CW00663107

Proceedings

15th International Conference on Information Visualisation

IV 2011

Proceedings

15th International Conference on Information Visualisation

London, United Kingdom
13 – 15 July 2011

Edited by
Ebad Banissi, Stefan Bertschi, Remo Burkhard, Urska Cvek, Martin Eppler, Camilla Forsell, Georges Grinstein, Jimmy Johansson, Sarah Kenderdine, Francis T. Marchese, Carsten Maple, Marjan Trutschl, Muhammad Sarfraz, Liz Stuart, Anna Ursyn, and Theodor G. Wyeld

Cover Image Credits
Memory, Difference, and Information: Generative Architectures Latent to Material & Perceptual Plasticity
Andrew Lucia1,2, Jenny Sabin1,2,4, Peter Lloyd Jones1,2,3,4
Sabin Jones LabStudio1, School of Design2, School of Medicine3, Institute for Medicine and Engineering4; University of Pennsylvania
Figure 7: Moderate (left), and rare (right) event information maps for an observer through a hallway.

Adaptive Visual Symbols for Personal Health Records
Heimo Müller1, Herman Maurer2, Robert Reihs1, Stefan Sauer1, Kurt Zatloukal1
(1) Medical University of Graz, (2) Graz University of Technology
Figure 7 – Selection of additional information embedded within the symbol.
Figure 8 – Explanations and configuration of symbols.

Los Alamitos, California

Washington • Tokyo

IEEE Computer Society Order Number P4476
BMS Part Number CFP1144D-PRT
ISBN 978-0-7695-4476-2
ISSN Number 1550-6037

Additional copies may be ordered from:

IEEE Computer Society
Customer Service Center
10662 Los Vaqueros Circle
P.O. Box 3014
Los Alamitos, CA 90720-1314
Tel: + 1 800 272 6657
Fax: + 1 714 821 4641
http://computer.org/cspress
csbooks@computer.org

IEEE Service Center
445 Hoes Lane
P.O. Box 1331
Piscataway, NJ 08855-1331
Tel: + 1 732 981 0060
Fax: + 1 732 981 9667
http://shop.ieee.org/store/
customer-service@ieee.org

IEEE Computer Society
Asia/Pacific Office
Watanabe Bldg., 1-4-2
Minami-Aoyama
Minato-ku, Tokyo 107-0062
JAPAN
Tel: + 81 3 3408 3118
Fax: + 81 3 3408 3553
tokyo.ofc@computer.org

Individual paper REPRINTS may be ordered at: <reprints@computer.org>

Editorial production by Lisa O'Conner
Cover art production by Joe Daigle/Studio Productions
Printed in the United States of America by The Printing House

IEEE Computer Society
Conference Publishing Services (CPS)
http://www.computer.org/cps

2011 15th International Conference on Information Visualisation

IV 2011

Table of Contents

1. Information Visualisation

1.1 Information Visualisation—Theory and Techniques

1.4 Information Visualization in Biomedical Informatics

2. Visual Analytics

2.1 Visual Data Mining and Analytics

2.2 GeoAnalytics

3. Knowledge Visualisation

3.1 Knowledge Domain Visualization

3.2 Knowledge Visualization and Visual Thinking

4. Design Visualisation

4.1 ArtSci—Intersection of Visualization, Art, and Design

5. Visualisation

5.1 Digital Art

5.2 Applications of Graph Theory

6. Geometric Modeling and Imaging

7. Visualisation in Built and Rural Environments

7.1 Built and Rural Environments Visualisation

7.2 Cultural Heritage Knowledge Visualisation

8. BioMedical Visualization

Preface

In today's information dependent society, most aspects of life are dependent and driven by data, information and knowledge. Visualisation of such commodities has added new impetus to the way these are applied. By studying the cultural heritage and history of art, we appreciate the power of visualisation has been identified back in the early days of civilisation. Modern day Computer Aided Visualisation has added momentum in developing tools that exploits 2D and 3D techniques, utilises metaphors adopted from many disciplines to communicate complexity of data and information within many application domains. The techniques are developed beyond visualisation to simplify the complexities, to reveal uncertainities, complete incompleteness, predict or project time dependent events and analyse visually.

This book on information visualization, compiled from the event of iV201, advocates that new framework will emerge from information rich disciplines like Humanity, Psychology, Sociology and Business as well as science rich disciplines. To facilitate this belief, iV2011 has the opportunity to reflect on the number of international funded projects as well as keynote lectures from distinguished speakers that pave the way this new frame work.

Joining us in this search are some 100 researchers who reflect and share a chapter of their efforts to the fellow researchers. The papers collected here reflect the vibrant state of Information Visualisation and bringing together researchers and artists and professional from more than 20 countries. It has allowed us to address the scope of information visualisation from a much wider perspective. Each contributor to this conference has indeed added fresh views and thoughts, challenged our beliefs and encouraged further our adventure of innovation. I, on behalf of all editors of this book, am grateful to all the authors for giving opportunity to share valuable work with the worldwide community from the platform of iV2011.

Ebad Banissi
On behalf of editors

Acknowledgments

We are deeply indebted to all of the contributors and all of the reviewers for their patience and cogent views of papers. They assisted the Information Visualization community with their expertise and feedbacks to shape this event effectively.

Special thanks go to all programme committee members and a truly unique team of organizing and liaison committee members who magnificently helped in shaping IV Forum.

I like to extend my sincere thanks to our keynote speakers: Professors Robert Spence, Francis T. Marchese, Rob Kitchin, and Theodor Wyeld.

Finally, we would offer sincere thanks to Graphicslink team for their continuous efforts in preparing, organising and handling the conference administration. Appreciation is also due to Lisa O'Conner, the Production Editor of IEEE Computer Society Conference Publication Services, for high standard editorial production of the Proceedings.

Organising & Liaison Committee

Conference Chair
Theodor Wyeld – Flinders University, Australia

Information Visualisation Theory & Practice
Ebad Banissi, London South Bank University, UK

Applications of Information Visualization
Liz Stuart – University of Plymouth, UK

Information Visualization Evaluation
Jimmy Johansson and Camilla Forsell, Linköping University, Sweden

Coordinated & Multiple Views in Visualisation & Exploration
Heimo Mueller, Medical University of Graz, Austria

Social media analytics, SMA
Andrew J. Cowell | Michelle L. Gregory
Pacific Northwest National Laboratory, USA

Visualization in Software Engineering
Francis T. Marchese – Pace University, USA

Visualization in Software Engineering Symposium Committee and Review Board:
Tom Arbuckle - University of Limerick, Ireland
Brian Berenbach - Siemens Corporate Research, Inc., USA
Seok-Won Lee - University of North Carolina at Charlotte, USA
Francis T. Marchese – Pace University
Stephen Morris - City University, London
Kurt Schneider - Leibniz Universität Hannover, Germany

Visualization, Art, and Design
Francis T. Marchese, Pace University, NY, USA (Chair)
Sarah Kenderdine, City University of Hong Kong (Chair)
Theodor G Wyeld, Flinders University, Australia (Chair)
Visualization, Art, and Design Symposium Committee and Review Board:
China Blue, Engine Institute, USA
Martin Dodge, University of Manchester, UK
Daniel Howe, City University of Hong Kong
Rob Kitchin, National University of Ireland, Maynooth
Ulf Langheinrich, Ghana
John McCormack, Monash University, Australia
Christine Nicholls, Flinders University, Australia
Hector Rodriguez, City University of Hong Kong
Jenny Sabin, The Nonlinear Systems Organization (Penn Design), USA
Dorrit Vibeke Sorensen, Nanyang Technological University, Singapore

Visualisation of the Semantic Web
Vladimir Geroimenko, University of Plymouth, UK

Visual Analytics
Dennis Groth - Indiana University, USA
Georges Grinstein, Computer Science Department, University of Massachusetts, USA

Knowledge Visualization and Visual Thinking
Stefan Bertschi, loginb consulting, http://www.loginb.com, knowledge@loginb.com
Remo Burkhard, ETH Zurich, http://www.ia.arch.ethz.ch, burkhard@arch.ethz.ch
Martin J. Eppler, University of St. Gallen, http://www.mcm.unisg.ch, martin.eppler@unisg.ch
Advisory Committee and Reviewers
Dominique Brodbeck, Macrofocus GmbH, http://www.macrofocus.com
Tom Crawford, Visualization Network, http://www.viznetwork.com
Serge Gebhardt, Jan Halatsch, Antje Kunze, Stefan Müller Arisona, ETH Zurich,
http://www.ia.arch.ethz.ch
Randy Goebel, University of Alberta, http://www.cs.ualberta.ca
Michael Granitzer, Wolfgang Kienreich, Vedran Sabol, Mario Zechner, Know-Center,
http://www.know-center.at
Michael Meier, vasp datatecture GmbH, http://www.vasp.ch
Jeanne Mengis, University of Lugano (USI), http://www.usi.ch
Peter Stoyko, Canada School of Public Service, http://www.csps-efpc.gc.ca
Andrew Vande Moere, KU Leuven, http://www.asro.kuleuven.be
Wibke Weber, Stuttgart Media University (HdM), http://www.hdm-stuttgart.de
Lukas Treyer, ETH Zurich

GeoAnalytics
Mikael Jern, NVIS Norrköping Visualization Centre, Linköping University, Sweden
Heidrun Schumann, University of Rostock, Germany
Sara Fabrikant, University of Zurich, Switzerland

Knowledge Domain Visualisation
Chaomei Chen Drexel University, USA
Katy Börner, Indiana University, USA
Jasna Kulji, Brunel University, UK

Human-Computer Interaction for Information Visualization
Dennis Groth - Indiana University, USA

Cultural Heritage Knowledge Visualisation
Theodor G Wyeld, Swinburne University of Technology, Australia
    Advisory, Programme and reviewing committee:
    Theodor G Wyeld, Swinburne University of Technology, Australia
    Sarah Kenderdine (Museum Victoria, Aust)
    Ekaterina Prasolova-Førland (NTNU, Trondheim)
    Teng-Wen Chang (NYUST, Taiwan)
    Brett Leavy (CyberDreaming, Aust)
    Malcolm Pumpa (QUT, Aust)
    Marinos Ioannides (HTI, Cyprus)
    Giovanni Issini (DFI, Italy)

Visualisation
Haim Levkowitz, Institute for Visualization and Perception Research And Graphics Research Laboratory, University of Massachusetts Lowell, USA

Mixed and Virtual Reality
Andrew J. Cowell, Pacific Northwest National Laboratory, USA
Ming Hou, Defence R&D Canada (DRDC) Toronto, Canada
Gui Yun Tian, University of Newcastle upon Tyne, UK

Digital Entertainment
Jian J Zhang, National Centre for Computer Animation, United Kingdom
Fotis Liarokapis, Director of Interactive Worlds Applied Research Group, UK

Computer Animation, Information Visualisation, and Digital Effects
Mark W. McK.Bannatyne, Purdue University, USA
Jian J Zhang, Bournemouth University, UK

Computer Animation & Especial Effects Show
Mark W. McK. Bannatyne, Purdue University, USA

Symposium and Gallery of Digital Art
Anna Ursyn, Chair, University of Northern Colorado, USA
    DART- Symposium and Online Gallery of Digital Art Advisory, Programme and reviewing committee:
    Dena Eber, Bowling Green State University, OH, USA
    Hans Dehlinger Professor Emeritus University of Kassel, GE
    James Faure Walker, Kingston University, UK
    LiQuin Tan, Rutgers University, NJ
    Marla Schweppe, Rochester Institute of Technology, NY, USA

Multimedia and E-learning
Mohammad Dastbaz, University of East London, UK

Cooperative Design and Visualization
Antje Kunze, Information Architecture, ETH Zurich Switzerland

Applications of Graph Theory
Carsten Mapel, University of Bedfordshire, UK
Adrian Rusu, Rowan University, USA

Web Visualization
Robina Hetherington, Open University, UK
Brian Farrimond, Liverpool Hope University, UK

Simulation Visualisation
Gui Yun Tian and Wai Lok Woo University of Newcastle upon Tyne, UK

Computer Games and their applications
Vittorio Scarano, Rosario De Chiara, Ugo Erra, ISISLab, Universita' di Salerno, Italy

Information Visualization in Biomedical Informatics (IVBI)
Georges Grinstein, Computer Science Department, University of Massachusetts, USA
Urska Cvek and Marjan Trutschl, Louisiana State University Shreveport, Louisiana State University Health Sciences Center, USA

Graphical Models and Imaging
Muhammad Sarfraz, Department of Information Science, Kuwait University, Kuwait
Programme and reviewing committee:
Malik Zawwar Hussain, Punjab University,PK
Natasha Dejdumrong, King Mongkut's University of Technology Thonburi, Thailand
Zulfiqar Habib, FAST National University of Computer & Emerging Sciences, PK
A. Zidouri, KFUPM, Saudi Arabia
Jarosław Miszczak, Institute of Theoretical and Applied Informatics, Polish Academy of Sciences, Poland
Arkadiusz Sochan Polish Academy of Sciences, Poland
Nouri, Fatma Zohra, Laboratoire de Mathematiques Appliquees, Universite Badji Mokhtar, Annaba (Algeria)
Mohamed Salah Hamdi,. Fachbereich Informatik, Universitaet Hamburg, Germany
Nacéra Benamrane, University of Sciences and Technology of Oran, Algeria

Visualisation in Built Environment
John Counsell, UWIC, UK
Farzad Khosrowshahi, University of Salford, UK
Richard Laing, The Robert Gordon University, UK

Programme Committee

Abdellatif Bettayeb (UK)
Adrian Rusu (USA)
AI Abdelmoty (UK)
Alex Garcia-Alonso (ES)
Alexander Lex (AT)
Alistair Morrison (UK)
André Skupin (USA)
Andrea Polli (USA)
Anna Ursyn (USA)
Anthony Robinson (USA)
Antje Kunze (CH)
Arzu Coltekin (CH)
Bannatyne, Mark W (USA)
Benoît Otjacques (LU)
Blaz Zupan (SI)
Brian Farrimond (UK)
Burkhard Remo (CH)
Camilla Forsell (SE)
Carla Maria Dal Sasso Freitas (BR)
Carlos Ferreira (PT)
Chalk, B S (UK)
Chaoli Wang (USA)
Cheng-Chieh Chiang (TW)
Chris Moore (UK)
Chris Shaw (CA)
Christian Tominski (DE)
Christin Seifert (AT)
Chun-Cheng Lin (Taiwa)
Claus Atzenbeck (DE)
Cliff Behrens (USA)
Connie Blok (NL)
Counsell, John (USA)
Craig, Paul (UK)
D. Graham (UK)
Daniel Weiskopf (DE)
Daryl Hepting (CA)
David Modjeska
Debora Testi (IT)
Devasis Bassu (USA)
Diansheng Guo (USA)
Dino Bouchlaghem (UK)
Eric CL Li (HK)
Feng Dong (UK)
Fotis Liarokapis (UK)
Francesco Bianconi (Italy)
Francis T. Marchese (USA)
Georg Gartner (AT)
Haim Levkowitz (USA)

Hans-Joerg Schulz (DE)
Harald Reiterer (DE)
Harri Siirtola (FI)
Heimo Müller (Austria)
Henrik Buchholz (GE)
Ho Van Quan (SE)
Hovhannes Harutyunyan (CA)
Hsu-Chun Yen (TW)
Hussein Karam (SA)
Jimmy Johansson (SE)
Jinwook Seo (KR)
Jonathan C. Roberts (UK)
jorgedel (ES)
Jörn Kohlhammer (GE)
José Antonio Macías (ES)
Joske Houtkamp (NL)
Kao, David L. (ARC-TNC) (USA)
Katherine A. Liapi (GR)
Keivan Kianmehr (CA)
Kenderdine, Sarah (AU)
Lihua You (UK)
Lik Shark (UK)
MacDorman, Karl Fredric (USA)
Malcolm Munro (UK)
Malcolm Pumpa (AU)
Maple, Carsten (UK)
Marc Streit (AT)
Margaret Bernard (USA)
margit pohl (AT)
Marjan Trutschl (USA)
Mark Apperley (NZ)
MARTIN TOMITSCH (AU)
Mats Lind (SE)
Matt Cooper (SE)
Mauro Figueiredo (Portugal)
Maylis Delest (FR)
Michael Granitzer (FR)
Mike Pitteway (UK)
Muhammad Hussain (SA)
Muhammad Sarfraz (KW)
Noritaka OSAWA (JP)
Pär-Anders Albinsson (SE)
Paul Cairns (UK)
Peter Ferschin (AT)
Peter Rodgers (UK)
Peter Wu (USA)
Philip Rhodes (USA)

Quang Vinh Nguyen (AU)
Riccardo Mazza (CH)
Richard Laing (UK)
Roberto Vivo (ES)
Robina Hetherington (UK)
Rosario De Chiara (Italy)
SASAKURA Mariko (JP)
Saturnino Luz (IE)
Shaimaa Lazem (USA)
Silvia Miksch (AT)
Sougata Mukherjea
Spence, Robert (UK)
Stefan Bertschi (UK)
Stefan Müller Arisona (CH)
Stefan Schlechtweg-Dorendorf (DE)
Stefan Seipel (SE)
Stefan Smolnik (USA)
Stewart Von Itzstein (DE)
Sven Fleck (DE)
Tammy S Knipp (USA)
Tao Ni (USA)
Tapani Sarjakoski (FI)
Tatiana von Landesberger (UK)
Teng-Wen Chang(TW)
Theresa-Marie (USA)
Tobias Schreck (GE)
Tom Arbuckle (IE)
Tomi Heimonen (FI)
Tumasch Reichenbacher (CH)
Tumasch Reichenbacher (CH)
Unsworth, Keith (NZ)
Urska Demsar (IE)
Vladimir Geroimenko (UK)
Volker Coors (DE)
Wai (Albert) Yeap (NZ)
Wesson, Jane (SA)
Wibke Weber (DE)
Wolfgang Aigner (AT)
Wong Hau San (HK)
Wong, Pak C (USA)
Xuelong Li (China)
Yan Zhang (UK)
Yong Yue (UK)
Yoshihiro Okada (JP)
Yousif Almas (UK)
zhang liangpei (China)

Reviewers list

Abd-Elsattar, Hussein Karam, Egypt
Adzhiev, Valery, UK
Aigner, Wolfgang, AT
Albinsson, Pär-Anders, SE
Alexander, Thomas, DE
Aljamali, Ahmad,KW
Alonso, A.García, ES
Andrienko, Natalia, DE
Aoyama, Hideki, JP
Apperley, Mark, NZ
Arbuckle, Tom, IE
Arisona, Stefan Müller, SG
Banissi, Ebad, UK
Behrens, Cliff, USA
Benamrane,, Nacéra, DZ
Bertschi, Stefan, UK
Bianconi, Francesco, IT
Blok, Connie, NL
Blue, China, USA
Borro, Diego, ES
Bresciani, Sabrina, CH
Burkhard, Remo, CH
Chang, Teng-Wen, TW
Chen, Yangjun, CA
Çöltekin, Arzu, CH
Conrad, Steve, USA
Cooper, Matthew, SE
Cory, Clark, USA
Counsell, John, UK
Cvek, Urska, USA
Day, Min-Yuh, TW
De Chiara, Rosario, IT
Dehlinger, Hans, DE
Dejdumrong, Natasha, TH
Delgado, Jorge, ES
Dong, Feng, UK
Dykes, Jason, UK
Eber, Dena Elisabeth, USA
Eppler, Martin, CH
Ferschin, Peter, AT
Figueiredo, Mauro, PT
Fleck, Sven, DE
Flynn, Ryan, UK
Gebhardt, Serge, CH
Geroimenko, Vladimir, UK
Graham, D., UK
Granitzer, Michael, AT
Graupner, Sven, USA
Grinstein, Georges, USA
Groth, Dennis, USA
Gwilt, Ian, AU
Habib, Zulfiqar, PK
Halatsch, Jan, CH
Halligan, Brian, USA
Harutyunyan, Hovhannes, CA
Heimonen, Tomi, FI
Hernantes, J., ES
Hetherington, Robina, UK
Hosobe, Hiroshi, JP

Howe, Daniel, HK
Huang, Mao Lin, AU
Hussain, Malik Zawwar, PK
Hussain, Muhammad, SA
Inselberg, Alfred, IL
Issini, Giovanni, IT
Kaczmarek, Elzbieta, PL
Kadaba, Nivedita R., CA
Kenderdine, Sarah, HK
Kennedy, Jessie, UK
Khosrowshahi, Farzad, UK
Kienreich, Wolfgang, AT
Klein, Karsten, DE
Kljun, Matjaz, SI
Knipp, Tammy Sue, USA
Kohlhammer, Jörn, DE
Kunze, Antje, CH
Kwolek, Bogdan, PL
Lazem, Shaimaa, USA
Lex, Alexander, AT
Lin, Chun-Cheng, TW
Lucia, Andrew, USA
Luz, Saturnino, IE
MacDorman, Karl, USA
Makalowski, Wojciech, USA
Marchant, Tom, USA
Marchese, Francis T., USA
Matuszewski, Bogdan, UK
McCormack, John, AU
Meier, Michael, CH
Miksch, Silvia, AT
Mountaz, Hascoët, FR
Mukherjea, Sougata, IN
Müller, Heimo, AT
Munro, Malcolm, UK
Nicholls, Christine Judith, AU
Osawa,, Noritaka, JP
Otjacques, Benoît, LU
Ozyer, Tansel, TR
Panse, Christian, CH
Pfister, Roland, CH
Piah, Abd. Rahni Mt., MY
Pohl, Margit, AT
Pumpa, Malcolm, AU
Rakkolainen, Ismo, FI
Rhodes, Philip, USA
Rhyne, Theresa-Marie, USA
Robinson, Anthony, USA
Rodgers, Peter James, UK
Rodriguez, Hector, HK
Rusu, Adrian, USA
Sabin, Jenny, AT
Sabol, Vedran, AT
Sarfraz, Muhammad, KW
Sasakura, Mariko, JP
Schlechtweg, Stefan, DE
Schumann, Heidrun, DE
Seifert, Christin, AT
Shariat,, Behzad, FR
Siirtola, Harri, FI

Skupin, Andre, USA
Smolnik, Stefan, DE
Sorensen, Dorrit Vibeke, SG
Spence, Robert, UK
Stuart, Liz, UK
Tominski, Christian, DE
Tomitsch, Martin, AU
Trutschl, Marjan, USA
Ursyn, Anna, USA
Vande Moere, Andrew, BE
Vietri, Andrea, IT
Virrantaus, Kirsi, FI
Von Itzstein, Stewart, AU
Walker, James Faure, UK
Ward, Matt, USA
Weber, Wibke, DE
Why, Ng Kok, MY
Wong, Pak Chung, USA
Wyeld, Theodor G, AU
Yen, Hsu-Chun, TW
Yuksek, Kemal, TR
Zechner, Mario, AT
Zeiller, Michael, AT
Zmazek, Blaz, SI
Zupan, Blaz, USA

1. Information Visualisation

IV 2011

The Effects of Image Speed and Overlap on Image Recognition

Timothy Brinded, James Mardell, Mark Witkowski and Robert Spence
Department of Electrical & Electronic Engineering
Imperial College London
London SW7 2BT
{*timothy.brinded04, james.mardell, m.witkowski, r.spence*}*@imperial.ac.uk*

Abstract—**Rapid Serial Visual Presentations (RSVPs) mimic the riffling of a book's pages and are widely employed as a way of gaining familiarity with a collection of images or selecting images of interest from a collection.**

In a typical RSVP a number of images within a collection enter a display in (say) the lower left-hand corner and move towards the opposite corner where they disappear ('diagonal RSVP'). If the rate at which images appear on the display is high, the speed with which images traverse the display may be such that the images overlap to some degree. As a consequence there is a need to know how much overlap can be tolerated without seriously affecting image recognition.

Diagonal RSVP was implemented for four different levels of overlap and four different image speeds in such a way as to separate the effects of these two parameters. Participants were required to identify theme images (such as 'ships' or 'cars') in a series of image sequences at various combinations of speed and overlap. In addition to recording their performance, participants also completed a questionnaire to gauge their opinion on perceived presentation speed and ease of recognition.

Results showed a significant effect of both overlap and speed on the percentage of correctly identified images. On the basis of the experimental results suggestions are made concerning interaction design for RSVP.

Keywords-**Inspection; Obscurement; Overlap; RSVP**

I. INTRODUCTION

Riffling the pages of a book in order to gain some familiarity with its contents or to conduct a search is a simple form of Rapid Serial Visual Presentation (RSVP) [1], [2]. The computational embodiment of RSVP leads to considerable flexibility in the *mode* of presentation, four of which are shown in Figure 1. In each mode images from a collection are introduced in turn at a given location, move along a trajectory and then disappear from view. The experiments in this paper use 'diagonal' mode (Figure 1a). In this diagonal mode, images appear in the bottom left and move at constant speed to the top right.

The technique of RSVP finds a wide range of applications. In e-commerce, for example, Wittenburg et. al. [3] explore various RSVP like designs, specifically for inclusion into consumer electronic products, notably for TV channel surfing and visualisation of VCR style fast-forward and editing tasks (Figure 1d). Tse et al. [4] investigated augmented 'gist' acquisition for film browsing. de Bruijn & Tong [5] investigated the selection of news reports on a mobile,

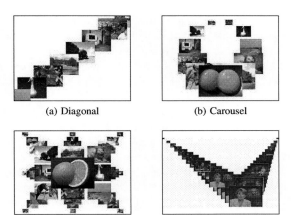

(a) Diagonal	(b) Carousel
(c) Volcano	(d) Video Browsing [3]

Figure 1. Typical RSVP Modes

notably in relation to inherently smaller screen dimensions. Most RSVP designs present images at a predetermined rate; Witkowski et al. [6] embed an RSVP design into a kiosk for product browsing and selection, in which the user has direct control of both image presentation speed and direction.

Cooper et al. [7] evaluated the comparative performance of users of six different RSVP designs, while monitoring their eye-gaze activities. de Bruijn and Spence [8] have investigated eye-gaze behaviour for a number of different RSVP visualisations, including a 'carousel' mode (Figure 1b). In 'carousel' mode, images appear small at the top of the screen, move clockwise increasing in size to the bottom, and disappear again at the top.

Corsato et al. [9] investigated both comparative performance and user preference for a number of more complex RSVP forms (including 'volcano' mode, Figure 1c). In 'volcano' mode images appear at the centre of the screen and successively move to the edges, reducing in size before disappearing. Corsato et al. also included a study of eye-gaze movement characteristics across the different modes tested, indicating that design has a substantial effect on gaze behaviour and that this is correlated with image recognition rates.

Wittenburg et al. [10] have considered the effects of simulated *depth* using perspective and occlusion methods. In

1550-6037/11 $26.00 © 2011 IEEE
DOI 10.1109/IV.2011.10

a related development Sun and Guimbretière [11] describe 'Flipper', a novel method for document navigation.

In RSVPs containing moving images it may often be preferable, for whatever reason, to cause the images to overlap each other to some extent, a condition illustrated for all the examples of RSVP shown in Figure 1. For any given image size, the number of images on the screen at any one time is determined by the interlinked factors of pace (rate of new images appearing onscreen), image speed and overlap.

The question then arises as to how occlusion of one image by the next affects a user's ability to recognise some feature of that obscured image. Since, for a given pace of image appearance on the display, overlap can be diminished or avoided by speeding up the movement of images, it is therefore essential to investigate the separate effects of image speed and overlap. The experiment described in this paper was devised to identify these independent effects on the ability of a user to recognise images satisfying a given theme (e.g. 'car', 'ship' or 'flower').

The approach adopted here to separate out the independent effects of overlap and image speed is presented in Section II by a specific but artificial experimental design. This design ensures that overlap and speed are independent.

The diagonal RSVP mode (see Figure 1a) was chosen for investigation because this mode or a minor variant of it is incorporated in most designs. The task assigned to the user was that of identifying, by space-bar press, those target images within a collection (of 200) characterised by a particular theme. Although unknown to the participant, there were always 10 target images in each presentation. After the presentation of each image collection, subjects were asked to answer three simple questions concerning their perception of image speed and identification success.

The experimental design is described in Section III. Section IV describes the experimental procedure used. Section V presents an analysis and discussion of the results obtained. Section VI provides a summary and further discussion of the experiment. In Section VII we derive, from the experimental results, some notes of guidance to the interaction designer faced with the task of designing an RSVP for a particular application. The final section presents some brief conclusions from the study.

II. INVESTIGATING OVERLAP

The purpose of these experiments was to test the combined effects of image speed and obscurement due to overlap as might be encountered in various RSVP designs. Our approach to a study of the effect of image overlap was to focus on two important features of an RSVP such as the exemplar shown in Figure 2. The two features are the degree of overlap and the speed at which the images move across the screen.

To isolate the independent effects of overlap and image speed the diagonal RSVP shown in Figure 2 was modified

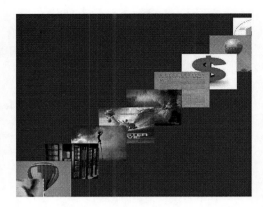

Figure 2.   A typical RSVP display as used in practice, showing image occlusion due to overlap

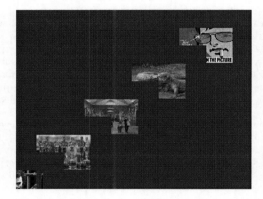

Figure 3.   A typical RSVP design modified for experimental purposes to address obscurement

as shown in Figure 3 purely for experimental purposes. This experimental RSVP was so arranged that throughout the investigation, the same number of images (or part images) were visible. The consequence of overlap was reflected in the varying obscurement of each image at one of four possible values illustrated in Figure 4. Independently of the degree of obscurement, four image speeds were investigated, but the rate at which images became visible (pace) was adjusted to keep the number of images on screen constant.

III. EXPERIMENTAL DESIGN

To investigate these parameters the number of images visible on the screen was kept constant, while the degree of obscurement was increased to emulate the effects of overlap. Four levels of obscurement were investigated: 0%, 25%, 50% and 75% (Figure 4). Figure 3 shows how this appears to the participant at 25% obscurement. At 0% obscurement the images just abut each other in this design.

The final experimental design adopted four linear image speeds across the screen, equating to 1005, 1612, 2246 and 2856 pixels/s. Table I indicates the consequences of this choice in terms of total travel time for any image across the whole screen, the rate at which images appear on the

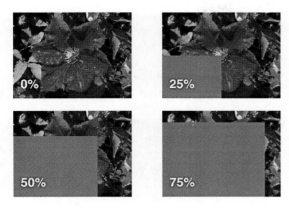

Figure 4. Levels of obscurement, as percentage area

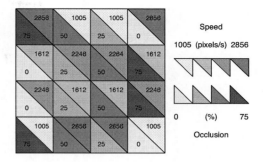

Figure 5. The Graeco-Latin square design

Table I
IMAGE SPEED SETTINGS

Travel Time (s)	Presentation Rate (images/s)	Test Duration (s)	Image Speed (pixels/s)	Image Speed (cm/s)
2.00	3.00	68.67	1005	24.15
1.24	4.84	42.57	1612	38.95
0.89	6.74	30.56	2246	54.27
0.70	8.57	24.03	2856	69.00

screen, the duration of each presentation of 200 images, and the equivalent speed in cm/s. Presentations were made on a 19" (48.3 cm diagonal) LCD monitor with a native display resolution of 1280x1024. Participants were seated a nominal 60 cm from the screen.

These final choices of obscurement and image speed were selected following pilot studies of eight participants. The trials were conducted both to test and refine the experimental software and procedures, and to ensure that the test parameters bounded the range of interest. Initial trials used obscurement levels of 0, 15, 30 and 45% and speeds of 666, 999, 1665 and 2856 pixels/s. It was clear that higher levels of obscurement were required to fully test the range of effects, and that the lower speed range was too slow to challenge the participants.

Each test represented a different combination resulting from varying the speed and obscruement of each image set. With four speeds and four levels of obscurement this resulted in 16 separate tests. To ensure a fair test this required 16 separate image sets each consisting of 200 unique images, so that participants only saw each image-set once.

Within each set, 10 target images drawn from a target theme were pseudo-randomly placed in the sequence. Participants used each target theme only once. Each target theme was drawn from one of 16 easily recognised categories: birds, cars, chairs, dogs, fish, flowers, aeroplanes, ships, horse, hot air balloons, hats, oranges, (military) tanks,

(British) phoneboxes, watches, and submarines. For each test the associated image set was also randomised to minimise the possibility of systematic error. The 3200 required images were sourced on-line, and represented a broad range of professional and amateur contributions.

The sequences were carefully chosen to equalise the relative difficulty of targets, the locations of identifying image features, and the target distribution within each set. In particular, care was taken to ensure that no target followed another by less than the time on screen, plus one second. This design also eliminates the possibility of attentional blink effects [12].

Prior to each presentation the participant was shown a screen indicating the target theme they were to identify. Participants were required to press the keyboard spacebar once (Figure 6) each time they identified a target image. The time of each spacebar activation was recorded automatically and subsequently compared to the actual time of target presentations to determine the accuracy data.

A Graeco-Latin square design [13] was adopted to distribute the combinations of speed and obscurment fairly. The square adopted is shown in Figure 5. The various schedules of combinations used for every participant were then derived from the square following normal practice.

During testing the experimenter was seated behind the participant, out of sight and otherwise non-interfering. This was done in an attempt to reduce potential impact of observation on the results (Figure 6), while allowing the experimenter full control of the procedure.

A. Subjective Questionnaire

As an integral part of the experimental design, each participant was required to answer three questions about their perceptions as to the speed of presentation, their confidence in seeing the targets and the overall difficulty of recognition during the test. The questions, as presented, are shown in Table II. Answers were recorded on an appropriate five-point scale, in the manner of a Likert design.

Since the participant filled out the relevant questions after each test (as opposed to at the end of the entire session) the

Figure 6.   View of the experimental set-up

Table II
INDIVIDUAL TEST QUESTIONS AND POSSIBLE ANSWERS

How did you find the speed of the presentation?	Very Slow	Slow	Just Right	Fast	Very Fast
How confident are you that you saw all the targets?	Not At All	Some-what	Fairly	Quite	Very Con-fident
Did you find it difficult to recognise the targets?	Very Dif-ficult	Diffi-cult	OK	Easy	Very Easy

responses were recorded with the most recent memory fresh in their minds.

IV. EXPERIMENTAL PROCEDURE

A total of 20 volunteers drawn from the general student and research population participated in the main experiment, 15 male, five female. Although none were directly familiar with the RSVP methodology, all were highly technically literate and experienced computer users.

After welcome, participants were seated comfortably, the general purpose of the experiment explained and consent obtained. Each participant was then shown an example of the diagonal RSVP presentation style to be used, at moderate speed and without obscurement. There was no interaction during the example presentation. Participants were carefully instructed to press the space bar on the keyboard once whenever they saw a picture with the target type in it, for example a 'dog'. Participants were not informed of the number of target images in each presentation sequence. Each participant was then asked if this was clear and any required clarifications were made.

Participants then each completed 16 presentation trials, at different speed and obscurement levels, in a schedule described previously (Figure 5). Prior to each of the sixteen presentations, an on-screen prompt informed the participants of the image theme they were required to identify, for example "In the next presentation, the theme you are looking for is dogs." The participant pressed the spacebar to start the presentation, when they were ready. Each of the sixteen presentations lasted between 24 and 69 seconds (Table I). At the end of each presentation they were then asked to answer each of the three questions from the questionnaire sheet, by highlighting one of the five options.

Following, and during, all sixteen presentations, any comments made by the participants were noted. The total time for each participant was between 15 and 20 minutes. No reward was offered for taking part.

V. ANALYSIS OF RESULTS

This section presents a discussion of the results obtained from the 320 individual presentations made during the main experiment, and summarises the results of the subjective questionnaire completed after each of the presentations. This discussion is broken down into different sections: a general overview of the results; a comparison and analysis of the effects of speed and obscurement; an examination of any learning effects; and an analysis of the participant questionnaire results. In the analysis that follows, the Accuracy measure reflects the number of instances where the participant recorded a space bar press while a target image was present on the screen (plus one second following to allow for reaction time, reflecting the design criteria, section III).

Accuracy is defined as the number of targets correctly identified within a sequence as a fraction of the total (10); these are the True Positives (TP). Accuracy may also be expressed as a percentage. False Positives (FP), where the participant indicated a target where none was present, were also recorded. The Accuracy measure is independent of the False Positive value.

A. General Overview of Results

Figure 7 provides an overview of the major findings of the experiment. The bubble chart shows the combined effect of obscurement and speed across the range of experimental parameters. The width of each bubble reflects the Accuracy of identification at each setting.

As expected, there is a pronounced effect on Accuracy of both speed and obscurement. However, it may be seen that the difference between 0 and 25% obscurement is very slight, in contrast to the more substantive effects between 25% and 50% and 50% to 75% obscurement. In contrast, Figure 7 indicates a progressive effect of speed on Accuracy. This is considered in more detail in section V-B, and is presented as an interpolated contour surface in Figure 16.

Figure 8 shows the average number of False Positives across the combinations of speed and occlusion. A False Positive indicates that a button press was recorded but did not correspond to a target.

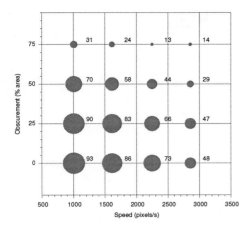

Figure 7.   Accuracy (%) when varying speed and obscurement

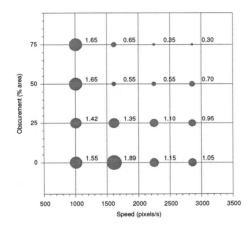

Figure 8.   False Positives when varying speed and obscurement

Whilst the actual numbers of False Positives are overall relatively small (all less than two per presentation) it is interesting to note the level of correlation between 'high difficulty' combinations (upper right, Figure 8) and smaller average instances of false positives. We postulate that this is due to participants 'giving up' on tests they deem too hard and appear to be hesitant to press the space bar if at all. Furthermore, we observed that participants would raise their fingers above the spacebar during these difficult presentations, while they would tend to rest their fingers on the bar during more tractable combinations.

B. Speeds and Obscurements

In order to allow a more detailed assessment of the difference between the different speeds and obscurements, Figure 9 and Figure 10 show the averaged results for speed and obscurement respectively. For example Figure 9 shows that at a speed of 1005 pixels/s there are 7.1 ($SD = 2.9$)

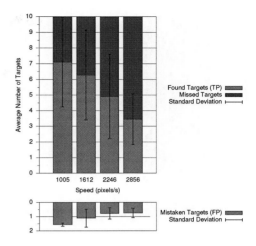

Figure 9.   Results across speeds

Table III
TABLE OF p-VALUES FROM THE TUKEY MULTIPLE COMPARISONS OF
MEANS ACROSS SPEEDS

Speed (pixels/s)	1005	1612	2246	2856
1005				
1612	0.0495			
2246	0.0000	0.0003		
2856	0.0000	0.0000	0.0001	

True Positives, for 1612 pixels/s, 6.3 ($SD = 3.1$), for 2246 pixels/s, 4.9 ($SD = 3.2$) and for 2856 pixels/s, 3.4 ($SD = 2.8$). Each is the result of averaging over the speed measurements across all obscurements (0%, 25%, 50%, 75%). We note the associated standard deviations (as denoted by the error bars shown on the figure) are fairly large, due to the range of obscurements used, and that the Standard Deviations (SD) are quite similar. Figure 9 also indicates a very strong negative linear correlation between speed and true positives ($R^2 = 0.986$).

Table III shows the Tukey multiple comparison p-values for all combinations of speed ($N \approx 80$), indicating that each of the four accuracy values are distinct at $p < 0.05$.

The False Positives shown in Figure 9 (lower) also exhibit a negative trend with increased speed, consistent with Figure 8. The relatively high SD across the False Positive values is indicative of the variability of the candidates' behaviours.

Figure 10 shows a non-linear relationship between obscurement and Accuracy. Note the similarity between 0% obscurement ($M = 7.5$, $SD = 2.6$) and 25% obscurement ($M = 7.2$, $SD = 2.6$). Table IV shows that the p-value ($p = 0.7580$) for a Tukey comparison between the 0 and 25% obscurements is clearly non-significant at the $p < 0.05$ level. This is in stark contrast to other Tukey comparisons of the remaining obscurements (25 to 50 and 50 to 75) as

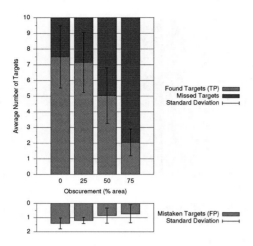

Figure 10. Results across obscurements

Table IV
TABLE OF p-VALUES FROM THE TUKEY MULTIPLE COMPARISONS OF
MEANS ACROSS OBSCUREMENTS

Obscurement (%)	0	25	50	75
0				
25	0.7580			
50	0.0000	0.0000		
75	0.0000	0.0000	0.0000	

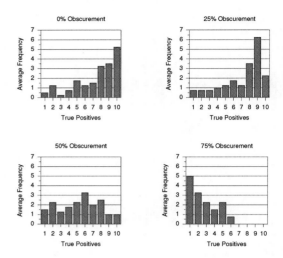

Figure 11. Effect of obscurement on accuracy

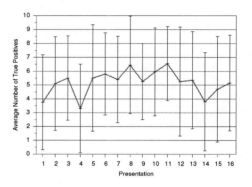

Figure 12. Potential learning effect

shown in Table IV, which are clearly distinct. Again we note a high variability in False Positives across the individual participants (Figure 10, lower).

Figure 11 emphasises the similarities between the effect on the spread of number of targets correctly identified at 0% and 25% obscurement (Figure 11, top left and top right). These are both heavily skewed toward the correctly identified part of the histogram. At 50% obscurement (Figure 11, bottom left), the spread of correctly identified targets is largely even, whereas 75% (Figure 11, bottom right) obscurement clearly indicates that few targets are identified correctly for the majority of presentations. There is a similar effect for speeds, but it is not as pronounced.

C. Learning Effect

Figure 12 shows the average score across all participants in the order of test presentation. To the extent possible the experimental design distributed *easy* and *difficult* combinations evenly across the presentations. The absence of any substantive improvement across the successive tests indicates that there is no significant learning effect for this type of RSVP design, implying that users found the RSVP style intuitive. Error bars indicate the Standard Deviation ($N = 20$). The error bars are large (and therefore only indicative) as each test position contains presentations at every speed and obscurement combination.

It should be noted that a potential 'learning effect' did play a part in the questionnaire, as participants would rate the slowest speed much slower than initially, once they had experienced the fastest possible speed (question one).

D. Participant Questionnaire Findings

This section presents the findings from the user opinion survey (Section III-A). Figure 13 summarises the results for question 1 "How did you find the speed of this presentation", asked after every presentation. The response 'Just Right' is assigned a value of zero, 'Fast' and 'Very Fast' positive values one and two respectively; the responses 'Slow' and 'Very Slow' values of minus one and minus two respectively; the permissible range is therefore −2 to +2. Fast values are shown on Figure 13 as filled upward pointing triangles, slow values as downward pointing triangles. Smaller triangles are therefore closer to the ideal.

It may be seen that the slowest speed (1005 pixels/s) was found to be very close to 'Just Right'. On average the second speed (1612 pixels/s) was considered just below

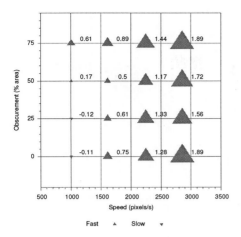

Figure 13.   Question 1: Speed (range −2 to +2)

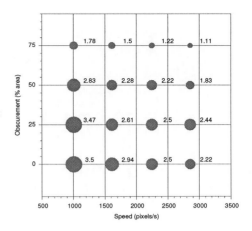

Figure 14.   Question 2: Confidence (range 1 to 5)

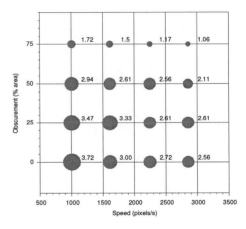

Figure 15.   Question 3: Difficulty (range 1 to 5)

'Fast'. The two highest speeds (2246 and 2856 pixels/s) were both between 'Fast' and 'Very Fast', with the highest speed almost uniformly considered 'Very Fast' (average 1.76 of maximum value 2). Recall that the range of speeds was partially determined by a sample of eight pilot study participants, where the trial's' slowest speed was evaluated as 'Very Slow', and which was also reported as unreasonably slow. Note that obscurement has little apparent effect on the perception of speed in these trials.

Figure 14 shows the results from the question: "How Confident were you that you saw all the targets?" with 1 being the lowest confidence answer ('Not At All') and 5 being the highest ('Very Confident'). It is interesting to note that participants were on aggregate only between 'Fairly' (3, central value) and 'Quite Confident' (4) even at the low speed, low obscurement presentations. Comparison with the measured Accuracy results shown in Figure 7 indicates that, on balance, participants were generally pessimistic about their performance under the most benign conditions compared to their actual performance. Confidence falls with increases in both speed and obscurement, largely mirroring the measured Accuracy values.

Figure 15 shows the results in response to the question "Did you find it difficult to recognise the targets?" Results are in the range 5 ('Very Easy') to 1 ('Very Difficult'). As with question two, for the benign settings for speed and obscurement, participants generally underestimate their performance regarding Accuracy, but become more realistic at the challenging settings.

VI. SUMMARY AND DISCUSSION

Figure 16 presents the results of fitting a cubic spline surface to the data shown in Figure 7 and indicates, for convenience, contours of constant Accuracy. The interaction designer may then choose a minimum desired accuracy level or range and simply read off a combination of speed and obscurement that would meet their requirements. Note that this Figure extrapolates the accuracy level to 100% obscurement (where it may reasonably be assumed that there can only be 0% Accuracy).

Note again that the effects of speed and obscurement are not generally equivalent, the effect of speed being largely linear over the range tested; whereas the effect of obscurement is minimal at low values, but increasingly pronounced at higher values. This is reflected in the shape of the contour lines presented in Figure 16.

Results from the subjective questionnaires indicate that the participants considered the speeds of presentation employed to range from 'Just Right' for the slowest speed to 'Very Fast' for the two faster speeds. Opinion about speed was apparently independent of the degree of obscurement used in the presentations.

Figure 17 shows the strong proportional correlation be-

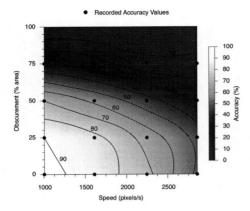

Figure 16. Accuracy, Speed and Obscurement

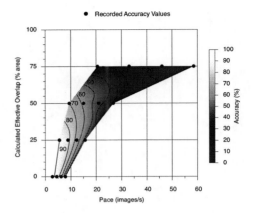

Figure 18. Accuracy, Pace and Overlap (calculated)

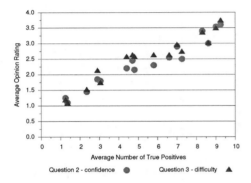

Figure 17. Correlation of Opinion to Performance

tween participants' opinion of their performance compared to the actual performance as measured, across all combinations of speed and occlusion. The linear regression fit, R^2, for question 2 is 0.94; R^2 for question 3 is 0.91.

It would seem to be an attractive property of a presentation design that users' intuitive perception of their performance matches that which they actually achieve. However, it remains unclear as to why participants are generally more pessimistic than they need be at slower speeds and lower obscurement levels, even though they are, by and large, properly pessimistic about their performance at the more challenging settings.

Given the ubiquity of the problems associated with speed and overlap in RSVP design, this paper has been concerned solely with design performance issues. While we have used a highly controlled experimental design, we consider our results may well prove useful for interaction designers developing a wide-range of RSVP designs. It should also be noted that the effects of image presentation rate on individuals' cognitive ability to both recognise and remember images has been extensively studied e.g. [14], [15], however such

considerations are beyond the scope of this paper.

VII. DESIGN CONSIDERATIONS

The experiment described in this paper keeps separate the effects of image speed and the degree to which images are obscured. In normal practice, this obscuration would be as a consequence of images overlapping, as shown in Figure 2. This artificial separation results in the obscurement of images shown in Figure 3. This ensures the same number of images (and part-images) are on the screen at the same time regardless of which speed or obscurement levels are selected.

The interaction designer may be more concerned with the effect on accuracy of pace, rather than image speed. Since image speed, overlap and pace are simply related, it is possible to transform the experimental data gathered in these experiments to generate Figure 18, under a single assumption. The assumption is that the accuracy of target identification is a function only of image speed and occlusion and is independent of pace. This conjecture is as yet unproven, though various previous studies give us some confidence in its validity. The assumption needs to be tested by future experiment.

Accepting the assumption, Figure 18 shows the freedom of design choice of pace and overlap available for a specified minimum Accuracy level of theme target. The area shown in Figure 18 represents the range of the experimental evidence, the other areas represent image presentation speeds that fall outside our previously identified useful boundaries (too fast or too slow).

VIII. CONCLUSIONS

This paper identifies and investigates the independent effect of image obscurement and image speed in a diagonal RSVP. We observed a strongly proportional effect of speed on accuracy, but that small amounts of obscurement had relatively little effect, although this increased markedly with further obscurement. Under the stated assumptions, we present our findings in a form (Figure 18) that allows a visual designer to choose an efficacious combination of image speed, overlap and pace to achieve a desired accuracy of target image recognition.

IX. ACKNOWLEDGEMENTS

The authors gratefully acknowledge the valuable discussions with Dr. Kent Wittenburg of Mitsubishi Electric Research Laboratories.

This work was financially supported by the Old Centralians' Trust of Imperial College London.

REFERENCES

[1] R. Spence, "Rapid, Serial and Visual: A Presentation Technique with Potential," *Information Visualization*, vol. 1, no. 1, pp. 13–19, Mar. 2002.

[2] O. de Bruijn and R. Spence, "Rapid Serial Visual Presentation: A Space-Time Trade-Off in Information Presentation," in *Proceedings of the Working Conference on Advanced Visual Interfaces (AVI 2000)*. Palermo, Italy: ACM Press, 2000, pp. 189–192.

[3] K. Wittenburg, C. Forlines, T. Lanning, A. Esenther, S. Harada, and T. Miyachi, "Rapid Serial Visual Presentation Techniques for Consumer Digital Video Devices," in *Proceedings of the 16th Annual ACM Symposium on User Interface Software and Technology (UIST '03)*. ACM Press, 2003, pp. 115–124.

[4] T. Tse, G. Marchionini, W. Drag, L. Slaughter, and A. Komlodi, "Dynamic Key Frame Presentation Techniques for Augmenting Video Browsing," in *Proceedings of the Working Conference on Advanced Visual Interfacesb (AVI '98)*, L'Aquila, Italy, 1998, pp. 185–194.

[5] O. de Bruijn and C. H. Tong, "M-RSVP: Mobile Web Browsing on a PDA," in *People and Computers XVII, Proceedings of HCI 2003*, 2003, pp. 297–312.

[6] M. Witkowski, B. Neville, and J. Pitt, "Agent mediated retailing in the connected local community," *Interacting with Computers*, vol. 15, no. 1, pp. 5–32, Jan. 2003.

[7] K. Cooper, O. de Bruijn, R. Spence, and M. Witkowski, "A Comparison of Static and Moving Presentation Modes for Image Collections," in *Proceedings of the Working Conference on Advanced Visual Interfaces (AVI '06)*. New York, New York, USA: ACM Press, 2006, pp. 381–388.

[8] O. de Bruijn and R. Spence, "Patterns of Eye Gaze during Rapid Serial Visual Presentation," in *Proceedings of the Working Conference on Advanced Visual Interfaces (AVI '02)*. New York, New York, USA: ACM Press, 2002, pp. 209–217.

[9] S. Corsato, M. Mosconi, and M. Porta, "An Eye Tracking Approach to Image Search Activities Using RSVP Display Techniques," in *Proceedings of the Working Conference on Advanced Visual Interfaces (AVI 2008)*. ACM, 2008, pp. 416–420.

[10] K. Wittenburg, T. Lanning, C. Forlines, and A. Esenther, "Rapid Serial Visual Presentation Techniques for Visualizing a 3rd Data Dimension," in *HCI International*, Crete, Greece, 2003, pp. 810–814.

[11] L. Sun and F. Guimbretière, "Flipper: a New Method of Digital Document Navigation," in *Extended Abstracts on Human Factors in Computing Systems (CHI '05)*. Portland, OR, USA: ACM Press, 2005, pp. 2001–2004.

[12] K. L. Shapiro, K. M. Arnell, and J. E. Raymond, "The Attentional Blink," *Trends in Cognitive Sciences*, vol. 1, no. 8, pp. 291–296, 1997.

[13] R. A. Bailey, "Orthogonal Partitions in Designed Experiments," *Designs, Codes and Cryptography*, vol. 77, no. 1-2, pp. 45–77, 1996.

[14] V. Coltheart, Ed., *Fleeting Memories: Cognition of Brief Visual Stimuli*, 1st ed. Cambridge, Massachusetts, United States: MIT Press, 1999.

[15] M. C. Potter, B. Wyble, R. Pandav, and J. Olejarczyk, "Picture detection in rapid serial visual presentation: Features or identity?" *Journal of experimental psychology. Human perception and performance*, Aug. 2010.

ImageCube: A Browser for Image Collections Associated with Multi-Dimensional Datasets

Yunzhu Zheng
Ochanomizu University
Tokyo, Japan
Email: yunzhu@itolab.is.ocha.ac.jp

Ai Gomi
Ochanomizu University
Tokyo, Japan
Email: gomiai@itolab.is.ocha.ac.jp

Takayuki Itoh
Ochanomizu University
Tokyo, Japan
Email: itot@is.ocha.ac.jp

Abstract—Image browsing techniques thus become increasingly important for overview and retrieval of particular images in large-scale collections. At the same time, there are various sets of images which are associated with multi-dimensional or multivariate datasets. We believe that image browsing for such datasets should be inspired from multi-dimensional data visualization techniques. This paper presents ImageCube, a scatterplot-like browser for image collections associated with multi-dimensional datasets. ImageCube locates a set of images into a display space assigning a pair of dimensions to X- and Y-axes. It suggests preferable pairs of dimensions by applying Kendall's rank correlation and Entropy on the display space, so that users can easily obtain interesting visualization results. This paper presents a case scenario that a user finds a preferable car from an image collection by using ImageCube.

Keywords-Visualization, Image browser, Multidimensional data.

I. INTRODUCTION

With the rapid development of the imaging technologies over the recent years, advanced visualization techniques for thousands of pictures are making big progress. At the same time, now we can obtain various sets of images which are associated with multi-dimensional or multivariate datasets via Internet. For example, we can obtain the images of recipes which have a variety of nutritional value, those of cars which have a variety of performance values, and those of medical which have a variety of diagnosis value, based on our specific requests. We think that image browsing techniques featuring multidimensional data visualization techniques are useful to explore such kinds of image datasets. Especially, multidimensional data visualization techniques are useful to explore and analyze features and structures in the datasets, including clusters, outliers or correlations. We believe it is interesting to explore and analyze such features and structures of multidimensional values assigned to images while browsing the images themselves.

Among various information visualization techniques, scatterplots is one of the most popular and widely-used visual representations for multidimensional data due to its simplicity, and visual clarity. Scatterplots visualize multidimensional datasets by assigning data dimensions to graphical axes and rendering data cases as points in the Cartesian

space defined by the axes. This approach has been widely used in visualization technique such as Rolling the Dice [2], which presents new interactive methods to explore multidimensional data. It applies a metaphor of rolling a dice, since as they implement an animation mechanism as they transform one scatterplot representation into another one by rotating a cubic space.

This paper proposes "ImageCube", an image browser featuring a multidimensional data visualization technique which is similar to Rolling the Dice. ImageCube can show the visualization through interactively selecting two dimensions from the multidimensional datasets of images applying scatterplot. Our implementation of ImageCube assists the dimension selection operations by suggesting interesting pairs of dimensions based on their correlations and entropies. ImageCube is helpful for users to obtain qualitative visualization results to explore and analyze features and structures of multidimensional values assigned to images.

We tested ImageCube with images of recipes and those of cars. Visualization results in the paper demonstrate that ImageCube efficiently supports users to obtain insightful visualizations.

II. RELATED WORK

There have been various image browsers related to Image-Cube. Also, there have been various techniques for multidimensional data visualization related to ImageCube. This section introduces several related techniques.

A. Image Browser

Overview and retrieval of image collections are important issues for their owners. Image browsing is therefore an active research topic and therefore recently many novel image browsers have been presented. This section categorizes the image browsers into two groups: browsers for structured/unstructured sets of images.

Many of image browsers for structured sets of images suppose that images forms trees or graphs. PhotoMesa [1] is one of the most famous image browsers for structured sets of images. It divides a window space by nested set of rectangles to represent the hierarchy of images, and then packs them in each of the rectangular subspaces.

On the other hand, many of other image browsers for unstructured sets of images scatter the images onto 2D/3D spaces like scatterplots. Several techniques applies dimension reduction techniques such as MDS (Multi Dimensional Scaling) or PCA (Principal Component Analysis) to locate the images [8] so that similarly looking images are placed closer on the display spaces. Several others directly assigns two or three values associated to the images to the axes of 2D/3D spaces [4].

MIAOW [3] is a hybrid technique that forms hierarchy while it assigns three values to axes of a 3D space. It divides the images according to latitudes, longitudes, and times which the images are taken, while assigns the three values to axes of a 3D space. The mechanism is somewhat similar to ImageCube; however, MIAOW just treats latitude, longitude, and time as three dimensional values. ImageCube presented in this paper is a more generalized image browser.

B. Multi-Dimensional Data Visualization

There have been various multi-dimensional data visualization techniques, including Parallel Coordinates, VisDB, and Worlds within Worlds. Some other techniques apply heatmaps or glyphs to represent multi-dimensional value. Meanwhile, Scatterplots is one of the most popular techniques to visualize multi-dimensional data. Many scatterplots implementations directly assigns two or three of the dimensions to axes of the visualization spaces, while others apply dimension reduction techniques. Scatterplot matrix is often used for overview of scatterplots selecting arbitrary pairs of dimensions; however, it requires very large display spaces if number of dimensions is large. If users do not want to use such large display spaces for scatterplots, they may need to interactively switch the pairs of dimensions to understand correlations between the dimensions. Rolling the Dices [2] is one of the novel techniques to assist the interactive selection of dimensions for scatterplots.

Dimension analysis is helpful to obtain fruitful knowledge from multi-dimensional data visualizations. Sips et al. [7] presented a view selection technique of multi-dimensional data visualization by applying the dimension analysis. Nagasaki et al. [5] presented a correlation-based dimension selection technique for scatterplots-based visualization of credit card fraud data. The correlation-based strategy is also useful to reorder the dimensions and improve the readability of Parallel Coordinates and scatter plots matrices [6].

III. BROWSING IMAGE COLLECTIONS WITH MULTI-DIMENSIONAL VALUES

This section presents our image browser ImageCube, which represents image collections by scattering the images. Specified arbitrary two dimensions, ImageCube calculates positions of images in a display space by assigning the

two dimensions to axes of the display space. It then groups the images based on their positions, and selects a representative image for each group. ImageCube initially displays the representative images, and provides a user interface to click the images so that other images in the same group with the clicked images are displayed in another window space. Dimension selection may be a problem for usability. ImageCube supports a function to recommend interesting pairs of dimensions so that users can easily select them.

A. Definition of Input Images

We suppose an image set $I = \{i_1, i_2, ..., i_n\}$ as input information, where i_i is the i-th image, and n is the number of images. We also suppose that an image $i_i = \{v_{i1}, v_{i2}, ..., v_{im} n_i, u_i\}$, where v_{ij} is the j-th value of the i-th image, m is the number of dimensions, a_i is the name of the i_i, and u_i is the URL or path of the i_i. Our implementation consumes input data files which describe names of the dimensions, multidimensional values, name of the images, and URL or path of the images. It then automatically generates and displays the selection menu from the input information, which are used to select arbitrary two dimensions as X- and Y-axes. Also, it calculates c_{ij}, the coordinate value of the j-th dimension of the i-th image, which is used as positions of images.

B. Multidimensional Visualization

ImageCube represents two dimensions in a single visualization as many scatterplots techniques do. When a user specifies the p-th dimension as the X-axis, and the q-th dimension as the Y-axis, ImageCube places the i-th image at (c_{ip}, c_{iq}). ImageCube senses click operations of users to display detailed information of the particular images on demand.

ImageCube supports a smooth dimension selection, by rotating the display space, like Rolling the Dice [2] supports. Suppose that the p-th dimension is assigned to the X-axis, and the q-th dimension to the Y-axis. When a user specifies the r-th dimension as the X-axis, ImageCube temporarily assigns the r-th dimension to the Z-axis, and therefore ImageCube places the i-th image at (c_{ip}, c_{iq}, c_{ir}). ImageCube then rotates the display space along the Y-axis, so that the XZ-plane gets the XY-plane, and the XY-plane gets the XZ-plane. Figure 1(Left) shows a capture of the rotation process.

C. Recommendation of Dimension Pairs

ImageCube automatically generates the selection menu featuring buttons of dimensions for X- and Y-axes. Here, a major challenge is how to easily get fruitful visualization results from multidimensional datasets according to user's needs. Therefore ImageCube provides a mechanism to recommend interesting pairs of dimensions so that users can easily select them. Current our implementation shows the

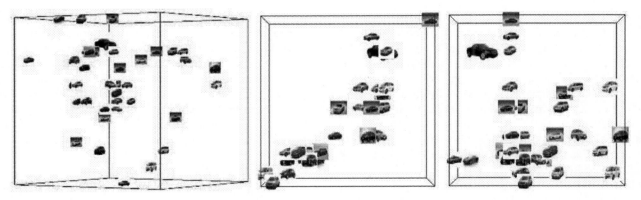

Figure 1. (Left) Image redeployment by rotation function of XY- and XZ-planes. (Center) A visualization result with a high-correlation pair of dimensions. (Right) A visualization result with a high-entropy pair of dimensions.

recommended pairs by coloring corresponding dimensions on the selection menu.

To realize the mechanism, we need to analyze the numerical features between arbitrary two dimensions. Current our implementation calculates the following two kinds of numerical features between arbitrary pairs of dimensions to obtain interesting visualization results:

- Kendall's rank correlation to obtain results which images are regularly aligned. See Figure 1(Center).
- Entropy to obtain results which images are evenly distributed. See Figure 1(Right).

Kendall's rank correlation: Correlation analysis is useful for multidimensional datasets visualization techniques, as discussed in Section II-B We apply Kendall rank correlation for the correlation analysis. The Kendall rank (τ) denotes the similarity of the orderings of the datasets ranked by each of the quantities, defined as follows:

$$\tau = \frac{4P}{n(n-1)} - 1 \qquad (1)$$

which is supposed as following.

- If the agreement between the two rankings is perfect (i.e., the two rankings are the same) the coefficient has value 1.
- If the disagreement between the two rankings is perfect (i.e., one ranking is the reverse of the other) the coefficient has value -1.
- If X and Y are independent, then we would expect the coefficient to be approximately zero.

ImageCube calculates the Kendall rank correlation for every possible pair of dimensions, and suggests the pairs which bring high correlations.

Entropy: ImageCube measures the distribution and randomness of the visualization results by applying Entropy. ImageCube internally divides the display space into N_s rectangular subspaces, and count the number of images p_i in

the i-th subspace. ImageCube calculates the sum of Entropy E_{sum} in the subspaces as follows:

$$E_{sum} = \sum^{N_s} (\frac{p_i}{N} \log \frac{p_i}{N}) \qquad (2)$$

ImageCube calculates the Entropy for every possible pair of dimensions, and suggests the pairs which bring high randomness.

D. Overlap Reduction

The simple image location strategy described in Section III-B easily causes overlap of images on the display space, while displaying large-scale image collections. To improve the understanding and usability, ImageCube reduces the number of displaying images by a clustering based on their positions on the display space. It generates groups of images that locate inside a constant radius of circles, and selects a representative image for each group. It initially displays only the representative images, and other images in the group of a representative image s will be displayed in another space, when a user clicks one of the representative images.

E. User Interface

Figure 2 shows our implementation of ImageCube. It features a drawing area in the left side of the window, and three tabs with user interface widgets in the right side of the window. The first tab in Figure 2 (Left) features widgets for setting viewing and drawing options.

The second tab in Figure 2 (Center) features buttons for selection of dimensions for assigning to X- and Y-axes. When a dimension is selected for the X-axis, labels of several buttons are colored in red, which denotes that higher rank correlation is obtained when the colored dimensions are selected for the Y-axis. Similarly, when a dimension is selected for the Y-axis, labels of several buttons are colored in red, because they are recommended for the X-axis. The labels may be also colored in yellow, which denotes that higher Entropy is obtained when the colored dimensions

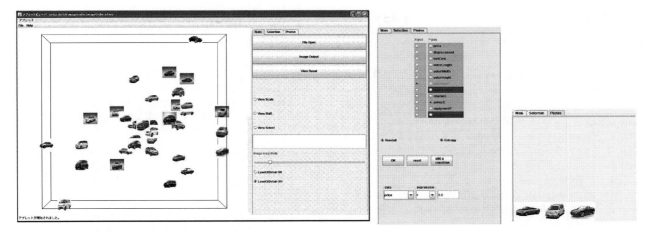

Figure 2. Our implementation of ImageCube. (Left) A drawing area, and a tab featuring widgets for setting viewing and drawing options. (Center) A tab featuring buttons for selection of dimensions for assigning to X- and Y-axes. (Right) A tab featuring a panel to display the images belonging to the clusters of clicked representative images.

are selected. This tab also features widgets for specifying the ranges of values. Images are not displayed if the values assigned to them are out of the specified ranges.

The third tab in Figure 2 (Right) features a panel to display the images belonging to the clusters of clicked representative images.

IV. EXAMPLE

We implemented ImageCube on Java 1.6.0 and JOGL (Java binding for OpenGL). We tested ImageCube on Lenovo ThinkPad T510 (CPU 2.4GB, RAM 2GB) with Windows XP SP3.

This section shows results of ImageCube applying 100 images collected from Japanese automobile catalog Web site [1]. We parsed HTML files introducing particular cars, to extract specifications and evaluations of the cars, and download their images. Consequently we obtained a 12 dimensional dataset including the following specification and evaluation values: 1) price, 2) displacement of the engine, 3) fuel cost, 4) outer length, 5) outer width, 6) outer height, 7) height of floor, 8) user evaluation of appearance, 9) user evaluation of interior design, 10) user evaluation of engine power, 11) user evaluation of equipments, and 12) user evaluation of cost performance.

We also constructed an image collection from Japanese recipe Web site [2]. We parsed HTML files introducing partic- ular recipes, and consequently we obtained a 7 dimensional dataset including the following values: 1) time required to cook, 2) energy, 3) amount of vegetable, 4) amount of salt, 5) amount of Calcium, 6) amount of fat, and 7) amount of Iron.

[1] http://autos.yahoo.co.jp/
[2] http://www.recipe.nestle.co.jp/recipe/

This section introduces a use case scenario with the image collection of cars. First of all, we were interested in correlations between prices and other variables. We checked correlation and Entropy between them, and found that dis- placement and fuel costs had relatively high correlations with the price. Figure 3(1) shows an example that price is as- signed to the X-axis, and displacement is assigned to the Y- axis. The example denotes that they are nearly proportional; luxury sedans are relatively expensive, and station wagons are relatively low cost in this collection. Figure 3(2) shows an example that price is assigned to the X-axis, and fuel cost is assigned to the Y-axis. Equipment evaluation also had high correlations with the price, but the distribution of the images was not linear. Figure 3(3) shows an example that price is assigned to the X-axis, and equipment evaluation is assigned to the Y-axis. It denotes that equipment evaluation increases proportional to the price of low-price cars, but it becomes flat if the price is higher. On the other hand, it was our surprise that appearance evaluation was not correlated to the price. Figure 3(4) shows an example that price is assigned to the X-axis, and appearance evaluation is assigned to the Y-axis, where it seems that expensive cars do not always obtain higher evaluations of appearance.

Be derived from the above surprising result, we were interested in what impact to the evaluation of appearance. Figure 3(5)(6) show examples that outer length or outer width is assigned to the X-axis, and appearance evaluation is assigned to the Y-axis. They denote that outer length or outer width is not well correlated with the evaluation of appearance. Actually, these pairs of dimensions had relatively higher Entropies. On the other hand, Figure 3(7) shows an example that height of floor is assigned to the X- axis, and appearance evaluation is assigned to the Y-axis. The result briefly denotes that appearance evaluations are better if floors are lower, which looks a common trend both for wagons and sedans. Actually, correlation of height of floor to appearance evaluation was relatively higher than others.

Finally, we checked what impacts to the evaluation of cost performance, and found that appearance evaluation was one of them. Figure 3(8) shows an example that appearance evaluation is assigned to the X-axis, and cost performance evaluation is assigned to the Y-axis. This high correlation denotes that appearance is very important for the user evaluation of cost performance. Again, it looks a common trend both for wagons and sedans.

This example demonstrates that we can discuss the trend of multi-dimensional values associated to the collections of images while looking at the images themselves. Actually, we could discuss what impacts to the evaluation of appearance and cost performance of cars, while looking at various values as well as designs of cars. We think this analysis tool can be applied to various fields dealing with images; for example, collections of medical images associated with medical checkup values, and collections of facial and cosmetic images associated with evaluations of subjects.

V. Conclusion and Future Work

This paper presented ImageCube, a scatterplot-like browser for image collections associated with multi-dimensional datasets. The paper described technical components of ImageCube, and introduced a use case scenario with a real image collection of cars on the Web.

Our current implementation of ImageCube supports a user interface to specify ranges of values to be displayed, however, our user case did in Section 4 did not use it. Moreover, the implementation does not suppose that tags or keywords are not associated to images. We would like to enhance them so that we can flexibly retrieve or narrow down interested images. Another our interest is implementation of dimension reduction schemes, and representations of three or more dimensions. We expect these bring us more various visualization results. Finally, we would like to test ImageCube with larger datasets including more images and higher-dimensional values, and subjectively evaluate with experimental users.

References

[1] B. B. Bederson, PhotoMesa: A Zoomable Image Browser Using Quantum Treemaps and Bubblemaps, *Symposium on User Interface Software and Technology*, 71-80, 2001.

[2] N. Elmqvist, P. Dragicevic, J. Fekete, Rolling the Dice: Multidimensional Visual Exploration using Scatterplot Matrix Navigation, *IEEE transactions on Visualization and Computer Graphics*, 14(6), 1141-1148, 2008.

[3] A. Gomi, T. Itoh, MIAOW: A 3D Image Browser Applying a Location- and Time-Based Hierarchical Data Visualization Technique, *Advanced Visual Interface (AVI10)*, 225-232, 2010.

[4] H. Horibe, T. Itoh, PhotoSurfing: A 3D Image Browser Assisting Association-Based Photo-graph Browsing, *NICOGRAPH International*, 2009.

[5] A. Nagasaki, T. Itoh, M. Ise, K. Miyashita, A Correlation-based Hierarchical Data Visualization Technique and Its Application to Credit Card Fraud Data, *1st International Workshop on Super Visualization (in conjunction with the 22nd ACM International Conference on Supercomputing)*, 2008.

[6] W. Peng, M. O. Ward, E. A. Rundensteiner, Clutter Reduction in Multi-Dimensional Data Visualization Using Dimension Reordering, *IEEE Symposium on Information Visualization*, 89-96, 2004.

[7] M. Sips, B. Neubert, J. P. Lewis, P. Hanrahan, Selecting Good Views of High-Dimensional Data Using Class Consistency, *Computer Graphics Forum*, 28(3), 831-838, 2009.

[8] J. Yang., J. Fan, D. Hubball, Y. Gao, H. Luo, W. Ribarsky, M. Ward, Semantic Image Browser: Bridging Information Visualization with Automated Intelligent Image Analysis, *IEEE Visual Analytics in Science and Technology*, 191-198, 2006.

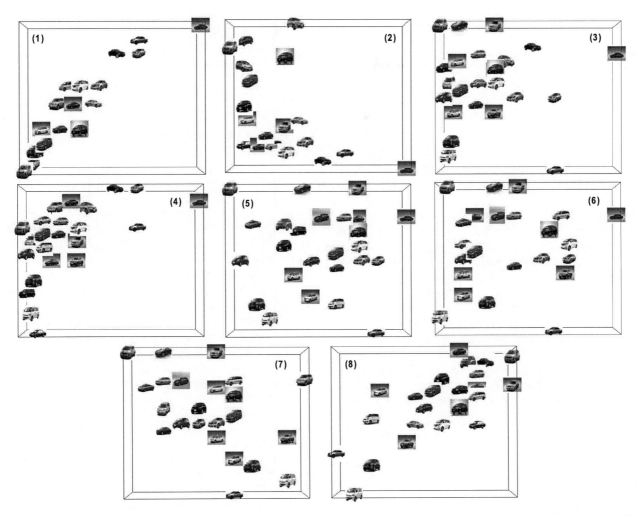

Figure 3. Examples with an image collection of cars. (1) Price for X-axis, and displacement for Y-axis. (2) Price for X-axis, and fuel cost for Y-axis. (3) Price for X-axis, and equipment for Y-axis. (4) Price for X-axis, and appearance evaluation for Y-axis. (5) Outer length for X-axis, and appearance evaluation for Y-axis. (6) Outer width for X-axis, and appearance evaluation for Y-axis. (7) Height of floor for X-axis, and appearance evaluation for Y-axis. (8) Appearance evaluation for X-axis, and cost performance evaluation for Y-axis.

Layered TimeRadarTrees

Michael Burch, Markus Höferlin, Daniel Weiskopf

Visualization Research Center, University of Stuttgart, Germany

{michael.burch, markus.hoeferlin, daniel.weiskopf}@visus.uni-stuttgart.de

Abstract

We introduce a novel technique for visualizing dense time-varying directed and weighted multi-graphs with an additional hierarchical organization of the graph nodes. Combining Indented Tree Plots and TimeRadarTrees, we show the temporal evolution of relations in a static view. The graph edges are layered around thumbnail wheels consisting of color-coded sectors that are representatives of the graph nodes. These sectors generate implicit representations of graph edges. Start and target vertices are perceived by inspecting the color coding of sectors in the context of other sectors and their orientations. The technique puts emphasis on newer relations and hence, these are mapped to a larger display space in the radial diagram. The benefit of our technique is reduction of visual clutter from which node-link diagrams typically suffer. The visualization focuses on an easy exploration of trends, countertrends, periodicity, temporal shifts, and anomalies in time-varying relational data. We demonstrate the usefulness of the approach by applying it to dense dynamic graph data acquired from a soccer match of the 2D Soccer Simulation League.

Keywords— **Dynamic Graph Visualization, Indented Tree Plots, TimeRadarTrees.**

1 Introduction

Visualizing dynamic relational data in information hierarchies with additional quantitative information applied to each relation is a challenging topic. Typically, this kind of graph data is represented by node-link diagrams with time displayed either by animation or by small multiples [2] of the graph at different time slices.

Animated diagrams normally use interpolation of node positions between time slices; new nodes are smoothly faded in and obsolete nodes are faded out to achieve a temporally coherent animation. The advantages of animation are its conceptual simplicity and its congruence of mapping because time from graph dynamics is mapped to visualization time: the user virtually sees the evolution of the graph. Another advantage is that the whole screen can be used to display the graph. However, animation is associated with high cognitive load for typical analysis tasks and, thus, viewed skeptically by psychologists [1]. Furthermore, the issue of how well the mental map of the graph is maintained arises [16].

Small multiples of different time slices shown side-by-side alleviate some of the cognitive issues of animation. In particular, this approach allows the user to explore several time slices simultaneously. However, small multiples need quite substantial screen space and therefore, only a few time slices can be shown.

To avoid issues of node-link diagrams, we adopt spatial circular layering to visually represent time, reminiscent of TimeRadarTrees [9]. To make the technique more scalable we extend the approach by multi-layered thumbnails and by the concept of center and thumbnail color wheels. Furthermore, we visualize a more general graph class than compound graphs: we allow relations between all nodes—leaf as well as inner nodes.

To interpret the graph relations in the diagram, we use differently oriented circle sectors of radial diagrams combined with color coding for each sector. In this way, we avoid explicit links as in node-link diagrams, but rather display links implicitly. The dynamic graph edges are layered as adjacency arcs around the corresponding sectors of a circular thumbnail (*ThumbWheel*) in the same temporal order as in the graph sequence. ThumbWheels are miniature representations for each vertex in the graph sequence and are located around a larger version of the sectors (*CenterWheel*) that provides the context of the vertex. The hierarchical organization of the graph vertices is represented by a radial extension of indented tree plots [10].

We decided to map time to spatial positions in the diagram in order to avoid typical issues of animation. In particular, this mapping reduces cognitive efforts when exploring trends, countertrends, temporal shifts, periodic behaviors, and anomalies. A viewer's mental map is automatically preserved by using a static diagram for dynamic data. Compared to node-link diagrams (static or animated), our approach exhibits the advantage of reduced visual clutter because explicitly drawn links are avoided, and it leads to lower computational costs because complex layout algorithms for effective node-link diagrams are not required.

1550-6037/11 $26.00 © 2011 IEEE

DOI 10.1109/IV.2011.93

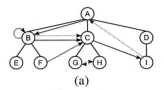 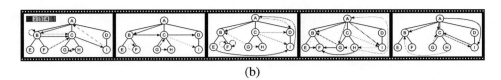

(a)   (b)

Figure 1: Node-link diagrams: (a) inclusion relations (black lines without arrow heads) and directed adjacency relations (colored lines with black arrow heads) in a node-link diagram; (b) a sequence of graphs as an animated node-link diagram.

Finally, our visualization technique additionally supports hierarchical information attached to graph vertices.

There are many applications for dynamic graph data with hierarchically structured elements such as relations in a hierarchically organized software system, the traveling behavior of tourists in a hierarchically structured world, or the relations among members in a social network.

In this paper, we illustrate the usefulness of the visualization technique by showing trends, countertrends, periodic behaviors, temporal shifts, and anomalies in soccer data of the World Championship 2010 of the 2D Soccer Simulation League. We choose this kind of data because it belongs to the class of dense graphs and understanding the semantics of the data is possible for non-domain experts, addressing a broad audience.

2   Related Work

There is a large body of previous work on visual analysis of large graphs, as summarized and categorized in the recent survey article by von Landesberger et al. [20]. The authors classify existing approaches according to the graph type to be visualized, the interactive features to explore a graph, and the algorithmic issues that have to be addressed.

For effective visual node-link representations of static and dynamic graphs alike, aesthetic graph drawing criteria should be observed [6, 7, 17]. As outlined in the previous section, a natural way of representing dynamic graph data is to show the time dimension by a time-to-time mapping as in animated sequences of node-link diagrams. This approach led to the development of many sophisticated graph layout algorithms that, amongst other criteria, target aesthetic graph drawing criteria and the preservation of a viewer's mental map [16]. A typical example of offline dynamic graph drawing is due to Diehl and Görg [11], who consider all graphs from the complete temporal sequence when they generate the layout of each graph in the sequence. A representative online dynamic graph drawing technique is the one by Frishman and Tal [13], who aim to maintain the global structure of the graph while allowing modifications between consecutive graphs. Our technique is independent from online or offline graph visualization aspects and allows us to quickly add graphs on-the-fly.

Cognitive issues with animation of graphs can be reduced by putting different time slices of the node-link diagrams side-by-side. This approach, however, still relies on node-link visualization with all its advantages and disadvantages. Recent work by Archambault et al. [3] compares the effectiveness of animation and side-by-side visualization with small multiples. Another alternative to small multiples is to draw a sequence of node-link diagrams in a single view as presented by Greilich et al. [15].

The layout problems of dynamic node-link diagrams can be avoided by resorting a completely different mapping of data to visual space. If one is not primarily interested in detecting varying paths in a graph sequence, matrix-based approaches have been shown to be more appropriate since they scale much better for the time dimension. Ghoniem et al. [14] investigated if matrix or node-link techniques for static graphs perform better for certain tasks.

The idea of matrix-based visualization can be extended to deformed spatial layouts. The TimeRadarTrees technique [9] displays dynamic compound digraphs in static diagrams by mapping time to space where graph relations are stacked into circle sectors. We build on this technique because we also generate a contextual view in the center (the CenterWheel) surrounded by miniature thumbnail representations (ThumbWheels). We enhance TimeRadarTrees by introducing an additional color coding of sectors in the CenterWheel and ThumbWheels. Moreover, we do not restrict the visualization to compound graphs, but we support relations between all possible nodes in the hierarchy.

To display the hierarchical information in the data sets, we adopt the indented tree plot technique [10]. We adapt this technique by deforming it from a linear layout to a circular layout that fits the CenterWheel. This kind of hierarchy visualization is useful because it does not occlude any other graphical elements in contrast to TimeRadarTrees and, hence, reduces visual clutter.

3   The Visualization Technique

Representing dynamic relational data in information hierarchies in a static diagram leads to the question of how different data dimensions can be visualized simultaneously. Effective encoding of graph vertices and edges,

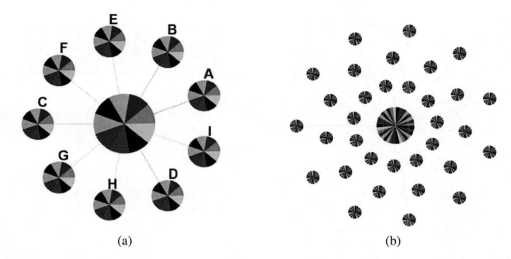

(a)   (b)

Figure 2: CenterWheel and ThumbWheels: (a) The large circle in the center—the CenterWheel—is divided into nine differently colored sectors. Nine miniature thumbnail copies—the ThumbWheels—generate a contextual view. (b) A contextual view for a larger node set may exploit several layers to display all ThumbWheels.

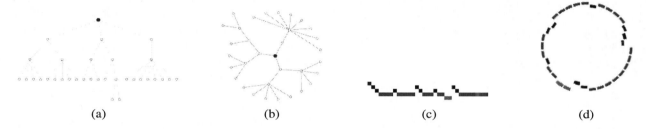

(a)   (b)   (c)   (d)

Figure 3: An example hierarchy consisting of 33 nodes displayed as (a) rooted node-link diagram; (b) radial node-link diagram; (c) indented tree plot; (d) radial indented tree plot.

as well as their directions and weights is required. Furthermore, multi-edges may occur that all might have different weights. Vertices are hierarchically organized, which leads to another type of structured relations. The representation of the time dimension among the graph edges is another challenge when using static diagrams.

In the following sections, we describe how all these different dimensions in the data can be visually encoded in a single static diagram with the goal to reduce visual clutter and to allow the user to easily detect trends, countertrends, periodic behaviors, temporal shifts, and anomalies in dynamic relational data between different hierarchy levels.

3.1 Implicit Link Representation

Figure 1 (a) shows a static graph that consists of inclusion edges (black lines without arrow heads). Separately, directed adjacency edges are indicated by colored lines with arrow heads, starting at a source node and pointing to a target node. The graph in Figure 1 (a) consists of

nine nodes where five of them are leaf nodes of a hierarchy (E, F, G, H, and I), and the four remaining nodes are inner nodes of the hierarchy (A, B, C, and D). Node A is the root node. Furthermore, there are nine adjacency relations, where the relation from node B to C appears twice (multigraph). Node B has a self-edge, i.e., source and target node are identical.

Figure 1 (b) depicts the dynamic case. A sequence of node-link diagrams is displayed where the weight of each adjacency relation is indicated by color coding. The hierarchical organization of the nodes is constant. The weights of some edges are constant in all of the timesteps. The weights of another edge are growing at a constant rate, which can be classified as a trend. There are also some nodes without any incoming edges throughout the sequence and nodes without outgoing edges at any time. Finding out these phenomena is difficult and needs some exploration time in Figure 1 (b).

To avoid explicit links as in node-link diagrams, we

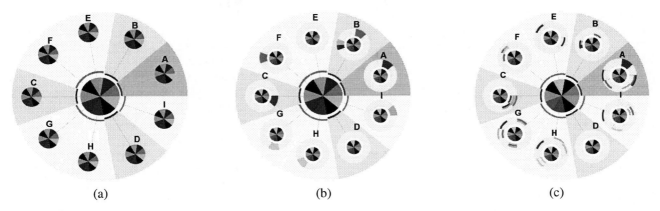

(a)   (b)   (c)

Figure 4: (a) The hierarchical organization of the nodes of Figure 1 is shown as a radial indented tree plot with additional color coding that depends on the depth of each hierarchical element. (b) Directed relations of the static multi-graph of Figure 1 are visually encoded as color-coded sectors and put on top of each representative ThumbWheel at the corresponding circle sectors. (c) Dynamic graph from Figure 1 is visually encoded as color-coded sectors.

instead use indirect encoding of correspondence between vertices by common orientation in a glyph. The glyph is designed as a circular area that is divided into as many sectors as vertices have to be represented.

Figure 2 (a) shows the glyph for the example of nine nodes. To improve the visual separation of the sectors, we apply a special color coding that makes neighboring sectors as distinct as possible. Humans are able to clearly and easily separate a certain number of distinct colors. The main idea here is to make visual objects as distinct as possible on several feature channels and to make use of the good perceptual grouping property of color [21].

In addition to the glyph above, the implicit link representation contains further smaller copies of the glyph located around the center glyph, adopting the concept of small multiples [2, 8]. The number of thumbnails is identical to the number of vertices to be represented. As a benefit, each single circle sector of the small thumbnail glyphs can be mentally connected to one of the sectors in the larger circle by using color coding and orientation information.

In the following, we use this ease of mental mapping to encode relations of a graph and a sequence of graphs implicitly: a directed link between any two vertices is implicitly represented by the combination of a sector in the CenterWheel and the sector in that ThumbWheel that is connected to the aforementioned sector in the CenterWheel.

The ThumbWheels do not necessarily have to be positioned at equal distances from the CenterWheel. As a benefit of the unique orientation of each circle sector, the corresponding ThumbWheel just needs to be positioned somewhere on the line starting at the CenterWheel and pointing radially in the direction of the corresponding sector.

Figure 2 (b) shows an example where the ThumbWheels

are placed on three different layers around the Center-Wheel. 33 ThumbWheels would be far too many to place them all equally distant from the CenterWheel. This would lead to overlap and occlusion. As a solution, we place these ThumbWheels on different radial layers; a guiding line connects each circle sector of the CenterWheel to the corresponding ThumbWheel.

3.2 Hierarchy Representation

To avoid visual clutter in the display we do not use a radial node-link diagram on top of the contextual view as, for example, in TimeRadarTrees [9]. To represent adjacency relations between any hierarchy level, we introduce the radial indented tree plot, adopting the linear indented tree plot technique [10]. These plots are well suited for our purpose because they are essentially one-dimensional zigzag curves that can be deformed to fit tightly around the CenterWheel. Other hierarchy representations such as treemaps [18], layered icicles [4, 19, 22], or traditional rooted trees [5, 12] are two-dimensional diagrams and, thus, would not be suitable for our goal of displaying all hierarchical elements on one common representative one-dimensional line.

Figures 3 (a)–(d) show how a tree diagram looks like in a rooted and radial node-link as well as indented metaphor. For the indented plot, we use a blue-to-red color gradient whose value depends on the depth of a hierarchical element. Indentation is used to express on which depth in the tree a node is located. Radial indentation means that nodes on a deeper level in the hierarchy are further away from the circle center. The root node of a radial indented plot is placed to the rightmost position of a circle and the following nodes are processed in a clockwise strategy and in depth-first order. This ordering of nodes also implies the same ordering of sectors in the CenterWheel. In this way, sectors and indented tree elements that point in the same direction also refer to the same node.

The contextual view from Figure 2 (a) is extended by this hierarchical information. The radial indented tree plot is displayed in the space between the CenterWheel and the ThumbWheels. Each hierarchical element is oriented in the same direction as its corresponding circle sector, see Figure 4 (a). The hierarchical organization of the graph nodes is additionally expressed by elongated grayish sectors, where the gray level depends on the depth of the corresponding hierarchy element.

3.3 Static Graph Representation

Each adjacency edge in a multi-graph consists of a start and a target node, and additionally of a list of weights attached to it. Suppose that a multi-edge originates at node A and points to node B and has weights $w_1, \ldots, w_n$. Then this edge is represented as a color-coded *adjacency arc* attached to the ThumbWheel that represents node A; the adjacency arc is located in the sector of the ThumbWheel that points in the direction of node B. To support multi-edges, this sector is subdivided into as many subsectors as edges in this multi-edge. Finally, the weights $w_1, \ldots, w_n$ are represented by color coding applied to the adjacency arcs.

As an illustrative example, we use the graph shown in the node-link diagram in Figure 1 (a). The adjacency edge starting at node B and ending at node C is a multi-edge consisting of two differently weighted edges. All edges of this graph are converted to circle sectors and placed on top of the respective ThumbWheels, see Figure 4 (b).

3.4 Dynamic Graph Representation

The main benefit of our visualization technique is the direct support for displaying dynamic directed multi-graphs in information hierarchies. Figure 1 (b) shows a sequence of five graphs in an animated node-link diagram with color-coded adjacency edges and additional hierarchical information. To map the dynamic graph data, we use the same principle as for the static case. Time starts in the circle center and grows radially outward. This means that displaying a sequence of graphs can be implemented by layering all edges starting at node A and ending at node B on top of the circle sector for node B of the thumbnail representing node A. The time-dependent relations lead to temporally varying weights that are again shown by color mapping. As a benefit, the growing display space in the sectors puts newer relations more in focus than older ones.

Figure 4 (c) is a visual mapping of the dynamic graph data from Figure 1 (b). Our diagram has the benefit that trends in the time series can easily be detected. For instance, one complete stack of adjacency arcs for the ThumbWheel of node A is colored blue. Using the contextual view, it is easy to identify that the sector corresponds to node B. We can conclude that there is a dynamic edge from node A to node B with the same weight throughout the sequence. Another interesting insight comes from the ThumbWheel sector from node C to node I: the edge weight is increasing over time. Node D is the only node without any outgoing edge in the sequence. Furthermore, the hierarchical information displayed as a radial indented tree plot can be used to understand between which levels of a hierarchy these relations occur. All these insights would be difficult to find out with animated node-link diagrams and even with a sequence of node-link diagrams placed next to each other as shown in Figure 1 (b).

3.5 Interactive Features

The visualization tool supports several interactive features: expanding and collapsing of hierarchy levels, changing the color coding of the CenterWheel and the ThumbWheels, applying different color codings for the adjacency relations, details-on-demand, zooming of ThumbWheels, changing the radial distance of ThumbWheels, selecting time intervals and the like.

4 Dynamic Relations in Team Sports

We use dynamic data of team sports as an example to demonstrate the usefulness of our visualization. In this section, we show the visualization of a soccer match of the 2D Soccer Simulation League World Championship 2010. Such data contains many features of interest: hierarchically ordered nodes, directed and weighted edges between node pairs on different hierarchy levels, as well as dynamic behavior of the relational data over time. Furthermore, these graphs belong to the class of dense graphs and our data set provides a textual description of nodes.

In detail, we consider the following data aspects of the soccer match:

- Hierarchical organization: the root node represents the match; both teams are on the second level. The team parts—goalie, defense, midfield, and offense—build the third level of the hierarchy. The players and the ball are the leaf nodes (Figure 5 (a)).

- We measure the Euclidian distance between the players and the ball on the soccer ground and use these relationships as adjacency edges. For the non-leaf nodes, the arithmetic means of all its elements is computed first and then the Euclidian distance from this average position to the position of any other hierarchical element is used. This leads to a dense graph.

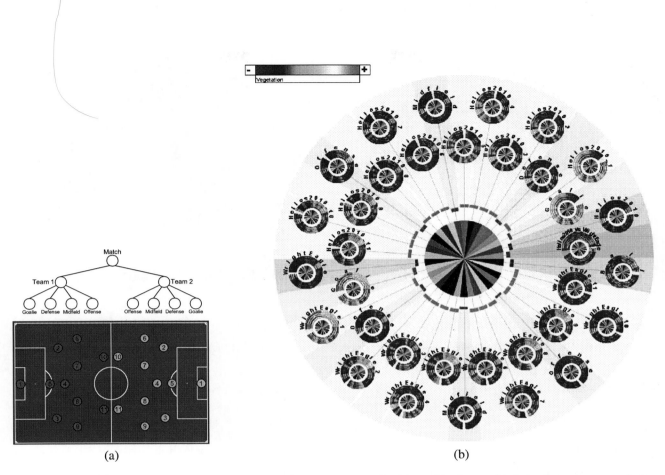

Figure 5: Hierarchy and dynamic relations in a soccer match. (a) The hierarchical organization of a soccer match (top image), along with the approximate spatial mapping of players (numbered nodes) to the soccer ground (bottom image). (b) Visualization of the 2D Soccer Simulation League World Championship 2010 final: Helios2010 vs. WrightEagle. Adjacency arcs show the Euclidian distances between players, team segments, and the ball during the soccer match.

- The dynamics of the data is obtained by measuring the positions in 100 millisecond intervals.

Figure 5 (b) represents an overview of all 6000 time steps of the dynamic graph data. The hierarchy consists of 34 elements and is represented as a radial indented plot with a blue-to-red color coding. We use a vegetation color mapping as illustrated in the upper left of Figure 5 (b). Zero-valued distances are encoded in light gray, which is typically the case for self-relations. Due to the large number of ThumbWheels, a second layer is created. Circular text labels are attached to each ThumbWheel.

A first observation from the diagram may be the dominating blue color. This expresses that distances between hierarchical elements are mainly not large. Four Thumb-Wheels are primarily in green to yellow color, which indicates that the corresponding players are farther away from the others. A closer inspection of this phenomenon reveals that these ThumbWheels belong to the goalies of both teams and the hierarchy container of their corresponding team parts.

Normally, the goalies remain in the penalty area and are hence farther away from other players and the ball. Another typical phenomenon can also be detected: offense players have mostly minimal distances to their defending counterparts. The midfield players of the Helios 2010 team are color-coded mainly in blue, which indicates that they are closer to other players and further apart from the two goalies, whose corresponding ThumbWheel sectors are colored in green. The midfield players of the WrightEagle team show a different behavior. The player with number eight has a larger distance to the defending players of the Helios 2010 team. The other two players of the WrightEagle's midfield do not share this behavior. These two players, number six and seven, have a larger distance to their own defense. Hence, the midfield of the WrightEagles focuses more on offense than the midfield of their opponent.

The ThumbWheels show periodic behavior in the distances. This originates from different actions during a soccer match: offense and defense. The ThumbWheel of the

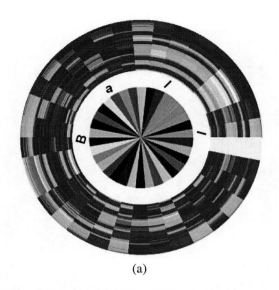 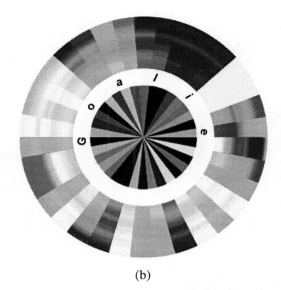

(a)   (b)

Figure 6: The enlarged ThumbWheel view for two graph nodes: (a) the ball object; (b) one of the goalkeepers.

ball exhibits that the midfield and the offense of the Helios 2010 team are most frequently close to the ball. Thus, we infer that these players are more often in possession of the ball.

Figure 6 (a) displays a scaled ThumbWheel of the ball, showing an interval of 100 seconds. The yellow and red color encodings unveil that the ball is often more distant from the goalies than from other players. The upper right circle quarter with a blue color coding indicates that the ball is close to the goalies and the defending players of Helios 2010, which is also the case for the midfield players of WrightEagle. We may conjecture that the WrightEagle team is in ball possession and attacks the opposite team.

The enlarged ThumbWheel of the goalie of the Helios 2010 team in the same time interval is illustrated in Figure 6 (b). Compared to the ThumbWheel of the ball, the color changes are smoother. The ball frequently changes its position abruptly since it can be kicked with high speed. Two sectors change from yellow to red, which indicates that the distance from the Helios 2010 goalie to the opposite goalie (and its corresponding goalie team part) is increasing.

This is just an example of the many insights that can be observed utilizing our visualization.

5   Conclusions and Future Work

In this paper, we have presented a novel technique for displaying time-varying directed multi-graphs in information hierarchies. The approach uses an implicit link representation to visually encode graphs. Relations are shown by adjacency arcs stacked on top of the corresponding

ThumbWheel sectors. The information hierarchy is displayed as a radial indented tree plot that allows us to visualize relations between any hierarchical element.

The cognitive effort is kept low for exploration of the dynamics, since we represent the dynamic data in a static diagram. Additionally, we preserve the mental map by displaying the graph nodes at a fixed position. In contrast to node-link diagrams of dense graphs, visual clutter is marginal since we do not have any crossing edges. We also do not need time-consuming layout algorithms. This leads to the advantage that graphs can be added on-the-fly without changing the graph layout.

We have demonstrated the usefulness of our technique by a data set of the 2D Soccer Simulation League. This data set consists of 34 nodes including a hierarchical organization, and a time-series of 6000 measurement points. The weights of edges are given by Euclidian distances for each pair of players, team parts, and the ball. Trends, countertrends, periodic behaviors, temporal shifts, and anomalies are easily detected in the diagram.

In future work, we will evaluate the strengths of implicit link representation in our technique compared to explicit link representation given in node-link diagrams. Although several interaction techniques are already available, additional interactive features will further enrich our novel visualization system.

Acknowledgements

This work was funded by German Research Foundation (DFG) as part of the Priority Program "Scalable Visual Analytics" (SPP 1335).

References

[1] B. Tversky, J. Bauer Morrison, and M. Betrancourt. *Animation: Can It Facilitate?* International Journal of Human-Computer Studies, pages 247-262, 2002.

[2] E. Tufte. *Envisioning Information.* Graphics Press 1990.

[3] D. Archambault, H. C. Purchase and B. Pinaud. *Animation, Small Multiples, and the Effect of Mental Map Preservation in Dynamic Graphs.* IEEE Transactions on Visualization and Computer Graphics, 17(4), pages 539-552, 2011.

[4] K. Andrews and H. Heidegger. *Information Slices: Visualising and Exploring Large Hierarchies Using Cascading, Semi-Circular Discs.* In Proceedings of the IEEE Information Visualization Symposium, pages 9-12, 1998.

[5] G. Di Battista, P. Eades, R. Tamassia and I. G. Tollis. *Graph Drawing: Algorithms for the Visualization of Graphs.* Prentice Hall 1999.

[6] F. Beck, M. Burch and S. Diehl. *Towards an Aesthetic Dimensions Framework for Dynamic Graph Visualizations.* In Proceedings of the 13th International Conference on Information Visualisation, pages 592-597, 2009.

[7] C. Bennett, J. Ryall, L. Spalteholz and A. Gooch. *The Aesthetics of Graph Visualization.* In Proceedings of Computational Aesthetics, pages 57-64, 2007.

[8] J. Bertin. *Semiology of Graphics: Diagrams, Networks, Maps.* Madison, WI: University of Wisconsin Press 1983.

[9] M. Burch and S. Diehl. *TimeRadarTrees: Visualizing Dynamic Compound Digraphs.* Computer Graphics Forum, 27(3), pages 823-830, 2008.

[10] M. Burch, M. Raschke and D. Weiskopf. *Indented Pixel Tree Plots.* In Proceedings of the International Symposium on Visual Computing, pages 338-349, 2010.

[11] S. Diehl and C. Görg. *Graphs, They Are Changing.* In Proceedings of Graph Drawing, pages 23-30, 2002.

[12] P. Eades. *Drawing Free Trees.* Bulletin of the Institute for Combinatorics and its Applications, pages 10-36, 1992.

[13] Y. Frishman and A. Tal. *Online Dynamic Graph Drawing.* IEEE Transactions on Visualization and Computer Graphics, 14(4), pages 727-740, 2008.

[14] M. Ghoniem, J.-D. Fekete and P. Castagliola. *A Comparison of the Readability of Graphs Using Node-Link and Matrix-Based Representations.* In Proceedings of the IEEE Symposium on Information Visualization, pages 17-24, 2004.

[15] M. Greilich, M. Burch and S. Diehl. *Visualizing the Evolution of Compound Digraphs with TimeArc-Trees.* Computer Graphics Forum, 28(3), pages 975-982, 2009.

[16] K. Misue, P. Eades, W. Lai and K. Sugiyama. *Layout Adjustment and the Mental Map.* Journal of Visual Languages and Computing, 6(2), pages 183-210, 1995.

[17] H. C. Purchase. *Metrics for Graph Drawing Aesthetics.* Journal of Visual Languages and Computing, 13(5), pages 501-516, 2002.

[18] B. Shneiderman. *Tree Visualization with Tree-Maps: 2-d Space-Filling Approach.* ACM Transactions on Graphics, 11(1), pages 92-99, 1992.

[19] J. T. Stasko and E. Zhang. *Focus+Context Display and Navigation Techniques for Enhancing Radial, Space-Filling Hierarchy Visualizations.* In Proceedings of the IEEE Symposium on Information Visualization, pages 57-65, 2000.

[20] T. von Landesberger, A. Kuijper, T. Schreck, J. Kohlhammer, J. J. van Wijk, J.-D. Fekete and D. W. Fellner. *Visual Analysis of Large Graphs.* In Eurographics State-of-the-Art Reports 2010.

[21] C. Ware. *Visual Thinking for Design.* Morgan Kaufman 2008.

[22] J. Yang, M. O. Ward, E. A. Rundensteiner and A. Patro. *InterRing: A Visual Interface for Navigating and Manipulating Hierarchies.* Information Visualization, 2(1), pages 16-30, 2003.

Drawing Semi-bipartite Graphs in Anchor+Matrix Style

Kazuo Misue and Qi Zhou*
Department of Computer Science, University of Tsukuba
Tsukuba, Ibaraki, Japan
misue@cs.tsukuba.ac.jp, zhouqi727@gmail.com

Abstract—A bipartite graph consists of a set of nodes that can be divided into two partitions such that no edge has both endpoints in the same partition. A semi-bipartite graph is a bipartite graph with edges in one partition. Anchored map is a graph drawing technique for bipartite graphs and provides aesthetically pleasing layouts of graphs with high readability by restricting the positions of nodes in a partition. For this research, the objects of the anchored map technique were extended to semi-bipartite graphs. A hybrid layout style of anchored maps and matrix representations are proposed, and an automatic drawing technique is shown. The proposed technique arranges the nodes in one partition on a circumference like the anchored map of bipartite graphs. It also divides nodes in the other partition with edges into clusters and represents them in the matrix representations to make it easy to see connective subsets.

Keywords-network visualization, graph drawing, semi-bipartite graph, anchored map, matrix representation

I. Introduction

Anchored map is a graph drawing technique for bipartite graphs [8], [9]. A *bipartite graph* consists of a set of nodes that can be divided into two partitions such that no edge has both endpoints in the same partition. The anchored map technique is based on the unrestricted placement of nodes such as with the spring-embedder model [1]. However, it restricts the positions of nodes in a partition to provide aesthetically pleasing layout of graphs with high readability.

The purpose of this research is to extend the object of the anchor map technique to semi-bipartite graphs. A *semi-bipartite graph* is a bipartite graph with edges in one partition. We see many semi-bipartite graphs in the real world. For example, relations between items and consumers who bought the items make up a bipartite graph. Taking into account friendships among consumers, it becomes a semi-bipartite graph. Relations between Web pages and visitors to the pages also make up a bipartite graph, and links between Web pages creates a semi-bipartite graph. We believe visual representations of semi-bipartite graphs help with observation and analysis of such relationships with semi-bipartite graphs.

In an anchored map, nodes whose positions are restricted are called "anchors," and the other nodes are called "free nodes." In this study, we assume nodes in the partition

* His current affiliation is with Nomura Research Institute.

with edges are free nodes. We can apply the anchored map technique to semi-bipartite graphs. However, it ignores edges between free nodes because there are no edges between free nodes in bipartite graphs. Therefore, edges among free nodes may bring about many problems in this situation. For example, adjacent free nodes may be placed apart from each other and edges connecting free nodes needlessly cross each other. These problems cause low readability of the layout.

We developed a new anchored map technique to solve such problems and draw semi-bipartite graphs as anchored maps. We took the following two measures.

- introduce aesthetic criteria considering edges between free nodes.
- introduce the matrix representation for the edges between free nodes.

We explain our new drawing technique we developed for semi-bipartite graphs as drawing objects. The combination of the anchored-map style and matrix representations is one of the most important features of this technique. We show the drawing standard, the aesthetic criteria, and a drawing procedure for semi-bipartite graphs.

II. Related Work

A. Bipartite Graph Drawing

Some studies on bipartite graphs have resulted in layout techniques as a building block of drawing a graph in the Sugiyama style [13]. For example, Newton et al. proposed a heuristic for two-sided bipartite graph drawing, where nodes in two partitions were laid out on two parallel lines [11]. Other studies tried to change the style for bipartite graphs. Zheng et al. described two layout models and proved theorems of edge crossing for these models [15]. Giacomo et al. proposed drawing bipartite graphs on two curves so that the edges do not cross [3]. These studies proposed techniques to minimize edge crossing in the two-sided style or its extended styles.

The anchored map technique [8] is also a drawing technique for bipartite graphs. We introduce research related to this in Section II-C because it is one of the most important precursors of this research.

B. Semi-bipartite Graph Drawing

To the best of our knowledge, there have been few studies on drawing semi-bipartite graphs. A semi-bipartite graph

1550-6037/11 $26.00 © 2011 IEEE
DOI 10.1109/IV.2011.24

model has been introduced by Xu et al. [14]. They gave a model of the gene ontology network as a semi-bipartite graph and proposed drawing methods.

C. Anchored Map

The anchored map technique restricts positions of nodes, called "anchors", in one partition, to provide aesthetically pleasing layout of graphs with high readability. Misue [8], [9] described a method for restricting the positions of anchors on a circumference.

Extensions were proposed for anchored maps. Ito et al. proposed an extension of the drawing space to three dimensions [6]. The positions of anchors are restricted on a spherical surface, so anchors have the freedom of two dimensions. Sato et al. proposed a method for showing clusters of free nodes [12]. Free nodes are divided into clusters by using similarities of sets of adjacent anchors and drawn with iso-similarity contour curves. We also use the idea of clustering free nodes. However, we divide them by using edges between free nodes and represent clusters as matrix representations. Ito et al. introduced another hierarchical structure into the partition of anchors and developed a technique using the hierarchical circular layout of bipartite graphs [7]. It is effective for visualization of large-scale bipartite graphs. The technique is related to our technique from the viewpoint that some structural elements are added to one partition. However, we add them to the partition of free nodes and propose a new representation style.

D. Matrix Representation

The techniques to express a network in the matrix representation are used for a long time. The matrix representation just displays an adjacency matrix, which is a mathematical expression of a graph. This enables quick reading of the adjacency of specific nodes, but it is unsuitable for tracing a path consisting of several nodes. Ghoniem compared matrix representation with node-link representation for easy reading of information from the representations [2]. MatrixExplorer is a tool that uses the matrix representation and a node-link representation to use the advantages of both representations [4]. In NodeTrix, matrix representations are locally combined with a node-link representation to provide advantages of the matrix representations [5]. The representation style used in this study was affected by NodeTrix. The matrix representation is combined with the anchored maps, which is a representation style of node-link diagrams.

III. Anchored Map + Matrix Representation

We propose a new representation style that combines an anchored map with matrix representation as a representation style of a semi-bipartite graph. We formalize the semi-bipartite graph and clarify the style by showing the drawing standard and the aesthetic criteria.

A. Semi-bipartite Graph

A *bipartite graph* is defined as $G_B = (A, B, E)$ with node partitions A and B, which are disjoint, i.e., $A \cap B = \emptyset$, and E is a finite set of edges, i.e., $E \subseteq A \times B$.

A *semi-bipartite graph* is defined as $G_{SB} = (A, B, E, F)$, where $G = (A, B, E)$ is a bipartite graph, and F is a finite set of edges connecting two nodes in B, i.e., $F \subseteq \{\{u, v\} | u, v \in B, u \neq v\}$[1]. We call the elements in set F "inner edges" of set B.

B. Combining anchored map and matrix representation

We devised a new drawing technique for semi-bipartite graphs. With this technique, nodes of set A are arranged on a circumference. Nodes of set B are divided into clusters by using inner edges. The clusters are arranged at appropriate positions expressing relations to other nodes and clusters well. Every cluster is represented in the matrix representation. Nodes in a matrix are arranged in an order that clearly expresses relations in the cluster.

C. Drawing Standards

The following standards are used for drawing anchored maps [9].

C1   Nodes are represented as bullets (or small icons).
C2   Nodes in partition A are arranged on a circumference.
C3   Nodes in partition B have no limitation with regards to the coordinate system.
C4   Edges of set E are represented as straight line segments.

We revised the drawing standards as follows to combine an anchored map with the matrix representation. We divided C1 into C1a and C1b and added C4b to C4.

C1a   Nodes in partition A are represented as bullets.
C1b   Nodes in partition B are represented as matrices or bullets.
C4b   Edges of set F are represented as matrices or straight line segments.

A node cluster is represented as a matrix. Therefore, edges of set F, whose endpoints are in the same cluster, are represented in a matrix. Other edges of set F are represented as line segments. The matrix representation of the clusters is the same as that widely used for general graphs. A row and column each corresponds to a node, and a symbol at the intersection of a row and column denotes that a node corresponding to the row and a node corresponding to the column are adjacent to each other.

---

[1] F is a set of undirected edges from this definition. If we want to express directed edges, we may use another definition such as $F \subseteq \{\langle u, v \rangle | u, v \in B, u \neq v\}$.

D. Aesthetic Criteria

The following rules are used for the aesthetic criteria of anchored maps [9].

R1   Nodes are separated mutually more than the lowest distance.

R2   Adjacent nodes are laid out as closely as possible (minimize the total length of edges.)

R3   The number of edge crossings is as small as possible.

R4   Anchors adjacent to common free nodes are laid out as closely as possible.

R5   Free nodes adjacent to common anchors are laid out as closely as possible.

We expanded the aesthetic criteria to cover semi-bipartite graphs as drawing objects and combine an anchored map with the matrix representation. We replaced rule R2 with R2', rule R4 with R4', and added rule R6.

R2'   Minimize the total length of edges.

R4'   Anchors connected to each other are laid out as closely as possible.

R6   Nodes adjacent to common nodes are laid out as closely as possible in a matrix.

Rule R2' is the same as R2 at a glance, but upon closer inspection they are different. The new representation style includes the matrix representation, and the edge lengths depend on the connecting points on a matrix. Therefore, we describe rule R2' with edge lengths rather than positions of adjacent nodes.

In addition, in a semi-bipartite graph, two anchors not sharing any free nodes may connect to each other via inner edges. We believe such anchors should be placed close to each other; therefore, we modified rule R4 to R4'.

We adopted rule R6 for the matrix representation to express clusters of free nodes. Rule R6 is formally defined by minimizing q in expression (1).

$$q = \sum_{f \in M} \sum_{u,v \in A(f)} |p(u) - p(v)|, \qquad (1)$$

where M is a set of free nodes represented in a matrix, and $A(f)$ is a set of nodes adjacent to the free node f in the subgraph[2] consisting of cluster M, that is, $A(f) = \{v \in M | \{v, f\} \in F\}$. $p(v)$ represents the position of node v in the matrix, i.e., $p : v \rightarrow \{1, 2, \cdots, |M|\}$.

We need to satisfy the aesthetic criteria as much as possible. We should give priority to rules because two or more rules may conflict. However, it is not easy to control the priority of rules using force-directed techniques. Therefore, we do not argue the priority here.

---

[2]the node-induced subgraph of G_{SB} by M

IV. DRAWING METHOD

A. Outline of Layout Procedure

The drawing procedure is as follows.

1:    Divide free nodes into clusters; creating a reduced graph

2:    Determine the anchor order

3:    Determine the positions of free nodes (i.e., free node clusters)

4:    Determine the free node order in matrices

5:    Link edges

Step 1: We divide nodes in set F into clusters by using inner edges. Each cluster includes nodes strongly connected to each other, and fewer edges connect different clusters. We used Newman's algorithm [10] to create such free-node clusters. Every cluster is replaced with a single node to create a reduced graph.

If we obtain a bipartite graph by this reduction, we can just use the current anchored map technique. In most cases, however, the reduced graph is also a semi-bipartite graph because it is generally impossible to make clusters so that there is no edge connecting the clusters. Therefore, a technique for laying out a semi-bipartite graph as an anchored map is necessary.

Step 2: Steps 2 and 3 are for obtaining the anchored map of a semi-bipartite graph. In step 2, anchor positions are determined using rules R2', R3, and R4'. The procedure is similar to that for bipartite graphs, but edges of set F should be considered.

Step 3: Free node positions are determined using rules R1, R2', R3, and R5. The procedure is also similar to that for bipartite graphs, but edges of set F should be considered as well. If we want to obtain an anchored map without matrix representation, we draw line segments connecting adjacent nodes after determining positions of the free nodes in step 3.

Step 4: The clusters made in step 1 are represented in the matrix representation. The order of nodes in the matrix is then determined if it satisfies rule R6.

Step 5: For an anchored map of a bipartite graph, each node is expressed at a point (a bullet or a small icon), and each edge is drawn in a line segment. We do not need to worry about routing of edges if the node positions have been determined. Conditions for anchored maps of semi-bipartite graphs are basically the same for bipartite graphs. However, there are four positions to connect an edge to a free node when the node is represented in a matrix. We have to choose one of four positions for every edge to satisfy rule R2' and R3.

B. Drawing Anchored Map for Semi-bipartite Graph

As stated above, steps 2 and 3 are used to obtain the anchored map of a semi-bipartite graph. Therefore, we explain them as a drawing technique of semi-bipartite graphs. The technique we explain here is an extension of the technique suggested in a previous study [8] on bipartite graphs.

1) Determining Anchor Order: Because we determined that the anchors are arranged on a circumference at equal intervals in the drawing standard, what we should do in this step is to determine the anchor order on the circumference. The basic algorithm to determine the anchor order is the same as in the previous study. We used a technique that gradually improves the order while evaluating which order would be good, that is, satisfy the rules.

We have to determine the exact positions of the free nodes to evaluate the goodness of the order of the anchor order. The positions are determined using the spring-embedder model, which consumes a large amount of computation time. Therefore, the previous study used an index called "penalty", which can determine the goodness of free node placement.

Some penalties were defined based on rules R2, R3, and R4 [9]. Because we cannot evaluate rules R2 and R3 if the positions of the free nodes are not determined, we use the value of a penalty assuming that the free nodes are placed at their ideal positions.

For semi-bipartite graphs, we cannot determine the ideal positions of free nodes by using only the anchor positions because we should consider edges between the free nodes. Therefore, the use of penalty derived from rules R2' or R3 may be difficult.

We defined a penalty using rule R4'. This penalty is expressed with expression (2).

$$p = \sum_{u,v \in A, u \neq v} p(u, v) \qquad (2)$$

$$p(u, v) = \frac{d_c(u, v)}{w_E \cdot p_E(u, v) + w_F \cdot p_F(u, v)} \qquad (3)$$

Let p_E and p_F be the number of elements of set E and the number of the element of set F included in a path, respectively. That is, $p_E(u, v) = |P(u, v) \cap E|$, $p_F(u, v) = |P(u, v) \cap F|$, where $P(u, v)$ is the path between node u and v. Suppose that $d_c(u, v)$ is the distance between anchors u and v on the circumference. w_E and w_F are constant numbers to give weights to the elements of F and elements of E included in the path. In our implementation, $w_E = 1$ and $w_F = 2$. We found these values from experience of experiments.

When nodes u and v are not connected, i.e., there is no path between u and v, let $p(u, v) = 0$.

2) Determining Positions of Free Nodes: After we determined the anchor positions, we fix the anchors at the positions and arrange the positions of free nodes using the spring-embedder model [1].

C. Drawing Matrices for Node Clusters

In step 4, nodes in clusters are represented in the matrix representation.

1) Determining Free Nodes Order: We make the row and column orders the same. Therefore, what we should do in this step is to determine the node order.

We propose a variation of the barycenter (BC) method to satisfy rule R6, i.e., to place nodes related to each other close together. The BC method is a heuristic algorithm which has been proposed to reduce edge crossings in the hierarchical layout of directed graphs [13].

Taking a hint from the BC method, we developed the algorithm shown in Figure 1 to determine the node order in a matrix. q in the algorithm is expressed by expression (1). For the number of repeat times m, we used the number of nodes in cluster M in our implementation.

```
give an initial order to every node in M
report m times {
    for each node,
        compute the barycenter of its adjacent nodes.
    sort all nodes by their barycenters.
    calculate q and record the order with the value.
}
select the order with the minimum value of q
```

Figure 1. Algorithm to determine node order in matrix

V. EVALUATION

A. Evaluation of Penalty

A good penalty precisely predicts how the final layout satisfies the aesthetic criteria. Because the penalty we propose is derived from rule R4', we can expect a certain effect for R4'. We conducted an experimental evaluation on how well the penalty can predict for rules R2' and R3.

We examined correlations between penalty values and total edge lengths (rule R2') and between penalty values and the number of edge crossings (rule R3). We generated 100 random semi-bipartite graphs with 10 and 15 anchors. The numbers of free nodes and edges were varied. For each graph, we randomly generated 1000 anchor orders to calculate correlation coefficients to reduce experiment time.

For the graphs with 10 anchors, 99% had a correlation coefficient over 0.6, and 73% had one over 0.8 for rule R2'. For rule R3, 84% of the graphs had a correlation coefficient over 0.6. The results for the graphs with 15 anchors are almost the same as with the 10 anchors. For rule R2', 98% of the graphs had a correlation coefficient over 0.6 and 70% had one over 0.8. For rule R3, 95% of the graphs had a correlation coefficient over 0.6. From these results, we believe the penalty we propose is effective in predicting the aesthetic criteria. We can expect it is especially effective in the predicting edge length (rule R2').

B. Evaluation of BC Method Variation

We conducted an experiment to examine how rule R6 is satisfied using the variation of the BC method.

For each randomly generated undirected graph, we calculated a value of rule R6 (q) for every node-order pattern. We also calculated q for the order found with the variation of the BC method, and examined the ranking of value of q in all patterns.

We generated 1000 random graphs with five, six, and seven nodes to examine the ranking of values of q. For the graphs with five nodes, 70% had a value in the top position. In other words, the method found the optimal orders of about 700 graphs. For the graphs of the other two sizes, 60% − 65% had optimal orders. From these results, we believe that the variation of the BC method is effective for rule R6.

VI. EXAMPLES AND DISCUSSION

We show examples drawn using the technique we developed. The semi-bipartite graph shown in this section was extracted from a social networking service. We expressed relations between users and communities using a bipartite graph and expressed friendships using inner edges. All examples represent the same semi-bipartite graph, and communities are represented as anchors.

Figure 2(a) shows an example drawn using the technique of a previous study [9]. The positions of all nodes were determined without regard to the inner edges. The edges were then drawn as straight line segments. In other words, the inner edges do not affect the placement of nodes.

Figure 2(b) shows an example drawn also using the technique of the precedent study. The positions of anchors were determined without regard to the inner edges. We used the inner edges when determining the position of free nodes by using the spring-embedder model.

Figure 2(c) shows an example of the same graph drawn with only steps 2 and 3 in the developed procedure. Free nodes were not divided into any clusters, and every free node was drawn as a bullet. We can see that the number of crossings of the inner edges in Figure 2(c) are less than those in Figure 2(b).

Figure 2(d) shows an example of the same graph drawn using the developed technique. Free nodes were divided into eight clusters, and each was drawn in the matrix representation. We can clearly see the clusters and roughly understand the connection patterns inside the clusters.

VII. CONCLUSIONS

We developed a drawing technique for semi-bipartite graphs. We extended the anchored map drawing technique of bipartite graphs and combined it with the matrix representation into a hybrid representation. In the new representation, clusters of free nodes are represented in the matrix representation, so we can easily see the connect components of the nodes consisting of inner edges, which is a feature of semi-bipartite graphs. We defined a penalty for arranging anchors in semi-bipartite graphs and developed a variation

of the BC method for determining the order of free nodes in a matrix.

There is room for improving the penalty we defined and the variation of the BC method we developed. We plan to develop more effective techniques through experimental evaluation.

ACKNOWLEDGEMENTS

This work was supported in part by the Okawa Foundation for Information and Telecommunications.

REFERENCES

[1] Peter Eades, A Heuristic for Graph Drawing, Congressus Numerantium 42, pp. 149–160, 1984.

[2] Mohammad Ghoniem, Jean-Daniel Fekete, and Philippe Castagliola, A Comparison of the Readability of Graphs Using Node-Link and Matrix-Based Representations, IEEE Symposium on Information Visualization 2004, pp. 17–24, 2004.

[3] Emilio Di Giacomo, Luca Grilli, and Giuseppe Liotta, Drawing Bipartite Graphs on Two Curves, Graph Drawing: 14th International Symposium, GD 2006, Lecture Notes in Computer Science, Vol. 4372, pp. 380–385, Springer Berlin Heidelberg, 2007.

[4] Nathalie Henry and Jean-Daniel Fekete, MatrixExplorer: a Dual-Representation System to Explore Social Networks, IEEE Transactions on Visualization and Computer Graphics, Vol. 12, No. 5, pp. 677–684, 2006.

[5] Nathalie Henry, Jean-Daniel Fekete, and Michael J. McGuffin, NodeTrix: A Hybrid Visualization of Social Networks, IEEE Transactions on Visualization and Computer Graphics, Vol. 13, No. 6, pp. 1302–1309, 2007.

[6] Takao Ito, Kazuo Misue, Jiro Tanaka, Sphere Anchored Map: A Visualization Technique for Bipartite Graphs in 3D, Proceedings of 13th International Conference on Human-Computer Interaction (HCI International 2009), Human Interface, Part II, HCII 2009, LNCS 5611, pp.811-820, 2009.

[7] Takao Ito, Kazuo Misue, Jiro Tanaka, Drawing Clustered Bipartite Graphs in Multi-Circular Style, Proceedings of 14th International Conference Information Visualization (IV10), pp.23-28, 2010.

[8] Kazuo Misue: Drawing Bipartite Graphs as Anchored Maps, Proceedings of Asia-Pacific Symposium on Information Visualization (APVIS 2006), CRIPT, vol. 60, pp. 169–177, 2006.

[9] Kazuo Misue, Anchored Map: Graph Drawing Technique to Support Network Mining, IEICE Trans. Inf. & Syst., Vol. E91-D, No. 11, pp. 2599–2606, 2008.

[10] M. E. J. Newman. Fast algorithm for detecting community structure in networks. Physical Review E 69, 066133, 2004.

[11] Matthew Newton, Ondrej Sýkora, and Imrich Vrt'o, Two New Heuristics for Two-Sided Bipartite Graph Drawing, Graph Drawing: 10th International Symposium, GD 2002, Lecture Notes in Computer Science, Vol. 2528, pp. 312–319, Springer Berlin Heidelberg, 2002.

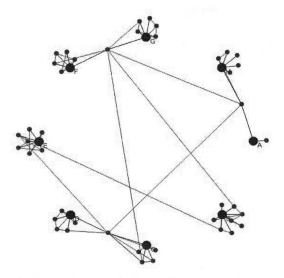

(a) Example drawn using technique of previous study. Nodes were arranged without regard to inner edges.

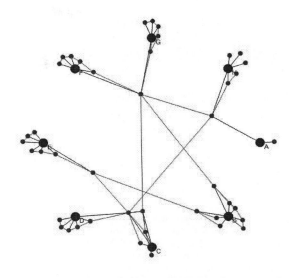

(b) Example drawn using technique of previous study. Anchors were arranged without regard to inner edges.

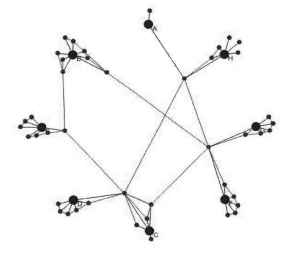

(c) Example drawn using part of proposed technique. Positions of nodes were determined with regard to inner edges.

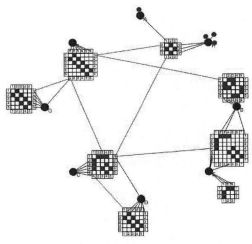

(d) Example drawn using proposed technique. Clusters of free nodes were drawn in matrix representation.

Figure 2.   Example of visualized semi-bipartite graph

[12] Shuji Sato, Kazuo Misue and Jiro Tanaka: Readable Representation for Large-Scale Bipartite Graphs, 12th International Conference on Knowledge-Based and Intelligent Information & Engineering Systems (KES 2008), LNAI 5178, pp. 831–838, 2008.

[13] Kozo Sugiyama, Shojiro Tagawa, and Mitsuhiko Toda, Method for Visual Understanding of Heirarchical System Structures, IEEE Transactions on Systems, Man and Cybernetics, Vol. 11, Issue 2, pp. 109–125, 1981.

[14] Kai Xu, Rohan Williams, Seok-Hee Hong, Qing Liu, and Ji Zhang, Semi-bipartite Graph Visualization for Gene Ontology Networks, Graph Drawing: 17th International Symposium, GD 2009, Lecture Notes in Computer Science, Vol. 5849, pp.244–255, Springer Berlin Heidelberg, 2010.

[15] Lanbo Zheng, Le Song, and Peter Eades, Crossing Minimization Problems of Drawing Bipartite Graphs in Two Clusters, Proceedings of Asia-Pacific Symposium on Information Visualization (APVIS 2005), CRPIT, Vol. 45, pp. 33–38, 2005.

Visualizing Tags with Spatiotemporal References

Dinh Quyen Nguyen, Christian Tominski, Heidrun Schumann
Institute for Computer Science
University of Rostock
Rostock, Germany
{nguyen|ct|schumann}@informatik.uni-rostock.de

Tuan Anh Ta
John von Neumann Institute
Vietnam National University - HCMC
Ho Chi Minh City, Vietnam
tuan.ta@jvn.edu.vn

Abstract—Nowadays, a great amount of data is created and distributed on the Internet. Tagging has become common practice to structure these data for easy access. Often the data and the associated tags contain spatial and temporal information.

In this paper, we develop general design strategies for visualizing spatially and temporally referenced tags similar to tag clouds on maps. Temporal information of tags is encoded through the visual appearance of text or through additional visual artifacts associated with the tags, whereas the location of tags on a map illustrates the spatial references. We demonstrate our solution based on an interactive visualization prototype for the exploration of both spatial and temporal references of Flickr tags.

Index Terms—Visualization, Tagging, Spatiotemporal Data, Flickr, Tag Clouds

I. INTRODUCTION

Keywords from an article or a book offer a special kind of linguistic summary for text. Beyond that, there is the concept of tagging, where any kind of media (e.g., music, movies, images) can be associated with textual tags in order to create such linguistic summaries.

Keywords or tags can be represented visually as tag clouds. In a tag cloud, not only the words are meaningful, but the appearance of the words (e.g., size, color, etc.) can be used to convey information, for example the importance or frequency of a word. Nowadays, tag clouds are commonplace on many websites because they efficiently communicate an overview of the site's content. In this work, we are interested in this topic of text visualization, but we consider two additional aspects: our tags are associated with geo-spatial and temporal information.

A photo hosting website such as Flickr is a prominent application scenario for spatiotemporal tags. When a photo is taken or uploaded it is automatically equipped with a time stamp. Additionally, many photos are also outfitted with spatial information such as precise geo-positions (i.e., latitude and longitude) or coarser areal information (e.g., west coast or city of Munich). Last but not least, the photographer or the user community may tag a photo with keywords (simply called tags) that describe the photo's content.

In turn, this means that tags are no longer just abstract linguistic objects. Instead, a tag carries meaning and embeds this meaning into a spatiotemporal frame of reference. Given such spatiotemporally referenced tags, a user might want to find out where certain tags occur, or how the tags are linked across different areas. He or she might also be interested in exploring the tags with regard to a specific time point or time interval of interest, or with regard to a specific temporal pattern (e.g., consecutive Sundays of a month). Examining how tags have evolved over time is also an interesting task.

While common tag clouds are useful for visually communicating tags, they cannot convey both spatial and temporal aspects. Yet, there are tag clouds that are capable of showing either the spatial or the temporal context of tags. Yahoo! Tag Maps [1] and Taggram [2] are examples of existing techniques for the visualization of tags on maps. On the other hand, Yahoo! Taglines [3] or Twitscoop [4], amongst some others, provide ways for the visual representation of tags over time.

We develop a first solution for the visualization of both spatial and temporal dependencies of tags. For the spatial component of the data, we utilize the concept of Taggram. In order to allow users to recognize temporal information, we enhance the visual representation of tags in Taggram. In accordance to McEachren's list of aspects of time [5], we aim to support users in answering the following set of questions:

- Q1: Does a specific tag exist at a particular time?
- Q2: When in time does a tag occur?
- Q3: How old is a tag at a specific time point (if existing)?
- Q4: For how long does a tag exist?
- Q5: How often is a tag used?
- Q6: How frequent or strong does a tag change over time?
- Q7: Is there any special temporal relationship (e.g., co-occurrence) between some tags in the cloud?

Our goal is to develop general designs for representing the different temporal aspects of tags. The suggested solution is two-fold: (i) time is encoded through the visual appearance of text (e.g., font size, text color, orientation, transparency, shape), and (ii) time is represented by additional visual artifacts associated with the tags.

The paper is organized as follows. In Section II, we take a brief look at related work and the fundamentals of Taggram. Section III introduces our general design strategies for the visualization of tags associated with temporal references. In Section IV, we present concrete design examples for the visualization of spatiotemporal Flickr tags developed based on our novel strategies and Taggram. Section V describes the interaction facilities provided to support the visual exploration. We briefly describe implementation aspects and report on preliminary user feedbacks in Section VI. Finally, Section VII concludes the paper.

1550-6037/11 $26.00 © 2011 IEEE
DOI 10.1109/IV.2011.43

II. RELATED WORK & FUNDAMENTALS

Because there is hardly any visualization that displays spatial AND temporal references of tags, we summarize previous work related to either space OR time. We also briefly explain Taggram, which is the basis for the spatial mapping.

A. Related Work

Tag clouds have become very popular on the Internet over the past few years. The aim of this kind of visual representation is to provide users with a simple and expressive overview of a larger body of content (e.g., a set of online news articles). Commonly, the basic technique is straight forward: display a set of words on the screen, where font size, color, and orientation visually encode some related information (e.g., frequency of a word). However, more information can be visually encoded with tag clouds:

1) Tag Clouds and Space: In the theory of perception, shape is a prominent visual variable for information acquisition [6]. Therefore, the shape of an area linking with a tag cloud can be used to represent contextual information of the tags (without losing the validity of those tags). For example, in DocuBurst [7], the hierarchical structures of the interrelated words are visualized as a polar treemap that can be explored interactively.

Many tag cloud visualization approaches focus on the question how to spatially layout (aka spatialize) words on the display? It is also the basic idea behind text typography, a special kind of information graphics [8]. Interestingly, it is also relevant to the problem of using tag clouds in geospatial data visualization. Taggram [2] is a recently developed technique that addresses this problem. However, Taggram only concerns the matter of spatial references of tags; temporal features have not been taken into account.

2) Tag Clouds and Time: Because online communities are usually dynamic, there are a number of implementations that integrate the one or the other aspect of time into tag clouds.

The tool Twitscoop [4] uses the slideshow approach. It updates the visualization every minute to reflect the currently most important keywords in Twitter. Yahoo! Taglines, for instance, uses animation to visualize changes of topics over time [3]. The user can choose from two animation schemes (river or waterfall), where time goes from left to right and top to bottom, respectively. If a tag cloud spans only a small number of time steps or if just the latest snapshot of the tag cloud is relevant, a dynamic visual representation (slide show or animation) is suitable, because the temporal changes are usually easily comprehensible.

In order to facilitate more detailed visual analysis, additional visual cues can be used. Stefaner uses animation as well, but additionally encodes information about the "age" of tags [9]. Cui et al. [10] use color to differentiate newer and older tags in the cloud. But comparisons of different time steps or different tags are still difficult to conduct. In this case, combining tag clouds with additional views (e.g., a temporal bar chart as in [10]) is one option to solve this problem. A similar implementation is offered by Cloudalicious [11].

While most approaches rely on basic techniques and show only one snapshot of a tag cloud at a time, only few attempts have been made to visualize data of multiple time steps concurrently or to support the analysis of temporal aspects such as frequency or rate of change. One such approach is SparkClouds [12], which combine spark lines with tags. But still, visualizing time-varying tag clouds remains an interesting research topic.

B. Taggram

We develop our solutions for the visual representation of spatiotemporally referenced tags based on Taggram [2]. Taggram is a flexible technique that deals with the spatialization of geo-referenced tags inside geographic regions. The key characteristics of this approach are:

- Tags are placed on a map according to the tags' spatial references. Regions of arbitrary shape are used as visual containers for the spatialization of tags. Tags that belong to a geographical region are placed inside that region in alphabetical order, following the main vertical axis of the region.
- Information related to tags can be encoded through text attributes (e.g., color or transparency) and also through additional visual artifacts that can be superimposed on the map. Note that size – conventionally a basic visual attribute of tag clouds – is used differently in Taggram: Tags that are close to the center of the region are enlarged, and tags with increasing distance to the center become smaller. The rationale behind this design is that normally the user prefers to explore tags at the center of a tag cloud [13].
- Because the number of tags in the data is usually larger than the number of tags that fit the available display space, tags can be dynamically scrolled inside the geographic region on demand. This way, users can stay focused on the region's center while exploring the alphabetically ordered tags.

With these characteristics, Taggram represents an excellent basis for our development. We can conveniently add more visual artifacts to the tags to represent their temporal aspects. In the next section, we will present general design strategies for the visualization of time-oriented tags.

III. GENERAL DESIGNS FOR THE VISUALIZATION OF TAGS WITH TEMPORAL REFERENCES

According to Aigner et al. [14], time-oriented data can exhibit a number of different characteristics, which leads to a variety of potential visualization designs. So, there are various ways to visualize temporally referenced tags. In our work, we focus on adapting the visual representations of the tags themselves, in order to arrive at designs that are suitable to answer the questions Q1 to Q7 listed in Section I. Note that the fact alone that a tag appears in a tag cloud enables users to recognize existence of the tag (Q1).

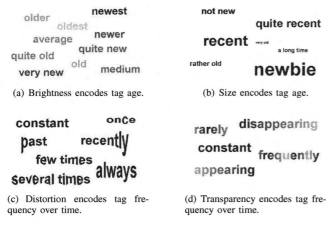

(a) Brightness encodes tag age.

(b) Size encodes tag age.

(c) Distortion encodes tag frequency over time.

(d) Transparency encodes tag frequency over time.

Fig. 1. Encoding temporal aspects with text appearance.

(a) The color of background rectangles indicates three different classes of tags.

(b) Color-coded segments visualize tag frequency over time.

(c) Color-coded cells of calendar tables help in discerning reoccurring patterns.

(d) Color-coded circular glyphs are useful to communicate cyclic patterns.

Fig. 2. Encoding temporal aspects with additional visual artifacts.

Next, we discuss two general design strategies for visualizing the temporal aspects: (i) by the visual appearance of the tags, and (ii) by additional visual artifacts associated with tags.

A. Temporal Aspects Mapped to Tag Appearance

Basic visual attributes such as color, size, or orientation are normally employed to visually encode information associated with tags. Visual attributes are also applicable to encode temporal aspects of tags. For example, one can use hue, saturation, or brightness to differentiate tags that have appeared at various points in time. Fig. 1(a) illustrates the encoding with brightness: more recent tags are darker and older tags are brighter. Similarly, text size can indicate how recent a word is (see Fig. 1(b)). For both encodings, the assumption is that recent tags are more important.

Provided that appropriate legends are displayed, such visual encodings allow users to discern a tag's age (Q3), and thus to estimate a tag's location in time (Q2). Conceptually, we are now able to visualize tags and a single data value per tag (e.g., age). But this is not enough for explicitly visualizing multiple time steps concurrently or for supporting the analysis of temporal aspects such as the frequency or rate of change. In order to arrive at conclusions for the questions Q4 to Q7, we need to consider other visual encodings.

One option is to modify the text rendering along the tag. The basic idea is to map individual time axes along the tags' horizontal orientation. That is, the beginning of a tag corresponds to the first time step and the end of a tag corresponds to the last time step. Given this mapping, we can vary the rendering along the tag. In Fig. 1(c), we show tags that have been distorted to visualize how frequent the tags appear over time. For example, the letters of "always" are larger throughout, indicating that the tag has been important at all points in time. On the other hand, the letters of "recently" increase in size towards the end of the tag, indicating a tag of growing importance. Similarly, one can vary other rendering parameters such as transparency as shown in Fig. 1(d).

Provided that there are no uncommonly short or long tags, these encodings along the tags' horizontal axes are suitable for indicating how tags have developed over time. For a more detailed exploration, however, varying basic visual attributes alone is not sufficient. Therefore, we suggest using additional visual artifacts as described next.

B. Temporal Aspects Mapped to Additional Visual Artifacts

By additional visual artifacts we mean enriching tags with additional graphical primitives. The main advantage of this solution, in comparison to the designs of the previous paragraphs, is its flexibility: By encoding temporal information with the visual attributes of the additional graphical primitives, we can visualize more complex temporal information. A positive side effect is that basic visual features of the tags (i.e., color, size, etc.) are kept for the traditional encoding of tag importance.

Fig. 2(a) shows a first simple example where a background rectangle has been added to each tag. The rectangle's color is used to indicate three groups of tags with different temporal behavior: appearing tags are green, disappearing tags are orange, and constant tags are gray.

More complex designs can communicate further information. Again, the basis is to construct an appropriate mapping of the time axis. For example, one can use color-coded segments along the horizontal extent of a tag to show the frequency of the tag over time (see Fig. 2(b)). This design is suited to visualize time in a linear fashion. Cyclic reoccurrence of tags can be made comprehensible with the help of table-based calendars (see Fig. 2(c)) or glyph-based cyclic artifacts (see Fig. 2(d)). These designs can also help in identifying any regular temporal patterns (e.g., tags occur only at particular weekdays).

With the aforementioned designs, the remaining questions Q4 to Q7 can be answered: The duration of tag existence, the frequency of tags, as well as the rate of change appear vividly in Fig. 2(b)-2(c), and temporal patterns are recognizable in Fig. 2(c)-2(d). Moreover, we can visualize time points together with time intervals, show linear time together with cyclic patterns, and switch to alternative perspectives, in order to explore the various temporal aspects of tags.

Further options are to compose different designs to show different temporal aspects as hybrid visual representations. However, care has to be taken to avoid cluttering the tags and to maintain the tag cloud's legibility. In this regard, an important aspect is to support user interactions such as zooming into details, highlighting tags or time points of interest, or interactive adjustment of the visual encoding.

The next consequent step is to extend these generic designs to address a more concrete visualization scenario.

IV. VISUALIZATION OF SPATIOTEMPORAL FLICKR TAGS

In contrast to the generic designs presented before, we now address the visualization of spatiotemporal tags as provided by Flickr. Furthermore, we take into account the fact that a user is usually interested in a specific time point, the so-called time of interest (TOI). In Fig. 3, for example, Fri, 8/20/2010 has been selected as TOI. The TOI divides the time domain into three parts: the time before the TOI, the TOI itself, and the time after the TOI. Note that the before and after parts might be empty, if the TOI is the beginning or the end of the time domain.

Given this additional TOI concept, we have to develop dedicated visual encodings, for which we again utilize (i) the visual appearance of tags and (ii) additional visual artifacts. Again, it is our goal to have at least a set of techniques that covers the questions Q1 to Q7.

A. Adjusting the Visual Appearance of Tags

The two visual designs that we present next are based on masking the tags. The designs operate on two different semantic levels. For the first design, we focus on qualitative statements regarding the existence of tags in the time domain. In the second design, we extend to quantitative assessments regarding the frequency of tags over time.

1) Encoding for Qualitative Statements: With regard to the TOI concept and the existence of tags, our design must be capable of communicating seven cases. The seven cases can be represented visually by color gradients, where red stands for existence, and gray indicates non-existence of a tag. The following list summarizes the seven cases of tag existence and the corresponding visual encoding: A tag exists

1) only at the TOI:
2) only before the TOI:
3) only after the TOI:
4) at the TOI and before:
5) at the TOI and after:
6) before and after the TOI:
7) before, after and at the TOI:

(a) Tags masked with gradient fills visualize tag existence.

(b) Tags masked with color-coded shapes visualize tag frequency over time.

Fig. 3. Visualization of Flickr tags on maps with temporal aspects represented by text appearance. (Recall that Taggram shows tags in alphabetical order and varies text size to attract the viewer's attention to the center of a region.)

To establish a visual association of a tag with one of the seven cases, the tag is masked with the gradient fill. This way, each tag is rendered according to the case it belongs to. Fig. 3(a) illustrates this with a sample data set extracted from Flickr: (1) tag "magical", (2) tag "messe", (3) tag "launsbach", (4) tag "licht", (5) tag "lowersaxony", (6) tag "nikon", and (7) tag "museum". Note that the combinatorial eighth case (i.e., the tag does not exist at all) must not be handled, because in that case the tag does not appear at all.

From the encoding presented here, the user can derive only qualitative information about tag existence (Q1 and Q2). How quantitative values such as tag frequency can be encoded will be shown next.

2) Encoding for Quantitative Assessment: Now our goal is to visualize data values associated with tags such as tag frequency (i.e., the number of occurrences of a tag over time per geographical region). What we need is a visual mapping of the time domain that is capable of showing quantitative values per time point.

To this end, we create series of visual segments (one for each time point) along the horizontal orientation of tags. We continue using the idea of the TOI and use different shapes for the segments. A diamond shape $\Diamond$ is used to represent the TOI, whereas time points before and after the TOI are represented as arrow shapes ≪ and ≫, respectively. We use colors from the ColorBrewer [15] to color-code each shape according to the tag's frequency at the corresponding time point. As tag frequencies might be distributed unevenly over time, additional color mapping concepts from [16] can be applied to redistribute colors for more effective visualization. For those time points where the frequency is zero, we use a hueless color to clearly indicate the non-existence of that tag at that time point.

These mapping steps result in visual representations like ◁◀◀◆▶▷ for each tag. Again, we mask the tags to integrate the visualization of the time-dependent frequency values with the visual appearance of tags. Fig. 3(b) illustrates such masked tags for a part of Germany for a time range of 8 days in August 2010. This design is suited to find answers to the questions Q3 to Q6. However, if the time domain is larger, differentiating the individual time points may become difficult. In such cases, one could exploit the hierarchical structure of time and represent aggregated frequencies of weeks or months, rather than those of individual days. Another option is to associate additional visual artifacts with tags.

B. Additional Visual Artifacts Associated with Tags

As indicated earlier, using the visual appearance of tags alone might not be sufficient for more complex questions or larger time domains. Therefore, we now consider adding visual artifacts to the tags on the map. Each artifact can then be used to visualize the temporal aspects in more detail.

1) Bar Charts Representing Temporal Developments: In this first design, we use bar charts as additional visual artifacts to visualize the existence and frequency of tags over a period of time (Q1 - Q6). We chose bar charts because they are an accepted method for visualizing time-dependent data and because they are easy to interpret.

The design of a bar chart per tag is straightforward: For each time point, we create a rectangular bar to show if the tag existed and how frequent it was. We add a small red dot to indicate the TOI. Color and height of bars are used to show tag frequency at individual points in time. The color-coding is the same as described in the previous section. Using a dual encoding with color and height has the positive side effect that we do not have to deal with the special case of non-existence, because in that case the bar has zero height and is invisible anyway.

The bar chart design is illustrated in Fig. 4(a) with a list of Flickr tags for the period of 8/9 to 8/29 in Germany, where Sat, 8/21/2010 has been selected as the TOI. From the bar charts in this visual representation, the user can easily see how tags appeared and if there are any linear temporal patterns. However, bar charts are not suited to find more complex and possibly reoccurring patterns.

2) Calendar Tables Representing Temporal Patterns: Color-coded calendar tables, whose horizontal and vertical axes represent independent levels of time, are promising alternatives. For example, a common design is to show weeks as rows of a table, which implies that columns represent

(a) Color and height of bars visualize tag existence and tag frequency.

(b) Color of the cells of calendar tables visualize tag frequency.

Fig. 4. Temporal aspects of Flickr tags visualized by additional visual artifacts. (Recall that Taggram shows tags in alphabetical order and varies text size to attract the viewer's attention to the center of a region.)

individual weekdays. Each table cell's color indicates tag frequency (or any other attribute users might be interested in).

The user can now spot more complex patterns (Q7), for example, tags that frequently reoccur only on particular week days. At the same time linear trends are discernable, for example, if the frequency increases from one week to the next. Several interesting patterns can be seen in the sample Flickr data visualized in Fig. 4(b) The tag "2010" is significant throughout, but the highest frequencies are on weekends (last two columns of the table). Quite nicely one can see that the event "wiesenbühne" appears in the middle of the first week (top row of the table) and disappears toward the weekend.

C. Discussion

The two basic design strategies (i.e., visual appearance of tags vs. additional visual artifacts) that we suggested have advantages and disadvantages alike. For both strategies the aim is to visualize additional temporal aspects while maintaining tag legibility. By changing only the appearance of tags, our options for encoding temporal information are limited, and thus only simple questions are supported. On the other hand, tag legibility is only marginally affected (provided that appropriate colors are used). Moreover, the encoding of a tag and its associated temporal aspects is overlap-free.

This is different when using additional visual artifacts. In this case, there can be significant overlap which could occlude possibly important temporal information, for example, when a letter occludes the cell with the highest frequency in a calendar table. This is the price to pay for the additional options that visual artifacts offer for the visualization.

We cannot tell which of the two strategies is best. But most likely there is no definite answer to this question at all. Rather a suitable solution must be selected depending on the data, the users' tasks, and their preferences. Therefore, interactive selection of encodings and their adjustment are important.

V. USER INTERACTION

The visual exploration of spatially and temporally referenced tags involves various aspects, and therefore requires sufficient means for user interaction. On the one hand, the user must be enabled to visit different places in space and to select different time ranges from the data. On the other hand, the visual encoding must be interactively adjustable to the users' needs and preferences.

We support these tasks with a number of interaction techniques. The users can zoom and pan to any place on the map, they can switch to their favorite visualization mode, and they can focus on tags with relevant temporal developments.

To make the different options for interaction easily accessible, we provide a custom-made user interface component, which borrows from the idea of floating menus. Fig. 5(a) shows the main menu with options, including home, settings, color adjustment, map display, photos, and tag selection. When the user clicks the tag selection, the component switches its interface accordingly. Fig. 5(b) shows this interface, which allows users to select the time range for which tags are to be displayed, the time point of interest, as well as the visualization mode (i.e., the different encodings introduced earlier).

Besides presenting tags with temporal dependencies on maps, we also support the users in interacting with the tags for further information exploration as described next.

One important task is to highlight the concrete locations in space where tags originate from. This is necessary because the Flickr database aggregates the spatial information of tags to larger regions. Our goal is to allow users to reestablish the connection of tags to specific locations.

To this end, we mark the concrete positions of one selected tag on the map as shown in Fig. 6(a). However, indiscriminately showing all locations could clutter the map with too many markers. Therefore, we restrict the highlighting to one selected time point, usually the TOI. If the visual encoding allows the identification of individual time points (e.g., segment-based appearance of tags, bar chart, or calendar table), the user can chose to select alternative time points for highlighting of locations simply by hovering the time points. In that case, the selected time point is additionally labeled with a tooltip containing date information (see Fig. 6(a)).

Similarly to highlighting spatial aspects, it makes sense to support interactive highlighting of temporal aspects. Identifying tags that co-occur is an interesting task (Q7) because it allows users to derive higher-level information from spatiotemporal tags.

Therefore, we allow users to select further time points in addition to the TOI. The visualization is then adapted so as to highlight those tags that co-occur on all selected time points (which is actually done by dimming the tags that do not co-occur). Fig. 6(b) demonstrates that this interactive highlighting can reveal facts in the data: It appears that there was a "lasershow" in "lowersaxony" in August 2010.

(a) Markers highlight concrete geo-positions for a selected tag.

(b) Selecting multiple time points reveals tag co-occurrence.

Fig. 6. Options for interacting with time-dependent tags on maps.

(a) Main menu.   (b) Time and encoding selection.

Fig. 5. Controller interface.

VI. IMPLEMENTATION AND PRELIMINARY USER FEEDBACKS

We implemented a web-based visualization application to illustrate the concepts introduced in the previous sections based on the available Flickr tags dataset. While the visualization part in our implementation exploits the graphics and interaction capabilities of Flash and ActionScript, the data part is based on MySQL and the Flickr web services APIs.

The Flickr APIs support queries for the relations of tags and geographical regions of the map using the services `flickr.places.tagsForPlace` and `flickr.places.placesForTags`. Both calls expect a range of dates as input and return lists of tags or places as output, respectively.

The corresponding data is as follows. At a particular date, a tag can be associated with various geo-coordinates inside a geographical region (normally concerning many photos). Because in Flickr a geographical region can be indicated through various levels of geographical abstraction (i.e., place types: locality, city, state, etc.), a tag listed for one place can be listed for other places at other administrative levels as well. For example, a tag listed for Berlin (level: city) may also be listed for Germany (level: country). We utilize this for semantic zooming as users zoom into particular regions of the map.

For a place (e.g. a city) and a given date, there exists a list of tags. Consequently, for multiple dates, there are multiple lists of tags, one for each date. Because our visualization client requires efficient access and iteration over multiple dates and geographical regions, we reorganize the retrieved query results in our own database, which consists of multiple lists of tags indexed by date and geographical region.

This data backend drives the efficient visualization of Flickr tags with spatial and temporal references in any Flash-enabled Web browser. Users can access the data for different places by navigating the Taggram-based map and different time ranges can be visited by using the query interface of the controller menu.

Using our implementation, we conducted a small informal test to collect first feedbacks about our visualization designs. Seven students (aged 22-26, 2 females, familiar with Tag Clouds and Yahoo! Flickr) have been asked to use our tool. As this was not a formal evaluation, we did not focus on any particular visualization task or question, but rather we were interested in the general acceptance of our designs for the visual exploration of Flickr tags.

In summary, six out of seven participants liked the fact that they can explore tag clouds concerning both space and time. They were strongly interested in the interactive visualization that highlights the co-occurrence of Flickr tags on the map for selected dates. Additionally, the exploration of temporal patterns (e.g., weekdays in a calendar-based artifact) got special attention.

On the other hand, there were also negative feedbacks. Firstly, adding visual encodings to tags was experienced as interfering with the legibility of the tags, which we expected to a certain degree. Secondly, some users asked for additional querying mechanisms, in particular a textual search for specific tags of interest.

VII. SUMMARY AND FUTURE WORK

In this paper, we have addressed the visualization of tags with both spatial and temporal references. We apply Taggram to visualize spatial dependencies of tags on a geographical map. Our design strategy for visualizing temporal aspects of tags has been twofold: employ (i) the visual appearance of text or (ii) additional visual artifacts associated with the tags. For both strategies, we described generic designs and developed visualization examples that support the users in interactively exploring spatiotemporal Flickr tags of user-selected time ranges on navigable maps (see Fig. 7). Using our application, the user can accomplish a number of visualization tasks, including identifying dates for which tags exist, finding local trends in the development of tags, and understanding tag co-occurrence over time.

Through this development, we have illustrated that incorporating additional visual cues into the representation of the raw data (i.e., the tags) is a sensible solution to account for additional spatial and temporal references of the data.

Still, many tasks are open for future work. In the context of visualizing temporal dependencies of tags, a more general formal study has to be carried out in order to identify the most suitable combination of visual variables (shape, size, value, grain, hue, orientation, and position). This also includes a comparison of our approaches with existing spatially and/or temporally referenced text visualization techniques. Another issue is that our development mainly focuses on the simple model of linearly ordered time. However, as temporal data can be multifaceted [14], future work may address other innovations for more complex and multi-perspective temporal data. Similarly, one can think of ways to extend our univariate visualizations to cope with multivariate data associated with tags.

ACKNOWLEDGMENT

This work is partly funded by the KAAD. Some of the colors that appear in this work are taken from ColorBrewer. Some of the icons that appear in this work are by Yusuke Kamiyamane.

REFERENCES

[1] S. Ahern, M. Naaman, R. Nair, and J. H.-I. Yang, "World Explorer: Visualizing Aggregate Data from Unstructured Text in Geo-Referenced Collections," in *Proc. of the ACM/IEEE-CS Joint Conference on Digital Libraries (JCDL)*. New York, NY, USA: ACM, 2007, pp. 1–10. [Online]. Available: http://doi.acm.org/10.1145/1255175.1255177

[2] D. Q. Nguyen and H. Schumann, "Taggram: Exploring Geo-data on Maps through a Tag Cloud-Based Visualization," in *Proc. of the International Conference on Information Visualisation (IV)*. IEEE Computer Society, 2010, pp. 322–328.

[3] M. Dubinko, R. Kumar, J. Magnani, J. Novak, P. Raghavan, and A. Tomkins, "Visualizing Tags Over Time," in *Proc. of the International Conference on World Wide Web (WWW)*. New York, NY, USA: ACM, 2006, pp. 193–202. [Online]. Available: http://doi.acm.org/10.1145/1135777.1135810

Fig. 7. Visualization of spatiotemporal tags on maps using different encodings.

[4] "Twitscoop," retrieved Mar, 2011. [Online]. Available: http://www.twitscoop.com/

[5] A. M. McEachren, *How Maps Work: Representation, Visualization, and Design*. New York, NY, USA: Guilford Press, 1995.

[6] J. Bertin, *Semiology of Graphics: Diagrams, Networks, Maps*. Redlands, CA, USA: Esri Press, 2011.

[7] C. Collins, S. Carpendale, and G. Penn, "DocuBurst: Visualizing Document Content using Language Structure," *Computer Graphics Forum*, vol. 28, no. 3, pp. 1039–1046, 2009.

[8] J. Clark, "Twitter List Profile Clouds," retrieved Mar, 2011. [Online]. Available: http://neoformix.com/2009/TwitterListClouds.html

[9] M. Stefaner, "Visual Tools for the Socio-semantic Web," Master's thesis, University of Applied Sciences Potsdam, 2007.

[10] W. Cui, Y. Wu, S. Liu, F. Wei, M. X. Zhou, and H. Qu, "Context Preserving Dynamic Word Cloud Visualization," in *Proc. of the IEEE Pacific Visualization Symposium (PacificVis)*. IEEE Computer Society, 2010, pp. 121–128.

[11] T. Russell, "Cloudalicious: Folksonomy Over Time," in *Proc. of the ACM/IEEE Joint Conference on Digital Libraries (JCDL)*. ACM, 2006, p. 364.

[12] B. Lee, N. H. Riche, A. K. Karlson, and S. Carpendale, "SparkClouds: Visualizing Trends in Tag Clouds," *IEEE Transactions on Visualization and Computer Graphics*, vol. 16, no. 6, pp. 1182–1189, 2010.

[13] S. Lohmann, J. Ziegler, and L. Tetzlaff, "Comparison of Tag Cloud Layouts: Task-Related Performance and Visual Exploration," in *Proc. of the IFIP TC13 Conference Human-Computer Interaction (INTERACT)*. Springer, 2009, pp. 392–404.

[14] W. Aigner, S. Miksch, W. Müller, H. Schumann, and C. Tominski, "Visual Methods for Analyzing Time-Oriented Data," *IEEE Transactions on Visualization and Computer Graphics*, vol. 14, no. 1, pp. 47–60, 2008.

[15] "ColorBrewer," retrieved Mar, 2011. [Online]. Available: http://www.colorbrewer.org/

[16] C. Tominski, G. Fuchs, and H. Schumann, "Task-Driven Color Coding," in *Proc. of the International Conference on Information Visualisation (IV)*. IEEE Computer Society, 2008, pp. 373–380.

Evaluating a Cube-Based User Interface for Exploring Music Collections

Arto Lehtiniemi
Nokia Research Center
Tampere, Finland
arto.lehtiniemi@nokia.com

Jukka Holm
Human-Centered Technology
Tampere University of Technology
Tampere, Finland
jukka.holm@tut.fi

Abstract—This paper studies the idea and feasibility of using a cube metaphor as a graphical user interface for exploring large music collections. In the implemented prototype, new music recommendations and related information are generated on the different faces of the cube based on the selected genre. In a user study with 40 participants, the cube was seen as an interesting and playful new concept that has great potential as a user interface. The prototype was considered to be inspiring and fun, and the participants appreciated to see extra information related to the currently playing track/artist. In the longer-term use, the prototype would have benefited from, e.g., text-based search functionality. Several other interesting ideas for the future development of the concept were also received.

Keywords-music; visualization; cube; playlist; music recommendation; musical genre; user study; user experience

I. INTRODUCTION

Streaming online music services such as Last.fm [8] and Spotify [14] have become increasingly popular, and the mobile versions of such services offer easy access to millions of tracks anytime, anywhere, and often at no cost. Music players typically represent collections as hierarchical lists, where the music is arranged according to artist, album, song, and genre names. One way to increase the expressive power of such a user interface (UI) without using extra space is to embed genre information in song, artist, and album text strings e.g. using a certain font typeface [5] or color. Another potential approach is to add small glyphs representing the musical genre, tempo, and release year next to each song in a playlist.

Modern music player applications may also include additional information such as lists of related artists, artist biographies, and the listening habits of user's social network. To show a large amount of information in an effective and user-friendly way, such UIs are often based on several different views or tabs. However, especially in the case of smaller devices such as mobile phones, it can be difficult to show all this information on the screen at the same time unless the lists are kept very short or the UI is crammed up with information.

In this paper, we propose to access music collections using a 3D cube-based graphical user interface. In the evaluated touch screen prototype, the main face of the cube includes a playlist of music recommendations, and the cube can also be rotated to access more information and functions. By clicking outside of the cube, another view for selecting playlists from different genres is opened. In addition to describing the prototype implementation, this paper discusses the results of a user study with 40 participants and suggests several ideas for further concept development.

II. RELATED RESEARCH

In the Grooveshark music recommendation system [1], the UI has been divided into several views (e.g. community, now playing, and my music), many of which contain several tabs. A similar type of approach has also been used in the mobile version of Spotify [14]. Different views are selected by clicking on buttons located on the bottom of the screen, and several views have further been divided into separate tabs. For example, the search view consists of artist, album, and track tabs.

In the academic literature, music collections and music recommendation services have been visualized using, e.g., maps, connections, sliders, discs, trees, graphs, scatter plots, and time series [7] [10]. In the following, we have briefly summarized some selected applications that offer a broad range of information and musical parameters to the user.

In [15], Torrens presents three different approaches (disc, rectangle, and tree-map) for visualizing music collections. Each visualization is able to present dimensions such as the number of tracks from a certain musical genre, sub-genre or artist, the release year of tracks, and a quantitative criterion chosen by the user (e.g. playcount, rating, added date, or last played date). As each visualization contains only one view, the UI contains a great variety of information and may thus be difficult to understand.

The same problem also applies to Pampalk & Goto's MusicRainbow [12], which arranges artists on a circular rainbow in such way that similar artists are located close to each other. By turning a Griffin Powermate knob, the user can jump to different regions on the rainbow or explore similar artists in the current region.

In the MusicSun from the same authors [13], the user drags a seed artist name to the center of a sun. The rays are labeled with words summarizing the search results. Also this application uses a single view to show a lot of information.

In the case of Musicovery [11], the user is able to search for music using parameters such as mood (dark, energetic, calm, and positive), decade, and musical genre. The search results are shown in a separate view with connections to similar artists. etc.

1550-6037/11 $26.00 © 2011 IEEE
DOI 10.1109/IV.2011.39

III. PROTOTYPE

Our cube prototype was implemented as a Flash application to enable the use of different platforms including computers and mobile devices. As suitable mobile devices or Apple iPad were not available at the time of implementing the prototype, the main platform was an HP Pavilion tx2500 touch-screen laptop. The main design drivers for the prototype were ease of use and easy access to a sufficient number of music player features. Different UI elements were designed in such a way that they could be operated with fingers.

When the user starts the prototype, he/she first sees the main face of the cube with the selected song playing (Figure 1). In addition to pressing the play/pause button, the user can move in the playlist by pressing the forward and backward buttons. Basic song related information (album cover art, artist/album/track name, and progress of the song) is also displayed on the cube.

The user is able to rotate the cube to any direction to access more information. In addition to the currently selected face of the cube, another face (in the case of Figure 1, the playlist view) is partially shown on the screen.

Figure 1.   Landing screen of the prototype including basic play controls and the partially visible playlist face of the cube.

The six different faces of the cube include Now Playing (landing screen), Playlist, Artist Albums, Similar Artists, Artist Information, and Friends (Figure 2). The Playlist face contains four songs with album art, artist names, and song names. The Artist Albums face displays other albums from the selected artist/track, and each album can be used to create a new playlist.

As the name implies, the idea of the Similar Artists face is to list some artists that are similar to the currently playing one. However, this feature was not implemented to the prototype, and the face was filled with some static artist names. The Artist Information face displays the correct album art and album name details, but the longer textual description was also simulated.

The last face, Friends, simulates a situation where the user already has some friends in the system. Several imaginary friends are generated automatically and shown on the screen. By clicking on the picture of friend, the user is able to view a playlist from that friend and select it as his/her current playlist.

Figure 2.   The six faces of the cube. From top left: Now Playing, Playlist, Artist Albums, Similar Artists, Artist Information, and Friends.

In addition to rotating the cube, the user is able to select the musical genre from a "genre map" view. This map can be accessed by clicking on the dimmed genre names located outside the cube. When the user clicks on this area, the currently visible cube is minimized and it animates back to the view shown in Figure 3.

The genre map consists of numerous miniature cubes that can be selected by clicking on the corresponding part of the screen. The map is divided into seven different genres (blues, heavy metal, hip-hop & rap, pop, rock, soul, and techno) using genre names and a color-coding that was partially based on [3]. When the user selects a miniature cube by clicking it, the cube increases to its full size and the main face of the cube (Figure 1) is shown.

Each miniature cube is mapped to a hand-picked seed song representing the corresponding genre. The resulting playlist is generated automatically on the server side using the music recommendation algorithms presented in [4], and the music is streamed from an updated version of Nokia Research Center's SuperMusic service [9].

Figure 3.   Genre map view for selecting the desired cube.

IV. RESEARCH METHOD

To study how well the prototype works in practice, we arranged a qualitative and quantitative user study as a part of a study on six novel music recommendation applications.

The user study had 40 participants. The initial research questions for the cube prototype were formulated as:

- Are users interested in using a cube-based interface to access music recommendation services and to generate playlists? Do they consider the concept fun and entertaining?
- Would the users be willing to replace their current music player with this type of application? Or could it complement traditional music players?
- How does the prototype work in general? How could it be developed further?
- How does the user experience change after using the prototype for a longer time?

The research method was a combination of observation, semi-structured interview, questionnaires, and evaluations done at home or any other preferred listening context. Each interview session lasted for circa 30 minutes, and all participants tested the software for the first time. The participants were not informed about how the prototype works or what they should do with it. Tutorials or help files were not included.

The interview sessions were arranged in various locations such as participants' homes, authors' homes, and the premises of Nokia Research Center and Tampere University of Technology. 37 of 40 interview sessions were arranged using a HP Pavilion tx2500 touch-screen laptop and three using a basic Dell Inspiron laptop. Evaluations at home were performed using participants' own computers.

In the beginning of the interview session, the participants had to fill in a short background information questionnaire. In addition to basic demographics (name, gender, year of birth and education), there were questions related to participants' music listening habits, musical taste, experience with music recommendation systems, and so on.

The participants were able to use the software freely for 5-15 minutes while being observed. After that, a short, semi-structured interview studying both hedonic and pragmatic aspects of the software was conducted. In the end, the participants had to rate a couple of quality aspects of the prototype using a seven-point Likert scale.

After the interview session, the participants were able to use an online version of the software at home or other preferred listening context for circa three weeks. In the end, they had to evaluate the prototype using a same type of questionnaire than during the interview.

The user study was conducted in Finnish. In the following, all terms, questions and answers have been translated from Finnish to English as closely as possible.

A. Participants

The participants were selected using convenience sampling from varying age groups (Figure 4) and education levels. The only requirement was that the participants had to listen to music every now and then. However, most participants who volunteered to the study were active music listeners.

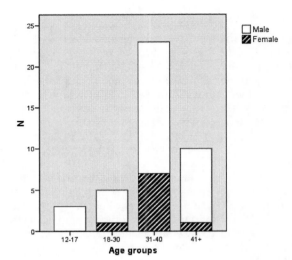

Figure 4. Age distribution of the participants.

All the participants were Finnish. 77% (31 participants) were male and 23% (9) female. The eldest one was 55, the youngest one 12, and the average age was 34.6. 63% were university graduates, while the rest were split between all types of education such as elementary school, college, and university students.

8% of the participants were professional and 50% hobby musicians. 50% considered listening to music as their hobby. During listening, 20% of the participants did not usually do anything else but concentrate on the music. All except two participants listened to music at least once a day, and the average time per day was 2.1 hours. The most popular genres included pop (85% of the participants liked it), rock (80%), metal (63%), soul, rnb & funk (60%), alternative & indie (55%), blues (55%), electronica & dance (50%), and jazz (50%). The least popular genre was gospel (5%).

43% of the participants searched actively for new music to listen to. The most common sources included the Internet (65%), friends (63%), magazines (33%), radio (33%), and Spotify (20%). 88% of the participants had used YouTube for listening to music, 51% had used Spotify [14], 32% Last.fm, and 29% iTunes Genius.

V. RESULTS

Based on the user study, we were able to answer our initial research questions and received a broad range of ideas for the future development of the concept. In this section, the results are discussed in a detailed manner. Both interview results and evaluations done at home are analyzed and compared against each other.

A. Interview

In the beginning of the interview session, the participants were able to use the prototype freely for 5-15 minutes while being observed. After that, various quality aspects of the prototype were studied by asking questions and filling in a questionnaire.

1) First Impressions: The most popular first impression was that the prototype was fun to use but also slightly confusing. The cube was seen as an interesting and playful new concept that has great potential as a user interface. Some participants felt that the prototype reminded them of Apple's innovations. However, there were some interaction problems when rotating the cube and some participants had several miss-clicks while playing around with the cube. As the selected cube did not indicate in any way to which genre the content was associated to, the link between the cube and the genre map view was seen as unclear. Still, 70% of the participants were positive about the idea of using a cube as a UI for music recommendation systems.

2) Quality Aspects: After the interview, the participants had to rate several quality aspects of the software on a seven-point Likert scale (1=totally disagree, 7=totally agree.). Both hedonic (a.k.a. emotional and experiential) and pragmatic (a.k.a. ergonomic, functional, and instrumental) aspects were studied. In [2], Hassenzahl et al. have shown that these can be independently perceived by the users. The statements to be graded were:

- "The program looked impressive"
- "The program was fun to use"
- "The program presented music in a novel way"
- "I believe that the appeal of the program will last and I will use it actively in the future"
- "The program had an extensive set of well-implemented features"
- "The program was easy to use" and
- "I was able to start the playback of desired music quickly."

In addition, the participants had to rate "My overall grade for the program" using a seven-point scale.

Figure 5 illustrates the ratings given by the participants as pairs of boxplots. The left plot of each pair represents ratings given after the interview, and the right plot represents ratings given after longer-term use. Numbers surrounding the outlier circles refer to certain users in the SPSS data. In the following, we concentrate only on the left side and leave the right side for discussion in the "Longer-Term Use" section.

On the positive side, most participants considered the program to be a novel way to present music collections (median 6.0). The prototype was also seen to be relatively fun and easy to use (both medians 5.0). When asked the question "Did you understand how the prototype works?" 78% of the participants gave a positive answer. However, 25% of these participants did not fully understand the operation of the genre map view.

The majority of participants felt that the prototype looked good. For the statement "The program looked impressive", the median was 5.0 but there were also several neutral or negative replies.

Only 53% of the participants thought that the prototype had enough features implemented. For 65%, the lack of a text-based search function was a major shortcoming. Still, the median for the statement "The program had an extensive

set of well-implemented features" was on the positive side (5.0). Except for the genre map view, 80% of the participants felt that the features were easy to find.

The lack of a search function also had an effect on some of the grades regarding the claim: "I was able to start the playback of desired music quickly." For this statement, the median was 5.0 but there was quite a lot of scattering in the results (mean 4.2, std. deviation 1.7).

65% of the participants felt that the prototype fit well to their current music listening habits. However, only 48% mentioned that they would like to use it for a longer time, and as a result, the median for lasting appeal was only 4.0. In addition to the lack of a search function, one important reason for this was that the users encountered some technical difficulties (e.g. network related problems) with the prototype during the test sessions. This also had an effect on the overall grades for the program (median 4.0).

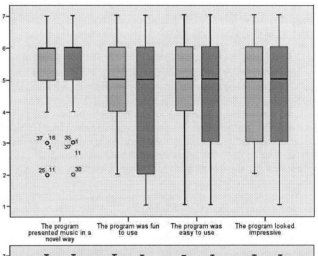

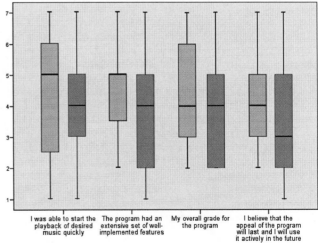

Figure 5. Boxplots for the quality aspects of the prototype. Ratings given at the end of the interview (boxplots on the left) and after longer-term use (boxplots on the right).

In general, those participants who believed they will use the prototype actively in the future also thought that the program looked impressive, was easy and fun to use, had an extensive set of well-implemented features, and that they found the desired music quickly. For all the pairs, Spearman's correlation was between $0.60 \leq rho \leq 0.79$ at the $p<0.001$ level (2-tailed).

Age, gender, or education level of the participants did not have statistically significant effect on the measured quality aspects.

3) Advantages of the Cube Approach: One of the greatest advantages of the cube prototype was the ability to map a great variety of data to the six faces. The participants appreciated to see information related to the currently playing track/artist and the ability to select other albums from the artist.

Mapping the information to a cube enabled the participants to see two different pages of information at the same time. It was commented that rotating a cube would be a faster and more intuitive way to display information than using ordinary tabs. Due of the cube analogy, it was also easier to understand "the bigger picture" of the UI.

B. Longer-term Use

The user study was arranged as a part of a study on six novel music recommendation applications. The participants were also able to use the online versions of five applications at home (or other preferred place) for circa three weeks. On average, the participants tested the cube prototype for 3-4 times during this evaluation period. When the evaluation period was over, the participants had to rate the same statements as during the interview and write some textual comments on the prototype.

By comparing the different boxplot pairs in Figure 5, one can notice that the medians for most of the statements did not change much during the evaluation period. In the longer-term use, the prototype was still considered to be novel, easy to use, and good-looking. In the case of the claim "The program was fun to use", there was more scattering in the results, i.e., there were several participants who graded the prototype worse after using it at home. Using the paired samples *t*-test, it was found out that this difference was also statistically significant ($t(36)=2.928$, $p=0.006$).

After the initial excitement, the prototype was considered to be too simple and lack some important features (see section "Ideas for Further Development"). This is well in line with [6], where it was found out that "Overall, while early experiences seemed to relate mostly to hedonic aspects of product use, prolonged experiences became increasingly more tied to aspects reflecting how the product becomes meaningful in one's life." A major shortcoming to 78% of the participants (cf. 65% after the interview) was the lack of a text-based search function. As the prototype contained only a limited number of genres, 50% of the participants felt that the music collection did not meet their needs and 18% mentioned that they did not use the prototype much for this reason. As a result, the medians for "I was able to start the playback of desired music quickly" and "The program had an extensive set of well-implemented features" dropped from 5.0 to 4.0.

Only 35% of the participants stated that they would like to use the prototype for a longer time (cf. 48% after the interview), and the median for lasting appeal decreased from 4.0 to 3.0. In addition to the lack of certain important features, limited amount of genres, etc., another potential reason for this was major and/or minor technical problems. 48% had some type of problems including program and server crashes.

The longer-term results supported well the findings of the interview. Participants who believed that they would use the prototype actively in the future also thought that they found the desired music quickly, that the program looked impressive, was easy and fun to use, and that it had an extensive set of well-implemented features. For all these pairs, Spearman's correlation was between $0.68 \leq rho \leq 0.89$ at the $p<0.001$ level (2-tailed).

Only 35% of the participants felt that the prototype fits to their current music listening habits. As the corresponding number after the interview was 65%, the user experience changed quite a lot in this respect. While only 10% thought that they could use the prototype as their main music player application, 48% answered that they could use it to complement other players. 83% of the participants preferred that the music comes from a music recommendation service instead of their own music collection (cf. 68% after the interview).

VI. IDEAS FOR FURTHER DEVELOPMENT

During the interview, we also received a broad range of ideas for the future development of the concept. One of the major shortcomings was the lack of search functionality, which also had an effect on the overall user experience. The ability to search for different artists and songs should be added to the future versions to complement the music recommendation algorithms. Other improvement suggestions included enhancements to the cube interaction, usability improvements, feature additions, and new concept ideas. In the following, these ideas have been explained in more detail.

A. Rotating the Cube

There was a lot to improve in the cube rotation implementation. Many participants performed several miss-clicks while rotating the cube, activated functions from the other faces of the cube, or launched the genre map view by accident.

It was said that the cube could rotate freely instead of using predefined and fixed positions. This would enable the user to place the cube in such way that up to three faces would be visible at the same time. Many users emphasized the ability to monitor many types of information simultaneously.

That said, the upper and lower faces (Related Artists and Artist Information) of the cube did not lock to a fixed position. Instead, the cube returned automatically to the previous position when the user lifted his/her hand off the cube. Based on the user study results, this approach should be changed in such way that the cube could also be locked to those positions.

As a potential future development, it was proposed that the cube could contain more than six faces. When rotating the cube, it could automatically generate more faces and perform as a "magic cube" with a navigation map displayed to the user. It was also mentioned that rotating the cube very fast could update or modify the contents of the playlist.

B. Selecting the Musical Genre

The greatest interaction problem with the prototype was launching the genre map. Only 29% of the participants noticed the dimmed genre names on the background screen and activated it intentionally. In total, 68% of the participants managed to activate the genre map, but the rest (39%) did it by clicking accidentally off the cube and then realizing the purpose of the background. It was said that the genre map background should be more visible and additional visual cues could be displayed. Several participants also proposed that the whole prototype should start from the genre map screen to make the interaction easier to understand.

Many participants did not understand that the small squares in the genre map represented miniature cubes, and they were just seen as squares that form the genre names. As one potential solution to the problem, the miniature cubes should be rendered in 3D as well. Also, there should have been a clearer way to recognize individual miniature cubes from the space and let the user know what kind of music they contain. For example, coloring the cubes using the selected genre-color mapping and providing additional tooltip/pop-up type of information screen could have been good solutions for this. In addition, those cubes that have already been accessed should have been marked in some way.

Some participants proposed that the genre map could have been larger than the screen. In that case, the user would be able to navigate in the genre space and zoom into individual small cubes to view more details. The map could include a time dimension, where the user could zoom in and out to find newer or older music from the selected genre. In the future, the genre map could also be dynamic and adapt to the listening preferences of the user. For example, when the user listens to a lot of rock music the portion of rock genre could be increased in the map.

C. Playlists

Due to the space limitations of the screen, the current implementation included only four songs per playlist. However, many participants requested that the playlist should be longer and a new playlist should be automatically loaded at the end of a playlist. To enable longer playlists, the content on the cube faces needs to be made scrollable.

Several participants stated that they would like to create their own playlists by combining individual songs from different cubes, or by smashing multiple cubes together to form a gigantic playlist. Saving and sharing of newly created cubes was also mentioned.

D. Friends

There were also some new concept ideas regarding the Friends view of the cube. Instead of displaying friends, there could be a list of people who actively listen to music recommended by that particular cube (~fans of the artists). There could also be a possibility to see what other songs those people listen to. The same type of ideology can be applied to friends list as well; only those friends that listen to the music offered by the cube should be displayed.

E. Enhancing the Cube

Several participants were interested in viewing their listening history in the cube. There could also be a button called "Never show me again" for deleting those cubes that the user does not like.

One interesting proposal included manipulating two cubes at a time. Data could be dragged easily from one cube to another (e.g. songs from one playlist to another) or outside the cube to delete it. This would enable easy and intuitive manipulation of the cube content.

Cubes could have different themes matching certain moods. For example, there could be artist specific cubes with the artist picture on one face of the cube. Other possible themes include kids, rainy day, holiday, music from the 70's, etc.

Some participants proposed replacing the current design with softer shapes (e.g. cubes with rounded edges). It could also be possible to unfold the cube to a 2D plate, where all of the information could be visible at once.

While most of the participants felt that the cube was easy to use, it was also proposed that the cube prototype should be enhanced with tooltips and other visual cues when performing the more advanced actions.

VII. CONCLUSIONS AND FUTURE WORK

In this paper, we studied the idea of using a cube as a user interface to discover new music. In the implemented software prototype, new music recommendations and related information are generated on the faces of the cube based on the selected genre. The main face of the cube includes a playlist of music recommendations, and the cube can also be rotated to access more information and functions.

The prototype was evaluated by 40 participants, and many interesting ideas for the future development of the concept were received. The idea of using a cube for music exploration was considered to be inspiring and fun, and the participants appreciated to see extra information related to the currently playing track/artist.

The cube was seen as an interesting and playful new concept that has great potential as a user interface. In the mobile domain, the cube concept could save valuable space from the user interface without compromising the usability and ease-of-use the system.

Mapping the information to a cube enabled the users to see two different pages of information at the same time. The participants felt that rotating a cube would be a faster and more intuitive way to display information than using ordinary tabs. Due to the cube analogy, it was easier to understand "the bigger picture" of the UI.

In the longer-term use, the prototype was slightly too simple and it would have benefitted from, e.g., text-based search functionality. Also, the users should have had more control over the selected musical styles and the contents of the playlists. Several other interesting ideas for the future development of the concept were also received. For example, the user could manipulate two cubes at a time, or cubes could have different themes matching certain moods. Other key ideas included adding a time dimension to enable the users to find newer or older music from the selected genre, and adapting the genre map to the listening preferences of the user.

REFERENCES

[1] Grooveshark, url: http://www.grooveshark.com.

[2] M. Hassenzahl, A. Platz, M. Burmester, and K. Lehner, "Hedonic and Ergonomic Quality Aspects Determine a Software's Appeal," Proc. CHI 2000 Conference on Human Factors in Computing Systems, ACM Press, April 2000, pp. 201-208.

[3] J. Holm, A. Aaltonen, and H. Siirtola, "Associating Colours with Musical Genres," Journal of New Music Research 38, vol.1, 2009, pp. 87-100.

[4] J. Holm and A. Lehtiniemi, "Evaluating an Avatar-Based User Interface for Discovering New Music," Proc. 9th International Conference on Mobile and Ubiquitous Multimedia, ACM Press, December 2010.

[5] J. Holm, A. Aaltonen, and J. Seppänen, "Associating Fonts with Musical Genres," Proc. 6th International Conference on Virtual Reality, Computer Graphics, Visualization and Interaction, 2009.

[6] E. Karapanos, M. Hassenzahl, and J-B. Martens, "User Experience over Time," Proc. CHI '08 Conference on Human Factors in Computing Systems, ACM Press, April 2008, pp. 3561-3566.

[7] P. Lamere and J. Donaldson, "Visualizing Music," url: http://visualizingmusic.com

[8] Last.FM, url: http://www.last.fm.

[9] A. Lehtiniemi, "Evaluating SuperMusic: Streaming Context-Aware Mobile Music Service," Proc. International Conference on Advances in Computer Entertainment Technology, ACM Press, December 2008, pp. 314-321.

[10] A. Lillie, MusicBox: Navigating the Space of Your Music. M.Sc. Thesis, MIT. 2008.

[11] Musicovery, url: http://www.musicovery.com.

[12] E. Pampalk and M. Goto, "MusicRainbow: A New User Interface to Discover Artists Using Audio-Based Similarity and Web-Based Labeling," In Proc. 7th International Conference on Music Information Retrieval, 2006.

[13] E. Pampalk and M. Goto, "MusicSun: A New Approach to Artist Recommendation," Proc. 8th International Conference of Music Information Retrieval, 2007.

[14] Spotify, url: http://www.spotify.com.

[15] M. Torrens, P. Hertzog and J-L. Arcos, "Visualizing and Exploring Personal Music Libraries," Proc. 5th International Conference on Music Information Retrieval, 2004.

Visualizing the Effects of Logically Combined Filters

Thomas Geymayer, Alexander Lex, Marc Streit, Dieter Schmalstieg
Institute for Computer Graphics and Vision
Graz University of Technology
Graz, Austria
tomgey@gmail.com, {lex,streit,schmalstieg}@icg.tugraz.at

Abstract—Filtering data is an essential process in a drill-down analysis of large data sets. Filtering can be necessary for several reasons. The main objective for filters is to uncover the relevant subsets of a dataset. Another, equally relevant goal is to reduce a dataset to which either visualization or algorithmic analysis techniques scale. However, with multiple filters applied and possibly even logically combined, it becomes difficult for users to judge the effects of a filter chain. In this paper we present a simple, yet effective way to interactively visualize a sequence of filters and logical combinations of these. Such a visualized *filter-pipeline* allows analysts to easily judge the effect of every single filter and also their combination on the data set under investigation and therefore, leads to a faster and more efficient workflow.

We also present an implementation of the proposed technique in an information visualization framework for the life sciences. The technique, however, could be employed in many other information visualization contexts as well.

Keywords-filter-pipeline, brushing, logical operations, inter-active, data analysis, compound filter

I. INTRODUCTION

Visualizing large amounts of data has been one of the grand challenges of information visualization for over a decade now. With ever more data being produced, the ability to efficiently extract knowledge out of data becomes more important. There are several ways to analyze large quantities of data. Examples are aggregation or drill-down techniques, focus and context methods, and so on. In the sense of visual analytics [1], [2], visualization is combined with computational methods, such as machine learning or statistics. However, in many cases, raw data has several undesired attributes: parts of it can be redundant, noisy or irrelevant for a given task. Also, most methods – either computational or visual – do not scale arbitrarily. Fortunately, there is a simple and yet effective method to reduce the data to a manageable size: filtering. Filtering allows parts of the data to be removed, based on a given criteria. A filter can be defined visually or textually as a processing rule. Filters can be based on fairly simple concepts, such as thresholds, or on more complex processes, such as a statistical evaluation of significance. Related concepts are dynamic querying [3] (selecting only a desired subset of a data set instead of removing undesired parts) and to some extent, also brushing (highlighting a subset of a data set).

It is common to use a combination of filters to continually refine the analysis result. In many cases, such combinations are equivalent to logical operations [4], [5]. While a logical AND is the most commonly used, other operations such as OR, XOR and uNOT are feasible as well.

While the reduced data set itself becomes more manageable, the overall filtering process and the individual effects of filters on the data set becomes increasingly obfuscated. To alleviate this, methods to visualize the combination of applied filters have been developed. Hong Chen [6] for example visualizes filters and other parameters of the visualization pipeline in a graph. However, to our knowledge, there has not been any technique that conveys not only the sequence of filters or brushes, but also the effects on the data size. Inspired by Minard's work, the famous *Carte Figurative des pertes successives en hommes de l'arme franaise dans la campagne de Russie 1812-1813* [7], which shows the continuous reduction of men in Napoleon's army during his Russian campaign, we have developed a visualization technique showing the effects of individual filters on a data set.

Our primary contribution is an interactive visualization technique for the effects of multiple filters, including the effects of logical operators applied to combinations of filters. This visualization technique enables users to understand the effects of individual and combined filters. A secondary contribution is a general and detailed analysis of requirements for visualizing multiple filters. Having these requirements at hand, we demonstrate how the proposed technique satisfies each of the specified requirements.

II. RELATED WORK

Much of how we interact with large quantities of data in visualization has its roots in the 1980s and early 1990s. Becker proposed some basic principles for dynamic data analysis [8], like linking & brushing – a technique that is commonly used today. In 1992 Ahlberg *et al.* [3] conducted an experiment with dynamic queries performed on a database with different combinations of graphical and textual input and output, respectively. As the different parameters used for the dynamic queries have the effect of refining the data set, this work is an early example of dynamically adapted filters.

1550-6037/11 $26.00 © 2011 IEEE
DOI 10.1109/IV.2011.52

In 1995 Martin and Ward propose an improvement of the XmdvTool which contains methods to combine multiple brush operations with different logical operations [4].

A recent example of an approach of filtering high dimensional data can be found in [9] where cross-filtering across multiple views is presented.

These works lay the foundation for modern visualization systems which widely employ combined filters or brushes to refine data sets or selections. However, only very few systems visualize these combinations in an explicit way. One notable exception is the work by Hong Chen [6] where node-link diagrams are used to visualize operations like a brush or selections. He also employs combined nodes which visualize logical or analytical operations. However, while individual operations are visualized, the effects of the operations on the data are not.

III. Problem Analysis

Users often find it hard to remember the steps conducted to get a specific result [9]. To support analysts and reduce the required cognitive load, we believe that an explicit representation of the filter sequence helps to understand the interdependencies between and consequences of filters. We elicited the following main requirements for such a filter-pipeline meta-visualization technique:

1) **Show Sequence**
   As filters are typically applied sequentially, it is essential to show the filters in the sequence they were applied.
2) **Show Consequences**
   To allow a user to judge how much data is removed by a filter, a filter visualization needs to show how many elements a filter reduces.
3) **Show and Create Compositions**
   A simple sequence of filters is equal to logical AND operations (*i.e.*, show all elements which are not removed by filter X and filter Y). Other logical operations such as OR and XOR cannot be visualized as easily. It is essential that such compositions are adequately represented in a dedicated filter visualization technique.
   In addition to the visualization of composed filters, it should also be possible to create composed filters based on pre-existing filters.

Aside from these main requirements for a filter visualization technique, there are several other requirements which provide added benefit to users:

4) **Modify Filters**
   An interactive filter visualization technique should enable a user to modify a filter (*i.e.*, change its parameters), to remove a filter and to move a filter to another position in the sequence of filters.
5) **Hide Filters**
   In some cases it may be desirable to hide filters.

A common example is an initial filter that removes noisy data. If such a filter removes a lot of data items, the consequences of subsequently applied, fine-grained filters become hard to perceive, due to the small change relative to the initial filter. One solution would be to use logarithmic scales for the amount of data removed. However, as log scales are not intuitive, we believe that the ability to hide filters is superior.

6) **Show Filter Efficiency**
   When a filter is visualized in relation to a previous filter, it is impossible to judge its effect on the global data set, since only the effects on the already filtered data set is shown. To make a user understand the consequences and the efficiency of a filter better, an effective filter visualization technique should also enable a user to see how much data a filter would remove from the complete data set.

In the following section we will describe how we address each of these requirements and challenges to create a simple and yet effective filter visualization technique.

IV. Method

Similar to the visualization of the reduction of men in Napoleon's army [7], we render each filter as a quadrilateral where the left side represents the input and the right side the output of the filter (see Figure 1). The size is chosen so that the largest visible filter always fills the available height, and the length is equally distributed over all visible filters. The height of the left edge of the filter encodes the elements going in, while the height of the right edge encodes the elements going out of a filter. Consequently, the difference in height (which is known to be the most powerful visual variable [10]) as well as the slope of the top edge to allow the user to easily judge the effect of the filter. To convey a sense of absolute numbers, we also chose to show the number of current elements and the number of elements each filter removes from its input. This can be seen more easily in figure 2.

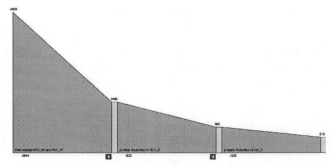

Figure 1: Sequence of filters. The result is equivalent to a logical AND operation of the filters.

A. Basic Sequence of Filters

We show a sequence of filters as equivalent to the logical AND operation, which simply concatenates one filter after each other, such that the output of a filter is passed to the next filter as input. This simple, yet effective method satisfies Requirements 1 and 2.

B. Compound Filters

For more advanced filter-pipelines, combinations of multiple filters into a single filter can be necessary. We provide the possibility to create meta-filters where all involved (sub)-filters are combined in one filter in the sequence of top-level filters. This can be achieved by dragging an existing filter and dropping it onto another already created filter. The whole meta-filter's input data is passed to each sub-filter. The output is then calculated based on the desired logical operations – most commonly an OR.

In order to visualize this combination, we experimented with two different approaches. One is to stack every involved sub-filter on top of each other (by means of a virtual z-axis orthogonal to the page) and embed this stacking into the overall meta-filter. Alternatively, we embed all sub-filters in the top-level meta filter without overlaps. In the following, we will briefly discuss the advantages and disadvantages of each method.

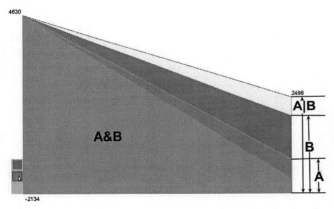

Figure 2: Two filters combined with logical OR, both sub-filters stacked over each other. The largest filter with the light yellow background is the resulting filter (A|B), the purple and red filter are the combined sub-filters (just A or just B) and the green filter on top of all filters represents the intersection of the elements filtered by both sub-filters (A&B).

Stacked Sub-Filters: As each sub-filter of the combined filter receives the same input, it is intuitive to render all sub-filters on top of each other at the same location (see Figure 2). The filters are sorted from top to bottom, where the topmost sub-filter (in our example rendered with a purple color) is the least effective one (the one that removes the least elements from the input data), thus guaranteeing that

no filter is completely occluded. The height on the left side of each filter is the total input of the compound filter and the height on the right side of each filter represents its individual output. Additionally, in the background, the union of all filters is rendered, visualizing the total influence of the combined filters on the filter-pipeline. In our example, this is the largest filter with the light yellow background.

It is also of interest to know which part of the input that passes all filters, which is the intersection of all individual sub-filter outputs (the result of an AND operation). We visualize this by adding another quadrilateral on top. According to the characteristics of set intersection this will always be the smallest quadrilateral (in Figure 2 it is rendered in green). This information can also be confusing to the user and misinterpreted as an additional filter. Thus, we only show it if the user moves the mouse over the filter. This allows him to detect inefficient filters, *i.e.*, filters that only contribute few or even no elements, apart from the elements also contributed by the other filters.

A problem with this approach is that it becomes cluttered easily. We found that for as little as three filters, especially if they are similar in terms of their efficiency, it is not easy to distinguish individual filters. Furthermore, it discontinues the flow of the data through the filter-pipeline, as all sub-filters have dead ends on their right sides without an equivalent at the left side of the next filter. Consequently, we devised an alternative method which addresses both issues.

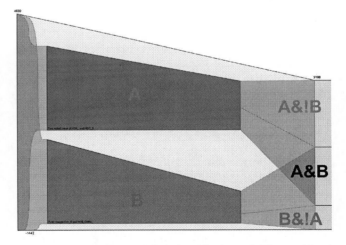

Figure 3: Two filters (labeled with A and B) combined with logical OR, visualized in parallel. The large filter in the background, rendered in light yellow, is the resulting filter. The left edge of the resulting filter is connected with the sub-filters using curved surface. On the right side, all intersections between the elements that are passed to at least one of the sub-filters are visualized – elements contributed only by filter A (A&!B), elements contributed only by filter B (B&!A), and elements contributed by both, filter A and B (A&B).

Separate Sub-Filters: As the sub-filters in a compound filter operate in parallel (contrary to the sequence of filters on the top-level), we considered also expressing this property in the visualization technique. Consequently, we render the sub-filters at a smaller scale in parallel inside the resulting compound filter. To provide a continuous flow of the data through the filter-pipeline, we connect the input of the compound filter to each sub-filter using curved shapes (see Figure 3). The shapes use the same color as the respective sub-filters, with transparency increased to allow a user to see the overlapping regions. Inspired by Kosara *et al.*'s work on categorical data visualization [11], we then calculate all possible intersections between the contributed elements of every sub-filter. Consequently, for a composition of two filters, if the underlying operation is an OR, there are two categories of elements: Those which are contributed by only one sub-filter, and those that are contributed by both. We render each set with a trapezoid using the same color as we did for the incoming surfaces (see Figure 3). To make the relative size of the set intersections more obvious, we use the space right of the filter to show the set sizes in detail. Moving the mouse over an intersection shows which filters are intersected for this sub-set.

With the technique of using separate sub-filters embedded in a meta-filter, we have successfully addressed Requirement 3.

C. Modifying Filters

The described filter visualization lends itself to allow interaction with the filters themselves. As discussed in Requirement 4, the essential operations are: modify, remove and move. We provide intuitive access to those features, for example by drag and drop for moving filters, or by double clicking on a filter for modifying it.

D. Hiding Filters

We have already discussed the issue of combinations of strong filters that initially remove large portions of the data, and more sensitive, refining filters that remove only smaller parts (see Section III, Requirement 5). Another issue, aside from the inability to perceive the effects of filters removing only a view elements, is the fact that composed meta-filters containing several sub-filters are hard to see because of the tiny amount of space available. These problems are illustrated in Figure 4. As a solution to this problem, we provide the possibility to hide a number of filters at the front of the filter-pipeline. This way, the remaining filters can be scaled up to the whole height, which makes their subtle effects on the filter-pipeline, as well as the embedded filters visible again. The effect is shown in Figure 4.

Below each filter, there is a button that enables the analyst to hide all filters from the front up to the corresponding filter.

If at least one filter is hidden, we show a button on the left margin to again display the hidden filters.

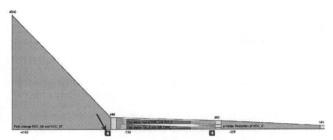

(a) Large filter followed by two small filters.

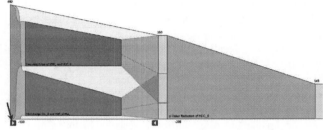

(b) The same pipeline but with the first filter hidden.

Figure 4: Hiding filters: By pressing the arrow button below the filter, the filter and all filters left of it are hidden. The example shown reduces the visible pipeline to only two filters which are scaled to the whole available height, as depicted in the lower image. Notice that the relative changes and the composition of the compound filter are much more visible when compared to the upper figure. By clicking on the button on the left border, the hidden filter can be made visible again.

E. Show Filter Efficiency

As every filter in the pipeline gets the output of its preceding filter, the amount of elements filtered is smaller (in most cases) than if it were applied on the whole input data set. However, as discussed in Section III, Requirement 6, it can be useful to get an idea on how the filter would behave if it were applied to the whole data set. This, for example, is desirable when the data is filtered to meet a pre-condition for a feasible runtime of a given algorithm. In such a case, a user can apply different filters at the same time, and judge whether he could meet the requirements with fewer filters.

We address this challenge by overlaying an transparent version of the filter, showing its size as if it was the only filter in the pipeline, on mouse over. This is shown in Figure 5.

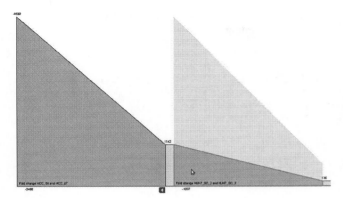

Figure 5: When hovering over the filter, its full size is shown in the background.

Having fulfilled all of the elicited requirements, we will now discuss how the described visualization technique is embedded in an information visualization framework, and give some examples on how the filter-pipeline is used.

V. VISUALIZATION ENVIRONMENT

The filter-pipeline view is a part of the Caleydo visualization framework[1] [12], developed at our institute. It is intended to be used for the analysis of large data sets from the life science domain, more specifically genetic and clinical data. Its multiple coordinated view system provides different ways to explore the loaded data set. For example, to explore gene expression data parallel coordinates, a hierarchical heat map, scatterplots and many further views are available.

As the initially loaded data sets in this domain are often very large, different types of filters are usually applied to reduce the size of the viewed data set, which is especially relevant to enable manual analysis performed by the user. The different views support various ways of brushing and consequently filtering data. In parallel coordinates it is possible to filter data where the gene expression values never leave a given interval and therefore, for example filter genes that are neither over- nor underexpressed. Another possibility to create a filter is to use the angular brush [13] which removes experiments with a deviation exceeding a visually specified threshold from the gene expression value of the selected gene of a specific experiment.

Caleydo also provides computational filters commonly used in gene expression analysis. One example is the fold-change filter that removes all elements which change less than a specified n-fold change to a reference experiment. Other examples are statistical variance tests, which ensure that outliers within control groups, which may be the result of errors in measurement, are removed.

The described filter-pipeline is used in Caleydo to convey the effects of complex combinations of filters. A typical scenario is shown in Figure 6.

[1]http://www.caleydo.org

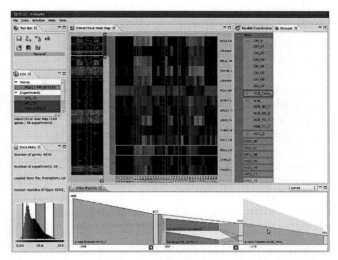

Figure 6: Example of using Caleydo with the described filter-pipeline view opened in the bottom right part of the window.

VI. IMPLEMENTATION DETAILS

The Caleydo visualization framework [12] is written in Java and is based on the Eclipse Rich Client Platform (RCP)[2]. The framework is designed in a modular manner where a minimal core contains integral parts, such as the data management, the event system, *etc.*. Everything else is outsourced into separate and completely independent plugins which communicate with each other by using the core's message-based event mechanism.

Each view can either use the Standard Widget Toolkit (SWT)[3] to create a user-interface by using the default widgets provided by the operating system, or for graphically more advanced or three dimensional user-interfaces use the OpenGL API provided by the Java Bindings for OpenGL (JOGL)[4].

In order to synchronize all views, the data set containing the data to by analyzed is stored centrally, so that each view can access it. View changes are handled first by the view under interaction itself and then propagated to all other views which in turn update their visualization based on the new context.

The statistical filters use the R statistics toolkit [14] for calculating the filter elements which are added to the corresponding list.

VII. CONCLUSIONS AND FUTURE WORK

As the amount of data to be analyzed is constantly growing, filtering it is a crucial part in the processing pipeline. Therefore, it is important that an analyst is supported in understanding complex sequences as well as compositions of filters. Visualization of those filters in the proposed filter-pipeline is an ideal tool for this task. It allows us

[2]http://www.eclipse.org/home/categories/rcp.php
[3]http://www.eclipse.org/swt/
[4]http://jogamp.org/jogl/www/

to understand even complex combinations of filters, and can be modified interactively until the desired result is achieved. Visualizing a sequence of AND combined filter is straight forward, but complex combinations, like a logical OR operation applied to several filters, require much care in visualization design.

We have presented two ways of visualizing compositions of logical filters (see Figure 7 for a complex scenario with four filters combined in an OR operation). The first one, a simple, stacked rendering of filters has shown to be very cluttered and hard to understand. Consequently we developed an alternative that shows each filter in parallel contained in a compound meta-filter, thereby providing an intuitive representation of a compound filter.

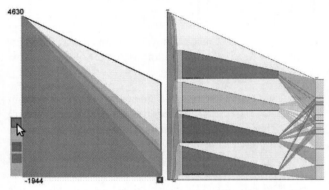

Figure 7: Comparison of different visualizations of compound filters as described in Section IV-B using four sub-filters.

Aside from these main objectives, we have elicited several minor requirements improving the interaction with such filter visualization techniques, and proposed solutions for each of the discussed points.

The support of the complete set of logical operations as well as nested filters, for example by using zoom levels, are promising directions for future research.

ACKNOWLEDGMENTS

We want to thank our partners from the Medical University of Graz, especially Dr. Karl Kashofer and Prof. Kurt Zatloukal, for providing both data and continuous feedback.

This work was funded in part by the Austrian Research Promotion Agency (FFG) through the *InGenious* project (385567).

REFERENCES

[1] J. J. Thomas and K. A. Cook, *Illuminating the Path: The Research and Development Agenda for Visual Analytics*. National Visualization and Analytics Ctr, 2005.

[2] D. A. Keim, J. Kohlhammer, G. Ellis, and F. Mansmann, Eds., *Mastering The Information Age - Solving Problems with Visual Analytics*. Eurographics, 2010.

[3] C. Ahlberg, C. Williamson, and B. Shneiderman, "Dynamic queries for information exploration: an implementation and evaluation," *Proceedings of the SIGCHI conference on Human factors in computing systems (CHI '92)*, pp. 619 – 626, 1992.

[4] A. R. Martin and M. O. Ward, "High dimensional brushing for interactive exploration of multivariate data," in *Proceedings of the Conference on Visualization (Vis '95)*. IEEE Computer Society, 1995, p. 271.

[5] H. Doleisch, M. Gasser, and H. Hauser, "Interactive feature specification for focus+context visualization of complex simulation data," in *Proceedings of the Symposium on Data visualisation 2003*. Eurographics Association, 2003, pp. 239–248.

[6] H. Chen, "Compound brushing," in *IEEE Symposium on Information Visualization (InfoVis '03)*. IEEE Computer Society, 2003, pp. 181–188. [Online]. Available: 10.1109/INFVIS.2003.1249024

[7] E. R. Tufte, *The Visual Display of Quantitative Information*, 2nd ed. Graphics Press, Cheshire, Coneeticut, 1983.

[8] R. A. Becker, "Dynamic graphics for data analysis," *Statistical Science*, vol. 2, no. 4, pp. 355–383, Nov. 1987. [Online]. Available: http://projecteuclid.org/euclid.ss/1177013104

[9] C. Weaver, "Cross-Filtered views for multidimensional visual analysis," *IEEE Transactions on Visualization and Computer Graphics*, vol. 16, no. 2, pp. 192–204, 2010. [Online]. Available: 10.1109/TVCG.2009.94

[10] J. Bertin, *Semiology of graphics*. University of Wisconsin Press, 1983.

[11] R. Kosara, F. Bendix, and H. Hauser, "Parallel sets: Interactive exploration and visual analysis of categorical data," *IEEE Transactions on Visualization and Computer Graphics*, vol. 12, no. 4, pp. 558–568, 2006.

[12] A. Lex, M. Streit, E. Kruijff, and D. Schmalstieg, "Caleydo: Design and evaluation of a visual analysis framework for gene expression data in its biological context," in *Proceeding of the IEEE Pacific Visualization Symposium (PacificVis '10)*. IEEE Computer Society, 2010, pp. 57–64.

[13] H. Hauser, F. Ledermann, and H. Doleisch, "Angular brushing of extended parallel coordinates," in *Proceedings on Information Visualization (InfoVis '02)*. IEEE Computer Society, 2002, pp. 127–130.

[14] R Development Core Team, *R: A Language and Environment for Statistical Computing*, 2010. [Online]. Available: http://www.R-project.org

Combined vs. Separate Views in Matrix-based Graph Analysis and Comparison

Alan G. Melville, Martin Graham, Jessie B. Kennedy
School of Computing
Edinburgh Napier University
Edinburgh, United Kingdom
{a.melville, m.graham, j.kennedy}@napier.ac.uk

Abstract—While much work has been done in the area of visualization for analysis of graphs, relatively little research exists into how best to use visualization for comparing graphs. We have developed a suite of general graph comparison questions that can be tailored to specific data sets, and compared the use of superimposed and juxtaposed views of graph matrices on an example data set. Our observations indicate that combined views are more useful in comparing general graphs, allowing for greater user accuracy in determining differences and their effects.

Keywords-Graph comparison, matrix visualisation

I. INTRODUCTION

Data sets from such widely varying areas as biomedical interactions, social networks, ontologies and software architectures can all be usefully represented in terms of the vertices and edges that make up a graph. As a result of this, the use of visualization techniques to assist in graph analysis has become commonplace over the last few years. So far this has concentrated on the analysis of single graphs - however more recently the requirement to analyze many graphs has become important. For example, with the increasing use of ontologies, users now need to understand how different ontologies compare, and software engineers need to understand how changes between revisions of code bases affect method call graphs, leading to an increasing demand for a reliable means of comparing graphs.

Graph comparison is a well-known problem in mathematics and computer science, with many algorithmic means of comparing structural similarities and differences in graphs. However, what we are concerned with is the visualization and thus visual comparison of multiple graphs, and what basic approach is best for finding differences between them.

To this end, this paper describes an experiment to compare two modes of visualizing multiple graphs in a matrix format – either as juxtapositions of separate matrix views or superimpositions into one combined matrix view. The aim of the experiment was to determine which of these two approaches, if any, would be more effective in allowing users to answer questions of a set of multiple graphs.

The rest of the paper is organized as follows: Section II describes previous work in comparative graph visualisation, Section III outlines a set of generic graph comparison questions, and Section IV outlines the methodology behind using these questions in evaluating differences between juxtaposed and superimposed views of the graph as matrices. The final sections discuss the results and conclusions of this evaluation.

II. PREVIOUS WORK

A review of existing research into single graph visualizations shows that there are two distinct alternatives for effectively representing a general graph: as a node-link diagram, and as an adjacency matrix of the graph. Both have strengths and weaknesses in single graph analysis which have been widely explored [1; 2; 3]. Research has also been undertaken into determining the best method to use for some types of graphs: Ghoniem et al. [4] examined locally sparse social networks, while Keller et al. [5] looked at connectivity models and the design structure matrix familiar to engineers. This research has shown that matrix-based displays are preferable to node-link displays for large or locally dense graphs and non-path-finding tasks. Node-link displays are better in general for smaller and simpler graphs and for path-finding. Other work has thus combined parts of these different representations such as Henry and Fekete [6] who overlay path-following edges on a matrix representation, and then alternatively [7] render dense sub-graphs as embedded matrices within a larger node-link representation.

For multiple graph visualizations, while there has been work done on the visualization and comparison of specific restricted graph types, such as planar graphs [8; 9] and trees [10; 11; 12], the general graph case has not been widely examined. Sairaya et al. [13] examined the issue of graphs associated with time series data and how best to indicate changes to the graph data at points in the time line; Telea et al. [14] looked at combining the graphs of RDF schemas with instances of the schemas, but in both cases the visualizations considered means of making alterations to node representations in order to show similarities or differences. Whilst these were effective, such alterations are data dependant rather than independent of both data type and graph type.

Collins and Carpendale [15] produced a comparison tool that used connections between node-link displays shown as pages of a book. The limitation of such a tool for lies primarily in the fact that only two pages can be adjacent to a

1550-6037/11 $26.00 © 2011 IEEE
DOI 10.1109/IV.2011.49

graph at any given time, thus limiting the number of graphs compared to three (one against two others).

Other research in this area has tended to look at some means of merging graphs for comparative purposes, [16; 17] and considered how best to compare node-link displays. Erten et al.'s [8] work in particular concluded that for collections of small graphs shown as node-link views, a combined view was superior to a juxtaposition of separate graph views for discovering similarities and differences between the set of graphs. Meanwhile, Beck and Diehl's recent work [18] showed the relations within and between multiple revisions of source code, combined into a single matrix view.

Freire et al.'s ManyNets [19] approaches multiple graphs from a different angle. It gives a table-based summary of statistics for large numbers of graphs, with graphs as rows and graph metrics as columns. Thus, the graphs can be sorted and compared on the basis of metrics such as edge counts, densities, in and out-degrees etc. in the same way a spreadsheet can be sorted.

Given that Erten et al. [8] had shown the superiority of a combined node-link view over separate node-link views for multiple graphs, we decided to investigate whether the same held true for the other main visualization method for graphs – the matrix. Thus, our aim was to determine whether a combined matrix would prove superior both in terms of user preference and of performance when compared to juxtaposed matrices.

III. GRAPH COMPARISON

As noted above, visual graph comparison has so far focused on node-link displays. We considered that since we are attempting to compare differences and similarities of graphs rather than analyze the information and structure of them or perform path-finding-based tasks, the intuitive nature of the node-link display would not necessarily have any advantage over the more abstract adjacency matrix. Since adjacency matrices are by definition planar, we examined means of comparing planar views. Erten et al covered three possible ways of laying out small planar graphs [8]; side-by-side, combined into a single planar view, and stacked one upon the other like a deck of cards. The recent IV seminar at Dagstuhl [20] looked at the first two of these options, describing them as juxtaposed and superimposed respectively, and also considered the uses of showing only the differences between data sets, possibly in an abstracted format.

We found during preliminary testing that the stacking option was quite confusing even for planar graphs of only fifteen or so nodes and accordingly decided to disregard this approach. We designed and built a visualization tool which enables comparison of graphs in matrix format both as juxtaposed single graphs and as a superimposed combine view. Using this tool we are able to visualize multiple general graphs in terms of their adjacency matrices. By offering a filter option to toggle common edges invisible, we are able also to allow a purely difference-based visualization.

Another issue we encountered was that of the stability of a matrix across multiple representations. In the superimposed state we show all the nodes that ever occur in the set of graphs along the appropriate axes, as all will come into consideration even if some are present in just one of the graphs. With regard to the juxtaposed matrices we have the issue of whether to show each matrix with just the nodes that occur in a particular graph, or to insert dummy rows/columns for nodes that do occur in other graphs but not in the current graph, which would preserve a consistent layout of nodes on the axes across all the juxtaposed representations.. The issue has been explored for dynamic node-link graphs by Purchase and Samra [21], who concluded that placement should either be fixed globally or per graph, either was not significantly better than the other, but definitely not a halfway blend of the two. We decided in the end to display only the nodes that were present in each individual graph.

To aid in the rationale behind the graph comparison test, we identified a series of 'standard' graph comparison questions. These could then be couched in terms of any experimental data set in order to produce a series of testable comparison tasks.

The general case graph comparison questions we considered were:

- Given a specific vertex in one graph, find it in a second graph;
- Given a specific vertex in one graph, find its *equivalent* in a second graph by
  - o Comparing its edges sets in and out
  - o Comparing those vertices to which it is connected as an origin
  - o Comparing those vertices to which it is connected as a target
- Given an identifiable edge in one graph, find it in a second graph;
- Given an identifiable edge in one graph find its *equivalent* in a second graph
  - o Compare its origin
  - o Compare its target
- Given multiple graphs, find the similarities between them in terms of
  - o Common vertices
  - o Common edges
  - o Common sub-graphs
- Given a given sub-graph in one graph, find its equivalent(s) in another graph

The experiment was intended to discover whether it was more effective comparing graphs when the matrix views were juxtaposed (laid out side-by-side in separate views), or combined into a single matrix view which allowed the individual graphs to be compared and contrasted in one view.

IV. METHOD

We tested a group of eighteen students, thirteen male and five female, with two sets of questions based on the generic tasks. We used both different types of visualization, and to eliminate bias the order in which the two visualizations were tested was varied between testers. We also included some initial questions on finding nodes in single graphs to allow users to familiarise themselves with the software.

After completing the first set of questions each tester attempted to answer the second set of questions using the visualization which they had not yet tried. After completing the tests, the testers were asked for comments and to express a preference for the type of visualization.

A. Data Set

The data set used in this experiment consisted of sports results, specifically the results of the annual SuperBowl game that decides which is the best team in America's National Football League. The graph shows teams as vertices and the games as directed edges from the winner to the loser. This data set was chosen for several reasons:

- It is easily comprehensible by non-expert users;
- It is small (29 vertices and 43 edges) enough to manage the number of differences to test our questions with, but complex enough to require testers take care when finding and interpreting those differences;
- The node-link graphs produced from this data set are non-planar with sufficient edge crossings and occlusion

to justify using matrix representations;
- It can be represented in different ways, allowing for direct comparison between versions;
- It has the rare property of uniquely identifiable edges, where the identity is not dependent on the vertices at either end – each edge is a SuperBowl game with a specific number. This enabled our users to more easily identify each specific difference and us to evaluate user accuracy.

We chose to use two graphs based on historic data which would enable information about the teams to be directly obtained from the comparison process. We then added a further two ahistorical graphs where results and opponents had in some cases been altered.

Thus, one pair of graphs (historic and altered) represented the teams by their current location (or in the case of the New York teams NYG or NYJ respectively). Thus in this representation, the Colts are shown as IND as their current home is Indianapolis, the Rams as STL (St Louis), and so on.

The second pair of graphs showed the teams by their home location when the game in question was played. For example, the Colts were shown as BAL (Baltimore) for

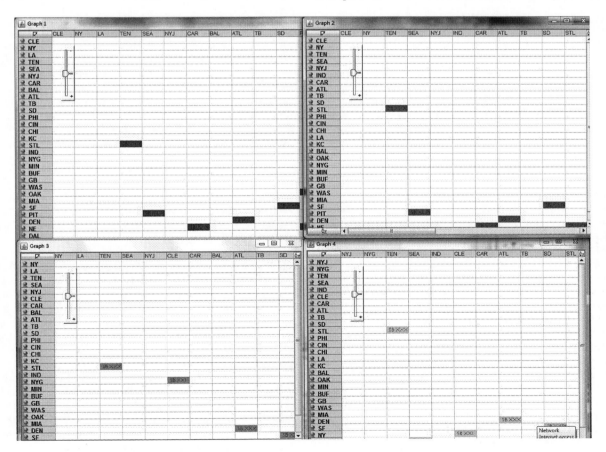

Figure 1.   Four graphs of SuperBowl results juxtaposed as individual matrix visualizations.

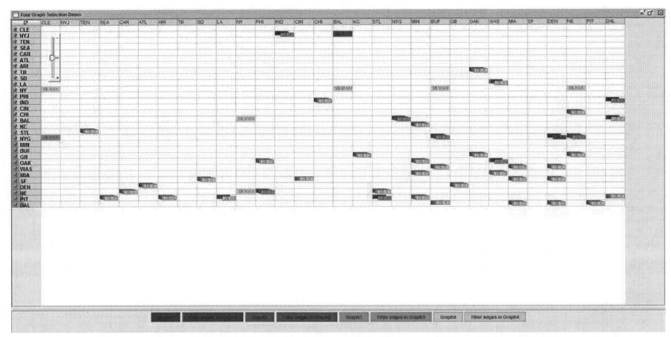

Figure 2.   Four graphs of SuperBowl results superimposed into one matrix visualization.

SuperBowls III and V, but IND for SuperBowl XLI; the Rams under LA for SuperBowl XIV, and STL for SuperBowls XXXIV and XXXVI and so on. This also meant that the two New York teams were shown under the same.

We then couched the generic questions we'd identified in terms of this data set. For example, rather than ask "which vertex has the highest out-degree?" we ask "which team won the greatest number of SuperBowls?" Likewise we ask "which graph shows a different loser than Denver Broncos (DEN) against the New York Giants (NYG/NY), and what is the team abbreviation?" (ans : graph 4 shows CLE as the target of the edge NY-CLE).

B.   Juxtaposed vs Superimposed Visualizations

The experiment compared and contrasted two distinct modes of visualizing multiple graphs in matrix form. One, the juxtaposition mode, showed one matrix per graph, divided as small multiples on the screen. The second displayed a single matrix visualization within which all the graphs were displayed in a combined structure. For all matrices, the vertices were shown on the axes and the edges as blocks within a grid. Where more than one edge (either a multi-edge in one graph, or multiple edges originating from different graphs) connected the same vertices, the blocks were reduced in size and offset from each other so that all edges were visible. Hovering the pointer over a filled block in the grid brought up a larger scale detail of the edge(s) in that block.

The juxtaposed visualization showed the test graphs in separate windows. These windows were linked so that a vertex or group of vertices selected in one graph would be highlighted in the others, and an edge or group of edges highlighted in one graph would likewise be highlighted in the others.

All the windows showed all vertices for all graphs (see Fig. 1). Given that an adjacency matrix shows all its vertices on each of its axes, this was necessary to more easily enable direct comparison where one graph contained a vertex (for example NY, representing New York) which was not present in the other. A visual comparison is much more difficult if the same vertices are not present in all views. In addition it is much easier to compare multiple matrices if all the vertices are placed in the same order; this means that edges joining a given two vertices always appear in the same position in the view.

Due to the choice of graphs used, we were able to more or less bypass the issue of vertex mapping, although it should be noted that LA in the game-time based graphs maps to both STL and OAK (in specific instances) in the current location graphs rather than to LA.

While the default setting of the axes placed vertices in degree order, which of course varied between the graphs, a facility was provided to enable re-ordering of the vertices on either or both axes. This facility was not linked between the views, since a user might wish to reorder the vertices in only one view at a time. The initial ordering was chosen specifically to make it easy to answer the first questions in each set, most of which to some extent involved finding vertices of given degree and were intended to give users practice in manipulating the visualizations.

A further feature of the views allowed a user to double click on any given vertex on either axis and by so doing to 'pull' all the edges associated with that vertex towards that axis. Thus if a user wished to see how many games a team had won, they could double click the team on the y-axis; to see how many losses, a double click on the x-axis would be used. This perforce reordered the axes and was again not linked, although the vertex selected would highlight in the other graph.

The second visualization superimposed the matrices into a single combined view (see Figure 2) using the combined vertex set. The same colours were used for each graph as were used in the juxtaposed view.

The functionality of this visualization was identical to that of the other visualizations with the addition of two buttons which enabled a user to toggle the visibility of any graph off or on at will. An example of this representation is shown in Fig. 2.

Finally we added a filter facility. This enabled users to select one graph and make its common edges with any or all of the others invisible. This facility takes advantage of the common vertex set to search each vertex in turn to determine if has multiple edges to other vertices from different graphs. In effect this gives a difference visualization mode to both the juxtaposed and superimposed states. Fig. 3 shows the filter in action in the superimposed view.

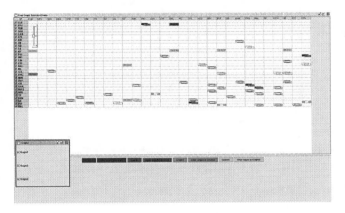

Figure 3.   Superimposed matrices with filter.

We found that all our users utilised these facilities at some point, but none suggested that we link the reordering so that reordering an axis in one view would automatically do the same in the other.

V.   RESULTS

The results showed that in terms of user preference, 13 out of the 18 testers preferred the combined view; only 4 preferred the separate windows and 1 had no preference.

The task-based results showed:

In determining which of the four graphs had a specific difference (a single edge)

View type	Result
Superimposed	Mean = 0.78; SD = 0.42; n=18
Juxtaposed	Mean = 0.56; SD = 0.5; n=18

In determining difference between vertices on a given edge (representation of SB V, the Colts as BAL or IND)

View type	Result
Superimposed	Mean = 0.83; SD = 0.30; n=18
Juxtaposed	Mean = 0.66; SD = 0.47; n=18

In determining a difference in vertices, the change being made in graph four where the SuperBowl game between NYG and DEN was instead between NYG and CLE.)

View type	Result
Superimposed	Mean = 0.83; SD =0.30; n=18
Juxtaposed	Mean = 0.56; SD =0.5; n=18

These results show a statistically significant improvement in accuracy for the superimposed visualization over the juxtaposed one. On the other hand, both visualizations scored almost identically in both finding a given vertex/edge in different graphs, and in determining the differences between in and out degree of any given vertex between graphs.

As shown by the figures above, it was in the area of finding equivalency (of both edges and vertices) that the superposition proved superior. Our testers found it very difficult to find which difference related where in the juxtaposed views, and much preferred (and were more correct) using the superimposed matrices.

VI.   CONCLUSIONS AND FUTURE WORK

Our main finding is that when comparing small graphs with matrix visualizations, it is significantly more effective to combine the visualizations into a single view rather than to link separate views; the accuracy of the comparison was better by nearly 50% in the former case.

This mirrors the same result Erten et al found for small planar graphs with node-link displays, the combined view being superior to that of the separate views. Likewise, Andrews et al [17] results were similar although with smaller ranges of difference.

We can therefore state that a combined tool for multiple graph comparison should be based around a superimposition of the graphs to be compared, regardless of whether the display technique is to be node-link or matrix-based.

We should be careful not to over-generalize this finding of a combined view being superior to separate views for comparison tasks. While the result of combining several general graphs is itself another general graph (in effect, a graph is its own plural), it may not apply to other data types, since combining them does not result in data of the same type. For example, the aggregate of multiple trees is a non tree-like graph of some description, and combining multiple data tables results in a data cube.

Future work may examine superposition versus juxtaposition versus differencing of other data types to determine if the above result holds for them also.

REFERENCES

[1]   H.C. Purchase. "Metrics for Graph Drawing Aesthetics," Journal of Visual Languages and Computing, vol. 13(5), pp.501-516, doi:10.1006/jvlc.2002.0232.

[2] H.C. Purchase, D. Carrington and J.-A. Allder. "Empirical Evaluation of Aesthetics-based Graph Layout," Empirical Software Engineering, vol. 7(3), pp.233-255, doi:10.1023/A:1016344215610.

[3] H.-J. Schulz and H. Schumann. "Visualizing Graphs - A Generalized View," Proc. 10th IEEE International Conference on Information Visualisation, IEEE Computer Society Press, 5-7 July 2006, pp.166-173, doi:10.1109/IV.2006.130.

[4] M. Ghoniem, J.-D. Fekete and P. Castagliola. "A Comparison of the Readability of Graphs Using Node-Link and Matrix-Based Representations," Proc. IEEE InfoVis, IEEE Computer Society Press, 10-12 October 2004, pp.17-24, doi:10.1109/INFOVIS.2004.1.

[5] R. Keller, C.M. Eckert and P.J. Clarkson. "Matrices or node-link diagrams: which visual representation is better for visualising connectivity models?," Information Visualization, vol. 5(1), pp.62-76, doi:10.1057/palgrave.ivs.9500116.

[6] N. Henry and J.-D. Fekete. "MatLink: Enhanced Matrix Visualization for Analyzing Social Networks," Proc. Interact, Springer, 10-14 September 2007, pp.288-302, doi:10.1007/978-3-540-74800-7_24.

[7] N. Henry, J.-D. Fekete and M. McGuffin. "NodeTrix: A Hybrid Visualization of Social Networks.," IEEE Transactions on Visualization and Computer Graphics, vol. 13(6), pp.1302-1309, doi:10.1109/TVCG.2007.70582.

[8] C. Erten, S.G. Kobourov, V. Le and A. Navabi. "Simultaneous Graph Drawing: Layout Algorithms and Visualization Schemes," Proc. Graph Drawing, Springer-Verlag, 21-24 September 2003, pp.437-449, doi:10.1007/978-3-540-24595-7_41.

[9] P. Brass, E. Cenek, C.A. Duncan, A. Efrat, C. Erten, D.P. Ismailescu, et al. "On simultaneous planar graph embedding," Computational Geometry: Theory and Applications, vol. 36(2), pp.117-130, doi:10.1016/j.comgeo.2006.05.006.

[10] J.Y. Hong, J. D'Andries, M. Richman and M. Westfall. "Zoomology: Comparing Two Large Hierarchical Trees," Proc. IEEE InfoVis Poster Compendium, IEEE Computer Society Press, 19-21 October 2003, pp.120-121.

[11] T. Munzner, F. Guimbretière, S. Tasiran, L. Zhang and Y. Zhou. "TreeJuxtaposer: Scalable Tree Comparison using Focus+Context with Guaranteed Visibility," ACM Transactions on Graphics, vol. 22(3), pp.453-462, doi:10.1145/882262.882291.

[12] M. Graham and J. Kennedy. "Exploring Multiple Trees through DAG Representations," IEEE Transactions on Visualization and Computer Graphics, vol. 13(6), pp.1294-1301, doi:10.1109/TVCG.2007.70556.

[13] P. Saraiya, P. Lee and C. North. "Visualization of Graphs with Associated Timeseries Data," Proc. IEEE InfoVis, IEEE Computer Society Press, 23-25 October 2005, pp.225-232, doi:10.1109/INFOVIS.2005.37.

[14] A. Telea, F. Frasincar and G.-J. Houben. "Visualisation of RDF(S)-based Information," Proc. International Conference on Information Visualization, IEEE Computer Socierty Press, 16-18 July 2003, pp.294-299, doi:10.1109/IV.2003.1217993.

[15] C. Collins and S. Carpendale. "VisLink: Revealing Relationships Amongst Visualizations," IEEE Transactions on Visualization and Computer Graphics, vol. 13(6), pp.1192-1199, doi:10.1109/TVCG.2007.70611

[16] S. Diehl, C. Görg and A. Kerren. "Preserving the Mental Map using Foresighted Layout," Proc. Joint Eurographics-IEEE TVCG Symposium on Visualization, Springer Verlag, 28-30 May 2001, pp.175-184.

[17] K. Andrews, M. Wohlfahrt and G. Wurzinger. "Visual Graph Comparison," Proc. 13th International Conference on Information Visualisation, IEEE Computer Society Press, 15-17 July 2009, pp.62-67, doi:10.1109/IV.2009.108.

[18] F. Beck and S. Diehl. "Visual Comparison of Software Architectures," Proc. 5th International Symposium on Software Visualization (SOFTVIS), ACM Press, 25-26 October 2010, pp.183-192, doi:10.1145/1879211.1879238.

[19] M. Freire, C. Plaisant, B. Shneiderman and J. Golbeck. "ManyNets: An Interface for Multiple Network Analysis and Visualization," Proc. ACM Conference on Human Factors in Computing Systems (CHI), ACM Press, 10-15 April 2010, pp.213-222, doi:10.1145/1753326.1753358.

[20] A. Kerren, C. Plaisant and J.T. Stasko. "Executive Summary of Dagstuhl Seminar on Information Visualization". Retrieved 21 March, 2011, from http://drops.dagstuhl.de/opus/volltexte/2010/2760/pdf/10241_executive_summary.2760.pdf

[21] H.C. Purchase and A. Samra. "Extremes Are Better: Investigating Mental Map Preservation in Dynamic Graphs," Proc. 5th International Conference on Diagrammatic Representation and Inference, Springer-Verlag Berlin Heidelberg, 19-21 September 2008, pp.60-73, doi:10.1007/978-3-540-87730-1.

Concentric Sliders to Display Partial Satisfaction of Query Criteria

Benoît Otjacques, Maël Cornil, Mickaël Stefas, Fernand Feltz
Public Research Centre – Gabriel Lippmann, Luxembourg
{otjacque, cornil, stefas, feltz}@lippmann.lu

Abstract

This paper describes a new approach called concentric planar slider to visually build queries and to pilot a data view. The purpose of this approach is to go beyond the binary satisfaction of the query criteria (satisfied vs. not satisfied). This UI control helps the user to know to what extent the dataset elements satisfy them. Two interactive sliders are combined in a planar setting. This plane is split into concentric zones that are associated to decreasing degrees of satisfaction of the query criteria. Various (potentially asymmetric) rules can be defined to express the non-satisfaction of a given criterion. These theoretical concepts have been implemented in a prototype whose main features are also described.

Keywords --- **Visual Query, Query Specification, Planar Slider, Sensitivity Information, Information Visualization.**

1. Introduction

Selecting some elements of a set according to certain criteria is a common task in many contexts. For instance, investors select funds and stocks according to the risk level and the expected return. People aiming to move may use the rent, the floor area and the walking distance to some facilities to choose their new apartment.

Sometimes, defining the precise selection criteria is challenging and the threshold values are adjusted many times during the querying process. In fact these threshold values often result in real life from an approximation or a negotiation process. The investors may adjust the acceptable risk level depending on the number of funds that were identified in the initial step of the study. Similarly, people can face some difficulties to choose an initial threshold for the maximum distance to the railway station when they are looking for an apartment.

These examples highlight a limitation of the usual way to build a query and to display the result set: the selection of items is based on binary satisfaction of conditions ("selected / not selected" approach). However, some years ago the 2005 Lowell Database

research self-assessment report [1] already pointed out the need to design database tools supporting approximate data or imprecise queries.

The purpose of the research described in this paper is to help users having only partial or imprecise information to define a query and to help them to adjust the selection threshold values to find the right answer to their ill-defined problem. More precisely, we have studied how to provide the user with an easy way to see more than the subset of items that strictly satisfies the query criteria on a binary basis. For instance, the investor want to identify which funds that do not appear in the initial result set have a risk level slightly above the acceptable threshold. Indeed, there might be some interesting "second choice" candidates.

2. State-of-the-Art

Mapping a question expressed in natural language into a formal expression using a demanding syntax like SQL or XQuery is not a trivial task (cf. e.g. [1] , [4] , [5]). Various strategies like Query-By-Example or natural language processing have therefore been proposed to avoid the user having to learn a formal query language. The work presented in this paper belongs to complementary research fields aiming to map the query terms and/or the query results to visual representations.

Dynamic queries (first reported in [13]) have become a standard way to combine interactively a visual specification of the query and the display of the result. In their usual implementations, each attribute of the elements of a data set $\{E_i\}$ is associated to a control (e.g. slider, check box, radio button) that is used to define the query criterion concerning this attribute. In the illustrative "apartment" example, the range of acceptable values for the rent and the floor area can be set via two sliders. The data view displaying the elements of $\{E_i\}$ is updated in real time when the selection control(s) are modified.

The simplest way to implement dynamic queries consists of highlighting the elements completely satisfying the Query (called $\{QE_i\}$ in the subsequent sections) in the data view. The two most common strategies are (1) to permanently display every element of $\{E_i\}$ and to visually mark (e.g. using a specific color)

1550-6037/11 $26.00 © 2011 IEEE
DOI 10.1109/IV.2011.9

the elements of {QE_i} or (2) to display only the elements of {QEi}. Note that the second solution is less affected by occlusion problems than the first one since fewer elements are displayed in the data view. Both solutions reduce the degree of satisfying the query to a binary value: either satisfying or not satisfying all its criteria.

In many circumstances the user does not need any explicit information regarding the elements that do not satisfy every criterion (subsequently called Elements of {NQE_i}). Nevertheless he/she may sometimes have some interest in those elements. For example, the investor may wonder which funds have a slightly disappointing return but a risk level compatible with the acceptable threshold.

Years ago Spence and Tweedie [10] identified this need and introduced the concept of sensitivity information that they defined as "the reduction in the number of violated limits achieved by movement of a limit". The basic idea consists in adding to the data view some information about how many criteria the elements of {NQE_i} satisfy. Spence and Tweedie's Attribute Explorer displays in dynamically linked histograms the number of criteria every element satisfies. A multi-level monochromatic scale (e.g. grey levels) is used to code the degree of satisfaction of the query criteria. This application visualizes the influence of modifying a criterion about a specific attribute. Unfortunately, it is not so easy to identify in histograms which criteria a given element E_i satisfies.

Keim and Kriegel [6] have also investigated this issue and have proposed the concept of relevance factor to represent the degree of satisfaction of the query criteria. Their application called VisDB codes the relevance factor with both the position and the color of pixels representing the elements {E_i}. VisDB is basically a specific type of chart and this approach is not easy to generalize to usual graphics layouts.

Other researchers focusing on the visual specification of queries have indirectly tackled the issue of giving to the user some information about the elements not included in the result set (i.e. {NQE_i}).

Jones [5] has proposed the VQuery tool based on Venn diagrams. Some ellipses (or circles) are associated to the query criteria. They can be moved in a plan and enabled (disabled) to form Venn-like diagrams defining a Boolean expression. The ellipses of the diagram include the number of elements (i.e. documents in his case study) satisfying the related criterion.

In InfoCrystal [11] all possible Boolean queries involving many criteria are represented by icons carefully positioned on a plan to show which criteria are satisfied. Infocrystal can also display the number of elements of the dataset {E_i} satisfying every combination of criteria. Its scalability in terms of number of query criteria is a major advantage of InfoCrystal.

KMVQL [4] is a visual query language that uses a Karnaugh map as the visual representation of Boolean queries. The elements E_i are represented by flower-like icons whose number and color of the petals inform the user regarding which criteria the related element satisfies.

Another example is Hotmap [3] designed in the context of information retrieval from the web. A set of n distinct squares associated to each query criterion (i.e. word/term in this context) are placed near each element of the query results set. Each square is colored according to the frequency of the related term in the result element. Hotmap shows the relationship between the criteria and the results but it does not help building the query itself. Also, HotMap does not display the whole dataset {E_i} but only a subset.

In the Filter-Flow approach [14] the criteria on the attributes are visualized by boxes placed sequentially (AND operation) or in parallel (OR operation). The width of a virtual flow passing through the boxes indicates the number of elements satisfying the criteria. Unfortunately, this representation is highly dependent of the order of the criteria (i.e. order of the boxes).

All these approaches have proposed valuable contributions regarding how to visually express a query. Although their focus was not on the visual display of the query result they acknowledge the need to provide the user with some information about the degree of satisfaction of the criteria.

3. Concentric Slider

Problem Statement

Our proposal does not allow the user to ask imprecise questions but rather focuses on the "results" facet. From a practical view point we aim to help the user to distinguish the elements E_i that are very far from satisfying the query criteria and those that have just failed to fulfill them.

To formally describe our problem we hypothesize first that the query Q is visually specified within a space having 2 dimensions.

Q is defined by a set of m criteria defining an interval of acceptable values for a subset of the n attributes of the elements E_i. We have limited this initial investigation to queries composed of two criteria ($m = 2$). In further research, we will investigate how to generalize this concept to a higher number of criteria ($m > 2$).

- $p \in R^2$, p is the point associated to the element E_i in the display space where the query Q is specified
- $x = (x_0, x_1, \ldots x_n)$, vector of all attribute values of E_i
- $x^* = (x^*_0, x^*_1, \ldots x^*_m)$, vector of attribute values of E_i that are involved in a query criterion, m<n
- Query $Q := \{ p \in R^2 \mid a \leq x^* \leq b \}$
  $a, b, x^* \in R^m$

We draw attention to the fact that this definition does not include all types of query. However, the definition specifies a class of query that is sufficiently generic to be studied.

Our goal in this context is to design a solution that (1) offers an intuitive way to define Q, (2) shows for each element the degree of satisfaction of the criteria and (3) is independent of the chart used in the display space.

Planar Slider Layout

The concept of dynamic queries has proven to be very powerful to build and interactively modify a query (cf. [2]). Therefore we have adopted this general paradigm. Each query criterion is represented by a slider defining the interval of acceptable values. We propose to place orthogonally the two sliders in order to define a plane (cf. Figure 1). This layout has an advantage on the use of two independent sliders because it visually links the two query criteria together, which offers some visual cues to easily perceive some aggregated information on both of them. In the example, the attribute A_1 is associated with the horizontal slider and the attribute A_2 to the vertical slider.

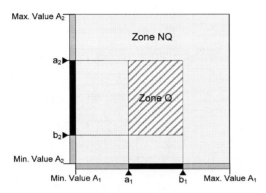

Figure 1 Planar Slider

This new control is called "planar slider". The cursors of the sliders define two distinct zones that together overlap the display space completely. The zone Q corresponds to the elements of $\{QE_i\}$ that satisfy the two query criteria. The zone NQ corresponds to the elements of the complement subset $\{NQE_i\}$. Each element E_i of the data set will therefore belong to only one zone. We remind that the elements E_i are not displayed in the planar slider but in the data view that can be any type of chart (e.g. bar chart, treemap).

Concentric Planar Slider

Let's take the example of someone looking for a new apartment. He/she can state that the rent should ideally be between 900 EUR and 1600 EUR and the floor area between 80 m^2 and 120 m^2 (these two criteria define the query Q). However, he/she is more sensitive to a higher rent than to a smaller floor area. Each bracket of 100 EUR above 1600 EUR would add a new serious constraint to his/her daily life. Simultaneously, his/her past experience tells him/her that each rent bracket of 150 EUR lower than 900 EUR corresponds to a significant decrease in terms of conveniences. Moreover he/she also requires that the floor area be no lower than 60 m^2. This is a typical use case that our proposal intends to tackle. The challenge is to help the user to assess whether an apartment not selected by the query Q can nevertheless be considered as a second choice option.

The concept of the concentric planar slider is illustrated in Figure 2. The zone Q corresponds to the complete satisfaction of the query (criteria regarding attributes A_1 and A_2 are fulfilled). The basic idea is to draw several concentric zones C_j around the zone Q showing increasing levels of incomplete satisfaction of the query criteria. The elements corresponding to zone C_1 are almost satisfying the criteria but the elements of zone C_4 are far from being acceptable. In order to offer a generic solution, the zones C_j are defined by two distinct distances for each query criterion (i.e. each slider). The distance d_{low} and d_{upp} are computed respectively from the lower and the upper limit of the interval defined by the criterion. In this two-dimensional concentric slider four distances are therefore required to define the concentric zones. This feature allows the user to specify four distinct ways of relaxing the criteria of the query.

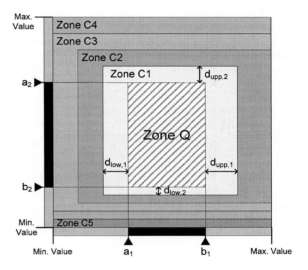

Figure 2 Concentric Planar Slider

The q concentric zones C_j can be formally defined by the expression:

$$C_j := \{p \in R^2 \mid (a-j\,d_{low} \leq x^* < a-(j-1)\,d_{low})\ \text{OR}\ (b+(j-1)\,d_{upp} < x^* \leq b+j\,d_{upp}\} \quad j = 1 .. q$$

with a, b, x^*, d_{low}, $d_{upp} \in R^2$ (*m*=2)

Two strategies are available to compute the incremental distances d_{low} and d_{upp}.

First, the distance from a given threshold can be expressed in absolute value (i.e. constant numerical value). For instance, the distance from the lower limit of the rent ($d_{low,1}$) is set to 150 EUR. In this example, each 150 EUR rent bracket below the ideal lower rent belongs to a specific zone C_j. According to our example, the distance from the upper limit of the rent ($d_{upp,1}$) would be set to 100 EUR due to the asymmetry of user sensitiveness to the rent.

Second, the distance from a given threshold can be computed as a relative variation of this threshold value (expressed in terms of percentage of increase/decrease).

For instance, the distance from the upper limit of floor area (e.g. $d_{upp,2}$) can be set to 10%. If the upper threshold is set to 120 m^2, this means that the first concentric zone C_1 corresponds to 120 – 132 m^2, the second one C_2 to 132 – 144 m^2, etc. Each of the four distances required to define the zone C_j can adopt either the "absolute value" or the "relative value" strategy to compute the increment between two adjacent zones.

Data View

The data view is the place where the elements E_i are visualized. We draw the reader's attention to the fact that the chart used in the data view can highlight other facets of the data than those underpinning the query Q. For instance, the data view can display a map to show the location of the apartments while the query involves the rent and the floor area. In another case, the data view can show the stocks quotes in a treemap and the query can involve the risk level and the expected return.

Our basic idea is to draw a visual relationship between the zone of the query control that an element belongs to (e.g. zone Q, C_1, C_2 …) and the display of this element in the data view.

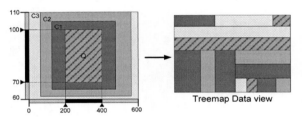

Figure 3: Concentric Planar Slider and Treemap

The zone Q is conceptually different from the zones C_j because the former refers to the satisfaction of the query criteria and the latter to their non-satisfaction. Consequently, we think that their related elements E_i should also be clearly distinguished in the data view.

We suggest to highlight the elements of {QE_i} (cf. zone Q) with a visual property v_1. Many visual properties can be used for this purpose, such as color, shape or icons. A visual property v_2 will be used to show how well the remaining elements belonging to {NQE_i} satisfy the query (cf. zones C_j). A continuous visual variable (e.g. color range) should probably be preferred for v_2 as this variable is linked to the degree of query satisfaction. If the user prefers to use the same visual property for both mapping (i.e. $v_1 = v_2$) it is recommended to select clearly distinct values.

Figure 3 shows how a concentric planar slider can be used to query data visualized by a treemap in the data view. In this example, the zone Q is mapped to the green color and the zones C_j to a monochromatic orange color scale. A double coding (i.e. background pattern) is used to facilitate the perception of zone Q. Each nested rectangle of the treemap is colored according to its degree of satisfaction of the query criteria. The treemap conveys some information regarding the structure of the

data set as well as the relative weight of a given attribute (e.g. market capitalization of the company). The concentric planar slider enables the exploration of the satisfaction of the two criteria: risk level and expected return of the company stock.

As a second example (cf. Figure 4), the concentric planar slider can be used together with a scatterplot. In this illustrative case, shape (v_1) is used to identify the elements of {QE_i} (cf. zone Q) that are represented by a star in the data view. A color range (v_2 = color) is used to show the partial satisfaction of the criteria by the elements of {NQE_i} (cf. zones C_j).

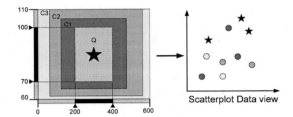

Figure 4: Concentric Planar Slider and Chart

Each combination of visual mapping for v_1 and v_2 has a different quality in terms of cognitive perception and semantic mapping. We do not discuss this aspect in this paper because of the exponential number of combinations and because this decision also typically depends on the use case. Moreover, we did not carry out any experiments to evaluate the relative performance of some competing settings. However, previous research regarding conjunction visual search may provide some decision criteria in this matter (cf. [12] p. 154-156, [8] p. 557-559). From a cognitive point of view, the visual mapping of the zones C_j to a continuous visual variable also faces the challenge of perceiving different values of this variable, (cf. JND Just Noticeable Differences concept thoroughly studied in psychophysics, e.g. [7]). The values associated to each zone C_j should therefore be carefully chosen. It is obvious that slight differences of hue will probably not be perceived by the user.

Our approach differs from Spence and Tweedie's concept of sensitivity information. Indeed, we do not display how many criteria a given element satisfies but we rather rely on a concept of distance. An element that satisfies the first criteria (A_1) but that is very far from satisfying the second criteria (A_2) will be located in a concentric area far from the center. Another element that just fails to satisfy both criteria A_1 and A_2 will be located in the concentric area near the centre. Moreover, our concept supports asymmetric zones around Q. In other terms, the sensitivity to the lower or upper limit of the query intervals can be different from each other. This feature allows the user to explore the dataset while taking into account query idiosyncrasies coming from the very nature of real life. Finally, the visual simplicity of the concentric planar slider makes it intuitive to realize what the settings currently in use are.

4. Prototype

The concept of concentric planar slider has been integrated into a software tool that we have incrementally designed and developed in past projects (cf. Figure 14: main user interface with a treemap used in the data view). This paper only discusses the concentric planar slider component but the application obviously offers additional features.

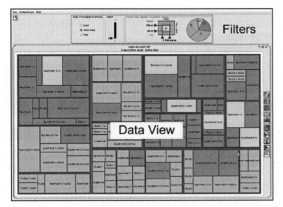

Figure 5: Main User Interface of the Prototype

Several interactive data views are available like tree view, pie chart, temporal chart, bar chart, table or treemap. The concentric planar slider is used to interactively query the dataset and to show in real time which zone (cf. Q, C_j) the elements displayed in the data view belong to. We remind that the data view can highlight some aspects of the data (e.g. hierarchical structure, temporal evolution, relative value of some attributes) that are not involved in the query.

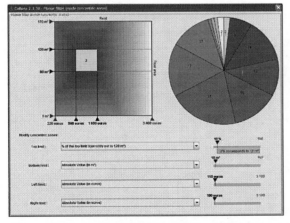

Figure 6: Concentric Planar Slider component

The main features of our implementation of the concentric planar slider concept are described below. The component can be integrated into the main window of the application (cf. Figure 5) or displayed in a separate one (cf. Figure 6). The features available in both settings are the same. They are directly accessed in the latter and via a contextual menu in the former.

Specifying the query Q requires choosing the two related attributes and the threshold values. The attributes are assigned via a contextual menu and the threshold values are set by moving the cursors of the sliders.

Moreover, the user can change the query Q simply be clicking into a given zone of the concentric planar slider. For instance, in Figure 7 the query Q_1 was first associated to the central yellow zone. Next the user has activated the top right zone to define a new query Q_2. The concentric zones C_j are automatically updated to refer to the new query Q_2. Color coding may be changed if appropriate. Regarding the zones C_j the user only need to select a basic color (e.g. green, blue) and the application automatically computes the needed shades.

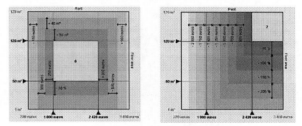

Figure 7: Changing query Q

The user can specify the strategies used to compute the concentric zones C_j. Two strategies (cf. section introducing the concentric planar slider concept) are available to define the four incremental distances (cf. Figure 2). Each border of the Q zone (top, right, bottom, left) can be given a distinct strategy whose settings may be interactively modified (cf bottom part of Figure 6). The chosen strategies can be reminded within the concentric planar slider by optional labeled arrows (cf. Figure 7).

The zones Q and C_j of the planar slider can display aggregated information about the elements that they include. In the example (cf. Figure 6), the number of elements belonging to the zone Q is displayed. However, other aggregation functions could be potentially useful, like the sum or the mean of a given attribute for the elements of the zone.

A pie chart is displayed on the right of the concentric planar slider (cf. Figure 6). This component shows the distribution of the elements E_i among the zones Q and C_j. Indeed, most of the time the elements are heterogeneously distributed according to the attributes used in the query. Consequently a small zone in the concentric planar slider can include much more elements of the data set than a larger zone. The pie chart, which is synchronized in real time with the settings of the concentric planar slider, can help the user to gain insight into the data from this point of view. For instance, he/she may want to know which proportion of the apartments have just failed to satisfy the criteria about the rent and floor area and are therefore located in the closest zone C_1 surrounding Q.

The application allows the user to focus on the elements that belong to a specific zone Q or C_j. The user can activate or deactivate individually each zone simply by clicking on it in the concentric planar slider or on its corresponding slice in the pie chart. The corresponding elements are visually marked in the data view (e.g. background color) while the elements belonging to inactive zones are visually deactivated (e.g. colored in grey). For instance, in Figure 8 the user has selected the elements satisfying the query (yellow) and those having just failed to satisfy it (green corresponding to C_1 zone)

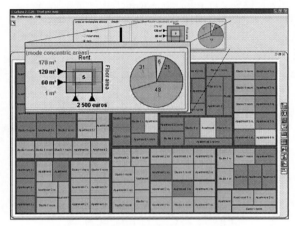

Figure 8: Focus on selected zones

The user can also add some absolute limits to the acceptable values of the attributes. For instance, the floor area of the apartment should not be lower than 60 m². He/she simply has to activate an optional specific cursor called "absolute limit" (cf. red line in Figure 9). The elements E_i beyond this limit will always be excluded and displayed as such in the data view (e.g. displayed in a specific color or pattern).

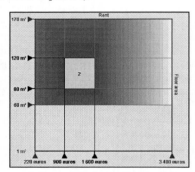

Figure 9: Absolute limits

Conclusions

The main contribution of this paper is the concept of concentric planar slider from a conceptual and practical point of view. We have proposed an evolution of the former concepts of sensitivity information and degree of satisfaction of query criteria and we have proposed a concrete way to implement our approach in a prototype.

Nevertheless, some questions remain open. First, the concentric planar slider is only discussed for a specific class of queries. Second, we propose an implementation only for queries based on two criteria. Further work will explore how to generalize the approach to a higher number of criteria because the orthogonal layout of the sliders is not appropriate in this case. Third, this new component will be included in the next release of our visualization tool. We plan to collect feedback in order to assess its usefulness and ease-of-use in real settings.

References

[1]   S. Abiteboul, R. Agrawal, P. Bernstein et al. The Lowell Database Research Self-Assessment. *Communications of the ACM*, 48, 5 (May 2005), 111-118.

[2]   C. Ahlberg, C. Williamson, and B. Shneiderman. Dynamic Queries for Information Exploration: an Implementation and Evaluation. *Proceedings of ACM Conference on Human Factors in Computing Systems* (Monterey, CA, USA, 3-7 May, 1992), ACM Press, 619-26.

[3]   O. Hoeber and X.D. Yang. The Visual Exploration of Web Search Results Using HotMap. *Proceedings of 10th International Conference on Information Visualization* (London, UK, 5-7 July, 2006). IEEE Computer Society. 157-165.

[4]   J. Huo. KMVQL: a Visual Query Interface Based on Kanraugh Map. *Proceedings of the working Conference on Advanced Visual Interfaces* (Napoli, Italy, 28-30 May, 2008). ACM Press, 243-250.

[5]   S. Jones. 1998. Graphical Query Specification and Dynamic Result Previews for a Digital Library. *Proceedings of the 11th Annual ACM Symposium on User interface Software and Technology* (San Francisco, CA, USA, November 01 - 04, 1998). ACM Press, 143-151.

[6]   D. Keim and H.-P. Kriegel. VisDB: Database Exploration Using Multidimensional Visualization. *IEEE Computer Graphics and Applications*, 14, 5, 40-49 (1994)

[7]   G. Mather. Foundations of Sensation and Perception, 2nd Ed., Psychology Press, Hove, UK. 2009.

[8]   S.E. Palmer. Vision Science, Photons to Phenomenology. MIT Press, Cambridge, MA, USA. 1999.

[9]   R. Spence. Information Visualization. ACM Press Books. 2001.

[10] R. Spence and L. Tweedie. The Attribute Explorer: information synthesis via exploration. *Interacting with Computers*, 11, 2 (December 1998), 137-146.

[11] A. Spoerri, A. InfoCrystal: a visual tool for information retrieval & management. *Proceedings of 2nd International Conference on Information Knowledge and Management* (Washington, DC, USA, 1-5 November, 1993), ACM Press, 11-20.

[12] C. Ware. Information Visualization, Perception for Design, 2nd Edition. Morgan Kaufmann Publishers, San Francisco, CA, USA. 2004.

[13] C. Williamson, C. and B. Shneiderman. The Dynamic Homefinder: evaluating dynamic queries in a real estate information exploration system. *Proceedings of the 15th ACM Conference on Research and development in information retrieval* (Copenhagen, Denmark, 21-24 June, 1992), ACM Press, 338-346.

[14] D. Young and B. Shneiderman. A graphical query / flow model for Boolean queries: An implementation and experimentation. *Journal of the American Society for Information Science*, 44, 6, 327-339. (1993).

Visual Clustering of Spam Emails for DDoS Analysis

Mao Lin Huang

School of Software, Faculty of Engineering & IT
University of Technology, Sydney
Australia
maolin@it.uts.edu.au

Jinson Zhang

School of Software, Faculty of Engineering & IT
University of Technology, Sydney
Australia
maolin@it.uts.edu.au

Quang Vinh Nguyen

School of Computing and Mathematics
University of Western Sydney
Australia
vinh@scm.uws.edu.au

Junhu Wang

[3]School of Information and Communication
Technology
Griffith University, Australia
J.Wang@griffith.edu.au

Abstract— **Networking attacks embedded in spam emails are increasingly becoming numerous and sophisticated in nature. Hence this has given a growing need for spam email analysis to identify these attacks. The use of these intrusion detection systems has given rise to other two issues, 1) the presentation and understanding of large amounts of spam emails, 2) the user-assisted input and quantified adjustment during the analysis process. In this paper we introduce a new analytical model that uses two coefficient vectors: 'density' and 'weight' for the analysis of spam email viruses and attacks. We then use a visual clustering method to classify and display the spam emails. The visualization allows users to interactively select and scale down the scope of views for better understanding of different types of the spam email attacks. The experiment shows that this new model with the clustering visualization can be effectively used for network security analysis.**

Keywords- Spam email, network security analysis, clustered visualization, information visualization, network intrusion detection, DDoS attacks

I. INTRODUCTION

Spam email is a common type of the cyber nuisance. It not only wastes resources, but also poses serious security threats [1]. Spam emails can be divided into two types: those with the attachment and others without the attachment. The attachments are normally the executable files that have virus hidden inside. The spam emails with no attachment usually have virus hidden inside of the message body.

DDoS attack is organized by a hacker who utilizes many computers as agents from different locations to launch a coordinated attack against one or more targets that consumes victim's network bandwidth, or consumes victim's resources so that legitimate users could not access to the targeted computers [2] [3] [4]. Spam email DDoS attacks cause the email system damage when it clogs mail server and network bandwidth [5].

Our research experiment is based on the dataset we collected from the email networking system running in the Library of the University of Technology, Sydney (UTS) which contains 4100 spam emails received in five month

time period of 2009. The email system is running on Microsoft Exchange Server. All of these spam email attacks come from 450 different sources (IPs). Some of these attacks have been identified as DDoS attacks.

In this project, we propose to use a visual clustering method [6][7] for assisting the analysis of email attacks, especially the DDoS attacks through the visual representation and classification of the spam emails. A clear clustered structure of the spam emails could help analysts to identify the unusual email events and the types of email attacks, including DDoS attacks.

We first analyze the behaviors of spam emails and then create a model for analysis. We use two coefficient vectors: *'density'* and *'weight'* of the spam email attack for analysis. We then use a visual clustering method to classify and display the spam emails. The visualization allows users to interactively select and scale down the scope of views for better understanding of different types of the spam email attacks for discovering DDoS attacks. The experiment shows that this new model with the clustering visualization can be effectively used for network security analysis.

II. BACKGROUND

A. Spam email with no attachments

The first type of spam emails are those with no attachments, in which the virus is hidden inside the message body and spreads when users open the message. There are several situations when a machine receives a spam email of this type:

- If there is a huge number of spam messages and unwanted emails are received on a victim email system in a short period, they will clog the email server, consume the network recourses and bandwidth towards a *network level DDoS attack* that will end up the email service in the victim's machine.
- If the virus has been opened, it will then be spreading inside the system and the system will be acting as an agent to attack other machines.

1550-6037/11 $26.00 © 2011 IEEE
DOI 10.1109/IV.2011.41

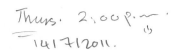

- An opened virus sometimes will kill a few or all system processes towards a system crash.

Message 1 shows the receipt of a no-attachment spam email in our email server.

```
|SMTP Messages\Inbound And Outbound
|Thank you for your patience
|Body of Message
|VIRUS=Trojan-Spy.HTML.Fraud.gen (Kaspersky5)
|Commonwealth Bank
|oficial@commbank.com.au
|undisclosed-recipients:;undisclosed-recipients
|ill@lib.uts.edu.au
|ill@lib.uts.edu.au
```

Message 1. Spam email with no attachment

B. Spam email with attachments

The second type of spam emails which is a typical spam email attack contains attachments that can be larger up to 20 MB each. There are several situations that could damage the system when a machine receives a spam email of this type:

- If there is a huge number of spam emails with large size of attachments arrived at the victim's system, *a network level DDoS attack* could occur.
- The executable attachment could bring worms, viruses and Trojans into the victim's system. The system could become an agent for spreading attacks to other systems when those executed attachments send viruses to other machines.
- When those executable viruses eat local disk spaces, memories and kill other applications, *an application level DDoS attack* could occur in the victim's system which will cause services denial to their users.

Message 2 shows the receipt of a spam email with the attachment in our email server.

```
12/06/2009 8:16:08 / / AM |Transport Scan Job
|SMTP
Messages\Inbound And Outbound
|You have received an eCard
|ecard.zip->ecard.exe
|VIRUS= VirTool:Win32/Obfuscator.FH
(Microsoft,CA(Vet),Command,Kaspersky5)
|Steve Hurst
|vaccinated5@spbdept.rbc.ru
|adt@lib.uts.edu.au
|adt@lib.uts.edu.au
```

Message 2. Spam email with attachment

C. Visualization in Network Intrusion Detection

The most common visualization approach to the problem of network intrusion detection is the use of IP Matrix. Koike et al. [8] have proposed a 2D IP matrix that is based on the 32-bits IP addressing space. This model divides 32-bits IP address into two groups: the global-level IP matrix and the local-level IP matrix. The global-level IP matrix is the highest 8 bits and next high 8 bits make a 2-D IP matrix model. The local-level IP matrix is the lower 8 bits × lowest 8 bits. It has been demonstrated that this IP Matrix visualization is effective in visualization and recognition of the infection of worms: a type of viruses. By using this IP matrix, the propagation of the Welchia worm and the Sasser.D worm can be visualized and identified.

Recently, Zhang et al. [9] further developed a 3D IP Matrix visualization called NetViewer that uses the highest 8-bits IP address as the location. The rest of 24-bits are classified into x-axis; y-axis and z-axis for the visual representation of the lower 24-bits of IP addresses in a 3D space. NetViewer can be used to detect the DDoS and Ports Scan attacks in the networks.

However, this approach has a number of limitations:

- *Unused IP addresses:* in this type of visualization, there are many unused IP addresses, and the display space is used wastefully. To use display space economically, some visualization techniques should be applied. However, it is not appropriate to eliminate non-existent IP addresses because there could be attacks from the spoofed IP addresses.
- *Unable to detect email virus:* This method is not appropriate to be used for detecting some other types of virus which uses different channels for infection. For example, in the case of an email virus, the next target is selected by using the user's address book, and these addresses have no relation to IP addresses. In this case, IP Matrix is not useful for prediction of email viruses.

Another approach which is specifically designed to deal with email viruses is called 'Two-mode visualization' [10]. During the email communication, there are several network 'nodes' involved, such as email server, network router and switcher. A large amount of information is recorded in the log files of these network 'nodes' which is hard to be represented. However, the Two-mode model has simplified those processes by using three stages:

- Sender sends an email to mail server
- Email exchanges between servers
- Receiver receives an email from mail server

Figure 1 shows the example visualization of the Two-mode spam email network. The *red nodes* represent email servers, *yellow nodes* represent clients (sender or receiver), *green edges* represent sending processes, and blue edges represent receiving processes. In Figure 1, we can easily see that three email servers are receiving a large number of spam emails (blue lines) and one email server spread huge viruses (green lines) into the network.

While the Two-mode visualization [10] could help analysts to guess email viruses, such as DDoS attacks, through the abstract views of the density of green edges (the outgoing emails) and blue edges (the incoming emails), it does not provide users with any quantified justification of particular types of the virus.

In this paper we will introduce a new analytical model that uses two coefficient vectors: *'density'* and *'weight'* of the spam email attack for DDoS analysis. We then use a visual clustering method to classify and display the spam emails. The visualization allows users to interactively select and scale down the scope of views for better understanding and quantified justification of different types of email virus, including DDoS attacks.

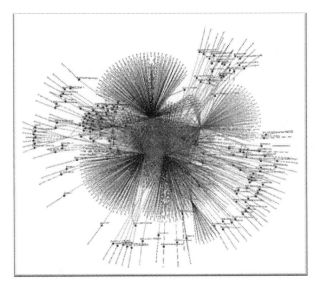

Figure 1.   Two-mode visualization of spam email network [10].

III.   CLUSTERED VISUALIZATION

Graphs which arise in Information Visualization applications are typically very large: thousands, or perhaps millions of nodes. The graph drawing competitions have shown that visualization systems for classical graphs are limited to (at best) a few hundred nodes. Attempts to overcome this problem have proceeded in two main directions:

Clustering: Groups of related nodes are "clustered" into super-nodes. The user sees a summary of the graph: the super-nodes and super-edges between the super-nodes. Some clusters may be shown in more detail than others. The clustering approach has been proposed several times in the graph drawing and information visualization conferences [6, 7], and is related to the overview diagrams" used by some web navigation facilities [11].

Navigation: The user sees only a small subset of the nodes and edges at any one time, and facilities are provided to navigate through the graph. This approach was taken by the WebOFDAV system [11].

A.   The graph level

In our visualization we use a graph model to represent spam emails and their attributes. A graph in our visualization is a classical undirected graph, consisting of *nodes* and *edges*. In our application it is likely a very large graph, containing hundreds or thousands of nodes. The graph may be dynamic, that is, the node and edge set may be changing; these changes may be a result of user interaction through the visualization, or they may be changed asynchronously by an outside agent.

B.   The clustering level

Our visualization uses clusters to represent set of groups of spam emails based on variety of similarity rules as defined above. The use of clustered visualization will significantly reduce a visual complexity of displaying large amounts of network related data. A *clustered graph C = (G, T)* consists of an undirected graph *G = (V, E)* and a rooted tree *T* such that the leaves of *T* are exactly the vertices of *G* as mentioned in [6]. Figure 2 shows a clustered graph. Our clustered visualization can operate on a clustered graph *C= (G, T)* by two basic operations, *create* and *destroy* a cluster. Both can be performed by user interaction, or by an algorithm attached to the visualization.

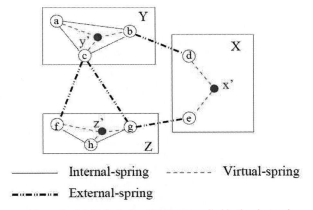

Figure 2.   Multiple Spring-Forces are applied in the clustered visualization.

C.   The abridgement level

The current Intrusion Detection systems lack in display focus. They do not consider user orientations and focuses of large amounts of data. The use of abridgement level in our visualization provides users with a *focus+context* viewing mechanism for navigating the large cluster tree. In many cases, the whole clustered graph is too large to show on the screen; further, it is too large for the user to comprehend. In our implementation, the clustered visualization draws only an ``abridgement" of the entire clustered graph at a time.

We now give a formal definition of ``abridgement". Suppose that *U* is a set of nodes of the cluster tree *T*. The sub-tree of *T* consisting of all nodes and edges on paths between elements of *U* and the root is called the *ancestor tree* of U. A clustered graph *C' = (G', T')* is an abridgement of the clustered graph *C = (G, T)* if *T'* is an ancestor tree of *T* with respect to a set *U* of nodes of *T* and there is an edge between two distinct nodes *u* and *v* of *G'* if and only if there is an edge in *G* between a descendent of *u* and a descendent of *v*. Our visualization has two elementary operations on abridgements; these change the basis of the abridgement. They are *open* a cluster and *close* a cluster.

D. The picture level

The picture level is concerned with the geometric position of the clustered graphs and its associated clustered trees as well as visual attributes to be associated to each displayed entity. Picture level of a clustered graph is shown in Figures 5. More formally, a *picture* of a clustered graph $C = (G, T)$ contains a location $p(v)$ for each vertex v of G and a route $c(u, v)$ for each edge (u, v) of G, in the same way as drawings for classical graphs. Further, a picture has a region $b(v)$ of the plane for each cluster v of T, such that if u is a leaf of T then $b(v)$ is located at $p(v)$, and if u is a child of v in T then $b(u)$ is contained in $b(v)$. The regions currently used by our visualization are rectangles.

Our visualization provides the usual operation of manually *moving* nodes in a picture. However, the main role of our visualization is animated automatic *layout*.

E. The force model

We use force-directed algorithm to draw the pictures of clustered graphs. It is based on the Spring-force model described by Eades [12]. Our visualization has three types of spring forces:

- *Internal-spring*- A spring force between a pair of vertices in the same cluster.
- *External-spring*- A spring force between a pair of vertices in different clusters.
- *Virtual-spring*- A spring force between a vertex and a virtual (dummy) node along a virtual (dummy) edge.

As well as spring forces, between each pair of nodes there is a gravitational repulsion force. The forces are applied additively to give an aesthetically pleasing layout of the graph. The sum of forces on each node is continually computed, and the movement of the nodes according to the forces drives the animation, as with the visualization.

F. Animations

In our implementation, the whole visualization is fully animated. Every transition, whether triggered by the user, visualization, or by another agent, has its own specific animation. This greatly reduces the cognitive effort of the user in recognizing the new view and change; we aim for a full preservation of the user's ``mental map''. More specifically, there are eight types of animation that are implemented in our system. Five of these are specifically related to the clustering.

G. Visual object (entity) design

We use visual object or entity to represent the spam emails for the display and analysis. Currently we use a Character String with the syntax below to represent spam emails and their attributes:

$$[r_{vt}]e[vt]\_[att]$$

where r_{vt} represents the repeating times of vt type of virus received in a time slot p, vt represents a particular type of virus, and att represents the attachment type of the virus.

IV. THE *DENSITY + WEIGHT* MODEL

Each spam email is represented as an attributed node in the visualization [13] which contains its domain-specific attributes, such as *receive-time; subject-name; sender-name; receiver-name; cc-receiver-name; source-IP; virus-type; attachment-type, etc.* Our model selects four most relevant attributes for the spam email analysis, which include *receive-time; virus-type; attachment-type and source-IP*.

A spam email that carries a particular type of the virus can be defined as an attributed node

$$e(t, vt, att, sip)$$

in which t indicates the arrival time, vt indicate the type of virus, att indicates the type of attachment and sip indicates source IP address.

We assume that in a certain time period p of the email communication between times t_x and t_y, a email server received a set of n spam emails as defined below

$$E_p = (e_1, e_2, ... e_n) \qquad (1)$$

and suppose that there are u types of the virus $VT = (vt_1, vt_2, ..., vt_u)$ that are identified, thus a subset of spam emails carrying a particular type of virus vt_i is defined as

$$E_{p,vt(i)} \subset E_p = \{ e \mid e \in E_p \wedge e(vt) = vt_i\} \qquad (2)$$

Suppose that there are w different source IP addresses $SIP = (sip_1, sip_2, ... sip_w)$ that are identified sending spam emails to the server during p period, thus a subset of spam emails sent from a particular source IP address sip_i is defined as

$$E_{p,sip(i)} \subset E_p = \{ e \mid e \in E_p \wedge e(sip) = sip_i\} \qquad (4)$$

Accordingly, a subset of spam emails which received from a particular source IP address sip_i and containing a particular type vt_j of virus is defined as

$$E_{p,sip(i), vt(j)} \subset \{ e \mid e \in E_p \wedge e(sip) = sip_i \wedge e(vt) = vt_j\} \qquad (5)$$

Thus, we can determine whether a particular source IP sending vt_j type of the viruses by the following Boolean function

$$(SIP(i)) = \begin{cases} 1, & Ep(i), sip(i), vt(j) \neq \phi \\ 0, & Ep(i), sip(i), vt(j) = \phi \end{cases} \qquad (6)$$

We then can calculate the total number of IPs whose have sent vt_j type of viruses to the server during p time slot as

$$w_{vt(j)} = |SIP_{vt(j)}| = \sum_{i=1}^{w} SIP(i) \qquad (7)$$

Suppose that there are v types of attachment (att_1, att_2, ..., att_v) have been identified, thus a subset of spam emails carrying a particular type of attachment att_i is defined as

$$E_{p,att(i)} \subset E_p = \{ e \mid e \in E_p \land e(att) = att_i \} \qquad (8)$$

Accordingly, the subset of spam emails received from a particular source IP address sip_i and containing a particular type att_j of attachment is defined as

$$E_{p,sip(i),att(j)} \subset \{ e \mid e \in E_p \land e(sip) = sip_i \land e(att) = att_j \} \qquad (9)$$

Thus, we can determine whether a particular source IP sending spam emails with att_j type of the attachments by the following Boolean function

$$(SIP(i)) = \begin{cases} 1, & E_p(i), sip(i), att(j) \neq \phi \\ 0, & E_p(i), sip(i), att(j) = \phi \end{cases} \qquad (10)$$

We then can calculate the total number of IPs whose have sent spam emails with att_j type of attachments to the server during p time slot as

$$w_{att(j)} = |SIP_{att(j)}| = \sum_{i=1}^{w} SIP(i) \qquad (11)$$

We now introduce two terms: *virus density* $d(vt_i)$ for measuring the attack pattern of vt_j type of virus and *attachment density* $d(att_j)$ for measuring the attachment pattern of att_j type of the attachments in p period. These terms are derived from (7) and (11) as shown below

$$d(vt_i) = \frac{W(vt(i))}{|E(p)|} \qquad (12)$$

$$d(att_j) = \frac{W(att(j))}{|E(p)|} \qquad (13)$$

where, $(0 < d(vt_i) < 1)$ and $(0 < d(att_j) < 1)$.

If the number of IPs $w_{vt(i)}$ or $w_{att(j)}$ is small, e.g. from a single source IP attack, the density value of $d(vt_i)$ or $d(att_j)$ will close to zero. For example

$$d(vt_i) = \frac{1}{|E(p)|} \approx 0$$

If the number of IPs $w_{vt(i)}$ or $w_{att(j)}$ is large, e.g. the number of source IPs is nearly equal to the total number of attacks, the density value of $d(vt_i)$ or $d(att_j)$ will close to one, and it means that a DDoS attack is most likely occurred. For example

$$w_{att(j)} \approx |E_p| \quad \text{or} \quad w_{vt(j)} \approx |E_p|$$

Suppose that in a time slot p, one type of the virus (or attachment) has the highest density and we call it d_{max} that can be expressed as

$$d_{max} = \max \{D(vt_i), D(att_j)\} = \max \{d_{vt(1)}, d_{vt(2)}, ..., d_{vt(u)}, d_{att(1)}, d_{att(2)}, ..., d_{att(v)}\}$$

in our detection model, we will consider d_{max} density as the possible attack first in the detection process.

We would also introduce the term: *weight SW(p)* to measure the system (email server)'s workload in handling the attacks in p time period. The system weight is defined below

$$SW(p) = \frac{E(p)}{M} \qquad (14)$$

where M is the maximum number of incoming emails that email server is capable to handle (or transfer) in a short time period p in our practices. Our email server which uses the Microsoft Exchange, can handle 240 emails ($M=240$) in 15 minutes time frame (around 16 emails per minute).

With *light weight spam email attacks*, they cost less than 20% of the system capability to handle or transfer these spam emails. Thus, it can be defined as a *light weight attack* if the system workload is between $0 \leq SW(p) < 0.2$.

Accordingly, we can define *a medium level spam email attack* if the system workload (or weight) is between $0.2 \leq SW(p) < 0.7$ in handling this attack, and *a high level email attack* if the system workload (or weight) is between $0.7 \leq SW(p) < 1.0$ in handling that attack.

If the system weight is great than one $1.0 < SW(p)$, then we consider that there is *a critical level of spam email attack* has occurred.

We can further define a scalability vector *AttackScale(p)* for the measurement of *DDoS* attack. It combines two vectors: the maximum virus density d_{max} and the system weight $SW(p)$ together. We have

$$AttackScale(p) = d_{max} \times SW(p) \qquad (15)$$

The vector *AttackScale(p)* indicates the scale of the most active type of spam emails (with attachment or with no attachment) that are current attacking the email server.

The outcome of our experiments showed that if $AttackScale(p)<0.2$ and $d_{max} \approx 1$, then a small scale DDoS attack is occurred. If $0.2<AttackScale(p)<0.7$ and $d_{max} \approx 1$, then a medium scale DDoS attack is occurred. If $0.7<AttackScale(p)<1.0$ and $d_{max} \approx 1$, then it is most likely that a large scale DDoS attack is occurred. If $1.0 \leq AttackScale(p)$, then a critical level DDoS attack is occurred and the email server could be down.

V. EXAMPLE: SPAM EMAIL VISUALIZATION

This section contains a sequence of screen dumps from Figure 3 to Figure 7 collected from our visualization system. They illustrate the visual analysis process for detecting DDoD attacks. These screens will show you how they achieve a better quality of the layout of clustered spam emails through the smooth transaction of views.

VI. FUTURE WORK AND CONCLUSION

This paper introduces the application of clustered data visualization for spam email analysis. We use a new analytical model called *density+weight* model that uses two coefficient vectors: 'density' and 'weight' for the virus and DDoS analysis. The visualization allows users to interactively select and scale down the scope of views for better understanding of different types of the spam email virus and attacks. The experiment shows that this new model with the clustering visualization can be used effectively for network security analysis.

Currently we use *character string* to represent the attributes of spam emails in the visualization. In the future, we will use a set of graphical nodes with rich graphic properties to represent spam emails. We will attempt to map the graphic properties to the email domain-specific attributes. For example, we will use different shapes, colors, sizes and brightness to represent the domain-specific attributes of emails, such as different types of viruses, types of attachments, and source IP addresses. Under this scheme, the user can gain the knowledge of classification of different spam emails through the visual interpretation.

REFERENCES

[1] M. Wanli, D. Tran, and D. Sharma, "A Novel Spam Email Detection System Based on Negative Selection," in *Computer Sciences and Convergence Information Technology, 2009. ICCIT '09. Fourth International Conference on*, 2009, pp. 987-992.

[2] C. Douligeris and A. Mitrokotsa, "DDoS attacks and defense mechanisms: a classification," in Signal Processing and Information Technology, 2003. ISSPIT 2003. Proceedings of the 3rd IEEE International Symposium on, 2003, pp. 190-193.

[3] C. Yu and H. Kai, "Collaborative Change Detection of DDoS Attacks on Community and ISP Networks," in Collaborative Technologies and Systems, 2006. CTS 2006. International Symposium on, 2006, pp. 401-410.

[4] X. Yi and Y. Shun-Zheng, "A Novel Model for Detecting Application Layer DDoS Attacks," in Computer and Computational Sciences, 2006. IMSCCS '06. First International Multi-Symposiums on, 2006, pp. 56-63.

[5] C. Dhinakaran, L. Jae Kwang, and D. Nagamalai, "An Empirical Study of Spam and Spam Vulnerable email Accounts," in Future Generation Communication and Networking (FGCN 2007), 2007, pp. 408-413.

[6] M. Huang and P. Eades, "A Fully Animated Interactive System for Clustering and Navigating Huge Graphs", *Graph Drawing' 1998*. pp.374~383

[7] M. Huang and Q. Nguyen, "A Fast Algorithm for Balanced Graph Clustering," *Information Visualization, IV'07. 11th International Conference*, 2007, pp. 46-52.

[8] H. Koike, K. Ohno, and K. Koizumi, "Visualizing cyber attacks using IP matrix," in Visualization for Computer Security, 2005. (VizSEC 05). IEEE Workshop, 2005, pp. 91-98.

[9] J. Zhang, P. Yang, L. Lu, and L. Chen, "NetViewer: A Visualization Tool for Network Security Events," in Networks Security, Wireless Communications and Trusted Computing, 2009. NSWCTC '09. International Conference, 2009, pp. 434-437.

[10] X. Fu, S. H. Hong, N. S. Nikolov, X. Shen, Y. Wu, and K. Xu, "Visualization and analysis of email networks," in Visualization, 2007. APVIS '07. 2007 6th International Asia-Pacific Symposium, 2007, pp. 1-8.

[11] M. Huang, P. Eades and R. Cohen, "WebOFDAV - Navigating and Visualizing the Web On-Line with Animated Context Swapping", *Computer Networks, 1998:* 638~642

[12] P. Eades, "A heuristic for graph drawing", *Congressus, Numerantium,* pp 149-160, 1984.

M. Huang, "Information Visualization of Attributed Relational Data", *in Proc. InVis.au, 2001*, pp.143-149.

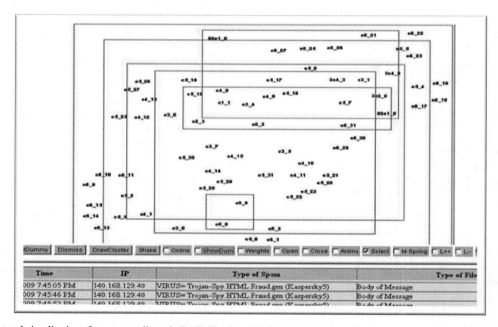

Figure 3.   A clustered visualization of a spam email graph $C=(G, T)$, where $G=(V, E)$ and $E= \phi$. Seven clusters are created in C based on the virus types received in a time slot p. However, this layout has many overlaps among clusters.

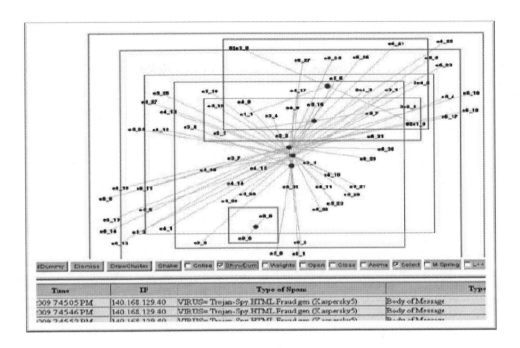

Figure 4.   The same layout as shown in Figure 3; however, the virtual nodes (red nodes) and edges are added. Each virtual node appears as the center point of a cluster linking with all the nodes in a particular cluster.

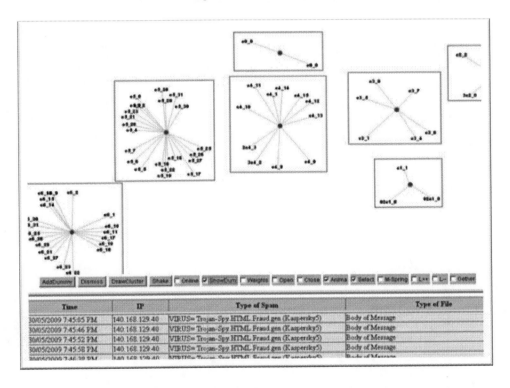

Figure 5.   After applying the 'virtual spring' forces along the red (virtual) edges, the overlaps among clusters are eliminated. We now can have a clear view of the clustering structure.

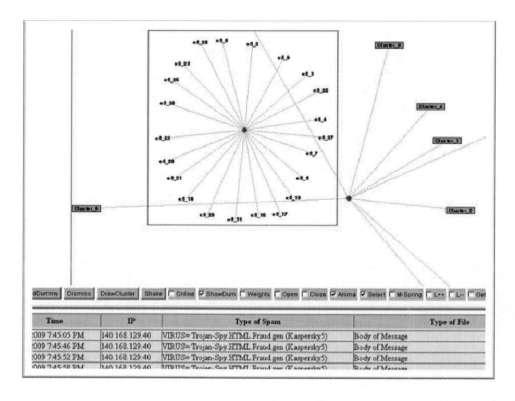

Figure 6.   From Figure 5, we can quickly identify that $d_{max} = d_{vt(5)}$, that is the 5th virus has the highest density with 31 repeating rate and 22 of them occurred within 7 minutes of p. To be able to see the detail of '*Cluster 5*' we close other six clusters through the '*close*' operation in the abridgement level of the clustering. After an inspection into the detail of vt_5, we found that all emails containing vt_5 are coming from different source IPs. Thus, *density* of this virus is $d_{vt(5)} =1$. However, the *weight* of the email system is $SW(p) = 0.20$ and the attack scalability is *AttackScale* $=0.20$. Finally, we confirmed our detection outcome: a small scale DDoS attack occurred in our email server.

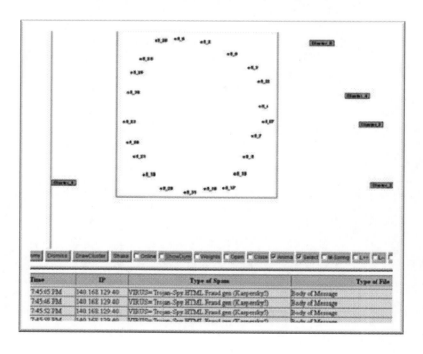

Figure 7. The same layout and visualization as shown in Figure 6; however, the virtual nodes (red nodes) and edges are disappeared.

Presenter
Edson Korti

Design considerations for drill down charts

Rafael Guimarães[1], Anderson Marques[1], Nikolas Carneiro[1], Aruanda Meiguins[2], Bianchi Meiguins[1]

Universidade Federal do Pará[1], Rede de Informática Ltda.[2]

{rafaelveras, andmarques, bianchism}@ufpa.br, nikolas.carneiro@gmail.com

aruanda@redeinformatica.com.br

Abstract

Frequency-based statistical charts are the most widespread visualizations and the preferred of Infovis novices. They are important in depicting categorical data and providing data abstraction on large datasets. The drill down feature enables better visual scaling by allowing navigation through aggregation hierarchies. In this paper we discuss design considerations that impact on the usability in drill down charts. We develop a tool based on pie chart in order to illustrate the discussion. Moreover, we suggest visual representations and an interaction model. Finally, we provide evidence on the benefit of using such techniques for visual analysis of categorical data through a short usability study.

Keywords— **information visualization; drill down chart; categorical data; multiscale; aggregation hierarchy.**

1 Introduction

Visual scaling is a major problem in information visualization. Item-based visualizations tend to be overloaded as the dataset size increases; hence, methods for data abstraction are commonly applied to data space and mapped by visual representations, reducing the scale impact. A simple approach is aggregating individual items into categories accordingly to a given attribute.

In addition, the combination of aggregates in hierarchical levels makes possible the classical incremental user experience described by the infovis mantra [13]. The class of multiscale visualizations takes advantage of this hierarchical aggregation model. Its main features include drill-down and roll-up interactions and visual aggregates.

In a study about how information visualization novices construct visualizations, Grammel et al. [4] observed that novices are strongly inclined to choose familiar types, especially pie and bar charts. Statistical charts are ubiquitous because, and also in consequence, they are very simple representations for data aggregates.

The multiscale approach has been applied to statistical charts in interactive business reports and visualization of OLAP (Online analytical processing) data, in virtue of the intrinsic drill down and roll up operations. In the former context, the scope is very limited, as the goal is mainly presentation; and in the latter the solutions are very tied to the OLAP technology [16, 10]. Additionally, in the design of drill down interfaces the perceptual infovis principles are often neglected, resulting in very limited tools, which go little beyond the basic double-click over slice in the pie chart. We believe that drill down charts might be further improved if some guidelines are taken into consideration. In this paper, we discuss these design elements in a general way, independent of application domain or technology, using as reference a tool developed under the infovis principles.

We focus on representational issues, such as coloring, information budget, navigational cues and layout, as well as in the interaction model, where navigation path and visual queries are discussed. The validity of the considerations is evidenced by a usability study where our tool is compared to a standard technique in the context of categorical data analysis.

2 Related work

Parallel Sets [8] is a visualization method for categorical data. It depicts categories using a frequency-based representation and applies the multidimensional layout of parallel coordinates. The taken approach is to show the distribution of categories simultaneously by several dimensions. Although this design favors the identification of relationships between dimensions, it becomes complex as the number of axis increases, with excess of information displayed. In our design we adopt a step-by-step solution.

A comprehensive and general model for hierarchical visualization is provided by Elmqvist and Fekete [2]. Our study is placed at a lower level of abstraction, as we implement many concepts described on it. The guidelines on interaction and visual representations are particularly interesting for this work, whereas the advices about adapting standard visualization techniques are useless, once we do not deal with any of the techniques analyzed.

Mansmann and Scholl [10] apply a tree-based hierarchical representation in the OLAP aggregates domain. A

1550-6037/11 $26.00 © 2011 IEEE

DOI 10.1109/IV.2011.65

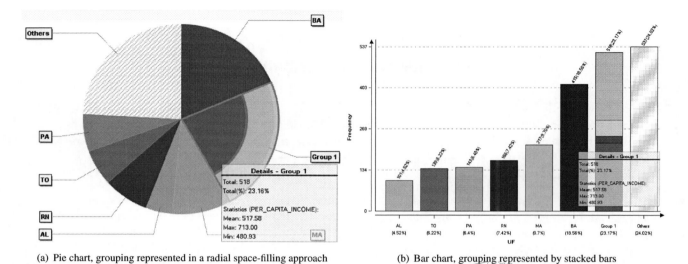

(a) Pie chart, grouping represented in a radial space-filling approach   (b) Bar chart, grouping represented by stacked bars

Figure 1: Representation of aggregates in statistical charts.

presentation model is defined in order to map data cubes to visual hierarchies. While drawing upon a solid conceptual model, it lacks refined interaction and representation design.

Our contribution does not consist in replacing any of the above work with a new model for hierarchical visualization. In a sense, we complement the above cited efforts by delivering good design guidelines for the subset of hierarchical charts inspired by the foundational studies of information visualization.

3 Aggregation and drill down model

Before focusing on the design aspects, in this section we briefly describe the underlying data and interaction model assumed for our drill down charts.

Multidimensional datasets are comprised of a set of attributes (or dimensions) and their values for each data item. The nature of attributes might be either categorical or quantitative, among some other classifications. Categorical attributes have discrete and reduced amount of distinct values (categories); and there is no implicit relationship among them, such as ordering or distance [8].

In simple aggregation, a set of items is grouped into one or more aggregates, each one representing a category of a particular categorical attribute. In an aggregation hierarchy, the groups are nested accordingly to an attribute hierarchy; therefore, a tree is built, whose root represents the entire dataset, nodes represent categories, and leaves are the individual items. As aggregation is best suited for categorical attributes, non-categorical ones can be converted in categorical through several classification techniques.

A *drill down path* is a navigation path through an attribute hierarchy. In a simple way, it contains the groups

selected in each hierarchical level. A drill down is a single "movement" downwards in a aggregation hierarchy. Drilling down on a group moves the analysis toward the group's children.

4 Representation

The choice of the chart type must be mainly driven by the fitness of visual entity in the representation of aggregates, the inherent complexity, and the amount of information conveyed [2]. Despite the criticism and controversy on using pie charts, familiarity [6] and simplicity are factors that can justify their employment. Pie charts use a space-filling approach to depict categories, which avoids the cluttering of the visualization space [7]. However, if there is a large number of categories or a high variance of frequencies, the perception over the smaller slices becomes difficult. It is crucial that even the minor categories are accessible, otherwise the drill down interaction becomes impracticable. Though we can apply some techniques to overcome this problem [15], in this case a bar chart may be more adequate.

Direct representation of aggregates is fundamental to provide a good level of abstraction. Visualizations like scatterplot, dot chart, or line chart are not well suited, again for the sake of drill down, which requires a reasonable area for clicking and because grouped data is best represented by areas than by individual points [8].

The visual aggregates can convey more information than just frequency, such as mean, mode, extrema, median, and percentiles [2]. As we are dealing with categorical data, it is necessary to provide a user control for defining which numerical attribute these measures refers to. Parallel Sets also allows the visualization of standardized relative

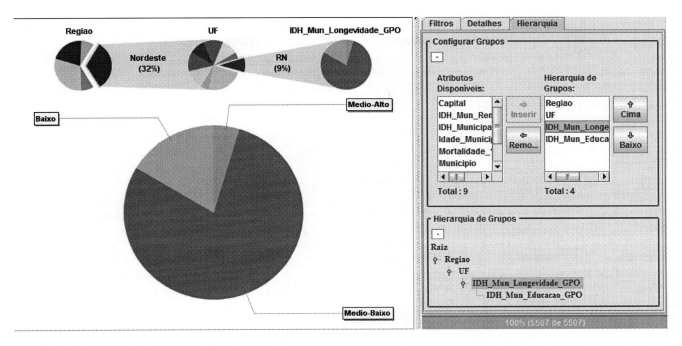

Figure 2: Workspace of drill down pie chart. On the left, full representation of the current level and the navigation bar. On the right, the lateral accessory panel with a control for defining attribute hierarchies and tree representation.

frequencies through embedded histograms [8]. In order to limit the information budget, we recommend the display of extra information in an indirect manner, via details on demand.

Figure 1 shows these visual principles applied to the pie and bar charts. Notice the two types of category composition presented in both examples. *Isolation* is intended to reduce the effort spent on analyzing great number of categories. This composition visually segregates the less important categories by applying a different texture, resulting in a chart with fewer visual items and a higher level of abstraction.

The second type, *Grouping*, is the union of two or more categories under an alias name. The main purpose of such composition is to allow drill down over multiple categories. In pie chart, we used a radial space-filling technique to represent the grouping, while in the bar chart, grouped bars were stacked vertically. This type of composition takes advantage of the user's domain knowledge [8].

5 Navigation

In the context of interaction design, an aggregation hierarchy may be classified as a discrete information space, i.e., it comprises a collection of discrete entities. The design of navigation across those hierarchies calls for a deep understanding of the stepped interaction fundamentals. In the previous section, we presented considerations about the visual representation of aggregates in charts. In the cur-

rent section, we discuss aspects of navigation across chart chains.

Users may be motivated to navigate discrete information spaces by several reasons. In our specific case, they would like to find the importance of a particular category in a restrict context, to establish direct comparisons between categories, or to enhance their mental model about the structure of the dataset. In order to accomplish these goals, users need to perform a number of 'movements' in the space. As Spence [14] pointed out, along this course, many questions arise, e.g., "Where am I?", "Where can I go?", "Where have I been?". An effective tool must provide cues to facilitate navigation.

We start by supporting the definition of a custom attribute hierarchy. Figure 2 presents the user control for this task. On the left there is a list with categorical attributes of the dataset. The user is allowed to build a hierarchy moving them to the list on the right . This user centered approach, in contrast to schema-based ones [10], gives the advantage of building a hierarchy that conforms to the structures of questions the user formulates about the data. The UI control, together with the explicit representation of the hierarchy (at the bottom of the panel), encodes residue [14], which is the indication of a distant content. In other words, it is necessary to make available the information about where the drill down will be taking the user. This information is located in the lateral accessory panel.

On the central panel, the initial chart presents the aggregates related to the first attribute of the hierarchy. A double-click on an aggregate uncovers its children classified by the categories of the next attribute. This process progress along the extent of the attribute hierarchy. This design ensures abstraction at all steps of traversing the aggregation hierarchy, i.e., the individual items are never exhibited. An alternative approach could be to enrich the experience by coordinating the chart view with an item-based visualization [17], or even to combine it in a hybrid approach. In the latter case, the item-based visualization would arise after the end of the drill down path. Then the drill down phase would act as a filtering section before the detailed visualization.

In order to track the users' interactions, we designed a navigation bar (Figure 2). We considered it should convey cues about the 'value' of each performed drill down (see *information scent* in [14]), the current localization in the drill down path, and provide a manner to easily revisit the previous levels. We adopted a design inspired by the breadcrumb navigation, originally applied to the web [12]; however, instead of using just text, as in web pages, we chose to use chart miniatures identical to those found along the drill down path. This decision is aimed to favor the cognitive process of recognition, instead of recall, which requires more effort [9, 11]. Each miniature is connected by a link representing a drill down, which shows the name of the selected aggregate as well as its relative value. By clicking over a miniature, the user jumps to the corresponding level, i.e., the full chart appears in the central panel.

6 Flexibility

Besides the basic drill down and roll up functionalities, it is necessary to take care of some details that determine the flexibility level of the tool as a whole. Basically, the flexibility issues are related to the freedom to modify the attribute hierarchy at any time and the consequences of nonlinear navigation. In this section we discuss the impact of possible alternatives.

Within our design, we can opt between two types of interaction flow. In the *linear flow*, the interaction is divided in two distinct, sequential phases. By this model, the *configuration time*—where the definition of the attribute hierarchy takes place—is completely isolated from the *exploration time*, where occurs the interaction with charts and drilling down. It implies that once the user has started to drilling down, it is not possible to reconfigure the path without all interaction state get lost. While this alternative is simpler to implement, it strongly limits the user's possibilities, imposing effort to reconstruct the navigation every time it is needed to make minimal changes in attribute hierarchy.

The other type is the *non-linear flow*, where configura-

tion and exploration time are not strictly separated, i.e., the user is able to change the drill down path in the course of navigation. It provides more flexibility, but increases the implementation complexity. Below, we explain two critical interactions with the attribute hierarchy in the exploration time, and how the tool must behave in order to avoid missing the previous navigation entirely.

6.1 Removing Intermediary Levels

The Figure 3 shows on the left an aggregation hierarchy. Groups labeled as *B1* and *B2*, for instance, refer to different categories of an attribute *B*. A hypothetical drill down path is highlighted in orange. If the user resolves to remove an intermediary step, most of the navigation must ideally be preserved. On the right, the figure shows the state immediately after the removal of the *B* attribute. The path between *A* and *C* is reconstructed, so the user remains "deep" in the hierarchy. In our tool, the correspondent visual feedback is provided by reorganization of both the chart in the current level—groups have now a new distribution; and the navigation bar.

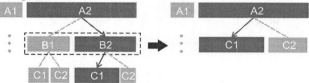

Figure 3: Reorganization of the drill down path after removing an intermediary level

6.2 Redirecting drill down

Another situation where part of navigation path needs to be automatically reconfigured is when the user wants to change the direction of a drill down at an intermediary level. The Figure 4 shows on the left a drill down path with four levels. On the right, is the result of changing the drill down in the second level. Farther navigation in the third level is maintained by just selecting the *C1* category among the *B1*'s children. However, it causes inconsistency in the fourth level, as the *D2* category has no representative items in that context, prohibiting drilling down over it. Consequently, the fourth drill down in the example should be discarded.

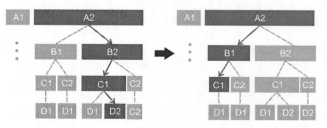

Figure 4: Redirecting a drill down in an intermediary level of drill down path

7 Guidelines

After the argumentation in the previous sections, we are able to derive some general guidelines to be applied in the design of drill down charts:

Choose charts whose visual items represent well data aggregates. Aggregates are better represented by areas than by dots or lines, for example. It will allow easy click for drill down and direct perception of the aggregate's value.

Provide localization cues. It is critical in order to avoid waste of time and confusion in the course of navigation. In our prototype, we deliver both the breadcrumb navigation bar and the tree representation for support localization.

Allow aggregation hierarchy definition at runtime. Instead of define a hard aggregation hierarchy before loading data into the visualization, definition at runtime is more adequate to the iterative nature of the visual exploration.

Dynamic and interactive aggregation. Allowing the creation of new aggregates in-place ease the incorporation of user domain knowledge in the analysis. Dynamic aggregation depends on direct representation of aggregates and visual metaphor's suitability. We recommend using different visual patterns for user-created items, such as the radial segmented slice for grouped items in our pie chart prototype.

Non-linear interaction flow. The user must be capable of defining the hierarchy and navigate it in a non-linear fashion. In relation to changes on the aggregation hierarchy, the interface must be fully adaptive, minimizing the impact over precedent navigation. As a rule of thumb, the navigation path must only be completely discarded when it becomes entirely inconsistent with the new hierarchy.

8 Usability Test

We developed the tool as a component within the PRISMA visualization platform [3]. PRISMA supports several standard visualization techniques, such as parallel coordinates, treemap and scatterplot. Along our experience with this platform, we noticed that, naturally, treemap is the preferred by users for analysing categorical data. This section presents an experiment to evaluate the usability of our design, based on a comparison with treemap visualization.

8.1 Participants

Fourteen individuals participated in the experiment. They are mostly professionals recently graduated in computer science, five women and nine men. All of them have experience using computers and four are familiar with information visualization.

8.2 Procedure

The participants were divided in two groups. Those who are familiar with visualization were distributed evenly among the groups in order to balance them. One group was associated with treemap while the other was associated with drill down pie chart. The treemap group could use the filtering capability of PRISMA, which consists in checkboxes located in a lateral panel; additionally, the treemap featured *in-depth navigation* and *direct node selection* [1]. The pie chart group could only use drill down to filter. Each participant of a group passed through a three phase trial using its tool. The first two phases were intended for training, while in the last we collected the evaluation data. The test was conducted by a supervisor, who instructed the users, took observational notes, and measured the users' performance (time and success).

Before starting a trial, each individual watched an explanation about how to use the tool, with duration from five to ten minutes. Afterwards, the person was invited to spend five minutes freely exploring a simple version of the classic titanic dataset (2200 items and four categorical attributes). During this and the next phase the participant could ask any questions about the tool.

Subsequently, we introduced the dataset used in the evaluation phase. It is about the research grants distributed to students by the Brazilian government through years 2007 and 2009. This dataset has 120.000 items and 10 categorical attributes. Each participant was allowed to explore it during five minutes.

The evaluation phase consisted in finding the answers for three questions about the dataset by exploring it. All questions required to filter the visualized data by categorical values:

1. Which governmental level (provincial, state or federal) distributed more doctorate grants for the *Pará* state through the years 2008 and 2009?

2. What about for *São Paulo* state?

3. In which year it was distributed more quantity of doctorate grants by the federal level for the southeast region?

The maximum time for completion of the tasks was respectively 180, 120 and 180 seconds. The measures collected for each questions were both task time and correctness of the answer. At the end of the trials, the participants filled out the NASA-TLX subjective workload assessment [5].

8.3 Hypothesis

In order to accomplish the tasks using the drill down chart, the participants needed to build an hierarchy with the attributes involved in the question (*state, region, year, type of grant, etc.*) and navigate it until reaching the chart showing the answer. In that case, each drill down is a filter.

The treemap provides visual access to the whole aggregation tree. Using it, participants needed to build similar hierarchy; then identify the answer in the big picture, or firstly, to limit the visual items through checkbox filtering or navigation.

We hypothesized that task times would be slightly shorter for the pie chart group, due to the high cost of localizing lower level groups on treemap when dealing with long hierarchies, as the visualization become cluttered. The time to interact with the checkboxes, which are an external control, would also impose more effort. Pie chart navigation would be also more effective than treemap navigation because of the positive influence of our navigation bar. For all these reasons, we expected that treemap would have the worst subjective workload.

8.4 Results

The average number of correctly solved tasks of treemap group (2.14) was better than the pie chart group (1.71). Only one participant using pie chart solved the first question correctly, against 3 from the treemap group. We noted that the common error of participants was forgetting to apply one of the required filters; therefore, we credit this behavior to the lack of attention. In the second task both groups were more successful: 5 correct using treemap and 4 using pie chart. All participants completed the third task correctly.

As expected, the average time of the pie chart group was shorter than the treemap group. The geometric mean for the 2nd task using pie chart was 21.7 against 35.8 seconds using treemap; and for the 3rd task was 73.1 against 90.6 seconds.

The results of TLX assessment also supported our claim about the subjective workload. The average value using pie chart was 40.3, against 46.4 using treemap.

Conclusions

In this paper, we approached the elements of designing drill down charts. Our contribution was to generate insight and advice about how to construct effective tools. Representation issues were discussed throughout the paper in order to clarify what cues are important to provide and what information can be depicted. The Section 5 provided

advices on navigation, a key point that strongly influence the success of drill down. The Section 6 presented two interaction issues that impacts on the flexibility of drill down charts.

In the usability study, we showed that even using limited charts it is possible to obtain good results. In a comparative experiment with treemap, our tool obtained better results in task time and workload index. We attribute the these results to some aspects of our design. Notice that the questions' structure requires incremental filtering to find the answer, over each dimension at a time. The low information budget provided by the multiscale layout ease that task as the categories of a dimension are only showed after drilling-down over the previous step, in contrast to Treemap, where all hierarchical levels are showed simultaneously.

Once the second question requires the partial reconstruction of the first visual query, we believe that our navigation bar was fundamental, allowing fast return to the step to be changed. The users were also able to dynamically aggregate two categories directly in the visualization space, for analysis of years 2008 and 2009 in the question 1. That is much faster than taking the attention out of visualization and handling checkboxes to filter by year (treemap does not support dynamic aggregation).

The experiment suggest that the proposed design was more effective for tasks that involved simple analysis of multidimensional categorical data. It does not mean that our tool is superior to treemap. In fact, there are many situations where drill down charts would be less powerful.

References

[1] Renaud Blanch and Eric Lecolinet. Browsing zoomable treemaps: Structure-aware multi-scale navigation techniques. *IEEE Transactions on Visualization and Computer Graphics*, 13:1248–1253, November 2007. ISSN 1077-2626.

[2] Niklas Elmqvist and Jean-Daniel Fekete. Hierarchical aggregation for information visualization: Overview, techniques, and design guidelines. *IEEE Transactions on Visualization and Computer Graphics*, 16:439–454, May 2010. ISSN 1077-2626.

[3] Paulo Godinho, Bianchi Meiguins, Aruanda Meiguins, Ricardo Casseb, Marcelo Garcia, Leandro Almeida, and Rodrigo Lourenco. Prisma - a multidimensional information visualization tool using multiple coordinated views. In *Proceedings of the 11th International Conference Information Visualization*, pages 23–32, Washington, DC, USA, 2007. IEEE Computer Society. ISBN 0-7695-2900-3.

[4] Lars Grammel, Melanie Tory, and Margaret-Anne

Storey. How information visualization novices construct visualizations. *IEEE Transactions on Visualization and Computer Graphics*, 16:943–952, 2010.

[5] S. G. Hart and L. E. Stavenland. Development of NASA-TLX (Task Load Index): Results of empirical and theoretical research. In P. A. Hancock and N. Meshkati, editors, *Human Mental Workload*, chapter 7, pages 139–183. Elsevier, 1988.

[6] Petra Isenberg, Anthony Tang, and Sheelagh Carpendale. An exploratory study of visual information analysis. In *Proceeding of the twenty-sixth annual SIGCHI conference on Human factors in computing systems*, CHI '08, pages 1217–1226, New York, NY, USA, 2008. ACM. ISBN 978-1-60558-011-1.

[7] Brian Johnson and Ben Shneiderman. Tree-maps: a space-filling approach to the visualization of hierarchical information structures. In *Proceedings of the 2nd conference on Visualization '91*, VIS '91, pages 284–291, Los Alamitos, CA, USA, 1991. IEEE Computer Society Press. ISBN 0-8186-2245-8.

[8] Robert Kosara, Fabian Bendix, and Helwig Hauser. Parallel sets: Interactive exploration and visual analysis of categorical data. *IEEE Transactions on Visualization and Computer Graphics*, 12:558–568, July 2006. ISSN 1077-2626.

[9] William Lidwell, Kritina Holden, and Jill Butler. *Universal Principles of Design, Revised and Updated: 125 Ways to Enhance Usability, Influence Perception, Increase Appeal, Make Better Design Decisions, and Teach through Design*. Rockport Publishers, second edition, revised and updated edition, jan 2010. ISBN 1592535879.

[10] Svetlana Mansmann and Marc H. Scholl. Exploring olap aggregates with hierarchical visualization techniques. In *Proceedings of the 2007 ACM symposium on Applied computing*, SAC '07, pages 1067–1073, New York, NY, USA, 2007. ACM. ISBN 1-59593-480-4.

[11] Jakob Nielsen and Robert L. Mack. *Usability inspection methods*, chapter Heuristic Evaluation, pages 25–62. Wiley, 1 edition, apr 1994. ISBN 0471018775.

[12] Bonnie Lida Rogers and Barbara Chaparro. Breadcrumb navigation: further investigation of usage. Technical report, Wichita State University, 2003.

[13] Ben Shneiderman. The eyes have it: A task by data type taxonomy for information visualizations. In *Proceedings of the 1996 IEEE Symposium on Visual Languages*, pages 336–, Washington, DC, USA, 1996. IEEE Computer Society. ISBN 0-8186-7508-X.

[14] Robert Spence. Sensitivity, residue and scent.: Concepts to inform interaction design for the support of information space navigation. *Information Design Journal*, 12:163–180, 2004.

[15] John Stasko and Eugene Zhang. Focus+context display and navigation techniques for enhancing radial, space-filling hierarchy visualizations. In *Proceedings of the IEEE Symposium on Information Vizualization 2000*, INFOVIS '00, pages 57–, Washington, DC, USA, 2000. IEEE Computer Society. ISBN 0-7695-0804-9.

[16] Kesaraporn Techapichetvanich and Amitava Datta. Interactive visualization for olap. In Osvaldo Gervasi, Marina Gavrilova, Vipin Kumar, Antonio Laganà, Heow Lee, Youngsong Mun, David Taniar, and Chih Tan, editors, *Computational Science and Its Applications – ICCSA 2005*, volume 3482 of *Lecture Notes in Computer Science*, pages 293–304. Springer Berlin / Heidelberg, 2005. 10.1007/11424857_23.

[17] Michelle Q. Wang Baldonado, Allison Woodruff, and Allan Kuchinsky. Guidelines for using multiple views in information visualization. In *Proceedings of the working conference on Advanced visual interfaces*, AVI '00, pages 110–119, New York, NY, USA, 2000. ACM. ISBN 1-58113-252-2.

A Task Based Performance Evaluation of
Visualization Approaches for Categorical Data Analysis

Sara Johansson Fernstad and Jimmy Johansson

C-Research, Linköping University, Sweden

{sara.johansson, jimmy.johansson}@itn.liu.se

Abstract

Categorical data is common within many areas and efficient methods for analysis are needed. It is, however, often difficult to analyse categorical data since no general measure of similarity exists. One approach is to represent the categories with numerical values (quantification) prior to visualization using methods for numerical data. Another is to use visual representations specifically designed for categorical data. Although commonly used, very little guidance is available as to which method may be most useful for different analysis tasks. This paper presents an evaluation comparing the performance of employing quantification prior to visualization and visualization using a method designed for categorical data. It also provides a guidance as to which visualization approach is most useful in the context of two basic data analysis tasks: one related to similarity structures and one related to category frequency. The results strongly indicate that the quantification approach is most efficient for the similarity related task, whereas the visual representation designed for categorical data is most efficient for the task related to category frequency.

Keywords— **Categorical Data, Quantitative Evaluation, Usability Studies, Parallel Sets, Quantification**

1 Introduction

Over the past decades the availability of complex multivariate data sets has increased within a variety of domains. A major challenge for data analysts is to discover patterns and to gain understanding and knowledge from the structures within the data. Different kinds of data have different characteristics that need to be taken into consideration when deciding which method to use for analysis. One data type which requires specialized analysis methods is categorical data. For categorical data there exists no similarity measure comparable with that of numerical variables. Due to this, the analysis of categorical data is often not as straightforward as for numerical data and fewer generic methods are available. Nonetheless, categorical data are common within many areas such as social sciences, biol-

ogy, chemistry and medicine; some examples being census data, organism classification data, DNA sequence-based data and molecular data. Efficient visualization methods can facilitate and speedup analysis considerably, and so the development of efficient methods for visual analysis of categorical data is an important issue within information visualization.

Two main approaches have been suggested for visual analysis of categorical data. One is to represent each category with a numerical value (quantification) and then analyse using visualization methods commonly employed for numerical data (from here on this approach will be called QuantViz). The other approach is to employ visualization methods specifically designed for the characteristics of categorical data (from here on called CatViz).

Although a range of methods for visual analysis of categorical data are available we cannot assume that all are useful and facilitate analysis and, even more, we cannot assume that all methods are equally useful for all types of tasks. Without proper evaluations of the usability of methods within specific task contexts, there is nothing but presumption to guide analysts as to which method to use. While quantification has been suggested several times as a method for efficient analysis of categorical data, very little evidence of its usefulness has been presented and no formal comparisons between quantification methods and visualization methods for categorical data have, to the best of our knowledge, been made.

1.1 Contributions

Through a usability study we now make a first attempt to evaluate the effectiveness and efficiency of employing quantification of categorical data prior to visualization. We also aim to provide an initial step of guidance in terms of establishing the usability of the two approaches in the context of performing basic analysis tasks. This is approached by comparing the performance of analysis using a QuantViz method with the performance using a CatViz method, while carrying out a number of tasks, details of which can be found in section 4.1.1. In this context performance is defined as a combination of accuracy and re-

1550-6037/11 $26.00 © 2011 IEEE

DOI 10.1109/IV.2011.92

sponse time. The main contribution of this paper is then a performance evaluation providing:

- A formal comparison of two methods for visual analysis of categorical data.

- An experimental study in the context of two basic data analysis tasks.

- Guidance as to which method may be most useful for different types of tasks.

It is worth noting that although the main goal of the study is not to compare the performance of one visual representation with another (e.g. parallel coordinates [9] vs. Parallel Sets [13]), but to compare one way of visually analysing categorical data with another (QuantViz vs. CatViz), the results of a comparison of a specific set of visualization methods is not generalizable to all available visualization methods. Hence, the results of this study are only true for the specific visualization methods and tasks of this study. This is a first step in evaluating the performance of quantification as a method for visualization of categorical data and has to be followed by additional evaluations focusing on other aspects before any general conclusions can be drawn.

1.2 Paper Overview

The remainder of this paper is organized as follows: Section 2 presents related research and in section 3 the design decisions of the study are described and motivated. Section 4 describes the study and presents the results, which are finally discussed in section 5.

2 Related Work

This section provides an overview of research in the areas of categorical data visualization, quantification and performance evaluation.

2.1 Visualization

Most visualization methods for categorical data are based on tables of category frequencies (contingency tables). The fourfold display [4] is one example where the cell frequencies of two-by-two tables are represented by quarter circles with size relative to frequency. Other examples are for instance the mosaic plots and mosaic matrices [4] where multivariate tables are represented by tiles whose sizes are proportional to the cell frequencies. In a Cobweb diagram [23] the categories are represented as individual nodes that are pairwise linked together using lines whose widths represent the deviation from independence of the category pair frequency. Parallel Sets [13] (described in more detail in section 3.2) has a layout similar to parallel coordinates where the categories of a variable are represented with a set of boxes. Another example using the layout of parallel coordinates is presented by

Havre et al. [7], where the polylines are spread over additional axes and sorted to display category frequencies and to avoid data overlay. The CatTree method [12] is an example of a tree-map based visualization for representation of hierarchically structured categorical data. In the Attribute Map View [14] categorical values are represented within attribute rows by rectangles whose sizes are relative to category frequency, and in the TreemapBar [8] bar charts are combined with tree-maps by embedding a tree-map visualization inside the rectangular space of the bars.

To conclude, CatViz methods are mostly designed for visualization of category frequencies and their efficiency is often highly dependent on data set size and structure. To the best of our knowledge no formal comparison has been made between the majority of CatViz methods and due to this the selection of method to use in this study is based on our subjective opinion that Parallel Sets (figure 1) is the CatViz method whose efficiency is least affected by data set size, being able to display approximately as many variables as parallel coordinates.

2.2 Similarity Measures and Quantification

Several algorithms usable for quantification of categorical data have been suggested. One of the more common being Correspondence Analysis (CA) [6] which is a method identifying associations between the cells of a frequency table. Tenenhaus and Young [22] describe how a number of different methods for quantification, such as Multiple Correspondence Analysis, Optimal Scaling and Homogeneity Analysis, all lead to the same equation. Hence, they are one method with a number of different names and will all be referred to as CA throughout the remainder of this paper. In Cuadras et al. [3] three methods for quantification are compared; CA, an approach using the Hellinger distance and a log ratio approach. They conclude that although CA and the Hellinger distance approach sometimes provide similar results, CA is the best due to a range of properties, whereas the log ratio approach often provides quite different results from the other two. Shen et al. [20] presents a framework for mapping categorical data to numerical values through calculation of similarities between data items and a reference set. The effectiveness of their method is compared with the effectiveness of other methods in the context of clustering and visualization. Ma and Hellerstein [15] presents a technique for ordering of categorical data, using a combination of clustering and domain semantics. In Rosario et al. [19] methods for numerical representation of categories using CA are presented. Two different CA computations and an arbitrary quantification with uniform spacing are compared for a number of categorical data sets using parallel coordinates. Johansson et al. [11] extended the quantification approach to mixed data sets by incorporating information about relationships among numerical variables into the process, and included the possibility of interactive modification to make use of the domain knowledge of expert users. Evaluating the performance of different quantification methods is not within the scope of this paper. We used CA in the study since it has been suggested several times as a method for quantification of categorical data, it is a generic method not designed for specific tasks such as clustering, and since a previous evaluation by Cuadras et al. [3] picked it out as a good quantification method compared to some other methods.

2.3 Evaluation

Different approaches can be taken to the evaluation of visualization methods, mainly depending on the objective of the study. In Plaisant [16] four main areas for evaluation in information visualization are listed; 1) controlled experiments comparing design elements, 2) usability evaluation of a tool, 3) controlled experiments comparing two or more tools, and 4) case studies of tools in realistic settings. The study presented in this paper can be defined as a controlled experiment comparing two approaches to visual analysis and is, hence, most closely related to Plaisant's first and third areas. A large number of studies have been performed within those evaluation areas and a full review is beyond the scope of this paper. In this study the performance of two visualization methods is compared in the context of specific tasks, defining performance as a combination of accuracy and response time. This is a common approach for quantitative evaluations and some previous examples are presented in for instance Stasko et al. [21] where the performance of two space-filling visualization methods for hierarchical data is compared, and in Plaisant et al. [17] where SpaceTree, a tree browser based on node link diagrams, is compared with Microsoft Explorer and a Hyperbolic tree browser. Similarly Johansson et al. [10] investigated the ability of humans to perceive relationships in 2D and 3D parallel coordinates and in Vrotsou et al. [24] a comparison was made between the performance using a 2D representation and a 3D representation for visual analysis of time-geographical data.

3 Design Decisions

Due to the fundamental differences between the QuantViz and CatViz approaches, a major concern during the design of this study has been to make decisions in terms of design in a way that makes it possible to perform a fair comparison, while not removing the basic differences and benefits of any of the methods. As CatViz method Parallel Sets is used (figure 1, described in detail in section 3.2) and the quantified data is visually represented using a multiple views set-up of three common visualization methods; parallel coordinates, table lens [18] and scatter plot matrix [1] (figure 2, described in detail in section 3.1). It might appear as an unfair comparison using multiple views for

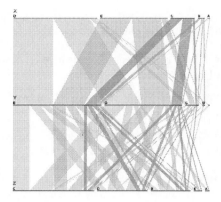

Figure 1: In Parallel Sets the variables are represented as horizontally laid out parallel axes. The categories within the variables are represented by vertical boxes with width corresponding to category frequency.

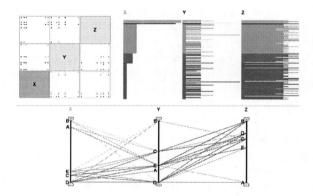

Figure 2: The multiple views used to represent quantified data, including a scatter plot matrix, a table lens and parallel coordinates. Colouring and table lens sorting is in this figure performed according to the leftmost variable.

the QuantViz approach while a single view is used for the CatViz approach. This is however a carefully considered decision based on the following:

1. Using multiple views facilitate analysis if the views complement each other. However, the use of multiple views increase the perceptual burden by demanding coordination of several sources of information.

2. Visualization methods for numerical data have different strengths and weaknesses and may complement and strengthen each other in a multiple view system.

3. Visualization methods designed for categorical data are based on category frequencies. They generally have the same strengths and weaknesses and hence do not complement and strengthen each other in the same way as methods for numerical data may.

Our aim has been to present all methods used in the study as advantageously as possible. The benefit of using multiple views depends both on visualization methods and the task at hand. For the tasks performed in this study we found no CatViz method that would complement Parallel Sets in a favourable way since all methods focus on category frequencies. Hence, using a single view was considered most beneficial for the CatViz approach. For the QuantViz approach on the other hand we could clearly appreciate that the features of for instance a table lens, which is able to display category frequencies, would complement the features of parallel coordinates in an advantageous way. Similarly a scatter plot matrix is able to display all pairwise correlations concurrently, which is not possible in parallel coordinates or table lens. Hence, using multiple views was considered most beneficial for the QuantViz approach. Another important issue was to avoid performance differences appearing due to interactive differences and features within the specific tools used in the study. To assure this the participants were presented with pre-prepared screen shots of the tools and were, hence, not allowed to interactively explore the data. Through this the individual differences between the tools were reduced as much as possible without removing the basic differences and benefits of any of the visualization methods. The visualization methods used and the layout rules employed when creating screen shots will be describe in the two following sections.

3.1 Quantification and Visualization

CA was used as quantification method, as this is a commonly used method for quantification purposes. CA is used for analysis of frequency tables where each cell represents the frequency of a combination of categories and it identifies similarity between cells by extracting independent dimensions in the table, using singular value decomposition. The first independent dimension, which explains most of the variance within the frequency table, is used as numerical representations of the row categories in the frequency table [6]. A multiple views layout is used for visualization (figure 2), including a scatter plot matrix, a table lens and parallel coordinates. These methods are commonly available and complement each other, and are hence considered to provide a good representation of benefits using the QuantViz approach. In general the QuantViz approach aims to perform analysis as if the data would have been numerical. Based on this the visualization methods employed for QuantViz in this study are used as if the data were numerical and hence basic implementations of the visual representations has been used. Although the visual representations could have been extended with additional features facilitating categorical data analysis, this is not used since the method would then no longer be a pure QuantViz method but a combined QuantViz/CatViz method. The only visual

enhancement used is displaying the category names next to the axes of the parallel coordinates to provide a link between the numerical representation of a category and its name. The layout rules used when preparing screen shots of this method are as follows:

1. Colouring is in all views performed according to the categories of the leftmost variable.

2. When tasks relate to one specific variable that variable is positioned to the left and sorting of rows in the table lens is performed according to it.

3. When tasks relate to two specific variables those are positioned as the two leftmost variables. Sorting of rows in the table lens is performed according to the second variable.

3.2 Parallel Sets

Parallel Sets [13] (figure 1) is a visualization method for analysis of categorical multivariate data where the variables of the data set are represented by horizontal parallel axes. Instead of displaying individual data items Parallel Sets focus on displaying category frequency. Within each variable the categories are represented by vertical boxes whose width corresponds to the relative frequency of the category. The width of the bands stretching between the categories of adjacent variables represent the relative frequency of a combination of categories. For this study a publicly available implementation of Parallel Sets has been used (http://eagereyes.org/parallel-sets). All screen shots of Parallel Sets within the paper have been created using this implementation, displaying synthetic data sets designed for this study. The tool's available features of reordering variables as well as categories have been used to prepare screen shots as follows:

1. Colouring is performed according to the categories of the topmost variable.

2. When tasks relate to one specific variable, that variable is always positioned as the top variable, and when tasks relate to two specific variables, those variables are always positioned as the two top variables.

3. For all variables the categories are internally ordered according to frequency, with highest frequency to the left and lowest to the right.

4 The Study

The aim of this study is to evaluate the effectiveness and efficiency of utilizing quantification followed by visualization for analysis of categorical data. More specifically, we want to evaluate the performance when carrying out basic data analysis tasks using the quantification approach compared to carrying out the same tasks using Parallel Sets.

Table 1: A data set including three variables (X, Y, Z) and six data items. If analysing the similarity of the three categories in variable X categories A and B are considered more similar to each other than they are to category C. This is true since the items belonging to categories A and B belong to the same categories in variables Y (D) and Z (F and G), whereas the items belonging to category C in variable X belong to a different set of categories in variable Y (E) and Z (H).

Item	X	Y	Z
1	A	D	F
2	A	D	G
3	B	D	F
4	B	D	G
5	C	E	H
6	C	E	H

Table 2: An example data set including three variables (X, Y, Z) and six data items. If analysing the similarity of the three variables, variable X and Z are considered more similar to each other than they are to variable Y. This is true since the data items belonging to the three categories in variable X belong to one category each in variable Z, and vice versa. Whereas they are spread over the two categories in variable Y.

Item	X	Y	Z
1	A	D	F
2	A	E	F
3	B	D	G
4	B	E	G
5	C	D	H
6	C	E	H

4.1 Method

To evaluate the performance the participants of the study carried out a number of tasks (described in detail in section 4.1.1) using the two visualization approaches. Performance was measured in terms of accuracy and response time, which were recorded for all tasks and stored in log files. Questionnaires were used to receive the subjective opinion of the participants in terms of difficulty of performing tasks and preference of visualization method.

4.1.1 Tasks

The tasks used in the study were selected to represent the basic elements of typical data analysis tasks, both specific to categorical data analysis and more general tasks. We focus solely on the basic elements of the tasks, which is motivated by the fact that the ability to efficiently perform the basic tasks is fundamental for the ability to efficiently perform more complex tasks. The overall task of data analysis is to identify structures and patterns within data. Most patterns, such as correlation and clusters, can be defined in terms of similarity. Hence, the most relevant general task to focus on are, in our opinion, the identification of relationships in terms of similarity. Additionally, when it comes to analysis of categorical data the frequency of categories, i.e. the relative number of items belonging to specific categories or combinations of categories, is often of major interest and is, as mentioned previously, the main property of focus in categorical data visualization. Based on this, the tasks of this study are separated into two classes: 1) identification of category frequencies, and 2) identification of similarity patterns. Within the two classes questions are asked relating either to structures within one variable or structures between two variables (from here on called 1VQ and 2VQ respectively). To be more precise, four tasks are defined as follows:

- Frequency task, 1VQ: *Which category in variable X is the most common?*

- Frequency task, 2VQ: *Which combination of categories in variables X and Y is the most common?*

- Similarity task, 1VQ: *Which two categories in variable X are most similar to each other?*

- Similarity task, 2VQ: *Which variable is most similar to variable X?*

In terms of similarity the following definitions were used;

1. Two categories are similar if they (in general) belong to the same categories within all (or most) variables in the data set (example displayed in table 1).

2. Two variables are similar if the category combinations for the variables are clearly separated, that is, if the data items of each category in variable X (in general) belongs to only one category in variable Y, and vice versa (example displayed in table 2).

4.1.2 Materials

The tests were carried out on an HP EliteBook 8540p laptop with an Intel i5 2.53GHz CPU, 4 GB RAM and an Nvidia NVS 5100M graphics card. An external Dell 20" monitor was used, set to a resolution of 1680 x 1050 pixels. The participants were presented with screen shots of the visualization methods together with the task to perform, included in figures of size 1100 x 800 pixels. The experimental environment used was designed in Matlab. To retain full control over relationships in the data synthetic data sets were created using Matlab. A total of 32 data sets were created, 16 designed for frequency related tasks and 16 for similarity related tasks, half of which where smaller data sets including three to four variables and three to five categories within each variable, and half being larger data sets including six to seven variables and six to eight categories within each variable. The data sets were designed to provide relatively clear answers to the tasks.

4.1.3 Experimental Design

The study was designed as a 2-factor within-subject design, where the two factors were type of analysis (QuantViz vs. CatViz) and type of task (Frequency vs. Similarity). The four separate experimental phases were hence:

1. QuantViz + Frequency
2. QuantViz + Similarity
3. CatViz + Frequency
4. CatViz + Similarity.

The presentation order of the four phases was counterbalanced using a Latin-square procedure [5], resulting in four different phase orders. The participants were randomly assigned to one of the four phase orders, assigning equally many participants to each.

Performing the tasks of this study includes interpretation of fairly complex visual representations, and hence some visualization experience was set as a requirement for participants. Due to this the participants were 15 researchers and students within areas related to visualization, aged between 22 and 35 years. Each participant performed 32 tasks in total (8 per phase), and no data set was used more than once per participant, avoiding that any structures asked for had been identified by chance during previous tasks. The presentation order of data sets and questions was randomized within each phase. However, since each task type includes two different kinds of questions (1VQ and 2VQ) and since the data sets were of different sizes, the randomization was limited by a certain level of control. During each phase it was ensured that equally many 1VQ and 2VQ were asked, and that half of each question type was asked using a smaller data set and half using a larger data set. No major performance differences were expected due to data set size and type of question, thus they were not treated as factors within the experimental design. However, information on size and question type was recorded to be able to identify unexpected results related to this.

4.1.4 Procedure

To assure that all participants possessed the basic knowledge needed to be able to interpret the visual representations, an initial introduction was held for all participants, either in small groups or individually. The introduction was in the form of a small scripted lecture where the

visual representations were described in detail as well as the basic concept of quantification. Furthermore, the rules used for screen shot layout was described. The concepts of frequency and similarity in the context of the study was also explained, and the basic task types were presented to the participants together with example images displaying how the structure asked for can be identified using each of the analysis methods. The explanations and example images were printed out and made available throughout the test. The participants were told that their response time would be measured and that they should try to answer as quickly as possible but to maintain high accuracy.

The test itself was performed individually and consisted of a training period and the experiment. The training period included a small number of test tasks using both analysis types and was used as a means for getting familiar with the experimental environment, methods and tasks. During the training period the participants were encouraged to ask questions to make sure they had understood the tasks. The experiment consisted of four separate phases, as described in section 4.1.3, where the participant was presented with 8 tasks and screen shots. Once the answer to the task was found the participant pressed a button, the screen shot was hidden and an interface for submitting the answer was displayed. For each task the response time was recorded from when the screen shot was displayed until the answer button was pressed. The answers provided, as well as response time and data sets used, were stored in log files. When a phase was finished a pause screen was displayed, allowing a break between the phases, and the participant was asked to answer two questions; 1) Did you find it difficult or easy to answer the questions using the visualization method? 2) Did you find it more difficult to answer the questions when the number of variables and number of categories increased? The questionnaire also encouraged the participants to provide additional comments on the method used and tasks performed. When all four phases were finished the participants were asked to answer a final questionnaire, including questions as to which analysis type the participant preferred using for each task type.

4.2 Result

This section will present the results of the study in detail. Results are reported both in terms of performance measures and questionnaire answers.

4.2.1 Performance

The measured data were initially not normally distributed. Due to this the response time was logarithmically transformed prior to statistical testing, and a repeated measures ANOVA [5] was carried out on the logarithmically transformed data, using an α value with a significance of $p < 0.05$. For accuracy a Friedman test was used for significance testing, since this data could not be logarithmi-

Table 3: Average response times in seconds for the four phases, overall average at the top and below split into one and two variable questions. Standard deviation is displayed within parentheses.

	QuantViz + Frequency	QuantViz + Similarity	CatViz + Frequency	CatViz + Similarity
Overall	26.73 (14.42)	16.15 (7.75)	10.55 (5.12)	32.45 (15.67)
1VQ	13.91 (10.58)	16.40 (9.68)	7.45 (3.31)	27.04 (11.88)
2VQ	39.56 (21.63)	15.90 (7.38)	13.66 (7.02)	37.85 (22.67)

Table 4: Descriptive statistics of the measured accuracy for the four phases, displaying median, minimum, maximum, 1st quartile and 3rd quartile. The maximum number of correct answers is 8.

	Median	Min	Max	Q1	Q3
QuantViz + Freq.	4	2	8	4	4
QuantViz + Sim.	8	6	8	8	8
CatViz + Freq.	8	4	8	8	8
CatViz + Sim.	6	4	8	6	7

Table 5: Descriptive statistics of the measured accuracy for the four phases separated into one and two variable questions. The maximum number of correct answers is 4.

	Median	Min	Max	Q1	Q3
Q + F + 1VQ	4	2	4	3	4
Q + F + 2VQ	0	0	4	0	1
Q + S + 1VQ	4	3	4	4	4
Q + S + 2VQ	4	3	4	4	4
C + F + 1VQ	4	4	4	4	4
C + F + 2VQ	4	0	4	4	4
C + S + 1VQ	3	2	4	2	4
C + S + 2VQ	3	1	4	3	4

cally transformed into a normal distribution. A post-hoc test was performed on accuracy, using pairwise comparisons according to Conover [2], to identify which phases are significantly different from each other.

The two factors of the study were visualization type (QuantViz vs. CatViz) and task type (Frequency vs. Similarity), resulting in four separate phases. Average response times of the phases are displayed in the top row of table 3 and the statistics of accuracy are displayed in table 4. In terms of overall response time, the average time for the two visualization methods were equal, as displayed in figure 3, and statistical analysis reports no significant effect of visualization type, $F(1, 14) = 3.112, p < 0.099$. However, there is a significant effect of task type, $F(1, 14) = 52.998, p < 0.001$, with frequency tasks being performed almost 25 % faster than similarity tasks, as displayed in figure 3. Furthermore, statistical analysis reports a significant interaction effect between visualization type and task type, $F(1, 14) = 122.007, p < 0.001$. This is also visible in figure 3 with similarity questions being performed considerably faster using QuantViz whereas frequency tasks are performed faster using CatViz. Accuracy results generally agree with response time, with high performance for similarity tasks using QuantViz and for frequency tasks using CatViz, as visible in table 4 and from the box plots in the left part of figure 4. Statistical testing confirms that the difference between the four phases is significant, $\chi^2(3, N = 15) = 32.929, p < 0.001$. Furthermore, post-hoc testing shows a significant difference between us-

ing QuantViz for frequency tasks and CatViz for similarity tasks, whereas there was no significant difference between using QuantViz for similarity tasks and CatViz for frequency tasks. These results indicate performance differences depending on the combination of visualization type and task type, with higher performance using CatViz for similarity tasks and QuantViz for frequency tasks. However, looking more closely into the results it appears as if question type also had a strong influence on performance.

The two bottom rows of table 3 display the response times of the question types, showing a noticeable difference between performing 1VQ frequency tasks and 2VQ frequency tasks using QuantViz. A similar relationship is identified for 1VQ and 2VQ frequency tasks using CatViz. The difference between 1VQ and 2VQ for similarity tasks is however not as explicit. Similarly, the difference in terms of accuracy between the question types is noticeable, as displayed in table 5 and in the right part of figure 4. Most obvious is the difference between 1VQ and 2VQ frequency tasks using the QuantViz approach. Here the accuracy of 1VQ is almost as high as the accuracy of performing frequency tasks using CatViz, whereas the accuracy of performing 2VQ frequency tasks using QuantViz has a median value of zero. Statistical testing of response time, with three within-subject factors; visualization type (QuantViz vs. CatViz), task type (Frequency vs. Similar-

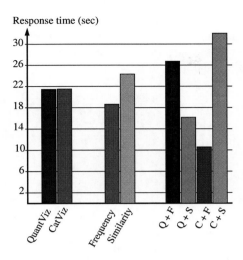

Figure 3: Average response time in seconds for visualization type (left), task type (centre) and the four combinations of task and visualization types (right).

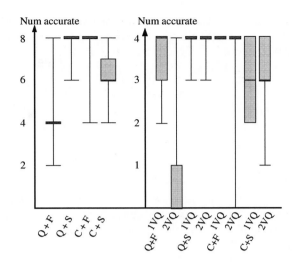

Figure 4: Box plots displaying number of accurate answers for the four phases (left) and phases divided based on question type (right). The red lines represent median values.

ity) and question type (1VQ vs. 2VQ), shows significant effects for task type, $F(1,14) = 64.137, p < 0.001$, and for question type, $F(1,14) = 137.625, p < 0.001$. Furthermore, the interaction effects where significant for visualization type and task type, $F(1,14) = 121.208, p < 0.001$, task type and question type, $F(1,14) = 43.758, p < 0.001$, and visualization type, task type and question type, $F(1,14) = 13.584, p < 0.002$, indicating that the performance difference in terms of response time is affected by the question type as well as by visualization and task type. Due to this additional statistical testing was performed separating the data into two sets based on task type. For frequency tasks significant interaction effects were found between visualization type and question type, $F(1,14) = 22.587, p < 0.001$, whereas no significant interaction effects were found for similarity tasks. In terms of accuracy, statistical testing shows significant difference between the conditions in table 5 with $\chi^2(7, N = 15) = 57.555, p < 0.001$. The post-hoc test showed a significant difference between 1VQ and 2VQ for frequency tasks using QuantViz, but no significant difference between 1VQ and 2VQ for any of the other phases. Worth noting is also that there were significant differences between performing 2VQ frequency tasks using QuantViz and both question types for frequency tasks using CatViz, whereas there were no significant differences between 1VQ frequency tasks using QuantViz and frequency tasks using CatViz, indicating that the overall difference between performing frequency tasks using QuantViz and CatViz may mostly depend on the low performance of 2VQ for frequency tasks using QuantViz, whereas the performance of

1VQ frequency tasks using QuantViz is almost as good as the overall performance of frequency tasks for CatViz. In terms of data set size, no major performance differences were found for any of the measures.

4.2.2 Questionnaires

The questionnaire answers strongly implied that CatViz was the preferred method for performing frequency tasks, as stated by twelve of the participants, and that QuantViz was the preferred method for performing similarity tasks, as stated by fourteen participants. Tables 6 and 7 provide more information on the participants opinions regarding the visualization approaches and tasks. Table 6 displays the number of participants finding it easy to solve the tasks for the four phases and table 7 displays the number of participants who found the tasks more difficult as the data set size increased.

Some participants found it both difficult and easy performing the tasks. Using QuantViz for frequency tasks a main comment on this was that it was easy for 1VQ (i.e. find the most common category in variable X) but difficult for 2VQ (i.e. find the most common combination of categories in variables X and Y). Regarding the increase in difficulty as the data set size grew, comments indicate that this was mostly true for 2VQ. Comments from the participants regarding using the QuantViz approach for similarity tasks indicate that the difficulty mentioned by some participants was mainly due to examples where more than one variable could be interpreted as similar. Using CatViz all participants found it easy to answer the frequency tasks, and most did not find the tasks more difficult as the data set size increased. An explanation made as to why it was easy to use

Table 6: Number of participants for each phase who found it easy to perform the tasks. Numbers within parentheses are total number of participants either finding it easy or both difficult and easy.

	QuantViz	CatViz	Total
Frequency	3 (8)	15	18 (23)
Similarity	12 (14)	4 (10)	16 (24)
Total	15 (22)	19 (24)	

Table 7: Number of participants for each phase who found it more difficult to solve tasks when data set size increased. Numbers within parentheses are the total number of participants either finding it difficult or both difficult and easy.

	QuantViz	CatViz	Total
Frequency	12 (14)	4	16 (18)
Similarity	8	15	23
Total	20 (22)	19	

this visualization approach was that the answers were obvious due to size and variable sorting. When it came to performing similarity tasks using CatViz a comment made as to what made it difficult was that it was almost impossible to follow the bands between the variables as they spread. Regarding increase in number of variables and categories, the main comment was that more bands, colours and categories generated more clutter.

5   Discussion and Conclusions

In general the performance results, both in terms of accuracy and response time, agree well with the subjective experiences reported by the participants through the questionnaires. For similarity related tasks a majority preferred using QuantViz, which was also the visualization approach for which the recorded performance was best for similarity tasks. For frequency related tasks on the other hand, a majority of participants preferred using CatViz, which also agrees well with the recorded performance. A result worth emphasizing is that when the tasks where split up into questions concerning the frequency of categories within one variable or a combination of categories in two variables, the performance was noticeably higher for the one variable questions using QuantViz. This was also mentioned by several participants who found the one variable questions easy during this phase, whereas two variable questions were perceived as more difficult. In terms of data set sizes no major performance differences were found. However, the participants reported an increase in perceived difficulty as the size increased. More specifically, a majority of participants experienced an increase in difficult for phases that were generally not perceived as easy, as can be identified through the inverse relationships between tables 6 and 7. Possibly the limitations of both approaches became more obvious as the tasks got more difficult.

As a final point of discussion it is important to again emphasize that although the study presented in this paper aims to compare the two main approaches to visual analysis of categorical data, and not to compare two visualization tools or two visual representations, the results can not be directly generalized to all visualization methods designed for cat-

egorical data, nor to all visualizations of quantified categorical data. However, it can be seen as an initial attempt to compare the effectiveness and efficiency of the two visualization approaches; not aiming to find an ultimate solution as to how categorical data is best analysed visually, but aiming to provide guidance as to which method might be most useful for a specific type of task and to encourage further evaluations of the two approaches.

Acknowledgements

We would like to thank Camilla Forsell for her kind advice on study design and analysis of results. This work was partly supported by the Swedish Research Council in the Linnaeus Centre CADICS and by the Visualization Programme coordinated by the Swedish Knowledge Foundation.

References

[1] Richard A. Becker and William S. Cleveland. Brushing scatterplots. *Technometrics*, 29(2):127–142, 1987.

[2] William Jay Conover. *Practical Nonparametric Statistics*. John Wiley & Sons, Inc, 1971.

[3] Carles M. Cuadras, Daniel Cuadras, and Michael J. Greenacre. A comparison of different methods for representing categorical data. *Communications in Statistics – Simulation and Computation*, 35:447–459, 2006.

[4] Michael Friendly. Visualizing categorical data: Data, stories, and pictures. In *Proceedings of the Twenty-Fifth Annual SAS Users Group International Conference*, 2000.

[5] Anthony M. Graziano and Michael L. Raulin. *Research Methods: A Process of Inquiry, 7. ed.* Pearson Education Inc., 2010.

[6] Michael Greenacre. *Correspondence Analysis in Practice, 2. ed.* Chapman & Hall, 2007.

[7] Susan L. Havre, Anuj Shah, Christian Posse, and Bobbie-Jo Webb-Robertson. Diverse information integration and visualization. In *Proceedings of SPIE, the International Society for Optical Engineering*, pages 60600M.1–60600M.11, January 2006.

[8] Mao Lin Huang, Tze-Haw Huang, and Jiawan Zhang. Treemapbar: Visualizing additional dimensions of data in bar chart. In *Proceedings of IEEE International Conference on Information Visualisation*, pages 98–103, 2009.

[9] Alfred Inselberg. The plane with parallel coordinates. *The Visual Computer*, 1(4):69–91, 1985.

[10] Jimmy Johansson, Camilla Forsell, Mats Lind, and Matthew Cooper. Perceiving patterns in parallel coordinates: Determining thresholds for identification of relationships. *Information Visualization*, 7(2):152–162, 2008.

[11] Sara Johansson, Mikael Jern, and Jimmy Johansson. Interactive quantification of categorical variables in mixed data sets. In *Proceedings of IEEE International Conference on Information Visualisation*, pages 3–10, 2008.

[12] Erica Kolatch and Beth Weinstein. Cattrees: Dynamic visualization of categorical data using treemaps. http://www.cs.umd.edu/class/spring2001/cmsc838b/Project/Kolatch_Weinstein/index.html, May 2001.

[13] Robert Kosara, Fabian Bendix, and Helwig Hauser. Parallel sets: Interactive exploration and visual analysis of categorical data. *IEEE Transactions on Visualization and Computer Graphics*, 12(4):558–568, 2006.

[14] Zhicheng Liu, John Stasko, and Timothy Sullivan. Selltrend: Inter-attribute visual analysis of temporal transaction data. *IEEE Transactions on Visualization and Computer Graphics*, 15(6):1025–1032, 2009.

[15] Sheng Ma and Joseph L. Hellerstein. Ordering categorical data to improve visualization. In *Proceedings of IEEE Information Visualization Symposium Late Breaking Hot Topics*, pages 15–18, 1999.

[16] Catherine Plaisant. The challenge of information visualization evaluation. In *Proceedings of the Working Conference on Advanced Visual Interfaces*, pages 109–116, 2004.

[17] Catherine Plaisant, Jesse Grosjean, and Benjamin B. Bederson. Spacetree: Supporting exploration in large node link tree, design evolution and empirical evaluation. In *Proceedings of the IEEE Symposium on Information Visualization*, pages 57–64, 2002.

[18] Ramana Rao and Stuart K. Card. The table lens: merging graphical and symbolic representations in an interactive focus + context visualization for tabular information. In *Proceedings of Human factors in computing systems: celebrating interdependence*, pages 318–322, 1994.

[19] Geraldine E. Rosario, Elke A. Rundensteiner, David C. Brown, Matthew O. Ward, and Shiping Huang. Mapping nominal values to numbers for effective visualization. *Information Visualization*, 3(2):80–95, 2004.

[20] Zhi-Yong Shen, Jun Sun, Yi-Dong Shen, and Ming Li. R-map: mapping categorical data for clustering and visualization based on reference sets. In *Proceedings of the Conference on Advances in knowledge discovery and data mining*, pages 992–998, 2008.

[21] John Stasko, Richard Catrambone, Mark Guzdial, and Kevin McDonald. An evaluation of space-filling information visualizations for depicting hierarchical structures. *International Journal of Human-Computer Studies*, 53(5):663–694, 2000.

[22] Michael Tenenhaus and Forrest W. Young. An analysis and synthesis of multiple correspondence analysis, optimal scaling, dual scaling, homogenity analysis and other methods for quantifying categorical multivariate data. *Psychometrika*, 50(1):91–119, 1985.

[23] Graham J. G. Upton. Cobweb diagrams for multiway contingency tables. *Journal of the Royal Statistical Society. Series D (The Statistician)*, 49(1):79–85, 2000.

[24] Katerina Vrotsou, Camilla Forsell, and Matthew Cooper. 2D and 3D representations for feature recognition in time geographical diary data. *Information Visualization*, 9(4):263–276, 2010.

Developing and Applying a User-Centered Model for the Design and Implementation of Information Visualization Tools

Lian Chee KOH, Aidan SLINGSBY, Jason DYKES, Tin Seong KAM

Lian Chee KOH is a PhD student at the giCentre, City University London, but is based in the School of Information Systems, Singapore Management University, e-mail:lckoh@smu.edu.sg
Aidan SLINGSBY is with the giCentre, City University London; email: sbbb717@soi.city.ac.uk ;
Jason DYKES is with the giCentre, City University London; email: jad7@soi.city.ac.uk ;
Tin Seong KAM is with the School of Information Systems, Singapore Management University; email:tskam@smu.edu.sg.

Abstract – The objective of this paper is to show how approaches for user-centered information visualization design and development are being applied in the context of healthcare where users are not familiar with information visualization techniques. We base our design methods on user-centered frameworks in which 'prototyping' plays an important role in the process. We modify existing approaches to involve prototyping at an early stage of the process as the problem domain is assessed. We believe this to be essential, as it increases users' awareness of what information visualization techniques can offer them and that it enables users to participate more effectively in later stages of the design and development process. This also acts as a stimulus for engagement.

The problem domain analysis stage of a pilot study using this approach is presented, in which techniques are being collaboratively developed with domain users from a healthcare institution. Our results suggest that this approach has engaged users, who are subsequently able to apply generic information visualization concepts to their domains and as a result are better equipped to take part in the subsequent collaborative design and development process.

Keywords- Information visualization, User-Centered approach, prototyping, problem domain characterization, requirements, design, Healthcare Patient Satisfaction Index

1 INTRODUCTION

The notion of user-centered design was described by Norman [9] and Nielsen [8] as the early and continuous inclusion of targeted end-users in the design and development process. Many researchers in the design and development of geographical information visualization tools have recognized the benefits of being consistent with this concept in the involvement of targeted users from the start to the finish of the design and development cycle of information visualization tools [15, 12, 13].

In visualization projects, domain users and visualization experts come together with a mutual objective. Frequently, their shared knowledge is limited. Whilst processes for capturing requirements are well established, means of sharing knowledge of visualization methods that may support and influence this process are less so. We have found that participatory visualization exercises can be effective in sharing knowledge about domain, visualization and their interaction through a process of 'co-discovery' [7, 3]. We propose a modification of Robinson *et al.*'s framework [12] that incorporates Roth *et al.*'s idea of early prototyping [13]. We also propose some additional activities at the beginning of the iterative user-centered process to inform and ensure engagement in our problem domain

analysis. These additions: *(a)* inform domain users about the concepts and techniques of information visualization, early in the process; *(b)* help visualization experts understand the work domain; and *(c)* act to build trust between both parties. At this stage 'patchwork prototypes' [4] – *ad hoc* combinations of existing tools, scripts and mocked-up examples – are used, some of which may contribute to eventual implementation. This early iteration involving data and interaction broadens Robinson *et al.*'s [13] and Roth *et al.*'s [12] Work Domain Analysis to a wider consideration of the *problem domain*. It is intended to better inform all participants about techniques, concepts and objectives, enabling them to participate more actively in the design and development process of information visualization applications to meet user needs.

We applied this approach to the design and development of an information visualization application for a government healthcare institution in Singapore. The study aimed to establish whether and how the introduction of prototypes to the healthcare domain users at the beginning of an iterative user-centered process, benefits both domain users and visualization experts. We also used the study to reflect on how each stage of the process should be implemented. The study involved an analyst and a manager from the Quality department. It applied this adapted iterative user-centered design approach to visualize responses to patient satisfaction surveys conducted on a sample population of patients discharged from the healthcare institution.

2 Background

Robinson *et al.* [12] recommended an iterative user-centered design process (Figure 1) that drew on Slocum *et al.*'s work [15]. The targeted end-users are actively involved in each of the six stages of this design framework, which involves significant feedback loops between stages:

> *Work Domain Analysis* – the task of gathering ideas and requirements from the end-users;
> *Conceptual Analysis* – developing the functionality and designs to be featured in the tool;
> *Prototyping* – the creation of working models of the tool's capabilities;
> *Interaction and Usability Studies* – the evaluation of the model's partial capabilities;
> *Implementation* – the creation of the tool with full features;
> *Debugging* – the validation of the tool's features before final deployment.

Roth *et al.* found several practical issues with this process [13]. Strict compliance to the previous process meant that the Work Domain

1550-6037/11 $26.00 © 2011 IEEE
DOI 10.1109/IV.2011.32

Analysis stage had to be completed before the creation of the working interfaces in the Prototyping stage. They reported that this is not practical where *(a)* initial scaled-down proof-of-concept projects do not have the resources to include user participation; *(b)* a new development team joins an existing project; *(c)* users are unavailable or non-existent during the development of the project; *(d)* an existing application is required to be extended to a broader group of users [13].

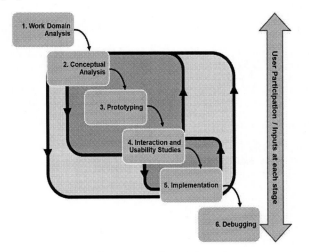

Figure 1: Robinson *et al.*'s six-stage user-centered design process [12].

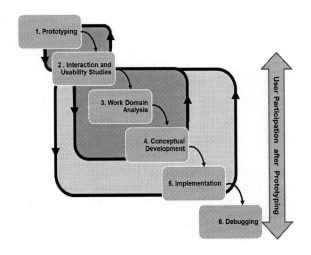

Figure 2: Roth *et al.*'s modified user-centered design process [13]

Figure 2 illustrates the modified iterative process proposed by Roth *et al.* [13]. The adapted approach is also focused on active domain user participation, with the added flexibility of making use of existing versions of the software or working interfaces prior to performing or revisiting Work Domain Analysis. This has the advantage that prototypes or existing versions of the software can be used to extract user ideas and viewpoints that may otherwise not have occurred to them [13, 4].

In our experience, potential users of visualization are often unlikely to know the true potential or scope of visual approaches or their possible impact on workflow at the early stages of design. Indeed Plaisant [10] reports that those new to or unfamiliar with information visualization concepts may struggle to participate effectively in

human-centred design. We therefore suggest another context in which this model, or variants of it, may be relevant, having found that many potential users of visualization have little experience of interactive graphics, the possibilities available or the kinds of analytical approaches that they encourage. This is particularly important as emerging methods of software development, APIs and toolkits are making interactive prototypes that can overcome these difficulties less expensive to generate [4, 11, 2].

As such, just like [13], we use prototypes prior to the work domain characterisation stage. We do so to engage interest, establish common understanding and engender creative thinking. However, we also use this process to characterize the problem domain and build confidence between experts in visualization and the problem domain. We find that this helps with knowledge sharing, trust building and 'orientation' and that it can be rewarding [7, 3]. This additional need for early prototyping, whereby users and visualizers engage in some initial learning before work domain analysis, differs from the other scenarios identified by Roth *et al.* [13] in that it is, in itself, user focused – the objective being to inform at a number of levels. We have found that a combination of broad and general learning about visualization possibilities and specific experience using data that are familiar to our users is successful in terms of being informative, engaging and likely to stimulate ideas [7, 3].

Our 'prototypes', range in terms of their functionality. We use both specific and focused *data prototypes* for *domain visualization*, with broader, more generic, *visualization examples* for *visualization awareness*. To use a visualization metaphor, these provide 'details on demand' and 'overview' in terms of visualization knowledge respectively and act as a stimulus for information exchange between visualizers and domain users. The *data prototypes* are interactive and use existing, modified, or rapidly coded applications with different levels of functionality that support the visual analysis of data provided by, and of interest to users. These are used in a Domain Visualization Workshop. The *visualization examples* may be interactive prototypes, but canned, animated or perhaps even static examples of visualization possibilities tend to provide coverage effectively. We use these in a Visualization Awareness Workshop. Thus, rather than using prototypes for 'formative studies' we use them much as they are employed by Roth *et al.* [13] in their work domain analysis "*to prompt useful ideas and reactions that users might not otherwise think to offer*" through structured activities at workshops in which we characterise the problem domain by sharing knowledge and establishing interest and needs.

Appropriate ordering of these stages is context dependent. Where participants have knowledge of some visualization possibilities and experience of exploratory analytical work, their existing applications may be used for initial Domain Visualization where strengths, weaknesses and needs are discussed [3], followed by Visualization Awareness in which additional opportunities are determined. Where participants have little experience of graphical approaches, Visualization Awareness may be an important first step, required to ensure that Domain Visualization is effective and successful.

This modified iterative process allows domain users to see and engage with some visualization at an early stage and this may stimulate creative thinking. Enabling users to see and interact with their own data through visualization has been shown to be very useful at this stage [7], with rapidly developed prototypes partially functional prototypes or existing versions of software being used to extract user ideas and viewpoints that may otherwise not have occurred to domain users whilst helping visualizers understand the domain and user priorities [3]. The ideas and viewpoints, together with user feedback gleaned through the Work Domain Analysis stage, can then be used as input into the Conceptual Development and more formal prototyping.

3   PROBLEM DOMAIN ANALYSIS

The Problem Domain Analysis stage is a process of characterizing the domain in which visualization is being applied and building understanding and confidence between experts in visualization and the domain users. Prototypes are key in this stage, for engaging interest and stimulating broad and creative thinking.

The **Visualization Awareness Workshop** is designed to introduce *general* information visualization concepts to the users, illustrating the range of information visualization techniques from standard statistical graphics to more specialized and innovative graphics designed for different types of research questions. The workshop seeks to engage users and allow them to gain a broad appreciation of the scope and characteristics of the information visualization approach and its tools and techniques. Structuring a workshop to help participants relate ideas and consider the application of visualization techniques to their own data analysis and communication scenarios is essential here – through discussion, imagination exercises and the like.

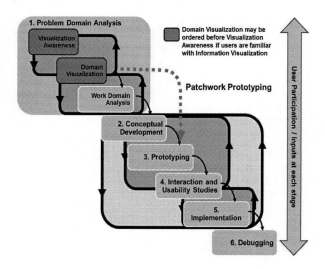

Figure 3: Modified version of Robinson *et al.*'s user-centered design process [12] with early prototyping as advocated by Roth *et al.* [13].

The **Domain Visualization Workshop** is another interactive session with a different emphasis. Here domain users can see and use *specific* examples of visualization techniques as applied to *their own data*. The visualization experts prepare *data prototypes* that showcase visualization techniques that are appropriate to the data supplied by the domain users. This may require several days' preparation on the part of the visualization experts, depending on how many prototypes are prepared and the nature of the prototypes, but patchwork prototypes [4] or existing software or components may be appropriate. The workshop demonstrates possibilities to the domain users of using visualization techniques with their own data. It also gives the visualization team the opportunity to gain initial user feedback and broad user requirements. The exchange of data, in itself, is a useful process that involves trust and learning on all sides. Ideally, domain users will achieve some insights from their data using these prototypes during this workshop [7].

These workshops may be re-ordered according to local needs. Engaging users in Domain Visualization before holding a Visualization Awareness Workshop may be appropriate in some circumstances, depending upon local knowledge of and experience with analytical and visual methods. In our vizLegends work [3], the domain users had significant prior exposure to visualization

approaches and techniques within their domain, unlike user groups in our subsequent study in Singapore. Our sequence of conducting the Awareness Workshop before the Domain Visualization is deliberate in this case, as our experience in working with various industry groups in the region in the field of software implementations had made us mindful to the fact that domain users in this case had little or no exposure to the concepts of information visualization. Without the initial workshop and prior knowledge about the way information visualization has been applied in various business domains, they would have been unable to participate effectively in the Domain Visualization.

As such, we recommend engaging users through workshops that inform, stimulate and are of interest to domain users. These workshops should inform Work Domain Analysis prior to Conceptual Development and more formal prototyping, and are designed and sequenced to introduce users to visualization applications that are relevant to their domain and knowledge and that ultimately use their data.

These workshops are followed by Work Domain Analysis sessions in which the requirements for a visualization application are collated.

4   A PILOT STUDY

We conducted a pilot study at a government healthcare institution in Singapore, to try this approach on domain users with little experience and knowledge about information visualization techniques. Senior management staff of the healthcare institution are contemplating the use of information visualization tools in the organization and had identified a group of departmental heads with analytical problems and questions, from the Business Development, Corporate Communications, Financial Control, Medical Affairs, and Quality departments to participate in this pilot study, with the aim of identifying potentially viable information visualization projects from these departments. The pilot study is still in progress and this paper only reports on the Problem Domain Analysis stage. We assess the impact of this process on the domain users though observational note-taking and by running informal feedback sessions during and after each stage in the process. As the domain users involved in the pilot study had had little exposure to information visualization concepts, we ran the Visualization Awareness workshop prior to the Domain Visualization session.

4.1   Visualization Awareness Workshop

We invited these domain experts, to a Visualization Awareness Workshop, which was facilitated by an information visualization subject expert. The domain experts had very little knowledge about information visualization techniques and concepts, but were keen to learn more about these and see how they might apply to their work domains.

The visualization team shared various non-healthcare specific applications of information visualization tools and techniques with the domain users, who were encouraged to reflect on and to share their views on how information visualization techniques could be applied within their respective domains. The team asked questions to prompt feedback about what participants liked or disliked about the various information visualization techniques, as the workshop progressed. Feedback from the domain experts was noted by the visualization team. In addition to eliciting feedback about the applications and methods presented, the visualization team sought to establish whether domain experts were receptive to the techniques and concepts presented. The prototypes were selected to provide a range of representative information visualization techniques and interactions applied to public information that would be familiar to workshop participants:

- The Hive Group Gallery[1], a collection of sample information visualization applications by industry, was used to illustrate an interactive tree map representation of a sales team's performance. This prototype was used to depict how high volume, hierarchical data could be visualized;
- Oakland Crimespotting[2], an interactive map of crimes in Oakland for understanding crime in cities, which focused on visualization of spatial and temporal data;
- News Dots[3], a social network visualization of the most recent topics in the news, to show how to visualize complex social relationships;
- Parallel Sets 2.1 (Parsets [6]) was used to illustrate the relationships between where purchasers were currently housed (either in public or private properties); property types that the purchasers had bought and regions where properties are located. (Figure 4). The highlighted region in Figure 4 shows that the most significant section of property transactions (23%) came from purchasers who were currently living in private housing, who bought condominiums located in the central region of Singapore.

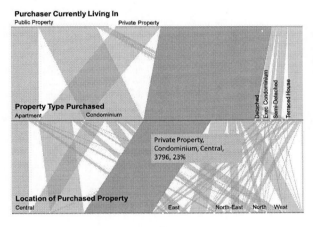

Figure 4: Parsets [6] visualization of property sales in Singapore.

In addition, generic interaction techniques such as select, filter, explore, abstract/elaborate, connect, encode and reconfigure [18], were demonstrated.

Feedback elicited from participants during the course of the workshop revealed that they had found the workshop informative and engaging, and were receptive to the interactive way data could be investigated using means that were previously unknown to them. Participants also thought that information visualization tools would add value to the way they analysed their domain data, but reflected their concerns that they might have to commit additional resources (and cost) in the form of expertise and special skillset upgrade in order to use the visualization tools.

Participants shared how information visualization tools could be applied in their respective work domains:

- exploring how doctors from various specialties collaborated;
- tracking trend of inpatient readmissions, falls or medication errors;
- analysing patient satisfaction survey data;
- trending financial results.

---

[1] http://www.hivegroup.com/solutions/demos/salesforce.html
[2] http://oakland.crimespotting.org/map/
[3] http://labs.slate.com/articles/slate-news-dots/

Domain users from Business Development arranged for a separate meeting shortly after the initial Visualization Awareness Workshop to discuss ideas that had occurred to them as a result of the workshop. This included ideas of tracking elderly patients using social network visualization techniques to enable more of the elderly to remain in their homes. Users from the Quality department also came forward indicating keen interest in applying information visualization techniques to the analysis of their patient satisfaction survey data. This kind of creative thinking is a typical response to Visualization Awareness, which stimulates ideas by broadening knowledge and encouraging its application and synthesis. Establishing focus in the problem domain and managing expectation is an important next stage.

Feedback obtained through this workshop and the subsequent meetings requested by the domain users, provided us with some evidence that participants were able to relate information visualization concepts to specific areas of work within their respective domains. The authors also gained some preliminary understanding of the kind of information analysis challenges faced by the various domain users, demonstrating the close relationships between these participatory learning events and work domain analysis as a problem domain is characterized. Further to this, the Visualization Awareness Workshop enabled the visualization team and domain users to identify domain problems or questions that were unsuitable for information visualization - due to the lack of data that available for analysis; or problems requiring solutions that were transactional or operational in nature; or users realising that they lacked the resources to commit to the implementation process.

Discussions with the healthcare institution's Management, Business Development and Quality Management departments led to a decision to focus on the patient satisfaction survey rather than the 'tracking elderly patients' alternative as data collection activities for this domain were ongoing.

4.2 Domain Visualization Workshop

Our domain experts wanted to analyse patient satisfaction surveys that were conducted by patients. The Quality department commissioned appropriately sampled telephone surveys of patients about how satisfied they were about the level of healthcare services they experienced, several weeks after they had been discharged from one of three departments: Emergency Department, Specialist Clinics and Inpatient Wards. Each of these departments contains various patient touch-points, where the department's staff has service delivery contact with patients (Figure 5).

Selected patients answered a series of questions about their overall satisfaction with the department that provided the treatment and the touch-points within that department. Surveys differed between departments, but all questions were measured on a 5-point Likert scale (1="very poor"; 5= "excellent"). Patients could also choose not to answer questions that were not relevant to their treatment. Respondents could also provide free-text comments for each question.

The patient satisfaction indices for overall patient experience and the various touch points were calculated as the percentage of total patients who responded with 4 ("good") or 5 ("excellent") for the relevant survey questions. Each month, the tele-survey company summarizes the survey responses into a set of static graphical reports that chart key patient satisfaction indices by departments and touch-points within the healthcare institution. The Quality department is provided with these results on a quarterly basis.

In this pilot study, we are working with Quality department to design an application that would allow their staff to visually analyse these results as they become available through the institution's intranet. A

Quality Manager and an analyst of the healthcare institution participated in this study.

Emergency Department	Specialist Clinics	Inpatient Wards
Registration	Registration	Admission
Triage	Doctors	Doctors
Doctors	Nursing Staff	Nursing Staff
Nursing Staff	Other Services	Meals
Other Services	Pharmacy	Ward Facilities
Pharmacy	Facilities	Other Services
Facilities		Discharge

Figure 5: Patient touch points in the segments of a healthcare facility

The patient satisfaction data in its raw form was obtained from the Quality department for the Domain Visualization Workshop. The workshop, which was held several weeks after the Visualization Awareness Workshop, presented a number of prototypes of visualization techniques using the patient satisfaction survey.

The workshop enabled the domain users to see the possibilities these techniques offered for visually analysing their own data. It also allowed the visualization team to learn more about existing means of analysing the data, to get feedback from the domain users on the prototypes presented, and the kinds of questions that the domain users wanted to be able to answer of their data.

The patient satisfaction survey data represented patients' responses to a telephone survey for each of the patient touch points and the patient's overall satisfaction with their episode of care. The patient survey data consisted almost exclusively of categorical variables. Parallel Sets [1, 6] and Mosaic Plots [5, 16, 17] are suited for this type of data [14] and these were the techniques chosen for presentation at this workshop.

The Domain Visualization Workshop was facilitated by an information visualization expert and attended by domain users from Quality department. Parallel Sets 2.1 (Parsets [6]) and JMP 8 (a SAS proprietary tool used to visualise mosaic plots) were used to visualize the patient satisfaction survey data.

The visualization team elicited feedback from the users about how they perceived the way they interacted with the prototypes, and the way their domain data was visualized. This was done through initiating discussions at appropriate points during the presentation and observational note-taking. The users liked the fact that these techniques allowed them to interactively explore their own data in new ways. They were able to see relationships between variables in their data that were not provided by the static reports they had been using. Users also suggested additional features that they would find helpful, that were partly informed by the Visualization Awareness Workshop. One such request was the ability to be able to drill-down to obtain details on demand, a capability not available in the applications that we were using.

After interacting with both the parallel sets and mosaic plots prototypes, domain experts expressed a preference for parallel sets prototype as compared to mosaic plots. The indication was that the parallel sets was deemed simpler and hence faster for users to understand. We might hypothesize that the parallel layout of this approach simplifies reading and comparison of the data dimensions, compared to the nested structure of mosaic plots. Participants in the workshop seemed to find it easier to conceptualize questions about their data, and to co-relate 3 or more data dimensions using parallel sets than mosaic plots through our prototypes.

At the end of the workshop, users indicated that they were enthusiastic about the prospect of now interactively exploring their domain data in ways previously not available to them. They were keen to continue working with the visualization team to design an information visualization solution based on the parallel sets prototype for use in their work domain. They had also begun to suggest broad ideas about the kinds of questions information visualization tools could help them answer as we began to capture requirements.

4.3 Work Domain Analysis

The visualization team held Work Domain Analysis sessions with domain experts to formally gather their requirements for an interactive visualization system. This was done through structured discussion to elicit the questions they would like answered using interactive visualizations. The following questions were prioritised:

- *What impact does 'very poor' (or alternatively 'excellent') satisfaction index at specific patient touch-points (Figure 5) have on the overall satisfaction index for each of the hospital department (Emergency Department, Specialist Clinics and Inpatient Wards)?* Users would like to verify whether particular touch-points perceived as main draws for patient complaints (or alternatively bouquets) are key contributors to the impact on overall satisfaction index for the healthcare institution;

- *Which days of the week, and peak hours for patient visits/admissions have greater impact on satisfaction index for specific patient touch-points?* To provide a feedback loop back to resource planning staff to improve patient's experience at service delivery touch-points even during busy periods;

- *How do the various touch-points within each of the hospital departments relate in terms of the department's overall satisfaction index?* To show how patients perceive service delivery by each touch-point within the department;

- *How can patients' free-text comments be used to back-up the results derived for patient satisfaction at the touch-points of each department?* Patient surveys may include (optional) patients' comments about each touch-point. Users would like to analyse comments for keywords that may lend support or clarify aspects of patients' satisfaction with service delivery.

5 DISCUSSION

We observed a number of benefits associated with early prototyping and the use of Visualization Awareness and Domain Visualization Workshops. In terms of successes:

- Domain users were able to relate the information visualization concepts and techniques to their current work and immediate needs within their work domain as a result of participating in a Visualization Awareness Workshop;

- Leading on from the previous point, domain users coming forward with their ideas on how information visualization concepts could be applied to their domain areas, in turn could lead to the identification of potential information visualization projects for an organization that is considering the incorporation of the use of information visualization tools into the organization;

- The Domain Visualization Workshop enabled domain users to better understand information visualization concepts that could be used to visualize the data as well as to enabling the developers to gain a better understanding of the problem domain – these findings are in line with those of [3];

- Our data owners became more demanding of their data and used ideas developed through the workshops to look for more sophisticated relationships in the data that they currently own – importantly demonstrating that our approach has an ongoing effect on analytical process.

We did observe some problems however in the case of domain experts who do not have experience of visualization:

- Whilst ideas about visualization were forthcoming at our workshops, participants were somewhat limited in their visualization aspirations and there was a tendency to select functionality that existed in data prototypes used during our Domain Visualization Workshop;
- Using existing (polished) software as *data prototypes* for domain visualization does not emphasize the preliminary nature of the designs and the prototypical (in terms of the visualization development project) nature of the methods being considered. Consequently participants were focused on tool rather than data at the initial interactions with visualization tools.

We consider the benefits reported here to be encouraging. Both concerns could be addressed either in the Domain Visualization Workshop or through feedback loops within the Problem Domain stages of our approach, to allow users to augment their knowledge as they experience and gain familiarity with visualization prototypes.

6 CONCLUSION

We modify Robinson *et al.*'s user-centered approach [12] to the design, development and implementation of information visualization applications in the context of work with potential users with little knowledge of visualization techniques. Our modification introduces *Domain Visualization* and *Visualization Awareness* Workshops early in the process and incorporates some of Roth *et al.*'s ideas about using prototypes [13] at this stage of user-centred design in visualization. These modifications are designed to enable those lacking experience in visualization to participate as informed users in UCD. They are also applicable to those with more experience and can help domain experts participate more effectively and to help build understanding and knowledge between those with domain knowledge and needs and those with visualization knowledge and capabilities.

We are applying this process to users in a government healthcare institution in Singapore. This pilot study is still in progress, but we are able to report on the Problem Domain Analysis stage.

Our reflections on the implementation suggest that the model has impact because:

- It informed domain users about a range of possibilities for visual analysis and equipped them to take an active part the process. They were able to suggest ways that these concepts could apply to their data and their problems that drew upon visualization to consider their data more comprehensively;
- It educated the visualization experts about domain-specific data, the questions of those data that the domain users find interesting and how receptive they are unfamiliar techniques;
- It engaged the domain users to take an active part in the process, evidenced by the further meetings that they called after the Visualization Awareness Workshop;
- It promoted trust between the domain users and visualization experts, enabling free and frank discussion at the workshops.

We observed that users new to information visualization, focused on tools rather than on questions about their data; and brought up ideas and questions about their data that were limited to what they had experienced in the prototypes used in the Domain Visualization Workshop. We believed that these issues could be addressed with iterations within the stages of the Problem Domain Analysis of our approach, where users could further expand the coverage of and

experience interaction with various prototypes and by structuring activities and presenting software in ways that emphasize this.

Future work will include development and deployment of a customized information visualization application using experiences and requirements derived from the Problem Domain Analysis stage of the pilot study to inform subsequent stages of the model.

REFERENCES

[1] F. Bendix, R. Kosara, and H. Hauser, "Parallel Sets: Visual Analysis of Categorical Data," in In INFOVIS '05: Proceedings of the Proceedings of the 2005 IEEE Symposium on Information Visualization (2005), 2005.

[2] M. Bostock and J. Heer, "ProtoVis: A Graphical Toolkit for Visualization", IEEE Transactions on Visualization and Computer Graphics, 2009 Nov-Dec, vol. 15, no. 6, pp 1121-1128, Dec 2009.

[3] J. Dykes, J. Wood, and A. Slingsby, "Rethinking Map Legends with Visualization," IEEE Transactions on Visualization and Computer Graphics, 2010 Nov-Dec, vol. 16, no. 6, pp. 890-899, Dec. 2010.

[4] I. R. Floyd, M. C. Jones, D. Rathi, M. B. Twidale, "Web Mash-ups and Patchwork Prototyping: User-driven technological innovation with Web 2.0 and Open Source Software," hicss, pp.86c, 40th Annual Hawaii International Conference on System Sciences (HICSS'07), 2007

[5] M. Friendly, "Visualizing categorical data: Data, stories, and pictures," in SAS User Group International Conference Proceedings, pp. 190–200, 1992.

[6] R. Kosara, F. Bendix, and H. Hauser, "Parallel Sets: Interactive Exploration and Visual Analysis of Categorical Data," IEEE Transactions on Visualization and Computer Graphics, vol. 12, no. 4, pp. 558-568, 2006.

[7] D. Lloyd, "Evaluating human-centered approaches to geovisualization," City University London, 2010.

[8] J. Nielsen, "Usability engineering". Boston, Massachusetts: Academic Press, Inc., 1993.

[9] D. Norman, "The design of everyday things." New York: Basic Books, 2002.

[10] C. Plaisant, "The challenge of information visualization evaluation," Proceedings of the working conference on Advanced visual interfaces, Gallipoli, Italy: ACM New York, NY, USA, pp. 109 – 116, 2004.

[11] C. Reas and B. Fry, "Processing: a learning environment for creating interactive Web graphics", ACM SIGGRAPH 2003 Web Graphics, San Diego, CA; ACM New York, NY, USA, 2003.

[12] A. C. Robinson, J. Chen, E. J. Lengerich, H. G. Meyer, and A. M. MacEachren, "Combining Usability Techniques to Design Geovisualization Tools for Epidemiology," Cartography and Geographic Information Science, vol. 32, no. 4, pp. 243–255, 2005.

[13] R. E. Roth, K. S. Ross, B. G. Finch, W. Luo, and A. M. MacEachren, "A user-centered approach for designing and developing spatiotemporal crime analysis tools," in Sixth international conference on Geographic Information Science, 2010.

[14] R. Scheaffer and N. Yes, "Categorical Data Analysis," NCSSM Statistics Leadership Institute, 1999.

[15] T.A. Slocum, D.C. Cliburn, J.J. Feddema, and J.R. Miller, "Evaluating the usability of a tool for visualizing the uncertainty of the future global water balance," Cartography and Geographic Information Science, vol. 30, pp. 299-314, 2003.

[16] M. Theus, "Interactive data visualization using mondrian," Journal of Statistical Software, vol. 7, no. 11, pp. 1–9, 2003.

[17] M. Theus and S. R. Lauer, "Visualizing loglinear models," Journal of Computational and Graphical Statistics, vol. 8, no. 3, pp. 396–412, 1999.

[18] J.S. Yi, Y. Kang, J.T. Stasko, and J.A. Jacko, "Toward a deeper understanding of the Role of Interaction in Information Visualization," Journal of Transactions on Visualization and Computer Graphic, vol. 13, no. 6, pp. 1124–1231, 2007.

Method to design coordinated multiple views adapted to user's business requirements in 4D collaborative tools in AEC.

Conrad Boton[1,2], Sylvain Kubicki[1], Gilles Halin[2]
[1]Henri Tudor Public Research Center, [2]Research Centre in Architecture and Engineering
{conrad.boton@tudor.lu, sylvain.kubicki@tudor.lu, gilles.halin@crai.archi.fr}

Abstract

The issue of multiple views coordination became more and more challenging in the architecture, engineering and construction (AEC) field since the apparition and the increasing success of 4D/nD CAD. In order to adapt visualization to user's business requirements in 4D-supported collaborative tools, this paper propose a method to design coordinated multiple views based on Model-Driven Engineering (MDE). The method enables user's visualization needs description, visualization modes comparison. The aim is to choose appropriate visualization modes business needs, to associate interaction principles and coordination mechanisms in order to compose coordinated multiple views adapted to actor's business needs. The paper presents a case study based on literature review and interviews with construction sector practitioners.

Keywords--- **AEC, 4D CAD, Coordinated Multiple Views, Visualization modeling, Model-Driven Engineering, CSCW, Business views**.

1. Introduction

Coordinated multiple views (CMV) are increasingly used since their introduction and several studies have been conducted to improve their use [1-4]. But in some complex and highly collaborative fields like architecture, engineering and construction (AEC), the use of CMV deserves special attention. A major issue concerns the adaptation of views to user's business requirements in such fields. Indeed, in the construction sector, each actor usually has a specific role which follows from the partner's primary business field. It usually results in specific views used for representing building-related information [5]. Moreover, several representation modes can represent the same concepts and actors choose one or the other of these modes according to their specific needs related to the tasks they have to achieve. Then, adapting visualization to user's business needs in collaborative work supporting tools implies being able to choose the best visualization modes and to associate to them the

most appropriate interaction and coordination mechanisms in order to design adapted multiple views.

Since the increasingly growing success of simulation tools based on 4D CAD (that associates a 3D view and a temporal view), the issue of multiple views composition and coordination becomes more and more important in the construction sector.

The following work relies both on Information Visualization and Human-Computer Interaction theories. It proposes a method to compose and coordinate adapted multiple views for users of 4D-based collaborative tools in construction projects.

2. 4D multiple views issue in AEC sector

The concept "multiple views" in general describes visualizations where multiple windows are used to represent data [6]. So, "a multiple view system uses two or more distinct views to support the investigation of a single conceptual entity" [1]. Many current windowing environments treat windows as independent and isolated, and users have to manipulate individually one window at a time, even when some contents or tasks are common among the windows [7]. But we will use "coordinated multiple views" when operations on the views are coordinated [6]. In this case, the same or different portions of the data can be displayed by windows and these windows can be tightly coordinated in "a variety of ways such that interacting with one component causes meaningful effects in others" [2]. So, coordination ensures that changes in one window are propagated to all other views keeping the analyzed data consistent [8]. In designing user interfaces, multiple window coordination is more and more effective [9] and CMV strategies are gradually more used in visualization and interfaces [7].

An important capability enhanced by coordination in Information Visualization is about flexibility regarding data; selection of a type of visualization mode for a given set of data; and coordination characteristics definition [8].

The Architecture, Engineering and Construction (AEC) industry is characterized by "its loose organization of the different participants that each perform a specific role in a building project and have a

1550-6037/11 $26.00 © 2011 IEEE
DOI 10.1109/IV.2011.15

specific view on the building project data" [5]. So, if the whole lifecycle of construction project can be covered by computer visualization usage [10], it has to support the highly collaborative aspect of the project. Indeed, in the sector, each discipline has to process a large amount of information related to the representation of a design object between disciplines. And from a stage to another, actors need to represent and share different kinds of information with various levels of abstraction [11]. Moreover, as we said, in the AEC field, several visualization modes can represent the same concept and actors choose one or the other of these modes according to their specific needs related to the task they have to perform. Indeed, cooperation assistance tools have to integrate interfaces that take into account the existence and the specificity of "business-views". "Business views" are the visualization modes that practitioners use in their daily work [12]. For example, tasks planning may be represented by a Gantt chart or by a PERT network and building elements can be depicted with a 3D model or a 2D plan. So to support the collaborative aspect of AEC projects, multiple views systems have to be adapted to users' business requirements and views have to be chosen wisely.

With the rise of 4D CAD as a reference simulation tool in the sector, the issue of coordination of multiple views becomes more important. 4D CAD consists in linking a 3D view of the building to a time view (works planning) to simulate the building construction over the time. Such visualizations respond to the four design rules related to diversity, complementarity, parsimony, and decomposition proposed by [1] about when to use multiple views.

The use of 4D simulation tools has a real impact in construction projects ([13]; [14]) and more recently, [15] showed that the collaborative use of 4D CAD is particularly useful during the pre-construction phase for comparing the constructability of working methods, for visually identifying conflicts and clashes (overlaps), and

as visual tool for contractors, subcontractors and suppliers to discuss and to plan project progress. But in the framework of this collaborative use, the adaptation of 4D multi-views to users' business requirements remains a challenging issue since the classical view (3D + Gantt) usually proposed to all practitioners in most of the current 4D tools seems not suiting the needs of every actors and situations of use.

In the next section, we propose a method aiming at designing adapted business multiple views for 4D collaborative tools in AEC sector.

3. Method to design adapted 4D coordinated and multiple views

3.1. The method's steps

We propose a multi-steps method to adapt visualization to actor's business needs in collaborative work supporting tools.

- The first step identifies the business needs of actors. This consists in formalizing the collaborative practices in order to identify the sub-practices performed by the different involved actors. Knowing these sub-practices helps to better define the business needs.
- In the framework of these collaborative practices, actors use groupware to perform their business activities. During these activities, we can identify specific usages that we have to understand and describe. The purpose of the second step is to determine the visualization needs for each actor. This step also highlights the actor's interactions and visualization tasks related to business practices. At this stage we use the taxonomy proposed by [16] to describe such visualization tasks with a single and accurate formalism (Fig. 2).

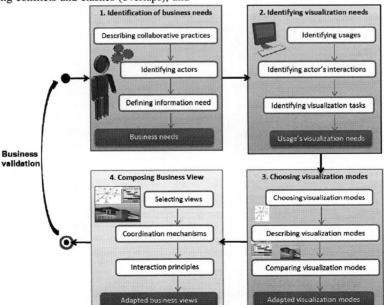

Figure 1: Method to compose business view

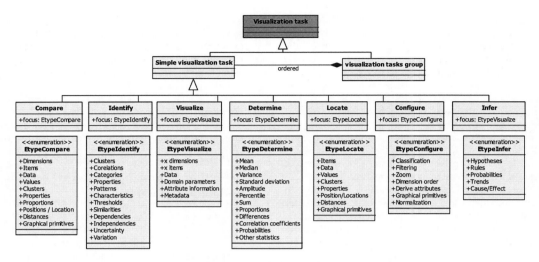

Figure 2: User's visualization tasks metamodel

- After visualization needs known, it is then possible to compare the possible visualization modes in order to choose the most appropriate in relation to the expressed needs. This is the subject of the third step in which the visualization modes are described and compared.
- When appropriate modes are selected for each actor, one can select those that may be composed together to form multiple coordinated views. To this end, it is important to study the coordination mechanisms and the interaction principles associated with the visualization modes (fourth step). At the end of this step, adapted business views are composed for each actor.

These views will then be validated to ensure that the propositions respond effectively to the expressed business needs. Fig. 1 depicts the steps of the method.

Model Driven Engineering (MDE) approach recommends the use of metamodels to define domain languages, so each model has to conform to its metamodel. In order to model visualization modes and to choose the most adapted ones, we propose to adapt and use the business view metamodel described in [17].

3.2. Formula for visualization modes ranking

We are working on a scoring system that would rank visualization modes according to usage needs. By assessing the criteria (technique, content, interaction principle, visualization tasks, etc.) an *adaptation score* (As) should be assigned to each visualization mode. This score is calculated for each actor and each sub-practice with the formula below. So, the relevance of a criterion is related to the information needs and to the visualization tasks.

$$As = \frac{\sum_{i=1}^{n} Nc_i}{n} \quad \text{with } Nc_i = \frac{\sum_{j=1}^{m} P_j}{m}$$

The score (Nc_i) of a criterion i is then the sum of its properties relevance (P_j) scores according to a visualization requirement. The visualization requirement is both an information need and a need for visualization tasks. Nc may vary between -1 and 1.

3.5. Composing coordinated multiple views

Exploration techniques and coordination control are two of the fundamental areas of coordinated and multiple views [6]. The utility of multiple coordinated views comes from users' ability to express multidimensional queries through simple forms of interaction [18]. To compose coordinated views, we use the eight guidelines proposed by [1] for the design of multiple view systems and the 2x3 taxonomy of multiple window coordination from [19]. Relied on these references and the state of the art proposed by [6], we are working to propose a metamodel of multi-views composition. This metamodel will take into account notions related to multiple views generation, exploration techniques, coordination and control, human interface and usability and perception.

4. Case study

We consider a case study related to site preparation collaborative context and apply our method to a specific collaborative practice: "Collaborative site scheduling". The case study is established on the basis of literature review and various interviews conducted. Indeed, we interviewed six practitioners with different roles from Luxembourg construction sector, in order to understand their common activities in the pre-construction framework and to better formalize the applied issue of this work. In this realistic case study we assume that in a given situation some actors are responsible for each of the sub-practices shown on table 1.

4.1. Step 1: Identifying business needs

For the case study, we show in table 1 the result of the first step. The sub-practices which will be performed are known such as the associated responsible actors. The information needs are also identified. We see that to list building elements, the architect needs to visualize the building representation and a pre-list of building elements. The supervisor needs a work breakdown structure (WBS) and a pre-list of construction activities, to define activities and the activities planning to develop the schedule. To estimate activities duration, sub-contractors will need the description on these activities while the contactor will have to visualize dates, activities durations and a building representation to create the activities sequences.

Sub-practices	Responsible actors	Information need
Building elements listing	Architect	Pre-list of building elements, building representation
Activities definition	Supervisor	WBS, pre-list of construction activities
Activities duration estimation	Sub-contractors	Activities description
Activities sequencing	Contractor	Dates, activities durations, building representation
Schedule development	Supervisor	Activities planning

Table 1: collaborative site scheduling practice

But this is not sufficient enough to choose appropriate visualization modes. It is necessary to add the visualization tasks to be sure to take into account the actor's visualization needs.

4.2. Step 2: Identifying visualization tasks

After understanding the context of the CP, the method's step 2 aims at identifying the visualization tasks the actors will have to perform. For this, sub-practices are divided into elementary usages that will call for specific visualization tasks. The visualization tasks model will help us in this description as shown in table 2.

We see that to list building elements, as visualization tasks, architect will need to *visualize data, locate items*, and *configure classifications*. The activities definition will lead to *visualize data, locate items, identify correlation* and *configure classification*. To estimate activities duration, sub-contractors have to *visualize data, configure filtering, determine means* and *infer hypotheses*. For activities sequencing, contractor will *visualize data, identify correlations and dependencies, infer trends, configure classifications* and *configure normalization*. The schedule development requires visualizing data, identifying correlations, inferring trends and configuring classification.

Sub-practices	Elementary usages	Visualization tasks
Building elements listing	Consult elements pre-list	*Visualize* (focus: *data*)
	Find appropriate elements	*Locate* (focus: *items*)
	Create elements listing	*Configure* (focus: *classification*)
Activities definition	Consult activities pre-list	*Visualize* (focus: *data*)
	Consult building elements	*Locate* (focus: *items*)
	Identify appropriate activities	*Identify* (focus: *correlations*)
	Create activities listing	*Configure* (focus: *classification*)
Activities duration estimation	Consult activities	*Visualize* (focus: *data*)
	Understand activities consistency	*Configure* (focus: *filtering*) *Determine* (focus: *means*)
	Estimate activities duration	*Infer* (focus: *hypotheses*)
Activities sequencing	Consult activities and durations	*Visualize* (focus: *data*)
	Study relationships and dependencies among activities	*Identify* (focus: *correlations*) *Identify* (focus: *dependencies*)
	Verify conflicts	*Infer* (focus: *trends*)
	Associate start/end dates	*Configure* (focus: *classification*)
	Define site planning	*Configure* (focus: *normalization*)
Schedule development	Consult activities listing	*Visualize* (focus: *data*)
	Consult actors listing	*Visualize* (focus: *data*)
	Associate actors and activities	*Identify* (focus: *correlations*)
	Include planning	*Infer* (focus: *trends*)
	Realize project plan	*Configure* (focus: *classification*)

Table 2: Actors' visualization tasks

After this step, the exact information that actors need to visualize and their visualization tasks are known. For each information need, many visualization modes may be possible. It is necessary to compare them in order to choose the best adapted ones according to actor's visualization tasks.

4.3. Step 3: Choosing adapted visualization modes

In this step, the business view metamodel (ref section) is used to describe the possible visualization modes for every expressed visualization need. In instance, for the sub-practice "Activities sequencing", actor need to visualize the dates, the activities durations and a building representation. The building representation could be a 2D plan or a 3D representation (Fig. 4). It is then necessary to describe these two visualization modes in order to compare them.

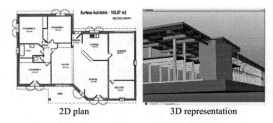

	2D plan	3D representation

Figure 3: Some visualization modes

Table 3 shows a comparison between these two visualization modes that could be used to represent building elements. For example, 3D representation is easy to understand and more attractive than 2D plan. More interactions are possible with 3D representations than with 2D plan. At the contrary, 2D representation is widely known and used compared to 3D.

	3D representation	2D plan
Technique structure	3D	2D
Graphical elements	Volumes	Lines, surfaces
Retinal attributes	Size, Shape, Colors, Form	Size, texture, Form
Known level	Very known	Very known
Business use level	Quite used	Very used
Data Nature	Physical Data	Physical data
Data spatiality	Spatial	Spatial
Temporality	No temporal	No temporal
Comprehensibility	Easy	Difficult
Concrete-Abstract	Concrete	Abstract
Attractivity	Attractive	Less attractive
Focus	Emphasizes whole	Emphasizes parts
Numericity	Non numeric	Non numeric
Dynamism	Static	Static
Possible interactions	Interactive zoom, Dynamic projection, Interactive deformation, Link&Brush	Interactive zoom, Interactive filtering, Link&Brush

Table 3: Visualization modes description

Using the adaptation score formula (table 4), we can establish that 3D representation is better suiting this sub-practice. The score in Table 4 are not validated yet and future works will focus on it and, more generally, on practitioner's evaluation of business views according to our criteria and their experience. Same work for each other sub-practices will lead to know which visualization modes are appropriate. So, for each actor, all visualization modes needed to achieve his usage are known.

Criteria	Proprieties	3D rep.	2D plan
Technique	Structure	0	-1
	Graphical elements	1	0
	Retinal attributes	1	0
	Business use	0	1
	Nc_1	0,5	0
Content	Data Format	1	1
	Mental perception	0	-1
	Data nature	0	-1
	Nc_2	0,33	-0,33
Interaction principles	Interaction level	1	-1
	Interaction type	0	-1
	Nc_3	0,5	-1
Visualization tasks	Visualisation tasks	1	0
	Nc_4	1	0
	As	0,58	- 0,33

Table 4: Visualization modes adaptation scores

4.4. Step 4: Composing adapted business multi-visualization

After selecting adapted visualization modes, a 4D tool designer would have to make sure that chosen views are compatible. This is the aim of the step 4, and we are still working on it. We will associate appropriate exploration techniques and coordination mechanism according to the needs of each actor. That will lead to a relevant collaborative 4D tool with adapted human interfaces. For example, within the case study, the resulting multiple views could be a "3D+Gantt" visualization for the architect, a "zoomed 3D+Gantt" view with a focus on zoom for contractors and subcontractors, and a "3D + Pert" view for supervisor.

We are still working to improve this step of the method, in order to have better 4D multiple views guidelines or patterns to support it.

Conclusions

The paper presents a method to design coordinated multiple views for 4D-based collaborative tools in order to adapt visualization to user's business needs. The metamodels that support the method are also presented and a case study showed how to use these method and models.

Future works will consolidate the method and a tool will be developed to support it. Both the tool and the method will be validated through confronting it to real business situations.

Acknowledgements

This article was supported by an AFR PhD Grant funded by the National Research Fund (FNR), Luxembourg.

References

[1] M.Q. Wang Baldonado, A. Woodruff, and A. Kuchinsky, "Guidelines for using multiple views in information visualization," *AVI '00: Proceedings of the working conference on Advanced visual interfaces*, New York, NY, USA: ACM, 2000, pp. 110-119.

[2] C. North, N. Conklin, K. Indukuri, and V. Saini, "Visualization schemas and a web-based architecture for custom multiple-view visualization of multiple-table databases," *Information Visualization*, vol. 1, 2002, pp. 211-228.

[3] A. Becks and C. Seeling, "SWAPit: a multiple views paradigm for exploring associations of texts and structured data," *AVI□04: Proceedings of the working conference on Advanced visual interfaces*, 2004, pp. 193-196.

[4] W. Berger and H. Piringer, "Peek Brush: A High-Speed Lightweight Ad-Hoc Selection for Multiple Coordinated Views," *2010 14th International Conference Information Visualisation*, Jul. 2010, pp. 140-145.

[5] G.A. van Nederveen and F.P. Tolman, "Modelling multiple views on buildings," *Automation in Construction*, vol. 1, 1992, pp. 215-224.

[6] J.C. Roberts, "State of the Art: Coordinated & Multiple Views in Exploratory Visualization," *Fifth International Conference on Coordinated and Multiple Views in Exploratory Visualization (CMV 2007)*, Jul. 2007, pp. 61-71.

[7] C. North and B. Shneiderman, "A Taxonomy of Multiple Window Coordinations," 1997.

[8] C. North and B. Shneiderman, "Snap-Together Visualization: Can Users Construct and Operate Coordinated Visualizations?," 2000.

[9] B. Shneiderman, *Designing the user interface: strategies for effective human-computer interaction*, Boston, MA, USA: Addison-Wesley Longman Publishing Co., 1997.

[10] D. Bouchlaghem, H. Shang, J. Whyte, and a Ganah, "Visualisation in architecture, engineering and construction (AEC)," *Automation in Construction*, vol. 14, Jun. 2005, pp. 287-295.

[11] M. Rosenman and J. Gero, "Modelling multiple views of design objects in a collaborative environment," *Computer-Aided Design*, vol. 28, Mar. 1996, pp. 193-205.

[12] S. Kubicki, G. Halin, and A. Guerriero, "Multi-visualization of the Cooperative Context in Building Construction Activity A Model-Based Approach to design AEC-specific Visualization Interfaces," *2007 11th International Conference Information Visualization (IV '07)*, Jul. 2007, pp. 590-595.

[13] S. Staub-French and A. Khanzode, "3D and 4D modeling for design and construction coordination: issues and lessons learned," *ITcon*, vol. vol. 12, 2007, pp. 381-407.

[14] N. Dawood and S. Sikka, "Measuring the effectiveness of 4D planning as a valuable communication tool," *ITcon Vol. 13, Special Issue Virtual and Augmented Reality in Design and Construction, http://www.itcon.org/2008/39*, 2008, pp. pg. 620-636.

[15] A. Mahalingam, R. Kashyap, and C. Mahajan, "An evaluation of the applicability of 4D CAD on construction projects," *Automation in Construction*, vol. 19, 2010, pp. 148-159.

[16] E.R.A. Valiati, M.S. Pimenta, and C.M.D.S. Freitas, "A taxonomy of tasks for guiding the evaluation of multidimensional visualizations," *BELIV '06: Proceedings of the 2006 AVI workshop on BEyond time and errors*, New York, NY, USA: ACM, 2006, pp. 1-6.

[17] C. Boton, S. Kubicki, and G. Halin, "Adaptation of user views to business requirements : towards adaptive views models," *Proceedings of IHM 2010, the 22th International Francophone Conference on Human-Computer Interaction*, Luxembourg: ACM, 2010, pp. 113-116.

[18] C. Weaver, "Look Before You Link: Eye Tracking in Multiple Coordinated View Visualization," *BELIV□10: BEyond time and errors: novel evaLuation methods for Information Visualization.*, Atlanta, GA, USA: 2010, p. 2 p.

[19] C. North and B. Shneiderman, *A Taxonomy of Multiple Window Coordinations*, 1997.

Evaluation of Parallel Coordinates for Interactive Alarm Filtering

Saad Bin Azhar and Mikko J. Rissanen
Industrial Software Systems
ABB Corporate Research
Västerås, Sweden
Email: {*saad.azhar, mikko.rissanen*}@*se.abb.com*

Abstract—Alarm management is a crucial part of many industrial systems used in generation, transmission and distribution of electric power as well as in production processes, for example in steel mills and oil refineries. Filtering of important alarms from unessential alarms is a critical task for operators of such systems, since failures may result in severe abnormal situations such as plant shutdowns. Currently, alarm filtering tasks are performed with alarm lists that offer limited interactivity. We evaluated an application of Parallel Coordinates for interactive filtering of alarm data by comparing its user performance against typical alarm lists. Statistical results demonstrate marginally significant evidence ($p<0.1$) for easy and moderate tasks while there is a highly significant evidence ($p<0.01$) for difficult tasks that Parallel Coordinates reduce alarm filtering time. Furthermore, Parallel Coordinates were found to reduce human mistakes.

Keywords-Evaluation; Parallel Coordinates; Alarm Management;

I. INTRODUCTION

Industrial processes or automation systems for utilities like electricity, gas, and heating or production plants for paper, steel and chemicals run into numerous abnormal situations every day. These abnormal situations have to be rectified for reliable and non-disruptive operation of utilities and production processes. An abnormal situation in such industrial applications is reported as "Alarms" which are information about the upset or abnormal conditions in the process. Alarms contain information such as the place the alarm occurred - a device or section of the plant - the description of the alarm - the actual problem - and other parameters like priority, category and time of occurrence.

Alarm management is the core of such industrial applications. Good alarm management is the key to ensuring safe and normal operations. Over time, processes and requirements in the industry change, this can result in alarms that have never been seen before. This reinforces the need for proper alarm management in such processes. [1]

Alarm management has many aspects, among which visualization of alarms holds much importance. Traditionally, alarms have been represented as lists typically referred to as Alarm Lists. This is mainly because legacy systems from the beginning of the digital era have always contained such representation of alarms. Though these lists serve as a good consolidated view of the alarms, they do not have a sense of trend or correlation in the alarms' data.

There are a high volume of alarms in today's industrial processes which have to be analyzed in order to identify patterns in these processes and especially anomalies in them. Alarms must be visualized in a manner which indicates problems by means of pointing out temporal as well as other non-temporal parameters of these alarms. Interesting patterns can be identified if the different parameters can be compared together to find correlations in the alarm data. A visualization technique which supports this kind of visual analysis of data are the Parallel Coordinates [2], [3].

This study focuses on the use of Parallel Coordinates for alarm management. The objective was to find results which either reject or support the use of interactive Parallel Coordinates as an effective, efficient and intuitive visualization method for analysis of alarm data. Two visualizations namely, Alarm List and Parallel Coordinates were evaluated to see if use of one method is advantageous over the other.

A. Alarm Management in Industrial Processes

Industrial processes for manufacturing, electricity generation and distribution, production, mining, refining and other processes dealing with real-time data acquisition and control, usually have a means of alarm management. Alarm management solutions can be as simple as lists or more advanced solutions that allow filtering and visualization of alarms in different ways for pattern identification for example Parallel Coordinates. The EEMUA guidelines on design, management and procurement of alarm systems define the sophistication of an alarm management system based on different factors among which the number of alarms is one factor [4]. Depending upon the application domain and its scope, the number of alarms in an alarm management system can range from a couple of hundreds to thousands at a time.

Applications like the one presented in Figure 1 have one main purpose, to present all the important parameters upfront and keep the operator informed about the processes' abnormal states i.e., alarms. This is a challenging task because of the large number of events occurring in such processes. These events could range from malfunctioning equipment to level of a tank's contents to temperature in

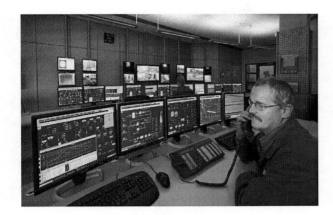

Figure 1. Alarm management in a process control application. The area on top of the screens in front of the operator show red blocks indicating alarms and part of the alarm list.

a furnace. Industries need to be able to visualize and filter important alarms from the rest of the alarms for purpose of complying with process requirements on production, safety and quality. [5]

B. Interactive Filtering and Visual Pattern Identification of Alarms

When analyzing alarms from an industrial process, not only is the volume of alarms very large, but there are several parameters within these alarms that need to be monitored. Data about the states of different parts of the process comes in every few seconds and it needs to be observed and acted upon to ensure error-free operation.

The operators should be able to pinpoint trouble areas and important events that occur while the process is running. Equipping the operators to filter out unwanted data helps in focusing on the more important and critical data related to alarms. Additionally, enabling the operators to visually identify patterns that show trends in the alarm data and analyze relationships inferred from these trends, critical information about the process can be revealed. This information can then facilitate maintenance and troubleshooting in industrial processes.

A visual pattern represents a typical behavior which shows the progress of certain process parameters over time. For instance, a certain alarm occurring at a particular time of day or at repeated intervals. However, a rather different and interesting pattern could be the relation between two parameters and how they affect each other and the overall process. For example, a particular type of alarm is always followed by another known alarm or, manual operation results in more high priority alarms. Among the two types of patterns mentioned, the latter is comparatively difficult to identify. Such patterns are usually not visible in lists unless the data is visualized in a way other than lists which supports identification of patterns. Visualizing such relationships could lead to better awareness about the processes' state and facilitate better decision making.

C. Alarm Lists vs. Parallel Coordinates

The Alarm List in Figure 2 shows the existing and typical way of representing alarms in the system. This list is typically very long depending upon the time of day, week, month or year and the nature of operations being carried out. While the number of alarms on a display can be reduced to some extent by means of shelving, suppressing and state-based alarming (see [1], [4]), the alarm lists are inherently incapable of visualizing patterns and relationships in the data. A study on comparison of tabular and graphical displays [6] indicates that lists or tabular visualization of data are not suitable of tasks like trend analysis, interpolation and forecasting as compared to graphical visualizations. However, the study also indicated that lists are better at identifying specific values than doing trend analysis as compared to graphical displays. The reason alarms lists have been in use for so long is because they have traditionally been best practices for displaying alarms. However, with the increased number of alarms in the current industrial applications due to changing requirements, better methods of visualizing and managing alarms are needed.

Category	Date	Time	Priority	Type	Message	Acknowledge
Power	2/24/2011	12:53 PM	1	MeasuredValue	Power Line load above 95% - restoring state	False
Controller	2/24/2011	12:53 PM	6	SpontaneousBreakerTrip	I/O unit failure - unable to recover	False
Power	2/24/2011	12:53 PM	6	MeasuredValue	Authorization failure code #536 - restoring state	False
General	2/24/2011	12:53 PM	1	SpontaneousBreakerTrip	Power Line load above 95% - error limit reached	False
General	2/24/2011	11:32 AM	2	MeasuredValue	Authorization failure code #653 - error limit reached	False
Controller	2/24/2011	8:35 AM	3	MeasuredValue	Breaker open failure - error limit reached	False
General	2/24/2011	8:10 AM	3	MeasuredValue	Threshold value 81 reached - unable to recover	False
Station	2/24/2011	7:14 AM	6	HighPriorityAlarms	Threshold value 10 reached - unable to recover	False
I/O	2/24/2011	5:39 AM	6	MeasuredValue	Breaker open failure - restoring state	False
Controller	2/24/2011	5:18 AM	3	HighPriorityAlarms	Breaker open failure - restoring state	False
Controller	2/24/2011	5:01 AM	5	HighPriorityAlarms	Power Line load above 95% - restoring state	False
General	2/24/2011	4:38 AM	6	HighPriorityAlarms	Breaker open failure - unable to recover	False
General	2/24/2011	4:24 AM	6	HighPriorityAlarms	Breaker open failure - alarm severity elevated	False
General	2/24/2011	3:57 AM	2	HighPriorityAlarms	Threshold value 34 reached - restoring state	False
Power	2/24/2011	3:33 AM	4	HighPriorityAlarms	I/O unit failure - error limit reached	False
Station	2/24/2011	3:30 AM	2	HighPriorityAlarms	Breaker open failure - restoring state	False
Controller	2/24/2011	3:25 AM	5	Protection	Threshold value 63 reached - unable to recover	False
General	2/24/2011	2:24 AM	5	HighPriorityAlarms	Authorization failure code #685 - unable to recover	False
Controller	2/24/2011	2:14 AM	4	Indications	Authorization failure code #983 - error limit reached	False
Station	2/24/2011	1:26 AM	4	MeasuredValue	Breaker open failure - alarm severity elevated	False
General	2/23/2011	9:41 PM	4	HighPriorityAlarms	I/O unit failure - error limit reached	False
Power	2/23/2011	9:27 PM	5	HighPriorityAlarms	Breaker open failure - unable to recover	False

Figure 2. A typical alarm list. A row in the list represents an alarm and each column corresponds to one or more attributes of the alarm.

Knowing the weaknesses and strengths of lists in terms of visual trend analysis, interpolation, forecasting and identification of specific values, the use of Parallel Coordinates together with lists was suggested as a means of filtering alarm data and identifying patterns visually [7]. As the concept is proposed earlier, this study sought to answer the following research question:

Do Parallel Coordinates improve filtering of alarms in terms of visual pattern identification and trend analysis?

A prototype application has been developed which includes a Parallel Coordinates plot as well as an Alarm List. Filtering and selection techniques were implemented in both the visualizations. There are seven different parameters in the Parallel Coordinates visualization that could be filtered with the help of slider controls in the user interface. The lines passing through the axes in Figure 3 represent the same alarms as in Figure 2 . Moving the sliders up and down on the axes filters the alarms which is reflected in both the Parallel Coordinates and the Alarm List.

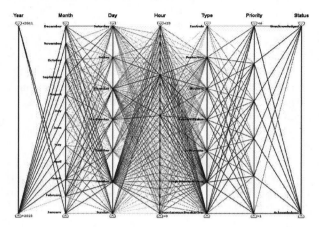

Figure 3. Parallel Coordinates representing alarms in the system. Each vertical axis represents a parameter of alarms. The lines passing through the axes represent alarms. Slider controls on each axis are used to filter alarms based on the values of the axis.

II. RELATED WORK

Siirtola has studied Parallel Coordinates and Reorderable Matrix visualizations and evaluated their use when coordinated or linked together [8]. A Reorderable Matrix is similar to a list in that its contents are symbols instead of text or numerical values. The study found coordination between the visualizations very useful in terms of reduced thinking overhead. The research also shows that the use of coordinated visualizations accelerates learning of complex user interfaces.

Cluster identification in different variants of Parallel Coordinates have been evaluated by Holten et al. [9]. The variants include the use of scatter plots, colors, opacity, smooth curves, and animation to supplement the standard Parallel Coordinates plot. It was found that with the exception of scatter plot variant, neither of the variants offered a considerable improvement.

Lanzenberger et al. have compared two InfoVis techniques namely, Stardinates and Parallel Coordinates [10]. The evaluation is based on task based user testing. The metrics for the evaluation were the task execution time for each of the visualizations. The errors from the user tasks were also used to judge the effectiveness of the techniques. Parallel Coordinates showed much better performance as compared to Stardinates.

Godinho et al. have developed a set of coordinated visualization tools called PRISMA - A Multidimensional

Information Visualization Tool Using Multiple Coordinated Views [11]. The tool was evaluated through user testing. Task execution time and errors were the main metrics for the evaluation. It was concluded that the use of Parallel Coordinates does not harm the performance of user tasks and helps improve filtering and visualization if coordinated with other visualizations [11].

All the mentioned related studies, in one way or the other, evaluate Parallel Coordinates with Lists and other comparable visualizations. However, results from previous studies do not reveal how much more effective and efficient Parallel Coordinates would be than lists in filtering tasks typical to Alarm Management in industrial systems.

III. METHODOLOGY

To evaluate the effectiveness and efficiency of Parallel Coordinates over the Alarm List, an empirical, test-case based user study was conducted. The experiment aimed at finding answers to the following questions:

- How significant is the gain in terms of efficiency (time) and effectiveness (error rate) when using Parallel Coordinates compared to Alarm List for filtering alarms?

- Which visualization method do the participants prefer in terms of usability factors namely, accuracy, efficiency, learnability, memorability, satisfaction and intuitiveness?

During the design of the prototype and while trying out the visualizations we observed that use of Parallel Coordinates made many difficult filtering tasks trivial and the amount of thinking required to finish the task was reduced. This formed the basis of our hypothesis.

A. Hypothesis

We hypothesized that use of coordinated Parallel Coordinates to filter alarms and identifying patterns in alarm data would be faster and more accurate as compared to Alarm List. The null hypothesis thus assumes that filtering does not improve when Parallel Coordinates are used.

$$H_0 : \mu PC = \mu_{AL}$$
$$H_1 : \mu_{PC} > \mu_{AL}$$

Where:

H_0 = *Parallel Coordinates does not improve filtering of alarms*

H_1 = *Parallel Coordinates improves filtering of alarms*

μ_{PC} = *Mean of group's performance using Parallel Coordinates*

μ_{AL} = *Mean of group's performance using Alarm List*

B. Participants

A total of 12 participants were involved in the evaluation, eight male and four female. They were between 24 and 56 years old, median age being 26 years. The participants used computers on a daily basis and almost all of them were from Information Technology or Engineering background. Some of the participants had background knowledge about the context of application but had not used these visualizations before.

C. Test Apparatus and Setting

The prototype application for the experiment was developed using the Geo Analytics and Visualization (GAV) framework [12], [13]. It runs on a desktop computer with displays set up similar to a real set up. The computer had large (17 inch), high-resolution (1280x1024 pixels), dual screens to show the visualizations side-by-side and was fast enough (Intel Pentium-IV 2.0 GHz) to instantaneously respond to user's actions. The experiment was recorded on video to capture participants' comments and actions while at the same time two experimenters timed the task execution and took notes as the participants performed the tasks.

D. User Tasks

The participants were required to do two types of tasks, *selection* and *filtering* for Alarm List and Parallel Coordinates. Tasks consisted of sub-tasks like *sorting* for the Alarm List and *reordering* the axes in the Parallel Coordinates.

There were two similar blocks of 11 tasks each (22 in total). Tasks were designed so that they have an equivalent and corresponding task for both Alarm List and Parallel Coordinates visualizations. This was done to ensure that both the visualizations are tested against the same use cases so their results can be compared.

The order in which participants performed tasks on the two visualizations was balanced to prevent skewed results(half of the participants performed tasks on the Alarm List first and then Parallel Coordinates, while the other half performed the tasks on Parallel Coordinates first). Tasks appeared in random order inside each block.

The tasks were categorized by their difficulty into groups based on the number of parameters involved and the steps needed to perform them correctly. Table I shows tasks used in the experiment. To accomplish a task, participants had to highlight alarms in the alarm list by selection or obtain a reduced set of alarms by filtering in the Parallel Coordinates.

E. Evaluation Criteria

Since this study essentially focused on design and evaluation of an Alarm Management solution, metrics in EEMUA [4] were considered in the experiment design. Although EEMUA metrics were not used in their entirety, the experiment utilized parameters such as operator response times and use of questionnaires in a similar fashion as in a real

Table I
LIST OF TASKS USED IN THE EXPERIMENT.

Easy tasks	
Task 1	Highlight all the Alarms that occurred from March 2009 to May 2009.
Task 2	Highlight all the Alarms that occurred during May 2009 and have Priority 5 or higher.
Task 3	Highlight all the Alarms that occurred for the month of March 2009 with maximum Priority.
Moderate tasks	
Task 4	Highlight all the Alarms that occurred for the month of April 2009 with Priority 5 or higher and are Unacknowledged.
Task 5	Highlight Alarms of type "Spontaneous Breaker Trip" having Priority 2.
Task 7	Highlight all the Alarms for the month of March 2009 with type "Protection" having the highest Priority.
Task 8	Highlight all the type "Control" Alarms for the month of March 2009 that are Unacknowledged, with Priority 3 or higher.
Task 9	Which Stations (Source) have currently the most number of high Priority, Unacknowledged Alarms?
Task 10	Which Stations (Source) have currently the most number of type "Protection" Alarms and are Unacknowledged?
Difficult tasks	
Task 6	Highlight Alarms that are Unacknowledged, are of type "Controls" and have minimum Priority.
Task 11	In April 2009 which Station (Source) got minimum "Control" Alarms with Priority 3 or higher?

world case. The following parameters were recorded during the experiment:

- Task Execution time (efficiency)
- Error rate (effectiveness)

Participants were asked to fill in a questionnaire to obtain subjective information such as accuracy, speed, learnability, memorability, efficiency, satisfaction and errors. Answers were recorded on a Likert scale by the participants. Another reason for using such a questionnaire was to capture the participants' perceived notion of the visualizations' characteristics like speed and accuracy. Answers from the questionnaire served as a verification of the observations from the experiment.

F. Test Protocol

Each participant was briefed about the evaluation procedure before the test. The experiment supervisor gave a 15-20 minutes introductory presentation to each participant about the motivation and context of the study, the two visualization methods and their use, and the tasks in order to familiarize him/her to the system equally. The participant was asked to perform some sample operations to get familiar with the prototype and 'think aloud' during the procedure. When the participant indicated being familiarized with the use of the prototype, the actual tests were conducted.

The test was conducted with each participant one by one and observed by two experimenters. The experimenters took notes, recorded execution times and errors for tasks, recorded the verbal communication and interviewed the participant for feedback after each test.

At the completion of the test, the participants were asked to fill out the questionnaire to acquire demographic information, their preferred technique in each task, the difficulties they had with each of the visualizations. The

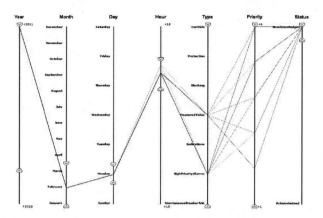

Figure 4. A view of the Parallel Coordinates plot with some alarms filtered to show unacknowledged alarms from first quarter of 2011, occurring on Mondays between 15:00 and 18:00. The Alarm List corresponds to this filtering and is reduced automatically to show only the alarms which match these criteria.

experiment took 50 to 70 minutes to perform all the tasks by one participant. The mean duration was 60 minutes. The participants were asked to execute the tasks as quickly as they could manage but with the aim of getting the right answers. Figure 4 shows the filtered Parallel Coordinates visualization similar to one of the evaluations.

A pilot test was conducted to check the clarity, completeness and impartiality of the testing protocol. The test design was iterated based on the findings from the pilot test before the actual evaluation was conducted. Results of the pilot test were omitted from the final analysis.

IV. RESULTS

The most pressing evidence was found in the task execution time per task together with the reduced number of errors. Figure 5 shows the mean, minimum and maximum execution times per task for Alarms List and Parallel Coordinates for all 12 participants and 11 tasks. Figure 6 summarizes the right and wrong answers for the same.

The results showed that there is indeed an improvement in the effectiveness and efficiency of the tasks performed when Parallel Coordinates were used. Use of Parallel Coordinates enhanced filtering and pattern analysis.

A. Task Execution Times per Task Difficulty

The participants performed better with the Parallel Coordinates in general. The task execution time using filtering on Parallel Coordinates was 392.82 seconds (61.5% faster) on average. Figures 7, 8 and 9 represent box plots of task execution time for easy, moderate and difficult tasks respectively.

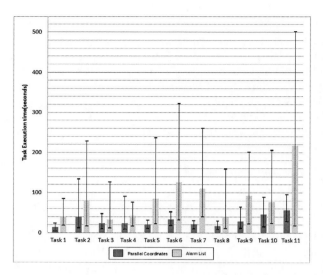

Figure 5. Mean task execution times on Parallel Coordinates and Alarm List for all tasks. Parallel Coordinates have shorter executing times on average.

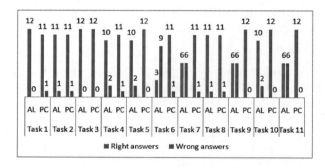

Figure 6. Number of right and wrong answers for each task using Alarms List(AL) and Parallel Coordinates(PC). Parallel Coordinates produced lesser wrong answers to tasks.

The observations for task execution times for the two groups (Parallel Coordinates and Alarm List) were statistically analyzed using single factor ANOVA. The analysis indicated that there is a significantly high efficiency gain in terms of task execution time for difficult tasks ($p < 0.01$) while for the simple and moderate tasks there was a marginally significant gain ($p < 0.1$) with moderate tasks having relatively higher performance gain as compared to easy tasks.

Comparing Alarm List and Parallel Coordinates, the results for difficult tasks namely, Tasks 6 and 11 both had a 73.7% decrease in mean task execution time with a drop in standard deviation from 79.6 to 10.3 for Task 6 and 130 to 22 for Task 11. The mean drop in task execution time for moderate tasks ranged from 40-80% when Parallel Coordinates were used. The standard deviation in execution times for moderate tasks shows that there was a considerable improvement in general. Among easy tasks, Tasks 1, 2 and 3 had 64%, 49% and 28% lower executions times in case of Parallel Coordinates with standard deviations lowered to 5.5, 32.8 and 13.2 respectively.

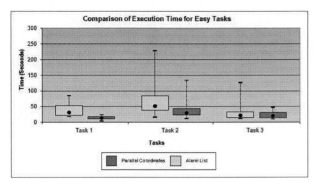

Figure 7. Task execution times (n=12 for each) for easy tasks. Parallel Coordinates do not offer considerable improvement from Alarm List.

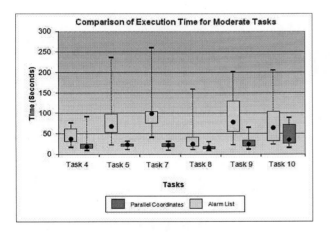

Figure 8. Task execution times (n=12 for each) for moderate tasks. There is a marked decrease in execution times when Parallel Coordinates were used.

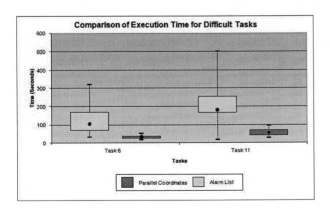

Figure 9. Task execution times (n=12 for each) for difficult tasks. Parallel Coordinates have highly significant effect on the filtering tasks in terms of execution time.

B. Error Rate

Out of the 132 tasks performed by total 12 participants, Parallel Coordinates produced 29.9% (126 as compared to 97 right answers) more correct answers than Alarm Lists. The error rate was reduced by 4.8% (6 as compared to 35 wrong answers) when Parallel Coordinates were used. Figure 10 represents the total right and wrong answers by participants on the Alarm List and Parallel Coordinates.

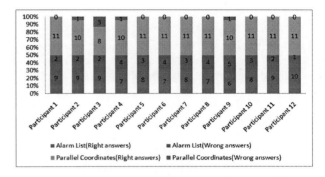

Figure 10. Number of right and wrong answers per participant (n=12) for both the Alarm List and Parallel Coordinates.

C. Subjective Satisfaction

Apart from the findings from the quantitative evaluation, the participants expressed subjective satisfaction on the questionnaire. Participants found the use of Parallel Coordinates faster, more intuitive, more accurate, easier to learn and remember, more supportive of pattern identification as compared to Alarm Lists. Figure 11 shows the findings of the questionnaire on participants' perceived notion of factors such as speed, accuracy, intuitiveness for Alarm List and Parallel Coordinates respectively.

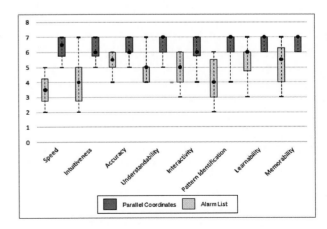

Figure 11. Participants perception of the Alarm List and Parallel Coordinates visualizations on a scale of one to seven, seven being highest.

D. Learning Effect

There was no considerable effect of learning on the participants' performance i.e. the order in which the participants used the Parallel Coordinates or the Alarm List, did not affect their performance on either visualization. Although the questionnaire results revealed that the participants preferred using Parallel Coordinates, statistical results show that their performance on either of the visualizations did not improve or reduce due to the order they performed tasks.

V. DISCUSSION

The results obtained from the evaluation were strongly in favor of use of Parallel Coordinates for Alarm filtering. Among the three categories of tasks, the increase in efficiency was not very high for easy tasks. The underperformance of Parallel Coordinates in Task 3 was thought to be attributed to one participant's extensive experience on working with list based visualizations on normal office applications, namely MS Excel. Only this one participant showed a tendency of having some difficulty in learning the use of Parallel Coordinates. The participant also had problems in the previous Task 2, but managed later tasks better.

For Parallel Coordinates in general, moderate and difficult tasks showed higher performance gain in terms of execution time. These results are representative of the reduced complexity of task execution in terms of execution time as well as thinking overhead for the participants. Overall, it can be said that the use of Parallel Coordinates improved the effectiveness and efficiency of filtering tasks which is supported by the alternative hypothesis as asserted by the statistical evaluation.

A limitation to this study was the scope of the experiment conducted. It should be investigated if more participants and a thorough and larger set of tasks will lead to more accurate results ($p<0.01$ for all tasks). Also, specific differences between various domains within the industry were not addressed in this study which are, e.g. number of priority levels and parameters in general, typical time interval between alarms and geographical distribution of alarms. The results here, however, demonstrate the advantages of Parallel Coordinates in alarm filtering tasks.

VI. CONCLUSIONS AND FUTURE WORK

This study evaluated Parallel Coordinates against conventional Alarms List for filtering and visual pattern identification of alarms. It was observed that it is in fact more efficient and more effective to use Parallel Coordinates. Use of Parallel Coordinates made it easier to perform difficult tasks in particular that consisted of multiple parameters. For easy tasks, performance gain was smaller. Thus we claim that Alarm Management in industrial applications could benefit from having Parallel Coordinates as the interface for filtering alarms and identifying patterns in alarm data especially when there are complex or difficult tasks at hand.

Future work covers a real world validation as a longitudinal study with operators in a real control room environment in e.g. electricity distribution or production plants using a full set of EEMUA metrics for alarm management.

ACKNOWLEDGEMENTS

We thank Christine Mikkelsen for valuable comments as well as Magnus Larsson and Martin Naedele for their support and all the participants for making the experiment possible.

We also thank Ammad Aslam and Bo Helgeson for their support.

REFERENCES

[1] B. Hollifield and E. Habibi, *The Alarm Management Handbook*. PAS, 2006.

[2] A. Inselberg, "The plane with parallel coordinates," *The Visual Computer*, vol. 1, pp. 69–91, 1985, 10.1007/BF01898350. [Online]. Available: http://dx.doi.org/10.1007/BF01898350

[3] A. Inslberg, *Parallel Coordinates: Visual Multidimensional Geometry and Its Applications*. Springer, 2009.

[4] *EEMUA 191: Alarm Systems. A Guide to Design, Management and Procurement.* Engineering Equipment and Materials Users Association, 1999. [Online]. Available: http://www.eemua.co.uk

[5] J. S. Alford, J. Kindervater, and R. Stankovich, "Alarm management for regulated industries," *CEP Magazine*, pp. 25–30, 2005.

[6] M. J. Lalomia and M. D. Coovert, "A comparison of tabular and graphical displays in four problem-solving domains," *SIGCHI Bull.*, vol. 19, pp. 49–54, October 1987. [Online]. Available: http://doi.acm.org/10.1145/36111.1045596

[7] C. Mikkelsen, J. Johansson, and M. Rissanen, "Interactive information visualization for sensemaking in power grid supervisory control systems," in *Proceedings of the 15th International Conference on Information Visualisation (IV2011)*, London, UK, 2011.

[8] H. Siirtola, "Combining parallel coordinates with the reorderable matrix," in *Proceedings of the conference on Coordinated and Multiple Views In Exploratory Visualization*. Washington, DC, USA: IEEE Computer Society, 2003, pp. 63–. [Online]. Available: http://portal.acm.org/citation.cfm?id=937938.937951

[9] D. Holten and J. J. Van Wijk, "Evaluation of cluster identification performance for different pcp variants," *Computer Graphics Forum*, vol. 29, no. 3, pp. 793–802, 2010.

[10] M. Lanzenberger, S. Miksch, and M. Pohl, "Exploring highly structured data: A comparative study of stardinates and parallel coordinates," *Information Visualisation, International Conference on*, vol. 0, pp. 312–320, 2005.

[11] P. I. A. Godinho, B. S. Meiguins, A. S. G. Meiguins, R. M. Casseb do Carmo, M. de Brito Garcia, L. H. Almeida, and R. Lourenco, "Prisma - a multidimensional information visualization tool using multiple coordinated views," in *Proceedings of the 11th International Conference Information Visualization*. Washington, DC, USA: IEEE Computer Society, 2007, pp. 23–32. [Online]. Available: http://portal.acm.org/citation.cfm?id=1270398.1271556

[12] S. Johansson and M. Jern, "Geoanalytics visual inquiry and filtering tools in parallel coordinates plots," in *Proceedings of the 15th annual ACM international symposium on Advances in geographic information systems*, ser. GIS '07. New York, NY, USA: ACM, 2007, pp. 33:1–33:8. [Online]. Available: http://doi.acm.org/10.1145/1341012.1341055

[13] M. Jern, S. Johansson, J. Johansson, and J. Franzen, "The gav toolkit for multiple linked views," in *Proceedings of the Fifth International Conference on Coordinated and Multiple Views in Exploratory Visualization*. Washington, DC, USA: IEEE Computer Society, 2007, pp. 85–97. [Online]. Available: http://portal.acm.org/citation.cfm?id=1270380.1270580

Evaluating a Potentiometer-Based Graphical User Interface for Interacting with a Music Recommendation Service

Arto Lehtiniemi

Nokia Research Center
Tampere, Finland
arto.lehtiniemi@nokia.com

Jukka Holm

Human-Centered Technology
Tampere University of Technology
Tampere, Finland
jukka.holm@tut.fi

Abstract— **This paper studies the idea of using potentiometers as a graphical user interface for interacting with a music recommendation service. In the implemented prototype, the user selects a musical genre and adjusts tempo and energy level potentiometers to fine-tune the playlist of new music recommendations. The look of the interface is changed to reflect the currently selected genre. In a user study with 40 participants, the idea of using potentiometers to access music collections was found to be suitable for discovering new music and to complement traditional music player applications. The prototype was seen to be easy to use and entertaining, and the graphical designs matched well with the musical genres. In the longer-term use, the prototype was slightly too simple and it would have benefited from e.g. text-based search functionality. Several other interesting ideas for the future development of the concept were also received.**

Keywords-music; visualization; skin; potentiometer; knob; playlist; music recommendation; musical genre; SuperMusic, user experience

I. INTRODUCTION

Modern music consumers are faced with a new kind of music discovery problem: how to find personally relevant and interesting music from the vast online collections containing millions of songs. One solution is to use one of the existing music recommendation systems, which are able to recommend new music based on a personal preference profile or one or more example songs. Such systems are usually based on collaborative filtering [25] or music content [22]. Content-based methods can be further divided into music signal analysis and manual content classification systems (e.g. Pandora [23]).

Many recommendation services such as Pandora and Last.FM [16] are essentially personalized radio stations, where the user gives input (e.g. artist, song, or genre name) to the system to receive recommendations of similar type of music. However, the fine-tuning of these stations can be rather limited, and the user does not have much control over music selected for the playlist. Another common restriction is the graphical user interface (GUI), which typically presents music as a list of tracks or using simple graphics such as album covers.

Some more interactive interfaces for discovering new music have also been proposed, such as navigating a

graphical 3D world [15] or turning a wheel [26]. Still, there is room for more innovation when trying to make the exploring of new music a playful and an entertaining experience. As argued in [3], the traditional HCI approaches are often too limited and must be extended to include enjoyment as well.

In this paper, we study accessing music recommendation services using a potentiometer-based prototype application for a touch screen PC. The metaphor is familiar to many from home appliances such as stereo systems and microwave ovens; turning a potentiometer clockwise increases the selected value and vice versa. In the prototype, the user first selects the musical genre to listen to, and then rotates tempo and energy level potentiometers to fine-tune the music selection. Turning the potentiometers offers instant feedback by changing the audible music to match the user selection, and creates a new playlist of music recommendations using SuperMusic [17]. To emphasize the selected genre, the look ("skin") of the interface is changed accordingly. By relying on clear associations between visual elements and musical genres, user's cognitive load can be reduced, and the users do not have to be musical experts or know the exact genre names to create representative playlists. Finding new music can be fun and targeted for everyone including young children.

To study the prototype in practice, a user study with 40 participants was arranged. This paper describes the results of the user study and the prototype implementation, and suggests ideas for the further development of the concept.

II. RELATED RESEARCH

The musical tempo or BPM (Beats per Minute) value is a common parameter in modern music player applications. In most cases, the tempo is selected manually using means such as text boxes, x- and y-axis location, sliders, wheels, or rings. By selecting the desired value or value range, the user can select fast or slow music fitting his/her current mood or listening context. According to several studies [13], fast tempi can result in expressions such as happiness, activity, and pleasantness, while slow tempi are generally associated with sadness, tranquilness, and the like.

One example of a commercial music player application with the tempo parameter is Apple iTunes, where the user can create smart playlists containing songs that match certain conditions. For example, one can add songs that are slower

1550-6037/11 $26.00 © 2011 IEEE
DOI 10.1109/IV.2011.51

than 120 BPM or faster than 200 BPM to the playlist. The parameters are set using pull-down menus and text boxes.

Van Gulik's artist map user interface [28] visualizes artist similarities by using colored circles located on an *x-y* space. Musical tempo can be mapped to circle color or location on the *y*-axis. In [29], tempo has been mapped to the *x*-axis and brightness to the *y*-axis.

In the Musiclens application [20], the user can adjust sliders such as tempo and mood to get new recommendations. Schedl et al. [26] have arranged the tracks of a music collection around a wheel in the order of maximum similarity. The wheel also functions as the track selector. To make the finding of certain styles easier, tracks from a selected genre or tempo are visualized on the ring using gray lines.

In some use contexts such as sports it may preferable to select the tempo automatically. One example of such a system is [18], where the system measures the step frequency of a runner and then creates a playlist with a suitable tempo.

In [9], 66% of the questionnaire participants were interested in using the tempo parameter either often or sometimes in their music player application. Despite the interest towards using the parameter, many digital music collections still do not contain pre-calculated BPM data. In such cases, automatic music tempo detection algorithms such as [4] can be utilized. Fortunately, the music collection used by the SuperMusic system already contained pre-calculated tempo metadata.

While several music player applications let the user to select songs based on tempo, the "energy level" and other similar type of parameters have not been commonly used. As the concept of energy level is slightly ambiguous and more difficult to understand than tempo, suitable signal processing algorithms are also more difficult to design. However, a couple of mood-based music applications do exist.

For example, Moody [19] is a mood-based playlist generator for iTunes. To start with, the user has to tag his iTunes library according to mood or download existing tags for the songs. This is done along two axes, where *y*-axis represents intensity and *x*-axis denotes happiness. As a default, the axes are color-coded in such way that red represents intensive but sad music, yellow intense and happy music, blue calm and sad music, and green happy but calm music. Once the library is tagged, the user can define new playlists based on mood. In the case of Musicovery [21], the user can select music according to mood (dark, energetic, calm, and positive), decade, and genre. Mood is selected by clicking on an *x-y* space.

In services such as All Music Guide [2], the moods of individual songs have been determined manually by a group of music experts. However, when such accurate data is not required, the moods can also be mapped to musical genres. In [11], we presented a list of genres that could be used as a starting point for making recommendations fitting the current mood of the user.

While all implementations discussed above have their own benefits, we feel that there are also some areas that could be improved or studied further. Firstly, we feel that the fine-tuning of music recommendations should be as easy as possible. In the case of Apple iTunes, for example, selecting music from a certain genre and tempo is typically done using smart playlists. Still, in [9] it was found out that 72% of the users were not willing to take such an effort. Secondly, as the above mentioned applications were developed for personal computers, many of them require quite a lot of screen space and are not directly applicable for touch screens and mobile devices. Thirdly, while there are some simple user studies on these applications, they have focused on traditional usability aspects instead of fun, enjoyment, or graphical design. Also, we are not familiar with applications that would use the combination of tempo and energy level potentiometers for accessing music collections.

In the case of our prototype, the goal was to develop a novel interface that would allow the users to create new music recommendation playlists in a fast and easy manner and fine-tune their contents using the familiar potentiometer metaphor. While we had to test the ideas using a touch screen PC, the prototype was designed in such way that it could easily be modified to operate on future mobile phones. We wanted to make the prototype highly visual and change the look of the player automatically according to the selected genre. By relying on clear associations between visual elements and musical genres, user's cognitive load can be reduced and finding new music can become easier and more fun. This type of functionality is not supported by the current line of music player applications.

III. PROTOTYPE

The prototype was implemented as a Flash application to enable the use of different platforms including personal computers and mobile devices such as Nokia N900. As suitable mobile devices or Apple iPad were not available at the time of implementing the prototype, the main platform was a HP Pavilion tx2500 touch-screen laptop.

One of the main design drivers was that the prototype should be so easy to use that it could be learned by using it for a short while. Due to this, the number of UI elements was kept to the minimum. The elements were designed in such a way that they could be operated with fingers.

When the user starts the prototype, he/she first sees the generic main view consisting of only two potentiometers or knobs (Fig. 1). By pressing the play button, the user can start listening to a playlist of rock and pop recommendations.

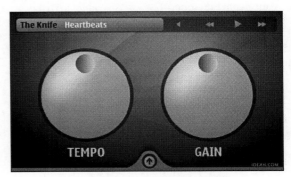

Figure 1.   Generic main view of the prototype.

The user can fine-tune the contents of the playlist by rotating the Tempo and Gain potentiometers. After each knob movement, a new playlist is automatically generated, the first song in the list starts to play, and music is streamed from an updated version of Nokia Research Center's context-aware music recommendation service [17]. By turning the Tempo knob clock-wise, faster songs are selected to the playlist. The Gain knob selects the overall energy level of the music in such way that higher values correspond to more energetic and aggressive sounding songs.

When the user presses the upward-pointing arrow located on the bottom of the screen, another screen for selecting the desired musical genre opens on top of the main view (Fig. 2). After selecting one of the five alternatives (soul, pop, rock, metal and electronica & dance) by pressing the corresponding icon, the user has to press the downward-pointing arrow to return to the main view for music listening.

Figure 2. Selecting the musical genre.

The appearance ("skin") of the main view is changed to reflect the selected musical genre (Fig. 3). The user can also fine-tune the music recommendations within the selected genre by turning the Tempo and Gain knobs.

The user can access the automatically generated playlist (top of Fig. 4) by clicking on the name of the currently playing song. The playlist consists of five songs. The chosen knob settings are displayed on the top left corner of the screen, which also works as a back button to the main view.

Songs details can be accessed by clicking on the corresponding track name. In the song details view (bottom of Fig. 4), the album cover is shown with more detailed information on the song. The user is able to listen to the track, remove it from the playlist by pressing the cross icon, and find more similar music. If the user presses the heart icon to retrieve more similar music, a new playlist is generated based on the selected track.

Figure 3. Skins used in the prototype. From top to bottom: soul, pop, rock, metal, and electronica & dance.

Figure 4. Playlist (top) and song details (bottom) views of the prototype.

A. Designing Skins and Icons

Musical genres are "categorical labels created by humans to characterize pieces of music" [27]. While categorizing music to different genres may be difficult and sometimes even artificial, they are commonly used in music player applications and recommendation systems including SuperMusic. For our research purposes, we selected five genres that we wanted to visualize using skins and icons: 1. electronica & dance, 2. heavy metal, 3. pop, 4. rock, and 5. soul. In a commercial product implementation, the number of genres should obviously be increased (in most of our previous research we have used 17), and the genre set should be localized for the target country or region.

The graphical designs were influenced by various things such as album cover art, movies, and the history of certain genres. Whenever feasible, we used colors and symbols from our previous studies [6] [10]. To enable studying how well the designs are recognized in practice, they were not labeled in any way.

Influenced by the movie Wall-E, we selected a robot theme to represent electronica & dance music (Fig. 2 and 3). In [6], most participants had already associated robots with electronica & dance, and the cover art of techno albums also uses them as common elements [24]. The selection of cyan color was based on the results of [10].

Designing the metal skin and the icon were straightforward tasks. According to our previous studies [6] [10], black color and the devil horns sign are mostly associated with metal music. The looks can be verified by studying album covers [1] or the history of the genre.

For pop, we selected a pink, soft, and happy theme. The decision was mainly based on our previous work on colors [10] and emoticons [11].

The rock and soul designs did not rely on any theoretical studies, but the decisions were based our instincts and knowledge of the genres. The rock theme was based on Gibson Les Paul, which is a guitar commonly used in rock bands all over the world. For soul, we used pictures of James Brown and a tweed-covered amplifier.

B. Used Music Recommendation System

The used music recommendation system was a new and enhanced version of Nokia Research Center's SuperMusic [17]. The system utilizes both textual metadata tags (describing genre and style) and audio signal processing. The similarity in terms of metadata tags is calculated at the artist level. For more details on the used music recommendation algorithms, see [8].

In the potentiometer prototype, each genre is represented with a set of prototypical seed songs. The songs were manually selected to be well representative of the corresponding genre, and there is a separate seed song for each Tempo and Gain potentiometer combination. Whenever the user turns the knobs to a new position, a new playlist is generated based on the corresponding seed song.

IV. RESEARCH METHOD

To study how well the prototype works in practice, we arranged a user study with 40 participants as a part of a study on six novel music recommendation applications. The initial research questions were formulated as:

- Are users interested in using potentiometers to access music recommendation services and generate playlists? Do they consider the concept fun and entertaining?
- Would the users be willing to replace their current music player with this type of application? Or does it only complement traditional applications?
- How does the prototype work in general? Is it fast enough and easy to use? How could it be developed further?
- How well do the looks of skins & icons and the music match?
- How does the user experience change after using the prototype for a longer time?

The research method was a combination of observation, a semi-structured interview, questionnaires, and evaluations done at home or other preferred listening context. Each interview session lasted for about 30 minutes. All participants tested the software for the first time, and they were not informed about how the prototype works or what to do with it. Tutorials or help files were not included.

The interview sessions were arranged in various locations such as participants' own homes, authors' homes, as well as the premises of Nokia Research Center and Tampere University of Technology. 37 of 40 interview sessions were arranged using a HP Pavilion tx2500 touch-screen laptop and three using a basic Dell Inspiron laptop. Evaluations at home were performed using participants' own computers.

In the beginning of the interview session, the users had to fill in a short background information questionnaire. Next, they used the software freely for 5-15 minutes while being observed. The participants were asked to describe their first impressions on the prototype, and various quality aspects of the prototype were studied by asking questions and filling in a questionnaire. Both hedonic (a.k.a. emotional, experiential) and pragmatic (a.k.a. ergonomic, functional, instrumental) aspects were studied. (In [5], Hassenzahl et al. have shown that these can be independently perceived by the users.) In the questionnaire, the participants had to rate several aspects of the software on a seven-point Likert scale (1=totally disagree, 7=totally agree). The statements to be graded were:

- "The program looked impressive"
- "The program was fun to use"
- "The program presented music in a novel way"
- "I believe that the appeal of the program will last and I will use it actively in the future"
- "The program had an extensive set of well-implemented features"
- "The program was easy to use" and
- "I was able to start the playback of desired music quickly."

In addition, the participants had to rate "My overall grade for the program" using a seven-point scale.

After the interview session, the users were able to use an online version of the software for circa three weeks. In the end, they had to evaluate the prototype by filling a questionnaire similar to the one used during the interview.

A. Participants

The participants were selected using convenience sampling from varying age groups and education levels. All the participants were Finnish. 77% (31 participants) were male and 23% (9) female. 8% (3) were 12-17 years old, 12% (5) 18-30 years old, 55% (22) 31-40 years old, and 25% (10) 41-55 years old. The average age was 34.6, and all participants from the 12-17 age group were male. 63% of the participants were university graduates, and the rest were split between all types of education. 8% were professional and 50% hobby musicians.

50% of the participants considered listening to music as their hobby. During listening, 20% did not usually do anything else but concentrate on the music. All except two participants listened to music at least once a day, and the average listening time per day was 2.1 hours. The most popular genres included pop (85% of the participants liked it), rock (80%), metal (63%), soul, rnb & funk (60%), alternative & indie (55%), and blues (55%), while the least popular genre was gospel (5%). The most popular listening contexts were home (55%) and the car (45%).

All major listening mediums were used, the most popular ones being computer (most important for 35% of the participants), traditional radio (23%), CD (18%) and mp3 players excluding mobile phones (15%). Only 5% named mobile phone's mp3 player as their main listening medium. On the average, the participants owned 302 music CDs and 4732 digital music (mp3, AAC etc.) files, and the number of CDs increased slightly with age. 43% of the participants searched actively for new music to listen to. The most

common sources included the Internet (65% of which 18% mentioned especially YouTube), friends (63%), magazines (33%), radio (33%), and Spotify (20%). 88% of the participants had used YouTube for listening to music, 51% had used Spotify, 32% Last.fm, and 29% iTunes Genius.

V. RESULTS

The combination of questionnaires and a semi-structured interview worked well, and the initial research questions were answered. In addition, we received a broad range of ideas for the future development of the concept. In this section, the results are discussed in a detailed manner.

A. Interview

In the beginning of the interview session, the participants were able to use the prototype freely for 5-15 minutes while being observed. After that, various quality aspects of the prototype were studied by asking questions and by filling in a questionnaire.

1) First impressions

For over 60% of the participants, the first impressions of using the prototype were very positive. Several participants considered selecting music with two knobs to be exciting, different, and novel. Most participants considered changing the skin based on genre selections to be a good idea.

Rotating the potentiometers was considered to be an intuitive way to select music, and "fine-tuning" within a selected genre was an especially appreciated feature. Rotating was seen very useful in exploring new music and for creating playlists in parties. One participant commented that this type of solution could very suitable for a casual listener, but too restricted for the active music consumers. Adjusting the tempo was seen as a very interesting attribute for music classification. One participant commented that "there are days when you want to listen to slower or faster music… For example if you have thousands of tracks in your collection and you want to quickly select some slow music."

A typical usage pattern was to first test how the minimum and maximum values affected the selection of the next track. After the basic operation of the knobs was understood, the users typically left them to a certain position reflecting their current mood. The knobs were not touched until the user got bored or felt that some other type of music would be more appropriate for the current mood and/or situation. Thus, the usage resembled closely the process of selecting and listening to a certain radio channel.

2) Quality aspects

During the interview, various quality aspects of the prototype were studied by asking questions and filling in a questionnaire. In the questionnaire, the participants had to rate several aspects of the software (see Section 4) on a seven-point Likert scale (1=totally disagree, 7=totally agree).

Fig. 5 illustrates the ratings given by the participants as pairs of boxplots. In the case of each pair, the left boxplot represents ratings given after the interview, and the right boxplot represents ratings given after longer-term use. Numbers surrounding the outlier circles refer to certain users in the SPSS data. In the following, we concentrate on boxplots on the left and leave the right side for discussion in the "Longer-Term Use" section.

As seen from Fig. 5, the prototype was received well in the interview. Most participants considered it to be a novel way to present music collections (median 6.0). While the conditions for using the Chi-Square test were not met, slight correlation between gender and novelty was found (Spearman's *rho*=0.35, significant at the p<0.05 level (2-tailed)), meaning that women considered the prototype to be slightly more novel than men. In the case of all other statements, the ratings did not correlate with participants' gender, age, or level of experience with modern music technologies such as music recommendation systems, and the conditions for using the Chi-Square test were not met.

The participants also thought that the prototype looked good or impressive (median 6.0). The minimalistic design was commented to be stylish, handy, and visually funny. The skins were said to be illustrative and good-looking.

The prototype was considered to be easy to use (median 6.0). After using the system for a while, 90% of the participants considered the general interaction to be good. When asked the question "Did you understand how the prototype works?" 75% gave a positive answer. In general, the participants felt that help files and/or tutorials were not required. However, several participants did not understand the meaning of the Gain knob, and 45% never found the playlist view. Almost 40% found the system to be a little confusing at start. The idea of tweaking knobs on a computer screen was new for many, and the relationship between knob positions and the generated playlists was not that clear. Some participants thought that rotating the knobs would affect the currently playing song instead of creating a new playlist for listening. However, many of these confusions were cleared rather quickly by simply exploring of the system.

The majority of participants felt that the prototype was fun to use (median 6.0), and the overall grades for the program were also high (median 6.0).

63% of the participants felt that the prototype fit well to their current music consumption habits. While 78% mentioned that they would like to use the prototype for a longer time, some were unsure of whether the appeal would last. The median for lasting appeal was 5.0, but there was more scattering in the results (mean=4.7, std. deviation=1.6) than in the case of most other statements.

Only 50% of the participants thought that the prototype had enough features implemented. For 38%, the lack of a text-based search function was a major shortcoming. As a result, the median for the statement "The program had an extensive set of well-implemented features" was 5.0 and several participants gave a grade of ≤4.0. Except for the playlist view, the features were easy to find.

The lack of search function might also have had an effect on some of the grades for "I was able to start the playback of desired music quickly." For this statement, the median was 5.0 but there was quite a lot of scattering in the results (mean 4.9, std. deviation 1.7).

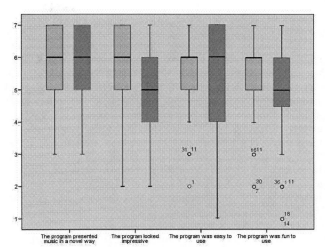

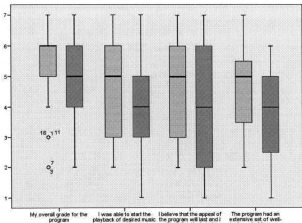

Figure 5. Boxplots for the quality aspects of the prototype: Ratings given at the end of the interview (boxplots on the left) and after longer-term use (boxplots on the right).

B. Longer-Term Use

The user study was arranged as a part of a study on six novel music recommendation applications. The participants were also able to use the online versions of five applications at home (or other preferred place) for circa three weeks. On the average, the participants tested the potentiometer prototype for 3-4 times during this time. In the end of the evaluation period, the participants had to rate the same statements as during the interview, rate the skins and icons, and write some textual comments.

By comparing the different boxplot pairs in Fig. 5, one can notice a drop in most of the grades. The only exceptions were novelty, which stayed the same, and ease of use, which increased slightly as the participants already had some experience with the prototype. In the case of the last four statements of Fig. 5, the drop was statistically significant. Using Wilcoxon's signed ranks test, the Z values for overall grade and lasting appeal were -2.19 and -2.46 at the p<0.05 level (2-tailed). For the statements "I was able to..." and

"The program had…", the Z values were -2.74 and -2.65 at the p<0.01 level (2-tailed).

In the longer-term use, the prototype was seen to be too simple and lack some important features (see section "Ideas for Further Development"). This is well in line with [14], where it was found out that "Overall, while early experiences seemed to relate mostly to hedonic aspects of product use, prolonged experiences became increasingly more tied to aspects reflecting how the product becomes meaningful in one's life". The lack of a text-based search function was a major shortcoming to 63% of the participants (cf. 38% after the interview). Due to the small number of available musical genres, 50% also felt that the music collection did not meet their needs, and 30% mentioned that they did not use the prototype much for this reason.

Only 55% of the participants stated that they would like to use the prototype for a longer time (cf. 78% after the interview). In addition to the lack of certain important features, limited amount of genres, etc., another potential reason for this was major and/or minor technical problems. Circa 33% of the participants had some type of problems including program and server crashes, pauses in the music playback, and other network related problems. The median for lasting appeal decreased from 5.0 to 4.0, and there was also more scattering in the results (mean=3.8, std. deviation=2.0) than in the case of other statements.

Logically, participants who felt that the prototype had an extensive set of well-implemented features also believed that the appeal of the program will last, and that they will use it actively also in the future (Spearman's *rho*=0.77, significant at the p<0.01 level (2-tailed)). The lasting appeal also correlated strongly (*rho*≥0.43) with all other statements except novelty (*rho*=0.25 with p=0.13).

58% of the participants felt that the prototype fit to their current music consumption habits. As the corresponding number after the interview was 63%, the user experience did not change significantly in this respect. While only 8% of the participants thought that they could use the prototype as their main music player application, 60% answered that they could use it to complement other players. 83% preferred that the music comes from a music recommendation service instead of their own music collection (cf. 80% after the interview).

1) Relationship between skins, icons, and music

The participants were also asked to rate how well the looks of skins and icons matched with the recommended music on a seven-point scale (1=did not match at all, 4= neutral, 7=perfect match). As seen from Fig. 6, the graphics performed well and most participants felt that the looks matched well with the related music recommendations.

In the initial interview, the participants had been asked to describe what type of music each skin & icon pair could possibly represent. This was done before listening to any music. The answers were given orally in participant's own words, and the number of genres was not restricted in any way. These first impressions revealed some reasons for the "negative" ratings of some of the designs.

The best ratings were given to the metal genre. During the initial interview, 93% participants associated the metal

graphics with some type of metal music. After listening to the songs at home, all except one participant still felt that the music and the graphics matched well (median 6.0). The results are well in line with our other studies sharing similar graphical characteristics. In [12], all parts of the metal avatar were mapped to metal music by ≥79% of the participants. In [7], the female metal character was also recognized best (median 6.0 on a seven-point scale).

Soul came next with the median of 6.0. However, the initial impressions during the interview were not that good. While 48% associated the graphics with soul music, 33% associated them with blues, 25% with jazz, and 13% with rock or rock 'n' roll. As the graphics should be easy to recognize without recall, there is still some improvement needed in this respect.

The same can be said of the rock graphics (median 5.5), too. During the initial interview, 65% of the participants associated the designs with rock but country and blues music were also mentioned several times.

In the case of pop music, the main problem is that the label may refer to almost any genre that is popular at the moment. This was also reflected in the results. Before listening to any music in the interview, 93% of the participants associated the pop graphics with pop music. However, after using the prototype at home, the median was 5.0, and there was quite a lot of scattering in the results. As the recommendations may not have matched some participants' own definition of what pop music is, other seed songs for the algorithm should also be tested.

To our surprise, the electronica & dance graphics performed worst in the study. In our previous studies [6] [8] [12], the genre has always been one of the winners. While the median was now 5.0, there were also quite a few "negative" (<4.0) responses. Also in this case, one possible explanation may be that the seed songs were not optimal; during the initial interview as many as 83% of the participants associated the graphics with electronic music.

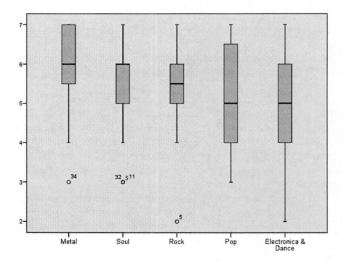

Figure 6. Boxplots for how well the recommended music matched with the looks of skins and icons.

VI. IDEAS FOR FURTHER DEVELOPMENT

During the interview, we also received several ideas for the future development of the concept. These included the operation of the potentiometers, selecting the genre(s), playlists, recommendations, and the user interface in general. In the following, these ideas have been explained in more detail.

While rotating the knobs was considered to be an intuitive way to select music, 17% of the participants thought that selecting music solely this way might be too restricted in the longer-term use. There are many use cases where the user wants to select a certain artist or song to listen to or use it as a seed song for the music recommendation system. However, these types of use cases were not in the scope of our study.

The operation of the Tempo knob was obvious to almost every participant. However, using the Gain knob was not that clear. When asked about its purpose, it was thought to adjust for example the balance between acoustic and electronic music, volume, compression level, roughness/smoothness, gloominess, or loudness/softness. As a result, the Gain knob should be renamed to something more descriptive (e.g. "Energy"), and some type of energy meter could also be shown on the screen.

In the current version of the prototype, the different knob positions are displayed in the form of "Tempo 2, Gain 4". However, there was a clear demand for a more informative numbering system that would clarify the meaning of the knobs and changes made. For example, it was proposed that the tempo could be displayed in beats per minute (BPM).

25% of the participants wanted to extend the prototype with more knobs to make the music selection more precise. Suggestions for the additional knobs included happy/melancholic, mainstream/underground, release year or decade, gender, and genre. When rotating the knobs, preview clips of the songs (e.g. chorus) could also be played.

Some participants considered the use of a generic default skin to be slightly confusing. While the default genre included mostly rock music, the skin was not recognizably related to any genre. It was proposed that the application should instead start with the genre selection view. Since the arrow button did not indicate in any way what it was used for, some participants had problems in opening the genre view for the first time. As one potential solution, it was proposed that the potentiometer and the genre views could be combined.

While the genre icons were seen to be distinctive, it was also proposed that there could be a textual explanation (such as a tooltip or a genre name) to avoid confusions. Music playback from the selected genre should start immediately to provide instant feedback on the selection. Over 20% of the participants were requesting a greater number of genres to select from, and roughly the same amount was interested in generating cross-genre playlists. The participants hoped that the knobs would work across genre boundaries in such a way that they could e.g. add fast pop and electronica songs to the same playlist.

In the current implementation of the prototype, playlists are accessed by clicking on the name of the currently playing song. In the beginning, 45% of the participants had problems in finding the playlist. While they paid great attention to how turning the knobs affected what type of music started to play, they did not know in advance that the prototype would generate playlists based on the knob positions. As one solution, it was proposed that the song name could be highlighted after turning the knobs. Another alternative would be to integrate the playlist with the main view.

In the playlist view, the user is able to request more similar songs by pressing the heart icon. However, 28% of the participants confused the icon with the "Like" button, which is often used to give positive feedback to a system or to add tracks to the favorites list. Still, the idea of requesting more similar songs from the service was considered to be good. When good music was found, the participants wanted to listen to more music from the same artist. Some also indicated that they would want to give feedback to the underlying algorithm by liking/disliking certain songs, and thus, gradually build their own personal music profile.

To fit well to the UI layout, each playlist contained only five songs. This was said to be too few, and the amount should be increased to around 20 as proposed in [17]. The prototype also lacked some important playlist related features such as adding songs to "favorites" and other playlists, selecting songs from one's listening history, and recommending songs to friends.

From observing the participants during the interview session, we learned that many problems could have been avoided by starting the prototype with the genre selection view. This would have removed the need for the confusing generic skin, and the users would have immediately seen the graphical effect of the genre selection. As a result, the prototype would have been even more easy to use and the general user experience could have been slightly improved.

One purpose of the prototype was to hide the overwhelming details of a massive music collection from the end user and provide easier access to the preferred types of music. However, several participants would have wanted to see a list of the complete music catalogue and lists of all artists and tracks belonging to the specified genre. One reason for this may be that the prototype hid too much information from the user and did not reveal the magnitude of the available music collection. Further studies are needed to verify if adding a search function would satisfy also this need.

Several participants mentioned that they were interested in getting more information on the currently playing song. The following information was seen as interesting: detailed artist info/biography, release year of the album, record label, and links to music videos, artist's website, and MySpace. Several participants mentioned that they would also like to access their own music library through the knobs.

VII. CONCLUSIONS AND FUTURE WORK

In this paper, we studied the idea of using potentiometers as a graphical user interface for interacting with a music recommendation service. In the implemented software prototype, new recommendations were generated based on the positions of tempo and energy level potentiometers as well as the selected musical genre. The graphical skin of the prototype changed according to the genre.

The prototype was evaluated by 40 participants, and the concept was considered to be suitable for discovering new music and to complement traditional music players. The prototype was seen to be innovative, handy, easy to use, and entertaining. The graphical designs matched well with the musical genres.

In the longer-term use, the prototype was slightly too simple and it would have benefited from the addition of e.g. text-based search functionality. Many interesting ideas for the future development of the concept were also received. These included adding more potentiometers (e.g. release year, vocalist gender, and mood) for fine-tuning the playlist even more, more advanced playlist modification capabilities, and visualizing the entire music catalogue. Despite the flaws, 60% of the participants commented that they could use the prototype to complement other music player applications. In the future, it would be interesting to test an improved version of the prototype as an alternative view to a traditional list-based music player.

During the last few years, automatic tempo detection technologies have improved to such a level that they are viable alternatives for use in commercial applications. In the case of the energy level parameter, there are still many challenges ahead. As the concept of energy level is slightly ambiguous and more difficult to understand than tempo, suitable signal processing algorithms are also more difficult to design. Another alternative would be to base the design on manually (user or expert) annotated metadata. For example, the application could search the database of All Music Guide [2] or Last.fm [16] for "aggressive" and other related keywords and map those songs to the scale of the potentiometer. Alternatively, the users could select or change the seed songs by themselves. Descriptive tags could also be shown on the screen while turning the potentiometers.

The potentiometer study was conducted as a part of a larger user study on six novel music player interfaces. After all the interfaces have been analyzed in detail, the results should be compared against each other and used to design the "perfect" next-generation music player UI.

REFERENCES

[1] N. Aldis and J. Sherry, Heavy Metal Thunder: Album Covers That Rocked the World. London, Mitchell Beazley, 2006.

[2] All Music Guide, url: http://www.allmusic.com.

[3] M. Blythe, K. Overbeeke, A. Monk, and P. Wright, Funology: From Usability to Enjoyment. Dordrecht, Kluwer Academic Publishers, 2004.

[4] A. Eronen, Signal Processing Methods for Audio Classification and Music Content Analysis. PhD Thesis, Tampere University of Technology, 2009.

[5] M. Hassenzahl, A. Platz, M. Burmester, and K. Lehner, "Hedonic and Ergonomic Quality Aspects Determine a Software's Appeal," Proc. CHI 2000 Conference on Human Factors in Computing Systems (CHI 2000), ACM Press, April 2008, pp. 201-208.

[6] J. Holm and H. Holm, "Associating Icons with Musical Genres," Proc. International Conference on Internet and Multimedia Systems and Applications (IMSA 08), ACTA Press, Aug. 2008.

[7] J. Holm and A. Lehtiniemi, "A Virtual World Prototype for Interacting with a Music Collection," Proc. 14th International Conference on Human-Computer Interaction (HCII 2011), Jul. 2011, in press.

[8] J. Holm and A. Lehtiniemi, "Evaluating an Avatar-Based User Interface for Discovering New Music," Proc. 9th International Conference on Mobile and Ubiquitous Multimedia (MUM 2010), ACM Press, Dec. 2010.

[9] J. Holm, "Popularity of Music Player Parameters and Features," Proc. International Computer Music Conference (ICMC 08), Aug 2008.

[10] J. Holm, A. Aaltonen, and H. Siirtola, "Associating Colours with Musical Genres," Journal of New Music Research 38, vol. 1, 2009, pp. 87-100.

[11] J. Holm, H. Holm, and J. Seppänen, "Associating Emoticons with Musical Genres," Proc. International Conference on New Interfaces for Musical Expression (NIME 2010), Jun 2010, pp. 383-386.

[12] J. Holm, H. Siirtola, and L. Laaksonen, "Associating Avatars with Musical Genres," Proc. 14th International Conference on Information Visualisation (IV 2010), IEEE, Jul. 2010, pp. 186-193.

[13] P. N. Juslin and J. A. Sloboda, Music and Emotion: Theory and Research. New York, Oxford University Press, 2001.

[14] E. Karapanos, M. Hassenzahl, and J-B. Martens, "User Experience over Time," Proc. CHI '08 Conference on Human Factors in Computing Systems (CHI 08), ACM Press, Apr. 2008, pp. 3561-3566.

[15] P. Knees, M. Schedl, T. Pohle, and G. Widmer, "An Innovative Three-Dimensional User Interface for Exploring Music Collections Enriched with Meta-Information from the Web," Proc. 14th Annual ACM International Conference on Multimedia, ACM Press, Oct. 2006.

[16] Last.fm, url: http://www.last.fm.

[17] A. Lehtiniemi, "Evaluating SuperMusic: Streaming Context-Aware Mobile Music Service," Proc. International Conference on Advances in Computer Entertainment Technology (ACE 08), ACM Press, Dec. 2008, pp. 314-321.

[18] N. Masahiro, H. Takaesu, H. Demachi, M. Oono, and H. Saito, "Development of an Automatic Music Selection System Based on Runner's Step Frequency," Proc. 9th International Conference on Music Information Retrieval (ISMIR 09), Sep. 2008.

[19] Moody, url: http://www.crayonroom.com/moody.php.

[20] MusicLens, url: http://finetunes.musiclens.de.

[21] Musicovery, url: http://musicovery.com.

[22] E. Pampalk, Computational Models of Music Similarity and their Application to Music Information Retrieval. PhD Thesis, Vienna University of Technology, 2006.

[23] Pandora, url: http://www.pandora.com.

[24] M. Pesch, Techno Style: Album Cover Art. Zurich, Edition Olms, 1998.

[25] B. Sarwar, G. Karypis, J. Konstan, and J. Reidl, "Item-Based Collaborative Filtering Recommendation Algorithms," Proc. 10th International Conference on World Wide Web, ACM Press, 2001.

[26] M. Schedl, T. Pohle, P. Knees, and G. Widmer, "Assigning and Visualizing Music Genres by Web-Based Co-Occurrence Analysis," Proc. 7th International Conference on Music Information Retrieval (ISMIR 06), Oct. 2006.

[27] G. Tzanetakis and P. Cook, "Musical Genre Classification of Audio Signals," IEEE Transactions on Speech and Audio Processing, vol. 10, no. 5, 2002.

[28] R. Van Gulik and F. Vignoli, "Visual Playlist Generation on the Artist Map," Proc. 6th International Conference on Music Information Retrieval (ISMIR 05), Sep. 2005, pp. 520-523.

[29] J. Zhu and L. Lu, "Perceptual Visualization of a Music Collection," IEEE Transactions on Speech and Audio Processing, vol. 10, no. 5, 2002.

Interactive Information Visualization for Sensemaking in Power Grid Supervisory Control Systems

Christine Mikkelsen* †, Jimmy Johansson†, Mikko Rissanen*

*ABB Corporate Research, Industrial Software Systems, Sweden
†C-Research, Linköping University, Sweden

christine.mikkelsen@se.abb.com, jimmy.johansson@liu.se, mikko.rissanen@se.abb.com

Abstract—Operators of power grid supervisory systems have to gather information from a wide variety of views to build situation awareness. Findings from a conducted field study show that this task is challenging and cognitively demanding. Visualization research for power grid supervisory control systems has focused on developing new visualization techniques for representing one aspect of the power system data. Little work has been done to demonstrate how information visualization techniques can support the operator in the sensemaking process to achieve situation awareness. To fill this gap, and with support from a field study, we propose solutions based on multiple and coordinated views, visual interactive filtering and parallel coordinates.

Keywords-Human supervisory control systems, sensemaking, information visualization, power grid visualization, field study

I. INTRODUCTION

Human Supervisory Control (HSC) system is a general term for systems that include an automation layer between the human operator and the system [15]. HSC systems can be found within a wide range of application domains and in this paper we will focus on control systems used for supervision of power grids. The main objective for an operator of such control system is to make sure that the power grid runs in "normal mode". That task involves information and data gathering from several different views of the power grid. The gathered information is used for building a mental model of the situation, a concept referred to as situation awareness [3].

Today's sophisticated and extremely complex power grids generate large amounts of data which needs to be analyzed by power system operators. Analyses of recent blackouts have shown that power grid operators ability to understand the situation is crucial and that problems with situation awareness have been one major factor that has affected the propagation of failures [4].

In recent years, sensemaking has been introduced as a process that should be considered while designing decision support systems for power grid supervision [4].

"Sensemaking is the active process of building, refining, questioning and recovering situation awareness." [7]

Sensemaking is related to situation awareness [3] and the conceptual model of sensemaking presented in [10], [11] defines situation awareness as the product of the sensemaking process. Their model is intended to describe the process of how situation awareness is achieved when the available information is uncertain or conflicting, and maintained or recovered after a surprising event, which are typical situations that an operator of a HSC system has to deal with. The metaphor frame is used to describe how humans start with some form of framework to make sense of data and events. This framework can, in the beginning of the sensemaking process, be minimal but it expands and becomes more elaborate when more data is acquired. The frame is a hypothesis about the connections among data and sometimes new information confirms the hypothesis but sometimes new data forces the user to reject the frame and thus the user has to replace it with another.

In this paper, we present findings from a comprehensive user study that describes how operators have essential problems with navigation and interaction with data in the system. Even if new visualization techniques that present data in a more intuitive way are used, there is still a need for intuitive navigation and interaction techniques that support the sensemaking process so operators can understand the situation and make the right decisions.

We propose visualization solutions for interactive analysis of data in a control environment that support sensemaking. The solutions have been influenced by the Visual Information-Seeking Mantra [16]: *"overview first, zoom and filter, then details on demand"* and are based on coordinated and multiple views (see [1] for a survey and user guidelines) and dynamic visual queries using parallel coordinates [8]. The proposed solutions are the result of an extensive user study with 76 participants from 16 different power utility control rooms in USA, India, Sweden, United Arab Emirates and Oman.

The remainder of this paper is organized as follows. Section II describes the fundamental views in the targeted system. In section III related work on interactive information visualization methods for power grid supervisory systems is discussed. Details of the method used for conducting the user studies are presented in section IV and the findings from the field studies are together with the proposed solutions presented in section V. The proposed solutions and future work are discussed in section VI.

1550-6037/11 $26.00 © 2011 IEEE
DOI 10.1109/IV.2011.100

II. BACKGROUND

An HSC system for power grid supervision usually includes the following fundamental views:

- **Geographical overview** - This is an overview of the power grid's geographical area, see Figure 1a. It includes, for example, transmission lines and substations that are mapped to their geographical location on the overview. The purpose of the view is to show overall status of the grid, for example voltage levels and if there are reported alarms in substations.

- **Single line diagrams (SLD)** - In addition to the geographical overview there is also a schematic view, called single line diagram (SLD), over the whole system showing more details, see Figure 1b. This schematic view focuses on the connectivity in the grid and does not maintain geographical distance between devices. The schematic view is also divided in sub-views showing individual substations with more details about devices and their status.

- **Alarm and event lists** - One of the most important views is the alarm list, see Figure 1c. The alarm list is usually a vertical list that represents reported alarms in the power grid. Each alarm that is reported to the alarm list has a number of alarm attributes that can be used for sorting and filtering. When a device in the power grid report a value that exceeds one of its limits then an alarm is sent to the alarm list. Usually a device has a number of different alarm limits and the first level is supposed to be used for alerting the operator about potential problems in the future if the value continues to increase or decrease. In addition to the alarm list there is usually an event list that includes recorded manual operations and other types of system events.

- **Detailed information views** - The single line diagrams display a subset of available information about devices in the power grid. The displayed information is typically numerical values which operators constantly need to supervise. Other information that the operator needs occasionally is displayed in separate detailed information views, see Figure 1d.

- **Automatic support function views** - The supervision of a power grid system is supported by automatic functions. One example is a function called contingency analysis which analyzes the effect of losing one or several transmission lines, due to damage or overload. The results from the automatic support functions are, in some cases, displayed on the schematic views or on the geographical overview but in some cases only in tabular lists, see Figure 1e.

Figure 1 shows an example subset of views that operators use while supervising a power grid system. Due to the size and complexity of the physical power grid system the information and data is spread over thousands of various

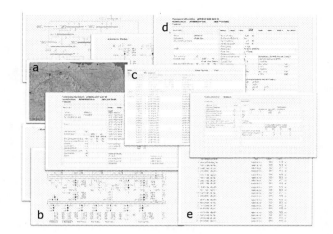

Figure 1. The wide variety of views in HSC systems for power grid supervision: (a) geographical overview, (b) single line diagram, (c) alarm list, (d) detailed information view and (e) automatic support function view.

views in the HSC system. The views represent different aspects of the system and are used for supervising the status and for performing manual operations. Most of the tasks performed by an operator involve some kind of decision making and thus the process of making sense of information to understand the current situation is very important.

III. RELATED WORK

During the last decade, research within power grid operations has focused on how to enhance situation awareness. Several visualization techniques have been developed to improve the representation of power grid data.

One early proposed technique for visualizing power system data is colour contouring [18]. Colour contouring is described as useful for representing voltage levels in the power grid. This technique has been validated in a follow-up study on the human factors aspects [13]. The study showed that the colour contouring display attracts the users' attention to the worst voltage violations quicker than the numerical display, but at the cost of worse performance when used for solving or removing the voltage violations. Overbye et al. also found that combining the numerical display with colour contouring resulted in worse performance in some situations, than just colour contours or numerical display alone, and their proposed explanation is that users are not able to ignore one dimension (numbers) while using another (colour contours).

Two other presented visualization techniques are static or animated arrows that represent power flow, and pie charts that represent the transmission lines' load percentage [12].

There are several attempts to utilize 3D views by mapping power system data to a three dimensional shape that is placed onto a tilted geographical map or schematics of the power grid. In some cases the tilted map is a terrain map representing additional aspects of the power grid. [2] used a terrain map in combination with colour contours to visualize results of power flow analysis and state estimation.

One example of visualizing the result of a contingency analysis is presented in [20]. In this case the presented solution also utilizes a third dimension by mapping attributes (height, colour and orientation) of bars, cones and other 3D shapes onto a tilted 2D plane with a single line diagram.

Thus, different kinds of 3D visualization techniques have been presented as solutions to enhance the way power system data is presented to the operator but few user studies have been performed to validate that 3D visual representations actually improve the performance. The user study presented in [19] only concludes that 3D displays could potentially be valuable tools but that more studies are needed. However, a number of situations where 3D can add value are presented. In particular they highlight 3D representations as a tool for improving the speed of high-level judgements of current operating levels in relation to upper and lower limits.

Evaluations of 3D displays in comparison to 2D displays have been done for various other domains with mixed results. The reason for the variety of conclusions in previous conducted evaluations is discussed in [17] and Smallman et Al. present their own comparison study where they found that information about a third dimension can be better obtained in a well-designed 2D display.

The fact that data in a power grid supervisory system has a spatial nature is the background for the work presented in [14]. They suggest several visualization techniques for different problems that would benefit from a geographical view. Their main idea is to map power system data onto different types of 2D icons within a geographical map, a similar solution as one of the solutions presented and compared in [17].

Some of the techniques summarized above, such as colour contours, animated arrows, 3D bar graphs on tilted 2D display and pie charts, have been implemented in power grid supervisory systems as solutions to fill the need for more intuitive displays that provide operators with better situation awareness.

The above summary of previous work shows that research within visualization for power grid operations has been focusing on developing visualization techniques that map power system information to one separate view for exploring a specific aspect of the data. There is little research about how these proposed techniques would fit into the whole decision making process to support sensemaking in situations when information needs to be gathered from several views.

IV. METHODOLOGY

To investigate what operators need in their supervisory role, and how they operate and make decisions in dynamic and complex systems, the best way is to observe them in their real environment [21]. Thus a number of field studies

were conducted in 2008 and 2010 covering 16 different power utility control rooms in USA, India, Sweden, United Arab Emirates and Oman. During each visit a selection of users, having different roles, were observed and interviewed. The goal was to gather as much information as possible about the different users' tasks and how they were using the system. How they navigated and interacted with information in the system to perform their tasks and making decisions was of special interest. Different types of control rooms (managing transmission (EMS) and/or distribution (DMS) power grids) located in three different continents was covered to capture differences between them. Figure 2 illustrates the role and geographical location distribution of the 76 studied users.

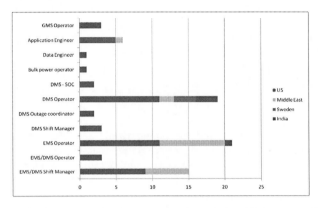

Figure 2.   Distribution of studied users (roles and geographical location)

We chose to do field studies instead of laboratory studies since it is difficult to replicate a true realistic situation with all interruptions and conflicting events that are going on in a control room. In addition, all control rooms have their own variations of the system and we were interested in finding out whether those variations affected the users' way of working. Another issue with laboratory testing is that it is difficult and expensive to get subjects with the right background to travel to the laboratory site.

The drawback of field studies is the lack of control. The opportunities for conducting the interviews with operators were strongly affected by the control rooms' organization and schedule and we had to adjust our methods depending on the available time in the control room and with the different users.

Generally a variation of different protocols for cognitive task analysis was used. In some cases a modified bootstrapping protocol [5] was enough to get the overall picture of the users' main tasks. In some cases we had the opportunity to observe a user while performing a task where he had to carefully analyze the situation and make critical decisions. In those cases an adapted version of the critical decision making method [6] was used to get a deeper understanding of the decisions the user had to make.

We aimed for an individual interview with each user, combined with naturalistic observations but in some cases the interview had to be done at the same time as the user was in operation due to the fact that replacement operators were not available. Thus the interview was constantly interrupted, but that also gave us additional and important information about how the system is used. The individual interviews together with the different cognitive task analysis protocols gave us deeper knowledge about the users' decision making process. Through the naturalistic observations we captured basic problems that users had with navigation and interaction with information in the system.

The information we got from the interviews and the conducted observations were mainly recorded with pen and paper and in some cases, with permission, they were audio recorded.

During the following phase, proposed solutions for dealing with the general findings were developed and implemented in a prototype. Finally the prototype was used in a qualitative validation of the results.

V. RESULTS

Several findings could be drawn from the field study, however in this paper we focus on the issues concerning the navigation between overview and details and alarm management.

A prototype was created in order to test and verify the proposed solutions during the development phase and in order to get qualitative response from end-users. The prototype was developed with C# as programming language and Windows Presentation Foundation (WPF) was used for the graphical user interface. The GAV Framework [9] provided us with the parallel coordinates control component.

A. Overview and details

Having an overview of the situation in the power grid has been highlighted by basically all types of users as critical and the most common views chosen for that purpose are the alarm list, in combination with single line diagrams (SLD). To have a complete overview the operators also have to find detailed information in many different views and it takes a lot of time and effort to just find the right views and place them on the available displays. One operator commented on moving from one alarm in the list to the station SLD and to find the right device is one of the most time-consuming tasks that operators face. Even if this statement came from a single operator it could be confirmed by observing other operators.

Another observation was a problem with the current function that takes the user directly from one alarm to the corresponding device on an SLD. The new view is opened on top of the alarm list and the user has to rearrange the views on his available displays to avoid hiding important

information on the alarm list. Thus this function is not used very often.

Our proposed solution to the above findings is to implement a system based on the concept of multiple and coordinated views. Figure 3 displays an alarm list view coordinated with an SLD view. A selection of one alarm in the alarm list will make the SLD diagram view automatically display the matching SLD for the device raising the alarm and with the device highlighted to guide the operator to directly understand where the device is located. Other alarms related to the same device is also highlighted in the list and gives the user an instant way to understand if the alarm is recurring or what the previous alarm from the same device was about.

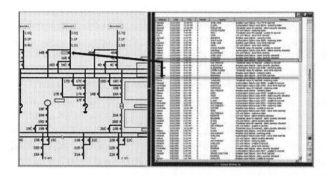

Figure 3. Selection of one alarm in the alarm list automatically displays the matching SLD and the device causing the alarm is highlighted. Other alarms related to the same device is also highlighted in the list

The geographical overview could also be coordinated with the alarm list and then a selection of one alarm in the list would highlight the related station in the geographical overview. Figure 4 demonstrates that the coordination should also work in the opposite direction and a selection of a station in the geographical overview would highlight the related alarms in the alarm list and the matching SLD would be displayed in the SLD view.

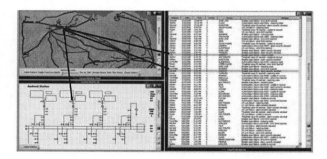

Figure 4. Substation selection in geographical overview highlights alarms in alarm list and displays the corresponding SLD with the alarming devices highlighted

The field studies also revealed a need to show more information about alarms in some kind of overview. This was specifically mentioned by operators in American control rooms. Several operators explained that when they receive a new alarm they have to find the right information in different places and often scroll down large tabular lists before they know what to do and how they should act. One operator would like to be able to extract more information from the overview and mentions which device has caused an alarm as an example. Today, he can only see that information in the SLDs if he zooms in on the right area. Also other operators said that details about devices are hard or slow to find. According to one operator, the SLD should show the details about breakers already in that view instead of another level of windows on top of a station's SLD. Others suggested that if the station name is clicked, the operators should see more detailed data on that station.

The above findings are all related to overview and details on demand and these problems could also be solved with the implementation of multiple and coordinated views since it provides a direct relation between the overview and details about objects and devices. Instead of mapping detailed information onto the geographical overview display or onto the SLDs, making them more cluttered, the user can easily find more information about an object by selecting it on the overview or SLD. The coordinated detailed view would then show more information about the object, see Figure 5. If the user selects another object the detailed view would automatically display the related information.

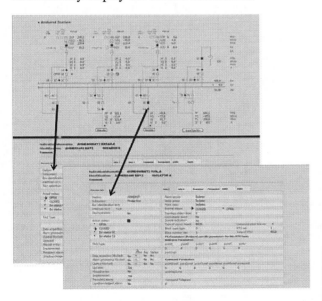

Figure 5. Selection of a device on SLD automatically display its detailed information view

Another problem that operators expressed is that they *"cannot measure disturbance"* in general. The overall disturbance must be deduced by using a number of different views of the system, which is cumbersome. One operator also said that *"we have to read all values in SLDs instead of seeing*

relevant things directly". Even if this statement came from one single operator the observations of the others confirmed this issue. These findings underpin the need for having good situation awareness.

Because of the complexity of the system it is difficult to have all needed information in one single view. Instead the operator has to navigate through different disconnected views and put the pieces of information together to a complete picture. The alarm list view is, for example, suitable for identifying the most recent alarms, since it is usually sorted chronological, and get more detailed information about them. But to find out where the alarms are located the operator has to first look at the alarm list and then find the interesting alarm on the geographical overview or on the SLDs. Thus, to understand where the most recent alarms are located the operator has to put information from the different types of views together and this is a cognitively demanding process.

By coordinating the displays the operator can easily answer the following questions: Where are the most recent alarms? How are alarms distributed in the power grid? Is there a specific part of the grid that is affected? The operator can select an alarm in the list and the geographical display highlights the station having the alarms selected and the operator can directly see where those alarms are located on the SLD.

Coordinated views also solve the problem of cumbersome exploration of various lists in the system. The alarm list is one example but there are many more. The items in the lists usually refer to one object in the system and the normal procedure is to navigate from one item in the list to a detailed view of the object in the SLD. This is done either using a function reached through the context menu that appears when right-clicking on the item or with a direct link. As a result the first view, the list, is either hidden or replaced by the new view, the SLD. The user must therefore re-arrange the views in order to monitor the list and get more detailed information at the same time or use backward and forward interaction to switch between the list and the details. If the user wants more information about another item in the list the same procedure must be performed again and this makes exploration of information a time consuming process.

Thus the proposed solution of implementing multiple and coordinated views is addressing both the problem with detailed views hiding the overview and the cumbersome way of navigating between overviews and details. The solution also addresses the problem of information scattered in different places in the system and the need to navigate through a number of views to build a mental model of the situation. Multiple and coordinated views support the operator in the sensemaking process by providing an intuitive way to explore data from different views and understand relationships among data.

B. Alarm management

One of the most critical issues that was found from the field studies were the information overflow that operators experience in critical situations. One operator described a specific situation when he received over 60 pages of alarms in 30 seconds. During that situation they missed important alarms about a transmission line that had a high load.

A major event in the system can be followed by a large number of alarms and events reported and the only view that operators can rely on in that situation is the alarm list. From the alarm list the operator needs to prioritize and find the root cause or causes of the problems and understand how the current situation can be resolved. Thus a large portion of the operators' daily work is going through pages of alarms.

It was also observed that too many alarms seems to make operators regularly ignore some of them and they need to trust their experience to identify the alarms that are essential. The need to manually narrow down alarms was expressed by several operators. In every control room except one, it was specifically mentioned that alarm filtering must be improved from their existing implementation.

Even if the users clearly expressed the need to narrow down the alarm list they also highlighted the fact that it is risky to filter alarms and filtering rules must be considered carefully since it is crucial that operators not miss important information. It is not possible to only look at the order of the alarms to detect the root cause alarm and filter out the rest. The alarm limits may also have been configured incorrectly, which makes it risky to use as the only filtering attribute.

Today each alarm is traditionally represented with a row in the list and has a number of different attributes that are divided in different columns. Examples of attributes are time, type and priority. The alarm list can be sorted by the different attribute columns and there is also a possibility to filter the list by entering limits to the attributes in a separate dialogue window. This functionality is not used according to the field studies and one explanation for that is that operators are afraid of missing important information. For example, if the list is filtered to only show alarms of priority 1-3, there is a risk that important information is passing by without notice since alarm limits may have been calibrated incorrectly. Each alarm that is reported to the alarm list has to be acknowledged by the operator to tell the system that it has been noticed. Only when it has been acknowledged and when the cause of the alarm has been cleared it disappears from the list.

One comment from an operator was: *"Every alarm counts in some way"*. This comment indicates that operators somehow use alarms that they, at first impression, seem to ignore. Even if the operator acknowledges some alarms without any further analysis they are still used in the creation of the mental model of the situation. Observations show that operators need the information hidden in the vast amount of alarms but also that they need an intuitive way to identify the alarms that they should focus on.

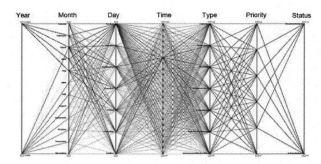

Figure 6. Parallel coordinates display showing alarm items as horizontal lines crossing alarm attributes values mapped to the vertical parallel axes

Thus operators need a more efficient and interactive way of filtering alarms without the risk of removing important information. The proposed solution is to coordinate the alarm list with a visualization technique that also can be used for interactive filtering of the alarm list. The suggested technique is parallel coordinates, see Figure 6, since it also can reveal hidden patterns in the huge number of alarms. In the parallel coordinates display, each alarm attribute is represented by a parallel axis and each alarm is represented with a line crossing through the vertical axis at the alarm's corresponding attribute value. From this view it is possible to explore alarm patterns and find out if there seems to be a correlation between some of the attributes, for example alarm type and time.

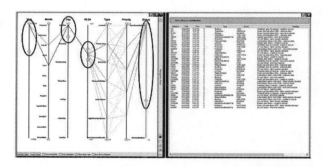

Figure 7. Interactive visual filtering of alarm list using the sliders in the coordinated parallel coordinate graph

Figure 7 demonstrates how the alarm list can be narrowed down by using the sliders on the vertical axis, in the parallel coordinate graph, representing the alarm attributes. Depending on the situation the user can have the option to either remove or fade the filtered alarms from the list and from the parallel coordinates display. The reason why the filtered out alarms should be faded out instead of removed is the risk of losing important information that is hidden in the alarms. The user can focus on a selection of the alarms but still keep the overview of all alarms and identify patterns.

Parallel coordinates is not a suitable representation for all alarm attributes. The location of the object that is sending the alarm is, for example, better shown on a SLD or on a geographical map. The solution with coordinated views solves this issue since an SLD and a geographical map can be coordinated with the parallel coordinates display and the alarm list, see Figure 8. Then the operator can carry out filtering operations by selecting regions of the map or of the single line diagram and look at alarms only from that specific region.

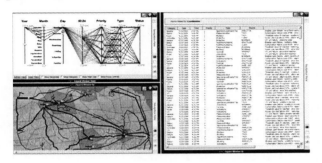

Figure 8. A coordinated geographical view provides a way to interactively filter out alarms based on regions

Thus, the final solution to coordinate the alarm list with a parallel coordinates display, a geographical overview and/or a SLD provide the operator with an intuitive way of exploring many alarms and detecting patterns. It addresses the need for narrowing down the number of alarms so that operators can focus on specific areas without the risk of losing important information.

VI. DISCUSSION AND FUTURE WORK

The field studies have shown that today the sensemaking process of reaching situation awareness is cumbersome. Operators are required to put pieces of information together from disconnected views in the system and the navigation between overview and details is especially challenging.

The developed prototype was presented to end-users during three focus groups meetings in USa, India and Denmark (including end-users from the Nordic countries). During the focus group session the end-users had the opportunity to try out the proposed interactive visualization techniques. The qualitative feedback from the end-users was gathered and will be used to refine the proposed solutions.

Overall the users were impressed by the proposed solutions and asked if they will be implemented in the real system. The users were also asked to fill in a questionnaire about how they felt about the different solutions. The answers from the questionnaire, in combination with verbal feedback, indicate that the multiple and coordinated views and parallel coordinates, in particular, have the potential to enhance the way operators interact with data in the system.

High learning threshold is usually listed as one of the major drawbacks of parallel coordinates. Thus one of the

objectives with the qualitative analysis of our proposed solutions was to find out if the end-users understand the visualization technique and how it can be used. Observations of the users while trying out the prototype, together with verbal feedback and the answers in the questionnaires show that users understand the parallel coordinates display. They started to discuss how it could be used for representing other types of data in the system. One operator said: -"*I am a part of a group that meets every week to discuss alarm patterns and parallel coordinates would therefore be very good for us. I mean having this tool for figuring out what the data is trying to tell you.*" Another statement made by an operator was: -"*The parallel coordinates would be very good; it would be possible to use this in real time.*" These statements indicate that the visualization technique is understood and can probably be used for identifying patterns in the alarms.

Another identified issue were the need to narrow down the number of alarms in the alarm list. The proposed solution, using parallel coordinates for representing alarms and providing a visual way to filter the coordinated alarm list, was evaluated in a quantitative and qualitative user study. Preliminary results, so far, indicate that the parallel coordinates display coordinated with the alarm list outperformed the alarm list alone in terms of execution time, correct answers to tasks and other usability attributes, in particular for tasks rated as difficult. The user study did not compare filtering alarms and selecting a subset of alarms in the parallel coordinates display alone. Thus the improved performance cannot be derived from only the parallel coordinates display but in coordination with the alarm list. However, subjective user responses were recorded and comments about the alarm list's strength when it comes to sequential sorting and the level of details in comparison with the parallel coordinates display were mentioned. This implies that the solution of coordinating multiple views support the user in the sensemaking process by providing a way to combine the strength of both representations.

Section III demonstrates the tendency to believe that new visualization techniques are the solution for problems with situation awareness. Visualization techniques play an important role but a single view containing all possible information an operator needs, to have complete situation awareness, would be to cluttered. The evaluation of colour contours showed, for example, that the combination of colour contours and numerical values had the worst performance [13]. When they were separated each of them was effective but for different situations. This underpins the fact that the best solution is to create visualizations that are effective for representing some aspect of the data and coordinate them together to build a complete mental model of the situation.

Adoption of the concept of multiple and coordinated views opens up a new way for exploring information and supporting the operators' sensemaking process to build situation awareness, not only from one view but from several.

This makes it promising to continue to develop customized visualization strategies for efficient identification of specific aspects of the system and by coordination find relationships between them.

The proposed solutions are based on results from field studies in the power grid system domain. It is possible that the proposed solutions could be applicable to other human supervisory control systems, used in other domains, where data and information is spread over a vast amount of various views, and where operators need intuitive way of navigating between overview and details.

Based on the results obtained in this work we will continue to investigate how multiple and coordinated views in combination with existing and new visualization techniques can improve operators' sensemaking process to achieve situation awareness in human supervisory control systems. Qualitative and quantitative evaluations of the proposed solutions in real world situations are discussed as the next step, both in the power grid system domain and in industrial process control.

ACKNOWLEDGEMENTS

We wish to thank the project leader Dilip Kota for arranging the field study and making things happen and Martin Naedele, Claus Vetter and Magnus Larsson for supporting this work.

We would also like to thank Missy Cummings and her researchers in the Humans and Automation Laboratory (HAL) at Massachusetts Institute of Technology (MIT), and Matthew Cooper at Linköping University for valuable input and discussions.

This work was partly supported by the ABB Industrial Software Systems program and partly by the Swedish Research Council in the Linnaeus Centre CADICS.

REFERENCES

[1] M. Q. Wang Baldonado, A. Woodruff, and A. Kuchinsky. Guidelines for using multiple views in information visualization. In *Proceedings of the working conference on Advanced visual interfaces*, pages 110–119, 2000.

[2] X. Bei, C. Yuksel, A. Abur, and E. Akleman. 3d visualization of power system state estimation. In *IEEE Mediterranean Electrotechnical Conference*, pages 943–947, 2006.

[3] M. R. Endsley. Toward a theory of situation awareness in dynamic systems. *Human Factors: The Journal of the Human Factors and Ergonomics Society*, 37:32–64, 1995.

[4] F. L. Greitzer, A. Schur, M. Paget, and R. T. Guttromson. A sensemaking perspective on situation awareness in power grid operations. In *Power and Energy Society General Meeting—Conversion and Delivery of Electrical Energy in the 21st Century, IEEE*, pages 1–6, 2008.

[5] R. R. Hoffman. Protocols for Cognitive Task Analysis. Technical report, State of Florida Institute for Human and Machine Cognition, May 2005.

[6] R. R. Hoffman, B. Crandall, and N. R. Shadbolt. Use of the critical decision method to elicit expert knowledge: A case study in the methodology of cognitive task analysis. *Human Factors*, 40:254–276, 1998.

[7] Robert Hutton, Gary Klein, and Sterling Wiggins. Designing for sensemaking: A macrocognitive approach. In *Sensemaking Workshop, CHI'08*, 2008.

[8] A. Inselberg. The plane with parallel coordinates. *The Visual Computer*, 1(4):69–91, 1985.

[9] M. Jern, S. Johansson, J. Johansson, and J. Franzén. The gav toolkit for multiple linked views. In *Proceedings IEEE International Conference on Coordinated and Multiple Views in Exploratory Visualization 2007*, pages 85–97, 2007.

[10] G. Klein, B. Moon, and R. Hoffman. Making sense of sensemaking 1: Alternative perspectives. *IEEE Intelligent Systems*, 21:70–73, 2006.

[11] G. Klein, B. Moon, and R. Hoffman. Making sense of sensemaking 2: A macrocognitive model. *IEEE Intelligent Systems*, 21:88–92, 2006.

[12] T. J. Overbye, , and J. D Weber. Visualization of power system data. In *Proceedings of the 33rd Annual International Conference on System Sciences*, 2000.

[13] T. J. Overbye, D. A. Wiegmann, A. M. Rich, and Y. Sun. Human factors aspects of power system voltage contour visualizations. *IEEE Transactions on Power Systems*, 18:76–82, 2003.

[14] T.J. Overbye, E. M. Rantanen, and S. Judd. Electric power control center visualization using geographic data views. In *REP Symposium on Bulk Power System Dynamics and Control - VII, Revitalizing Operational Reliabilityi*, pages 1–8, 2007.

[15] T. B Sheridan. *Telerobotics, Automation, and Human Supervisory Control*. MIT Press, 1992.

[16] B. Shneiderman. The eyes have it: A task by data type taxonomy for information visualizations. In *VL '96: Proceedings of the 1996 IEEE Symposium on Visual Languages*, pages 336–343, 1996.

[17] H.S. Smallman, M. St. John, H.M. Oonk, and M.B. Cowen. Information availability in 2d and 3d displays. *Computer Graphics and Applications, IEEE*, 21(5):51 –57, 2001.

[18] J. D. Weber and T. J. Overbye. Voltage contours for power system visualization. *IEEE Transactions on Power Systems*, 15(1):404–409, 2000.

[19] D. A. Wiegmann, T. J. Overbye, S. M. Hoppe, G.R Essenberg, and S. Yan. Human factors aspects of three-dimensional visualization of power system information. In *IEEE Power Engineering Society General Meeting*, 2006.

[20] S. Yan and T. J. Overbye. Visualizations for power system contingency analysis data. *IEEE Transactions on Power Systems*, 19(4):1859–1866, 2004.

[21] C. E. Zsambok. *Naturalistic Decision Making*. Lawrence Erlbaum Associates, 1996.

Gesture-Based Input for Drawing Schematics on a Mobile Device

Daniel Chivers, Peter Rodgers

Department of Computer Science, University of Kent, Canterbury

dc355@kent.ac.uk, P.J.Rodgers@kent.ac.uk

Abstract

We present a system for drawing metro map style schematics using a gesture-based interface. This work brings together techniques in gesture recognition on touch-sensitive devices with research in schematic layout of networks. The software allows users to create and edit schematic networks, and provides an automated layout method for improving the appearance of the schematic. A case study using the metro map metaphor to visualize social networks and web site structure is described.

*Keywords--- **Gesture-Based Input, Sketching Input, Metro Maps, Schematics, Mobile Device.***

1. Introduction

Visualizing complex, interconnected information using a metro map is a common metaphor. Data from many application areas has the potential to be visualized in this way, for example metro map diagrams for astronomical data and web trends, are shown in [15]. Other types of data drawn as a metro map, such as thesis structure and a business plans can be found at [8]. Typically, these examples have been drawn by hand using vector graphics applications, requiring a great deal of time and effort. An alternative approach is to use an existing metro map and change the labels to make the new data fit the existing structure, as can be seen in [14], which is based on the London Underground. However, this method is restricted to data sets that can fit into an existing layout. These examples are evidence that users want to visualize data using a metro map metaphor but the difficulty in creating this style of diagram by hand means that it has not been explored to its full potential.

Mobile touch based devices have a great potential for creating schematics as they allow users to conveniently and effectively capture complex ideas in a clear, easy to read schematic at any time. With this in mind our aim was to develop a piece of software to meet these needs.

The application we have developed, SchemaSketch (see Figure 1), facilitates the fast drawing of metro map style schematics and allows the user to create them in such a way that the schematic contains information about the underlying connections. This makes it much easier for the user to reposition stations, as all lines remain connected when nodes move. The software can be downloaded from:
http://cs.kent.ac.uk/projects/schemasketch/iv2011.

As the diagram contains structural data, it is also possible to perform automatic layout techniques to attempt to improve the schematic. An example of this automatic layout has been implemented into SchemaSketch. Inspired by the methods developed in [7], the application attempts to position nodes to satisfy a series of criteria based upon aesthetic quality of the diagram.

We have developed SchemaSketch to run on portable Android devices, which allows the user to draw their ideas whilst away from a computer. For example, whilst on public transport or for workers out in the field where a larger computer may be impractical. In addition, touch screen devices, such as mobile phones, are commonly used which makes the system widely accessible.

There are few current applications that support schematic drawing of metro maps. Example applications which claim to, such as [2] and [5], are general purpose vector based graphic applications and do not allow easy modification of drawn schematics, as they do not preserve connectivity information.

We have examined previous work in gesture based input [1], sketch recognition and beautification of hand

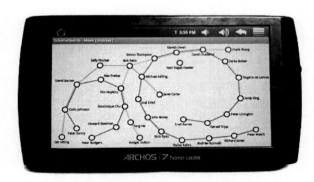

Figure 1: SchemaSketch running on an Archos 7 HT device using Android v1.5

1550-6037/11 $26.00 © 2011 IEEE

DOI 10.1109/IV.2011.50

drawn sketches [6][9][12] in order to decide on an efficient and intuitive input mechanism for drawing schematics. Although full sketch recognition can provide more advanced functionality by supporting a variety of symbols, it comes with a performance overhead in recognition, as well as a mechanism to determine when the user has finished one symbol and moves onto the next. Mechanisms to circumvent this include a waiting time between pen strokes [12], but this hinders the input flow of the user. Simpler gesture recognition, where each gesture corresponds to a symbol, can provide the functionality we require and will ensure the user is not disturbed by workflow pauses.

Previous work on automatic metro map includes work that applies a force directed approach [13]. Other research uses a series of criteria to measure aesthetic elements of the schematic, such as line straightness, octilinearity and line length between nodes [7][10]. User tests, such as those carried out in [4], have shown that diagrams that conform strongly to combinations of these criteria have increased readability. Although these papers use different methods for optimisation, we have chosen to implement a method inspired by that in [7] due to its flexibility, as aesthetic criteria can be modified relatively easily.

In the remainder of this paper, Section 2 describes in detail the user interface of SchemaSketch, as well as implementation details of gestures, connections, and labels. Section 3 describes the layout and optimisation techniques including implementation of layout criteria used by SchemaSketch to optimise drawn schematics. Section 4 describes our results and provides some examples of the software in use, as well as discussing current problems. Section 5 outlines potential future work. Finally, Section 6 gives our conclusions.

2. Interface and Implementation

We have developed a software tool that allows a user to hand draw schematics on a touch based mobile device. The application, SchemaSketch, has been written to run on mobile devices running Google's Android operating system. It has been developed on v1.5 but is compatible with newer releases and will accommodate a variety of screen sizes. It provides two operating modes for creation of schematics, draw (input) and move (modification), which can be toggled in the main menu. These two modes of operation are described in Sections 2.1 and 2.2 respectively.

2.1. Draw Mode

This mode allows schematics to be created by using sequences of gestures to input objects (see Section 2.3 for details on gesture recognition). The following list describes the objects that can be drawn in the schematic.

- *Station* – SchemaSketch provides two different types of station object, a circular station and a line station. These two stations are visually different and are input using different gestures, however they are treated the same from a connectivity perspective. Circular stations are intended to be used for representing junction stations, whereas line stations are intended for use in situations where the station has two or less incident edges. Stations are used to connect together multiple edges, of the same or different colour. A label can be added to either type of station object.

- *Edge* - Provides a connection between two stations. SchemaSketch provides support for different coloured edges to be drawn. Parallel edges (of a different colour) can be drawn between two stations. Edges allow the formation of metro lines. Metro map lines are considered to be several connecting edges of the same colour.

Whilst in this mode, the menu provides the following options:

- *Eraser* – Changes the pen to an eraser pen that will remove everything drawn over.
- *Undo* – Undo the last action.
- *Colour* – Change the colour of the Edge.
- *Clear All* – Clears all objects from the screen (requires confirmation).
- *Mode: Move* – Switch to the move mode (see Section 2.2).

The draw mode also allows the user to add labelling to the schematic, see Section 2.5 for details.

2.2. Move Mode

This mode allows the manual modification of a drawn schematic, by enabling drag and drop functionality for stations and labels.

Whilst in this mode, the menu provides the following options:

- *Eraser* – Changes the pen to an eraser pen that will remove everything drawn over.
- *Undo* – Undo the last action.
- *Optimise* – Uses a hill climbing multicriteria optimiser method to produce a more optimised schematic (see Section 3).
- *Load/Save* – allows the loading and saving of drawn schematics to a file.
- *Mode: Draw* – Switch to the draw mode (see Section 2.1).

The draw mode also allows the user to manually move labels on the schematic, see Section 2.5 for details.

2.3. Gestures

Multiple gestures are used to input the various objects defined in Section 2.1. Gestures are recorded as a sequence of time-stamped points. When the user makes a gesture, SchemaSketch will attempt to recognise the gesture based on a series of rules.

- **Minimum direct length to be classified as an edge.**
  Direct length refers to the distance between the start and end points of the gesture. For a gesture to be an Edge object, this distance must be greater than 45 pixels.

- **Minimum straightness to be classified as an edge.**
  The straightness of a gesture, G, is calculated using Equation 1.

$$straightness(G) = \left(\frac{dist(G_{Start}, G_{End})}{actualLength(G)} \right)$$

Equation 1

actualLength(G) is calculated using Equation 2. The straightness calculation will produce a value between 0 and 1. A value of 1 is a perfectly straight line. For a gesture to be classed as an edge, *straightness(G)* must be greater than 0.9.

If a gesture passes the minimum direct length test and minimum straightness test, it can be classified as an edge, otherwise it is potentially a station. Differentiating between the two types of station is performed by the three following rules.

- **Minimum actual length to be classified as a station.**
  Actual length refers to the length of the gesture if it was straightened out, and is calculated using Equation 2, where n is the number of points in the gesture and p_i is the ith point along the gesture.

$$actualLength(G) = \sum_{i=1}^{n-1} \left(dist(p_i, p_{i+1}) \right)$$

Equation 2

actualLength(G) must be greater than 10 pixels for the gesture to be a station. This means any gesture shorter than 10 pixels will not be recognised and nothing will be added to the diagram. This is useful for discarding unintentional screen touches.

- **Minimum straightness to be classified as a line station.**
  The straightness is once again checked using Equation 1 and if *straightness(G)* is greater than 0.5 then it will be classified as a line station. Although stations and edges are both straight lines, edges require a higher *straightness(G)* value because the

longer a gesture, the easier it is to get a high *straightness(G)* value.

- **Minimum average radius to be classified as a circular station.**
  If *straightness(G)* is less than (or equal to) 0.5 this last check is performed to identify a circular station gesture. We calculate the average radius of the shape (we know the shape is curved, as *straightness(G)* is low). First we calculate the centre point of the gesture, by averaging x and y co-ordinates of all points. Using this, we can calculate the average radius using Equation 3, where n is the number of points in the gesture and p_i is the ith point along the gesture.

$$radius(G) = \frac{\sum_{i=1}^{n} \left(dist(G_{centre}, p_i) \right)}{n}$$

Equation 3

If *radius(G)* is greater than 10 pixels, this gesture can now be classified as a circular station, otherwise the gesture will not be recognised and nothing will be added to the diagram.

These rules result in stations being drawn either by a short, straight gesture or a circular shape with start and end points close together. Edges are drawn by a long, straight gesture.

2.4. Connections

SchemaSketch connects edges to stations based upon location of the gesture. Starting an edge in the vicinity of a station will connect that edge to the station; conversely, drawing a circular station around an unconnected end of an edge (or multiple edge ends) will connect the edges to the newly drawn station. Line stations will also connect to multiple edges provided they are close enough. When the user is drawing, any object that an edge can connect to will display a highlighted "hotspot" which is the object's connection radius.

Drawing a line station that intersects an edge will insert it at that point along the edge, or if the station is close enough to a free end, it will attach to that.

2.5. Labelling

Labels can be added to stations whilst in draw mode. Touching on a station will open a text input dialog allowing the user to enter a label name.

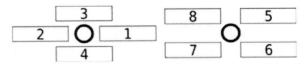

Figure 2: Possible positions for labels relative to their parent node. The values indicate the priority of each position

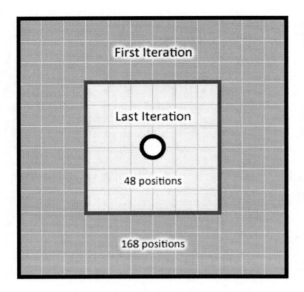

Figure 3: Distance nodes are moved during first and last optimisation iterations

Whilst in move mode, labels can be moved manually by dragging them around their parent. There are eight positions in which a label can be placed, these positions relative to the parent node are *North, North-East, East, South-East, South, South-West, West* and *North-West,* as shown in Figure 2. A label will initially be placed in position 4 (*South*).

3. Layout and Optimisation

SchemaSketch includes a multicriteria optimiser to produce more easily read schematics. This optimiser is inspired by work performed in [7]. SchemaSketch's specifics are outlined in Section 3.1. We have chosen to use a subset of the criteria used in this prior work for optimising node and label positioning, as many of these criteria are not appropriate for our case.

3.1. Optimiser

SchemaSketch's optimisation process uses a number of iterations of station movements, currently set to 10. During each iteration, each station is examined in turn and placed in available grid positions around it. As well as moving stations, clustering methods (based on those that group lines in [7]) are applied to move groups of stations.

The optimiser uses a cooling method to attempt to reduce the number of position checks the algorithm performs. Figure 3 shows the distance nodes are moved; during the first iteration, each node is tested in all positions up to six squares away (168 positions), this distance decreases linearly down to three squares (48 positions) during the last iteration. Fractional values are rounded up to the nearest integer. Stations are not permitted to go beyond the limits of the screen.

At each station or cluster movement, a series of criteria are calculated and summed to produce a value representing a measurement of the aesthetic quality of the schematic; the lower this value the better - a value of zero indicates all criteria have been satisfied. The criteria used for this value are explained in Section 3.2. This value is recorded for each position the station or cluster is moved to, and once all positions have been tested it is moved to the position that yielded the lowest criteria value (indicating the best aesthetic quality).

After optimisation of the stations, the labels are examined in turn to determine their best position. They are tested in a single step. Figure 2 shows the order in which label positions are considered (from 1 to 8). At each position, the label criteria are calculated and labels are moved to the position with the lowest summed criteria value. The criteria used in the label positioning stage are explained in Section 3.3. Testing the labels in order of position preference ensures that if multiple positions have the same summed criteria value, it will be placed at the first found.

3.2. Station Criteria

This section explains the station positioning criteria used to determine the quality of the layout.

The criteria values often have a squared component, this is to ensure that the worst criteria are penalized more strongly. For criteria such as line straightness, this also provides the desirable behaviour that fewer sharper bends are penalised more than multiple smaller bends.

The calculations produce values which vary greatly by criterion (up to many orders of magnitude different), this is because the criteria are measured naturally on different scales. Using these unweighted values would put more emphasis on the criteria that were naturally larger, it is therefore necessary to weight the values so that they can be comparable.

Basic weighting involves multiplying the unweighted value by 1 over the maximum possible value; this constrains the value to between 0 and 1. However, it would be incorrect/not possible to scale all criteria in this way as they may never reach the maximum in practice, or alternatively they may not have a maximum. Therefore, to calculate weightings, we created a series of example graphs and recorded the unweighted criteria values. We averaged the values and used the inverse of the result as the weighting.

The first stage of optimisation is to snap all stations onto a grid. This is accomplished by examining all stations and moving them to the nearest grid position. If multiple stations contest a grid position, the original position of contested stations will be checked, and the closest one moved. This grid has multiple advantages to simplify the optimisation process. 1) By using a grid we can minimise the number of possible station positions that we are required to check, greatly speeding up the process 2) By moving stations to fit to a grid, we get the benefit of helping the octilinearity of edges between stations 3) Station/station occlusion checks are not necessary providing the grid spacing is greater than the station's bounding box diameter.

The five station criteria that we use are:

1. **Octilinear Layout.** This criterion is to keep the graph as octilinear as possible; this means keeping all angles at multiples of $45°$. The octilinear layout criterion sums the measure for each edge. The measurement for an edge is a square of the difference in angle from the nearest multiple of $45°$.

2. **Minimise Edge Crossings.** Edge crossings should be kept to a minimum. The edge crossings criterion is measured by checking all pairs of edges for an intersection, and then summing the number of intersections and squaring it.

3. **Line Straightness.** Lines, a group of connected edges that share the same colour, should be as straight as possible and when bends are required they should be as small an angle as is attainable. The line straightness criterion sums a calculation for each line bend. The line bend calculation is the square of the angle the bend makes, penalising a line more if it contains sharper bends.

4. **Equal Edge Lengths.** Edges between stations should be of equal length, and they should also try to achieve a desirable target length, t. This length has been defined as three grid squares. The criterion sums a calculation for each edge. The edge calculation squares the difference between the edge length and the desirable length. As we are using an octilinear layout for the graph, we must account for diagonal edges. Because of this, we adjust the value of t to be three times the diagonal distance across a grid square when necessary.

5. **Occlusions.** Stations and edges should be positioned in a way that they do not obscure any other part of the schematic. Possible occlusions include station/station, station/edge, and edge/edge. Because the optimiser is based on a grid positioning system, it cannot place one station on top of another and therefore station/station occlusions cannot happen. Also, the *Minimise Edge Crossings* criterion includes edge/edge occlusions and so this need not be dealt with here. This means that this criterion only needs to check for station/edge occlusions. The number of indirectly connected station/edge occlusions is counted by checking each possible pairing for an intersection, and this result is squared to create the occlusion criterion.

3.3. Label Criteria

This section explains the criteria used for label positioning. As label criteria are not included in the main layout of the schematic, they do not require weighting. In terms of priority, labels will only be placed in a consistent position when it is possible to do so without introducing occlusions. The two label criteria are defined as following:

1. **Occlusions.** Labels should not overlap edges or other labels. This criterion is measured by calculating the label bounding box and checking against each edge and other label for an intersection. The number of intersections is counted to create the value.

2. **Position Consistency.** It is desirable for adjacent labels to be similarly positioned. This is achieved by penalising labels that are not in the same position as their neighbours. All labels with exactly one or two neighbouring stations are checked and given a scoring based upon their position consistency (one point per difference in label positioning to both other stations). The value is the sum of the consistency values for all such stations.

The work described in [7] uses additional criteria, but these have been omitted because they are application area specific or ineffective in our model. In particular, some criteria are designed for use with data that has a spatial component such as metro maps that contain geographic relationships between the stations. These criteria include those that prevent large distortions and changes in topology, so retaining some geographical accuracy. Another criterion used by this previous work, angular resolution, which maximizes the angle between incident edges at a station has not been used. However, its effect is also performed by the octilinear criterion, so there is no need for a separate calculation.

4. Results and Examples

The following sections provide examples of data sets that can be displayed in a metro map style using the application. The examples shown also illustrate the optimisation method.

As illustrated in [15], there is clearly a use for software that allows the drawing and optimisation of metro map style schematics using abstract data, as the examples that can be found there have been time-consumingly drawn by hand.

SchemaSketch is still at the proof-of-concept stage, hence it cannot currently replace a vector graphics program for complete creation of metro map style schematics because of the aesthetic appearance of the final diagrams. However, we believe the software illustrates the potential for saving users considerable time by allowing fast and easy drawing of schematics. In addition, the built in optimiser can further aid users by helping them optimise their graphs according to a set of criteria. In Section 5 we discuss the export of drawn schematics to multiple file formats, which would allow the user to switch to a vector graphics software package for further editing.

4.1. Social Networks as a Metro Map

Here we demonstrate how the metro map metaphor can be used for the visualization of social networks. Stations are used to represent individuals, and different coloured lines correspond to the type of relationship between them. Figures 4 and 5 show an example of a

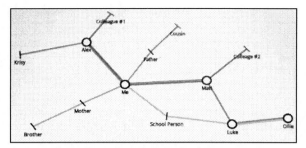

Figure 4: Social network before optimisation

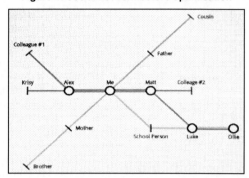

Figure 5: Social network after optimisation

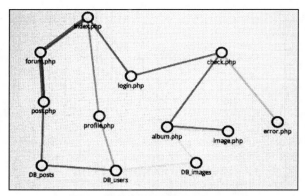

Figure 7: Website before optimisation

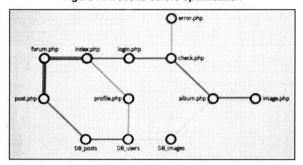

Figure 8: Website after optimisation

social network drawn as a metro map, before and after optimisation. Here we show the family and friendship relationships centred on one individual.

Another example of where this type of visualization may be desired is for the display of personnel structure within a company or department, for example academic staff in a research institute can belong to multiple research groups. These can be represented as the coloured lines as shown in Figure 6. This schematic was conceived using SchemaSketch to draw the initial structure and plan an effective layout of the stations (as can be seen in Figure 9); it was then re-created using a vector graphics drawing application.

4.2. Website planning as a Metro Map

As well as social networks, the structure of a website (from either an end user or a developers perspective) can be effectively visualized using the metro map metaphor. Figures 7 and 8 illustrate how a website can be visualized from a developers perspective by representing the individual pages and database tables as stations, and

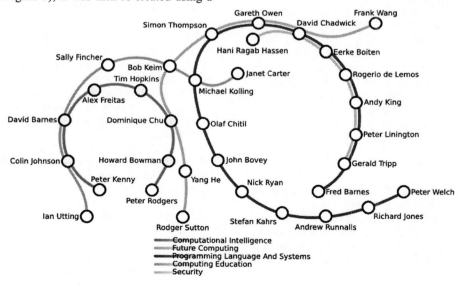

Figure 6: Metro map style schematic showing staff research areas in the University of Kent, Canterbury

the lines as aspects of the system, for example pages that require user authentication.

A designer may wish to plan the pages or services of a website for personal use or to show to a customer. The metro map at [3] illustrates an example of this use in practice. There, the designer of this diagram explains how he struggled to understand how aspects of the system were related when designing a course plan. Designing the system as a metro map allowed him to see the related aspects that could be combined into topics for the course.

In addition to this, a metro map based site diagram could be made into an interactive diagram to allow users to click on the stations to take them to that page, as well as providing a more interesting overview than the commonly used hierarchical text structure.

4.3. Issues with the System

Currently the canvas size is restricted to the size of the screen. This can be problematic as it limits the size of the schematic that can be drawn. A larger, scrollable canvas, and/or a zoom function would be beneficial to users by allowing them to draw schematics that are not limited in size. This would of course increase computational time for optimisation, but we believe this to be a reasonable trade-off. This size limitation problem sometimes manifests when the optimisation method is run. The optimiser will attempt to spread out schematics that are very dense, because it will attempt to normalise edge lengths, and if there is not enough room for the expansion, schematics will remain squashed into the available space. Figures 9 and 10 show an example of where a dense graph has been squashed onto a canvas that is too small for the optimiser to function correctly. The optimiser does not have enough canvas space to be able to move the stations to more desirable positions.

Besides canvas space, it is possible that the optimiser will remain in a state of local minima. A method in which the optimiser is allowed to make changes for the worse (such as Simulated Annealing) may be able to alleviate these local minima problems, but would increase the search space of the optimiser and increase optimisation time.

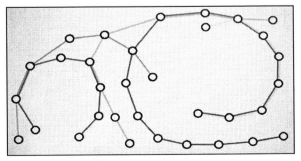

Figure 9: Dense graph before optimisation

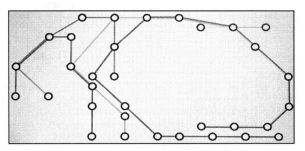

Figure 10: Dense graph after optimisation

5. Future Work

The multicriteria optimiser implemented in SchemaSketch allows the easy addition of new criteria. We plan to introduce new experimental criteria for use in user tests in an attempt to find out how much these affect the readability of metro style schematics. Examples of these additional criteria include symmetry, station balancing, parallel lines and station alignment.

The current version of SchemaSketch supports loading and saving of schematics, but this is limited to a bespoke file type. Future work would allow implementation of a mechanism to allow the user to export the schematic for use in other applications. It would be particularly beneficial to allow export to a vector format, for example *.svg*, so that users could import the diagram into other applications and make further edits.

SchemaSketch is not at the stage at which it could replace a vector graphics program for illustration of metro map style schematics in terms of aesthetic quality. However, with implementation effort, this may be an achievable goal and future projects could involve improving the visual quality of the schematics produced.

We have found that a metro map can be an interesting and practical visualization for any data set that contains multiple items which share relationships. There are many data sets like this around on the Internet, where many items are given "tags" (metadata describing a theme or concept) to relate them to the other items. For example, a metro map schematic could be produced from a set of photographs that have been tagged with metadata (for example, Flickr encourages this form of tagging). It would be possible to create a schematic by using line colours to represent tags and so produce a visualization of how all the items are linked together. Unlike simple tagging, it would be easy to see past the first order relations, which may reveal interesting results.

The application area for SchemaSketch is also currently limited due to it supporting only a small number of symbols. The gesture based input system can be modified to allow addition of new symbols which would allow SchemaSketch to be used for specialist applications. For example, electrical symbols could be introduced to allow the design of electrical schematics. This is a viable example of the particular benefits of a mobile device – an electrician may want to plan out electrical circuits whilst out on call, and it would be much more practical to use a small mobile device than a laptop.

Mobile devices use much slower processors than desktop computers, and therefore the optimisation process can take a long time to run. Optimisation time also increases rapidly as more stations and edges are added to the schematic. To make it suitable for mobile devices, optimisation techniques can be introduced to minimise processing time, for example when a station is moved all criteria are currently recalculated. It would be possible to optimise this process so that only the required criteria are calculated on the stations that have changed. Stations with degree 2 could also be combined into a single edge with a weighting indicating the number of stations along them, this would greatly reduce the number of criteria calculations.

6. Conclusions

There are no applications which successfully support schematic drawing of metro maps in the style of Henry Beck's classic London Underground design. Nevertheless, data from a variety of areas is suitable for visualization in this manner.

In answer to this problem we have created SchemaSketch, an application that facilitates the drawing of metro map style schematics on Android devices using a gesture based touch interface. SchemaSketch contains information about the underlying graph structure and this allows easy use of automatic layout techniques to optimise the schematic. SchemaSketch includes a multicriteria optimiser which repositions nodes to satisfy a series of criteria based upon aesthetic quality.

Using SchemaSketch, we have investigated the use of the metro map metaphor for diagramming abstract data collections, such as social networks and websites. During these investigations we have found that metro maps can be an interesting and practical visualization for data sets that consist of multiple items which share relationships.

We have demonstrated that there are practical applications for software such as SchemaSketch, and that even at this early stage of the project's life it can greatly aid users who wish to visualize information in this style.

References

[1] Dean Rubine, *"Specifying Gestures by Example"*, in Proceedings of the 18th annual conference on Computer Graphics and interactive techniques, vol. 25, 1991, pp. 329-337.

[2] Edraw Soft, http://www.edrawsoft.com/, accessed 23/02/2011.

[3] The Moodle 2.0 Administration Map, http://www.synergy-learning.com/blog/moodle/the-moodle-2-0-administration-map/, accessed 24/02/2011.

[4] Helen C. Purchase, Robert F. Cohen and Murray James, *"Validating Graph Drawing Aesthetics"*, in proceedings Graph Drawing 1995. Lecture Notes in Computer Science, vol. 1027, 1996, pp. 435-446.

[5] iMapBuilder, http://www.imapbuilder.com/, accessed 23/02/2011.

[6] Isaac Freeman and Beryl Plimmer *"Connector semantics for sketched diagram recognition"*. AUIC '07 Proc. 8th Australasian conference on User interface 64. ACM, 2007.

[7] Jonathan Stott, Peter Rodgers, Juan Carlos Martínez-Ovando, and Stephen G. Walker. *"Automatic Metro Map Layout Using Multicriteria Optimization."* Transactions on Visualization and Computer Graphics, 16(1):101-114, January 2011.

[8] Keith V. Nesbitt, *"Getting to more Abstract Places using the Metro Map Metaphor"*, in Proceedings of the Information Visualisation, Eighth International Conference, 2004, pp. 488-493.

[9] Levent Burak Kara and Thomas F. Stahovich, *"Hierarchical Parsing and Recognition of Hand-Sketched Diagrams"*, in Proceedings of the 17th annual ACM symposium on user interface software and technology, 2004, pp. 13-22.

[10] Martin Nöllenburg and Alexander Wolff, *"A Mixed-Integer Program for Drawing High-Quality Metro Maps"*, in proceedings Graph Drawing 2006. Lecture Notes in Computer Science, vol. 3843, 2006, pp. 321-333.

[11] Maxwell J. Roberts, *"Underground Maps After Beck"*, Capital Transport Publishing, 2005.

[12] Milda Gusaite, E. Kazanavičius and T. Barkowsky, *"Dynamic Scene Analysis and Beautification for Hand-draw Sketches"*, Masters thesis, Kaunas University of Technology, 2006.

[13] Seok-He Hong, Damian Merrick and Hugo A.D. do Nascimento, *"The Metro Map Layout Problem"*, in APVis '04: Proceedings of the 2004 Australasian Symposium on Information Visualization, vol. 35, 2004, pp. 91-100.

[14] Simon Patterson, The Great Bear, http://www.olivercloke.com/simon-patterson-the-great-bear, accessed 23/02/2011.

[15] Ten examples of the Metro Map Metaphor, http://blog.visualmotive.com/2009/ten-examples-of-the-subway-map-metaphor/, accessed 23/02/2011.

Visualization of Sensory Perception Descriptions

Andreas Kerren, Mimi Prangova
School of Computer Science, Physics and Mathematics (DFM)
Linnaeus University
SE-351 95 Växjö, Sweden
Email (corresponding author): andreas.kerren@lnu.se

Carita Paradis
Centre for Languages and Literature
Lund University
SE-221 00 Lund, Sweden
Email: carita.paradis@englund.lu.se

Abstract—On the basis of a large corpus of wine reviews, this paper proposes a range of interactive visualization techniques that are useful for linguistic exploration and analysis of lexical, grammatical and discursive patterns in text. Our visualization tool allows linguists and others to make comparisons of visual, olfactory, gustatory and textual properties of different wines from different parts of the worlds, from different grape varieties, or from different vintages. It also supports the immediate creation of visual profiles for descriptions of sensory perceptions for exploratory purposes as well as for purposes of confirmatory investigations of linguistic patterns in text and discourse and their correlations to metadata variables.

Keywords-multivariate visualization; interaction techniques; text visualization; scatter plot; dynamic queries; wine reviews;

I. Introduction

In this paper, we present our work on the development of an interactive information visualization tool to be used on corpus data. The tool has been developed on the basis of 84,864 wine reviews, or tasting notes as they are also sometimes called, from the Wine Advocate[1] journal. Thanks to the capacity of the tool to handle large amounts of data and to its dynamic interface, it can be used for exploratory work as well as for confirmatory investigations in linguistics [1].

Wine reviews are descriptions and evaluations of wines written by professional wine tasters. They have a strict rhetorical structure and consist of three parts, starting with production facts and ending with an assessment and a recommendation of prime drinking time. The middle of the text, which is the most important part, is devoted to an iconic description of the wine tasting procedure from the taster's inspection of the wine's visual appearance through smelling, tasting and feeling its texture, i.e., from *vision* through *smell*, *taste*, and *mouthfeel (touch)* [2], cf. sample review (1).

> (1) "This great St.-Estephe estate has turned out a succession of brilliant wines. The 2005, a blend of 60% Cabernet Sauvignon and 40% Merlot, has put on weight over the last year. An opaque ruby/purple hue is accompanied by a sweet nose of earth, smoke, cassis, and cherries as well as a textured, full-bodied mouthfeel. While the tannin

is high, there is beautifully sweet fruit underlying the wines structure. It will require 8-10 years of cellaring after release, and should drink well for three decades." (Wine Advocate 170, April 2007)

The visual appearance of the wine in (1) is described in terms of its clarity and color using the descriptors 'opaque ruby/purple'. The olfactory perceptions are primarily described through concrete objects, e.g., 'earth, smoke, cassis, and cherries', but also in terms of a gustatory property, 'sweet', while taste and mouthfeel are described through various gustatory and tactile properties ('high' (tannin), 'sweet' (fruit), 'textured, full-bodied'). Because almost all wine reviews describe the wines in terms of four different perceptual modalities, i.e., visual appearance, smell, taste and texture, they are a gold mine for linguistic explorations of descriptions of human sensory perceptions in discourse. Of particular interest are the descriptions of olfactory perception. There is no specific olfactory vocabulary, neither in English nor in (most) other languages of the world. Olfactory descriptions have to be made using words from other domains. In wine reviews, words for taste or words for objects such as fruit, herbs or flowers of different color are used. In general, dark objects are used in descriptions of red wines and pale objects describe white wines. In other words, olfactory descriptions are primarily made on the basis of the smell of objects and also their color and taste. Exploring patterns for perceptual descriptors and the context of their use in wine reviews provides useful information not only about the relations between descriptors of odor and other modalities, but also about language, perception and cognition in general [3].

Our tool supports the visual analysis of the corpus of wine reviews from the Wine Advocate. The wine reviews are available in the form of two databases that contain a large number of wines, metadata about the wines, and the actual reviews. In order for linguists to arrive at a better understanding of different text types, different discourses and their vocabularies, large corpora are of crucial importance. At the same time, it is also a challenge to identify linguistic patterns in large corpora, to organize the data, to make statistical calculations and to present the data to

---

[1]https://www.erobertparker.com/entrance.aspx

1550-6037/11 $26.00 © 2011 IEEE
DOI 10.1109/IV.2011.38

readers in intuitive and clear ways. The contribution of this paper is to find solutions to some of these challenges. The first challenge is that we have to be able to represent large amounts of multivariate data. For that purpose, advanced interaction techniques are essential, because they ensure the opportunity for selecting a subset of tasting notes and for getting detailed information about the tasting notes in order to proceed with further analyses. Secondly, we have to find an efficient way to interactively visualize the text of the individual wine reviews, which brings us to the field of interactive text visualizations. Thirdly, a number of compatible visualization approaches have to be combined in order to efficiently explore the language used in the descriptions of the wines.

The remainder of this paper is organized as follows. Section II gives a general overview of the advantages of our tool for linguists. Then, we discuss related approaches in Section III within the field of information and text visualization as well as in the field of linguistic analysis of sensory descriptions. In Section IV, we describe the wine database. Our own approaches to the visualization of wine tasting notes by using information visualization (InfoVis) techniques are presented in Section V. Initial results are briefly outlined in Section VI. We conclude in Section VII and suggest some investigatory paths for future work.

II. LINGUISTIC BACKGROUND

Advances in visualization offer important possibilities for organizing, presenting and analyzing linguistic data, in which case visualization techniques provide a way to view language in another formats than as linear stretches of letters. Visualization techniques offer the tools to capture lexico-semantic usage patterns and to represent interactions of different dimensions of language structure that characterize different texts and discourses. As demonstrated in the introduction, descriptions of wines in wine magazines are short texts with a very strict rhetorical structure. The language of such texts are of interest to linguists at various different discursive levels. Linguists want to know about what kind of words are used to describe the wines' visual properties, what kind of descriptors are used for olfactory, gustatory and tactile perceptions. They are interested in what words and expressions are used where in the texts. For instance, what kind of temporal expressions are used in different parts of a text, and what expressions of personal opinion, such as 'should', 'drinkable', 'recommend' are used where in the texts and why. More generally, linguists take an interest in how all linguistic patterns combine into what might be our understanding of the discourse beyond the text itself. In other words, visual imagery provides a way to represent things that would otherwise go unnoticed. The added value of the visualization tool presented in this paper is that it can be used interactively. The data can be easily explored, and because parameters and combinations of data and metadata

can be changed, many questions regarding the potential of the data receive on-the-spot answers. As a result, new patterns emerge that can generate new research hypotheses about language use in different genres and text types.

III. RELATED WORK

Using both corpus methodologies including visualization of the data and experimental psychophysical techniques, Morrot et al. investigated the interaction between visual appearance and odor determination in wine description and wine tasting [3]. Their work presents the results of a study carried out with the help of a tool called ALCESTE. It is based on statistics about the distribution of words in a corpus of text to determine groups of words that co-occur in the same context. They found that the descriptors used to characterize white and red wines were different in terms of the colors of the objects used in the descriptions respectively (i.e., dark objects describe red wines and pale objects white wines). In addition to the corpus study, they also carried out a psychophysical experiment, which confirmed the corpus data, demonstrating the impact of vision on the human odor perception. In comparison to ALCESTE, our visualization tool gives users more possibilities to browse the text, to filter out uninteresting cases, and to interact with the visualizations. Thus, it does not afford pure statistical numbers only, but gives analysts an opportunity to explore the dataset and to get a better understanding of the texts' structure and content.

Another visualization approach, called Wine Fingerprints, has been discussed by Kerren [4]. In contrast to the tool presented in this paper, Wine Fingerprints focus on wine attributes, such as wine color, rating, grape type, price, or aroma, and not on the actual wine reviews. This data forms a multivariate data set, part of which can be hierarchically structured into a so-called aroma hierarchy. The Wine Fingerprints approach has various applications for business and industry in that it can create visual patterns of combinations of wine attributes and support comparisons of visual, olfactory and gustatory properties of different wines from different parts of the worlds, from different grapes, from different vintages etc. Both customers and companies can make visual comparisons of wines and select wines on a pictorial basis instead of on the basis of a list of multimodal perceptual attributes.

For the purpose of information visualization of complex textual data, we use different well-known techniques and interaction approaches. The general design of our visualization tool is based on standard coordinated and multiple view visualization techniques as described in Section V-A. An excellent starting point for related work of this kind of visualization techniques is the annual conference series on Coordinated & Multiple Views in Exploratory Visualization (CMV) or the work of Roberts [5].

In order to specify the layout of our tool and to define the functional requirements, we were inspired by the FilmFinder tool for exploring film databases [6]. It was one of the first tools, which integrated the concept of a two dimensional scatter plot with color coding, filtering, and details provided on demand (dynamic queries). The developers realized different encoding and interaction techniques for the representation of multivariate data.

The research project Many Eyes provides alternative methods for data analyses using innovative visualization techniques [7]. One of the approaches for supporting text analysis is the representation of a given text as a word tree [8]. The purpose of this visualization method is to afford an insight into the different contexts in which a word is encountered in an unstructured text. We used this concept in one of the text visualizations of our tool to facilitate rapid exploration of the wine tasting notes' content.

An approach for visual literary analysis, called Literature Fingerprinting, was presented by Keim and Oelke [9]. This work supports the visual comparison of texts by calculating features for different hierarchy levels and by creating characteristic fingerprints of the texts. Such features might be word length or measurement of vocabulary richness.

Salton and Singhal analyze the relationships between text documents according to different topics. They developed a tool called Text Theme [10] to represent such correlations visually. Single topics can then be identified and be compared with the help of textures or color coding. In contrast to this approach, our tool operates more on the syntactic level, i.e., higher-level themes cannot be compared directly.

Tag clouds provide information about the frequency of words used in a corpus of text [11]. This approach uses different font sizes for each word in the text to indicate how often this word is used by comparison with the others. Several extensions and approaches exists, such as Wordle or ManiWorlde [12], [13]. We use a simple tag cloud implementation to represent the word frequency in a group of tasting notes.

Stasko et al. developed a visualization tool for analyses of textual reports called Jigsaw [14]. The goal of their tool is to aid investigative analysts to faster understand the content of reports in order to predict possible threats and to prepare defensive plans accordingly. The main analysis unit in their work are pre-defined entities in the texts and the goal of the implemented visualizations is to represent relations and connections between these entities. As distinct from their work, our tool is not designed to focus on the significance of specific entities extracted from the texts but rather on the exploration of their content and linguistic constructions.

IV. NOTES ON THE DATA SET

The wine tasting notes are stored in two databases that contain information about different wines as well as the tasters' comments about them. In each database, the tasting notes are represented in different ways. The first database contains descriptive information about the wines, their unique ID number, their origin, vintages, wine ratings, dryness, color and the complete original wine review. The second database contains the same tasting notes including ID numbers, but they are segmented into words and word-class tags (so-called word tags, such as nouns (NN) or adjectives (JJ) [15]). The latter database was built from the former, the original database, by using the WineConverter tool, developed by Ekeklint and Nilsson from the computer linguistics group at Växjö University, Sweden. The result of this segmentation is a new structuring of the wine tasting notes where each word is described by additional information that accurately specifies its position in the text of the full tasting note. The location of each word in a tasting note is determined by the following information: ID number of the tasting note, number of the corresponding sentence in the tasting note, position of the word in this sentence, the word itself, and the word tag given to this word.

In order to get a better overview of appropriate visualization approaches for representing the tasting notes and their attributes, we had to take the great amount of analyzed data into consideration. Table I provides a list of substantial statistical numbers derived from the dataset to give an idea about the sheer quantity of the data to be visualized.

Table I
STATISTICAL NUMBERS DERIVED FROM THE WINE DATABASES.

Number of tasting notes	84,864
Total number of words used in the tasting notes	8,332,666
Number of different words used in the tasting notes	46,000
Maximum length of the tasting notes	496
Number of word classes	43
Number of vintages	104
Range of wine rating values	1 to 100

V. VISUALIZATION FRAMEWORK

In order to provide an overall perspective of the analyzed wine tasting notes, we follow Ben Shneiderman's mantra of information visualization: "overview first, zoom and filter, details on demand" [16]. This gives users an initial overview of the explored data and the possibility to proceed with investigation of its subsets. For this, we combined several visualization approaches to achieve our goals: scatter plots, tag clouds, word trees, bar charts / histograms, and a world map. The scatter plot is used to be the main entry point for using our tool as described in the following.

A. Visual Representations

1) Scatter Plot: The purpose of this visual representation is to give a first overview of the data. Because of the large number of tasting notes (cf. Table I), we decided to use a scatter plot for their initial display, i.e., each single tasting note is represented by a blue circle. This approach also

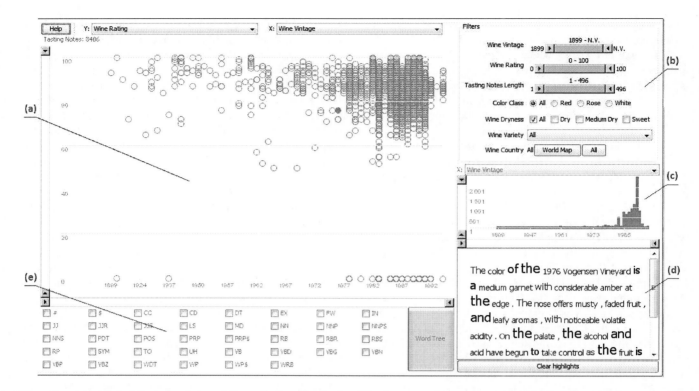

Figure 1. A snapshot of the main window of the application after starting. Note that one tasting note was selected in the scatter plot; its tag cloud is shown in the bottom right corner.

saves space and gives an idea about the distribution of the tasting notes on the basis of the values of two selected wine attributes, see Figure 1(a). Attributes currently supported by the scatter plot visualization are all possible pairs of Wine Rating, Wine Vintage, Color Class, Tasting Notes Length, and Wine Country.

2) Bar Charts and Histograms: Getting statistical information helps analysts to better understand the visualized data and finding the desired set of tasting notes. Bar chart diagrams are traditional approaches to statistical data visualization. In this work, they are supplied in order to show the number of tasting notes that correspond to the values of a specific wine attribute (Figure 1(c)).

3) Text Visualization: The visualization approaches that we apply for the representation tasting notes are word trees and tag clouds.

Word Tree: The word tree visualization facilitates rapid querying and exploration of text bodies [8]. In our tool, a word tree describes the sequence of words and phrases used in a group of tasting notes. The structure of the word tree is organized into two main groups of nodes: word tags and words. There are three prerequisites for proceeding with the word tree visualization:

- users need to select a group of tasting notes for further analyses,
- a specific tasting note for deriving the initial data (from now on referred as *root tasting note*), and

- the word classes of the words in this root tasting note that they would like to analyze.

The first three levels of the word tree contain data from the root tasting note. The other levels consist of data from the whole group. The root node of the tree is artificially added, and it contains the static text "Tags", which suggests that the following level is composed of word tags. The second level contains the selected word tags that correspond to words in the root tasting note. The third level consists of all the words from the root tasting note that belong to the word tags on the previous level. Figure 2 gives an example of the word tree and the organization of its nodes. The levels of the tree alternate with each other to represent either word tags or words that correspond to the tags on the previous level. The children of each node representing a word class are the words from the analyzed group of tasting notes that belong to this word class. For instance, the word tree in Figure 2 displays two (selected) word tags of the root tasting note, i.e., "JJ" (adjectives) and "NN" (nouns, singular common). By looking at the children of "JJ", the user can see that the root tasting note has four adjectives, e.g., "coarse". Then, by looking at the next two deeper levels, the user can see that "coarse" has two successors: one noun (plural common; "NNS" → "flavors") in another note from the analyzed notes group (black) and one determiner ("DT"→ ", this") in the root tasting note.

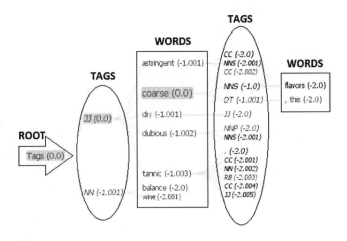

Figure 2. A word tree that shows the node organization into two main groups: word tags and words. Furthermore, there is another partition of the tree nodes as well: nodes that contain data from the root tasting note (colored in red) and nodes that contain data only from the other tasting notes (colored in black). The DOI value of each node is given in brackets on its right side.

Our word tree visualization represents a large data set of words and word tags. It is restricted by the size of the display and people's perceptive capabilities. To cope with these restrictions, our implementation applies the idea of Degree-Of-Interest (DOI) trees that provide a solution of these problems. They combine Focus&Context visualization techniques and degree-of-interest calculations to find a proper layout that fits within the bounds of the display. The technical idea is the use of a degree-of-interest function, which assigns a number value (DOI value) to each node indicating how interested the user is in this node. This value is then used as a criterion to determine, which of the nodes should be visible, which of them are in the focus and how they should be displayed [17], [18]. The nodes in the focus have the greatest DOI value and are slightly magnified. The size of all other nodes is directly proportional to their individual DOI value. An exception to this rule is the tree element that was selected last, which is the most magnified element, in spite of the fact that it has the same DOI value as the other focus nodes. Figure 2 demonstrates a degree-of-interest tree where the DOI value of the nodes are given in brackets on the right side of the node label.

Tag Clouds: The tag cloud visualization makes use of different font sizes for the words in a corpus of text to give a hint about the frequency of their usage. There are two prerequisites for the application of tag cloud visualizations to a tasting note's text. A group of tasting notes needs to be defined for further analyses, and one of them has to be selected for its text visualization. The text of the selected tasting note is then visualized by using the tag cloud metaphor, where each word has a different font size depending on how often this word occurs in the whole group of tasting notes, cp. Figure 1(d).

4) World map visualization: The origin of a wine is important information, visualized in a way that gives a rough overview of the wine-producing countries of the world. A natural approach for visualizing it is an interactive world map indicating the density of wine production in different countries. Figure 5 shows a world map representing information about the wines produced in different parts of the world that have been tasted and described in the tasting notes. The color saturation is directly proportional to the density of wines produced in each country.

B. Interaction and Coordinated Views

We combined the visualization approaches described in Section V-A with appropriate techniques for user interaction to build an efficient tool for analyzing wine tasting notes. The following subsections give a notion about the user interface and the overall layout of the application. In detail, there are five particular views intended to build an efficient overview visualization as displayed in Figure 1:

(a) a scatter plot (showing the distribution of tasting notes),
(b) filters (to reduce the complexity by filtering),
(c) bar charts and histograms (to show statistical data),
(d) tag clouds (for text visualization), and
(e) tag checkbox panel (to select specific word classes).

All aforementioned views are coordinated by standard highlighting and brushing techniques.

1) Distribution of Tasting Notes: The scatter plot axes on the left and bottom sides of the display correspond to one wine attribute each. Range sliders [19] are added to the axes in order to make it possible for the users to change the range of the wine attributes' values and therefore the scope of tasting notes visualized in the scatter plot. The number of visible tasting notes can be observed at the upper left corner of the scatter plot (8,486 in our screenshot example of Figure 1). Another possibility given to the user is to change the wine attributes plotted on the x-axis and y-axis by selecting other attributes from the combo boxes on the top of the display.

There is a drawback appearing as a consequence of the scatter plot concept and the data stored in the database: it might happen that more tasting notes share the same values for both of the wine attributes plotted on the axes. Such tasting notes overlap when they are visualized at the same spot in the scatter plot. This makes the selection of an element from the display more complicated. We added a tooltip to each element to give the user a hint about the number of overlapping tasting notes at the specific position (Figure 3(a)). Thus, an individual element can be selected from a popup list of the overlapping tasting notes, as shown in Figure 3(b). The selected tasting note differs from the others in its blue color in the scatter plot and in the popup list.

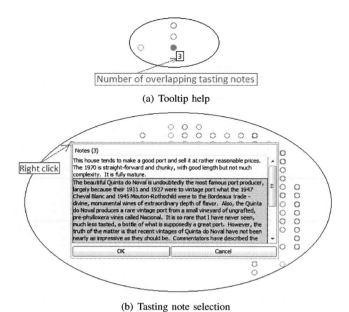

(a) Tooltip help

(b) Tasting note selection

Figure 3. Overlapping tasting notes in the scatter plot view.

Figure 4. Types of filters implemented in the application.

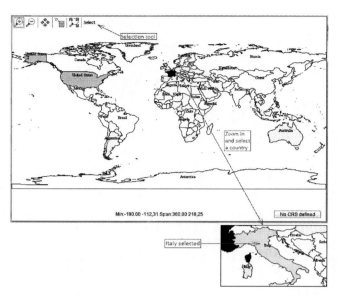

Figure 5. World map providing information about the tasted wines produced in different countries. It is also possible to use this view as an interactive filter for the specification of single countries.

2) Filtering: Filters are used to facilitate the task of the users to interact with the visualization and to find the best subset of elements to be further analyzed. Figure 4 shows a screenshot example of filters supported by our tool. By the current selection only those tasting notes are considered in the different views, which corresponding wines have a vintage between 1899 and 1978, a rating between 30 and 70 points, a length between 51 and 496 words, a red color, no specific dryness, geographical information, and made from Cabernet Sauvignon grapes.

The world map filter is a realization of the geographic visualization approach described in Section V-A4. It provides users with the opportunity to filter out tasting notes on the scatter plot depending on their origin (Figure 5). Different standard functionalities are supplied to assist working with the map like zooming in, zooming out and panning to a specific region of interest. Users have the possibility to select

a country on the map and our tool visualizes only those representations of tasting notes of wines produced in the specified region.

To provide a better software maintenance, we use a specific property file that contains a list of wine attributes and their required filter types. In this way, filters are dynamically created on the basis of this information and can be easily added or removed.

3) Statistical Information: The property file also contains a list of wine attributes that can be represented by bar chart diagrams. Figure 6 presents snapshots of histograms implemented in the application. An individual bar chart or histogram is created for each of the listed attributes showing the number of visible tasting notes corresponding to each of their values (Figure 6(a)). Only one of the diagrams is visualized at a time in order to save space. We added range sliders to the x- and y-axes to assist users in changing the range of visualized attribute values and to get a closer look at a specific section of the diagram, see Figures 6(b) and 6(c) where the vintage range was modified.

4) Word Frequency Analysis: After the selection of a tasting note in the scatter plot view, its text is visualized using a tag cloud approach (cf. Section V-A3). The font size of each word is estimated according to the frequency of its occurrence in all elements visible at the same time, including the selected one. Figure 7(a) shows a tag cloud example generated by our application.

The tag checkbox panel contains all word tags available. A coordinated interaction exists between the tag cloud view and the checkbox panel. On the one hand, when the user

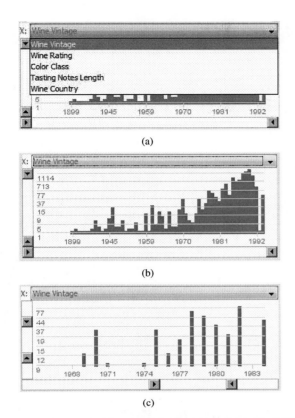

(a)

(b)

(c)

Figure 6.   Screenshots of an interactive histogram for attribute "Wine Vintage".

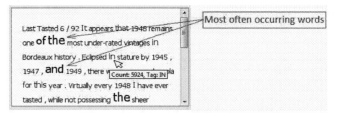

(a) Tag cloud visualization implemented in the application

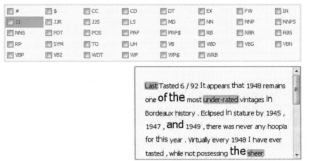

(b) Tag cloud interaction together with the tag check box panel

Figure 7.   Word frequency analysis

selects a word from the tag cloud visualization, all words of the same class (i.e., with the same word tag) are highlighted in the tag cloud together with the tag itself in the tag checkbox panel. Figure 7(b) demonstrates this interaction after selecting the word "Last" in text of the tasting note. On the other hand, when a word tag is checked in the checkbox panel (such as "DT"), then it is highlighted together with the words corresponding to this tag in the text.

5) Sentence Structure Analysis: The basic concept and structure of the word tree visualization was already described in Section V-A3. Figure 8 presents an additional example of a word tree generated by our system. The visualization consists of three basic components: (a) a display containing the word tree, (b) a text area presenting the text of the root tasting note, and (c) a text area presenting the currently constructed sequence of words. All nodes that build a path from the root node to the currently selected node are in focus. Selecting a node from the tree changes the focus to the nodes contained by the path from the root to this node. A smooth animation is used to change the state of the tree to the newly selected focus [17]. The nodes in focus are highlighted with another background color and slightly enlarged. In the example, the node selected is "raspberries", and therefore, all nodes from the root to the

node "raspberries" are in the focus. These nodes constitute a sequence of words which forms part of one or more tasting notes in the current scatter plot. This sequence is displayed at the bottom of the word tree, and it is also highlighted in the root tasting note if included there.

In Figure 8, the actual sequence of words is "glass, offering aromas of ripe raspberries.". The node labels are in red since they are contained in the root tasting note. Often, the tree depth and width exceed the display bounds. It is not possible all the nodes to be visualized in the space available. In order to surmount such problems, different techniques are integrated into the visualization, e.g., zooming in, zooming out, and panning controls [17].

There is a close relation between word tree visualization and the scatter plot. The word tree is constructed according to all combinations of words beginning with words from the root tasting note and followed by words from the whole group of tasting notes visualized in the scatter plot. This means that each sequence of words specified by the word tree exploration is contained in at least one tasting note of the current scatter plot selection. This relation is indicated by highlighting those tasting notes in the scatter plot (by a filled blue circle), which contain the sequence of words construed by the word tree (Figure 9(a)). The tool makes sure that highlighted elements are always visible. To distinguish them, their texts are in blue in the popup list of overlapping tasting notes. In the given example, there is only one tasting note that contains the sequence of words "glass, offering aromas of ripe raspberries" and its text is in blue in the popup list, see Figure 9(b).

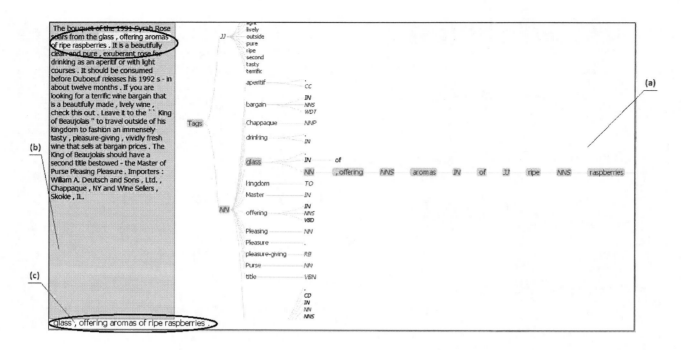

Figure 8. Word tree visualization consisting of three basic components. The tree node labels corresponding to words that are contained by the root tasting note are colored in red.

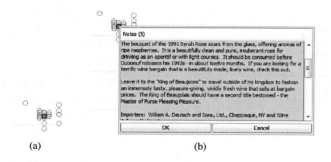

(a)   (b)

Figure 9. Highlighting of tasting notes in the scatter plot that contain the currently sequence of words constructed by the word tree.

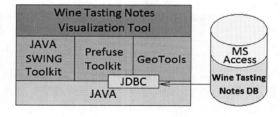

Figure 10. Software architecture of the tool.

C. Implementation Aspects

The tool's software architecture can be represented by four logical layers as shown in Figure 10. Because the original database containing the wine tasting notes was created using Microsoft Access®, we also decided to use this database management system (DBMS). The programming language that we decided to use for the implementation of the application is JAVA. We used four open source JAVA libraries to implement the required functionalities. The JDBC library was employed for establishing connectivity between the JAVA programming language and the database [20]. The graphical user interface was created with the aid of the JAVA Swing Toolkit [21]. We used the Prefuse Toolkit for the following interactive visualizations: the scatter plot,

the bar chart diagrams and the word tree [22]. The world map visualization was created by the functionalities of the JAVA GIS Toolkit GeoTools [23].

Scalability Issues: The selected visualization approaches are appropriate for representing large amounts of data. From a theoretical point of view, there is almost no restriction placed upon the number of visualized tasting notes. The scatter plot and the bar chart diagrams provide different interaction techniques that give users the opportunity to focus on a subset of elements for further exploration. The tag cloud visualization represents the text of one tasting note using different font sizes for its words. With an increase in the number of tasting notes, the proportions between the font sizes of the words in the visualized text will be affected – not the number of the words. This feature makes the tag cloud visualization even more attractive. The word tree facilitates for users to explore the correlations beginning from a set of visible words and proceeding with other words which appear as a result of previous choices. This approach allows the exploration of unbounded sets of words. However, increasing the number of tree nodes makes it more complicated to browse through the tree and to preserve the mental map. Because there is no upper limit for the number of tasted wines produced in the visualized countries, the world map is not restricted by the amount of visualized data either.

That said, our implementation currently imposes some restrictions on the functionality of the tool. The scatter plot together with the filters, the tag cloud visualization and the bar chart diagrams perform well for a number of up to 3,000 tasting notes. For more elements, the tool becomes slower and thus less interactive. One way of improving the application's performance is to migrate the database to another, more efficient DBMS. The current DBMS and the database schema are in fact the main bottleneck of our implementation. Because of the inappropriate design of the wine database, the word tree visualization cannot be efficiently built for more than 60 tasting notes. In order to overcome this restriction, the design of the database should be modified in such a way that it represents the tree structure of the words in the tasting notes. The response time of the world map view for standard user interactions takes about six seconds, which is a relatively long time. Here, we have to find out whether the GeoTools Toolkit API may provide a solution to this performance problem or if we have to move to another library.

VI. RESULTS

Our tool offers possibilities for the exploration, the analysis and the presentation of large and complex amounts of data in ways so that linguists can make use of them in investigations of the structure of texts and discourses and of the lexical resources that languages have for the expression of meaning domains. Not only can visual images communicate concrete information, but they can also represent abstract information in the form of visual imagery, which is of particular significance in the case of wine descriptions of subjective sensory modal representations, which by nature are transitory and volatile. Through these techniques, textual data can be visually represented at a glance and can be interactively explored at the same time. This is clearly an innovation in linguistic research. The most essential part of wine descriptions is concerned with the description of passing sensory perceptions. They are captured by our visualization approaches in the form of scatter plots, tag clouds, word trees, and bar chart diagrams. Given the availability of tagged corpora, dynamic visualization techniques open up for linguistic advances through typological comparisons across different text types, different times and different languages. For instance, with the aid of the various filters of metadata we can explore linguistic patterns across subsets of tasting notes, subsets of ratings of wines, or subsets of grapes. And we can apply filters, such as only tasting notes containing more than 400 words, only sweet wines, only wines from Spain, etc., in various different combinations. The tool provides direct feedback in the form of interactive visualizations and is immediately able to answer questions such as: Do tasting notes have the same format across time? Or how do wines pattern that are described with the attribute 'sweaty saddle'? Thus it offers the possibility for linguists to play around with the variables and get a picture of the differences in the distribution of tasting notes in relation to the changes we make using the different filter settings straight away. We also obtain statistical information related to choices that we make in the form of bar chart diagrams and tag clouds. These functions are particularly important for the setting of parameters more accurately and for the subsequent formulation of new hypothesis for corpus investigations of text.

VII. CONCLUSION AND FUTURE WORK

This work is concerned with various approaches for visualizing wine tasting notes that can be used to support linguistic analyses. Our data sources are large databases containing tasting notes and metadata related to the wines tasted. Linguists are interested in the language of such texts and the possibilities offered by the language to describe sensory perceptions to better understand descriptions of them. The purpose of our tool was to visualize this data in a way that would help linguists to get a better picture of wine descriptions. All solutions presented in this paper were carefully discussed with linguists during their development.

There are several improvements that can be made to enhance the visualization tool for wine tasting notes. In Subsection V-C, we discussed several problems with the current DBMS and the database schema. An improvement of this situation would be one of the first candidates for the next software revision.

Another issue would be the tag clouds that can be improved. There are function words that occur very frequently in general language like "a", "the", "of", etc. They are visualized by the largest font sizes and therefore attract the attention of the users from other words that are more important and more interesting for linguistic analyses. An obvious solution to avoid this problem would be to create a user-defined black list of words that could be disregarded and excluded from the calculations. The tool could thereby avoid their overestimation.

The world map visualization and its performance could be improved too. It would be useful to add more interactive features to the map visualization. For example, the map could be extended by visualizing vintages, i.e., time-series data. Another idea would be to add an interactive control for tracing the wine production density in different countries on the basis of the wines' vintages. Range sliders or other controls could be integrated to change the time period of the data visualized on the map.

Finally, we recognize that our visual analyses are also related to tasks in the field of Sentiment Analysis. It would be very interesting to develop our tool also in this direction, see for example the handbook chapter [24].

ACKNOWLEDGMENTS

We would like to thank Ilir Jusufi for carefully proof-reading the final version of this paper.

REFERENCES

[1] M. Prangova, "Visualization of sensory perception descriptions," Master's thesis, Linnaeus University, School of Computer Science, Physics and Mathematics, Växjö, Sweden, 2010.

[2] C. Paradis, "A sweet nose of earth, smoke, cassis and cherries: Descriptions of sensory perceptions in wine tasting notes," in *Proceedings of the 7th AELCO International Conference*, Toledo, Spain, 2010.

[3] G. Morrot, F. Brochet, and D. Dubourdieu, "The color of odors," *Brain and Language*, vol. 79, no. 2, pp. 309–320, 2001.

[4] A. Kerren, "Visualization of workaday data clarified by means of wine fingerprints," in *Proceedings of the INTERACT '09 Workshop on Human Aspects of Visualization*, ser. LNCS, vol. 6431. Springer, 2011, pp. 92–107.

[5] J. C. Roberts, "Exploratory visualization with multiple linked views," in *Exploring Geovisualization*, A. MacEachren, M.-J. Kraak, and J. Dykes, Eds. Amsterdam: Elseviers, December 2004. [Online]. Available: http://www.cs.kent.ac. uk/pubs/2004/1822

[6] C. Ahlberg and B. Shneiderman, "Visual information seeking: tight coupling of dynamic query filters with starfield displays," in *Proceedings of the SIGCHI conference on Human factors in computing systems: celebrating interdependence*, ser. CHI '94. New York, NY, USA: ACM, 1994, pp. 313–317. [Online]. Available: http: //doi.acm.org/10.1145/191666.191775

[7] IBM Research, "Many Eyes," http://manyeyes.alphaworks. ibm.com/manyeyes/, 2011.

[8] M. Wattenberg and F. B. Viégas, "The word tree, an interactive visual concordance," *IEEE Transactions on Visualization and Computer Graphics*, vol. 14, pp. 1221–1228, November 2008. [Online]. Available: http: //portal.acm.org/citation.cfm?id=1477066.1477418

[9] D. Keim and D. Oelke, "Literature Fingerprinting: A New Method for Visual Literary Analysis," in *IEEE Symposium on Visual Analytics Science and Technologie*, Sacramento, CA, USA, 2007, pp. 115–122.

[10] G. Salton and A. Singhal, "Automatic text theme generation and the analysis of text structure," Cornell University, Ithaca, NY, USA, Tech. Rep. TR94-1438, 1994.

[11] O. Kaser and D. Lemire, "Tag-Cloud Drawing: Algorithms for Cloud Visualization," in *Proceedings of Tagging and Metadata for Social Information Organization (WWW '07)*, Banff, Canada, 2007.

[12] F. B. Viegas, M. Wattenberg, and J. Feinberg, "Participatory visualization with wordle," *IEEE Transactions on Visualization and Computer Graphics*, vol. 15, pp. 1137–1144, November 2009. [Online]. Available: http://dx.doi.org/10.1109/TVCG.2009.171

[13] K. Koh, B. Lee, B. Kim, and J. Seo, "Maniwordle: Providing flexible control over wordle," *IEEE Transactions on Visualization and Computer Graphics*, vol. 16, pp. 1190–1197, November 2010. [Online]. Available: http: //dx.doi.org/10.1109/TVCG.2010.175

[14] J. Stasko, C. Görg, and Z. Liu, "Jigsaw: supporting investigative analysis through interactive visualization," *Information Visualization*, vol. 7, pp. 118–132, April 2008. [Online]. Available: http://portal.acm.org/citation.cfm? id=1466620.1466622

[15] B. Santorini, "Part-of-speech tagging guidelines for the penn treebank project," University of Pennsylvania, Department of Computer and Information Science, Philadelphia, PA, USA, Tech. Rep. MS-CIS-90-47, 1990, (3rd Revision).

[16] B. Shneiderman, "The eyes have it: A task by data type taxonomy for information visualizations," in *Proceedings of the IEEE Symposium on Visual Languages (VL '96)*, 1996, pp. 336–343.

[17] J. Heer and S. K. Card, "Doitrees revisited: Scalable, space-constrained visualization of hierarchical data," in *Proceedings of the working conference on Advanced Visual Interfaces (AVI '04)*. New York, NY, USA: ACM, 2004, pp. 421–424.

[18] S. K. Card and D. Nation, "Degree-of-interest trees: A component of an attention-reactive user interface," in *Proceedings of the working conference on Advanced Visual Interfaces (AVI '02)*. New York, NY, USA: ACM, 2002, pp. 231–245.

[19] D. A. Carr, N. Jog, H. Prem Kumar, M. Teittinen, and C. Ahlberg, "Using interaction object graphs to specify graphical widgets," University of Maryland, Department of Computer Science, College Park, MD, USA, Tech. Rep. CS-TR-3344, 1994.

[20] Oracle, "The Java Database Connectivity," http://java.sun. com/products/jdbc/overview.html, 2011.

[21] ——, "JAVA Swing Toolkit," http://java.sun.com/docs/books/ tutorial/ui/overview/intro.html, 2011.

[22] The Berkeley Institute of Design, "Prefuse Visualization Toolkit," http://prefuse.org/, 2009.

[23] GeoTools, "The Open Source Java GIS Toolkit," http://www. geotools.org/, 2010.

[24] B. Liu, "Sentiment analysis and subjectivity," in *Handbook of Natural Language Processing*, 2nd ed., N. Indurkhya and F. J. Damerau, Eds. Chapman and Hall/CRC, 2010.

Lyricon: A Visual Music Selection Interface Featuring Multiple Icons

Wakako Machida
Ochanomizu University
Tokyo, Japan
Email: matchy8@itolab.is.ocha.ac.jp

Takayuki Itoh
Ochanomizu University
Tokyo, Japan
Email: itot@is.ocha.ac.jp

Abstract—This paper presents "Lyricon", a technique that automatically selects multiple icons of tunes block-by-block, and effectively displays the icons. Here, Lyricon selects icons based on not only musical features, but also lyrical keywords. In other words, Lyricon can reflect not only the features of the tunes but also the story of lyrics on its icon selection. Users can understand both impression of the sounds and the content of the lyrics, and they can choose songs which is suitable for their feeling based on the visual impression of the icons. Besides, embedding Lyricon on GUIs of music players is convenient to play specific parts of songs.

Keywords-Visualization, Icon selection, Lyrics, Music player

I. INTRODUCTION

Today, people can enjoy their favorite songs easily and freely due to the evolution of portable music player products and free video sharing Web sites. We often demand smoothly working song selection mechanisms because we often store large number of tunes. Sometimes user cannot remember the melody of the song and the lyrics, only by looking the titles or artist names of the tunes on the song selection panels. We think that "music visualization" is useful to solve the problem.

Lyrics are very important on recent popular hit songs. There are many big sale songs which lyrics are key points, such as answer songs those lyrics reply to another song, and songs on compilation albums which collect multiple artists' songs following particular themes (e.g. "sea", "love"). As a feasibility study for lyrics, we asked the following two questions to 86 students in our university:

- "Are you usually conscious of lyrics while listening to the music?"
- "Do you often choose the music based on lyrics?"

We got results that 66 students answered "yes" for the former question, and 42 students answered "yes" for the latter question. These results indicate that lyrics may be informative for many people while selecting the songs they want to listen to.

This paper presents "Lyricon", a music visualization technique that represents musical structure by multiple icons, taking lyrics into account. Lyricon automatically selects multiple icons of songs block-by-block, and provides a user interface to effectively display the icons. Lyricon selects icons based on not only musical features, but also lyrical features. We have designed Lyricon to represent musical and lyrical features by multiple icons, not by a single icon, because story of lyric may be too complex to explain by a single picture. We can apply this idea to selection of larger pictures as well as icons; however, in this paper we focus on icon selection, because icons are smaller than pictures, and therefore suitable to display in limited sizes of GUIs.

Figure 1 shows examples of selected icons. Users can understand both impression of the sounds and the content of the lyrics when they look at the icons selected by Lyricon, even before listening to the song. This paper discusses the detail in Section III. Moreover, embedding Lyricon on GUIs of music players is convenient for partial play of tunes. This paper presents potential user interfaces of Lyricon in Section IV.

II. RELATED WORK

There have been several novel techniques for icon generation or selection. Setlur et al. presented Semanticons [1] that synthesizes small pictures to generate semantics-matched icons. It can represent various semantics by single icon; however, the technique is not music-specific. Music Icons [2] by Kolhoff et al., and MIST [3] by Oda et al., generate/select icon pictures according to musical features. However, these techniques do not take lyrics into account. Moreover, these techniques assign only one icon for each tune, and therefore it may be often difficult to represent changes or structures of tunes.

There have been several novel techniques for visual representation of lyrics-based information. Xu et al. presented a technique to create slide shows according to the story of lyrics [4]. Framework of Lyricon is also applicable to slide show generation; however, we preferred to develop an icon selection technique, because we think we can understand the features and story of the songs more quickly by looking at sequences of icons. Neumayer et al. presented a technique to visually represent clusters of songs taking both features and lyrics into account [5].

III. MULTIPLE ICON SELECTOIN

This section describes our multiple icon selection technique consisting of the following technical components:

1550-6037/11 $26.00 © 2011 IEEE
DOI 10.1109/IV.2011.62

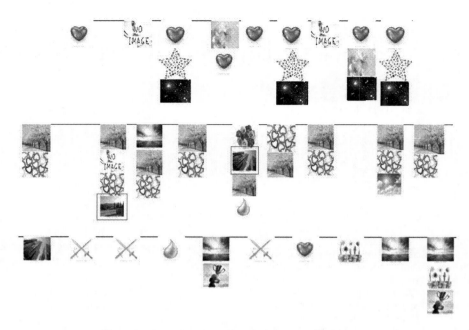

Figure 1. Examples of icon selection resutls of three songs.

1) Preparation during system development:
   a) Category and keyword selection
   b) Musical feature selection
   c) Icon selection
2) Process during input of new songs:
   a) Lyrical processing for icon candidate selection
   b) Musical feature processing for final icon selection

Following sections describe these processing units. Section III-A to Section III-C describes preparation processes. Section III-B describes steps 1 to 3. Section III-D and III-E describes lyrical and musical processes for icons election. Note that our implementation supports songs those lyrics are written in Japanese, but the mechanism of Lyricon is not limited to Japanese songs.

A. Preparation(1): Category and keyword selection

Our implementation prepares "categories", and sets multiple keywords and icons into the categories. A category contains a set of related keywords that can be the main theme of the lyrics and its synonyms. At the same time, the category contains a set of multiple icons which bring different impression. Let us formulate categories, keywords, and icons, as following:

- Categories as $C = \{c_1, ..., c_{Nc}\}$, where N_c is the number of categories.
- Keywords belonging to c_i as $K_i = \{k_{i1}, ..., k_{iNki}\}$, where N_{ki} is the number of keywords belonging to c_i.
- Icons belonging to c_i as $X_i = \{x_{i1}, ..., x_{iNxi}\}$, where N_{xi} is the number of icons belonging to c_i.

- Adjectives of icon x_{ij} as $A_{ij} = \{a_{ij1}, ..., a_{ijNaij}\}$, where N_{aij} is the number of adjectives of x_{ij}.

To define categories, we first asked the following question to 86 students in our university:
"What kind of topics or themes do you occasionally want to use to select songs?"

We got many topics as the result of the question, and used 23 topics such as "Love", "Summer", and "Christmas", as categories. Then, we extracted synonym of the categories from Japanese thesaurus dictionary [6], and selected frequently used words as keywords. We scanned the lyrics of randomly selected a lot of Japanese hit songs, and divided the lyrics into words. We used "Chasen" [7] for this process. Then, we matched the words extracted from the lyrics with the synonym extracted the dictionary, and finally selected frequently matched synonym as keywords of the categories. Our current implementation prepares 23 categories and 248 keywords.

B. Preparation(2): Musical feature selection

At the same time, Lyricon uses several musical feature values. Our current implementation uses MIRtoolbox [8], working on MATLAB, for musical feature calculation. We had a feasibility study of features calculated by MIRtoolbox by applying randomly selected 26 Japanese hit songs. We subjectively estimated that 10 features were especially meaningful for our purpose. We then selected 3 features from the 10 features by the following procedure. We assigned pairs of inverse meaning of adjectives for each feature. For example, we assigned "fast" and "slow" for the feature "Tempo". At the same time, we calculated the 10 feature

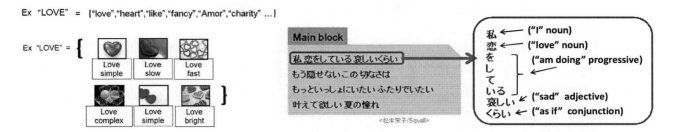

Figure 2. (Left) Keywords and icons of a category. (Right) Morphological analysis.

values for the songs as shown in Figure 2(Right). We then applied the following procedure for each feature. We asked 6 examinees to subjectively divide the 26 songs into two groups according to one of the pairs of adjectives, such as "fast" and "slow". At the same time, we divided the songs according to an automatically determined threshold value of the feature corresponding to the pair of adjectives, such as "Tempo". We then calculated the average concordance rate between the subjective and automatic division. Finally, we determined the feature can be used for Lyricon, if the two division results were sufficiently similar.

As a result of above mentioned process, we selected the following three features:

- *Tempo.* "slow" and "fast" are used as adjectives.
- *Percentage of high-tone range.* "simple" and "rich" are used as adjectives.
- *Percentage of inharmonic tones.* "primitive" and "complex" are used as adjectives.

Here, the word "simple" may point songs which sound naively because of small number of musical instruments or less sound effects. On the other hand, the word "rich" may point songs which feature many musical instruments or use various sound effects. The word "complex" may point songs which apply complicated chords or tensions like Jazz music. On the other hand, the word "primitive" may point songs which do not apply complicated chords or tensions.

C. Preparation(3): Icon selection

Lyricon supposes to prepare several icons for each category. It also supposes that one or more adjectives, slow, fast, simple, rich, primitive, or complex are assigned to every prepared icon. The assigned adjectives are referred to select icons. Figure 2(Left) shows an example of a category "love", which contains 9 keywords, and 6 icons. Lyricon firstly specifies the category corresponding to the contents of song by keyword matching between each category and lyrics, and then selects the most adequate icon in the specified category based on musical features, referring the adjectives of icons.

During our experiments, we prepared enough number of icons for each category. We then showed the icons and adjectives assigned to the icons to 12 examinees, and asked

if the adjectives matched to the icons. We did not use icons which less than half of examinees agreed that they matched.

D. Lyrical analysis for icon candidate selection

Since Lyricon assigns icons block-by-block, we would like to use lyrics divided based on blocks of the songs. We used "Lyric Master" [9] to obtained lyrics of Japanese hit songs which are divided block-by-block.

Lyricon then analyzes morphologic of each block and divides the block of the lyric into words by using "Chasen". Figure 2(Right) shows an example of the morphological analysis.

Let us describe a set of words in a block as $W = \{w_1, ..., w_N\}$. If a word wk completely matches to the keyword k_{ij}, Lyricon determines that the block is related to the category c_i. In this case Lyricon treats the set of icons X_i as the candidates to be assigned to the block, and finally one of the icons x_{ij} is assigned to the block.

E. Musical feature analysis for final icon selection

Lyricon also calculates feature values selected in the preparation process. We selected three features, "Tempo", "Percentage of high-tone range", and "Percentage of inharmonic tones", as described in Section 3.1. Lyricon then selects the adjectives of the song according to the calculated feature values. Our current implementation selects at least one adjective from the selected 6 adjectives described in Section 3.1 by the following procedure.

Let the three feature values F_1, F_2, and F_3, and these ranges $[F_{1min}, F_{1max}]$, $[F_{2min}, F_{2max}]$, and $[F_{3min}, F_{3max}]$. Here, we define the relevance of the song to the two adjectives of the i-th feature value as R_{ia} and R_{ib}, calculated as $R_{ia} = F'_i$, and $R_{ib} = 1.0 - F'_i$.

When there are multiple icon candidates in a same category specified from a block of the lyric, Lyricon selects one of the icons which is assigned the adjective bringing the maximum Ria or Rib value.

IV. USER INTERFACE

We implemented visual music selection interfaces that display the multiple icons selected by our technique on two platforms: Windows PC and Android OS.

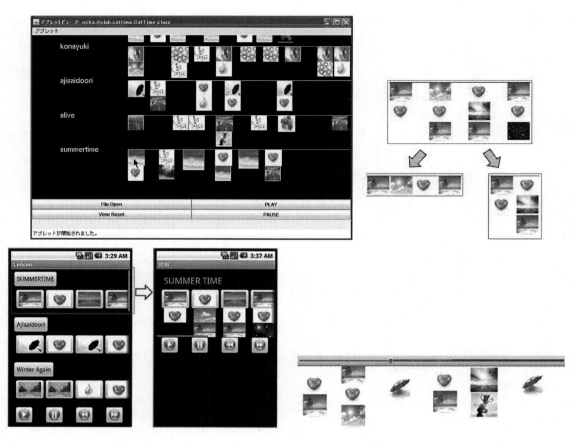

Figure 3. (Upper-Left) User interface implemented for Windows PC. (Upper-Right) Zooming user interface. (Lower-Left) User interface implemented for Android OS. (Lower-Right) A scroll-bar of a music player software

Figure 3(Upper-Left) shows our implementation of the user interface for Windows PC. It horizontally displays a set of icons for one song, and vertically aligns the sets of icons. Users can select their favorite songs by clicking the names of songs. They can start or stop of playing the songs by pressing the downside buttons. Also, users can click icons so that Lyricon can start the play of songs from the corresponding parts of the songs.

Here, this mechanism occupies large area of window space to completely show the selected icons of many songs. To solve the problem, we implemented a level-of-detail mechanism to control the number of displayed icons. It vertically reduces the number of displayed icons according to change of heights of windows. Also, it vertically reduces the number of displayed icons according to change of widths of windows. Figure 3(Upper-Right) illustrates the mechanism.

Figure 3(Lower-Left) shows our implementation of the user interface for Android OS. It features start, pause, next, and previous buttons as orange buttons. It also features horizontal and vertical scroll bars: users can browse icons through a song using the horizontal scroll bar, and many

songs using the vertical scroll bar. The user interface initially displays the most important icon for each block. When a user clicks a name of a song, the user interface zooms up so that all icons of the specified song are displayed.

We think that Lyricon can be also applied to icon indication along scroll-bars of media players. Figure 3(Lower-Right) shows an illustration of the application. Users can easily play the song from any block that they want to listen, by looking at the icons.

V. RESULTS

A. Examples

Figure 1 shows examples of the multiple icon selection results applied to real Japanese hit songs. Theme of the song displayed in Figure 1(upper) is love, and the icon selection result clearly represents the theme. Theme of the song displayed in Figure 1(center) is Japanese cherry, which blossoms during graduation and enrollment season in Japan. It displays an icon of country and an icon of city, because the central character of the song graduates from a school in a country and then moves to a city. The icon selection result narrates such story of the song. The former part of lyrics displayed in Figure 1(lower) negatively contains keywords "fight" and "tear", but the latter part of the lyrics positively contains keywords "love" and "flower". The icon selection result well represents the change of the nuance.

These results demonstrate that the icon selection results by Lyricon clearly represents the theme of the songs, and story of the lyrics.

B. Subjective evaluation of icon selection results

We showed printed icon selection results for examinees, and asked them several questions. Examinees were 13 female university students majoring computer science.

1) Impression of songs associated by looking at icons: We asked 50 examinees to look at sequences of icons which expressed the whole songs, and asked to answer their impression of the songs. We prepared 10 sequences of icons, and asked to freely write keywords imagined to be contained in the lyrics of the songs, and impressions imagined to be led from musical features of the songs. We extracted adequate keywords and impressions from their answers, and calculated adequate answer rates, which are the rates of the number of adequate answers against the total number of answers.

Table I shows the adequate answer rates for keywords and impressions. This result denotes that the answers were very adequate for several songs (e.g. icon set 2, 5, and 6). The icon set 2 is selected for a summer love song, which have fast and bright musical features. Figure 1(Upper) shows this icon set. Lyricon successfully selected icons of summer and love icons, and examinees adequately mentioned keywords including summer and love, and impressions including fast and bright.

On the other hand, we could not get high adequate answer rates for some of other songs. Icon set 7 was selected for a song of family love, but many examinees imagined a song of love between a man and a woman looking at icons of heart. We need to apply more sophisticated natural language processing techniques to distinguish between family love and man-woman love. Icon set 10 was selected for a song of urban life struggling against business and economics. We did not prepare adequate categories and keywords for such songs. We need to prepare wider categories and keywords for more variety of songs.

2) Selection of icons from lyrics: We asked 50 examinees to read lyrics of 7 songs, and then choose the best sequence of icons for the lyrics. We prepared 10 similar sets of icons for each song, and asked them to choose one of the icon sets for the song.

Table II shows correct answer rates, which are the rates of the numbers of correctly answered examinees against the total number of them. This result denotes that the rates were totally good, and Lyricon works well to associate semantics of songs by looking at the sequences of icons. On the other hand, this result denotes that there were several mistakable

icon sets. For example, lyric 2 in Table II was a Christmas song, but some of examinees selected another icon set shown in Figure 1(upper). We assume that some of examinees associated the Christmas day from icons of hearts and starts from the wrong icon set. We would like to gather such mistakable examples and discuss how to improve in our future experiments.

VI. CONCLUSION AND FUTURE WORK

This paper presented "Lyricon", a technique for automatically selecting multiple icons of tunes block-by-block. Lyricon firstly selects candidates of icons according to words of lyrics block-by-block, and then selects suitable icons from the candidates according to musical features. Lyricon also supports user interfaces to effectively and adaptively display the icons. This paper demonstrated the effectiveness of Lyricon with examples and subjective evaluation results.

As a future work, we would like to reexamine the icons and keywords. Section V-B discussed that several songs bring mistakable results, or consist of important words which are not prepared by our implementation. We would like to prepare more categories, keywords, and icons to support more variety of lyrics. Also, we would like to have more experiments to find more mistakable results and discuss how to improve.

Also, we need to improve the implementation. Section V-B also discussed that interpretation of lyrics is mistakable while Lyricon just extracts keywords. We would like to apply more sophisticated natural language processing techniques to solve the problem. Another issue is that Table I suggests adequate answer rates for impressions were a little bit worse than those for keywords. We think one reason may be selection of musical features, and therefore we would like to discuss how to improve the processes of musical features.

As another future work, we would like to extend Lyricon to allow users to edit the categories, and to add keywords and icons. For example, we assume it is effective if users can add their favorite photographs or original pictures which they can easily imagine the songs.

REFERENCES

[1] V. Setlur, C. Albrecht-Buehler, A. A. Gooch, S. Rossoff, B. Gooch, Semanticons: Visual Metaphors as File Icons. Computer Graphics Forum (Proc. of Eurographics), Vol. 24, No. 3, pp. 647-656, 2005.

[2] P. Kolhoff, J. Preub and J. Loviscach: Music Icons: Procedural Glyphs for Audio Files, Brazilian Symposium on Computer Graphics and Image Processing (SIBGRAPI'06), pp. 289-296, 2006.

[3] M. Oda and T. Itoh: MIST: A Music Icon Selection Technique Using Neural Network, NICOGRAPH International, 2007.

[4] S. Xu, T. Jin, F. C. M. Lau, Automatic Generation of Music Slide Show Using Personal Photos, 10th IEEE International Symposium on Multimedia, pp. 214-219, 2008.

Table I

ADEQUATE ANSWERS RATES, WHERE ANSWERS ARE KEYWORDS IMAGINED TO BE CONTAINED IN THE LYRICS, AND IMPRESSIONS IMAGINED TO BE LET FROM MUSICAL FEATURES.

Icon set	1	2	3	4	5	6	7	8	9	10
Rate(keyword)	0.97	0.96	0.87	0.96	0.94	0.86	0.18	0.98	0.85	0.25
Rate(impression)	0.57	0.88	0.62	0.63	0.98	0.85	0.33	0.35	0.24	0.28

Table II

CORRECT ANSWER RATES OF SELECTION OF ICON SETS FOR LYRICS OF SONGS.

Lyric	1	2	3	4	5	6	7
Rate	0.92	0.76	0.82	0.80	1.00	0.84	0.96

[5] R. Neumayer, A. Rauber, Multi-Modal Music Information Retrieval - Visualisation and Evaluation of Clusterings by Both Audio and Lyrics. 8th International Conference on Computer-Assisted Information Retrieval, 2007.

[6] Japanese WordNet, http://nlpwww.nict.go.jp/wn-ja/

[7] Chasen, http://chasen.naist.jp/hiki/Chasen/

[8] O. Lartillot, MIRtoolbox, http://www.jyu.fi/hum/laitokset/musiikki/en/ research/coe/materials/mirtoolbox

[9] K. Maehashi, Lyric Master, http://www.kenichimaehashi.com/lyricsmaster/

Chameleon – A Context Adaptive Visualization Framework for a Mobile Environment

Paulo Pombinho, Ana Paula Afonso, Maria Beatriz Carmo

Departamento de Informática, Faculdade de Ciências, Universidade de Lisboa

ppombinho@lasige.di.fc.ul.pt, {apa, bc}@di.fc.ul.pt

Abstract

The evolution of mobile devices, especially the integration of sensors, is fostering the development of context aware visualization applications. The adaptation to usage contexts is crucial to overcome the diverse limitations that exist in a mobile device, namely the screen size. However, most of the currently develop applications focus on specific contexts. In this paper we propose an adaptive visualization framework that has the goal of enabling the development of applications that use a diverse set of contexts and adaptation methods.

1. Introduction

The rapid evolution, on a global scale, of the telecommunication infrastructures has allowed the massification of users with access to wireless communication networks and to the mobile internet. According to the International Telecommunication Union report [1], mobile phone networks presently cover almost 90% of the world population, and it is expected that this number should reach 100% in 2015.

On the other hand, people increasingly feel the need to use, in a mobile environment, tools and applications that enable them to become productive in scenarios where they, previously, were not. This need can be seen in the circa 5 billion mobile network subscriptions and in the almost 2 billion people with internet access.

The conjunction of the growing desire for mobile productivity with the new available infrastructures, has been operating a change in our society.

While in the past, people planned and chose the various options of their day-to-day, in advance, often in the comfort of their home, they are now preferring to do it on the spot, in a mobile environment, using services or applications available in mobile devices. This need for more complex applications in a mobile environment can be seen in the growing demand for smartphones, which in some countries, in 2011, are expected to exceed the number of standard phones [2].

One of the features that has been fostered by advances in mobile phones and the, already frequent, integration of global positioning devices, are location based services. These services have gained much popularity because they allow a user to know, with some ease, what points of interest exist in their neighborhood (restaurants, hotels, and so on). However, despite extensive research with the aim of minimizing some of the limitations of the visualization of points of interest in mobile devices, there are still some unsolved problems.

The major limitation of a mobile device is its reduced screen space. Thus, whatever is shown onscreen has to be important to the user [3]. Moreover, the usability of these systems should be taken into account, since inexperienced users will not enthusiastically adopt these services if the complexity of the interaction and its restrictions are not removed [4, 5].

The adaptation to usage contexts is a key feature to mitigate the limitations in the usability of small screens. According to the definition of Reichenbacher [6], adaptive visualization concerns the adjustment of all components of the visualization process, such as the interface, the information extracted from the data and the data codification, according to a particular usage context.

With the growing amount of geo-referenced information available, the search for visualizations adapted to the specific usage context of each user will increase. The adaptive principle is especially important to increase the usability of the visualization of information in mobile devices and to reduce the cognitive load inherent to mobile usage contexts.

In recent years, the search for context-aware solutions has shown significant advances. However, research in this area has focused on computational contexts or device location context. Consequently, in the information visualization area, for mobile devices, the applications have explored only these contexts and the associated adaptations.

However, current context models and adaptive applications suggest richer and broader context dimensions beyond location and computation. The adaptation of information visualization techniques to other contexts has already been explored in some studies [6, 7, 8].

Despite the existence of some works that explore a larger number of different contexts, they are usually focused in a specific domain, making its reuse in other domains difficult.

1550-6037/11 $26.00 © 2011 IEEE
DOI 10.1109/IV.2011.34

The aim of this work is the creation of a framework that can facilitate the creation of adaptive applications for the visualization of points of interest that can deal with a diverse set of contexts and adaptation methods. To achieve this objective we adopt the classification and terminology adopted by Reichenbacher [6], and divide the main components of the visualization framework into adaptation objects, adaptation methods and usage contexts. The fundamental idea is to understand what adaptation methods adapt which objects depending on the different usage contexts present.

In the next section we will describe some of the related work. In section 3 we will review and categorize the different usage contexts, the adaptation objects and the respective adaptation methods. In section 4 we present our proposed framework and in section 5 we refer some case studies that have used this framework. Finally, in section 6, we present the conclusions and the future work.

2. Related Work

In 2001 Reichenbacher suggested an outline of a conceptual framework for adapting the display of geo-referenced information in mobile environments [9]. In this conceptual framework, the key elements identified are the user, the context and the current task. These elements should be responsible for adapting the visualization.

In 2008, Reichenbacher differentiates between adapted visualization, which is a display where tools are offered for changing the characteristics of the visualization, and adaptive visualization, in which the characteristics of the display are automatically changed according to the current usage contexts [6]. Reichenbacher identifies as basic building blocks of an adaptive visualization application, the context dimensions, the objects that can be adapted, and the adaptation methods. Thus, an adaptation method may receive one or more objects to adapt and use as adaptation parameters the values of the different contexts.

Bradley van Tonder and Janet Wesson [10], propose a model that incorporates an adaptive interface in the design of a map visualization system for mobile devices. Their model consists of four main components: A "Data Model" that contains the information that is being visualized in the system; a "Knowledge Base" that manages and obtains the four different types of context used (namely user profile, user task, time and location); the "User Monitoring and Modelling Component" that is responsible for accepting the user interaction data to try and automatically determine the user's preferences and behavior; and finally the "Adaptation Engine" that manages the adaptations of the visualization (visual representations, detail level, zoom level), information (filtering) and interface (menu options).

Lastly, Panagiotakapoulos and Lymberpoulos [11] propose an active context-aware platform for the monitorization of patients suffering from special phobias.

An ontology based context model was designed that used a diverse set of contexts to be able to provide a complete set of data that describes the current situation of the patient. The proposed framework is composed by six main components: "Context Providers" that are responsible for obtaining the diverse context data from the sensors and external sources; an "Aggregating Agent" that gathers all the data obtained from the context providers and analyses which data is useful; an "Inference Agent" that interprets the data from the previous component to generate high level contexts; a "Profile Agent" responsible for managing the profile information about the patients; a "Service Adaptation Agent" that queries the two previous agents to decide which actions should be taken; and finally the "Service Coordination Agent" responsible for managing the communication between the different agents present in the framework.

Despite the existence of the adaptive frameworks described, they are either too focused on a specific domain, making their reuse in other domains very difficult, or they do not have in consideration the diversity and quantity of the different usage contexts that are possible to be obtained in a mobile environment.

Thus, it is necessary to create a framework that is sufficiently generic that it may be reused in different domains and that has different types of context in consideration.

3. Contexts, Objects and Adaptation Methods

To be able to develop a framework that can effectively manage the adaptation to different contexts, it is necessary to understand, in advance, what is the relationship between the different contexts available in mobile environments, the adaptation objects that typically exist in mobile point of interest visualization applications, and the different adaptation methods.

As an example to understand this relationship, suppose it is late at night and the user is searching for a gas station in a mobile application, the information that is presented to the user (the adaptation object) should be adapted through the use of a filtering function (adaptation method) that selects locations that are open at that current time (the usage context)

In the following sections we will present and categorize the contexts, objects and methods of adaptation that are the building blocks for the creation of the adaptive framework.

3.1. Mobile Environment Contexts

We have chosen to categorize context, using a combination of the categorization that were presented by [12] and [13], since it represents the most comprehensive categorization for mobile environments. Thus, we consider five categories: Computation Context, User Context, Physical Context, Temporal Context and Historical Context.

Next, we will describe the various context dimensions identified for each category (as illustrated in figure 1) and the approaches for acquiring these contexts. As we have already stated, the identification of the contexts are crucial for the process of adaptation of the visualization.

Figure 1. Context dimensions categorization

3.1.1. Computation Context. This category concerns all the technical features of the device, the device's connection to a network, and also the collection of possible resources accessible by the device.

The characteristics of the device can be automatically obtained during the applications installation. These specifications include the type and speed of the CPU, memory and storage capacity, screen size, resolution, number of colors, and also what input and output peripherals are available.

The characteristics of the network connection can be obtained in real time (for example, the available bandwidth) or specified by the user (for example, the cost of using the network).

3.1.2. User Context. The contexts directly related to the user include his profile, the user's spatial characteristics and the task he is doing.

The different characteristics of the user profile can be configured directly by the user, and include contexts such as age, language and nationality, experience in using the device and application, disability, and preferences.

One of the main contexts that, due to the type of use of mobile devices, is constantly changing, is the spatial context. The user's location has the potential to be the most important context in mobile visualization applications. This context can be obtained by a satellite positioning system like the GPS or inferred through the use of other integrated sensors. Equally important, the orientation of the user and therefore his focus of attention, can be obtained from a digital compass.

Other properties that may be important are the speed and acceleration of the user and the type of movement he is doing. This information can be obtained by analyzing the real-time GPS data and the information obtained from an accelerometer.

Finally, a crucial context is the knowledge about what task the user is (or will be) performing. This context can be specified by the user or automatically inferred by using information from historical contexts (described below).

3.1.3. Physical Context. The physical features surrounding the user can be divided into visual and sound conditions, weather conditions and surrounding environment.

The lighting conditions and noise levels at the location where the user is located may be obtained, respectively, through the device's camera and microphone.

Weather conditions can be obtained by combining different contexts: temperature, humidity, barometric pressure and intensity of ultraviolet (UV). This information can, in turn, be obtained in two different ways. On the one hand, it is possible to use a set of sensors (thermometer, hygrometer, barometer, and UV sensor) integrated on the device, that show the exact conditions in the location of the user. Alternatively, if it is sufficient to use approximate information, an online meteorological web service can be used instead.

The context of the surrounding environment can be obtained by analyzing, for example, the type of buildings (for example, public buildings, residential, factories or tourism), the surrounding terrain (for example, gardens, buildings, sea or mountain) or traffic conditions. In the case of traffic conditions, these can be obtained through the use of available online servers.

3.1.4. Temporal Context. These contexts correspond to the time of day, date, day of week, season of the year, among others. They can be obtained from the device's internal clock and calendar. Alternatively, online time servers can also be used to check if the date/time definitions are correct.

3.1.5. Historical Context. Lastly, the historical context of the previous choices made in the application can be obtained through the logs that were stored in the previous uses of the system. These logs may consist, for example, in the list of places the user has previously visited, previous queries, and also the different choices made by the user.

3.2. Adaptation Objects

Regarding the adaptation objects, we want to identify what objects commonly exist in a mobile visualization application that can be adapted depending on the different contexts.

The approach followed in this work is inspired by the proposal in [6], in which three distinct categories are suggested: Visualization, User Interface and Geospatial Information. This way, our categorization of the adaptation objects is as follows:

3.2.1. Information. Consists on the data presented to the user. It includes: the type of filtering done to the information, the amount of information that is presented, the ranking of their relevance and the area being considered.

3.2.2. Visualization. This category contains the graphical elements directly related to the information visualization in the device. For instance it includes: element codification (raster, vector), how the elements are arranged on the screen (positioning, size, color and opacity), the characteristics of the maps used (scale, orientation, legend, projection and center coordinates), its level of detail, the iconography used, and the use of generalization operators.

3.2.3. Interaction. Finally, the interaction category comprises the objects related to the applications interface. Includes: Use of different mechanisms or methods for the input of data, using different techniques for the selection of objects, moving the map and scale change operations.

3.3. Adaptation Methods

Finally, regarding the adaptation methods, these can be viewed as an association between the different contexts and the adaptation objects and are responsible for adjusting one or more adaptation objects. Thus, these methods can be classified, not only, in relation to the different categories of context, but also in relation to the different categories of object they adapt. This relationship can be seen in Figure 2.

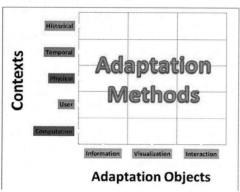

Figure 2. Adaptation methods categorization

For the sake of simplicity, the examples of adaptation methods, described below, are grouped by the context category they adapt to.

3.3.1. Computation Context. The knowledge of the characteristics of the device may enable the application to proceed with different types of adaptation: the computational load of the application may be adjusted by disabling more complex features if the device is a less powerful one; the detail and size of the icons used may be increased of reduced depending on the size and

resolution of the screen; and alternate modes of interaction may be applied depending on the input and output devices available.

The network connection characteristics may be used to allow a better use of the available resources, through the use of a cache and by choosing the best time to obtain the needed data.

Regarding the cost of using the network connection, this information allows the application to know whether to give priority to speed (in case of billing by time) or to prioritize the reduction of the amount of data (in case of billing by amount of traffic).

Finally, the use of the information about the nearby available resources (printers, screens among others) may allow a better interconnection of the mobile devices with the different devices in its vicinity.

3.3.2. User Context. Concerning the user profile, characteristics such as age, language and nationality may influence the visualization used, adapting, respectively, the type of graphics used, the language and time definitions and the currency.

The type of interaction may also be adapted according to the experience in using the device and the application, the disabilities and the preferences of the user. Through these contexts it is possible to present more complex interfaces to the users, or more simple ones, depending on their needs and capabilities.

Lastly, the information presented can also be adapted according to the user interests, the locations he has marked as important (for example, his home and work place) and also cultural and social elements.

In relation to the spatial characteristics, the location context allows the application to show information about what is near the user. In the same way, the orientation context of the user can be used to show only the information about what is in front of him, or where the user is looking.

Properties such as speed, acceleration and the type of movement done by the user, may be used, not only, to calculate where the user is headed and to estimate how long he will take to arrive there, but also to adapt the way information is presented (for example, reducing the magnification of a map as the speed increases) or the type of interaction available (for example, using different techniques to select objects on the screen in the user is walking or running).

As already happens in systems like Google Latitude [14], the geographic proximity of friends and family can be used to assist the search for locations that are in the proximity of both users.

The knowledge about the task the user is engaged in is crucial to allow the presentation of the most relevant information that can be most helpful to aid the user.

3.3.3. Physical Context. Information about lighting conditions and noise levels present at the location where the user is standing are important to adapt the way information in transmitted to the user. The lighting conditions context can enable the application to adapt the colors used and the screen's brightness and contrast in a way that it can be easier for the information displayed to be correctly understood. Concerning the noise levels, it is possible to increase or reduce the volume of the device depending whether he is, respectively, in a noisy or silent location.

The information about the weather conditions can be used to show different information depending on the current conditions. If the user is, for example, looking for a restaurant, if it is a sunny day with comfortable temperature , the application may raise the relevance of a restaurant with a terrace, and the reverse if it was cold and rainy.

Using information about the surrounding environment it is possible to filter the information presented to the user taking into account such surroundings. If the user is near the sea the application could show beaches, or museums if the user is near a touristic area.

Traffic conditions can be, as is already done in systems like TomTom HD Traffic [15], used to suggest alternative information that avoids crossing locations that have traffic congestion.

3.3.4. Temporal Context. The temporal information may allow different types of adaptation.

The way the visualization of information is done (for example, the colors and icons used) can be altered depending on the time of the day (for example, using different colors whether it is night or day).

Using the local time context, it is possible to filter the presented information, taking into account the schedules of the locations and whether they are open or closed. Similarly, the presentation of information about events may take into account the current date and filter information that is still a long time away.

3.3.5. Historical Context. The analysis of the logs recorded over the previous uses of the application may allow, in combination with other contexts, to anticipate the needs of the user and automatically display the most relevant information at each moment.

4. Framework

To be able to make an effective management of the relationship between usage contexts, adaptation objects and adaptation methods, we propose the Chameleon, a Context Adaptive Visualization Framework for Mobile Environments.

This framework (Figure 3) consists of three main components, which correspond to the adaptation objects (in blue, on top), the adaptation methods (in green, on the middle) and the usage contexts (in red, on the bottom). The focus of our work is on the adaptation of the information and the visualization and not on the adaptation of the user interface. The modules that will not be focused on our work are presented with a black background.

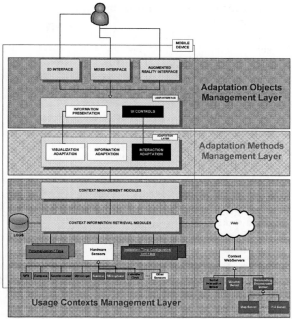

Figure 3. Chameleon Framework (detailed view of each layer in Figure 4, 5 and 6)

In the next subsections we will describe these three layers.

4.1. Adaptation Objects Management Layer

In the developed framework, the user can interact with three distinct primary interfaces (Figure 4): one consisting on a display of information on a 2D map representing the neighborhood of the user, another in which the information is presented using augmented reality techniques and, finally, a mixed interface in which a 2D map is presented simultaneously with an augmented reality view.

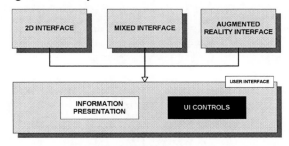

Figure 4. Adaptation Objects Management Layer

Thus, the elements that compose these distinct interfaces form the set of adaptation objects. For these, management is divided in two modules: User Interface Controls (which will not be the focus of this work) and the information presentation module (corresponding to the information and visualization categories of adaptation objects).

From a programmatic perspective, each adaptation object will be responsible for knowing and calling the different adaptation methods it relates to.

4.2. Adaptation Methods Management Layer

Regarding the Adaptation Methods Management Layer, it consists in three modules that manage the different types of adaptation (Figure 5). This way, the interaction adaptation module is responsible for managing the adaptations of objects directly related with the user interface control.

The information adaptation module and the visualization adaptation module will manage the information and visualization adaptations, respectively, requested by the adaptation objects that correspond to the information presentation module.

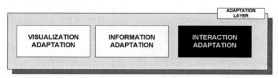

Figure 5. Adaptation Methods Management Layer

Thus, each adaptation method will be responsible for implementing different versions of the adaptations, allowing for some flexibility according to the type and value of the available contexts.

4.3. Usage Contexts Management Layer

Lastly, the layer responsible for managing the contexts is composed of two main sets of modules (Figure 6).

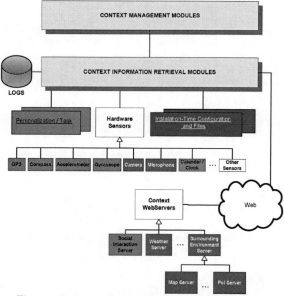

Figure 6. Usage Contexts Management Layer

The Context Management Modules are responsible for managing, calculating and communicating the contexts themselves. The Context Information Retrieval Modules communicate the required data to obtain / calculate the different contexts with the previous modules.

Regarding the latter modules, they are divided into five groups: an internal database in which historical records are stored, a set of dynamic files that contain personalization information and information about the user's current task, fairly static files created in installation time and configuration, a set of hardware sensors integrated with the mobile device and, finally, a set of context servers available via the Web.

Thus, the modules corresponding to each context should be responsible for obtaining the data required, from the Context Information Retrieval Modules, that allows them to calculate the value of the context.

4.4. Flow of Information

As an example of a possible flow of information, considering the adaptation of a map image to the location context: we have an adaptation object "Map" that will communicate with the required adaptation method, so that it may adapt the map picture to a new location.

This adaptation method will then request the "Location Context" module for its value. The "Location Context" module will then be responsible for asking the GPS sensor module the new coordinates or, if GPS is not available, use alternate sensors that may allow it to calculate the new location.

After obtaining the necessary information, the context module should calculate its value and return it to the adaptation method that called it. This method, after receiving the context information will then be able to adapt the map picture to the new location, returning it to the interface.

5. Application of the Framework

Parts of the proposed framework have been applied in some case studies that explore different types of usage contexts and some visualization and information adaptation methods that adapt some objects from the information presentation module. The different visualization applications developed are describe below.

In [16] an application for the visualization of points of interest on a 2D map interface was tested. This application used some adaptation methods that filtered the points of interest shown to the user depending on the location context and the user's search preferences, to show only the most relevant ones. Additionally, the icons were also adapted, taking into account the relevance of the points of interest associated with them and their location relative to other icons, by changing their graphical symbols to represent more than one point of interest and also conveying the most relevant ones.

In [17] a location and orientation aware application for the search of points of interest in mobile devices that uses, not only the location of the user, but also his orientation was presented. The location and orientation contexts are obtained through the use of position (GPS) and orientation (digital compass) sensors.

The developed application uses an augmented reality interface and adapts the way the different points of interest (and their information) are shown, according to their relative orientation. The interface also includes a dynamic adaptation of the indication of the device's orientation, complemented with the capture of real time pictures, using the device's integrated camera.

Finally, the choice of which stored picture (for each point of interest) should be shown is adapted by automatically selecting the one that most closely resembles the user's current location and orientation contexts. The addition of these pictures helps the user to compare what he is currently seeing in the real world, and correctly identifying the shown point of interest.

In [18] we have presented a point of interest aware application that uses the user's indoor location context to adapt the information displayed about the points of interest that exist in the vicinity of the user. To be able to correctly identify the position context of the user, we have proposed an indoor positioning method that does not need previously installed physical infrastructures in a building. Furthermore, this approach does not need external sensors, avoiding the restriction of the user's natural movements when using a mobile device and walking indoors.

6. Conclusions and Future Work

In this paper we have presented a review of the different types of adaptation objects, adaptation methods and usage contexts that may exist in a mobile scenario and categorized them.

Using this insight, we developed an adaptive visualization framework that has the goal to allow an efficient management of the relationship between objects of adaptation, methods of adaptation and usage contexts.

The proposed framework is composed of three main layers that correspond and manage the usage contexts, adaptation methods and adaptation objects. This framework aims to be sufficiently generic so that it can be used to a very diverse set of domains, and also to allow the knowledge and use of the very diverse types of context that exist in a mobile use scenario.

Although we have already done some case studies that use parts of this framework, we still need to create it, in a more global approach. To do this, we intend to create a more complex case study that uses a diversified set of contexts, objects and adaptation methods.

Acknowledgements

The work presented here is based on research funded by the FCT - Fundação para a Ciência e Tecnologia (Portuguese Science and Technology Foundation) through the SFRH/BD/46546/2008 scholarship.

References

[1] International Telecommunication Union. World Telecommunication / ICT Development Report 2010 – Monitoring the WSIS Targets, A Mid-Term Review. *Geneva, Switzerland,* 2010.

[2] Entner, N. Smartphones to Overtake Feature Phones in U.S. by 2011. [online] Available in http://blog.nielsen.com/nielsenwire/consumer/smartphones-to-overtake-feature-phones-in-u-s-by-2011/ [accessed in 30 January 2011].

[3] Holtzblatt, K. Designing for the Mobile Device: Experiences, Challenges, and Methods. In *Communications of the ACM, 48 (7), pp. 33-35.* 2005.

[4] Chittaro, L. HCI Aspects of Mobile Devices and Services. In *Personal and Ubiquitous Computing, Springer-Verlag,8 (2), pp. 69-70.* 2004.

[5] Burigat, S. and Chittaro, L. Visualizing the Results of Interactive Queries for Geographic Data on Mobile Devices. In *Proceedings of the 13th Annual ACM International Workshop on Geographic Information Systems, ACM Press, pp. 277-284.* 2005.

[6] Reichenbacher, T. Mobile Usage and Adaptive Visualization. In *Encyclopedia of GIS, part 16. Heidelberg: Springer-Verlag, pp. 677-682.* 2008.

[7] Nivala, A. –M. and Sarjakoski, L. T. User Aspects of Adaptive Visualization for Mobile Maps. In *Cartography and Geographic Information Science, Towards Ubiquitous Cartography, 34 (4), pp. 275-284.* 2007.

[8] Cai, G. and Xue, Y. Activity-Oriented Context-Aware Adaptation Assisting Mobile Geo-Spatial Activities. In *Proceedings of the 11th IUI, pp. 354-356.* 2006.

[9] Reichenbacher, T. Adaptive Concepts for a Mobile Cartography. In *Journal of Geographical Sciences, 11, pp. 43-53.* 2001.

[10] Tonder, B. v. and Wesson, J. Using Adaptive Interfaces to Improve Mobile Map-Based Visualization. In *Proceedings of the SAICSIT, pp. 257-266.* 2008.

[11] Panagiotakopoulos, T. C., and Lymberopoulos, D. K. Monitoring of Patients Suffering from Special Phobias Exploiting Context and Profile Information. In *Proceedings of the 8th IEEE International Conference on BioInformatics and BioEngineering – BIBE 2008, pp. 1-6.* 2008.

[12] Schilit, B., Adams, N. and Want, R. Context-Aware Applications. In *Proceedings of the IEEE WMCSA, Santa Cruz, California, pp. 85-90.* 1994.

[13] Chen, G. and Kotz, D. A Survey of Context-Aware Mobile Computing Research. In *Technical Report, Department of Computer Science, Dartmouth College.* 2000.

[14] Google Latitude. [online] Available in: http://www.google.com/latitude/ [accessed in 30 January 2011].

[15] TomTom HD Traffic. [online] Available in: http://www.tomtom.com/services/service.php?id=2 [accessed in 30 January 2011].

[16] Pombinho, P., Carmo, M. B., and Afonso, A. P. Evaluation of Overcluttering Prevention Techniques for Mobile Devices. In *Proceedings of the Information Visualization (IV2009), pp. 127 – 134.* 2009.

[17] Pombinho, P., Carmo, M. B., Afonso, A. P., and Aguiar, H. Location and Orientation Based Queries on Mobile Environments. In *Proceedings of the Computer Graphics, Visualization, Computer Vision and Image Processing 2010 International Conference.* 2010.

[18] Pombinho, P., Afonso, A. P., and Carmo, M. B. Point of Interest Awareness Using Indoor Positioning with a Mobile Phone. In *Proceedings of the 1st International Conference on Pervasive and Embedded Computing and Communication Systesm.* 2011. (to appear).

Visualization of Complex Relations in E-Government Knowledge Taxonomies

Per Myrseth, Jørgen Stang, David Skogan
Det Norske Veritas
{per.myrseth, jorgen.stang, david.skogan}@dnv.com

Abstract

The successful collaboration and interoperability between fully and partially related E-government subject domains requires well understood and high quality definitions of terms and a unified view of the relationships between the defined terms. The common terms and corresponding relation are defined in knowledge taxonomies (or even ontologies) and several good tools exist to create and maintain these models for the appropriate sub domains. The engineering process is carried out in a multi-user environment including remote workers editing the taxonomy. However, the sheer complexity and size of the full models dictates more powerful and dedicated visualization tools to graphically inspect, assess and diagnose the full taxonomies. This article describes a case where a social network analysis (SNA) tool is used as a part of a regime for the quality assurance of a knowledge taxonomy for e-government interoperability. In addition to the visual aids provided by the SNA tool, some comments are also made as to the applicability of SNA centrality metrics to knowledge taxonomies.

*Keywords --- **Visualization, knowledge taxonomies, social network analysis, ontology, e-government, metadata, data quality**.*

1. Introduction

In order to make governmental data collection and public interfaces more effective and less error prone, the Norwegian government has over the past few years made a substantial effort to harmonize and build common knowledge taxonomies across governmental departments. The ultimate goal of this initiative is manifold; (i) avoid duplication and inconsistencies when collecting data from the public by eliminating inherent data entry redundancy (asking for the same information in multiple data entry (web) forms), (ii) enable pre-filled forms only requiring user confirmation, (iii) reuse collected information for multiple regulations, and (iv) to ensure governmental rules are applied consistently within and across departments.

The quality of the resulting knowledge taxonomy will be determent to the users trust and the general usefulness of the common model. The syntactical data quality is maintained by continuously measuring well defined modeling rules and by defining responsibility matrices and feedback loops to the appropriate data modeler[1]. At the same time, there is a need for efficient tools and process to utilize existing models to identify and learn from both best practices, mal practices and inconsistencies in the existing terms and taxonomies. Hence, leveraging an educational process as the knowledge taxonomy is actively in progress. This in turn requires effective visualization of the taxonomies which goes well beyond what is provided by the OWL or UML modeling tools normally used for defining the models.

By considering each term as an actor (node) and the relations between them (the taxonomy) as inter actor communication (edges), visualization and analysis tools frequently employed for social network analysis can be applied to both birds eye views of large scale taxonomies as well as provide useful drilldowns for diagnosis and pattern matching at a finer granularity. Identified patterns could include overlaps, inconsistencies, dangling (unresolved) entities and wanted or unwanted clusters. Also, the layered model design approach used for the governmental knowledge taxonomies described here could well lend itself to 3D visualizations by orthogonally offsetting each layer and so emphasizing on the layer connectivity [2].

In addition to the pure visual and educationalist aspects of applying SNA tools to knowledge taxonomies, we also attempt to relate several centrality metrics [3] to the taxonomy and determine if these metrics can provide useful characteristics of the taxonomy, in particular we consider; (i) inbetweenes centrality, (ii) degree centrality and (iii) closeness centrality. These SNA metrics are tested and evaluated as diagnostic metrics for a set of quality patterns we describe in a multi-user taxonomy / ontology engineering environment.

2. E-governmental metadata framework

The Norwegian Semantic Repository of Electronic Services (SERES) e-governmental metadata framework is designed to provide an effective means of connecting data submitted by the public (paper based or web forms based) to the governing rules and regulations. Also, the framework will support interoperability between

1550-6037/11 $26.00 © 2011 IEEE
DOI 10.1109/IV.2011.90

departments to prevent data inconsistencies and duplication.

2.1. Architecture

The metadata framework architecture comprises three distinct entity layers; (1) *implementation*, (2) *structure* and (3) *semantics* [1]. Each layer contains entities with a set of properties and relations to other entities. The implementation layer defines the entities as they are entered by the user, the structure layer defines aggregated (related) types that can be reused by several implementation entities, and the semantics layer defines the terms that are being used by the departmental subject matter experts. At the moment, the collected metadata can be termed a knowledge taxonomy, however, as the model evolves and become more mature it is intended to be extended to an ontology which can be used for inference engines. Figure 1 illustrates how the model can be used to define a taxpayer in the current implementation.

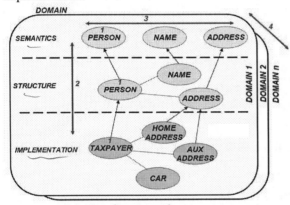

Figure 1 – Metadata example

The numbers 1-4 indicate levels of quality assurance, (1) by entity, (2) between entities, (3) across terms in the semantic layer and (4) between domains 1 through *n*. The visualization activity described here mainly supports (2) and (3) and to some extent (4). Several syntactical rules have already been defined and is routinely used to verify (1) and (2) in figure 1[1]. However, manual inspections are necessary to combine both modeling and domain expertise to ensure optimal model consistency and integrity. The total number of entities in the tax domain (all three layers) is currently in excess of 80 000.

2.2. Modeling process

The current modeling process is largely based on a bottom-up process. Skilled data modelers are collecting implementation entities from web based input forms and relate these entities to both the structure layer and the semantics layer. If no suitable entity is found in the above layers the modeler either modify existing or create new entities. Generally both the implementation layer and the semantics layer will provide rich descriptions of

the collected data and the legal terms respectively. On the other hand, the structure layer will be more generic and hence contain fewer entities than the other two layers; however, the structure layer will provide a large number of properties on each entity to facilitate efficient reuse by entities in the implementation and semantics layer. Possible reuse of governmental terms have previously been studied both on national and international levels [4].

To successfully develop a working taxonomy that will support both transactions between layers and domains, different skills and tools will be required. Subject matter experts proficient in the appropriate legal terms and definitions will develop the semantics layer whereas executive officers specialized in data modeling will contribute to both the implementation and the structure layer. This disjoint workflow will present challenges when it comes to how to eventually map and represent the governing terms efficiently and unambiguously; from the semantic layer to the interface presented to the public in the implementation layer. It is considered a particular high risk that subject matter experts could be reluctant to contribute if they perceive that the quality of underlying layers are low. To build their trust in the supporting structure an efficient vehicle for model discussions and communication must be established at a level that will efficiently span the user communities. The dedicated UML modeling tools and other table based repository browsers are generally useful to display subsets and verify specific hypothesizes. However, they do not provide good model overviews that can be used for collaboration at a general level, both to discover existing structures as well as to learn how to connect to or extend entities at a particular level. Also, patterns for best- or mal- practices that are not a part of any modeling guidelines or existing hypothesizes can be readily identified. This knowledge can subsequently be formalized in the guidelines and added to the routine syntactical verification. An efficient and powerful visualization of the e-governmental knowledge taxonomies is considered a substantial contribution to this discovery and collaboration process.

The rest of this article introduces Social Network Analysis (SNA) and describes how it can be used for both tentative taxonomy analysis as well as for providing good 2D layouts and visualizations. To further enhance the visualizations, the layered nature of the models are exploited to offset each layer in a 2.5D layout which can be viewed in 3D visualization tools such as provided for the extensible 3D markup language (X3D).

3. Social network analysis overview

Social network analysis (SNA) have been used for decades [5] to model the interactions between actors in a community. The area of application is wide and includes communication, transportation, sensor networks, knowledge discovery, chemistry, physics and anthropology [6]. Also, the suitability of SNA applied to ontology discovery has been described in [7] and the notion of network and data islands (cohesion, connectivity) in the context of quality assurance of taxonomies and ontologies is used in [16].

3.1. 2D Layout algorithms

Frequently, the considered networks do not have an explicit geometric layout and several algorithms have been devised to distribute the nodes in 2D or 3D space. The resulting layouts will aim to optimize visualization by clustering nodes with high communication frequency and spreading out disjointed data islands. Most of the work showed here use variations of force direction algorithms [8] as provided by the GUESS [9][10] visualization tool. The force direction algorithms generally consider edges as forces (or springs), thus pulling highly connected nodes together until some sort of equilibrium is achieved. In addition, the resulting layouts are non-overlapping and largely symmetrical. Figure 2 shows a typical example of a force directed layout applied to the knowledge taxonomy found in a subset of the Tax Administration domain.

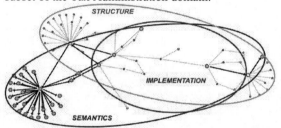

Figure 2 – Force directed layout of a subset of the Tax Administration metadata

Figure 2 is meant for illustrating the 2D layout only, however, by simple means such as color coding the layers and using different circle radius for entities (large) and properties (small), the usefulness for visualizing the knowledge taxonomies is evident.

3.2. Orthogonal 3D offsets

Several network layout algorithms offer 3D layouts and this was initially introduced to the e-governmental metadata. However, the resulting layouts offered little or no improvements on the 2D layouts as long as the third dimension was applied randomly and not as a contribution to clarify the inherent layered structure of the taxonomy. To alleviate this, the layout generation was performed in two separate steps; (1) a force directed algorithm was used to generate an initial 2D layout, optimizing the layout based on connectivity and aesthetics, and subsequently (2) each layer was offset orthogonally relative to each other to produce the model showed in figure 3.

As compared to the 2D layout, the layout in figure 3 offers a clear separation between individual layer connectivity and inter-layer connectivity.

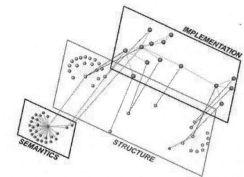

Figure 3 – Orthogonal offsets on force directed layout

Another example is given in figure 4 where a circular layout has been generated to visualize degree centrality for the same model.

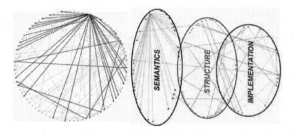

Figure 4 – (a) 2D and (b) 3D views of circular layouts

Both views (a) and (b) in figure 4 effectively highlights the degree centrality, however, the 3D models also illustrate the degree centrality per layer and connectivity between layers.

3.3. Centrality metrics

Several characteristic metrics have been developed to measure the performance of networks, where the majority is concerned with social aspects to assess how the individual nodes impact and interact with the overall network. In the work described here we focus on the centrality metrics. *Degree centrality* measures the number of direct connections for any node in the network. In the context of social networks this measures the individual's level of immediate connections. The *closeness centrality* is similar to degree except it also considers reach, meaning it will measure how well connected and how far an individual's connections can extend. *Inbetweeness centrality* measures how many nodes much pass through an individual's node to successfully communicate. Typically high inbetweeness indicates individuals with few direct connections; however, they are crucial by indirectly connecting other nodes. Removing nodes of high inbetweeness will typically result in disjointed clusters on either side of the removed node. In the case study presented in section 4, we argue for how the centrality metrics can be used to characterize the e-governmental knowledge taxonomies.

3.4. Model patterns

Our experience from multi-user taxonomy / ontology engineering during the last 10 years, we have learned that to achieve further quality improvements the engineers need tools to identify challenges, not related to single nodes, but related to patterns of nodes. The engineering quality patterns targeted in this article are listed below. We have used well established SNA centrality metrics, and visually inspecting the 2D and 3D models to identify the quality patterns in the taxonomy. The taxonomy used in our test bed is a subset from the Tax Administration. Section 4 describes the particular cases where the patterns were identified and possible relations to the SNA centrality metrics.

Overlap – Full and partial overlaps are considered here. In addition Soundex [11] (similar sound) and edit distance [12] (similar spelling) could be investigated. Full overlaps occur when two or more entities in the implementation layer refer to identical properties in the structure layer, and partial when they share a subset of properties.

Abundance – Entities in the semantics layer can be modeled standalone or with a rich set of relations to other nodes. The abundance pattern denotes rich semantics entities where the underlying entities fail to take advantage of the expressiveness and rather refer repeatedly to a single entity.

Incomplete – Many entities will have a good match in expressiveness across all three layers. Still, some matching properties might fail to be connected reducing the actual expressiveness as compared to the possible expressiveness. The incomplete pattern comprises entities which underutilize the potential connectivity offered by the above entities.

Inconsistency – Entities in the implementation layer can refer both to entities in the structure layer and entities in the semantics layer. To produce valid taxonomies the same implementation entity is not allowed refering to unrelated entities in the semantics layer. The inconsistency pattern hence denotes all constellations where an implementation entity both directly refers to a semantics entity and indirectly (via the structure layer) refers to another unrelated semantics entity.

Ambiguity pattern – The ambiguity pattern is a variation of the inconsistency pattern, however, the implementation entity does not misrepresent by inconsistent references. Rather, the entity properties refer to a different structure entity than the owning entity. Hence, one single implementation entity refers to two different structure entities.

All the above patterns are believed to adversely affect the quality of the model, both as a knowledge taxonomy and as an ontology. The list of patterns could easily been extended by e.g. dangling nodes. However, the assessment of the exact implications is outside the scope of this article and should be investigated in further work.

4. Case – Norwegian Tax Administration

To illustrate the described visualization, metrics and patterns we use production data from the Norwegian Tax Administration metadata repository. The metadata have been subjected to a rigorous syntactical data quality assessment and has been found to score close to 100% for compliance with the modeling guidelines. Hence the purpose of the visualization exercise is to add quality metrics to the already defined syntactical validations. This case limits itself to describe the discovery of additions to syntactical rules; however, future scenarios will also include the assessment of compliance to the real world and any inter-departmental issues.

4.1. Overview

The complete metadata for the Tax Administration office was extracted to produce figure 5. Several interesting characteristics can be noted at this level.

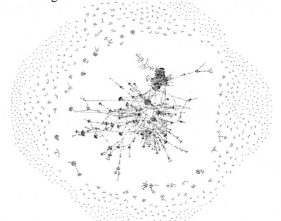

Figure 5 – The overall structure of the metadata

The main core is well connected and represents the model entities which are mature and have evolved over time. The disjointed clusters appearing at the fringe represents work in progress, where single nodes or groups of nodes have been defined but are not fully integrated in the domain. It is expected that a timeline animation would illustrate how entities travel from the outskirts of the model to the core as they evolve. Separate domains could be compared as a function of density and number of clusters to give a relative indicator of maturity.

4.2. Metrics

The impact of the SNA centrality metrics on the knowledge taxonomy is illustrated in figure 6. The figure depicts the metadata for one particular input form used by the Tax Administration. High degree centrality was found to denote well defined entities underutilized by other entities. For example the semantics entity *vehicle* could relate to a number of specific vehicles, however, none or few of the specializations were used. On the other hand, high closeness centrality identified well defined *and* well used entities, and high inbetweeness typically identified key values or nodes unintentionally left dangling.

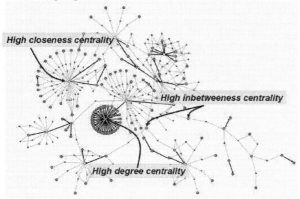

Figure 6 – SNA centrality for metadata

High inbetweeness for non-key nodes would typically increase the degrees of separation [15] between the implementation level and the semantics level, indicating that several of the patterns described in the next section could be expected to be found.

4.3. Patterns

By visually inspecting the networks, several recurring patterns could be identified. Similar techniques have previously been applied to identify access patterns on web pages [13].

The overlap pattern shown in figure 7 forms dense symmetrical clusters where all or subsets of the property connections (small circles) are identical.

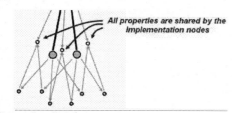

Figure 7 – Overlap pattern

The abundance pattern shown in figure 8 is described previously and is closely linked to degree centrality.

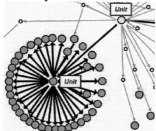

Figure 8 – Abundance pattern

Several entities were similarly defined across all three layers, however, the property connections would only run across the two bottom layers. This is labeled an incompleteness pattern and will result in *increased* inbetweeness centrality and *decreased* closeness centrality.

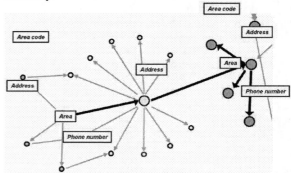

Figure 9 – Incompleteness pattern

Implementation level entities should only refer to one entity in the structure level, however, the ambiguity pattern shown in figure 10 shows how this is circumvented by referring to properties on disjointed structure entities. This will *increase* the degree centrality and again *decrease* the closeness centrality.

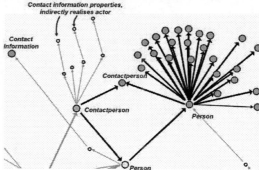

Figure 10 – Ambiguity pattern

In a similar fashion to the ambiguity pattern, implementation level entities should only connect to the semantics layer in closed loops (ie. the semantics entity should be identical or connected). Figure 11 shows an example of the inconsistency pattern. The *account* implementation entity refers both directly to *account* and indirectly to *account number* in the semantics level.

Figure 11 – Inconsistency pattern

The inconsistency pattern has largely the same effect on the centrality metrics as the ambiguity pattern; the

162

closeness centrality will *decrease* whereas the degree centrality will become more prominent.

5. Discussion

Social network analysis metrics and visualizations have been applied to aid the quality assurance, pattern discovery and communication of complex knowledge taxonomies for e-government metadata carried out in a multi-user engineering environment. Several patterns in the model were identified and provided useful input to best practices and validation rules. Full and partial overlap, inconsistencies and data islands (clusters) could easily be spotted and communicated to both domain experts and data modelers. The layered nature of the e-government metadata suggested a 2.5D visualization technique. The overall layout was calculated in 2D and each layer was subsequently offset orthogonally to aid the inspection the entities both individually and for interlayer integrity.

The social network analysis centrality metrics were found to have clear impacts on the metadata structure. The top nodes (key candidates) were found to have high *inbetweenness* centrality as all nodes should be reached from the top. Low *inbetweeness* for top nodes frequently indicated unwanted disjoints in the model. High *degree* centrality indicates well defined entities with low usage, whereas high *closeness* centrality indicates central nodes with rich definitions and high usage. Also, the majority of the common modeling patterns that were identified could be expressed directly as functions of the centrality metrics.

Social network analysis has proved a useful tool to diagnose and inspect complex knowledge taxonomies. Several issues could be identified which would be onerous to detect with more traditional means such as tree structures and table views. However, it did introduce some added complexity and some users could be deferred by the more elaborate navigation in a 2D/3D graphical world as opposed to classical table based interfaces. In addition to user adoption, more work is also required to further investigate both scalability and how to benefit further from existing social network methodologies. Animation could also be employed to show both how modeling trends change as a function of time and also how the usage of terms evolve (semantic drift [14]).

Most importantly, the visualization of the e-governmental metadata structures have shown substantial promise as a test bed for bridging the gap between subject experts and data modelers, offering a less specialized view than typically provided by the dedicated tools applied to the data collection (*implementation layer*) in one end and to the definition of the legal terms in the other end (*semantics layer*). The visualization of the knowledge taxonomies will also be important to improve the subject matter expert's trust in the model.

Often this trust is fragile and will be based on incidental perceptions, visualization will make the model more accessible and transparent and hence the perceptions can be solidly funded in how the model actually is implemented.

Acknowledgements

This work was carried out as part of the Semicolon project (project no. 183260/S10), funded by the Norwegian Research Council, Det Norske Veritas and other Semicolon participants.

References

[1]   P. Myrseth, J. Stang and V. Dalberg, A Data Quality Framework Applied to E-Government Metadata, *The International Conference on E-Business and E-Government (ICEE2011)*, Shanghai, China, 2011

[2]   W. Peng and L. SiKun, Social Network Visualization via Domain Ontology, International Conference on Information Engineering and Computer Science (ICIECS 2009), Wuhan, China, 2009

[3]   R.A. Hanneman and M. Riddle, An Introduction to Social Networks, *url: http://faculty.ucr.edu/~hanneman/nettext/*, University of California, 2005

[4]   S.M. Lui and C.C. Yu, Information Reuse Among Government Websites in Asian Countries, *International Conference on Information Information Reuse and Integration (IRI 2007)*, Las Vegas, USA, 2007

[5]   J.A. Barnes, Class and Committees in a Norwegian Island Parish, Human Relations vol.7 no1, 1954

[6]   U. Brandes, Social Network Analysis and Visualization, *IEEE Signal Processing Magazine*, November, 2008

[7]   B. Hoser, A. Hotho, R. Jaschke, C. Schmitz and G. Stumme, Semantic Network Analysis of Ontologies, Proceedings of the 3rd European Semantic Web Conference, 2006

[8]   Bas van Schaik, Force-directed Methods for Clustered Graph Drawing, *url: http://www.cs.uu.nl/docs/vakken/gd/bas2.pdf*, Universiteit Utrecht, 2005

[9]   E. Adar, GUESS: A Language and Interface for Graph Exploration, *Conference on Human Factors in Computing Systems (CHI 2007)*, Montreal, Canada, 2007

[10] NWB Team, Network Workbench Tool. Indiana University, Northeastern University, and University of Michigan, http://nwb.slis.indiana.edu, 2006

[11] D. Knuth, The Art of Computer Programming, *Addison-Wesley*, 1968

[12] A. McCallum, String Edit Distance, *Computational Linguistics*, University of Massachusetts Amherst, 2006

[13] M. Kawamoto and T. Itoh, A Vizualisation Technique for Access Patterns and Link Structures of Web Sites, *International Conference Information Vizualisation (IV2010)*, London, 2010

[14] J. A. Gulla et. al., Semantic Drift in Ontologies, *International Conference on Web Information Systems (WEBIST 2010)*, Valencia, Spain, 2010

[15] P. Laddha, Degree of Separation in Social Networks, url: *http://arxiv.org/find/grp_cs/1/au:+Laddha_Prerana/0/1/0/all/0/1*, Cornell University Library

[16] S. Tartir &al, Metric Based Ontology Quality Analysis, *International Conference on Data Mining (ICDM 2005)*, Texas, USA, 2005

xLDD: Extended Linguistic Dependency Diagrams

Chris Culy, Verena Lyding, Henrik Dittmann
Institute for Specialised Communication and Multilingualism
European Academy Bolzano/Bozen
Bolzano/Bozen, Italy
{christopher.culy, verena.lyding, henrik.dittmann}@eurac.edu

Abstract—Extended Linguistic Dependency Diagrams are an innovative visualization of a data structure that is increasingly important in linguistics and language studies. It uses standard InfoVis techniques in ways new to linguistic diagrams to encode more information than is possible with previous visualizations. The goal is to make the diagrams easier to use, by allowing easier identification of the parts of the diagram of interest to the user. In addition, we aim to construct reusable tools to aid in language analysis and study. Preliminary evaluation supports the validity of the approach and suggests further improvements.

Keywords- dependency diagrams, linguistics

I. INTRODUCTION

Visualization of language-based information (LInfoVis) is becoming increasingly important, from cloud tags and Wordle [1], to more advanced visualizations (cf. e.g. [2] for an overview, and [3], [4] for detailed examples). Despite this, tools for language professionals, and others interested in language structures, still do not make much systematic use of visualization techniques (but cf. [5] for an overview and [6] for some LInfoVis tools).

Our general goal is to address this gap in InfoVis by developing a series of general tools for language visualization that can be easily adapted and incorporated into specific applications. Taking advantage of lower level toolkits, these tools also address the special nature of language data (it is not only nominal, but it is not mappable to other more compact representations), as well as the specialized data structures used in language analysis. Extended Linguistic Dependency Diagrams (xLDD) are an instance of this type of tool, designed for a data structure that is important, if not particular, to one aspect of linguistics. While many InfoVis visualizations of language information are centered around words or meaning (see the references cited above), xLDDs are diagrams of language structure.

II. DEPENDENCY STRUCTURES AND DIAGRAMS

A. Basic Dependency Structures and Diagrams

A dependency structure is a directed (usually acyclic) graph representation of relations between parts of a sentence. "Basic" dependency structures represent binary relations between words in a sentence, such as "subject of", "modifier of", etc. "Basic" dependency diagrams are a visualization of basic dependency structures in which the words are presented in their normal reading order, with directed arcs (usually labeled with the corresponding relations) connecting the words. In Fig. 1 is an example, using xLDD, which follows the Expert Advisory Group on Language Engineering Standards (EAGLES) recommendation for (basic) dependency diagrams [7]. (English examples are from the Wall Street Journal, as analyzed in the PARC 700 collection of dependency structures [8] and reinterpreted in the Kalashnikov 691 [9].)

Dependency diagrams have a clear family resemblance to Arc Diagrams and their descendants [10], though dependency diagrams predate Arc Diagrams, having been used at least since 1984 in Word Grammar [11], and perhaps earlier.

As with other graphs, it is important to remember that the dependency structures are the data structures and the dependency diagrams are *one* way of visualizing those data structures. In fact, linguists also use other visualizations of dependency structures, e.g. the ANNIS2 [12] project uses two other (node-link pseudo-tree) visualizations of dependency structure (see also DgAnnotator [13] and TrED [14]). While linguists do not consistently make this distinction between the data structure and the visualization(s), we will continue to refer to the visualizations here as dependency diagrams as opposed to dependency structures.

Dependency *structures* have become increasingly popular in the linguistics communities, with databases of dependency structures for real sentences now available for various languages. Visualizations of dependency structures are therefore more and more important. Dependency *diagrams* are a convenient way of visualizing the relations among words in a sentence while maintaining the original order of the words. This allows the user to see the connections between the relations and the order of the words. However, it is more difficult to see the hierarchical organization of the relations. Other visualizations of dependency structures as attribute-value matrices [8] facilitate the exploration of this hierarchical relational structure, at the cost of losing the information about word order. Each visualization is (more) appropriate for certain use cases and less for others.

1550-6037/11 $26.00 © 2011 IEEE
DOI 10.1109/IV.2011.42

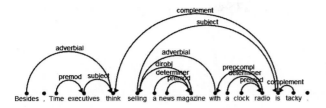

Figure 1. Basic Dependency Diagram

B. Extended Dependency Structures and Iissues

Basic dependency structures provide the basic information only, and in fact almost all dependency structures have information beyond words and the relations between them. Typically this extended information is about the words rather than the relations, and often includes the lemma ("dictionary form") of the word as well as its part of speech ("noun", "verb", etc.). Some dependency structures have even more detailed grammatical and/or semantic information, e.g. "it" is third person singular and inanimate.

This extended information presents both challenges and opportunities for visualization. On the one hand, there is the question of how to integrate the extended information into the diagram in a clear way. On the other hand, having this extended information gives us many more opportunities for visualization and the types of this additional information (typically nominal) allow us to use standard InfoVis visual encoding techniques, e.g. color to indicate the parts of speech.

There is an additional issue for all dependency diagrams, and that is that many real-life sentences are quite long, (the average sentence length in the PARC 700 collection is 19.8 words). Unlike in text, we cannot wrap the sentence in a dependency diagram onto successive lines, so compressing the representation horizontally is one of the challenges xLDD addresses. Vertical compression is another challenge addressed by xLDD, since the circular arcs typically used (at least in automatically drawn dependency diagrams, as well as in Arc Diagrams) take a lot of vertical space.

III. xLDDs: EXTENDED DEPENDENCY DIAGRAMS

A. Architecture

Extended Linguistic Dependency Diagrams (xLDD) are implemented in JavaScript using the Protovis [15] framework. The architecture is shown in Fig. 2.

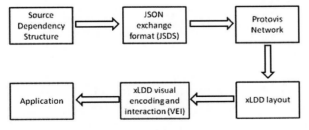

Figure 2. xLDD Architecture

The first step is to process the original dependency structure representation. Unfortunately, there is no consensus as to what information should be included in a dependency structure, and hence no standard representation. For the purposes of xLDD, we have created a simple JSON format for dependency structures (JSDS), which requires the information necessary for basic dependency structures, while still allowing extended information. We have written converters for a few dependency structure formats, most notably for the format used in CoNLL-X (the conference of the Association of Computational Linguistics' Special Interest Group on Natural Language Learning) Shared Task on Multi-lingual Dependency Parsing [16], as well as for the format used in the Kalashnikov 691, based on the PARC 700. The PARC 700 dependency structures cannot be used directly, since they do not include word order information, a point we will return to below.

The JSDS format is then converted to a Protovis Network object which is the input to the xLDD layout module. As is standardly done, the layout calculates the position of the nodes, as well as some supplementary information about the dependency graph structure.

Once the positions of the nodes have been calculated, the Visual Encoding and Interaction (VEI) component constructs the visual presentation of the diagram, including colors, shapes, etc. as well as interactions. The xLDD VEI component incorporates a useful set of default visual encodings and interactions. These default encodings and interactions are customizable, making the VEI component a flexible wrapper around the xLDD layout. However, the xLDD layout can always be used separately, without the xLDD VEI component.

The final step is to incorporate xLDD into an application. Of course, the details of that incorporation, including which kinds of visual encoding and interactions to expose to the end user, depend on the goals and uses of the particular application.

B. Addressing Space Issues

Fig. 3 shows an example of an xLDD which illustrates the ways in which we have addressed the challenges of space constraints. In this example, the words are presented on different levels, descending from left to right until the quotation mark, and then restarting at the initial level. In addition, words are indented to the left ("staggered") under the higher word on the previous level.

To address the issue of circular arcs taking large amounts of space, we use elliptical arcs instead. The only informational difference is that the height of an arc is no longer equal to the distance between its endpoints, but rather proportional to that distance. There is no significant information loss in using elliptical arcs instead of circular ones, since only the relative distance between endpoints is relevant, not the absolute distance. In fact, this can even be an advantage as it mitigates the tendency of circular arcs to give more visual weight to longer arcs, due to the quadratic increase of the space/area below circular arcs.

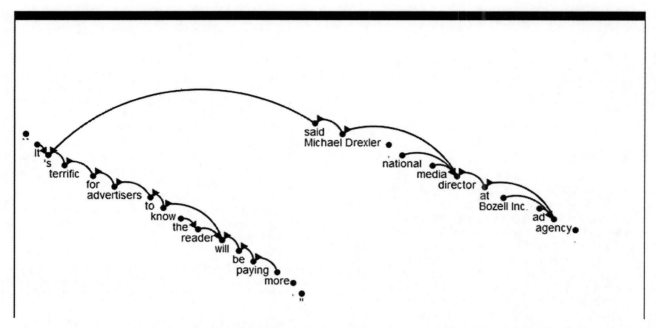

Figure 3. xLDD Diagram for a longer English Sentence; using elliptical Arcs all above and Levels + Staggering

To address the issue of sentences taking up large amounts of horizontal space, we use a combination of two techniques, namely levels and staggering. Varying the vertical position of the words (the level) allows us to offset words horizontally (stagger) so that they overlap a bit vertically (though not graphically). However, since staggering can be distracting, the default implementation uses staggering only when the sentence would extend beyond the visible area. (Cf. [17] for another visualization of dependency diagrams which uses levels but not staggering.)

Of course, sentences, and their relation arcs, can still be too large for the available visual area, so the default implementation of the xLDD VEI component provides for panning and zooming. However, the use of elliptical arcs, levels and (intelligent) staggering does increase the range of sentences that can be displayed in a given space.

C. Visual Encoding and Interaction

As mentioned above, extended dependency structures have extra information beyond just the words and their relations. Any of this information can be visually encoded and/or made available through interaction. In particular, we use color and size for the words, the nodes above them, and the arcs. We can also use the vertical level of the words to encode information. Finally, in contrast to most other visualizations of dependency structures, we can position the arcs above or below the text (cf. [18] for a similar approach, but for non-interactive diagrams). An example is in Fig. 4, where arcs showing dependents of verbs are above the text, and others below. In addition, arcs involving punctuation are thinner than other arcs. In terms of the use of color, the main dependencies of verbs are blue, relations between prepositions and their objects are green, and conjunction relations are yellow. Fig. 4 also shows the results of panning the diagram. In terms of showing the non-basic information textually, the default implementation in the xLDD VEI provides a dendrogram view of the information (shown for "allenatore" in Fig. 4), similar to the attribute-value matrix representation that is familiar to linguists, and this view is shown by double-clicking the node. Of course, other possible interactions and visualizations of this information are possible as well; the default implementation provides just one.

In addition to double-clicking the node, other standard types of interaction are available, such as mouse hover, clicking, selecting nodes by dragging, etc. As mentioned above, the default implementation of the xLDD VEI also provides panning and zooming.

166

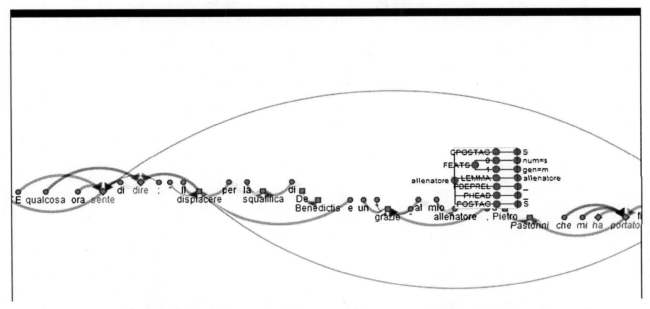

Figure 4.   xLDD Diagram for an Italian Sentence from Corpus PAISÀ [19]; mixed Levels, Colors, also shows Info on Word.

IV.   EVALUATION

A.   Procedure

Based on an annotated sample of the PAISÀ corpus [19] we created nine different displays:

1. Basic dependency diagram
2. Arcs above and below the text according to their dependency type
3. Arcs of one dependency type above the text and all other arcs below
4. Arcs colored according to their dependency type
5. Arcs of one dependency type colored red and all other arcs colored gray
6. Descending text, with steps at every noun
7. Descending text, with steps at every word
8. Descending text, with steps at every word, and words staggered horizontally
9. Text descending for the first half of the sentence and ascending for the second half of the sentence

After a short introduction to dependency diagrams, to interactions in xLDD and to the annotations, the users were asked to find occurrences of a specified dependency type. In test 1 in addition to records of the results, we collected think-aloud protocols of the users' impressions and reasoning during completion of the tasks. In test 2, besides the results, the time to completion was recorded for each xLDD display. Following the two tests users were asked to give evaluative feedback on xLDD.

All subjects have a language-related background, ranging from language didactics to different degrees of formal linguistic training. All but one have a good understanding of syntactic structures, but are more familiar with tree representations than with dependency diagrams. Two subjects are of Italian mother tongue, the other two subjects have basic knowledge of Italian with good reading comprehension skills

B.   Results

Overall the testing showed that users were able to understand and use xLDD autonomously after a short introduction. In general, they preferred visual cues over text-based indications (e.g. details in the pop-up window for each lemma) for solving the given tasks. It even turned out that the visualizations highlighting the requested dependency type enabled the testers to complete the tasks without having to read and understand the sentences.

Of the innovative xLDD features, color coding and the systematic placement of arcs above and below the text were most appreciated, while descending text by levels and staggering of words lead to initial confusion. Highlighting dependencies that are relevant for the given task by means of color or placement of the arcs on one side of the text as opposed to the other dependency types was considered very useful, as it supported the understanding of what is important and helped to reduce visual clutter. Leveled and staggered displays were perceived as less readable and confusing or not useful. The evaluative feedback made clear that users expected positional placement of words to have a meaning, which they were not able to deduce, and that in fact if levels and staggering would be applied systematically they might have potential to be useful for some tasks. Overall, people asked for control over which dependencies to show and how to show them, as well as the integration of xLDD with a specific application (e.g. a corpus query engine).

Regarding the interaction with the xLDD interface the testers criticized the overlap of arcs/arrows and words, especially when zoomed out, that make the visualization difficult to read (e.g. determine the directionality of an arc) and hamper the smooth interaction with units of interest (e.g. tooltip on hover, details on double-click). Furthermore, the shape of the cursor was considered unintuitive and we noticed some difficulties with panning involving the draggable areas. One user suggested to use varying line widths of arcs for highlighting, another user suggested to provide different curvatures of arcs – these are both features that are already implemented in xLDD but were not applied in the testing displays.

Test 1 and test 2 yielded similar results, however the time recording confirmed that besides the visual features of xLDD, sentence length also has a considerable impact on the readability of the dependency diagram. To deduce more differentiated significant results from time recording a larger scale user study would be needed. In particular it would be interesting to test how leveled and staggered displays impact efficiency in solving tasks – besides being perceived as more or less helpful (our preliminary testing did not control for all the variables). In fact, the users' behavior showed that they were aiming to get a view of the full sentence, which was achieved by zooming out (with its disadvantages), but is also attained by leveling and staggering.

Asked for possible application contexts, there was a consensus among all users that xLDD would be most useful in the language learning and teaching, assuming that the user could take control over what dependency types and additional information to display, and how to display it.

V. FUTURE DIRECTIONS

There are a few refinements that we would like to make to xLDD. In response to the user feedback, we would like to further experiment with different shapes of arcs and arrows, changing them dynamically when zooming. Refining the panning and choosing appropriate arc curve shapes are also on the list of things to do. Another improvement would be to allow different textures (e.g. dashes) for the arcs, though this would be a bit challenging since Protovis does not currently support line textures. Other technical challenges lie on the linguistic side. As mentioned above, not all dependency structures include the connections with the actual words in the original sentence, so they cannot be used directly with xLDD (though they can be used in other visualizations). One goal is to reconstruct those connections with the words for certain major dependency structure formats, where possible, as in e.g. [9], though without changing or omitting information as done in those efforts.

An additional linguistic issue is the presence in some dependency structures (like the PARC 700) of items that do not appear in the original sentence, but which are analytical constructs (such as "understood" subjects, e.g. in *I want to go* "I" is understood as the subject of "go" in addition to "want", although "I" only occurs in the sentence once). We have done some preliminary tests with dependency structures semi-automatically reconstructed from the PARC 700, but until we can come up with an automatic reconstruction of the PARC 700, we will have to wait on seeing how extra items are best visualized.

The original motivation for this work was to provide a visualization of the dependency structures available in the PAISÀ corpus of Italian [19]. We have a proof of concept application allowing search results from PAISÀ to be displayed dynamically, from which Fig. 4 was taken, but we intend to make a more flexible, comprehensive application. This application will also let us explore concretely what kinds of information (if any) could usefully be encoded using levels.

Finally, we intend to release xLDD under an Open Source license.

VI. CONCLUSIONS

xLDD is a new way of visualizing dependency structures, which incorporates standard InfoVis techniques. It uses features, such as coloring and placement of arcs above and below the text and using the technique of levels plus staggering to reduce the amount of horizontal space needed for the visualization. The preliminary results are promising, and give indications about what needs to be focused on and improved for integration into specialized applications. The application in a language teaching and learning context seems particularly promising considering the user feedback, and we hope that xLDD will in addition be adopted and adapted by other linguistic projects.

As noted above, many InfoVis visualizations of language information are concerned with words or meaning, but xLDDs are diagrams of language structure. They are thus an example for how the many other specialized linguistic diagrams in a range of subfields from phonetics to discourse analysis could also benefit from a modern InfoVis treatment.

ACKNOWLEDGMENT

Dick Hudson kindly provided us with background on the origin and nature of dependency structures. We also thank our colleagues for the cheerful participation in the usability testing.

REFERENCES

[1] Wordle url: http://www.wordle.net/

[2] Christian Rohrdantz et al., "Visuelle Textanalyse," Informatik Spektrum, vol. 33(6), Dec. 2010, pp. 601-611, doi: 10.1007/s00287-010-0483-x.

[3] Martin Wattenberg and Fernanda B. Viégas, "The word tree, an interactive visual concordance," IEEE Transactions on Visualization and Computer Graphics, vol. 14(6), Nov.-Dec. 2008, pp. 1221-1228, doi: 10.1109/TVCG.2008.172.

[4] Frank van Ham, Martin Wattenberg, and Fernanda B. Viégas, "Mapping text with phrase nets," IEEE Transactions on Visualization and Computer Graphics, vol. 15(6), Nov.-Dec. 2009, pp. 1169-1176, doi: 10.1109/TVCG.2009.165.

[5] Chris Collins, Gerald Penn, and Sheelagh Carpendale, "Interactive visualization for computational linguistics," ACL-08: HLT Tutorials, 2008, http://www.cs.utoronto.ca/~ccollins/acl2008-vis.pdf

[6] Chris Culy and Verena Lyding, "Visualizations for exploratory corpus and text analysis," Proc. of the 2nd International Conference on Corpus Linguistics (CILC-10), May 13-15, 2010, pp. 257-268.

[7] EAGLES url: http://www.ilc.cnr.it/EAGLES96/segsasg1/node44.html

[8] Tracy H. King, Richard Crouch, Stefan Riezler, Mary Dalrymple, and Ronald M. Kaplan, "The PARC 700 Dependency Bank," Proc. of the 4th International Workshop on Linguistically Interpreted Corpora, held at the 10th Conference of the European Chapter of the Association for Computational Linguistics (EACL'03), 2003.

[9] Tomas By, "The Kalashnikov 691 Dependency Bank," Proc. of the Sixth International Language Resources and Evaluation (LREC'08). May 28-30, 2008, Nicoletta Calzolari (Conference Chair), Khalid Choukri, Bente Maegaard, Joseph Mariani, Jan Odjik, Stelios Piperidis, Daniel Tapias.

[10] Martin Wattenberg, "Arc Diagrams: visualizing structure in strings," Proc. IEEE Symposium on Information Visualization (InfoVis'02), IEEE Computer Society, pp. 110-116. doi: 10.1109/INFVIS.2002.1173155.

[11] Richard Hudson, English Word Grammar. London: Blackwell, 1984.

[12] ANNIS2 url: http://www.sfb632.uni-potsdam.de/d1/annis/visualizations.html

[13] Pisa DgAnnotator url: http://medialab.di.unipi.it/Project/QA/Parser/DgAnnotator/

[14] TrED url: http://ufal.mff.cuni.cz/~pajas/tred/

[15] Mike Bostock and Jeffrey Heer, "Protovis: a graphical toolkit for visualization," IEEE Transactions on Visualization and Computer Graphics, vol. 15(6), Nov./Dec. 2009, pp. 1121-1128, doi: 10.1109/TVCG.2009.174.

[16] CoNLL-X url: http://nextens.uvt.nl/~conll/

[17] TDS url: http://staff.science.uva.nl/~fsangati/TDS/

[18] Calligramme Dep2pict url: http://wikilligramme.loria.fr/doku.php?id=dep2pict:index

[19] Corpus PAISÀ url: http://www.corpusitaliano.it

Collaborative Augmented Reality Application for Information Visualization Support

Edson Koiti Kudo Yasojima, Bianchi Serique
Meiguins
Universidade Federal do Para - UFPA
Belém-PA, Brasil.
koitiyasojima@gmail.com, bianchi.serique@terra.com.br

Aruanda Simões Meiguins
Centro Universitário do Pará – CESUPA
Belém-PA, Brazil
aruanda@redeinformatica.com.br

Abstract— In today's information systems, strategies for decision making and accurate results in a short time are crucial in many knowledge areas of industry, economic, medical etc.. To support this demand to store and interpret relevant information, the area of information visualization coupled with several others, such as intelligent systems and data mining, is increasingly taking place in academic research and market. Aiming to increase to level of interaction and accurate results, this article presents a collaborative augmented reality application for information visualization support.

Keywords- Information Visualization; Collaborative Environments; Augmented Reality

I. INTRODUCTION

Augmented Reality offers new ways of man-machine interaction, today with the internet and cloud computing people can share data and knowledge in collaborative environments. Using information visualization, users can organize large amounts of data in context and interpret them for patterns. Using these concepts, this paper proposes a tool that uses augmented reality and information visualization tools to manipulate data in a distributed manner between one or more users, allowing the sharing of knowledge using dynamic ways to interact with them.

A. Information Visualization (IV)

One of the main ideas of information visualization is to make the user interact with a large amount of data using a context, creating images which can be interpreted by a human [1].

According to [2], IV promotes a small but crucial task in cognitive systems. Through visions, applications open up a channel for human-machine communication. Humans have a better interpretation when a context is illustrated by pictures and interact with it.

Applications that use information visualization are becoming increasingly essential; this is because the human and technology produce ever more data. The storage capacity of hardware is expanding more and more, as well as processing of information. Applications of Information visualization are designed to collect and organize large amounts of data and show them to the user in a context where he can understand them. But the contexts generated are produced by the person who handles, generating different types of interpretations by other users and can cause misunderstandings about the data [3].

Using the augmented reality together with the information visualization, enables new ways to organize and display data to the user a more interactive and interesting.

B. Augmented Reality (AR)

Unlike virtual reality, which transports the user to the virtual environment, augmented reality keeps the user in their physical environment and transports the virtual environment to the user space, allowing interaction with the virtual world with more naturality. New interfaces multimodal and are being developed to facilitate the manipulation of virtual objects in user space, using their hands or simple interaction devices. And to achieve its objectives, the AR needs to integrate the graphical information in the real environment [4] [5].

AR provides new ways of user interaction, creating a more realistic and interesting application in various fields of knowledge, like education, marketing, industry, medicine etc. [6].

With the evolution of hardware devices, more applications with AR are being developed focusing on the lay public [7] [8].

C. Collaborative Environments

With the evolution of Internet, multi-user applications are more and more used by people. This kind of software provides real-time capabilities that enable manipulation of data between multiple people within the same context [9].

1550-6037/11 $26.00 © 2011 IEEE
DOI 10.1109/IV.2011.44

Collaborative environments using augmented reality have been studied to evaluate and propose improvements in the forms of interaction and communication. The use of AR in a collaborative context has been a promising business when it relates to collaboration. Several ideas have been implemented in this context. It also reveals concerns when it says about the interaction, new ways of interacting emerge, opening new research to usability testing and user acceptance for the application [10] [11].

II. RELATED WORKS

Little research attention has been focused in collaborative information visualization using augmented reality. Many users still rely on using or implementing IV tools with new features but not giving attention to the environment of the user space

A single-user application developed by [12] in augmented reality using information visualization. Using the technique of scattering data and other graphics it is possible to manipulate objects through the use of markers in the application.

Test cases of the tool have shown that the ratio of success is 80% for tasks considered easy [12].

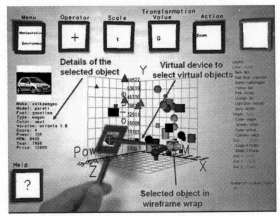

Figure 1 Information Visualization Tool with AR [12]

III. ARCHITECTURE

The project aims to create an environment in RA, in which multiple users can interact in a vision of data dispersion. Interacting through configuration of color, shape and using filters, a context can be construed and interpreted in real time enabling the interpretation of several clients at the same time, unlike single-user environments.

The architecture in a global aspect would include a central server that would have as its main goal, and synchronize customer data, and receive and forward messages between clients when any modification is made in a vision.

Server will work to provide synchronization between clients. It will get the data from the users and synchronize to the others that have the same view. If one client changes the data, the others will be notified.

For the detailed class architecture we will have as follow:

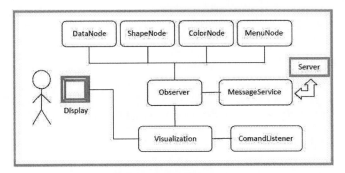

Figure 2 Client Class Architecture

- Observer: this class will be responsible for observing for changes in some nodes responsible for managing certain activities such as changing the color, shape or performance of the filter. And communicate to the server and other connected clients.

- MessageService: this class will be responsible for receiving notifications of class Observer, package them and send to the server; in addition, it will receive and unpack messages.

- Visualization: it will hold the organization of data from the observer and mount the display to the user; moreover, receive human interactions inputs through Listeners (CommandListener) like movement, keyboard, voice etc.

- Node: are responsible for managing settings and application data, for example, setting the color and shape, and perform data filtering and provide menus for interaction.

IV. PROTOTYPE

In the context of a collaborative environment, users can work on a problem and more accurate results or at least more closely meet the goal compared to a single user environment. Moreover, collaboration can enhance interaction in the aspect of communication and discussion of the problem by manipulating shared objects [14] [15].

The prototype used augmented reality to implement a 3D scatter plot IV technique in a collaborative environment enabling users to work in the same view, allowing the manipulation of the displayed data. Main points of this application are:

- Answer all the basic features of information visualization tool.

- Enable the display of data through the technique of scattering data in three dimensions.

- Carrying out operations on data such as filtering and additional settings.

- Generate a basic architecture for the construction and expansion of the prototype.

- Conducting usability tests.

The prototype uses markers to display 3D objects on the screen through these objects, users can manipulate data in accordance with menus, pointer and voice. Using a 3D pointer the user can select the desired action and the column that will be applied to action.

All changes made and applied in the menu are reflected to all users who share this view. Applications and changes are optional and free to all users, not necessarily compelling to interact with the tool, which can only be as a spectator.

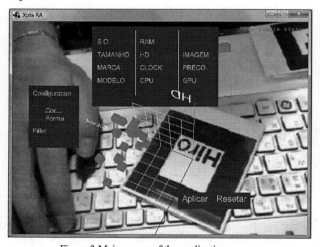

Figure 3 Main screen of the application

When setting up a color, the user may notice a change in the 3D scatter plot and the color change by using another marker, and can view the color legend accordingly.

Figure 4 Discrete attribute color change and Table reference of the colors

Figure 5 Continuous attribute color change and Gradient color bar

Besides the color setting, you can also configure the geometric shape of objects; however this operation is restricted to columns that have discrete attributes.

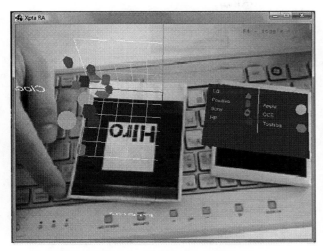

Figure 6 Shape change and Table reference of the shapes

The main menu also allows the realization of filters, filtered data is removed from the dispersion (are hidden) and clean the viewing. The filter supports columns that have discrete values and continuous.

In the continuous filter, the tool makes a categorization of data according to ranges of values, divided into five classes: 0% to 19% of the total value is very low, 20% to 39% are down 40% to 59% are medium 60% to 79% are high, 80% to 100% is too high.

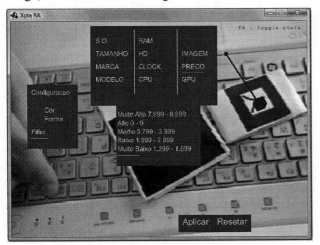

Figure 7 Filter menu

The user can also select any desired attribute using the pointer.

Figure 8 Selecting attribute with the pointer

If the user does not have a webcam connected to the computer, the application can be used without it, providing a simple virtual environment. In this environment mouse and keyboard are used to make interactions on the data displayed. Also, details on demand are displayed like the color marker.

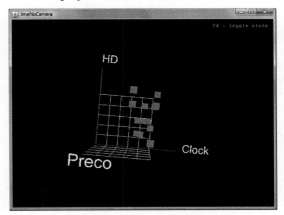

Figure 9 Application without camera

V. TECHNOLOGIES AND IMPLEMENTATION ASPECTS

A. NyARToolkit

NyARToolkit [17] is an abstraction of ARToolkit [18]; it was written for Java and provides functions for integrating 3D objects with the real world using markers.

B. JMonkey Engine

JMonkeyEngine is a game engine written in Java and provides support for developing 3D games, according to the official site [19], has the following features:

- Free and Open Source within the BSD license.

- Compatibility with different versions of the OpenGL graphics library, and supports various operating systems.

- Uses a shader-based architecture for rendering 3D graphics objects.

- Has a graphical editor for various development platforms, besides to have a self.

- Abstracts and automate different types of routines and construction of objects as well as the use of textures.

C. *Application Restriction and Evolution*

The tool was developed in order to accept new modules, using a hierarchy of nodes, new IV techniques can be developed using the JMonkeyEngine and added to the Observer. Moreover, it is necessary that the view is adapted to the listeners and actions pre-defined by the programmer, allowing a better coupling.

Other issue that needs to be taken in mind is the resolution of the webcam that necessarily must be equal to or greater than 800x600, otherwise the screen view will be too small to allocate the objects.

VI. TEST CASES

To validate the usability and accuracy rate of the application, according to the evaluation method proposed by [15], users of the software will be submitted to a short training and soon after will use the tool to make some assumptions that involve pre-defined tasks of:

- Identification
- Determination
- View
- Comparison

From the results collected, the usability of the features of the application will be evaluated in a level of severity which can be:

- Level 0 (no importance): Does not affect usability;
- Level 1 (mild): No need to immediately fix the problem;
- Level 2 (simple): Problem of low priority (can be repaired);
- Level 3 (severe): Problem of high priority (that need to be repaired);
- Level 4 (catastrophic): Too serious (which needs to be repaired).

Changes in the application will be made if there is a need to adjust to the concepts covered in the project.

CONCLUSIONS

As shown by [16] according to some experiments in augmented reality and IV, showed that end users have an easy adaptation and learning, as more engaging is the tool, users have more interest in learning and interpretation of data.

Further, the augmented reality, allows the use of new forms of interaction to manipulate or data.

In technical terms, the project aims to assist the search, data interpretation patterns and generating knowledge for users in a social and collaborative context.

As future work, we can highlight the implementation of new visualization techniques, in addition to improving operations with existing interactions, and execute the test cases to improve the usability.

Some issues during the development of the application are listed below:

- Study of applications for recognition and voice processing.
- Develop and synchronize the command listeners.
- Improve the accuracy of pointer and improve the depth (Z axis) of the rendered items on the screen.
- Enhance slow due to the generation of 3D text and selecting items in menus.
- Installation of tools and libraries for application execution.
- Add texture to markers and improve realist of the application

REFERENCES

[1] Spence, R. *Information Visualization: Design for Interaction* Barcelona: ACM Press. 2. ed., 2007.

[2] Ware, C. Information Visualization: Perception for Design. Elsevier Inc. 2º Edition. 2004.

[3] Valiati, E.R.A.; Freitas, C.M.D.S.; Pimenta, M.S. Using multi-dimensional in-depth long-term case studies for information visualization evaluation. Proceedings of the 2008 conference on BEyond time and errors: novel evaLuation methods for Information Visualization. 2008.

[4] Regenbrecht, Holger T.; Wagner, Michael T. Interaction in a collaborative augmented reality environment. CHI '02 extended abstracts on Human factors in computer systems - CHI '02. 2002.

[5] Kirner, C.; Tori, R. Fundamentos da Realidade Aumentada, In Fundamentos e Tecnologia da Realidade Virtual e Aumentada. VIII Symposium on Virtual Reality, 2006.

[6] Medicherla, Padmavathi S.; Chang, George; Morreale, Patricia. Visualization for increased understanding and learning using augmented reality. Proceedings of the international conference on Multimedia information retrieval - MIR '10. 2010.

[7] Hirose, Michitaka; Tanikawa, Tomohiro. Overview of the digital museum Project. Proceedings of the 9th ACM SIGGRAPH Conference on Virtual-Reality Continuum and its Applications in Industry. 2010.

[8] Ren, T.; Wang, Y. A Japanese text based mobile augmented reality application. ACM SIGGRAPH ASIA 2010 Posters. 2010.

[9] Diehl, S. Distributed Virtual Worlds. Springer-Verlag. 2001.

[10] Billinghurst, M.; Kato, H. Collaborative augmented reality. Communications of the ACM Volume 45. 2002.

[11] Billinghurst, M. Usability testing of augmented/mixed reality systems. ACM SIGGRAPH ASIA 2008 courses. 2008.

[12] Casseb do Carmo, Ricardo Melo; Meiguins, Bianchi S.; Gonçalves, Aruanda S.; Pinheiro, Sérgio Clayton V.; Godinho,

Paulo Igor A. Coordinated and Multiple Views in Augmented Reality Environment. 2007 11th International Conference Information Visualization IV 07. 2007.

[13] Nini, B. Batouche, M.C. Virtual object manipulation in collaborative augmented reality environment. 2004 IEEE International Conference on Industrial Technology, 2004. IEEE ICIT '04. 2004.

[14] Büscher, Monika; Christensen, Michael; Grønbæk, Kaj; Krogh, Peter; Mogensen, Preben; Shapiro, Dan; Ørbæk, Peter. Collaborative Augmented Reality Environments: Integrating VR, Working Materials, and Distributed Work Spaces. Proceedings of the third international conference on Collaborative virtual environments - CVE '00. 2000.

[15] Pillat, Raquel M.; Valiati, E. R. A.; Freitas, Carla M. D. S. Experimental study on evaluation of multidimensional information visualization techniques. Proceedings of the 2005 Latin American conference on Human-computer interaction - CLIHC '05. 2005.

[16] Meiguins, Bianchi S.; et al. Multidimensional information visualization using augmented reality. Proceedings of the 2006 ACM international conference on Virtual reality continuum and its applications - VRCIA '06. 2006.

[17] NyARToolkit url: http://nyatla.jp/nyartoolkit/wiki/index.php

[18] ARToolkit url: http://www.hitl.washington.edu/artoolkit/

[19] JMonkey Engine url: http://www.jmonkeyengine.com

A Tool to Support Finding Favorite Music by Visualizing Listeners' Preferences

Satoko Shiroi
Department of Computer Science
University of Tsukuba
Ibaraki, Japan
shiroi@iplab.cs.tsukuba.ac.jp

Kazuo Misue
Department of Computer Science
University of Tsukuba
Ibaraki, Japan
misue@cs.tsukuba.ac.jp

Jiro Tanaka
Department of Computer Science
University of Tsukuba
Ibaraki, Japan
jiro@cs.tsukuba.ac.jp

Abstract—In recent years, music-finding services have been increasing. If we have explicit information specifying pieces of music, we can find music to our taste using such services. This paper describes a tool to support music discovery. The tool visualizes a relational structure among music genres and the music-preference data of many listeners to make the users aware of their favorite music without explicit information. A case study is described to illustrate the usefulness of the tool.

Keywords-preference; music genre; sub-genre; relational structure

I. INTRODUCTION

In recent years, music distribution on the Internet has been actively developed, and it has become increasingly easy for many listeners to obtain music. We can search for and buy songs at online shops like the iTunes store[1] and Mora[2]. Song titles and artists' names of songs are useful clues to finding the desired songs. If we have such information for our favorite songs, we can quickly find and obtain them using the services of online shops because these shops offer a huge database of music information.

We believe that there are many songs that we would like, but we do not have the necessary clues for them; we want to find songs without having these clues.

We propose a means of support for finding preferred songs without explicit clues. We focus on music genres and listeners' preferences. Music genres are groups of songs classified by their features[2]. Listeners' preferences are useful in filtering favorite songs from a huge collection of songs[1]. We visualize a relational structure among genres and sub-genres of music and listeners' music preferences. We have developed a tool to support the finding of favorite songs by visualizing these relational structures. The tool does not explicitly recommend songs, but rather provides an environment where users become aware of their taste in music.

In this paper, we describe a tool to support music discovery using music-preference data. First, we explain music genres and music-preference data. Then, we give an overview of our tool and operation of the tool, and

describe a method for drawing relational structures. Finally, we describe our case study and offer conclusions.

II. RELATED WORK

A. Using Music Genres

Yaxi et al. focused on customer-defined music genre tags defined by users of Last.fm[3][3]. They visualized collaborative tags using Euler diagrams. The users can search songs by traversing the genre structure hierarchically. Their tool gives readable visualizations when the number of genres is small. We allowed listeners to look for their favorite songs from a wider range by showing larger relational structures with more music genres and sub-genres.

B. Using Listeners' Music Preferences

Takekawa et al. combined listeners' preferences and features of music such as rhythm and tempo [4]. This combination gives other clues for music searching. They used MIDI data as the music data, so it is easy to obtain music features and combine them with users' preferences. However, their method covers a very limited number of songs. Ito et al. analyzed chord progressions of music and divided them into clusters [5]. They enable the use of chord progressions as clues to finding favorite songs. However, the users need knowledge of the music theory related to chord progression. We developed a tool that allows users to search their favorite songs without expert knowledge of music.

C. Using Artists

Sarmento et al. developed a visualization tool to show networks consisting of similarities of artists and user-defined tags in the data set of Last.fm[6]. They provided the users with high-precision browsing of these networks. We provide higher-precision browsing to show the relational structure among genres using music-preference data.

III. CLUES TO FINDING FAVORITE SONGS

A. Structures of Music Genres

Music genres are categories of songs classified by their musical features. Examples of genres are *pop*, *rock* and *folk*.

[1]http://www.apple.com/jp/itunes/whats-on/
[2]http://mora.jp/

[3]http://www.lastfm.jp

Table I
A CONCRETE EXAMPLE OF MUSIC-PREFERENCE DATA

Listener	Song	Artist	Genre	Sub-genre	Music information	Record
white_luc	AM to PM	Christina Milian	R&B	dance	http://bit.ly/eAR4uC	2010/12/01
pommedepin	Misty	HitchcockGoHome!	folk	post-rock	http://bit.ly/byeNnZ	2010/12/01
tedman1990	Champagne	CAVO	rock	alternative rock	http://bit.ly/1QeGW	2010/12/02

Music genres may have sub-genres. Sub-genres are more detailed categories of songs. For example, *rock* has sub-genres such as *hard rock* and *progressive rock*. Some genres may share sub-genres; this means that a genre structure is not a tree. For example, the genre *pop* includes a sub-genre *pop punk* and *punk* also includes this sub-genre. Some songs may belong to some genres, but not belong to any sub-genres.

The relational structure among music genres work as a guide to finding favorite songs. We aim to support searching of listeners' favorite music by visualizing the relational structure among music genres.

B. Listeners' Preferences

Many listeners tweet and share their favorite songs using online services; one of the best-known services is Last.fm. By collecting such tweets, we can observe listeners' music preference. The preferences data includes the listener's name, song title, artist's name, genre, sub-genre, timestamp, and other information (e.g., the artist's official website and a site that introduces the song). Table 1 shows a concrete example of the data.

We considered using the preference of users with the same properties, for example, of the same generation. This is because we think people with the same properties have similar preferences. Here, we focus on generation as the users' property. We collected preference data of listeners of the same generation to extract the relational structure among genres.

C. Visualizing Structure of Genres and Listeners' Preferences

A genre structure constructed using listeners' preference data may be useful for finding favorite songs, but the structure is too complicated for many listeners to understand. Therefore, visualizing the structure helps listeners to identify the relationships between genres and sub-genres and guides them in finding their favorite songs. The relational structure among genres is a graph. We adopted a node-link diagram to show the relationships between genres and sub-genres.

We can observe which genres are much listened to by analyzing many listeners' music preferences. We therefore visualize which genres are listened to more or less by using size and the opacity of the colors of elements in the diagrams. This allows users to intuitively obtain preference information for the same generation. The users may find their favorite songs by referring to genres and sub-genres,

and comparing their preference with those of other users. Furthermore, we want to give listeners an 'awareness" of their own preferences and show the differences among listeners' preferences.

IV. TOOL TO SUPPORT FINDING FAVORITE MUSIC

We developed a tool to support music discovery based on the discussion in the previous section. We visually represent listeners' preference data to help find users' favorite songs.

A. Overview of the Tool

Figure 1 shows the initial screen of the tool. Before starting to use the tool, users have to specify their generation and preference data. Here, we introduce examples of the screen using the first author of this paper, who is in her twenties.

In Figure 1, the blue filled circle in the right-hand side of the window represents listeners. We call the circle the listeners' node. The node represents the set of listeners in the same generation; in our example, we have listeners in their twenties. The circles in the middle column of the window represent genres. We call them genre nodes. The text labels in the left-hand side of the window represent sub-genres. We call them sub-genre labels. We connect the listeners node and the genre nodes, and the genre nodes and the sub-genre labels with curved lines. We call the curved lines links. The size of a genre node indicates how often songs belonging to the genre are listened to by other listeners. For example, in Figure 1, *rock* an the top of the screen, is the biggest circle. Therefore, we understand that listeners in their twenties listen to rock music a lot.

The white lines surrounding the listeners node, genre nodes and links, and highlighting of the sub-genre labels with pink, represent the user's own preferences. We can compare our favorite genres and sub-genres with other listeners in the same generation by looking at the white lines and highlighted labels.

Genres have different colors. It is therefore easy to observe connecting links by their different colors. We understand that sub-genres connect with many genres. For example, in Figure 2, *indie* (the second top) is a sub-genre connected to four genres. We find a sub-genre connected to many genres by different colors of genres. Links have opacity. In this way, the tool shows how to listen to songs belonging to a genre related to a sub-genre for other listeners. For example, in Figure 2, comparing the link connecting *rock*

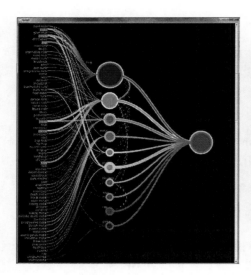

Figure 1. The initial screen of the tool.

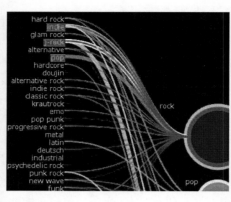

Figure 2. Links connecting genres and sub-genres.

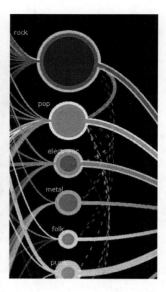

Figure 3. Links connecting two genres.

and *krautrock* (twelfth from the top) and the link connecting *rock* and *emo* (thirteenth from the top), we find that the latter link has a deeper opacity than the former. The tool shows that a link has many songs if the link opacity is deep, and the link has few songs if the link opacity is paler. In this way, we can compare the number of songs in sub-genres by the opacity differences.

Some songs belong to many genres but do not belong to any sub-genres. In this case, the tool shows a pair of genres connected through a dotted line. We therefore understand the relationship between two genres if an artist belongs to some genres but not to any sub-genres. Figure 3 is an extended illustration of links connecting a pair of genres. The links connecting a pair of genres have opacity, the same as links connecting a genre and a sub-genre. From the differences in the opacities, we can compare the number of songs belonging to specific genres.

B. Operation of the Tool

The tool displays artists' names by clicking a genre node or a sub-genre label. The artists' names shown represent other listeners' favorite artists. We therefore consider that it is easy for users to search unknown artists. We show an example of clicking a genre node, in Figure 4, and clicking a sub-genre label, in Figure 5. These allow users to find their favorite artists from a list of artists' names.

1) Finding Many Unknown Artists: The tool shows the names of many artist listened to by many listeners. Therefore, if we search for unknown artists, we can find them by focusing on artists not highlighted in white or pink.

2) Finding Many Artists in User's Own Favorite Genre: We can find many artists' names in a genre because genres have many sub-genres. For example, if users focus on their

favorite genres, they know that they listen to two or three sub-genres, but the genres have many sub-genres. Therefore, we can search artists from unknown sub-genres. Focusing on a genre highlighted in white, and sub-genres related to genres not highlighted in pink, allows users to find many artists.

3) Finding Many Artists Focusing on Genres Relationships: As mentioned in Section III-A, a genre has many sub-genres, and a sub-genre belongs to a number of genres. Some songs do not belong to any sub-genres, but belong to a number of genres. A genre and a sub-genre, and a pair of genres, are connected by links showing relationships, and genres have colors. The tool therefore allows users to find many artists by traversing links, comparing the differences in link colors.

V. DEVELOPMENT OF THE TOOL

In this section, we first describe the music-preference data used in our research. Next, regarding the visual presentation of the used data, we show how to define the size of genre nodes and how to draw links.

A. About Music-preference Data

Last.fm is a popular music social network service. Last.fm synchronizes with iTunes[4] or Windows Media Player[5], and gathers data on music listened to by users. The service also shows listeners who liked users' preferences for music and artists whom users may like. The service allows users to register their favorite songs by clicking the "Love track" button.

---

[4]http://www.apple.com/jp/itunes/what-is/
[5]http://windows.microsoft.com/ja-JP/windows/products/windows-media-player

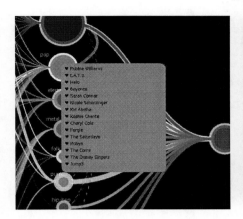

Figure 4. Clicking a genre node *pop*.

Figure 5. Clicking a sub-genre label *classic rock*.

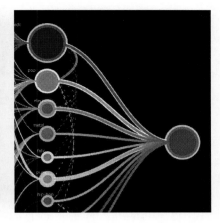

Figure 6. Link connecting genre nodes and listener node.

If the users set up a collaboration service on Twitter[6] and Last.fm, they can tweet automatically about their favorite songs adding "#lastfm", that is, a hash-tag.

We gathered tweets with the hash-tag "#lastfm", using the Twitter searchAPI[7]. The gathered tweets data includes user name, song title, artist's name, URL where the song information appears, and time-stamp. Information about genres and sub-genres was obtained manually from customer-defined tags of Last.fm. We used the gathered tweets data and the genres and the sub-genres obtained from customer-defined tags of Last.fm as listeners' preference data.

We extracted the genres and the relationship among genres from listeners' preference data. The total set of songs is $M = \{m_1, m_2, m_3, \cdots, m_n\}$. The set of extracted genres is $G = \{g_1, g_2, g_3, \cdots, g_k\}$. The set of sub-genres is $S = \{s_1, s_2, s_3, \cdots, s_l\}$. Genre $g_i \subset M, (i = 1, 2, \cdots, k)$ is a subset of songs, and sub-genre $s_j \subset G, (j = 1, 2, \cdots, l)$ is a subset of genres.

B. Deciding the Radius of a Genre's Node

The radius of a genre's node is decided by the ratio of the number of songs contained in a genre to the total number of songs M. Expression (1) shows how to obtain the radius of the node that represents the intended genre $g_i (i = 1, 2, \cdots, k)$:

$$ r_i = c_1 \cdot \frac{|g_i|}{n} + c_2 \tag{1} $$

Where c_1 and c_2 are constants, and n is the total number of songs. For some genres, the ratio becomes very small, regardless of the number of songs. We therefore set a minimum radius of c_2 to ensure that all genre nodes can be seen.

[6]http://twitter.com/
[7]http://apiwiki.twitter.com/w/page/22554679/Twitter-API-Documentation

C. Links Using Curved Lines and Color Combination of Links

1) Using Curved Lines and Making Links: We connect the listeners node and genre nodes, and genre nodes and sub-genre labels by links of curved lines. Using curved lines allows bundling of some links and decreases the hiding of links. By focusing on connecting of nodes or labels, we can guess the number of songs from crowding of the links. We have been inspired by Holten's edge bundles[7].

2) Color Combination of Links: We assign opacity to links connecting genre nodes and sub-genre labels. The opacity shows how many songs a sub-genre contains. We show how to set up the opacity α by expression (2):

$$ \alpha_j = c_3 \cdot \frac{|s_j|}{n} + c_4 \tag{2} $$

Where c_3 and c_4 are constants, and n is the total number of songs; $\alpha = 0$ indicates complete transparency and $\alpha = 1$ indicates complete opacity. For some sub-genres, the ratio becomes very small, regardless of the number of songs. We therefore set c_4 as the minimum.

Links connecting the listeners node and genre nodes use gradations of each genre color and each listener's color. If connected links use only color, there may be inconsistencies between the nodes and the root parts of the link connected to the nodes when some nodes use a number of colors. In order to avoid this, we use gradation and we use the same color for the node and the link connected to the node. Figure 6 shows an enlarged view of the link connecting the listeners node and genre nodes.

VI. CASE STUDIES

To verify the availability of our tool, we performed case studies.

Table II
RESPONSES OF EACH USER IN EACH PATTERN

Pattern	User A	User B
Pattern 1	Pendulum (electronic) Pupa (electronic) Muse (alternative) Mellodrone (indie rock)	McFly (pop rock) Hurts (synthpop)
Pattern 2	not discovery	kagraa (j-rock) Supercar (j-rock) Omar A.Rodriguez-Lopez (progressive rock) Bullet For My Valentine (metalcore)
Pattern 3	Fort Minor (hip-hop) Handsome Boy Modeling School (hip-hop) Bad Religion (punk)	Sparks (new wave) anNina (j-pop)

Table III
RESPONSES OF EACH USER WHEN THEY SEARCH FREELY

Pattern	Artist	Genre or Sub-genre
Pattern A	Dr. Dog	indie
Pattern B	The Corrs	folk
Pattern C	Hocico My Chemical Romance Emil Bulls	dark electro emo nu-metal

A. Users

We asked a graduate student and an undergraduate student, who are studying information technology, to use our tool. They listen to music in their daily life. We prepared their music-preference data. User A likes the genres *rock*, *pop*, and *folk*, and the sub-genres *j-rock*, *punk rock*, *j-pop*, and *indie*. User B likes the genres *rock*, *electronic*, and *metal*, and the sub-genres *j-rock*, *progressive rock*, *new wave*, *post-rock*, *j-pop*, and *metalcore*.

B. Setup

We gave the users a five-minute explanation of how to use our tool, and then we asked them to use our tool. We showed the users a screen displaying highlights of their preferences. We asked them to search artists using the three patterns below, and to preview artists' songs on YouTube[8].

Pattern 1
    Search artists from genres or sub-genres of listeners with similar tastes.
Pattern 2
    Search unknown artists from their favorite genres or sub-genres, and find songs.
Pattern 3
    Search artists from their favorite genres belonging to other genres or sub-genres, and find songs.

If users find their favorite music, we ask them to record in their response sheets the artists' names and genre names or sub-genre names that they found. However, if users do not find their favorite music, we ask them to write "not found" in their response sheets.

Next, we asked users to search artists freely. We then asked them to describe in their response sheets how to search and find artists. Finally, we asked them to write freely about their overall impression of using our tool. We used listeners' preference data for users belonging to the same generation in our case study.

C. Results

We show the results for the three patterns in Table II. Responses are shown as "artist (genre or sub-genre)".

Regarding the three patterns, user A followed the genres he was interested in by tracing the links connecting the

[8]http://www.youtube.com/

nodes, using the mouse cursor. He specifically searched *electronic* and *hip-hop* in Pattern 1 and Pattern 3. In Pattern 3, he discovered two *hip-hop* artists. However, overall, he did not follow sub-genres very much.

User B followed the genres and sub-genres she was interested in by tracing the links connecting the nodes and labels, using the mouse cursor. She specifically searched *pop*, and genres and sub-genres related to *pop* in Pattern 1 and Pattern 3. For example, she found all artists belonging sub-genres of *pop* in Pattern 1 and Pattern 3. User B focused on sub-genres rather than on genres.

Both users followed the colors of the links because genres have colors. However, when they followed sub-genres, they seemed to lose their way. When they reached genres or sub-genres of interest, they previewed some of the artists instead of all the artists. We interviewed them about how to search artists. They commented> "When searching artists, first I searched artists whose names I have heard of. Next, I searched artists' names that interested me."

Next, we asked the users to search artists freely. The users searched artists in the following patterns.

Pattern 4
    Search artists in sub-genres that connect most genres.
Pattern 5
    Search artists in genres that they listen to a lot, but that other listeners do not listen to very much.
Pattern 6
    Search artists in sub-genres that belong in their favorite genres.

Pattern 4 and Pattern 5 are how user A searches for artists, and Pattern 6 is how user B searches for artists. In Table III, we show the results for each pattern.

D. Discussion

Both users used our tool in a similar way in Pattern 1 to Pattern 3. However, we obtained different results from user A and user B. User A mainly searched artists from genres he listened to a little. User B searched artists from sub-genres similar to her favorite genres. The focus of each user is different. However, in Pattern 1, they could search music they like from genres or sub-genres that they do not usually listen to because they focused on what other listeners listen to. As in the case of Pattern 1, we believe that in Pattern

3 they could search their tastes in artists from the genres or the sub-genres because they focused on the relational structure among the genres. Color-coding of genres and curved lines connecting genre nodes and sub-genre labels support the understanding of the relationships among genres. We therefore believe that our tool supports searching a wide range of songs.

In Pattern 2, user B could find the artists she likes; however, user A could not. This is because the listeners' preference data we used included a lot of Western music, rather than Japanese music. Both users commented: "We want more data with Japanese music." We had gathered the data by combining the services of Last.fm and Twitter, and Last.fm is more widely used by overseas users. Therefore, overall, there were few Japanese music data. However, with Pattern 2, it is possible to find unknown artists in the user's favorite genres or sub-genres.

When we asked users to search artists freely, we saw that they searched in a different way than we had expected.

In Pattern 4, user A searched by focusing on the genre relationships, regardless of his favorite genres and sub-genres. We obtained the following comment from user A: "I found a sub-genre contained many genres by color-coding of genres. Therefore, I got interested and searched artists." The color-coding of genres is therefore considered to be effective in showing the relational structure among genres.

In Pattern 5, we found that the user searched artists based on the differences between the other users' preferences and their own preferences. Our tool shows the user's music-preference data by highlighting in white. The tool shows other listeners' music-preference data by other colors. The opacity of each link shows how many songs sub-genres contain. We obtained the following comment from user A: "I could look at my music preference objectively by comparing my music preferences with those of others." Therefore, using colors and opacity is considered effective in comparing a user's music preference with others.

Pattern 6 shows how to search artists in unknown sub-genres of personally preferred genres. A genre has many sub-genres. Comparing one's music preferences with sub-genres, it is often the case that there are unknown sub-genres. By showing these sub-genres, users can search a lot of music in their favorite genre.

VII. CONCLUSIONS

We developed a tool to support listeners' tastes in music by showing listeners' music preference, and the relationships between genres, by visualizing the listeners' preference data.

Through our case study, we made it possible to identify users' tastes in music. By showing a user's preference data and those of others at the same time, we enabled users to look at their music preferences objectively.

ACKNOWLEDGMENTS

The authors would like to thank all the case study participants, and Dr. Simona Vasilache and the anonymous reviewers for their valuable comments.

REFERENCES

[1] Yoshinori Hijikata, "User Profiling Technique for Information Recommendation and Information Filtering", *Transaction of the Japanese Society for Artificial Intelligence vol.19, no.3*, pp.365-372, 2004 (in Japanese).

[2] Satoshi Masuda, "What is Musical Genre?: The Topology of Sounds, Concepts, and Power", *10+1 No.28*, pp.27-30, 2002 (in Japanese).

[3] Yaxi Chen, Rodrigo Santamaria, Andreas Butz, Roberto Theron, "TagClusters: Semantic Aggregation of Collaborative Tags beyond TagClouds", *Proceedings of 10th International Symposium on Smart Graphics, Springer Press*, pp. 56-67, 2009.

[4] Kazuki Takekawa, Yoshinori Hijikata, Shogo Nishida, "Implementation of a Content-based Music Search and Recommendation Method", *DEWS2007 (The Institute of Electronics, Information and Communication Engineers, 18th, Data Engineering Workshop)*, pp.1-8, 2007 (in Japanese).

[5] Takayuki Ito, Reiko Miyazaki, Misuho Oda, Makiko Nagasawa, Chiemi Watanabe, "Visualization of Musical Information Using "HeiankyoView"", *IPSJ SIG technical reports 2008 (50)*, pp.71-76, 2008 (in Japanese).

[6] Luis Sarmento, Fabien Gouyon, Bruno G. Costa, "Visualizing Networks of Music Artists with RAMA", *International Conference on Web Information Systems and Technologies (WEBIST 2009)*, pp.232-237, 2009.

[7] Danny Holten, "Hierarchical Edge Bundles Visualization of Adjacency Relations in Hierarchical Data", *IEEE Transactions on Visualization and Computer Graphics 2006*, pp.741-748, 2006.

Comparing static Gantt and mosaic charts for visualization of task schedules

Saturnino Luz
School of Computer Science and Statistics
Trinity College
Dublin 2, Ireland
Email: luzs@cs.tcd.ie

Masood Masoodian
Department of Computer Science
The University of Waikato
Hamilton, New Zealand
Email: m.masoodian@cs.waikato.ac.nz

Abstract—A mosaic chart has been proposed for representation of events on a timeline. While early studies demonstrated the effectiveness of mosaics in supporting visualization of multimedia records on a meeting browser, the usability of mosaics as a static timeline visualization has not been studied in more general settings. This paper investigates the use of the mosaic charts for visualization of project schedules. A user study was conducted to compare a building project schedule encoded alternatively as a mosaic or as a Gantt chart. Although the study focused on static graphs, for which the Gantt technique is usually very effective, results showed that the users were as fast and accurate at answering the questions using the mosaic representation as they were using Gantt charts. The analysis and experiment indicated algorithmic, space-filling and interpretation limitations of the mosaic technique. We suggest possible design improvements to overcome some of these limitations.

Keywords-Timelines; Gantt charts; Screen design; Information Visualization;

I. Introduction

Visualization of multiple chronologies spanning a common time period is usually done through timelines. A ubiquitous example of timeline is the Gantt chart, a tool which has been used for representation of task schedules since the beginning of the last century [1]. The fact that Gantt charts are still widely used in a number of areas testifies to how intuitive and effective the idea of representing temporal data streams as rectangular bars stretching along a timeline can be.

Although Gantt charts were initially conceived for the paper medium, where space constraints are not usually a cause for concern, the representational recipe for Gantt charts has undergone little change since Henry Gantt's time. In fact, a case could be made that because Gantt charts serve broader group coordination purposes as shared organizational artifacts they are irrevocably bound to the paper medium. Tufte [2], for instance, acknowledges the strengths of timeline visualizations, but elsewhere he claims that Gantt charts are ill-suited to computer screens and can only be useful if drawn on large sheets of paper and made available in public spaces [3]. Despite these concerns the static metaphor of Gantt charts also carries through to interactive contexts, and timelines have evolved and mi-

grated into the electronic medium [4]. They are now widely used in a variety of systems that deal with sequential data, including project management applications, browsing of multimedia collections [5] and meetings [6], representation of patient history and planning in health informatics [7], [8], visualization of travel itinerary information across time-zones [9], [10] and many others.

As timelines were incorporated into interactive systems, certain innovations were introduced which facilitated data input and presentation of multiple views. However, the basic design concept remained roughly the same. While the coordination roles of timeline artifacts such as paper Gantt charts have been either neglected or assumed to be performed elsewhere (through, for instance, integrated collaborative environments, etc) the screen real-estate limitations of the new medium have often been addressed through standard graphical user interface techniques such as scroll-bars, zoom and pane, and overview plus detail.

Leaving aside the coordination issue, which this paper will not address, and focusing solely on the timeline as a user interface component, one could argue that the transition to the electronic medium facilitated by the aforementioned techniques has not been entirely satisfactory either. For instance, if vertical scroll-bars are used the user's ability to align events decreases. Even in cases where the entire diagram fits on the same screen one needs to consider that visual sensitivity to spatial alignment decreases as the distance between the targets increases [11]. The difficulty is also accentuated if alignment needs to be recognized across intervening parallel lines, as is often the case in Gantt charts. The basic design premise of Gantt charts, i.e. that each event type be allocated a horizontal line, contributes to making these limitations quite common in practice. As the number of event types (task types, in Gantt charts) increases, so does the height of the chart. This results in wasteful space allocation since most diagrams will be dominated by blank spaces representing inactivity. As the graph grows vertically with the number of event types, the user's ability to recognize concurrent events and exclusively inactive intervals is also greatly impaired.

Luz & Masoodian [12] introduced "temporal mosaics" as an alternative to timelines for visualization of multiple

1550-6037/11 $26.00 © 2011 IEEE
DOI 10.1109/IV.2011.53

Figure 1.   The same set of events represented in temporal mosaic (left) and Gantt (right).

streams of events and their dependencies and relationships. Unlike a timeline, which grows vertically on demand, a temporal mosaic is a form of visualization that starts with a fixed height and allocates space proportionally to the number of overlapping tasks in a given time interval. Task types are no longer tied to particular lines but are represented through colour codes, as illustrated in Figure 1. Temporal mosaics preserve the representation of *overview*, even as the available drawing area is reduced, and facilitate the detection of concurrent and overlapping events, even as the number of events to be represented increases.

Temporal mosaics have been used in a mobile meeting browsing system [13] and evaluated for usability and effectiveness in a multimedia browsing task [12]. Although the evaluation showed that users performed better when using the mosaic-based browser, the tasks they were asked to perform were not typical schedule visualization tasks, and involved dynamic, interactive elements such as playing audio events and alternating between timeline and textual views.

This paper addresses these issues by assessing the use of mosaics in a static (non-interactive) and more familiar schedule visualization task. A user study is reported which compared user performance at answering questions about building schedules represented in mosaic and Gantt charts. Results are presented for accuracy, time to answer, and difficulty ratings. The main findings are discussed, limitations of the mosaic technique are analysed, and methods and guidelines for addressing those limitations are proposed.

II. EVALUATION

As mentioned above, the mosaic technique has been found in a previous study [12] to be effective for visualization of meeting recordings, where the number of event types is relatively small, and the vertical axis can be faceted to group events according to media source (audio, text). In contrast, the evaluation described in this section compares the mosaic visualization with the more familiar Gantt visualization, in a more complex context where the number of event types is much greater than the number of event types used in the previous study.

Furthermore, although we anticipated that temporal mosaics would be most useful for interactive dynamic visualizations systems, particularly for small-screen devices, in this comparison we were mostly interested in finding out whether users could readily understand the mosaic mapping in a static representation, and perform temporal inferences

based on it at least as effectively as when using the Gantt chart. Therefore, we chose a building schedule visualization task as the basis of our evaluation.

A. Method

In this study, a single project schedule was displayed to the participants as mosaic or Gantt timelines in conjunction with a question about the schedule, followed by a difficulty rating question. The project schedule used in the experiment is shown in Figure 2, in its mosaic and timeline forms.

A within-subject design was employed. All subjects were given a written tutorial explaining both forms of the visualization. The tutorial consisted of a short text which described the types of visualization to be used (i.e. Gantt and mosaic), illustrating each type with graphs similar to those actually used in the study. At the end of this tutorial the subjects were directed to the live visualization trial.

Table I
SAMPLE QUESTIONS.

Type	sample question
e	*No more than 3 tasks should be scheduled for the same day. Is this a problem with the current plan?*
i	*How many days are free in the first two weeks?*
c	*All the windows are installed by the same person and should happen in the same days. Is this possible in the current schedule?*
d	*How many days does the bathroom plumbing take in total?*
o	*Painting a room should finish before its carpet can be installed. Is this a problem for the bedroom schedule?*

Each trial consisted of a set of 10 pairs of questions, displayed one at a time in conjunction with either the mosaic or Gantt representation of the project chart. For each pair, we randomly allocated images to questions according to a uniform probability distribution. Therefore, in addition to randomizing the presentation sequence so as to minimize order effects, we randomized the question-image pairs in order to minimize possible learning effects. The types of questions employed in this trial were exclusion (e), duration (d), inactivity (i), concurrence (c) and ordering (o). Examples of each type of questions are shown in Table I.

All questions were multiple choice and the choices were presented through drop-down lists. Once the participants selected their response from a list of choices, the system recorded the time taken to answer the question, and then presented them with a request to rate the difficulty of the question they had just answered on a Likert scale ranging from 1 (easy) to 7 (difficult). The participants were told that the time taken to rate a question would not count towards the total task completion time. A prize (book voucher) was offered to the participant that answered the questions most accurately in the shortest time.

The study had 23 participants: 14 were male, 9 female; 11 were academics, 7 were students and 5 had other occupations. The system recorded 460 answers and ratings.

183

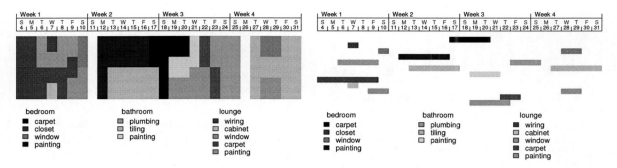

Figure 2. Scheduling constraints used in the study, represented as mosaic and Gantt charts.

B. Results

Remarkably, very little difference was observed in accuracy and answer time results for Gantt and mosaic charts. Mean error rates were practically identical. Macro-averaged (over mean error per question) the error rates were 15% for mosaic and 15.1% for the Gantt chart. Mosaic users took an average of 20.4 seconds to answer a question while Gantt timeline users took 21.2 seconds, but the difference was not found to be statistically significant (t[436]=0.5, p = 0.5).

Difficulty ratings were also very similar, with mosaic being rated slightly less difficult than Gantt timelines on average (2.3 versus 2.4, not significant). Since participants were randomly presented with both alternative visualizations for each question type, it is likely that these ratings accurately reflect their assessment of the relative difficulties of mosaic and timeline. Time-rating correlations were found to be quite robust. Pearson's product-moment correlation was 0.68 ($p < 0.001$) for Gantt and 0.62 ($p < 0.004$) for mosaic, showing that subjects tended to find more difficult those questions they took longer to answer.

A detailed breakdown of answer times and error rates per question is shown in Figure 3. While some questions were probably too easy, as is the case of the ones about inactivity (11 and 12), other seemingly straightforward questions such as question 4 proved surprisingly challenging. Question 4 reads: "All the windows are installed by the same person, and should be installed in the same days. Is this possible in the current schedule?", requiring a simple concurrence detection task. It is possible that the problems found by the subjects in answering this question stem from difficulties in interpreting the text itself, rather than the graphics. However, the low accuracy observed in both conditions seems to indicate otherwise.

We also grouped the answers according to type (concurrence, inactivity, duration, exclusion and ordering) and plotted the combined results for speed, accuracy and ratings (Figure 4). The only group for which one of the visualization styles had a noticeable advantage was the group of concurrence assessment questions, for which mosaic users were faster (and practically as accurate as timeline users).

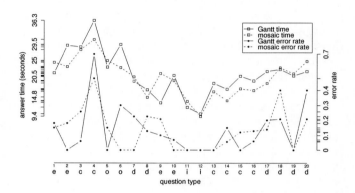

Figure 3. Answer times and error rates.

C. Discussion

Temporal mosaic matched the Gantt timeline visualization very closely for all types of event relationship detection tasks. Mosaic users performed well at detecting event overlaps, as expected, but they also did well at assessing event duration. The latter is somewhat surprising, since in the meeting visualization task evaluation carried out previously [12] users often mistakenly assumed event duration to be proportional to the area occupied by the event representation on the graph. We infer from this that since in the schedule visualization study participants were presented with both Gantt and mosaic charts, the former (for which interpretation of duration is clearly unambiguous) helped them form the correct mental model when using the latter. The mosaic visualization should, therefore, aim to utilize this mental model of timeline that most people already have due to their familiarity with Gantt charts. An improvement to the mosaic design along these lines could be to draw thin horizontal bars spanning the maximum width of each mosaic area as a way of suggesting the right mapping of width to time duration.

As noted above, of the questions that required detection of concurrency, question number 4 can be regarded as "difficult", specially if answered against a Gantt chart. They took a long time to answer it but still made many mistakes.

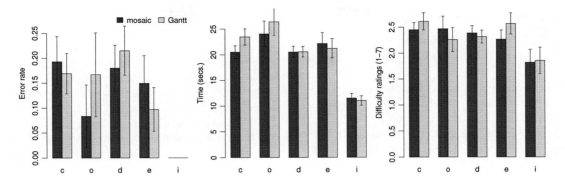

Figure 4. Answer time, accuracy and ratings by type of question.

Similarly, the questions concerning inactivity (11 and 12) can be regarded as "easy" in both visualizations. Question 18 illustrates the issue of misinterpretation of event duration in the mosaic visualization discussed above. Mosaic users did not take too long to answer the question but eventually answered it incorrectly. Closer examination of question 18, which reads "How many days does the bathroom tiling take in total?", also suggests that the respondents might have been misled by the placement of the legend for bathroom directly under week two, which happens to be exactly where the first period of tiling activity ends (see Figure 2). This was particularly problematic for the mosaic representation since it happened to extend right down to the beginning of the legend, causing its users to overlook the second period of tiling activity which starts much later, in week four.

Finally, the study revealed a shortcoming of the mosaic drawing algorithm, which sometimes produces the undesirable result of rendering an event that should be drawn as a single contiguous rectangle as two rectangles discontinuous ("broken") across lines. An example of such discontinuous drawings occurred for the lounge carpeting task (days 22 and 23). Figure 5 illustrates the problem: the two rectangles marked (a) in the zoom area should have been drawn as a single rectangle. This seemingly caused the high number of errors made by mosaic users in question 2 ("Putting carpet in a room and painting that room can't coincide. Is this a problem for the lounge schedule?") while Gantt users always answered correctly. A few of the participants pointed out that they were confused by the fact that the area corresponding to carpeting appeared not as a single rectangle spanning the 22nd and 23rd but as two adjacent rectangles, one at the top and one at the bottom of the screen. This indicates that discontinuity is undesirable. The question however is, can discontinuity always be avoided in mosaics? In the next section we address this question.

III. DISCONTINUITY IN MOSAICS

Let us start by formalizing the issue of discontinuity in mosaic visualization based on Algorithm 1, which is a

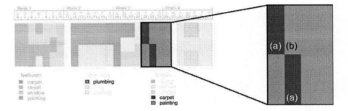

Figure 5. Example of discontinuity.

simplified version of the original mosaic drawing algorithm [12].

```
1  drawMosaic
2     assign a unique colour c_i to each event type e_i
3     for each time step t
4        n ← number of events between t and t−1
5        h ← height of drawing area / n
6        for (i in 1:n)
7           set fill colour to c_i
8           drawRectangle(t−1, (i−1)/h, t, i/h)
```

Algorithm 1. Mosaic drawing.

We say that a representation for an event e on the mosaic is a *discontinuous representation* if e extends from time t_b to t_e and there are times t_i and $t_j = t_i + 1$ ($t_b \leq t_i < t_e$) such that the vertical sides of the rectangles representing e at t_i and t_j do not coincide or overlap. In the case of Figure 5 the problem could have been avoided by reordering the plumbing event (b) to be drawn below the carpeting event (a). However, this forward ordering strategy will not always guarantee continuity. In fact, for any 2-interval sequence consisting of an interval t with $m > 3$ events, immediately followed by an interval t', containing $m - 2$ events that also occur in t, Algorithm 1 will produce at least one discontinuous representation. This is also true of the algorithm proposed in [12].

Let $e_1, \ldots, e_m$ be the m events represented in interval t. Assume that t is followed by interval t' containing $e'_1, \ldots, e'_{m-2}$. If h is the height of each rectangle for each

e_i in t, then the height h' of each e'_i will be:

$$\begin{aligned} h'(m-2) &= hm \\ h' &= h\frac{m}{m-2} \end{aligned} \tag{1}$$

At best all m events in t will be ordered, say, from e_1 to e_m, and all events in t' correspondingly ordered, i.e. $(e_1, \ldots, e_{m-2})$ so that, for all e_i in t and e'_j in t', $i = j$. Let $h_0(e_i)$ be the vertical coordinate for the top side of the rectangle that represents e_i, and $h_1(e_i)$ the coordinate for the rectangle's bottom corner. Clearly, in order for continuity to hold, $\forall_i h_1(e_i) > h_0(e'_i)$. According to (1), the general pattern of the sequence is the following:

Therefore, for $h_1(e_i) > h_0(e'_i)$ to hold for all i we need:

$$\begin{aligned} ih &> \frac{(i-1)hm}{m-2} \\ i &< \frac{m}{2} \end{aligned} \tag{2}$$

In other words, for $i = m - 2$ inequation (2) can only be satisfied by $m < 4$.

A. Strategies for avoiding discontinuity

A possible strategy for dealing with the discontinuity issue would be to alter the mosaic drawing algorithm so as to allow the rectangles (tiles) to have variable heights within intervals. In this case, vertical space would no longer be allocated equally among concurrent events. Before drawing a rectangle for event e' we would check if drawing the next rectangle in the same time interval would result in discontinuity. If so, we would reduce the height $h_1(e')$ so as to keep $h_0(e'_{i+1}) < h_1(e_{i+1})$. The visual result would be a mosaic in which the events at the top of the graph would seem "compressed" in certain intervals, producing a visually less intuitive design.

Another possibility would be to allow all segments (not only the next segment to be drawn) to be reordered once the continuity constrain has been violated. However, this strategy would be much costlier, since an exponentially large space of possible arrangements would need to be searched. Moreover, it does not guarantee continuity, as can be easily verified by trying to lay out a set of events $\{e_1, \ldots, e_6\}$ on a 3-interval mosaic, such that the first interval contains $\{e_3, \ldots, e_6\}$, the second contains $\{e_1, \ldots, e_6\}$ and the third $\{e_1, \ldots, e_4\}$. Fortunately, such unsolvable

continuity constraints rarely arise in practice. Therefore, a heuristic that seeks to minimize the number of discontinuous representations by looking ahead one interval and reordering streams appropriately before drawing will suffice in most situations. The required modification to the drawing algorithm of temporal mosaic is straightforward. Algorithm 1 can be modified so that the events occurring between $t-2$ and $t-1$ are stored in a vector, and the events between $t-1$ and t are reordered prior to drawing so that the events that also occurred in the previous interval are drawn as closely to their height in that interval as possible.

IV. DESIGN PRINCIPLES FOR DRAWING MOSAICS

The results of the study presented in the this paper can be used to define a series of visual design principles which can be incorporated into the algorithm for drawing temporal mosaics to improve its effectiveness.

In terms of visual variables [14], the basic difference between the temporal mosaic and a conventional timeline is that the latter relies on position, size (and occasionally colour) as its core attributes while the former trades position for colour (and optionally texture) as the plot's underlying visual variables. An event representation based on colour rather than position risks undermining visual continuity. Preserving visual continuity is the most important aspect of conventional timelines such as the Gantt chart, while space efficiency is the most beneficial aspect of temporal mosaics. Therefore, the overall aim of the design principles outlined below is to preserve, as much as possible, the visual continuity of individual tasks across the time axis, while also utilizing space more efficiently across the tasks axis.

A. Avoiding discontinuity

Visual discontinuity is the least desirable aspect of the mosaics visualizations, and therefore should be avoided when possible. As demonstrated, even though there are some cases where discontinuity cannot be avoided, an approximation algorithm can be employed which deals with the cases in which it can be avoided, as described above.

B. Visual alignment against the time axis

Timeline visualizations such as Gantt charts allow viewers to scan space reserved for each task, which is aligned against the time axis, to see all the instances of that particular task across time. Although this is not the case for mosaics, as no specific area is reserved for each task, it may still be possible to provide some visual alignment against the time axis especially for tasks that occur more frequently. One way of achieving this is to analyze the entire tasks dataset to calculate the frequency, or duration, of each task and then order the tasks according to their frequency or duration, so that task mosaics can be drawn in the order of their frequency or duration (e.g. top to bottom along the tasks axis). Although this does not guarantee alignment, it is likely to lead to higher frequency tasks being drawn in a narrower visual space along the time axis (e.g. always closer to the top).

C. Selection of colours

Selection of colours to represent different tasks in Gantt charts is not usually very important, as space is used to preserve the visual continuity, and separation, of individual tasks. In temporal mosaic, on the other hand, the association between colours and different tasks is crucial to the effectiveness of the visualization. It is very important to carefully choose colours that would allow individual tasks to be easily identified and separated from other tasks, particularly when the number of tasks increases. There are a number of colour selection criterion, based on graphic design principles, that could be adopted. The most important criteria is that tasks that are likely to co-occur, and hence be drawn close to one another, should be complementary so that they are easily distinguished from one another. This selection criteria could be combined with the task ordering and drawing sequence, as described above.

D. Enhancing visual continuity

Visual continuity of individual tasks could also be enhanced by combining some elements of Gantt timelines with temporal mosaics. Although such improvements can be added more easily in interactive visualization systems (e.g. by overlaying Gantt timelines over mosaics), in static visualizations connecting lines could for example be used to join occurrences of different instances of each task across the entire mosaic visualization.

V. CONCLUSION

The study presented above demonstrated that, despite its different visual style, temporal mosaic preserve the intuitiveness of timelines while using space more effectively. It also showed that first-time users of temporal mosaic are able to match the performance of Gantt users for speed and accuracy. Results and user feedback indidated possible improvements and guidelines for drawing mosaic charts.

Although our focus here has mainly been on evaluation of "static" mosaic and timeline visualizations, we believe that much can be gained by providing interactive alternatives to these static visualizations. Therefore, in parallel to this research, we have also been developing a prototype tool for interactive creation, visualization and manipulation of scheduling tasks using Gantt and mosaic techniques, as well as different combinations of both [15].

ACKNOWLEDGMENT

Saturnino Luz is supported by the Science Foundation Ireland (Grant 07/CE/I1142) as part of the Centre for Next Generation Localisation (www.cngl.ie) at Trinity College Dublin.

REFERENCES

[1] H. Gantt, "Organizing for work," *Industrial Management*, vol. 58, pp. 89–93, 1919.

[2] E. R. Tufte, *The Visual Display of Quantitative Information*, 2nd ed. Graphics Press, 2001.

[3] ——, "Project management graphics: ET notebooks (Ask ET," http://www.edwardtufte.com/bboard/q-and-a-fetch-msg?msg_id=000076, 2002, (retrieved November 2010).

[4] S. F. Silva and T. Catarci, "Visualization of linear time-oriented data: A survey," in *Procs. of the International Conference on Web Information Systems Engineering (WISE)*. Hong Kong: IEEE, 2000, pp. 310–319.

[5] D. Huynh, S. Drucker, P. Baudisch, and C. Wong, "Time quilt: scaling up zoomable photo browsers for large, unstructured photo collections," in *CHI '05: Human Factors in Computing Systems*. ACM, 2005, pp. 1937–1940.

[6] M.-M. Bouamrane and S. Luz, "Meeting browsing," *Multimedia Systems*, vol. 12, no. 4–5, pp. 439–457, 2007.

[7] S. Cousins and M. Kahn, "The visual display of temporal information," *Artif. Intell. in Medicine*, vol. 3, no. 6, pp. 341–357, 1991.

[8] R. Kosara and S. Miksch, "Visualization methods for data analysis and planning in medical applications," *International Journal of Medical Informatics*, vol. 68, no. 1–3, pp. 141–153, 2002.

[9] M. Apperley, D. Fletcher, B. Rogers, and K. Thomson, "Interactive visualisation of a travel itinerary," in *AVI '00: Proc. of Advanced Visual Interfaces*. ACM, 2000, pp. 221–226.

[10] M. Masoodian, D. Budd, and B. Rogers, "A comparison of linear and calendar travel itinerary visualizations for personal digital assistants," in *Procs. of OZCHI'04: Conf. on Human-Computer Interaction*, 2004, pp. 124–133.

[11] S. J. Waugh and D. M. Levi, "Spatial alignment across gaps: contributions of orientation and spatial scale," *Journal of the Optical Society of America*, vol. 12, no. 10, pp. 2305–2317, 1995.

[12] S. Luz and M. Masoodian, "Visualisation of parallel data streams with temporal mosaics," in *Proc. of the 11th Intl. Conf. on Information Visualisation*. Zurich: IEEE Computer Soc., 2007, pp. 196–202.

[13] ——, "Visualisation of meeting records on mobile devices," in *Handbook of Research on User Interface Design and Evaluation for Mobile Technology*, J. Lumsden, Ed. IGI, 2008, pp. 1049–1067.

[14] J. Bertin, *Sémiologie graphique*. Gauthier-Villars Mouton, 1967.

[15] S. Luz and M. Masoodian, "Improving focus and context awareness in interactive visualization of time lines," in *HCI '10: Proceedings of the 24th BCS Conference on Human Computer Interaction*, British Computer Society. Dundee, Scotland: ACM Press, 2010.

A Visualization Interface Applied in the Brazilian T-Commerce Scenario

Anderson Marques[1], Nikolas Carneiro[1], Rafael Veras[1], Aruanda Meiguins[2], Bianchi Meiguins[1]
Universidade Federal do Pará (UFPA)[1], Rede de Informática Ltda.[2]
{anderson.gmarques@gmail.com, nikolas.carneiro@gmail.com, rafaelveras@ufpa.br,
aruanda@redeinformatica.com.br, bianchi.serique@terra.com.br}

Abstract

With the spread of sales in electronic commerce and the popularization of interactive devices for digital television, grows the demand for applications that supports services over this platform, considering that television devices are present in 95% of brazilian households. In order to supply this demand, this work proposes a visualization interface for visual analysis of products in electronic commerce, through the Interactive Digital TV, the t-commerce.

Keywords: Information Visualization, Interactive Digital Television, t-commerce.

1. Introduction

The use of information visualization (InfoVis) applications becomes more common every day, once it favors the analysis of large amounts and different types of data in an intuitive and interactive way, revealing the relationships between data. There are several reasons for this popularity, one of them is the evolution in the means of data transmission and the dynamism in decision making the globalized world imposes on society.

In this context, the popularization of the Interactive Digital TV (iDTV) brings a new environment for applications, in a similar way to what happened to the internet, whose popularization led a natural tendency for the port of applications [10]. However, the porting of applications to the iDTV environment should consider the inherent limitations of this platform. These limitations are more noticeable about interaction devices and processing power [10].

Actually, according to the Brazilian iDTV middleware (GINGA) [11], the interaction device is limited to the Integrated Receiver-Decoder (IRD) controller. Along this work we use IRD to refer to the any device that attends to the specification created by the Brazilian Digital Television System (Sistema Brasileiro de Televisão Digital, SBTVD) for interactivity, be it a Set-top Box (STB) or a TV with embedded interactive resources.

The GINGA midlleware was specified by the SBTVD with the goal of abstracting the hardware platform for developers. The middleware defines the interaction modes and two subsystems for development of applications, Ginga-J (a Java based environment for procedural applications) [11] and Ginga-NCL (for declarative applications based in the Nested Context Language - NCL) [12].

The major innovation is the possibility to gain a wide range of new services through TV, such as the t-commerce. Other key point is that the middleware would provide a better social/digital inclusion, since it specifies internet access, is a specification free of royalties and more than 95% of the Brazilian population has at least one TV device [13].

In order to provide an application that enables the viewer to perform a analysis and easy the choice among products of the same type, this paper presents a prototype tool for iDTV that uses the treemap visualization technique to help the viewer to perform the analysis.

Section 2 presents issues faced by the development of an IV interface for the iDTV environment. Section 3 enumerates some related works, both on IV development for limited environments and works about the GINGA middleware and its possibilities. Section 4 presents the objectives of this work, the design process of the interface and the results acquired in this early stage of development. Section 5 present a scenario to exemplify the use of the application and Section 6 bring some final considerations.

2. InfoVis issues in iDTV

Even, by definition, information visualization is a computer independent human perception task, the computer support has being an important factor for improvements in this field [19]. It is due to the elevated memory capability, high processing power, improved video devices and interactivity resources availability, which can be used to potentiate visual and cognitive human systems [17].

When developing applications for a new environment, it is necessary to deal with several issues, besides the problem the application is supposed to solve.

1550-6037/11 $26.00 © 2011 IEEE
DOI 10.1109/IV.2011.66

As example, we can point the technologies to use (both on development as on the production environment) and the limitations imposed by the environment.

Issues largely discussed in the IV field become even worst in the context of iDTV. An example is the representation of large datasets, which in low performance environments (such as iDTV), impose severe scalability restrictions.

Another quite discussed point in InfoVis is interaction. About this issue, the SBTVD specification defines IRD controllers as input interface. The controller functionalities-buttons are following: confirm, exit, back, directional, contextual shortcuts (through the colored-buttons: red, green, yellow and blue), information and menu [18]. So, to assure compatibility among the diversity of IRDs, we use just the minimum set of keys to represent the listed above, assigning the "back" functionality to the red button.

The iDTV environment faces a great challenge about interactivity, due to the lack of devices that allow better interaction capabilities. Unlike a personal computer (PC), there is no mouse or other kind of pointing device, which makes the specification of a bi-dimensional point a laborious activity [15] . This is a serious lack for a visualization tool, since a set of operations and functionalities are based on, or improved by, pointing interactions (like clicking, drag and drop, zooming, selection and navigation operations [21] .

Another strong concern is the data scalability. Considering the hardware limitations, there are severe constraints about what can be loaded into the IRD. The amount of represented items also leads to navigation questions. Since the interaction device is limited and navigation can require much effort, it can result in an un-motivational characteristic for the viewer.

3. Related works

Into the iDTV environment we found the LuaOnTV [4], a framework that aims to optimize the build of iDTV applications. The framework provides several GUI components rendered directly in Lua, allowing the development of dynamically generated interfaces. Unfortunately, the projected presented some issues on performance and its development is stopped for while.

Pinheiro et al. [3] implemented multiple coordinated techniques (Teemap and scatter plot over maps), to display information on mobile devices. The main feature of this work is the capability to soften the impact on data analysis in limited devices.

Ghisi [6] defined models of *t-Commerce* based in three features: presentation (Presentation Model), form of payment (Form of Payment Model) and content associativity (Content Associativity Model).

Hur [5] designed and implemented a system that provides a personalized yellow page service for IPTV end-users to create an interesting partnership in the business directory market. This system shows the commercial possibilities for a t-commerce application in an IPTV system.

Our work presents an own implementation of graphical components, instead of using LuaOnTV [4] , based on the considerations discussed by Pinheiro [3] and taking into account the presentation model and the content associativity model recommended by Ghisi [6] We present a dynamic generated GUI, based on data loaded in each run. This means that the prototype is general purpose and adaptable to different dataset. This is an important requirement in a comparison tool in sales support as it allows using of the application for various products types without requiring code changes.

4. Proposed work

We present a prototype of a general purpose iDTV application for t-commerce support, which uses the treemap visualization technique. When attending to a service in the iDTV environment, this prototype also contributes to the digital inclusion, and consequently to social inclusion, among the Brazilian people [16] .

Some characteristics of the interface are listed below:

- Dynamic generation of the user interface;
- Navigation through items and user controls, using the remote control arrows;
- Selection of items and details on demand;
- Usage instructions at any time;
- Dynamic configuration of the visualization hierarchy;
- Dynamic configuration of items size and color;

Usually, data has a hierarchical structure or, at least, can be hierarchically organized. This data organization eases the analysis if the data are small, because it reduces the complexity of the data [7].

Usually, data has a hierarchical structure or, at least, can be hierarchically organized. This data organization ease the analysis, because it reduces the complexity of the data. In this context, among the different ways of representing and presenting data, we choose the treemap technique. According to Johnson [7] this technique makes easy to the user view a large volume of data, considering that human beings have the innate ability to recognize the spatial configuration of elements in a picture and understand the relationship between them.

Considering the two aspects of the brazilian middleware, Ginga-NCL and Ginga-J, we choose Ginga-NCL, instead of Ginga-J, to develop the prototype, due to the maturity of this option compared to the other one [8], [14].

The NCL is only used as a layer to define the positioning of the graphical user interface and to capture the interaction events in to the prototype. The Lua layer is responsible for most of the application functionality and is divided into four groups: the visualization, responsible for rendering the treemap in accordance with the standard configuration, the configuration manager, which records the user-configurable settings into a configuration model, the data manager, responsible for loading and organizing data, and the cart, that records selected registries by the user and returns them to the Broadcasting Service Provider (BSP).

During the development of the prototype we choose to use just two contextual shortcuts, because a smaller number of interactions would be easier for the end user to get used to the application usage.

The prototype was defined to be a tool in a step prior to the buying process via TV, specifically, in the choice of products. The Figure 1 shows the architecture of all the life cycle of the prototype and what happen before the viewer start to interact with the TV.

The architecture of the prototype is divided in four environments: development area, BSP, Ginga Set-Top-Box, and the viewer interaction environment.

In development area, basically, the designer defines which available products will be in the database script. The BSP is responsible for send to the clients' STB the database and the prototype, it also get the products selected by the client and load the shop application with them. The Ginga Set-Top-Box is responsible for receive end run the prototype, processing the viewer interactions. Finally, in the viewer interaction environment, the viewer is able analyze and interact with the visualization, being able to adapt the prototype for its needs.

First of all, (1) a Designer write a database script to selecting just the items to be displayed in that execution (i.e. the products that will be offered or are related to that commercial), and then (2) the database script will be processed by the Service Server and extract a subset of the products dataset. This reduced dataset is what is send to BSP and anchored to that execution context (dataset + tv commercial or content) (3).

Further, with the database updated, (4) the application's life cycle begins when the BSP provide to the viewers both the executable application and the dataset to be used. So, the Ginga Set-Top-Box, interpret and load the prototype, displaying it into the TV (5). The Ginga Set-Top-Box uses some metadata from the TV to properly render the application (6). After these steps, the viewer receives the visual information through the TV. In turn, the viewer has the first contact with the visualization (8), and then start to interact to the interface prototype, analyzing, comparing, and choosing their products. After the viewer analyze and choose products, (9) he can opt either by buying or not the selected products.

Once started, the app will end only in two ways: the user can exit the application without beginning the purchase application, via the button "Exit", or sending the selected products to the BSP and waiting for the purchase application to start, through button "Buy". It is important to say that the scope of this work does not include the purchase application.

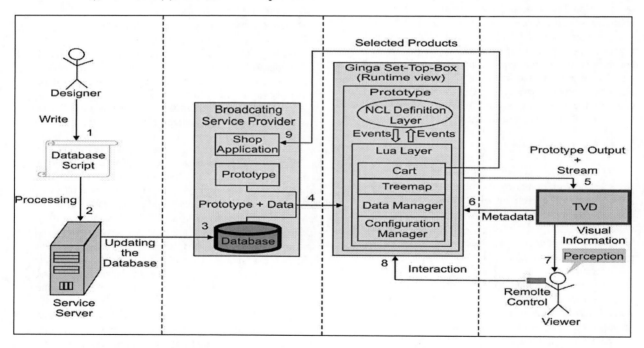

Figure 1: Architecture prototype splited into association areas showing in details the four environments (development area, BSP, the viewer's Ginga Set-Top-Box, and the viewer's interaction environment).

4.1. Details of functionality and forms of interaction of the prototype

After examining the main issues discussed in Section 2, we performed some tests with databases bigger than 100 items, thus, we highlight three *issues*.

First, when we loaded the database bigger than 100 items the treemap visualization in iDTV became cluttered. The second issue we found is about performance. The time averaged to plot all items in the interface was equivalent to 18 seconds, which is not a satisfactory result.

As the preparation of the visualization is up to an expert, the problems above cited are unlikely to occur, while they are easily solved by some preprocessing on the database (e.g., filtering). On the other hand, if the user is allowed to load any database, in other word, if the application is in the viewer's STB permanently there is a possibility of the viewer load a database bigger than 100 items which became a cluttered visualization and unsatisfactory performance.

And third, in order to overcome such difficulties, we decided to link the application database with the TV content, which according to Morris [9] is classified as *Service Bound* application.

In the iDTV environment the main form of interaction between the viewer and the application is the remote control. However, it does not provide means for reaching any bidimentional point in the TV. Considering this constraint, we designed the navigation in order to avoid unpleasant impacts on the ordinary functions of the TV, such as channel choice. So we decided to use only the directional arrows, the "ok" button, and the contextual shortcuts of the remote control.

In order to avoid the constraint above, considering the limitation of the interactivity device and the hierarchical organization of the treemap technique, we have designed a tree-based navigation for the prototype.

Basically, to go down in the navigation tree the end user should click in the "ok" button. To navigate among the treemap groups, treemap items, or among the GUI's buttons, the viwer should use the directional arrows. And finally, to return a level in the navigation tree the viewer use the "red" button. We opt to put all the graphical components (e.q. buttons, labels, radiobuttons) in the tree.

Starting the application, the prototype displays an area for the visualization, one for the "instructions" and one for configuring the visualization (Figure 2). The area A is the visualization area, where the viewer can navigate between treemap groups and items, the area B, presents a set of "instructions" to help the viewer to identify the possible interactions with the tool, and finally, the area C contains the buttons responsible for configuring the treemap: "Set Hierarchy", "Set Size", "Set Color" and "Set Label", more two, the buttons "Buy" and "Exit".

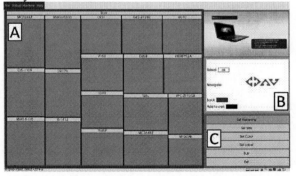

Figure 2: A – Visualization area, B - Area for instruction to the viewer. C – Configuration area

In the navigation structure, the visualization is "sibling" of the control buttons, and the items and groups of the treemap are children of the visualization. When navigating between items or groups, viewers can see the details of that item/group in the area A according to Figure 3. We chose to plot the details on the items in a reserved area instead of rendering them over the visualization so, at no time, the user lose the visibility of other treemap items. Details can be seen in Figure 3.

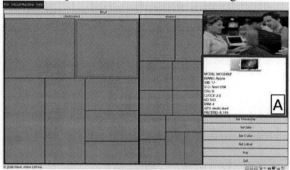

Figure 3: A - Details on demand of an item selected in the prototype

Considering the limitations on the interactivity device and the absence of any prior training of the viewer to use the tool, we define an interaction pattern to be used whenever possible. The configurations of hierarchy, size and label, respectively activated by the buttons "Set hierarchy", "Set Size" and "Set Labels" follow this pattern. By selecting one of the buttons mentioned, the area defined for the configuration (where the buttons are rendered) is redrawn, giving space to a group of radiobuttons that refers to the eligible attributes in each configuration (Figure 4). Only a subset of the attributes from the database is available for each type of configuration, as follows: categorical attributes for hierarchy configuration; continuous attributes for size configuration, and all the attributes for label configuration. To complete de configuration it is necessary that the user navigate to the button for the desired attribute and confirm this by pressing "OK/ENTER" then the display area is updated following the new configuration.

At the current stage of development of the prototype, the possibility of setting the color is limited just for categorical data. It is due to the lack of a user control that offers a good interactivity to continuous attributes, since the use of slider like controls are laborious through remote control.

The Figure 4 shows the *treemap* colors configured for the attribute GPU. The items with value "dedicated" for the cited attribute are colored in green, while items with value "shared" are colored in red. This configuration is available via the "Set Color" button. It is intended to preserve the pattern for setting the colors, making easier the process of familiarizing with the tool for the viewer.

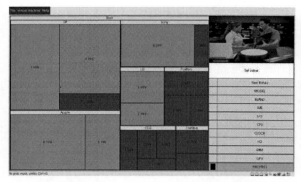

Figure 4: Reconfiguring the labels of the colorful items in Treemap.

About the "Buy" button, it sends the BSP data from products into the cart and ends the application. The way that BSP handle this data and starts the buying application is beyond the scope of this project.

5. Scenarios

This section describes an example of using the prototype, in order to show the use of resources for the extraction of information products in iDTV. The database selected for the sample was constructed with information from the local notebook market, it contains 10 columns being 6 categorical and numerical 4, with a total of 18 records. The database contains information on the model, brand, clock, operating system, storage capacity of hard disk, main memory of the notebooks, among others.

In the iDTV environment we face a severe limitation of interaction devices and processing power of the STB (Set-top Box). These limitations imply in a reduced dataset to be rendered because as large is the number of items, more difficult is to the viewer reach all of them using the remote control.

As a test environment, we used a virtual machine that simulates a STB with Brazilian middleware Ginga [20]. In the first scenario we tried to analyze what would be the notebook with the lowest price that has the Windows 7 operation system and 2 GB RAM.

To find a laptop with these features, the first step was reconfigure the treemap hierarchy to make it possible to distinguish the notebooks that had Windows 7 operational system. Then we reconfigured the size to the price of the laptops, so the smaller rectangle represents the cheaper laptop in the goup. Finally, in order to get the goal of the scenario, leave clearer view and allow the viewer to make a conscious purchase, we chose to reconfigure the labels of the treemap items according to the RAM of the notebooks into the dataset. Thus, it was possible to navigate between items on the treemap and observe details about the cheaper laptop with Windows 7 operational system. Figure 5 illustrates the notebook and its details on demand.

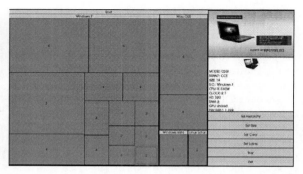

Figure 5: Notebook storage capacity of hard disk and dedicated GPU found after analysis in TreeMap.

As a second scenario, we decided to find a notebook database of who has the lowest price between the ones with 4GB of RAM (Random Access Memory) and Mac OSX operating system. To enable it to perform this scenario, we reconfigured the size of the treemap items according to the price attribute, then it was necessary to redefine the hierarchy of items according to the amount of RAM, so that was can see faster notebooks that had equal to 4GB RAM. To be successful in the analysis was necessary to change the labels of items in accordance with its operating systems, in order to view the notebook that had the Mac OSX operating system. After the end of the configuration of the visualization, it was easy to identify the notebook that followed the elements required for analysis. Figure 6 show the scenario.

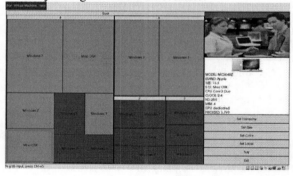

Figure 6: Lowest price notebook with 4GB RAM and Mac OSX system operational.

6. Final Remarks

This paper presented a prototype tool which allows the viewer to perform a comparative analysis of products of the same type, in order to ease his choice at buying process. The prototype is being developed for the brazilian iDTV middleware, Ginga, using the treemap technique to the help the viewer analysis.

It is important to point that the dynamic generation of interfaces is a factor of importance in a comparative tool, since it allows the reuse of graphical user interface for various datasets.

During the development phase of the prototype some difficulties come up, such as:

- For the development of dynamic interface was necessary the development of the vast majority of graphics components such as buttons, radiobuttons, labels, etc.
- To make possible to navigate between items on the treemap, it was necessary to develop a navigation algorithm that use only arrows as input.

Because the development and test environment adopted was only composed by a virtual machine simulating a GINGA STB, it was not possible to estimate the performance of the application in a real scenario.

As future work, it is possible to highlight the following topics:
- Develop the color setting mechanism, for continuous attributes;
- Develop the client using Lua, for the purchase of products by a viewer;
- Create a real test scenario to the iDTV, i.e., test the application into a commercial GINGA STB;
- Realize usability tests;

References

[1] KLEIN, J. A.; KARAGEN, S. A.; SINCLAIR, K. A.. Digital TV For All: A report on usability and accessible designer. Cambridge, UK: The Generics Group, 2003.

[2] HAMILTON, S.. 1997. E-commerce for the 21st century. Computer. Vol. 30. pp. 44.

[3] PINHEIRO, S. C. V., MEIGUINS, B. S., MEIGUINS, A. S. G., ALMEIDA, L. H., 2008. *A tourism information visualization analysis tool for mobile devices.* Proceedings. 12th International Conference Information Visualization. pp. 264 - 269.

[4] LuaOnTV (2011). Available at: http://luaforge.net/projects/luaontv/. Last acceded in January 5th, 2011.

[5] HUR, S. J., KANG, S. J., CHOI, W.. *A Development of a System Providing a Personalized Yellow Page Service Based on an Interactive Video Application Service.* Proceeding of International Conference on New Trends in Information and Service Science - NISS'09. pp. 1154-1157. 2009.

[6] GHISI, B. C.; LOPES, G. F.; SIQUEIRA, F.. *Conceptual Models for T-Commerce in Brazil.* Proceeding of Workshop on Interactive Digital TV in Emergent Countries at EuroITV – Emergent iDTV. pp. 22-27. 2010.

[7] JOHNSON, B., SHNEIDERMAN, B.. *Treemaps: a space-filling approach to the visualization of hierarchical information structures.* Proceeding of the 2nd International IEEE Visualization Conference, pp. 284-291, October 1991.

[8] COSTA, A. L. V. da., MELO, M. de.. *Desenvolvimento de aplicativos para TV Digital: Comparativo entre módulos do Ginga.* 10ª Escola regional de computação Bahia-Alagoas-Sergipe (ERBASE), 2010.

[9] MORRIS, S., SMITH-CHAIGNEAU, A.. *Interactive TV Standards.* Focal Press, 2005.

[10] KLEIN, J. A.; KARAGEN, S. A.; SINCLAIR, K. A.. Digital TV For All: A report on usability and accessible designer. Cambridge, UK: The Generics Group, 2003.

[11] SOUZA, G. L., LEITE, L. E. C., BATISTA, C. E. C. F., 2007. *Ginga-J: The procedural Middleware for the Brazilian Digital TV System.* Journal of the Brazilian Computer Society. 2007, Vol. v12, pp.47-56.

[12] SOARES, L. F. G., RODRIGUES, R. F., MORENO, M. F.. 2007. *Ginga-NCL: the Declarative Environment of the Brazilian Digital TV System.* Journal of the Brazilian Computer Society. 2007, Vol. v12, pp. 37-46.

[13] IBGE - Brazilian Institute of Geography and Statistics. 2009. National Survey by Household Sampling - Summary of Indicators. 2009. Rio de Janeiro.

[14] COSTA, A. L. V. da., MELO, M. de. 2010. *Desenvolvimento de aplicativos para TV Digital:Comparativo entre módulos do Ginga.* 10ª Escola regional de computação Bahia-Alagoas-Sergipe (ERBASE)

[15] FERRETTI, S., ROCCETTI, M., 2006. *MHP Meets the Web: Bringing Web Contents to Digital TV for Interactive Entertainment.* Eighth IEEE International Symposium on Multimedia, 2006.

[16] ÁVILA, P. M. de., GATTO, E. C., ZORZO, S. D.. *Recommender: Helping Viewers in their Choice for Educational Programs in Digital TV Context.* 40th ASEE/IEEE Frontiers in Education Conference, 2010. pp. S1E-1.

[17] WARD, M., GRINSTEIN, G., KEIM, D. Interactive Data Visualization. 2010.

[18] ABNT NBR 15606-1, *Associação Brasileira de Normas e Técnicas, Digital terrestrial television – Data coding and transmission specification for digital broadcasting, Part 1: Data coding specification.* 2ª ed. 2010.

[19] SPENCE, R. Information Visualization: Design for Interaction, 2007.

[20] GingaNCL (2010) Ferramentas Ginga-NCL. Available at : http://www.gingancl.org.br/ferramentas.html. Last acessed in: october 18th , 2010.

[21] SHNEIDERMAN, *Designing the User Interface: Strategies for Effective Human-Computer Interaction,* 1997. Addison-Wesley Longman Publishing Co. ISBN:0201694972.

Analyzing Soccer Goalkeeper Performance using a Metaphor-Based Visualization

Adrian Rusu[1], Doru Stoica[2], Edward Burns[1]
[1]Department of Computer Science, Rowan University, U.S.A.
[2]Department of Physical Education, University of Craiova, Romania
rusu@rowan.edu, doru_stoica_2005@yahoo.com, burnse15@students.rowan.edu

Abstract

The dimensionality of soccer statistics relating to goalkeeper specific data can be difficult to interpret. Leveraging our existing statistical analytics tool, Soccer Scoop, we developed a goalkeeper visualization add-on that can assist a team manager. With the newly developed goalkeeper visualization tool, a team manager can compare a single goalkeeper between two games, measure the overall performance of the goalkeeper both for games played at home or away, as well as to devise the appropriate training exercises needed to strengthen any visible weakness. To keep with the continuity of the visualization styles of our first tool, Soccer Scoop, the goalkeeper visualization applies similar techniques, such as glyphs, details on demand, color, and Gestalt principles.

1. Introduction

The interpretation and relation of data collected by team managers in the field of athletics, for purpose of developing pre-game objective scenarios such as tactical set plays, drills, or other player performance monitoring tasks, can be daunting considering the high dimensionality of the data. Managers of a team can gather data using many disparate methods that relate to specific player attributes such as speed, precision, or other performance values, however relating this data in a unified manner may be hard to achieve. The analysis of this data may be useful in determining the success or failure of a team or players as they progress, however with the high dimensional and disparate nature of most data collected in athletics, many team managers continue to ignore, hide, or inaccurately interpret data that would otherwise be beneficial if presented appropriately.

Our first step with introducing a solution to this dilemma was Soccer Scoop, a visualization tool that fulfills the need for player-to-player comparisons relating to team performance and dynamics by providing a metaphorically unique way to visualize and interpret data [3]. With Soccer Scoop we used a variety of natural field elements to represent several data categories that cross reference specific key player elements and allowed for the quick visualization of data. The overall goal achieved was to create a metaphor-based data visualization [10], that was appealing to the manger of the team thus minimizing overall cognitive effort surrounding team player and attribute analysis. Although Soccer Scoop solves the problem for analysis of data for players specific to various field positions within the game of soccer, it does not provide a visualization for the data as related to the goalkeeper position.

To further enhance the data and analytics capabilities of the Soccer Scoop application, we developed the goalkeeper visualization that allows for managers of a team to view soccer goalkeeper specific performance attributes. The goalkeeper visualization application presents a single visualization that maintains similar metaphoric and usability characteristics established within our Soccer Scoop application. Leveraging similar visual cues and appealing visual styles allows for team managers to adapt easily to the goalkeeper visualization without the need to learn an entirely new tool. The goalkeeper visualization is called the Goalie Viewer and shows vital information on a single player. Additionally, the goalkeeper visualization allows for the comparison of the vital statistics of the individual player with other games in which they have played, as well as a comparison of two different characteristics for the same goalkeeper for the same games. It can also allow for the comparison of different goalkeepers on other teams for the same game or between different games. The visualization represents the goalkeeper's attributes as an actual soccer goal with various data entities adorned throughout.

Our combined Soccer Scoop and Goalie Viewer visualization tool provides features for soccer statistical field data, gathered by soccer managers based on players' characteristics. We are not aware of any other tool used for the same purpose. Other soccer tools that allow for simulation of pre-game training initiatives for play-by-play analysis exist: "Grass Roots Coaching" [2] is a drill viewer visualization tool that encompasses the overall sequences of play drills related to both offense and defense, and "TactFOOT: Soccer Coaching Tactical Software" [1] is a visualization tool that allows for the creation of training exercises and drills through simulation animations.

Since the goalkeeper visualization is integrated with the original Soccer Scoop visualization application, the user is able to toggle between the various available visualizations, including the Goalie Viewer. Toggling between the other visualizations and the newly developed Goalie Viewer visualization is performed by clicking on the appropriate view button as available within the application, a technique which facilitates easy transitions between visualizations within the same tool [9].

1550-6037/11 $26.00 © 2011 IEEE
DOI 10.1109/IV.2011.57

Our application is intuitive and innovative in design and allows for the presentation of all goalkeeper attributes and key elements associated with performance. These qualities allow for even the most technically deficient team managers to quickly adopt the system.

The paper is structured as follows: in Section 2 we define categories, attributes, and characteristics as established in our tool, in Section 3 we present principal elements of our visualization, in Section 4 we provide implementation details, in Section 5 we present actual field data as it is being interpreted in our program, in Section 6 we provide future enhancements ideas, and conclusions are described in Section 7.

2. Background

We first define specific attributes (data model) that characterize goalkeeper performance, and then present a solution for goalkeeper analysis, both for individual comparisons between games and player-to-player between games. The overall goalkeeper dynamics of a specific player are represented and modeled using specific structure of data elements provided for the requested goalkeeper visualization. The data model contains three main data categories with attributes, with the target of allowing for the observation of both offensive and defensive goalkeeping, establishing a determination of performance level, and exposing specific performance characteristics that would otherwise remain hidden without a proper method of presentation.

We define the data model for goalkeeper to be similar to that of the original data model as provided for the original player visualizations, as presented in [3]. The main categories are: execution mechanics, tactical utility, and common mistakes in execution. What differs is that each of the categories are crossed by characteristics specific to goalkeepers: ball catching, plunge, boxing ball, diverting ball, hand throwing, blocking, dribbling, and ball kick. Execution mechanics for goalkeeper is comprised of precision, fluency, coordination, easiness, and rapidity.

The precision attributes for a goalkeeper elements are denoted by a corresponding percentage value, corresponding to each of the characteristics specific for goalkeepers: percentage of success related to ball catching (from long, medium, or short range shots), catching the ball during a plunge, boxing the ball to the side, diverting the ball to avoid goals, hand throwing to teammates, removing the possession of the ball from the opponent or removal of danger during blocking, percentage of time when the ball is 50 inches from the leg, and the percentage of success of ball kicking to teammates.

Fluency, coordination, ease, and rapidity are all Likert values represented by a scale of: unsatisfactory, satisfactory, good, and very good.

Tactical utility of an individual goalkeeper is distinct for each data element as described above and denoted by the following aggregation value totals respectively: number of times the goalkeeper manages to take possession of the ball, plunged and the ball stayed with his own team, managed to extricate game space (players unwind and go after the ball), diverted the ball's trajectory outside of the goal area, safely sent the ball to a teammate who managed to receive the ball and keep it under his control, went out of the goal to block the striker and decreased his shooting angle, controlled the ball with his foot in order to waste time, and kicked the ball beyond midfield.

The common mistakes in execution category is comprised of specific goalkeeper data for foot or hand, trunk, and slow execution of movement attributes. These attributes are all represented using a similar, corresponding Likert scale; however, foot or hand, and trunk values are more specific to the physical performance characteristics of an individual player. Foot or Hand attribute is broken down into the following representative elements: wrong position with arms and elbows apart, as well as ball catch which does not cover the back of the ball enough and does not provide it's amortization (corresponding to ball catching), while in plunge momentum does not resort to added steps, or arms are spread apart during flight, or landing is made with hands outstretched (corresponding to plunge), the jump from the ground is performed with whole foot or arm is not sufficiently extended from the elbow joint when the ball is hit (corresponding to boxing ball), the ball is amortized with the palm of the hand (corresponding to diverting ball), the ball is released late from the hand, making a curved path or for long distance throws, the center of gravity is not transferred from the back foot onto the front foot (corresponding to hand throwing), throwing feet first or does not choose the right time of the attack (corresponding to blocking), ankle is tense when the ball is touched (corresponding to dribbling), and impetus is too short (corresponding to ball kick). The trunk attribute of the goalkeeper data represents the following element values, respectively, corresponding to each of the characteristics listed above: trunk is not tight, contact with the ground is not made on the side of the trunk and not in natural sequence of its segments, during the flight trunk muscles are not tense to help hit the ball with more power, there is no synchronization between the trunk and the arms which divert the ball depending on the ball's trajectory and velocity, trunk does not execute a twisting motion after the ball leaves the hand, blocking the ball is executed with the trunk - thus the risk of injury is high, the trunk is not bent forward and is rigid, and the trunk is leaning backwards.

As with the original concept as followed by our earlier soccer player visualizations, our goalkeeper visualization tool was designed to encapsulate and integrate all of the three categories and respective data elements into a single viewing instances. This was accomplished by implementing a goalkeeper metaphor which uses a variety of unique visual cues, objects, and color styles; goal posts, goalkeeper player, and various sections of the goalkeeper player body model [4]. A simple glyph-based system [7] was incorporated by leveraging the natural objects of the player model in order to represent common mistakes in execution such as foot or hand and trunk attributes.

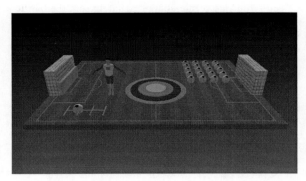

Figure 1. Goalie Viewer is integrated within the new version of the Soccer Scoop

3. Goalie Viewer Visualization

The goalkeeper visualization as presented in this paper was designed to be integrated within the original Soccer Scoop visualization software (see Figure 1).

The Goalie Viewer visualization, as shown in Figure 2, allows the manager of a soccer team to review an individual goalkeeper on a given team for a specific game. Additionally, it allows for the comparison of two goalkeepers of different teams for same or different games. Like our previous work, this visualization can be toggled to show different goalkeeper-specific characteristics: ball catching, plunge, boxing ball, diverting ball, hand throwing, blocking, dribbling, and ball kick. For example, in Figure 2, Plunge characteristic has been selected, and the same goalkeeper is projected in the same visualization twice to compare his performance in two different games.

Overall, Goalie Viewer comprises of several visualizations with varying cues and visual styles that present information for execution mechanics (divided into its associated attributes of precision, fluency, coordination, and rapidity), tactical utility, common mistakes in execution, and slow execution of movement (divided into its associated attributes foot or hand, trunk, and slow execution of movement) for the respective characteristic.

It is important to recognize that the complete visualization is integrated into a soccer goal model. This is to keep with the continuity of our other player visualizations by providing the key aspect of familiarity [5]. In it is a necessary usability factor that the user must feel connected with the overall visualization and must be able to realize the various abstractions as related to goalkeeper data. If the presentation is foreign or not recognizable to the team manager or general user, the overall information may be misinterpreted or even not visible to the viewer.

To implement comparative goalkeeper analysis, the visualization uses two instances of the same visualization. The mesh goalkeeper model uses color coded [6] regions to represent the category of common mistakes in execution. By default, if data is not available, color white is used. Otherwise, the Likert scale corresponding to the attributes of this category is assigned color values as follows: green represents very good, yellow represents good, orange represents satisfactory, and red represents unsatisfactory. Hand and foot is considered one attribute, so goalkeeper's hands and feet will always have the same color. For example, in Figure 2, the goalkeeper on the right side performs very good on one or more of the following actions: resorts to added steps while in plunge momentum, arms are close to each other during flight, landing is made with arms bent (the value associated to plunge for hand or foot attribute). The trunk of the goalkeeper is associated with the trunk attribute. For example, in Figure 2, both goalkeepers have good evaluations for making contact with the ground on the side of the trunk and in natural sequence of its segments (the value associated to plunge for trunk attribute). Slow execution of movement attribute is represented by the thighs of the goalkeeper. For example, in Figure 2, both the right and left goalkeepers have white thighs, which represents that data is not available for this attribute.

The category of tactical utility is represented in the visualization by the angle of a player model directly positioned from a gradient meter model that is color coded to red, yellow, and green to represent numerical ranges such as 0-5 for poor, 5-10 for good, and 10-20 for great, respectively. The player model works like a meter that will allow a team manger to visually recognize the performance of the goalkeeper during a specific game based on appropriate skill category. A straight goalkeeper is naturally associated with great work, so the player-meter metaphor would lead a team manager to understand goalkeeper's performance without much effort or knowledge of the data. For example, in Figure 2, the goalkeeper on the right side has been able to plunge and keep the ball with his team more than ten times (the value associated to plunge for tactical utility category).

Within the execution mechanics category, precision attribute is represented using the scale of the player model. Scale of the player model relative to size of the goal is associated to a percentage value for each skill attribute. The larger the player model the greater (and thus better) the precision; smaller models have poorer precision. This visualization technique allows for a team manger to quickly compare an individual goalkeeper or goalkeepers by associating precision with the idea that a taller goalkeeper relative to goal height will ultimately possess more precision performance overall. For example, in Figure 2, the goalkeeper on the right side has more precision in catching the ball than the goalkeeper on the left side.

Within the execution mechanics category, the right goal posts (or left depending on the side) and the top goal posts within the visualization represent the attributes of fluency, coordination, easiness, and rapidity, respectively. The posts (right or left) are separated into three sections; fluency at top of post, coordination in middle, and easiness at base of the post. Each attribute is color coded to denote the appropriate Likert scale value. For example, in Figure 2, the goalkeeper on the right side has very good values for his rapidity and fluency, and good values for coordination and easiness of plunge.

When developing a visualization, the main goal is making it as intuitive as possible for the target user. By leveraging the natural elements of a goal such as posts, or the mesh goalkeeper model positioning, a team manager is able to deduce the many performance characteristics as associated with a particular goalkeeper. When the team manager observes that the goalkeeper model is small compared to another model for blocking, they should be able to deduce that they need to practice at blocking. Finding the connections between the data and the overall visualization by the use of metaphors makes our visualization an effective analysis tool.

Figure 2. Goalie Viewer allows the manager of a soccer team to review or compare goalkeepers

4. Implementation Details

The initial release of our Soccer Scoop application was designed and written using the Java language framework and using JOGL, a Java implementation of the OpenGL graphics library, and implemented in the Netbeans IDE. Although this suited well for cross platform deployment, we decided to take the original design into the realm of 3D while leveraging a more unified programming model that could incorporate UI, data, and media. We chose Windows Presentation Foundation (WPF), implemented in the Visual Studio 2010 IDE, for the Soccer Scoop redesign, as well as for implementing the Goalie Viewer as presented in this paper. WPF is a development platform available within the .NET 3.0 Framework that provides a consistent programming model for building next generation software applications. It uses DirectX for graphics processing and provides a separation between both the user interface and the business logic layers which are generally written in the C# programming language. It was designed to unify some of the common elements of user interfaces such as documents, text, 2D and 3D rendering, vector graphics, and runtime animation. In WPF, the presentation or UI layer can be written in XAML, which is a derivative of XML, to define the many elements or models; however, it is also possible to define these models within the business logic layer with traditional graphics using the C# programming language. For the purposes of our design, we implemented the 3D models using XAML and implemented any transformations or animations using C# graphics programming. Version control was supported by Microsoft's Visual Studio Team System (VSTS) platform through Team Foundation Server.

Integrating field data into the Goalie Viewer is achieved through uploading a user created CSV file or by means of form field input within the main Soccer Scoop application before accessing the goalkeeper visualization.

5. Results

The application and analysis of actual goalkeeper data is critical in determining the usefulness of the Goalie Viewer visualization tool. In this section we explore the overall functionality of our goalkeeper visualization by presenting several case studies that leverage captured goalkeeper data. The data consists of a single goalkeeper of a second division team from Romanian soccer championship as an observation over a fifteen game period. These games were played both home advantage and away. Each data table comprises specific data attributes that provide for a detailed description of the goalkeeper within a single game, so a total of fifteen data tables have been collected. The data tables contain specific values for categories, attributes, and characteristics, as described in Section 2.

5.1 Observing performance deficiency

In this analysis, as seen in Figure 3, a goalkeeper was observed to have a performance deficiency with diverting balls that remained consistent between games. This deficiency lies within the tactical utility category required for the technique. The angle of the goalkeeper shows that he has diverted less than five balls outside of the goal area in both games considered (left and right). Upon viewing the visualized data specific for diverting the ball from the goal, one can see that although the player may possess this deficiency within the tactical utility attribute, overall fluency, rapidity, coordination, easiness, as well as precision appear to be improving from the game depicted on the right side to the game depicted on the left side. These attributes are represented as the green and yellow colored left goal posts in contrast to the orange colored posts relative to the right goalkeeper. Improvements in precision can be observed by comparing the size differences of the player models. Similarly, by comparing goalkeeper's performances over several matches, it has been observed that he is also deficient in his blocking characteristic spanning several categories (not shown in Figure 3).

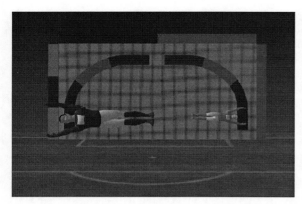

Figure 3. This figure represents a comparison of a goalkeeper between games in order to determine a performance deficiency.

5.2 Observing hidden performance qualities

It is as equally important to discover performance qualities as it is discovering deficiencies. In this case study, the performance attributes of an individual goalkeeper were compared between several games in order to detect exceptional qualities. Observation and analysis of the data through the goalkeeper visualization exposes ball kick as an exceptional performance characteristic (see Figure 4). It is evident through the visualization that the goalkeeper exceeds expectations for the two games selected, as shown by the mostly green and yellow coloring associated with the various elements of the metaphor. This is an important feature; by focusing in on performance qualities, the manager of a team is able to discover hidden talents of a specific goalkeeper.

Figure 4. Goalie Viewer reveals the hidden performance qualities of a goalkeeper

5.3 Comparison of an individual goalkeeper characteristic between home and away games

Managers of soccer teams are sometimes limited to visual or statistical memory when attempting to compare and evaluate the performance of a goalkeeper between

games home or away. Even considering the fact that a team manager may collect data between remote games, accurately interpreting this data may be still unclear as it is sometimes difficult to cross reference matrices [8]. Additionally, detecting performance improvements or deficiencies just by glancing at the numbers may not be easy. Our goalkeeper visualization solves this problem by providing the team manager insight into how their goalkeepers perform in games played at home relative to games played away. In this case study, we show how Goalie Viewer can be leveraged to determine performance gains or declinations between home or away games.

Results for one home (left side) and one away (right side) game for the ball boxing characteristic are presented in Figure 5. At first glance, it can be observed that there is a clear advantage when a goalkeeper plays at home versus away. It is evident that for some games there is a decline in the performance areas of tactical utility, precision, and rapidity as related to ball boxing. Additionally, the goalkeeper is much more prone to foot or hand mistakes. The only attributes that seem to remain consistent for the ball boxing characteristic are fluency, coordination, easiness, and trunk mistakes. Although specific of an individual goalkeeper, a performance may also be dependent on the performance of the overall team. Playing away may require the goalkeeper to contribute much more during the match, thus leading to more mistakes. As such, an evaluation of the general performance of a goalkeeper may in fact be indicative of team play. These discoveries can ultimately assist with the development of coaching exercise or other training practices that focus specifically on the performance deficiency that may be in need of improvement.

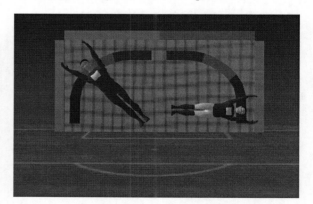

Figure 5. This figure represents a comparison between a goalkeepers performance at home (left) versus performance at away (right) games.

5.4 Results Summary

We presented three case studies that use various scenarios in order to find hidden information, such as performance deficiencies or qualities, as well as comparison between home and away matches, for selected characteristics. These scenarios represent a small subset of what the Goalie Viewer can be used for, in terms of evaluating the performance of a goalkeeper.

The main intent of the Goalie Viewer visualization tool is to empower team managers with the ability to evaluate, analyze, and observe the performance of an individual goalkeeper between games or with other goalkeepers of other teams between games so that decisions regarding the development of appropriate training or practices exercises can be devised. Our goalkeeper visualization tool quickly presents not only the best performance attributes of a goalkeeper, but also highlights any deficiencies that can be encouraged by the coach to develop, thus ultimately improving overall goalkeeping performance.

6. Future Enhancements

In this section, future enhancements to the goalkeeper visualization, as well the overall Soccer Scoop application are considered. First, the possible future inclusion of object animations using several animation principles within the Soccer Scoop software will allow for additional visual cues that may represent other various data elements not yet considered. For example, the animation principle of timing may represent a player's specific attribute such as coordination, while the principle of slow-in/slow-out may be representative of attribute related to easiness or rapidity. Second, allowing for the input of the data by the team manager on the field in real-time could be made possible by implementing a mobile, web-enabled version of the system that would send data ideally through a XML Web Service allowing for data that can be analyzed during a training session or game already in progress. Last, integrating other methods of data input such as accelerometers and/or gyroscopes devices worn by the players into the Soccer Scoop software package would allow for real-time input that would possibly eliminate the need for traditional data entry methods, thus allowing team mangers to focus on analysis through real-time monitoring.

7. Conclusions

In this paper we presented the Goalie Viewer addition to our original Soccer Scoop visualization application that is centric around goalkeeping performance data. Our tool represents individual goalkeeper dynamics specific to a particular game, however like our previous efforts in the realm of player visualizations, the goalkeeper visualization allows for establishing an analysis of goalkeeper-to-goalkeeper between games, as well as between teams. This fulfills the need for team manager coaching analysis related to specific goalkeeper performance data. Leveraging our unique quick-glance observation technique, we are able to metaphorically encapsulate and represent a complete set of skill-set categories centric around goalkeeping with their associated attributes and cross referenced elements by establishing a goal model that uses natural objects to represent the data. With analysis through quick observation as implemented by our goalkeeper visualization, team managers benefit with the ability to evaluate the goalkeeping with focus on performance qualities or deficiencies, and thus empowering them to not only take control of their team, but perhaps allowing them control over the outcome of the game.

References

[1] TactFoot: Soccer Coaching Tactical Software. Retrieved from http://www.tactfoot.com, 2010.

[2] Soccer & Football Coaching, Drills, & Training in the UK, Europe, & America. Retrieved from http://www.grassrootscoaching.com, 2005.

[3] A. Rusu, D. Stoica, E. Burns, B. Hample, K. McGarry, and R. Russell. Dynamic Visualizations for Soccer Statistical Analysis. Proceedings of the 14th International Conference on Information Visualisation (IV), pages 207-212, 2010.

[4] Jack Ox. Visualization and the art of metaphor. Proceedings of the 6th ACM SIGCHI conference on Creativity & cognition, pages 307-308, 2007.

[5] Phil Turner. Being-with: A study of familiarity. Interacting with Computer, Volume 20, Issue 4-5, pages 447-454, 2008.

[6] Haleh. H. Shenas and Victoria Interrante. Compositing color with texture for multi-variate visualization. Proceedings of the 3rd international conference on Computer graphics and interactive techniques in Australia and South East Asia, 2005.

[7] Beth Yost and Chris North. Single complex glyphs versus multiple simple glyphs. Conference on Human Factors in Computing Systems, pages 1889-1892, 2005.

[8] A. Telea, P. de Hillerin, and V. Valeanu. Visualization of multivariate athlete performance data. The Seventh IASTED International Conference on Visualization, Imaging and Image Processing, pages 123-128, 2007.

[9] Darius Pfitzner, Vaughan Hobbs, and David Powers. A unified taxonomic framework for information visualization. Proceedings of the Asia-Pacific symposium on Information visualization, Volume 24, pages 57-66, 2003.

[10] Miller, Todd and Stasko, John, "The InfoCanvas: Information Conveyance through Personalized, Expressive Art", Short Paper, CHI 2001 Extended Abstracts, Seattle, WA, April 2001, pp. 305-306.

Exploratory to presentation visualization, and everything in-between: providing flexibility in aesthetics, interactions and visual layering

Alexander Baumann[1], Andrew S. Dufilie[1], Sebastin Kolman[1], Srinivas Kota[1], Georges Grinstein[1],
William Mass[2]
UMass Lowell, Institute for Visualization and Perception Research[1],
Economic and Social Development of Regions[2]
{baumann.alex@gmail.com, adufilie@cs.uml.edu, saby83@gmail.com,
Srinivas_Kota@student.uml.edu, grinstein@cs.uml.edu, william_mass@uml.edu}

Abstract

It is often necessary to perform exploratory analysis on datasets in order to determine the patterns to show as presentation visualizations for a target audience. In many cases, exploratory packages do not offer enough flexibility to alter application look and feel in order to produce the required presentations of the data. Runtime modifications of aesthetic, interactive and visualization layering properties allow new interfaces to be defined that can best suit a target audience. Modifications to these properties allow advanced exploratory systems to be reduced down to limited presentation visualizations, and everything in between. This paper explores the design and applications of such runtime application flexibility within the web-based visualization environment Weave.

1. Introduction

Data visualization often takes many forms depending on the task and who is viewing or interacting with the output. For some datasets, the patterns inherent in the data, or interpretations of the data, are already known. However, exploratory visualization is often necessary to interpret data that is too complicated to understand in strictly tabular form. In both cases, the ultimate goal is often presentation visualization – whether presenting results directly from an exploratory system or after recreating the same discoveries in systems that provide more support for presentation including control of fonts, colors, and annotations for example. Users interacting with such systems range in expertise from novice to expert and each will use the software in different ways to satisfy their own needs.

Most systems offer modifications for visualization properties, colors, fonts, and other aesthetic settings, but limited choices for more complex aesthetic, interactivity and visualization properties that would allow further customization of the system to better suit the target audience. Systems with more presentation or confirmatory visualization focus often provide extra aesthetic settings in order to allow the presenter to make sure the final visualization looks the way they want it to. Systems do not often provide choices for ways in which the user interacts with the visualizations in order to target

different user levels, other than by virtue of different types of visualizations or applications being more or less simpler to understand and use (as determined by how they were designed).

Runtime modifications to user interfaces is of interest to the intelligent user interface (IUI) sub-field of HCI [1] as it relates to changing the interface to handle the personal preferences of users, the simplification of tasks and guiding users through new features. Such designs require the ability to dynamically define and modify user interfaces as the user interacts with the system. Other automatic transformations of user interfaces at runtime such as that of the Fluid architecture [2] allow dynamic modification of "the default user interface by substituting or augmenting components with appropriate alternatives which best match the user's needs and preferences."

Manual modifications to user interfaces (as opposed to automatic intelligent modification) allow users or designers (in the case of Weave administrators) to design very specifically targeted user interfaces as they work. Modifiable markup (XML, etc) representations of user interfaces like that of Luyten and Coninx [3] encode the hierarchy and properties of user interface components to define layout. This type of representation is extensible, allows rapid prototyping and can even often be cross-platform if the component definitions are generalized. This is similar to the design used in Weave: session states (as part of the session history) define all application properties, including user interface hierarchy.

2. Background and Motivation

Weave (WEb-based Analysis and Visualization Environment) is a data visualization framework designed and engineered at UMass Lowell as part of a joint effort between the Computer Science department, the Economic and Social Development of Regions program, and the Open Indicators Consortium (OIC) [4] whose members consist of government agencies and non-profit organizations looking for tools to provide interactive data visualizations to their constituencies and the general public.

Weave is designed to provide visualization tools to many different levels of experienced users. The highest-

1550-6037/11 $26.00 © 2011 IEEE
DOI 10.1109/IV.2011.82

level user will be referred to in this paper as an *administrator*, emphasizing the ability to control any aspect of Weave. Many administrators use the software to do exploratory visualization and then present their findings to their target audience. The features available to users are specified by an administrator who can turn on and off various functionality to for example simplify the user interface or limit user interactions. The resulting presentation will be referred to as an *instance* of Weave.

It became clear early on when working with the OIC that each member's needs were going to be different. The differences were in the data they had to present, how they wanted the resulting visualizations to look, and how they wanted users to interact with these visualizations. Their target audiences ranged from advanced analysts with similar needs, to end users who may have simply wanted to see a visualization with minimal interaction., including for example hovering over a point to retrieve more data. In order to satisfy this, aesthetic and interactive properties of the software were parameterized so they could be changed at runtime, rather than relying on writing code within the framework or predefining initialization files. We selected a layered approach to visualizations in order to provide runtime modifications of visualizations to create new visualization types.

3. Framework flexibility

Weave is a data visualization framework for the web. Each application has parameterized aesthetic, interaction and visualization properties that can be modified through a simple interface and thus yield customized applications at runtime. The parameterization of properties allows the resulting presentation visualizations to be edited at any time by another user with administrator privileges, meaning a final simplified visualization could later be edited to show different patterns or data, or become the basis for further analysis. The same application can be used for both exploratory analysis (to determine the patterns to show to the users), and to provide the resulting interactive presentation visualizations to their end users. The parameterizations of all user-editable values within the system are stored in a state that is for the basis for session histories within Weave, referred to as a *session state* within this paper.

User defined layout (position, size) of visualizations was accomplished by creating a windowing environment within the web browser that allows users to work with tools as they would windows on their operating system. These windows can also be modified to disable resizing, moving, closing, minimization and maximization. By removing all the controls and borders on a window, visualizations can be drawn in a static layout, allowing the creation of dashboards and other presentations that are meant to have fixed positioning. Windows within the system can also be nested within one another so that for example a legend window could be added to a bar chart window, or a histogram could be placed on the axis of a scatterplot showing the distribution of points on that given axis. Figure 1 shows a choropleth map

visualization with a nested map window showing the same map at the entire world view. Although the framework does not provide such a map tool, it can be created at runtime by modifying session state, offering a new visualization type without writing any code to do so.

Figure 1 Map of state boundaries with nested second map showing the world view.

The state created by the parameterization of all the objects used in the system can be modified manually to control settings that do not yet have a user interface. When a class is instantiated it shows up in the session state in the same hierarchy it has internally in the code. Thus various nested components can be copied and pasted into other components, such as adding the definition of a scatterplot to the layers present in a map visualization, allowing point-based data to be added to a map. This state also allows code prototyping and new visualization type creation by copying and pasting various sub-components into other tools. Variables in the session state can be linked to one another, meaning on any change every other variable that are linked are updated. This allows, for instance the font used in a label for each record on a tool to be sized by a data value, or the creation of a selection in a map to set the subset of the data that is used in a line chart.

3.1. Flexibility in aesthetic properties

Aesthetic properties of a visualization are often most important for a final presentation, but can come into play when doing exploratory analysis. In certain cases, changing the background color of a visualization can help provide better contrast between the background and foreground, and can be easier to deal with under certain lighting conditions, such as when using a projector. Similarly, changing fonts and other size properties can aid in seeing what the user is working on when the objects being dealt with are too small. Color deficiencies also highlight the need for flexible color choices. Custom color mappings can be created for various tools, allowing users to present the data visually exactly as they see fit, or to match some scheme they are trying to convey. Figure 2 shows modifications to aesthetic properties such as choice of colormap, background color of tools and removal of window borders to have a static dashboard-like layout.

Presentation visualization often focus more on these settings to match a desired look (branding) for a group, create visualizations appropriate for specific audiences (older individuals, ADA compliance, etc), and to annotate results to aid understanding. In the case of administrators familiar with the data or trying to show known trends, presentation visualization may be the only goal. Data mappings can be chosen and the various aesthetic qualities of the visualization can be tweaked for the given audience. In many cases, trends in the data are not known, or the results are not what was expected, meaning that exploratory analysis is necessary.

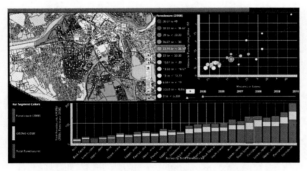

Figure 2 Weave showing fixed layout and customization of aesthetic properties

Weave uses the same system for analysis and presentation visualization, with transitions between the two (and any combination thereof) possible via modifications to the session state. Multiple parameters can be changed at once, stored, and then reapplied later. For instance, a state that shows a tool or the application in presentation mode can be stored, along with a state that shows the same objects in exploratory mode.

Applying the state parameters that define a given user view (exploratory, presentation or any combination thereof) provides seamless transitions between different views, as opposed to having to recreate all the parameters each time. Administrators can find new patterns and trends to highlight without having to recreate presentation views after each data mapping change that is made. This is similar to a system that allows switching between different views or modes, except that the states that can be applied are entirely administrator defined and can include any number of aesthetic, interaction, and visualization parameters to customize what each instance or user view will look like and do.

3.2. Flexibility in user interactions

Interactivity is extremely important when presenting to end users.. However, for many users, especially novice ones, too much interactivity or a having a complex interface is discouraging. Therefore, providing interactivity in a layered approach allows customization from detailed and fully interactive to simple and minimally interactive. Depending on the domain and user base, minimally interactive, highly simplified tools may even be desired by users who are very familiar with the data and even visualization techniques. One such example is an expert user presenting findings to a group of people who are less familiar with the data, using simpler canned presentation visualizations to highlight findings rather than overwhelming the crowd with too complex an interface.

When creating different pages, an administrator will either start from a blank slate view or more often from a previous state with similar properties. Exploratory analysis allows finding patterns to present in visualizations that can be shown to users at various skill levels. This is handled by creating different user views, with the original administrator view always accessible. These views can be named and saved and each are defined by the settings provided by the administrator. This includes aesthetic settings, interaction settings and all the data mappings and visualizations that are present in the instance – with the goal being to present some information to a user or allow them to explore some data using the interfaces chosen by the administrator.

Administrators need to access all the properties of data mapping within each tool, choosing a parameter to map to (such as X or Y in a scatterplot) and choosing what data to map to this parameter (from what can be a complex hierarchy of a large amount of possible data choices). Once desired mappings are found, these can be saved for later reuse, for the purposes of comparison or to save time. Presets for properties such as X and Y in a scatterplot can also be used to provide a simpler method of navigating data patterns to other end users, allowing them to simply choose from one of several options rather than from the entire available data. Similarly, presets can be created that cover more than one property, such as both X and Y of a scatterplot at the same time (i.e. "Height vs. Weight"). This approach of allowing an administrator to save presets is an example of how functionality can be provided that can both aid administrators in their work (save time by storing commonly used presets), and offer simpler user interfaces to other users (presets that the user can change to see canned views of the data). Creating such an interface is thus simple due to the session state approach where each preset is simply the subset of parameters for a given tool required to represent the given mapping.

Linking of parameters across the session state allows other complex forms of application modification, such as using the interactions within a visualization tool to filter the data within another. Examples of this include using the selection created in a given tool as the subset of records shown in another, or using mouse probed records as a subset in another tool. During an in person meeting with members of the OIC, the line chart visualization tool was modified in real time to show only the records selected in other visualization tools, and then show any other record that is probed in another tool on top of this selection, allowing comparison between selected records and mouse probed records. Figure 3 shows runtime modification to Weave in order to support this requested functionality. The flexibility of the system allowed us to prototype this during the meeting to test alternative functionality and then add this as a feature within the framework code after a consensus was reached.

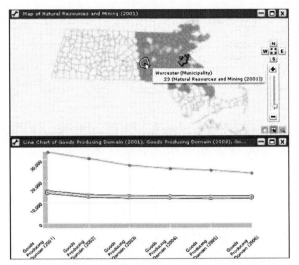

Figure 3 Line chart modified at runtime to show selection with probed record overlaid

3.3. Flexibility in visual layering

Besides taking advantage of existing tools, administrators may have the need to create composite visualizations that better handle their needs. Such new tools can be coded into the framework, but they can also be made at runtime. Some examples include changing what kind of glyph is drawn for each point on a visualization tool, or placing a bar chart at a specific location on a map. Figure 4 and figure 5 show two types of composite tools created by manually copying and pasting layers between visualization tools.

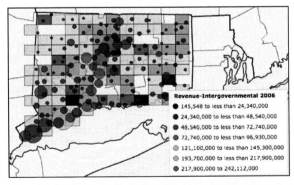

Figure 4 Composite of a binned scatterplot and regular scatterplot on top of a map (CT/NY area)

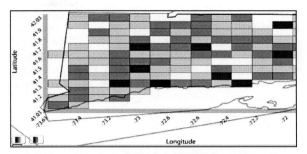

Figure 5 Composite of a binned scatterplot with map layer added (CT/NY area)

The user interface used by administrators to code new tools is simple enough for non-programmers to use, and is more desirable for general usage (including by programmers) that does not require additional functionality not already available within the given tool layers and glyphs. Modification can also be done by manually editing the session state or by accessing the provided API to more dynamically modify the session state at runtime. In both cases, no modification to the framework code is needed.

The visualization tools within the Weave framework have been written with support for multiple layers present on each visualization, with each record represented as a glyph that can itself be a visualization, and with selection, mouse probing and other features abstracted out so that these features are automatically enabled. This means one could, for example, create a scatterplot that uses a geographic shape for each record being shown (i.e. a scatterplot of state data that draws the state shape for each record) or a scatterplot of pie charts or even other scatterplots. These new visualizations can be prototyped at runtime, and if particularly useful, coded within the framework as new tool types.

4. Applications

The Weave framework offers great flexibility in the creation of applications with each application having interfaces to support the modification of aesthetic, interaction and visualization properties. Other applications can be created using the framework and new features can be added to existing applications at runtime by modifying the session state. The following includes some example use of this flexibility to highlight the benefits gained.

Although different views can be made that are suited for different target audiences, a single view might not satisfy a user over time as they become more experienced with the system and the data. A user interface can be created that allows users to "unlock" features by requesting to step up in complexity (from novice, to intermediate, etc).

In order to allow reusability of session states, we define the concept of "templates" in which portions of session states can be applied to other states. These templates can be loaded and have various properties filtered out to only apply what is desired from the state. For example, only the aesthetic properties could be loaded and the data mappings could be filtered out, modifying the appearance of a visualization tool while retaining its data mappings. Alternately, the data mappings could be loaded without modifying the aesthetic or interaction settings.

4. Future work

As the development of Weave continues and the needs of our users change, more flexibility will be added to the system. Currently, certain modifications to the application at runtime are too difficult for most administrators to handle, such as using the selection in a given tool to define the subset of another, or creating a new visualization with the same data mappings as a different type of visualization (e.g. a line chart with the same data as a scatterplot). User interfaces will be developed that support these modifications. The framework provides so much flexibility already that most of the future work involves user interface design. We also will provide an administrator with the ability to define taxonomies of interactions, allowing a user to add interactions to their current tools rather than losing any work they did at the lower user level. Additionally, these user levels could be unlocked by tracking what the user is doing within the system and determining whether to expand their available features.

Creating new visualization types at runtime is currently only possible by manually modifying session state and is too difficult for any but the simplest cases to be done by a technically proficient administrator. Layers should be movable between visualizations through user interaction and which glyph to use in each visualization an option within the tools. The newly created visualizations should be savable as tools that can be reused within the system, rather than just one-off tools.

Although Weave currently offers an API to modify the session state, this API must be further enriched to provide functionality that administrators will want to modify at runtime. This API can be used to program new features at runtime that make use of existing framework functionality and that cannot be made by simply modifying session state. Offering runtime scripting and macros is another example of how the API could perform various functions on the session state, such as cascading all windows, duplicating an existing tool, or applying a series of aesthetic settings to an existing state.

In order to aid in framework development, one idea suggested was to create dummy class structures in the code that are based upon a current session state. Since each state is used to instantiate a class, it could also be used to create the code necessary to represent the layering structure and parameters modified in a given visualization defined at runtime. This would speed up the development of new visualizations while encouraging the use of runtime experimentation.

Conclusions

Runtime modification of user interfaces allows users to customize how they interact within the system. In the case of Weave, administrators have the need to customize user interfaces for a target audience that varies in skill level. For data analysis software packages this allows interfaces to be defined that can present the same data to different audiences for the purposes of solely presentation (most naïve users) through highly interactive exploratory analysis (most advanced users). Runtime modification of aesthetic, interaction and visual layering allow administrators to create customized user interfaces without modifying application code. By parameterizing user interface choices and controls, and making those available both through an API and user interfaces at runtime, features of an advanced exploratory visualization system can be reduced or simplified to target less technical users and provide interactive presentation visualizations.

Acknowledgements

We would like to acknowledge the Open Indicators Consortium membership for their continued support and feedback and the members of the IVPR lab at UMass Lowell who have implemented various parts of Weave.

References

[1]   Patrick A.M. Ehlert. Intelligent User Interfaces: Introduction and Survey. Delft University of Technology DKS03-01. 2003.
url:
http://www.kbs.twi.tudelft.nl/Publications/Report/2003-Ehlert-DKS03-01.html

[2]   Fluid proposal – A customizable user interface
url:
http://wiki.fluidproject.org/display/fluid/A+Customizable+User+Interface

[3]   Kris Luyten and Karin Coninx. An XML-Based Runtime User Interface Description Language for Mobile Computing Devices. In *Proceedings of the 8th International Workshop on Interactive Systems: Design, Specification, and Verification-Revised Papers*. DSV-IS '01. Springer-Verlag, London, UK, 1-15. 2001.

[4]   Open Indicators Consortium
url: http://www.openindicators.org

Moving from Folksonomies to Taxonomies:
Using the Social Web and 3D to Build an Unlimited Semantic Ontology

Konstantinos Gkoutzis
Faculty of Science and Technology
University of Plymouth
Plymouth, United Kingdom
konstantinos.gkoutzis@plymouth.ac.uk

Vladimir Geroimenko
Faculty of Arts
University of Plymouth
Plymouth, United Kingdom
vladimir.geroimenko@plymouth.ac.uk

Abstract—The Semantic Web was introduced in 1999 as a method of interrelating information to help computers derive conclusions based on the links between data. With the rising popularity of Social Networks though, unconnected pieces of information have only chaotically increased instead of becoming parts of well-organised Taxonomies.

In this paper, we suggest a system which will take advantage of the Social Web and put it to work so that it will operate under the common cause of categorising old and new data into an unlimited Semantic Ontology. This ontology will be created gradually and ever-changing, like a versatile encyclopaedia of information compiled from interconnected data. With the addition of a 3D Web interface on top of the ontology management mechanisms, the entire experience will become more user friendly, providing graphical presentation of all opinions and interpretations in a clear and comparable manner.

Keywords-semantic web; social networks; 3d; information visualisation; knowledge management

I. INTRODUCTION

We live in the Information Era, where knowledge is everything and everywhere. The proper management of knowledge presupposes the existence of mechanisms for organising information, in order to match the appropriate pieces together. When the Internet came along, it offered users the ability of having access to many different types of electronic data. Unfortunately, these data are still mostly uncategorised and the human mind simply cannot absorb and process the increasingly huge amount of information available. This is the reason why computers are utilised to gather and present information in a more streamlined manner, so that people are able to browse through the findings in a faster and more efficient way.

XML and all the technologies that are based on it, like the Semantic Web [1], provide the facilities for electronic devices, even of a different nature, to communicate with each other and exchange data in a commonly acceptable way. This is really useful, especially when it comes to making machines responsible for information gathering and the delivery of coherent results which a human can understand and rely upon. The Semantic Web is already trying to organise information into standardised structures called Ontologies [2]. This will gradually create a common ground for all topics, making information sharing easier and more automated.

Social Networks can benefit from the use of Semantic Ontologies to improve their simple, yet unsophisticated, method of tagging which is based on keywords rather than logical concepts. Adding Semantics may require more time than plain old word tagging, but the long-term gains can prove to be profitable in the quality of search results and in data categorisation.

With the number of 3D-based virtual communities increasing every day, both for Social and Gaming worlds, combining all the aforementioned technologies can result into a powerful online tool which will offer ease of use and meaningful search results [3].

II. BACKGROUND AND RELATED WORK

At the original proposal of the World Wide Web in 1989 [4], most could not predict that it would become as widespread as it eventually did. Despite initial expectations, the Web has turned into a killer app of the Internet, gradually taking over the roles of other applications like E-mail, Usenet Newsgroups and IRC.

While the number of websites and webpages kept rising, it became impossible for a human to memorise all the available Web addresses or manually search through online data for specific information. That is the reason why Search Engines were invented, aiming to provide faster searching through a large amount of webpages based on requested keywords. After many attempts, and a variety of algorithms for page ranking, new age Search Engines are beginning to adopt the Semantic Ontology model to categorise their data in order to provide faster and more relevant results.

A. Search Engines and the Semantic Web

Computers are programmed by people to respond in a predefined way to specific actions. Artificial intelligence scientists have made several attempts to make computers come up with original ideas but, up to this point, it has not been achieved. Given the fact that computer applications can only follow the rules programmed into them (or the rules that those rules produce), they cannot yet cross the line from computing to improvising.

Since Search Engines are computer applications too, their search results are bound to be calculated and precise, based on mathematical formulae for text searching. This way, results may match the given words or phrases, but the meaning is totally lost. A search for the word "apple" will return many links to webpages and pictures of apple trees, as well as Apple computers, among a lot of other things. Researchers suggest [5] that in the circumstance of the results being too many, users usually go through the first few pages and then either accept what they found as the truth or just give up.

The most practical method to deal with this problem is to help the computer "understand" what each piece of information "means", by using the relations between interconnected objects. The Semantic Web project is trying to address this issue by grouping information into Ontologies, which are logically organised datasets, a formal and well defined version of Taxonomies [6]. This means a user could specifically search for the fruit called apple, retrieving more relevant results. A few Semantic Web based Search Engines already exist [7, 8].

Computer users have grown accustomed to the habit of text search engines where they must type in keywords which they believe are related to their search. Those keywords are then matched to the index of the engine by using proprietary algorithms and a result list is produced, usually ordered by relevance or link popularity.

Semantic Web based search engines are trying to redefine this procedure. They may still be asking the user to type in text but they match those keywords to ontology items thus making results more logically relevant, rather than just plain keyword relevance [9]. This is feasible because ontologies organise items based on logical connections derived from the item meaning.

As time passes, ontology standardisation will play an increasingly significant role in information categorisation and exchange. Scientists will be able to compare their research with others faster and in great detail due to the specific nature of ontology definitions. All individuals can benefit from the advantages of Semantic annotation, for example while searching for music that sounds like their favourite band or for a movie to watch based on which films they have enjoyed so far [10]. It is only a matter of presenting the idea of well-organised data to the Social Web communities in a useful and inviting way.

B. The Power of Social Networks

Soon after the Web became available to the public in the early 1990s, many users became interested into creating their own personal website to present themselves, their businesses or their interests. Certain companies begun giving away size-limited Web space for free on their servers and in exchange they placed advertisements on top of each webpage. This way, Web "citizens" began interacting with each other, linking their websites, exchanging virtual "awards" and comments in electronic "guestbooks", as well as publishing their personal thoughts, ideas, pictures or even poems and passages. Separated from the commercial websites, the personal websites had a life of their own, either organised in communities or independently posting articles and news of interest to this new "global village".

Near the end of the 1990s, users started calling their personal websites "blogs", a contraction of the words "Web" and "log", leading to the creation of a new trend in the Web culture [11]. This eventually lead to the creation of the first "online social networks" in the early 2000s, a term also popularised as "Web 2.0" by Tim O'Reilly of O'Reilly Media [12]. Social networks reused all the well-known technologies of the Web but, instead of offering free Web space, they prompted users to upload all their information and material inside a standardised personal profile page.

Friendster, MySpace, Facebook, LinkedIn and other well known Social Web giants became increasingly popular because they responded to the need of people to keep in touch with their friends or acquaintances and participate into activities together, like groups or games. Many companies, like YouTube, Flickr, Delicious and others, followed the Social paradigm by adding mechanisms to increase community participation and cooperation.

What all of the above websites have in common is that they categorise their data by using Folksonomies. This term was coined up around 2004 [13] from the words folks and taxonomy and basically defines the method of using keywords to describe the content of a data object. Blog articles, images, video and sound files stored all over the Web have been annotated using the words that uploaders chose to describe their data. Those words might or might not be related to the content, depending on the perception (or mood) of each uploader. It may be an extremely fast way to annotate data but, due to the lack of standards, many tags are vague, misspelled or simply wrong.

When the Social Web eventually merges with the Semantic Web, the users will be the first to benefit because, after the Semantics have been agreed upon, data sharing will be seamless and instant. It may take longer to annotate data than plain old keywords, but visualisation techniques can be used to speed up the process.

C. 3D Environments and Virtual Worlds

With the rise of the computer age in mid 20th century, every type of business tried to get the best out of the new technological achievements. Even though at first computers only had text command interfaces, they eventually became able to present graphics. These graphics were initially plain, but as computer capabilities increased, so did the complexity of the designs.

The computer game industry has taken advantage of 3D graphics and moved from classic point-and-click games to 3D gaming. From first-person shooters to massively multiplayer online role-playing games, 3D graphics improve the gaming experience by offering a more realistic gameplay to the users.

With the Social Networking niche in mind, companies decided to combine 3D gaming environments with online communities, such as Second Life, Active Worlds and IMVU, among others. These programs, though, require the users to download extra Windows applications, which execute separately from the Web browser in order to access the 3D environment. This fact not only prevents application mobility but also isolates the actual program from the Web realm, leaving only the account management on the company website.

A notable attempt to combine browser based 3D graphics with a Social Network was Google "Lively", which was launched, popularised and shut down in 2008. Lively used Flash, as well as a proprietary plug-in, in order to execute inside the browser and the final result was a fully in-browser 3D experience. Despite its initial success, Google decided to discontinue "Lively" shortly after its inauguration to focus more on their core search [14]. A similar Flash application called "Smeet" still exists, created by a German company.

As far as 3D search engines are concerned, there have only been a few attempts. In 2005, a company called "INOZON" announced [15] that they would be creating the first 3D based search engine, running inside a browser, but eventually the project fell apart. Another example was "Ergo" by Invu, launched as beta in 2007, running in an application outside the browser, offering a visual environment for searching information [16].

Although all these attempts are recent, a Web language to express 3D graphics started to be formed as early as 1994 and was called VRML (Virtual Reality Modelling Language). Since that time, it managed to become a standard and reached version 2.0, before being succeeded by X3D.

X3D is an XML based language which aims to popularise a file format to display 3D graphics by using XML syntax [17]. This makes 3D graphics ideal to parse and present inside browsers or to use with any type of XML related API. At this moment, though, X3D is not widely used and its commercial utilisation is limited. Also, Web browsers require extra add-ons to display the X3D environment. Being standardised with HTML5, the latest version of HTML, will help this format to gradually gain more recognition, while the X3DOM [18] project is already trying to bypass the need of a plug-in.

HTML5 will also bring instant embedded support of WebGL, a language based on JavaScript which offers in-browser interactive 3D graphics, as well as CSS3 which will also offer 3D transformations. The basic aim of HTML5 is to be able to run in all types of devices and support the creation of Web applications without the need of extra plug-ins. This will bring the Web to an entirely new level.

III. THE FUTURE WEB: SOCIAL, SEMANTIC AND 3D

What the Web needs now is a new idea, to make users feel that all these advancements can indeed improve the current status quo.

Introducing 3D visualisation techniques to the Social Web would be a start but by itself it would only appear like a "cool" looking improvement of the graphics. There has to be essential change in the way we perceive data annotation and information acquisition. The Social community is a power strong enough to fill websites with a plethora of multimedia files gathered in many different ways. The users only need to become accustomed to a new method of tagging data, in order to make them part of a Semantic Ontology.

This is why we propose the creation of a system that will have the properties of the Social Web, but with a 3D Web interface on top and a Semantic Ontology behind it. It will be a new age Web application, merging the aforementioned technologies into a 3D Social community, which will constantly be improving an underlying, unlimited, Semantic Ontology.

A. Creating an Information Driven Community

The proposed system will have a search engine which will not only check indexed keywords for similarities to a given input, but will also classify data to specific categories of an unlimited catalogue. This catalogue will be created gradually as users add new multimedia objects or change the already existing ones. Some organisations, such as Wikipedia, Dmoz or Open Source Software communities, have managed to maintain quite a high level of data quality, even though they are not always edited by professionals, but by earnest individuals who dedicate their time to adding and correcting the website material.

The users of this system will enjoy the advantages of a 3D Social community, such as 3D avatars and personalised virtual "lounges", and at the same time will contribute to the creation of an infinite and global source of knowledge. This way, not only they will be able to participate into Social Networking activities but they will also play an important role into rating the quality of the information available in the system by voting up or down additions and changes based on the correctness of the submission.

This participation will make the Web community more active and raise awareness against spam and phishing attempts because data will be immediately comparable due to the nature of ontology objects. Users will be required to make all changes and additions using their real name which will radically reduce the cases of "trolling" (i.e. uploading inflammatory or off-topic data).

Using an overall reputation based scheme, the level of user access to the system will be altered depending on how their additions and changes are ranked. Thus, material which contains mistakes or is miscategorised will be voted down and gradually replaced by correct ones, while at the same time the overall reputation status of the uploader will decrease, restricting their access to website features.

B. Making Data Management User Friendly

The most interesting factor of the system is that the users do not have to possess any type of Semantic Web or XML knowledge in order to use it. The 3D Web interface will help them to add, change or search for specific website objects by creating new compositions. In order to manage or look for data, users will select 3D objects and connect them to each other, thus graphically compose what they are adding or seeking.

An example connection of three objects is presented in Figure 1. More specifically it has been composed to look for a "Person" who is working for a "Business" in a specific "Location".

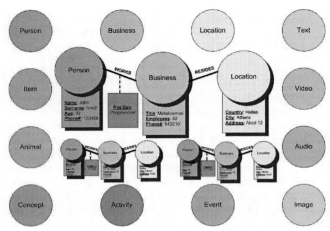

Figure 1. Draft layout of a query in a custom user interface.

We call this method "Semantic Synthesis", from the Hellenic word "synthesis" which means "composition". It is interesting to note that the term "Semantic Synthesis" was initially used by Igor' Mel'cuk in 1965 [19], for his Meaning Text Theory which was the suggestion of linking words of different languages together, based on their meaning (i.e. semantically). In our system the objects will be semantically connected to compose (synthesise) specific queries or additions. The associations between the objects will be assigned roles, based on a list of supported role objects for each relation.

In addition to the connection roles, extra information may be provided for each selected item, in a menu offering a choice of specific properties available for each object. As soon as the query or addition has been synthesised, there will be an option to either add it or search for it. Figure 1 also shows possible search results below the synthesised query.

The positive factor of showing results this way is that they can be selected and then further explored with additional queries. Specifically designed mechanisms will help the user quickly shift through the results. Some are currently being evaluated based on their performance for a variety of different queries. The whole search experience must be fast and always produce relevant results which means that the total time spent and the quality of the results are the most important factors.

To create these mechanisms, information must be viewed not only as words and phrases, but as objects which are all parts of the same unified system. That is where the 3D Web interface will come in handy, to give users a look and feel of actually connecting objects.

Ultimately, the user may search through the information provided by our system and then explore links to external websites for extra references, such as images, videos and additional, not yet stored, material.

C. Social Semantics Drawbacks

Web citizens have been tagging online data sources for many years now. Apart from the obvious powerful virtual workforce of collective intelligence they comprise [20, 21], there are also certain negative aspects to it. The current drawbacks of Social Semantics are summed up by three basic factors of human nature: responsibility, credibility and objectivity.

When people publish data on the Internet, they do not always take the time to label and organise them based on the existing standards for each category, thus making their meaning vague for a computer. This lack of responsibility can be avoided by utilising predefined methods for adding and manipulating objects so that they carry at least some basic annotation, which will be aided by using visual objects and Semantic Synthesis.

Even if this problem is surpassed, no one can guarantee that the categories and relations the user has selected are appropriate for that object, because not everyone is a field expert on everything they post online. That is why users will have the ability of voting additions up or down, which will affect the overall reputation of the uploader appropriately.

Finally, the biggest problem of all is objectivity. Even for an organised consortium of scientists and field experts it would be difficult to agree on a common methodology for characterising every possible piece of information. The only way to prevent the debates from reaching a total deadlock is to try and present all opinions in a very specific and comparable way, so that each researcher can then determine what applies to their specific case.

Philosophy and Sociology will play an important role in the definition of most data categories (e.g. ideas and concepts) which are unsubstantial by nature. Gradually, all views and suggestions will be synthesised and depicted, allowing users and researchers to compare them side by side in a more streamlined manner.

IV. METAKOSMOS

All of the above will be joined together in a system called "Metakosmos", from the Hellenic words "meta", which means "after", and "kosmos", which means "world" or "universe". The name reflects the ultimate purpose of the system, which is to create a graphical virtual world of organised information about the entire real world.

A. Social Knowledge Management

Metakosmos will be a 3D Social Web community that will store its information by taking advantage of Semantic Web Ontologies. The system will have two types of users: unregistered (visitors) and registered (members). Visitors will only be allowed to use the search engine, without being able to adjust the user interface or participate to the addition, categorisation or correction of data. Members will be able to use the website to its full extend.

Additionally, the members will be able to edit their user interface on the website by choosing which items should appear at their home screen, also known as their "lounge". They will select those items by searching through the available categories offered by the website or by adding new ones. They will also be able to add new items to the system, rearrange existing data or even correct mistakes that may exist such as, for example, object miscategorisation or misspelling.

Collecting consistent data is essential for any search engine, especially for one that needs to store them inside an ontology. Members will have to correctly synthesise the data, based on their understanding, in order to add them to the system in the appropriate categories. Other members with better understanding or expertise on a domain will be able to suggest corrections, if needed.

Members that offer a lot to the website, either by adding new material or by correcting existing items, will receive an increased reputation status which will allow them to influence the system faster. Clearly, members that do not cooperate respectfully will receive a decrease of their reputation status, giving them less and less access in influencing the system.

All the user interaction will bring out the social aspect of the system, uniting the members under the common cause of keeping everything organised and as accurate as possible. The additions or changes which are well defined and correctly categorised will be voted up by the members, thus increasing the overall reputation status of the person who synthesised them. In contrast to this, constant mistakes and sloppiness will cause members to vote items down, decreasing the reputation of the person responsible.

Five reputation levels will be used: Ignored (0%), Trainee (25%), Notable (50%), Popular (75%) and Perfect (100%). Newly registered users will start as Trainees and then, depending on how well they adjust, their reputation will increase or drop. If their additions or changes are constantly voted down they will eventually reach the Ignored status which would mean that their new additions will be automatically pre-voted down and they will also be unable to make any changes to the system.

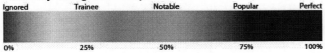

Figure 2.   The five suggested reputation levels.

The Metakosmos system will aim to provide simplicity to all users, whether they are technology amateurs or experts, as well as offer scalable complexity based on customisable options, while maintaining the same effective search experience despite of the settings.

B.   Synthesising, Integrating and Sharing

By reintroducing the term of "Semantic Synthesis", users will be called to select predefined objects, connect them in a way they consider meaningful, add literal parameter information and finally search for matching results stored in the system. Additionally, registered members will be able to synthesise additions or any needed changes to the system. All of the syntheses will be Semantic Web based, even though the website users will only see the 3D visualisation representation.

Metakosmos will aim to set certain standards which other developers will be able to follow so as to interact externally with the system or to implement additional capabilities for the user interface. Currently set as future work, is creating the mechanisms to integrate Semantic Syntheses from other

websites, as well as to share local syntheses with external Web applications by exporting them in an appropriate form.

As time passes, more and more websites will appreciate the advantages of using Semantic Ontologies, making data sharing and integration simpler and instant. Semantic annotation will gradually replace the keyword cloud tagging of Folksonomies, allowing increased access to data of all types and formats.

C.   Adding a 3D User Interface

In order to make Semantic annotation easier and more straightforward, 3D visualisation elements will be used to depict the various Semantic objects that comprise each synthesis. Usability will be an important factor of this new age 3D community, in order for it to get accepted by the general public and integrated into everyday life. It has to combine simplicity with scalable complexity, based on custom options, while maintaining the same effective search experience for all users.

To achieve this, an extra layer of graphics is added on top of text searching, making search queries visually accurate and, as a result, retrieving more relevant search results. With the help of the underlying Semantic Web ontology, as well as with the introduction of 3D graphics, users will be able to query content both textually and visually, depending on their personal preferences and the nature of their search. This way, they will be able to retrieve highly relevant results, which can be presented in many different forms.

With the upcoming official arrival of HTML5 [22] and the constantly increasing improvements of Web 3D graphics like X3D, X3DOM, WebGL and CSS3, the Metakosmos system will obtain its final form and gain its place among the first 3D Social Web communities, while at the same time participate in the storing and categorisation of global knowledge on a large scale.

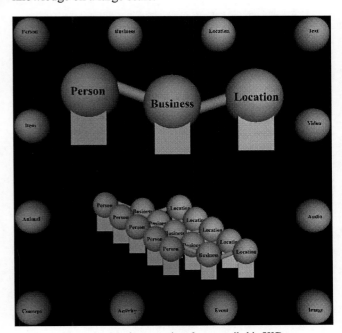

Figure 3.   Mock-up user interface compiled in X3D.

V. Conclusions and Future Work

When the Metakosmos PhD thesis is complete, the first prototype will be launched online in order to offer users a preliminary beta testing of the system.

The initial version will be a visually searchable and updatable catalogue which will aim to produce useful and relevant results as quickly and as accurately as possible. This means minimising unsolicited advertisements, preventing misinformation and yet presenting all possible views of each subject, both concisely and thoroughly, based on the personal preferences each user sets. Gradually, more and more users and websites will be able to create and exchange their information syntheses and come up with ways to merge and unify new and old data as efficiently as possible.

Eventually, new functionalities will be added to the system which will give members increased access in affecting their user interface themes, thus making searching and editing further adjustable. Additionally, Web Services will be launched to make information integration and sharing more automated for external applications.

The merging of the Social Web with the Semantic Web is an inevitable advancement which will lead to increased information organisation and universally useful data mining. The addition of the 3D Web interface on top of the ontology management mechanisms provides an extra level of simplicity in order to make the experience more user-friendly. Although keyword search will be also available, the proposed visual search environment is only a glimpse of what the future of the Web holds.

REFERENCES

[1] T. Berners-Lee, J. Hendler, and O. Lassila, "The Semantic Web," Scientific American, May 2001, pp. 34-43.

[2] H.P. Alesso and C.F. Smith, Thinking on the Web: Berners-Lee, Gödel, and Turing, John Wiley & Sons, 2006, pp. 16.

[3] V. Geroimenko and C. Chen, Visualizing the Semantic Web: XML-based Internet and information visualization, Springer, 2006, pp 3-18.

[4] World Wide Web CERN Proposal: http://www.w3.org/History/1989/proposal.html.

[5] iProspect, "Search Engine User Attitudes," May 2004; http://www.iprospect.com/premiumPDFs/iProspectSurveyComplete.pdf, Accessed: 1 February 2011.

[6] W. Pidcock and M. Uschold, "What are the differences between a vocabulary, a taxonomy, a thesaurus, an ontology, and a meta-model?," 2003; http://www.metamodel.com/article.php?story=20030115211223271, Accessed: 1 February 2011.

[7] Swoogle: http://swoogle.umbc.edu/.

[8] Hakia: http://www.hakia.com/.

[9] D. Li, et al., "Swoogle: a search and metadata engine for the semantic web," ACM, 2004.

[10] Jinni: http://www.jinni.com/.

[11] J. Wortham, "After 10 Years of Blogs, the Future's Brighter Than Ever," 2007; http://www.wired.com/entertainment/theweb/news/2007/12/blog_anniversary, Accessed: 1 February 2011.

[12] T. O'Reilly, "What Is Web 2.0 - Design Patterns and Business Models for the Next Generation of Software," 2005; http://www.oreillynet.com/pub/a/oreilly/tim/news/2005/09/30/what-is-web-20.html, Accessed: 1 February 2011.

[13] Folksonomy: http://vanderwal.net/folksonomy.html, Accessed: 1 February 2011.

[14] Lively: http://googleblog.blogspot.com/2008/11/lively-no-more.html, Accessed: 1 February 2011.

[15] INOZON: http://www.prweb.com/releases/2005/02/prweb211778.htm, Accessed: 1 February 2011.

[16] Ergo: http://www.yourergo.com/help.php, Accessed: 10 May 2009.

[17] V. Geroimenko and C. Chen, Visualizing information using SVG and X3D: XML-based technologies for the XML-based Web, Springer, 2005, pp. 3-20.

[18] X3DOM: http://www.x3dom.org/.

[19] A.K. Zolkovskij and I.A. Mel'cuk, "O vozmoznom metode i instrumentax semanticeskogo sinteza [On a possible method and instruments for semantic synthesis (of Texts)]," Nauchno-texnicheskaja informacija, vol. 1, no. 6, 1965, pp. 23-28.

[20] H. Halpin, V. Robu, and H. Shepherd, "The complex dynamics of collaborative tagging," ACM, 2007.

[21] V. Robu, H. Halpin, H. Shepherd, "Emergence of consensus and shared vocabularies in collaborative tagging systems," ACM Trans. Web, vol. 3, no. 4, 2009.

[22] HTML5: http://dev.w3.org/html5/spec/.

The Fractal Perspective Visualization Technique for Semantic Networks

Curran Kelleher, Georges Grinstein
University of Massachusetts Lowell
{ckellehe@cs.uml.edu, grinstein@cs.uml.edu}

Abstract

We introduce a novel interactive visualization technique for semantic networks supporting continuous semantic graph browsing. Our visual semantic graph representation is a nested object visualization representing a view into the graph from a node's viewpoint. In this view, panning and zooming interactions drive graph traversal. We call the visualization technique Fractal Perspective, because it has approximate fractal structure (self similarity at multiple scales) and represents a kind of "perspective projection" from graph space to display space in which distant objects (in graph space) appear smaller (in a dynamic display space). This is work in progress, and this paper should be considered primarily a concept paper with a brief description of a very early prototype harnessing multi-touch interaction.

1. Introduction

We address the problem of visually representing a semantic graph such that the graph is intuitively and efficiently browsable. One is tempted to imagine that the semantic graph data structure and related reasoning algorithms may partially approximate the way humans store memories and think. If this is even remotely true, an interactive visual tool representing semantic graphs offering intuitive interactions for data navigation (and ideally creation and manipulation as well) could serve as a revolutionary information recording, manipulation and communication technology.

Static visual representations of trees and graphs exist, as well as standards for representing semantic graphs, but these areas have not yet been combined to form a semantic graph browsing tool based on interactive data visualization concepts. There are some examples of dynamic representations in limited environments with an underlying semantic framework (see thebrain.com for example). However the semantic graph data structure, and thus the Semantic Web, still lacks a compelling and usable visual interface for data navigation, manipulation and creation. Were one created, it may serve as a catalyst for the adoption of the Semantic Web as a mainstream technology for personal and organizational information management, visualization and analysis.

We see the task of building visual interfaces for the Semantic Web as a significant step toward achieving several grand challenges, namely enabling memories for life, lifelong learning environments, and cognitive partners for humans. To this end, we propose a novel visualization technique for semantic graphs we call Fractal Perspective as a first stab at the problem.

2. Related Work

Our work combines elements of tree visualization and graph visualization. TreeMaps, introduced by Ben Shneiderman in [1], are visual representations of hierarchies whose nodes have associated numeric values. In a TreeMap, packed squares represent nodes, and color represents their associated numeric values. The Voronoi TreeMap, introduced by Balzer et. al. in [2], is a TreeMap variant where nodes are visually decomposed into Voronoi tessellations rather than packed squares. Circular TreeMaps have also been introduced by Wetzel [4], in which circles are the nesting unit.

Labeling of nodes in a TreeMap is only possible when overlaying the label to summarize a region (see Figure 1), or when enough padding is added such that labels can fit within the padding and be associated unambiguously with a particular node. Sometimes only the leaf nodes are visible in a TreeMap, but padding can be added to make all intermediate nodes visible. For our application, we prefer a nested object visualization technique which both allows unambiguous labeling and coloring of all intermediate nodes. As illustrated in Figure 2, the Circular TreeMap seems more amenable to unambiguous labeling and all-node coloring than the TreeMap or Voronoi TreeMap.

Researchers have produced many radial visual representations of a depth-limited or "node centric" tree view. In these representations, nodes are presented with varying levels of detail based on their distance from the root node, providing an effective focus plus context visualization. Interactive systems employing these visualizations have a browsing state which defines a particular node to be the root of the visualization at any given time. The mutability of this state via user interaction is the key element which enables interactive browsing of trees using these visualizations.

1550-6037/11 $26.00 © 2011 IEEE
DOI 10.1109/IV.2011.107

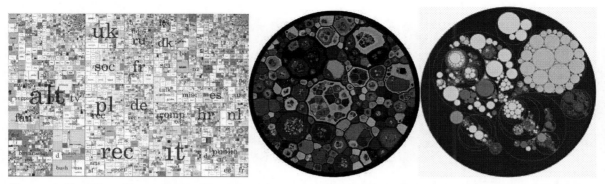

Figure 1. TreeMap, Voronoi TreeMap and Circular TreeMap. Images left to right from [3],[2] and [4].

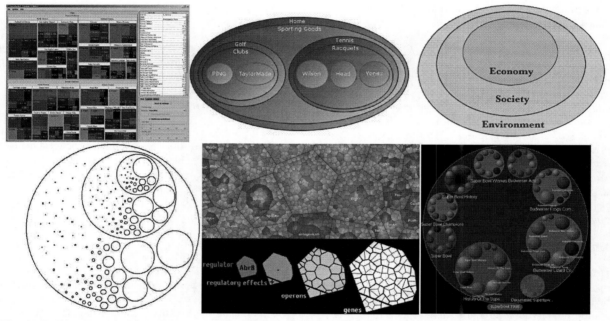

Figure 2. TreeMaps and variants used on semantic data spaces. Images left to right from (top) [1],[5],[6] (bottom) [9] – a Circular TreeMap visualization of Wikipedia structure,[8] – a Voronoi TreeMap gene ontology visualization, and [7] – a federated content search result viewer using nested circles.

Semantic graphs are directed graphs with labeled nodes and edges. Resource Description Framework (RDF) is a flexible data model for federated knowledge representation based on the semantic graph data structure. RDF is the foundation of the Semantic Web, Tim Berners Lee's vision for a global web interlinking data, computational agents and people, also called the "Network of Linked Data" or the "Giant Global Graph".

When confronted with the problem of visualizing semantic graphs, typically labeled node-link diagrams are used, with the distinction between Resources (object nodes) and Literals (data nodes) visually encoded (as in Figure 4). This approach does not scale, because as the size of the graph increases the size of the nodes and labels decreases, leading to unreadable visualizations.

We found only a few applications of visualization techniques to semantic data spaces in general. We were particularly impressed by the clear legend of Jörg

Bernhardt [8](center of figure 2) depicting four hierarchical levels of a gene ontology including regulators, regulatory effects, operons and genes, with summary labels at the regulator level. Cartographic map navigation has many often noted advantages over other visualizations, the primary advantage being that it involves multi-scale generalization - including details appropriate to the scale at which the space is viewed. Panning and zooming over cartographic maps are the only two interactions necessary to explore the entire vast space represented by a multi-scale cartographic map. These interactions are made extremely intuitive by the (now conventional) multi-touch interactions of pinch zooming and drag panning. The addition of inertial processors to the multi-touch panning and zooming interaction make it even more instinctive (arguably because as humans we are used to manipulating masses with inertia).

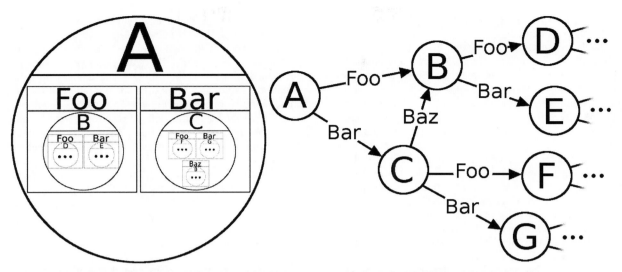

Figure 3. Fractal Perspective (left) and the corresponding node-link representation (right).

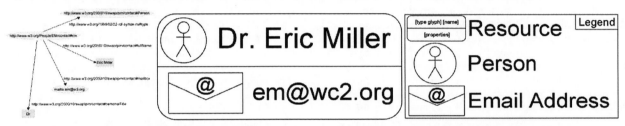

Figure 4. An example ontology-specific visual language we'd like to enable users to define using the Fractal Perspective concept. The left image is a node link RDF visualization taken from [12]. On the right is a mock up visual language based on the Fractal Perspective concept which uses domain specific visual encodings to unambiguously and compactly visualize the same information represented in the node link diagram on the left.

2. Our Contribution

Our aim with this work is to apply the intuitive multi-scale navigation techniques used by interactive (particularly multi-touch) cartographic maps to the task of browsing a semantic graph. We also plan to apply this technique to browsing data cube structures. Though interactive navigation of hierarchical data cube dimensions was our original intent for this work, we address instead the problem of visually navigating semantic graphs because it has became clear in our research that the data cube structure itself can be represented within a semantic graph [10], and so solving the semantic graph navigation problem with sufficient flexibility implicitly solves the data cube navigation problem (or so we believe at this time).

We introduce a novel mapping between the data structure resulting from a rooted depth-limited semantic graph traversal and a nested object visualization. In our proposed interactive system, there is a mutable browsing state which consists of the root node for the visualization, a scaling factor (zoom), and a translation vector (pan). Multi-touch zooming and panning interactions affect the scaling and translation components of the browsing state while viewing children of a certain

node. When the user zooms into a particular node so far that no part of the enclosing node is visible, the root of the browsing state changes to the newly focused node. At this point, a transformation of the scaling and translation components occurs such that the new browsing state results in the same visualization as the old one, just with a new root node (the scale and translation are projected from the space of the outer node to the space of the inner node). In this way, we establish an equivalence between browsing a multi-scale 2D space and browsing a semantic graph.

In Figure 6, circles represent windows through nodes, squares represent windows through edges, and ellipsis (...) represent nodes which have the potential for expansion. Nodes below a certain size threshold are left unevaluated, and are evaluated when the user zooms in on them (during retrieval, a progress animation is displayed in place of the ellipsis). In our proposed system, a force directed layout algorithm acts on the children of each node independently. Layout occurs on each set of child nodes independently, and the layouts of multiple child sets are combined during rendering using object containment.

2.2 Visual Languages for the Semantic Web

The basic specification of our Fractal Perspective visualization technique deliberately leaves out the details of how nodes and edges be represented visually. The only requirement is nesting. We view the visual language used in Figure 3 to be one of an infinite sea of potential visual languages for representing semantic graphs using the Fractal Perspective concept mapping connection to containment. Some of these may use explicit graphical objects for representing edges, some may express the edge label via some visual aspect of the node pointed to by that edge. We hope to enable the refinement of ontology-specific visual languages which have particular visual representations for particular ontology classes, properties and literals. For example, the fact that a Resource is of type Person could be represented by placing a stick figure next to the name of a node (as in Figure 4). As another example, an envelope glyph could be used to represent a person's email rather than a box labeled "Email". In Figure 4, the image on the left represents the traditional node-link semantic graph visualization technique used in [12]. The images to the right represent an ontology-specific visual language for describing people; a compact visual representation of the same semantic graph represented in the left side image.

In our proposed system, a visual language in which labeled circles represent nodes and labeled squares represent edges is taken to be the default. This is generic and can represent any semantic graph. We hope to enable users to progressively define ontology-specific visual languages by annotating each class and property with information specifying how to encode them visually. For a given class or property, the following can be specified: how is the label derived (e.g. from a class property, from a regex on the URI)? What shape should be used to represent a class or property instance? How should that shape be styled (color, texture)? What class properties drive which visual channels, if any?

We hope the rough conceptualization presented here can eventually lead to the formulation of a kind of "Grammar of Semantic Network Visualizations" built upon concepts from Wilkinson's Grammar of Graphics, Bertin's Semiology of Graphics, and the Semantic Web. A statement in such a grammar would be a formal version of the kind of legend shown in figure 4, describing exactly how elements in the semantic graph map to visual representations.

It is worth noting that our proposed visualization technique enables dynamic visualization of incremental (edge-by-edge) data requests. As more data is retrieved, the details of the visualization are filled in. This approach fits perfectly with the Linked Data paradigm [11] in which each node is identified by a URL, and outgoing edges for that node are retrieved in a group by accessing ("dereferencing") that URL. Our proposed system could enable navigation of Linked Data in a fluid manner in which requests can be literally seen coming in, causing incremental nested refinement of the visualization.

Our belief is that once ontology-specific visual languages are defined, Linked Data can be traversed and comprehended with ease by the masses using our technique. We plan to develop a prototype implementation for mobile multi-touch devices utilizing intuitive gestures for pan and zoom. We imagine that the more familiar one becomes with the various ontology-specific visual languages defined, the more quickly one is able to mentally register the semantic structure - the real meaning and implications - of the data encoded in the visualization. Our hope is that eventually, this technique will be used by many to communicate complex webs of meaning more effectively than existing techniques such as plain text, tree maps or node-link diagrams.

3. Future Directions

One disadvantage of our nested object approach is that nodes reachable by more than one path are represented more than once on the display. For example, node "B" is displayed twice in Figure 3: once within node "A" and once within node "C". In future work, we hope to address this issue by introducing visual elements which express equivalence between multiple representations of the same node by drawing a visual connecting element, and also perhaps to apply attractive forces which pull those nodes together to reduce clutter.

Imagine a physical setting in which several multi-touch tablets are arranged on tables surrounding a large high resolution display. On each tablet imagine a nested object view representing a window into a depth-limited graph neighborhood navigable via multi-touch panning and zooming. On the large display imagine a node-link diagram of the full graph, with a distortion bubble surrounding the locations of each nested object viewpoint. This would allow all nodes and edges seen by each viewer to also be seen by all in the room on the large display. At the same time, nodes outside the view of any user would be shrunk or represented by aggregate nodes on the large display. Each local nested object visualization is isomorphic to the contents of the distortion bubble surrounding its viewpoint represented in the node-link visualization. This is one potential direction we are considering, which would enable real time collaborative exploration of massive semantic graphs.

We would also like to explore how a system using this visualization technique can be built in which a small multi-touch device (such as an iPad) is used as a controller for a much larger display (such as a powerwall) showing the same view into the graph. In this scenario, the two devices must maintain a synchronized browsing state. The smaller device will only be able to display a few nesting levels, while the large display will look exactly the same as the small display, except that the smallest nodes in the small display could be filled in with several additional nested levels of detail.

4. Conclusion

We present the conceptual formulation of a novel visualization technique using nested graphical objects to facilitate visualization and navigation of semantic graphs. In the nested object view, some objects represent nodes and some represent edges, and each type of object is communicated using a clear visual encoding. We hope to evolve this work to enable user definable ontology-specific visual languages. Our approach has the disadvantage that nodes reachable via distinct paths are represented more than once in the display. We frame this work as a step toward building intuitive visual interfaces for the Semantic Web, which we see as ultimately a step toward achieving the grand challenges of enabling memories for life, lifelong learning environments, and cognitive partners for humans.

References

[1]   Schneiderman et al. "Treemaps for space-constrained visualization of hierarchies". url: www.cs.umd.edu/hcil/treemap-history/

[2]   M. Balzer, O. Deussen. "Voronoi Treemaps". IEEE Symposium on Information Visualization (InfoVis), 2005

[3]   Treemap View of 2004 Usenet Returnees url: scimaps.org/maps/map/treemap_view_of_2004_57/

[4]   K. Wetzel. "Pebbles - using Circular Treemaps to visualize disk usage". url: http://lip.sourceforge.net/ctreemap.html

[5]   Using the Nested Set Data Model for Breadcrumb Links. Jason Mauss. 2005. url: http://www.developer.com/db/article.php/3517366/Using-the-Nested-Set-Data-Model-for-Breadcrumb-Links.htm

[6]   Wikipedia contributors. "Sustainability." Wikipedia, The Free Encyclopedia. 21 Mar. 2011.

[7]   Rivadeneira, W., & Bederson, B. (2003). A study of search result clustering interfaces: Comparing textual and zoomable user interfaces. url: http://www.infostrategist.com/NavOpenSourceWeb/Oceania04_Images.html

[8]   Jörg Bernhardt; Henry Mehlan; Julia Schüler; Michael Hecker. "Ontology Maps" (E.M.A.-University Greifswald, Institute for Microbiology; Jahnstrasse15;17487 Greifswald; Germany)

[9]   Lizorkin, Medelyan, Grineva. "Analysis of Community Structure in Wikipedia" (Poster). 18th International World Wide Web Conference. 2009.

[10]   Richard Cyganiak, Dave Reynolds, Jeni Tennison. "The RDF Data Cube vocabulary". url: publishing-statistical-data.googlecode.com/svn/trunk/specs/src/main/html/cube.html

[11]   Tim Berners-Lee. "Linked Data". 2006-2009. url: www.w3.org/DesignIssues/LinkedData.html

[12]   Frank Manola, Eric Miller, "RDF Primer". Web resource, url: www.w3.org/TR/rdf-syntax/

Linguistic analysis of genomic islands revealed recent acquisition of genetic materials by *Mycobacterium tuberculosis* from alpha-Proteobacteria

Oleg N. Reva, Oliver Bezuidt

Bioinformatics and Computational Biology Unit, Biochemistry Department, University of Pretoria, Lynnwood Rd., Hillcrest, Pretoria 0002, South Africa.

Abstract

Important genes may flux among bacteria by horizontal transfer and trigger substantial evolutionary changes. Novel genome linguistic and visualization approaches helped to identify genomic islands in Mycobacterium tuberculosis *and trace their origin down to alpha-Proteobacteria. The identified genomic islands are distinctive from prophage inserts common for Mycobacteria. Donor-recipient relationships were visualized for the analysis on a two-dimensional map. A database of genomic islands found in bacterial chromosomes has been created and it is freely available on-line at http://anjie.bi.up.ac.za/geidb/geidb-home.php.*

Keywords: genome linguistics, mobile genetic element visualization, Mycobacterium tuberculosis.

1. Introduction

DNA fragments encoding functional enzymes, transcriptional regulators and virulence factors are fluxing through the bacterial taxonomic walls. They endow environmental and clinical strains of bacteria with new unexpected properties. Lateral genetic exchange, particularly of drug tolerance genes has been recognized for a long time; however the ontology of genomic islands and their donor-recipient relations remain generally obscure because of methodological problems. Horizontally transferred genes are highly mutable and the mobilome entities having been inserted into host chromosomes undergo multiple events of fragmentation, partial duplications and deletions. Prediction of insertion sites in host chromosomes also remains to be a challenge.

This work demonstrates the applicability of genome linguistics methods to study and visualize intrinsic relationships between mobile genetic elements in bacterial genomes. *Mycobacterium tuberculosis*, a bacterial pathogen which is a leading cause of human death worldwide, was selected as a subject for this study. Emergence and evolution of this deadly pathogen are still ambiguous and were not resolved even after comparative studies and sequencing of multiple strains of this genus had been performed.

2. Results

Linguistic methods were applied to study the distribution and relationships of genomic islands (GIs) in available genomes of *Mycobacterium*. Complete genome sequences of organisms used in the study were obtained from the NCBI FTP server (ftp://ftp.ncbi.nih.gov/genomes/Bacteria/). GIs were identified by SeqWord Genomic Island Sniffer (SWGIS available at www.bi.up.ac.za/SeqWord/sniffer/), a tool that detects inserts of foreign DNA in bacterial genomes by comparison of the biased distribution of tetranucleotides in the core genome and accessory elements [1]. Statistical methods implemented in SWGIS are explained in depth in our previous publications [1, 2]. The identified GIs were grouped by their compositional similarity of oligonucleotide usage (OU) patterns (Fig. 1). These were further analyzed by pair-wise blast2seq and blastp methods where the protein encoding genes of GIs were searched against local DNA and protein databases of genes/proteins of all sequenced bacteria, plasmids and phages. The latter was performed to check if the GIs that cluster together share blocks of genes that are in the same order and to also deduce the types of genes that are highly likely transferred across genus or species borders.

Multiple GIs were found in genomes of virulent and environmental species of *Mycobacterium*. These GIs share similarity in both sequence and OU pattern (Fig. 1). An exception was *M. leprae* whose genomic islands did not share any similarity with GIs of other Mycobacteria (data not shown but check http://anjie.bi.up.ac.za/geidb/geidb-home.php). In Fig. 1 GIs identified in *M. tuberculosis*, *M. bovis*, *M. avium*, *M. marinum*, *M. vanbaalenii*, *M. abscessus* and *M. smegmatis* are represented by white nodes and species of other genera by grey nodes. Each node presents one GI referred by NC numbers of the host organism as in the NCBI database followed by colons and reference numbers of GIs as in GEI-DB (http://anjie.bi.up.ac.za/geidb/geidb-home.php) where more information about these GIs is available.

1550-6037/11 $26.00 © 2011 IEEE
DOI 10.1109/IV.2011.18

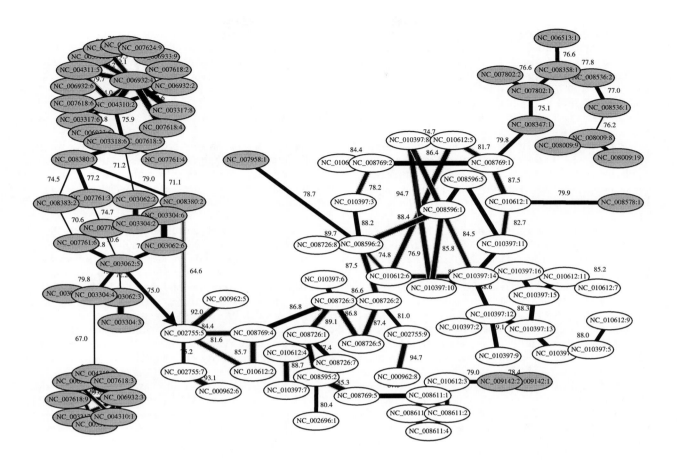

Figure 1 GIs identified in *Mycobacterium* genomes and other organisms share compositional similarity

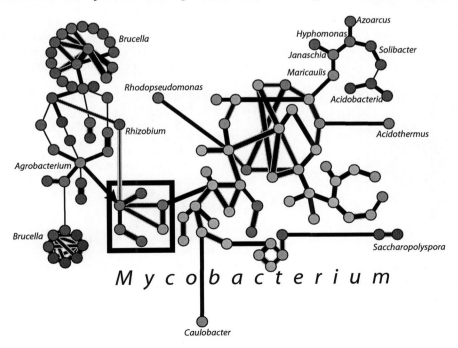

Figure 2 Stratigraphic analysis of GIs

Numbers in Fig. 1 represent compositional similarity indices ranging from 0 (completely dissimilar) to 100 (identical OU patterns) [2]. The edges depicted by borders link GIs which share identical DNA sequences longer than 100 bp identified by blast2seq. The layout was created by an in-house Python program that incorporates executable files of Graphviz 2.26.3 for Windows.

Furthermore, six GIs identified in *M. tuberculosis*, *M. bovis* and *M. marinum* (framed in Fig. 2) showed similarity in both DNA sequence and oligonucleotide composition with the GIs distributed among alpha-Proteobacteria, particularly those of *Rhizobium* and *Agrobacterium*.

To determine the relative time of GI insertions, the similarity in pattern of GIs and their host chromosomes was calculated for all organisms. The results are depicted by grey gradient colors in Fig. 2.

GIs that significantly deviate from their hosts (recent inserts) are dark; and those that underwent genomic amelioration [3] and became more similar to their hosts are light grey. Most mycobacterial GIs are ancient inserts and are shared among different species of *Mycobacteria*. Few of the *M. tuberculosis*, *M. bovis* and *M. marinum* GIs which showed to be in possession of OU patterns similar to *Rhizobium* and *Agrobacterium* GIs are relatively recent acquisitions (framed in Fig. 2). Comparison of the patterns of the GIs and host genomes was revised (Fig. 3). The two large grey circles indicate OU pattern variations in core sequences of the host organisms. OU patterns of genomic islands of *M. tuberculosis* and *A. tumefaciens* (black and white circles respectively) were plotted according to the calculated distances between them and OU patterns of the chromosomes.

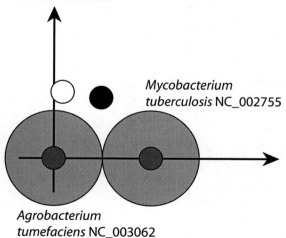

Mycobacterium tuberculosis NC_002755

Agrobacterium tumefaciens NC_003062

Figure 3 Donor-recipient relationships between GIs and host organisms of *Agrobacterium* and *Mycobacterium*.

It was found that mycobacterial GIs are compositionally more similar to *Agrobacterium* chromosome and its mobilomes and that they most likely had originated from this source. Plotting was done by an in-house Python program.

Conclusions

Ancient inserts in mycobacterial genomes were mostly found to be prophages as determined by the analysis of their genes. 43 GIs (unframed in Fig. 2) contain 910 annotated genes among which 386 were hypothetical or unknown. Functional genes are listed in Table 1.

Predominance of phage related genes suggests that these GIs are mostly prophages. Genes that are harbored by the *Mycobacterium* GIs of the alpha-Proteobacteria origin (framed in Fig. 2) encode several transferases, esterases, mmcH proteins and hypothetical proteins organized into operon structures (Fig. 4) which may be involved in the biosynthesis of some yet unknown compounds. In Fig. 4 shaded areas link regions sharing DNA sequence similarity determined by blast2seq. The compared genomes are NC_000962 (*M. tuberculosis* H37Rv); NC_002755 (*M. tuberculosis* CDC1551); NC_008769 (*M. bovis* BCG str. Pasteur 1173P2); and NC_010612 (*M. marinum* M). Numbers that appear after colons are the reference ids of GIs as in the GEI-DB (http://anjie.bi.up.ac.za/geidb/geidb-home.php). Lengths of GIs are also indicated in Fig. 4.

BLASTP search retrieved similar proteins in a great variety of bacterial plasmids and phages with conserved syntenies of genes, particularly in the plasmid pSOL1 from *Clostridium acetobutylicum* ATCC 824. Acquisition of genetic materials from intracellular parasitic and symbiotic species of alpha-Proteobacteria by an ancestral strain of *Mycobacterium* may be an event that had triggered the evolution of former saprophytic organisms towards the parasitic lifestyle.

Table 1 Protein encoding genes in mycobacterial GIs.

Gene categories	*Number of genes*
Phage related proteins, integrases and transposases	91
Dehydrogenases	31
Transcriptional regulator	23
Peptide synthetase and polyketide	13
Membrane proteins	23
Monooxygenase	11
Glycosyl transferases	11
Oxidoreductase	10
Dioxygenase	9
PE-PGRS proteins	7
Esterases	5

Acknowledgements

Funding for this research was provided by the MetaLingvo grant 71261 of the National Research Foundation (NRF) of South Africa.

References

[1]   H. Ganesan, A.S. Rakitianskaia, C.F. Davenport, B. Tümmler and O.N. Reva. The SeqWord Genome Browser: an online tool for the identification and visualization of atypical regions of bacterial genomes through oligonucleotide usage. *BMC Bioinformatics* 2008, 9:333.

[2]   O.N. Reva and B. Tümmler. Global features of sequences of bacterial chromosomes, plasmids and phages revealed by analysis of oligonucleotide usage patterns. *BMC Bioinformatics* 2004, 5:90.

[3]   J.G. Lawrence and H. Ochman. Amelioration of bacterial genomes: rates of change and exchange. *J Mol Evol* 1997, 44:383-397.

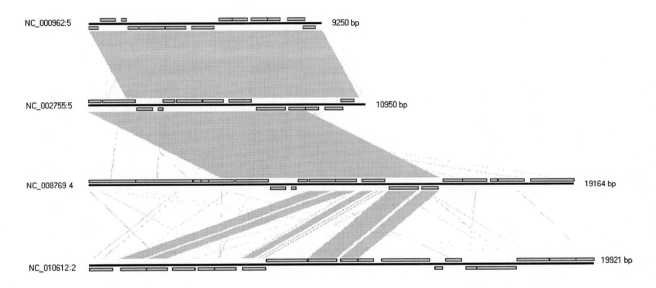

Figure 4 Homologous genes and operons in GIs shared by *Mycobacterium*

Adaptive Visual Symbols for Personal Health Records

Heimo Müller[1], Herman Maurer[2], Robert Reihs[1], Stefan Sauer[1], Kurt Zatloukal[1]

(1) Medical University of Graz, (2) Graz University of Technology

Abstract

As a hub of information controlled by the patient, personal health records (PHR) collect information from the patient medical history including a wide variety of data sources as patient's observations, lab results, clinical findings and in the future maybe even personal genetic data and automatic recordings from monitoring devices. This development will on the one hand make health care more personalized and user controlled but on the other hand also overloads consumers with a huge amount of data. To address this issue we developed a framework for adaptive visual symbols (AVS). An AVS can adapt its appearance and level of detail during the communication process. Finally we demonstrate the AVS principle for the visualization of personal health records.

1. Introduction

A Personal Health Record (PHR) is in line with the following definition of the National Alliance for Health Information Technology:

> *"An electronic record of health related information on an individual that conforms to nationally recognized interoperability standards and that can be drawn from multiple sources while being managed, shared, and controlled by the individual."* [1]

Traditionally electronic health records (EHR) are produced by health care providers, maintained at hospitals and doctors offices and are archived at some central place. In contrast to this a PHR is owned and maintained by a patient, who controls the access to it and it includes a lot of additional information about the lifestyle and the subjective well-being of patients. PHR exist a long time in paper format, e.g. "baby books", a personal calendar for women who track their menstrual cycles, medication lists or notes about medical directives. However WEB 2.0 technologies empowered PHRs with the possibility to share medical data between different computers and users, and to interlink personal medical notes with information sources on the Internet. Several commercial and non-profit institution already provide PHR data repositories. Microsoft's Health Vault, Google Health, and Dossia are the biggest players in this field.

A PHR typically holds information about the (family) medical history, medications, allergies and reactions, problem lists (diseases and conditions), contact information from healthcare institutions or immunizations and links to patient portals. PHRs can even include advanced features as healthcare providers' exams, scanned images, such as CT scans or dental images, drug interaction checks, therapeutic modalities, occupational therapies, advance directive forms, living wills, organ donor authorization, appointments, scheduling, and financial information, such as explanation of benefits. [2]

This comprehensive list shows, that the amount of information within a PHR can be incredibly large, which makes it difficult to (a) overlook the whole data set, (b) access detail information in an easy and effective way and (c) communicate the semantics of data items to different user groups. All three challenges are directly related to the development and evaluation of user interfaces dealing with PHRs. Usability engineers have today quite a number of methods to evaluate the quality of an interface [3]. If such usability tests give good results the design process is finished

1550-6037/11 $26.00 © 2011 IEEE
DOI 10.1109/IV.2011.87

220

and the users and the designer are happy, however when this is not the case we have two choices :

(A) The user adapts its behaviour to the (not perfect) user interface; or

(B) The user interface will be redesigned according to the input from the usability tests, and we restart the evaluation.

Usually alternative (A) is chosen, not due to the fact, that the user interface designer and the usability engineer are lazy guys, but because of the long delay in the feedback cycle (B) and the orientation of the user interface toward the lowest common denominator of all users requirements, see Figure 1.

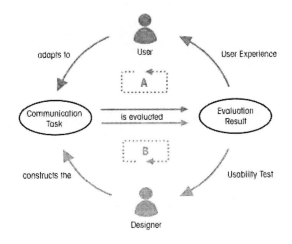

Figure 1 - Feedback cycles in user interface design

The solution to this problem seems to be obvious: just let the user interface adapt its visual appearance and codes to the needs of the user. This can be achieved by capturing user input and adapt visual signs according to the previous experience and knowledge of the user, just in line with the statement of Heinz von Foerster "the hearer and not the speaker determines the meaning of an utterance" [4].

2. Related Work

2.1 Dynamic Visual Languages

The underlying assumption of Dynamic Visual Languages is that by the beginning of the next decade computers allowing the presentation of high resolution moving images will be as ubiquitous as today's mobile phones. This will for the first time allow to implement a novel concept of communication systems that employs modern multimedia concepts (animations, movies, interactive pictures, dynamic maps, etc.) in combination with dynamic visual languages (i.e. visual languages in which symbols can change in shape, color, size, etc. in time).

Putting it differently, there is no reason why information in the future should be recorded only using static text, static images and such, but rather it is conceivable to build on earlier attempts to construct new artificial languages that are not based on letters, but on icons. It was Otto Neurath [5] who showed with his isotypes that in many aspects symbols are superior to textual representations; a number of attempts to construct full communication systems based on symbols have been developed since. A brief survey of the main approaches is given in [6]. However, even in earlier papers such as [7], [8], [9], [10] and [11] the idea to use dynamic symbols, rather than static symbols has been discussed: the idea that symbols can change size, colour, shape, contours or can move and even change position to convey additional semantic meaning is rather appealing: why not e.g. use a symbol for 'eye' and to use the same symbol when slightly moving to indicate the verb associated with the noun, i.e. 'seeing'. This and other techniques as explained in above cited papers, techniques such as orthogonality, macros and using picture dictionaries that explain the same items in a variety of languages, changing the level of abstraction where desirable, etc. are the reasons why it does not seem far-fetched that written language, communication and interfaces as we now know them will be partially replaced by methods involving dynamic visual languages.

2.1 Adaptive Interfaces

A good overview about adaptive interfaces can be found in [12] and [13]. Intelligent interfaces do not exist in isolation, but rather improve their ability to interact by constructing an user model based on the interaction. This brings the problem of intelligent interfaces close to the area of machine learning, where the user plays the role of the environment in which the learning occurs and the user model corresponds to the learning knowledge base. In such a scenario the interaction acts as performance task, on which learning should lead to improvements [14]. Many applications of adaptive interfaces focus on information filtering and recommendation task, e.g. in content-based filtering and collaborative filtering applications. Intelligent interfaces can be divided into 3 classes [13]:

(A) Adaptation within direct manipulation interfaces by adding extra interface objects for predicted future commands.
(B) Intermediary interfaces: The nature of interaction is changed in order to act as an intermediary between the user and the direct manipulation interface.
(C) Agent interfaces: In this case the user retains full control over the direct manipulation interface and is advised by an autonomous agent.

Our approach focus on a combination of user adaption and intermediary interfaces introducing active communication objects, which can adapt their semantic depth (the level of detail, which is presented to the user) according to needs of the user.

All intelligent interfaces have as central part a user model [14] [15]. Extensions to the simple model of stereotypical user models are programmable user models [16], user models for demonstrational user interfaces [17] and comprehension based user models [18]. In a programmable users model the mental representations and the user behavior results in a cognitive model of the user. Using an Instruction Language (IL) the user interface designer describes the knowledge, which a user needs to perform a specific task. The Instruction Language can be seen as programming, which is translated to a run able cognitive model. [19]

2.2 Visualization of PHR

Aigner and Miksch [20] give an overview of visualisation methods for computerized protocols and temporal patient data. Their work takes in account graphical patient record summary by Powsner [21], VIE-VISU by Horn 2001 [22], time lines and life lines by Plaisant [23] and time tubes by Konchady [24].

Jiye An et al. present a level of detail (LOD) information navigation model, which classifies patient's whole EHR into different detail levels according to their clinical relevance and they introduce a novel navigation and visualization method based on the LOD model. [25]

3. Adaptive Visual Symbols

Building on a number of previous studies in the field of static and dynamic visual languages [5], [6], [7], [8] and [9] we developed a model, where each basic sign is able to adapt its visual appearance and level of detail. In order to achieve this goal we propose a new type of interface object, the Adaptive Visual Symbol (AVS).

An AVS consists of

Intended Denotation	Formal or natural language description of its mission.
Coding	Representation of the intended denotation.
Semantic Inspection	Method for the analysis of the receiver reactions.

An AVS is modelled in an object oriented way, i.e. it has an internal state (data) and autonomous behaviour (methods), see Figure 3. In order to achieve the overall goal - congruence between the intended denotation and the constructed denotation – the semantic inspection method adapts the presentation process (rendering, level of detail, presentation speed, additional explanations). The fundamental innovation of an AVS lies in the distinction between the semantics of a message and the used visual sign.

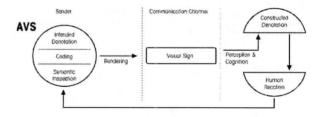

Figure 3 – Adaptive Visual Symbols

A semantic inspection method does an analysis of the communication process in three constitutive levels:

Level 1: *The communication process was successful*
The receiver has seen the symbol and the construction of the denotation has started. Semantic inspection can be achieved by recording user interactions (e.g. the symbol was touched) or by a simple eye tracking systems. [26]

Level 2: *The construction of the denotation at the receiver is finished*
Analysis of user interactions and/or facial expressions [27] can be used as indicators for the completion of the interpretation task This does not mean that the intended denotation is concordant with the constructed denotation.

Level 3: *The constructed denotation is concordant to the intended denotation*

In this case we can distinguish between (a) simple denotations, e.g. a command or question, where the fulfilment of the command deals as direct confirmation, and (b) complex denotations, e.g. a part of a medical treatment. In the case of a complex denotation concordance can only be measured in a wider context.

Experiments have shown, that it is sufficient to provide feedback mechanisms at level 1 and 2 in order to implement an adaptive visual communication process. If the receiver has a completely wrong constructed denotation, the following communication steps will fail even at level 2 tests, if they are constitutive.

4. Symbols for PHRs

The basic element of a medical history is an event. Main attributes of an event are it's type together with a short description, localisation, main outcome and the event's temporal range.

Figure 4 – Visualization of a medical event

Together with medical doctors we developed a visual language [28], which transform a part of textual diagnosis in a visual symbol, see figure 4. In this approach each visual symbol represents either an observation or procedure in a treatment history and corresponds to an unique ICD10 coding [29] as widely used in health care institutions. With the help of such a visual summary experts can overview a medical case within seconds, see figure 5.

Figure 5 – Visualization of a medical finding, as used by medical experts.

This very condensed (visual) representation of a medical finding is on the one hand effective when used

by trained medical experts in their day-to-day business, but on the other hand still too complicated and not self-explaining for patients. Based on input gained in focus groups from patients and considering design principles described by John Maeda [30] we re-worked the visual language, see figure 6.

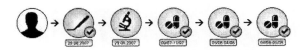

Figure 6 – Visualization of the same disease history as in figure 5, but from a patient's perspective. Each symbol tells the "what" and "when" and has an optional indicator for the outcome (green checkmark)

In particular the "patient style" visual language builds on the following principles and methods:

- Remove obvious facts and add more meaningful symbols for patients.
- Focus on emotions.
- Organize information.
- Provide a gesture-based interface for information organization and semantic inspection.

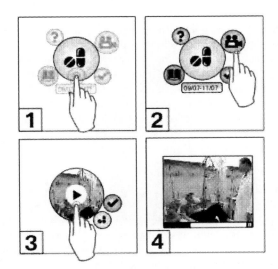

Figure 7 – Selection of additional information embedded within the symbol

Figure 7 shows the application flow of the user interaction with adaptive symbols. When the user touches the border (1) the symbol shows additional information, e.g. personal notes, the doctors diagnosis, web links or a even a video recording (2). The user can move the new information item to the center, where an iconic representation is shown (3). In this case the master symbol of the event, e.g. a chemotherapy treatment is moved to the bottom right area. The iconic representation itself holds the user-interface, i.e. the video content is played by pushing the play button in the center of the symbol (4).

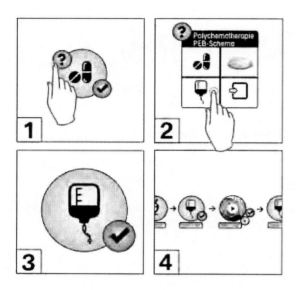

Figure 8 – Explanations and configuration of symbols

Figure 8 shows how a symbol explains itself. By touching the border of the symbol, a small question mark appears in the top left area (1). This button activates an explanatory interface (2), where the user gets a short textual explanation and can change (or upload) an alternative symbol (3). In our example the symbol for chemotherapy was changed from a pill to an infusion bottle. Please note, that the symbol is changed for every chemotherapy event (4).

5. Conclusion

We developed a framework for adaptive visual symbols for the visualization of personal health records. With the help of adaptive symbols an user can summarize his medical history with the desired complexity and visual style. The adaptive and flexible approach can even support the visualization of "universal health records" (UHR) as proposed by John Morgenthaler [31]. UHRs are the union of electronic health records as used by health care provides and PHR both shared in a granular way. With the help of the framework, implemented as actionscript library (FLEX), a demonstrator application was realized. We prospectively plan to move to a HTML-5 approach in order to support multitouch tablet devices and gesture based interaction paradigms.

6. Acknowledgments

This work was funded by the FIT-IT programme (813 398) and by the Austrian Fonds zur Förderung der wissenschaftlichen Forschung (FWF, L427-N15). Medical data were provided in the context of the Austrian Genome Programme GEN-AU and the CRIP project. Our thanks are due to all partners projects, for their contributions, critical reviews and various discussions. The study has been approved by the Ethical Committee of the Medical University of Graz.

7. References

[1] The National Alliance for Health Information Technology report to the Office of the National Coordinator for Health Information Technology on defining key health information technology terms April 28, 2008. Chicago, IL: National Alliance for Health Information Technology; 2008, pg 6.

[2] S. Kahn (Eds), A Community View on How Personal Health Records Can Improve Patient Care and Outcomes in Many Healthcare Settings, Northern Illinois Physicians for Connectivity (NIPFC) and Northern Illinois University Regional Development Institute (NIU RDI), 2009.

[3] A. Holzinger, Usability Engineering Methods for Software Developers, Communication of the ACM, Vol. 48, 2005, pp. 71-74.

[4] H. von Foerster, Cybernetics of Cybernetics (2nd edition), Future Systems, Minneapolis, 1996.

[5] O. Neurath, International picture language, University of Reading, 1978.

[6] H. Maurer, R. Stubenrauch, D. Camhy, Foundations of MIRACLE - Multimedia Information Repository, A Computer-supported Language Effort, J.UCS Vol 9, No 4., 2003, pp.309-348.

[7] J. A. Lennon, H. Maurer, MUSLI: A hypermedia interface for dynamic, interactive, and symbolic communication; J.NCA vol 24, (2001), 273-291.

[8] J. A. Lennon, H. Maurer, Augmenting text and voice conversations with dynamic, interactive abstractions using P2P networking; J.NCA vol. 24 (2001), 293-306.

[9] H. Maurer, P. Carlson, Computer Visualization, a Missing Organ and a CyberEquivalency; Collegiate Microcomputer, vol. 10, no. 2 (1992), 110-116.

[10] J. A. Lennon, H. Maurer, MUSLI- A Multisensory Interface; Proc. ED-MEDIA'94, AACE (1994), 341-348.

[11] D. H. Jonassen, R. Goldman-Segal, H. Maurer, Dynamicons as Dynamic Graphic Interfaces; Intelligent Tutoring Meida vol. 6, No.3-4 (1996), 149-158.

[12] P. Patrik, Intelligent User Interfaces – Introduction and survey – Research Report DKS03-01 / ICE 01, Delft University of Technology, 2003.

[13] E. Ross, Intelligent User Interfaces: Survey and Research Directions, Technical Report: CSTR-00-004, Bristol, 2000

[14] P. Langley, User modeling in adaptive interfaces. Proceedings of the Seventh International Conference on User Modeling. Banff, Alberta: Springer, (1999), pp. 357-370.

[15] P. Brusilovsky, D. W. Cooper, Domain, task, and user models for an adaptive hypermedia performance support system, Proceedings of the 7th international conference on Intelligent user interfaces, (2002), pp. 23-30.

[16] R. M. Young, T. R. G. Green, T. Simon, Programmable User Models for Predictive Evaluation of Interface Designs, in K. Bice and C. Lewis (eds.) Proceedings of CHI'89 Human Factors in Computing Systems, ACM Press, New York, (1989).

[17] B. Myers, Creating User Interfaces by Demonstration, Academic Press, (1988).

[18] W. Kintsch, Comprehension: A Paradigm for Cognition, MA: Cambridge University Press, (1998).

[19] Y. W. Sohn, & S.M. Doane, Evaluating Comprehension-Based User Models: Predicting Individual User Planning and Action. User Modeling and User Adapted Interaction. 12(2-3), (2002), pp. 171-205.

[20] W. Aigner, S. Miksch, CareVis: Integrated Visualization of Computerized Protocols and Temporal Patient Data. Presentation: Workshop on Intelligent Data Analyis in Medicine and Pharmacology (IDAMAP-2004), Stanford, USA; 06-09-2004; in: "Workshop Notes of the Workshop on Intelligent Data Analyis in Medicine and Pharmacology", (2004)

[21] S. M. Powsner S.M., E. R. Tufte., Graphical summary of patient status. The Lancet 334, 1994, pp. 386-389.

[22] W. Horn, C. Popow. L. Unterasinger. Support for fast comprehension of ICU data: visualization using methaper graphics. Methods of Information in Medicine 40, 2001, pp. 421-424.

[23] C. Plaisant, B. Milash, A. Rose S. Widoff. B. Shneiderman, LifeLines: visualizing personal histories. Proceedings of the ACM CHI 96 conference on Human Factors in Computing Systems, 1996, pp. 221-227.

[24] M. Konchady, R. D'Amore, G. Valley, A web based visualization for documents. In: Procceddings of the workshop on new paradigms in information visualization and manipuation, ACM press, 1998, pp. 13-19

[25] Jiye An, Zhe Wu, Hushan Chen, Xudong Lu, Huilong Duan: Level of detail navigation and visualization of electronic health records, Prpceedings of Biomedical Engineering and Informatics (BMEI), 2010, pp. 2516 – 2519.

[26] M. Argyle, M. Cook, Gaze and Mutual Gaze, Cambridge University Press, London, (1977).

[27] M. Pantic, Facial gesture recognition from static dual-view face images, International Conference on Measuring Behaviour, (2002), pp. 195-197.

[28] H. Müller, S. Sauer, K. Zatloukal, T. Bauernhofer. Interactive Patient Records. Proceedings of IV'10 - 14th International Conference on Information Visualization, London (2010)

[29] ICD-10: international statistical classification of diseases and related health problems: tenth revision. World Health Organization 2004.

[30] J. Maeda, The Laws of Simplicity (Simplicity: Design, Technology, Business, Life), The MIT Press, 2006.

[31] J. Morgenthaler, Moving Toward an Open Standard Universal Health Record, http://www.smart-publications.com/articles/view/moving-toward-an-open-standard-universal-health-record/, last visited Feb. 2011.

Interactive Drug Design in Virtual Reality

Ching-Man Tse, Hongjian Li, Kwong-Sak Leung, Kin-Hong Lee, Man-Hon Wong

Department of Computer Science and Engineering, Chinese University of Hong Kong

{*cmtse,hjli,ksleung,khlee,mhwong*}*@cse.cuhk.edu.hk*

Abstract—Discovering new drugs for emerging diseases has been a challenging task. There are numerous drug design techniques including fragment-based and diversity-oriented methods but their accuracies and efficiencies are low. By incorporating visualisation, biomedical experts can interact with the process to produce drug-like ligands more efficiently. The paper presents an interactive drug design algorithm which generates lead candidates against a protein. A set of drug candidates, created by an inhouse fragment-based method and docked on the target protein, are visualised in the virtual reality settings. Biomedical experts can investigate and select some of the ligands for further processing, aided with distance and bonding information. It also assists the user to drag and rotate the ligand to the binding site they find suitable. The algorithm runs iteratively and improves the quality of lead candidates every step. The paper compares the quality of resulting ligands between interactive and automatic approaches.

Keywords-Interactive Drug Design; Virtual Reality;

I. INTRODUCTION

The momentum in searching for compounds of medical uses continues to grow as diseases are more difficult to cure owing to drug resistance. Out of the possible configurations of the molecules which may have medical purposes [1], only a minority of the molecules were synthesised and exploited. It becomes crucial to design new molecules which can be of medical values but not explored. Computational methods have been employed because of low cost and high efficiency.

There are numerous computational techniques, mainly fragment-based and diversity-oriented, to generate drug candidates for wet-lab experiments [2], [3]. Fragment-based method constructs a library of structurally diverse small molecules that could become fragments of active drugs [4], [5]. The drug candidate starts with low affinity for the target in which is systematically altered and enlarged, generating high affinity, drug-like lead compound. Diversity-oriented method produces a library of structurally diverse drug-like compounds, usually from common intermediates [6], [7]. The compounds are then screened and high affinity candidates are optimised for further analysis. The accuracy of both strategies rely on the screening procedure, which could be a docking program in a recent approach [8].

In addressing the accuracy issues, there are interactive approaches which enable optimisation to the compound using the user's knowledge about structure-activity relationship [9]. The algorithm visualises a set of drug candidates for the user to choose from and generate new candidates based on

their choice using evolutionary algorithm. It overcomes the difficulties in creating the fitness function to assess drug design. However, it considers solely on the structure of the drug candidates while the target protein is often known especially for pharmaceutical companies.

We propose an interactive algorithm for drug design with a known target protein. Visualisation plays an important role in displaying ligand-protein structure in 3D. The user can then investigate the structure and determine whether a drug candidate is viable. While there are good visualisers such as JMol and ligand editors by MolSoft, manipulating a drug candidate around requires adequate depth information. Virtual reality enables immersive experience to the user where conventional visualisation techniques cannot. The program generates a set of drug candidates by evolutionary algorithm and refined by chemical rules and docking. The user gives feedback by translating or rotating the candidates and remove them if found unsuitable. Our study shows the resulting lead compound is lighter in molecular weight which is more readily absorbed and has comparable affinity to the automatic method.

The detailed design and algorithm is presented in section III. Experiments are described in section IV A discussion on the advantages and improvements of the interactive approach is given in section V.

II. RELATED WORK

There are many attempts in combining visualisation with the biomedical field. Visualisation and sometimes virtual reality are brought into place to help solve complex biomedical problems such as protein docking and drug design.

1) Interactive Drug Design: A drug design tool Molecule Evoluator [9] uses atom-based evolutionary approach to explore multiple configurations of drug candidates. The tool displays numerous configurations in 2D for the user to choose from and modify. The evaluation however depends completely on the user. In addition, when the target protein is available, the tool cannot take advantage of the information by estimating the affinity such as docking.

2) Virtual Reality in Biomedical Field: The function and interaction of proteins depend heavily on their conformations which are best visualised in virtual reality. The advantages of comparative visualisation was investigated in [10]. There is a shortcoming in their visualiser that it does not support the standard Protein Data Bank [11] format. An attempt to assist protein docking using virtual reality was made in [12]. The user guides a ligand to the binding site of a protein with real-time feedback from their system. The user needs to control the whole process for the algorithm to work.

III. Methods and Design

The program consists of an interface which displays the ligand-receptor pair in virtual reality and a computational module to provide feedback. We first explain the algorithms in the computational module and then describe the features of the interface.

A. Hybrid Drug Synthesis

The drug synthesis algorithm employed in our program combines the strength of fragment-based and diversity-oriented approaches. A diversity-oriented approach creates structurally diverse molecules with their molecular masses usually close to those of drug-like compounds. In addition, it explores molecules that escape the attention of human or even nature. A fragment-based approach produces numerous sets of compounds not represented in existing libraries, filling the gap of 'chemical space'. It is suggested that tremendous amount of compounds can be represented in a library of few fragments.

The program accepts a small molecule and a receptor of Protein Data Bank (PDB) format. The small molecule is then be optimised to bind into the receptor. The program uses a fragment library ranging from hydroxide to benzene to add onto the small molecule. Evolutionary algorithm (EA) is employed to generate multiple instances of the small molecule and maintain diversity. It is based on biological principles such as natural selection and usually involves mutation and crossover operations. There are four operators implemented, namely, mutation, crossover, merge and split. The detail of the operators are as follows.

(1) Mutation: This replaces a hydrogen atom in a small molecule with a random fragment from the library. A hydrogen atom on the fragment is removed such that a non-hydrogen atom is attached to the small molecule. The small molecule is optimised by rotating the fragment to achieve minimal torsion.

(2) Crossover: Two small molecules are selected and exchange some of their fragments. The implementation resembles genetic programming that a subtree of two different molecules are selected and swapped. The small molecule is in a graph-based representation and cannot contain incomplete cycles. Thus, when a random atom on the fragment is selected, excluding the common initial compound, all dependent atoms are checked and selected for the exchange. Two small molecules are optimised and generated.

(3) Merge: An operation similar to crossover that two small molecules are chosen. All fragments on one of the small molecule are transferred to the other small molecule, removing some hydrogen atoms. Only the larger small molecule is returned, decreasing the number of small molecules in the set by one.

(4) Split: This transfers some randomly chosen fragments on a small molecule to the initial common compound. The valences of the small molecule which loses fragments is corrected by adding hydrogen atoms. Two small molecules are optimised and returned, increasing the number of small molecules in the set by one.

Apart from the mentioned operators, there are two special methods to produce larger variance to the small molecules which is restrictive to invoke.

Join Ring: This is an advanced mode of mutation that the ring in the fragment is joined to a ring on the small molecule, forming consecutive rings. Both the fragment and the small molecule must contain ring structures to perform. Two adjacent atoms on the ring are checked to find a matching pair in another ring. If the rings cannot be joined, the usual mutation is carried instead.

Decrease Bond Order: If there is a double or triple bond in the small molecule, the order of that bond is decreased by one. Hydrogen atoms are added to correct the valences. The small molecule is optimised and contains more bonds to add fragments.

Using the operators and methods mentioned, a set of small molecules is generated. The user can investigate the structures of the generated small molecules. However, it usually takes tens of different small molecules for the evolutionary algorithm to work well. The user may not want to explore the whole population. In addition, the decision of the user can benefit from computing affinity between the small molecules and the receptor. A docking algorithm is integrated as the fitness function of the evolutionary algorithm. An external docking program AutoDock Vina [13] is integrated because it is fast and relatively accurate. Its bundled tool, MGLTools, computes the flexible side chains and partial charges of the small molecule and receptor.

A compound follows certain chemical rules. If the graph representation is evolved freely, invalid molecule may arise. The Lipinski's rule of five [14] is applied to check the validity of the resulting small molecules evolved. The rules describe the number of acceptors, donors, molecular weight and solubility of a compound to be drug-like.

While the evolutionary approach can work on its own, there are several disadvantages. Firstly, the docking method may not be accurate enough in optimisation and sometimes incorrectly estimates the potency of the lead compound. Secondly, the compounds are difficult to compare. It is necessary to compare the physical and chemical properties among compounds which cannot simply represented by similarity index or subgraph differences. Lastly, evolutionary algorithm requires parameters tuning to work well. For this complex problem, the number of parameters is high which does not appeal to the users. In addition, it is more effective to adaptively adjust the parameters based on situations.

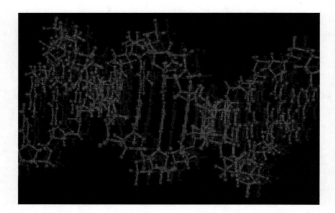

Figure 1. Stereo effect in anaglyph mode (red-and-blue). Using a spectacles with red and blue filter on each side, the disparity between the two superimposed DNA creates a perception of depth. The DNA appears in white in VR. This figure shows the effect without the spectacles.

Figure 2. Stereo effect in shutter mode. Superposed images are displayed alternatively in temporal frames. The spectacles synchronise with the monitor such that each eye perceive the correct image. This figure shows the effect withour the spectacles.

We, therefore, introduce an interactive solution incorporating human intelligence. The fitness and similarity are decided by the users using their expert knowledge. The parameters of the evolutionary algorithm are adjusted based on the feedback of the user. This interactive approach relies on a rigorous visualisation implementation.

B. Interactive Interface in Virtual Reality

Realistic visualisation is important in biomedical research, especially in the field of drug design. Virtual reality (VR) environments allow a detailed inspection on molecular structure and offer a different quality than standard 3D representation.

The interface is developed in C++ and OpenGL programming language which is portable across platforms. The interface can visualise PDB format in standard 3D, red-and-blue stereo or shutter stereo mode. When paired with the drug design algorithm, the interface provides feedback to the user and computes the parameters for the algorithm. The standard 3D visualisation enables users without equipment to produce virtual reality environment to use the drug design algorithm.

The red-and-blue stereo mode (Figure 1) is a compromise in visualising structures in single colour which works on common monitors. It could display depth information better than the standard 3D which is crucial when judging the binding position. The shutter stereo mode (Figure 2) requires a high frequency monitor and special spectacles, but provides the best experience. Molecules visualised in this mode are rich in colour and depth information is presented precisely.

There are several display styles the interface supports which visualises different levels of information. The supported styles include DNA backbone model, ball-and-stick model, cartoon representation and van der Waals filling model. The van der Waals filling model requires surface mesh computation which can take up to half a minute

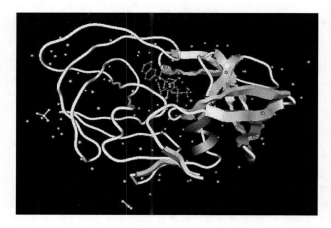

Figure 3. Cartoon representation of 3XME. Alpha helices and beta strands are represented by ribbons and arrows respectively. The ligand 1F1 is presented by ball-and-stick model inside the protein

upon the initial rendering. After the initial rendering, all models can be manipulated in real-time in stereo on common machines.

The ball-and-stick model (primary structure) is used to display the chemical aspects of the molecules. This is the only model available to the small molecules. This mode is used to visualise the bonding between a small molecules and its receptor.

The cartoon representation (secondary structure) reveals information on the shape and size of a protein. This mode uses simplified symbols such as arrows and ribbons to represent beta strands and alpha helices of the protein.

The van der Waals filling model (surface representation) visualises each atom in the protein using their van der Waals radius. This mode presents surface information of the protein which allows investigation on the binding sites.

The display capabilities of our interface may not be comprehesive as the mature display tools such as JMol,

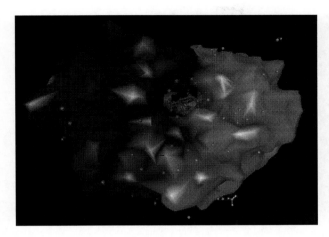

Figure 4. Surface model of 3XME. The protein is coloured according to its chains and a binding site is clearly shown.

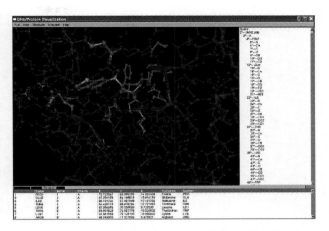

Figure 5. Interface of the interactive drug design program. Table on the right displays atom information in a hierarchy. Table on the bottom shows information in group such as chains and residues. The hydrogen bonds between the ligand and protein 3XME are displayed in the main window, with non-interacting residues faded out

which supports a variety of visualisation choices. When compared with the editing tool from Molsoft, their tool has more modification options and a well-established evaluation function. Nevertheless, the interface we developed has more features than the existing tools. It includes multiple stereo modes for different hardware configurations. In addition, our tool evaluates multiple drug candidates and assigns fragments automatically which can reduce the effort of the user.

The interface has a collision detection algorithm integrated to support dragging by the user. The user can select the protein by atom, residue or chain levels. It is done by directly clicking on the visualised proteins or the names in the list which contains the sequences in text form. In addition, bonding between the small molecule and the protein can be highlighted. The residues which bond directly with the small molecule is shown normally while the other fades out. The bonds are calculated using hydrogen bond or distance criteria.

When the interface is used with the drug design algorithm, the initial small molecule and the receptor must be specified. Two parameters, the number of small molecules generated and investigated, are defined by the user. A sufficient number of small molecules to be generated can encourage diversity among the population and reduce the chance of premature convergence. The user only needs to investigate a portion of the generated small molecules. A subset is selected for investigation according to the affinity, calculated by the docking program, and the molecular weights of the small molecules. The initial population is then created by mutating the specified small molecule.

During each generation, the user investigates a set of small molecules and decides whether to accept or remove them. Only one ligand-protein pair can be investigated at a time due to the complexity of the structure to be drawn. The user is assisted by a variety of information to make the decision. The statistics of the small molecule, including number of donors, acceptors, estimated logP and molecular weight, are displayed. The docked structure is visualised in virtual reality with possible hydrogen bonds drawn. The structure can be rotated and zoomed in for more details. The user can cycle through different model styles and highlight the interacting residues. The small molecule can be dragged and rotated, hydrogen bonds are updated in real-time. The user can specify to use the modified structure in the next generation of the drug design algorithm.

Based on the decision of the user, parameters of the drug design algorithm is dynamically calculated. The adaptive parameters includes mutation rate and crossover chance. These parameters are changed each generation depending the investigation result. When the user removes a majority of the small molecules for investigation, the mutation rate becomes high in order to create structurally diverse small molecules, which covers more 'chemical space'. In contrast, when the user accepts most small molecules, crossover is encouraged to create similar compound of the accepted ones. The molecular weight also plays a role in changing the parameters. There is an implicit molecular weight in the algorithm, which is the average of molecular weights of the small molecules for investigation. After the user accepts a certain number of small molecules, their average molecular weight is calculated. If the new weight is smaller than the implicit weight, it means that the user prefers smaller compound. The split operator will be invoked more often. The opposite applies that merge operator is used more often when the averaged weight is larger than the implicit weight. The two advanced methods, join ring and decrease bond order, need to be instructed by the user and are not used normally. The program can be stopped any time when the user is satisfied with the generated small molecules.

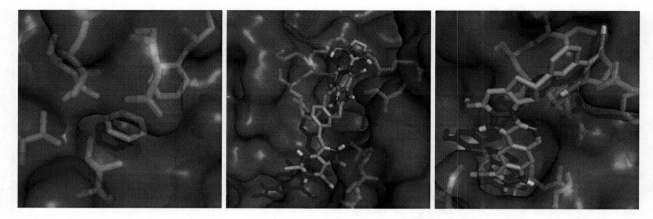

Figure 6. Putative binding site on EV71 protease. (a) Initial scaffold in binding site. (b) Resulting lead candidate by the automatic algorithm. (c) Resulting lead candidate by the interactive algorithm.

IV. EXPERIMENTS

We conducted experiments on the program using several receptors and compounds from the ZINC database [15]. We will explain one of the experiments which illustrates the idea of the interactive drug design algorithm. An automatic drug design algorithm, AutoGrow, was chosen for comparison. This algorithm is fragment-based and utilises evolutionary algorithm.

The receptors chosen are glycogen synthase kinase 3 beta (GSK3β), HIV reverse transcriptase, HIV protease and Human Entrovirus 71 3C protease. Their corresponding PDB ID are 1J1B, 2ZD1, 3KFN and 3OSY where the first three have known binding sites and inhibitors. We screened all compounds in the ZINC databases against the receptors using the docking program. Five initial compounds were selected which have high affinity and work on the automatic drug design program. The fragment library used for both programs was the same which contained 46 small fragments. For the interactive program, a population of 50 was set. The number of small molecules for investigation was 10. For the automatic program, it used the same population size. The number of elitists was set to 10. Their program required to set the number of molecules produced by mutation and crossover, where they were set to 20 and 20 respectively.

Both programs were executed for eight generations. We only interacted with the first generation of small molecules to save effort. The program was run the end which took about two hours in total. The interactive apporach had an average of 10% better affinity. Moreover, the automatic program is not aware of physico-chemical property such that the molecular weight of the resulting compounds were 60% higher on the extreme, which were not drug-like.

In figure 6, the comparison indicates that the automatic program misplaced the binding region of the initial scaffold. The interactive approach created a compound of 8.9% better affinity and comparable molecular weight. In addition, the resulting compound of the interactive approach contained large consecutive rings not in the initial compound which is difficult to achieve in automatic methods.

V. DISCUSSIONS

In this paper, we have described an interactive approach over the evolutionary algorithm for drug design. The graph representation preserves most of the information available in the structures. It is also suitable for fragment-based methods which have the potential benefit of easier synthesis. We used standard PDB format for displaying and processing which effectively utilises online resources. In addition, the interface can be used as a standard visualiser to display structure in virtual reality when not paired with the drug design algorithm. We have achieved real-time interation with the molecule in stereo mode, while the evaluation process may take longer time.

Adopting an interactive approach, we overcome the most difficult aspect in evolutionary algorithm for drug design, creating the appropiate fitness function. The evolutionary algorithm is specially designed to dynamically adjust itself each generation by the decision of the user. We have decided not to display all the small molecules in the population because the user may not want to screen tens or hundreds of compounds before passing them back to the algorithm. Instead, a portion of small molecules, which the algorithm thinks they are good, are visualised for investigation. The parameters of the evolutionary algorithm are calculated based on the decision about the selected set of small molecules. Through this design, we have abstracted the complicated parameter tuning process into simple reasoning.

There are many advantages to user interaction. The most attractive advantage to drug design is the feedback from the users can produce compounds which can be synthesised more easily in laboratory. With more expert knowledge, the resulting compounds will be more likely to be synthesisable. Another advantage is the user can use whatever domain knowledge they have, whereas the developers may not possess. It is particularly difficult to assume all required knowledge is integrated beforehand. A third advantage is user-friendliness. Tuning the evolutionary algorithm can be tedious when there are a lot of parameters. The interactive approach reduces the tuning process to simple questions: whether to accept a small molecules or use certain methods. Nonetheless, using an interactive program can be more time-consuming than an automatic approach. The outcome may not be objective which depends on the perception of the user.

Considering the feedback of the users, we have planned to allow greater flexibility in the interface such as real-time modification to the small molecules. At the moment of writing, only translation and rotation are available to the user. With more explicit chemical rules implemented, the user can modify atoms or fragments on the small molecules. In addition, with recent capability to display in virtual reality on webpages, it is beneficial to have a web-front which encourages a larger user base.

CONCLUSIONS

We have designed and implemented an interactive approach to the drug design. Through visualisation on the docked structures in virtual reality, domain experts can investigate and manipulate with higher precision. Incorporating human intelligence in the fitness function, we overcome difficulties associated with physico-chemical properties of compounds. It also combines the domain knowledge of the user and processing power of computers.

ACKNOWLEDGEMENTS

We thank Bobby Tang and Bean Lam for developing the interface of the program. The research is supported by the grant CUHK414708 from the Research Grants Council of the Hong Kong SAR, China.

REFERENCES

[1] R. S. Bohacek, C. McMartin, and W. C. Guida, "The art and practice of structure-based drug design: A molecular modeling perspective," *Medicinal Research Reviews*, vol. 16, no. 1, pp. 3–50, 1996. [Online]. Available: http://dx.doi.org/10.1002/(SICI)1098-1128(199601)16:1%3C3::AID-MED1%3E3.0.CO;2-6

[2] P. J. Hajduk, W. R. J. D. Galloway, and D. R. Spring, "Drug discovery: A question of library design," *Nature*, vol. 470, no. 7332, pp. 42–43, Feb 2011. [Online]. Available: http://dx.doi.org/10.1038/470042a

[3] G. Schneider and U. Fechner, "Computer-based de novo design of drug-like molecules," *Nature Reviews Drug Discovery*, vol. 4, no. 8, pp. 649–663, Aug 2005. [Online]. Available: http://dx.doi.org/10.1038/nrd1799

[4] I. D. Kuntz, "Structure-based strategies for drug design and discovery," *Science*, vol. 257, no. 5073, pp. 1078–1082, Aug 1992.

[5] P. J. Hajduk and J. Greer, "A decade of fragment-based drug design: strategic advances and lessons learned," *Nat Rev Drug Discov*, vol. 6, no. 3, pp. 211–219, Mar 2007. [Online]. Available: http://dx.doi.org/10.1038/nrd2220

[6] R. S. Bohacek and C. McMartin, "Multiple highly diverse structures complementary to enzyme binding sites: Results of extensive application of a de novo design method incorporating combinatorial growth," *Journal of the American Chemical Society*, vol. 116, no. 13, pp. 5560–5571, Jun 1994. [Online]. Available: http://dx.doi.org/10.1021/ja00092a006

[7] D. R. Westhead, D. E. Clark, D. Frenkel, J. Li, C. W. Murray, B. Robson, and B. Waszkowycz, "Pro-ligand: an approach to de novo molecular design. 3. a genetic algorithm for structure refinement," *J.Comput.Aided Mol.Des*, vol. 9, no. 2, pp. 139–148, Apr 1995.

[8] J. D. Durrant, R. E. Amaro, and J. A. McCammon, "Autogrow: a novel algorithm for protein inhibitor design," *Chem.Biol.Drug Des*, vol. 73, no. 2, pp. 168–178, Feb 2009.

[9] E.-W. Lameijer, J. N. Kok, T. Back, and A. P. IJzerman, "The molecule evoluator. an interactive evolutionary algorithm for the design of drug-like molecules," *Journal of Chemical Information and Modeling*, vol. 46, no. 2, pp. 545–552, 2006. [Online]. Available: http://pubs.acs.org/doi/abs/10.1021/ci050369d

[10] E. Moritz and J. Meyer, "Interactive 3d protein structure visualization using virtual reality," in *Proceedings of the 4th IEEE Symposium on Bioinformatics and Bioengineering*. Washington, DC, USA: IEEE Computer Society, 2004, pp. 503–. [Online]. Available: http://portal.acm.org/citation.cfm?id=998667.998837

[11] H. M. Berman, J. Westbrook, Z. Feng, G. Gilliland, T. N. Bhat, H. Weissig, I. N. Shindyalov, and P. E. Bourne, "The protein data bank," *Nucleic acids research*, vol. 28, no. 1, pp. 235–242, January 1 2000.

[12] A. Anderson and Z. Weng, "Vrdd: applying irtual eality visualization to protein ocking and esign," *Journal of Molecular Graphics and Modelling*, vol. 17, no. 3-4, pp. 180 – 186, 1999. [Online]. Available: http://www.sciencedirect.com/science/article/B6TGP-3YN94J2-3/2/fe8e17c8cb8f8f0c3309af690b83b04a

[13] O. Trott and A. J. Olson, "Autodock vina: improving the speed and accuracy of docking with a new scoring function, efficient optimization, and multithreading," *J.Comput.Chem.*, vol. 31, no. 2, pp. 455–461, Jan 2010.

[14] C. A. Lipinski, F. Lombardo, B. W. Dominy, and P. J. Feeney, "Experimental and computational approaches to estimate solubility and permeability in drug discovery and development settings," *Adv.Drug Deliv.Rev.*, vol. 46, no. 1-3, pp. 3–26, Mar 2001.

[15] J. J. Irwin and B. K. Shoichet, "Zinc: A free database of commercially available compounds for virtual screening," *Journal of Chemical Information and Modeling*, vol. 45, no. 1, pp. 177–182, 01/01 2005, doi: 10.1021/ci049714+; M3: doi: 10.1021/ci049714+. [Online]. Available: http://dx.doi.org/10.1021/ci049714+

Development of an Interactive Ramachandran Plot in Weave

Shweta Purushe, Sanjay Krishna Anbalagan and Georges Grinstein

Institute for Visualization and Perception Research, Department of Computer Science, University of Massachusetts Lowell

{shweta_purushe@student.uml.edu, sanjay_anbalagan@student.uml.edu, grinstein@cs.uml.edu}

Abstract

Current software systems having Ramachandran Plots do not support interactivity with the visualization. Current web-based Ramachandran Plot tools provide only primitive analysis and simple report generation features. In Weave (Web-based Analysis and Visualization Environment), we have developed an improved Ramachandran Plot with interactivity that facilitates better analysis, sequence searching features and supplementary visualizations. Weave provides essential features facilitating broader amino acid analysis, statistical computations and the advantages of a more general web-based application.

1. Introduction

The conformation of a protein, its domains and folds is governed by the Phi (φ) and Psi (ψ) angles of the protein backbone [1, 2]. These angles are the torsional angles that describe the rotation of a polypeptide backbone around the two bonds on either side of the Cα atom [Figure 1]. The Ramachandran Plot is a two-dimensional scatter plot of φ and ψ pairs overlaid on a predicted distribution of the amino acids which constitute the given polypeptide. For multiple decades this plot has been used to decipher steric hindrances and constraints in proteins. It was designed by Ramachandran *et al* [1] to study the structure of the protein backbone in terms of the two aforementioned angles.

We have developed a new web-based interactive visualization environment, called Weave, which provides a number of different visualization tools including histograms, linegraphs, barcharts, scatterplots, radial visualizations, for example [9]. Weave supports linked highlighting, data subset generation and selection all enabling better user involvement and analysis. In addition, Weave includes an editor that communicates with several 'R' statistical packages and an equation editor to allow quick mathematical and statistical calculations on the data being visualized.

We recently developed an interactive Ramachandran plot enabling the visualization of protein data imported from the Protein Data Bank (PDB) [9].

In this paper we provide the background to Ramachandran plots, why they are useful, discuss the implementation of the plot in Weave and identify future work.

2. Background

Proteins are vital components of our diet and also form structural components of the human anatomy. Proteins are polymers of units called amino acids. The structure of the protein backbone has the following appearance.

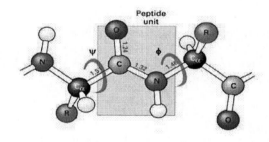

Figure 1: Planar structure of the protein backbone and the   and   angles [4]

The psi angle (ψ) defines the limit to which the Cα – C bond can rotate in 3D space and the phi angle (φ) defines the limit of rotation of the N – Cα bond [1]. Ramachandran [1] put forth the idea that if the protein backbone were planar and in the trans configuration, the overall conformation (shape in 3D space) can be defined by specifying these ψ and φ angles.

Different secondary structure elements in proteins have characteristic (φ, ψ) distributions and can be visualized in the plot [1]. Each dot on the plot represents a single (φ, ψ) pair for a single amino acid in the peptide sequence. Theoretically the (φ, ψ) pairs can assume any values. However due to steric constraints the ψ and φ angles have particular values permissible within certain regions [Figure 2]. These three regions are the β sheet, the α helix and the α_L helix. The two axes in the Ramachandran plot range from 180° to -180° allowing a clear and convenient distinction between these different regions. Figure 3 shows the plot for high-resolution data.

The regions of the plot containing the highest density of the dots are the "allowed" regions of the plot. These represent low energy areas and highly possible conformations of the protein. The empty areas of the plot are those regions which represent forbidden values for (φ, ψ) pairs and are high energy, unstable conformations of the protein.

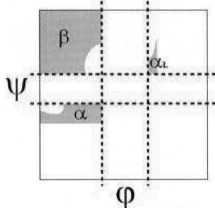

Figure 2: The three allowed regions of the Ramachandran plot are those having the highest density (in grey) [4].

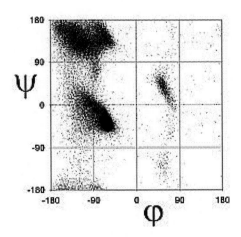

Figure 3: The Ramachandran plot for high resolution data [4].

Figure 4 shows the contour lines which were supplemented by Richardson [7 and 8]. He and his coworkers studied the 98% and 99.98% contour lines around the three cluster regions to demarcate the exact limits of the Ramachandran plot.

When a protein is plotted on the Ramachandran plot, on the basis of their ψ and φ angles, we can identify those regions of the plot where the amino acids are

concentrated and how they are spread thus indicating the major secondary protein conformations in the protein [1]. When determining the overall structure of any protein by any of the methods available such as NMR, X ray crystallography, or homology modeling, biologists resort to tools such as the Ramachandran plot to identify those particular amino acid residues that require special attention to convert existing unrealistic conformations in the model to chemically realistic ones [1, 2].

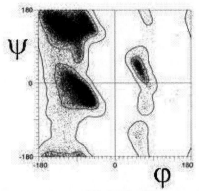

Figure 4: The Ramachandran Plot with contours [4].

3. Motivations

Although Ramachandran plots have been used extensively to date, they are primitive and lack user involvement and analysis. The Ramachandran Plot of the Sirius Visualization Software developed by the San Diego Computer Center and the RamachandranPlot2 developed by IISc, Bangalore [10], generate reports and tables respectively. However, they do not provide interaction and thus hamper complete analysis. STING Millennium Suite [11] does offer many programs for protein structure analysis; however linked visualization and highlighting are not consistently available. Once plotted, the protein data cannot be interactively explored. There is also no feature that allows the user to visualize subsets of the protein sequence within the entire sequence context. We summarize our motivations below.

- Interaction is extremely important to facilitate analysis by the user. Any visualization and analysis tool must allow interaction and tweaking of the visualization by the user.
- Data subset selection is necessary. The user might be interested only in a particular conformation within the protein or only a particular sequence of amino acids at a particular position.
- As part of the analysis certain statistical computations on the protein dataset might be necessary. Simple metrics such as amino acid counts and relative distributions are often needed.

- Multiple methods to explore the protein dataset should be provided. The user may want to explore or search for certain motifs (amino acid signatures) in the dataset.
- Since most visualization systems, as does Weave, provide the above requirements for other visualizations it made sense to integrate Ramachandran plots in Weave.

4. Results and Discussion

Although our first prototype was a standalone web-based Ramachandran plot, our goal was to incorporate it in Weave [9]. Protein data from PDB is available over the internet, and can be loaded into Weave and visualized on-the-fly. Weave offers a quick, easy and comprehensive system for the Ramachandran Plot.

4.1 Interactivity

Interactivity is the strongest and most significant feature of the Ramachandran plot in Weave. It was achieved through linked highlighting, subset selection and tweaking different parts of the plot [Figure6 and 7]. Each of these if discussed below.

4.2 Subset Selection

Data subset selection is allowed in the tabular data as well as in the Ramachandran plot. The selected subset can be exported to other file formats, visualized separately, obtained as a separate table and analyzed.

This allows the user to investigate and analyze particular amino acids relative to the whole protein sequence. In addition to this, increased transparency of the non-selected items allows us to focus on the selected ones within the context of the entire protein sequence.

As can be seen in Figure 6, the amino acid residues selected in the Ramachandran plot on the right pop up in a separate visualization which remains linked to the plot. This can be done using the popup button on the far right-hand bottom of the plot. Each such selection produces a new visualization.

4.3 Supplementary visualizations

As mentioned earlier Weave provides a variety of visualization tools that allow the user to extend the analysis quickly and efficiently. Figure 7 shows the use of one such visualization, the histogram. The histogram indicates the counts and relative distributions of the amino acids within the protein sequence used. These can be colored according to different variables as desired by the user. When the cursor is moved over any of the bars, linked highlighting occurs in the Ramachandran Plot as well as in any other visualization that is being used. This

highlighting is in the form of a shadowed halo surrounding each corresponding selected data point accompanied with a tooltip displaying the given data.

Additional supplementary visualizations such as pie charts or colored histograms could also be used. Weave provides support for multiple simultaneous linked visualizations that can be displayed all at the same time.

4.4 Accompanying Statistical Editors

'The R Project', a powerful tool for statistical computations is integrated with the Ramachandran plot. The 'R text editor' is another tool available in Weave, which can be used for analysis of the protein dataset. This editor communicates with several packages of 'R'. Scripts for different types of analyses can either be written or can be pasted in. Weave provides the flexibility of storing images generated by the 'R' text editor as well.

We successfully used 'R' scripts to cluster amino acids on the basis of their different properties, such as hydrophilicity and charge.

4.5 Motif Searching

Using 'R' we developed scripts for motif searching within the protein sequence in the dataset. As seen in Figure 6, the required sequence can be pasted within the accompanying motif searcher to find any motif of interest. The retrieved searches can be highlighted in a color of choice. Motif searching can be indicative of antigenic determinants and could provide clues regarding domain conformations. Fast and thorough searches throughout the sequences could hint at potential drug targets.

5. Ramachandran Plot in Weave

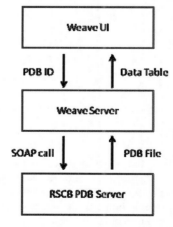

Figure 5: Flow of Control while using the Ramachandran Plot in Weave

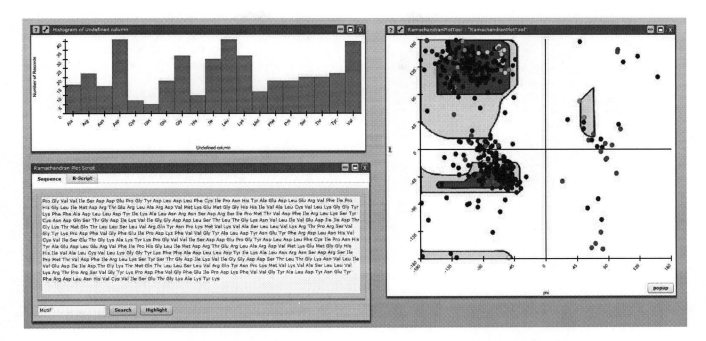

Figure 6: Ramachandran Plot in Weave shows the plot on the right, the supplementary histogram on the upper left and motif search on the bottom left.

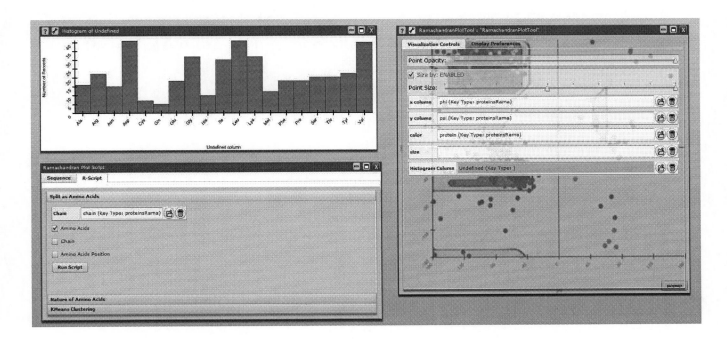

Figure 7: A pop up panel which can be moved provides additional controls for the Ramachandran Plot including the mapping of visual attributes to parameters.

Weave's interface accepts the PDB ID of a given protein, and calls the RSCB Protein Data Bank.PDB in turn returns a typical PDB file to Weave, where the file can be further mined to filter different protein properties of interest. The Ramachandran plot utilizes the Phi and Psi angles [9].

6. Conclusion

Weave not only provides an interactive Ramachandran plot but also serves as a rich visualization environment offering other tools and statistical and mathematical computational abilities. In contrast to the other similar systems, Weave enables greater user involvement and analysis.

We have described an interactive tool that has the potential for protein conformations and amino acid composition –dependent studies.

Our work focused on developing the technology required to incorporate a functional Ramachandran Plot into Weave.

7. Future Work

We are working on improving data import from the PDB of all available proteins into Weave. We intend to add a feature that provides metadata about the protein in addition to its atom coordinates and amino acid details. This metadata will include information about the protein, how and when it was discovered, and its function and purification techniques.

Visualizing biomolecules, proteins in this case, in a three dimensional space, gives us a better idea of different domains, motifs and the overall protein conformation. We will be developing parallel tools for visualizing proteins in 3D space within the Weave framework. This will be accompanied with linked highlighting throughout all current active tools giving an idea of the 3D spatial orientation of the motif of interest within the entire protein.

Although the motif searching feature is in its infancy, it holds the potential to become a very powerful mining tool which could eventually be used to search, visualize and analyze entire genomes.

We are working on a stronger coupling of the Ramachandran Plot with the advantages that the 'R project' text editor has to offer. This will be followed by a user study and evaluation.

Weave is available as an open source project [9].

References

[1] Ramachandran.G.N, Ramakrishnan.C. and Sasisekharan.V. (1963) Stereochemistry of polypeptide chain conformations. *J. Mol. Bioi*, 7, 95 - 99.

[2] S. Roy, D. Martinez, H. Platero, T. Lane, M. Werner-Washburne. Exploiting Amino Acid Composition for Predicting Protein-Protein Interactions. *PLoS ONE*, 2009, 4(11): 7813.

[3] T. Hopp, K. Wood. Prediction of protein antigenic determinants from amino acid sequences. *Proc. Nati. Acad. Sci.* USA, Vol. 78, No. 6, pp. 3824-3828, June 1981

[4] The Mysterious Regions of the Ramachandran Plot : http://boscoh.com/protein/the-mysterious-regions-of-the-ramachandran-plot

[5] Kabsch.W. and Sander.C. (1983) Dictionary of protein secondary structure: Pattern recognition of hydrogen bond and geometrical features. *Biopolymers*, 22, 2577-2637

[6] Hooft, R.W.W., Sander.C. and Vriend.G. (1996a) Verification of protein structures: Side-chain planarity. *J. Appl. Crystallography.*, 29, 714-716.

[7] Richardson, J. 1981. The anatomy and taxonomy of protein structure. *Adv. Protein Chem.* **34**167–339.

[8] Richardson, J.S. and Richardson, D.C. 1988. Amino acid preferences for specific locations at the ends of α helices. *Science* **240** 1648–1652.

[9] The Open Indicator Consortium (OIC): www.openindicators.org

[10] Gopalakishnan K, Saravanan S, Sarani R, Sekar K. *RPMS*: Ramachandran plot for multiple structures *J. Appl. Cryst.* (2008). 41, 219-221

[11] Goran Neshich et al .STING Millenium: a web-based suite of programs for comprehensive and simultaneous analysis of protein structure and sequence. Nucleic Acids Research 31: 13 Pp 3386-3392.

Characterization of Atherosclerosis Plaque in OCT Images Using Texture Analysis and Parametric Equations

Amr Elbasiony
Computer Science
University of Massachusetts Lowell
Lowell, USA
Email: aelbasio@cs.uml.edu

Haim Levkowitz
Computer Science
University of Massachusetts Lowell
Lowell, USA
Email: haim@cs.uml.edu

Figure 1. Sample OCT speckle structure.

Abstract—It has been long thought that the main cause of a heart attack is the narrowing of an artery from the buildup of fatty plaque inside the artery wall. Postmortem autopsy studies on patients who have died after a myocardial infarction (heart attack) found that many of those did not have their arteries severely narrowed by plaque. Instead, thrombosis (blood clots) near ruptured lesions were identified as the actual main cause. The search for the type of culprit lesions has established that the formation of a lipid-rich pool covered by a thin fibrous cap (thickness less than 65 micrometer) was structurally unstable and likely to rupture. Subsequently, the term vulnerable plaque has been used to refer to this type of plaque.

Optical Coherence Tomography (OCT) is a new imaging modality capable of providing the required micrometer scale resolution to detect such tissue. With a resolution of approximately 15 micrometer, OCT is considered the most promising imaging modality for identifying vulnerable plaque.

We present a complete framework for reliable tissue characterization of different plaque types using OCT images. Our framework utilizes texture analysis as delineating features. In addition, a parametric classification technique is presented. The characterization performance of the proposed framework is assessed and evaluated.

Keywords-optical coherence tomography; texture analysis; parametric classification; framework; visualization

I. INTRODUCTION

OCT is a new imaging modality that uses safe non-ionizing infrared laser to generate high resolution images of tissues. Much like ultrasound, in which the image is built using the backscattered signal, OCT generates gray-scale images from the backscattered infrared signal. Due to its high resolution, OCT is considered the most promising imaging modality for detecting the vulnerable plaque in vivo as well as for studying its natural progression [1]–[8].

Texture analysis [9] has been utilized in both the segmentation and characterization of different types of images. While texture is a hard-to-formalize concept, it is generally described as repetitive patterns of elementary constructs formed by intensity/color variations. Texture measures can be broadly divided into three major types, spectral, statistical, and structural measures. Spectral measures are, loosely speaking, frequency domain measures that rely on the repetitive nature of texture patterns. Statistical measures, on the other hand, are spatial domain measures that rely on the ordered distribution of texture patterns. Finally, structural measures rely on the geometric properties of texture elements.

A close examination of OCT images reveals a texture structure (figure 1) formed by the distribution of intensity variation spots known as speckle. Speckle appears in OCT images as a result of multiple interferences between coherent waves [10] scattered from coarse (at the microscopic level) surfaces. While speckle is generally viewed as a source of noise, it has been suggested [11], [12] that it may be possible to use texture analysis to differentiate between tissue types based on features of their speckle.

To date only a few attempts have been made to utilize OCT speckle texture analysis. Qi et al. [13], [14] used center-symmetric auto-correlation (CSAC) for the texture features and principal component analysis (PCA) for the classification to develop computer-aided diagnosis CAD algorithms that aid the detection of dysplasia in Barrett's esophagus. Jang et al. [15], [16] used the normalized standard deviation as a texture measure to demonstrate the capability of OCT to quantify macrophage density. Zysk and Boppart used spatial and Fourier-domain analysis to identify

1550-6037/11 $26.00 © 2011 IEEE
DOI 10.1109/IV.2011.23

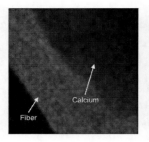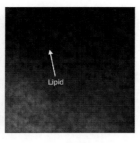

Figure 2. Closeup samples of the three plaque types.

tumors in human breast. Baroni et al. [17] estimated the first and second order gray level statistics through the histogram and the co-occurrence matrices to discriminate between different layers of retinal tissue. Lingley-Papadopoulos et al. [18] used 74 texture features representing the three approaches to texture analysis (statistical, structural, and spectral) to detect bladder cancer. Linearly correlated features were removed by calculating the correlation matrix for the feature set. Based on the results of the feature selection process, a decision tree was created to perform classification. Pitris et al. [19] used an autoregressive spectral estimation to calculate the spectral density of each section of the image. They utilized Principal Component Analysis (PCA) to reduce the number of variables per spectrum followed by Multivariate Analysis of Variance (MANOVA) to maximize the separation between categories before applying the k-Means algorithm.

Statistical texture analysis can provide valuable information about the physical properties of the imaged object. The ability to consistently quantify the intensity distribution from any arbitrary image location can provide the quantitative means to associate image content with its corresponding physical meaning.

II. FEATURE SELECTION

In tissue characterization, feature selection is the discovery of the set of quantitative measures that can best delineate between different types of tissues. The selection of the optimal feature set is not a trivial problem. Early studies utilized features similar to those employed by physicians during their diagnoses. This is not always the best strategy as most of these features tend to be qualitative and judgmental in nature, not particularly suitable for computerized techniques. Another strategy is to start with a large number of features then use a space reduction method (e.g., PCA, ICA, MANOVA) to reduce the dimensionality of the set to a practical size. This doesn't always produce an applicable feature set. In fact, it can even produce very disappointing results since these are generic techniques that don't consider any specifics about the characterization problem.

Our approach to feature selection is to first investigate the characteristics of the image textures we are trying to classify,

then propose features that can capture these characteristics as quantitative measures. Figure 2 presents closeup samples of the three plaque types. While there is an obvious difference in the intensity range between fibrous plaque and the other two types, the difference is not as clearly discernible between calcified plaque and lipid plaque. Looking at the texture element scale, one can see that fibrous plaque has the smallest texture elements while lipid plaque posses the largest texture elements. In terms of structure and order, calcified plaque comes in between the lipid plaque at the high end and the fibrous plaque at the low end (fibrous plaque has smaller rapidly changing elements that appear more random compared to the larger slowly changing elements in lipid).

We propose two texture measures to differentiate between the three types of plaque. The first measure is the normalized variance (variance divided by mean intensity value). This measure should capture the variation in the texture element size as well as the sharp versus slow transitions in the intensity values at the texture element scale. The second texture measure, entropy, is intended to quantify the structure and order in a given region. Entropy has long been used to quantify statistical correlation (lack of statistical correlation to be exact) in data analysis.

$$\sigma^2 = \frac{1}{N} \sum_{i=1}^{N} (I_i - \mu)^2 \tag{1}$$

where σ^2 is the variance. N is the number of intensity values in the selected region. I_i is the i_{th} intensity value and μ is the mean intensity given by:

$$\mu = \frac{1}{N} \sum_{i=1}^{N} I_i \tag{2}$$

$$E = - \sum_{i=1}^{N} p(I_i) \log p(I_i) \tag{3}$$

where E is the entropy and p is the probability of intensity value I_i.

III. METHOD

Our method consists of two phases. The first phase, is a learning phase where we estimate the texture parametric equations. In this phase, we collect large number of data points from the three types of plaque. We fit suitable polynomials to the data to estimate the parametric equations that govern the relationship between the normalized variance and the entropy for each of the plaque types as shown in figures 3-5.

The second phase is the characterization phase. Given an image region to characterize, we calculate the normalized variance and entropy from the given region. We call these, the observed measures. We substitute the observed normalized variance in the parametric equation of each of

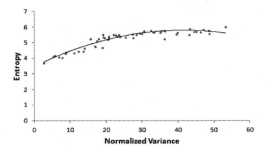

Figure 3.   Fibrous Plaque.

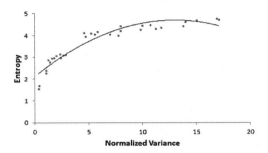

Figure 4.   Calcified Plaque.

the plaque types and calculate the corresponding entropy. We find the absolute difference between the calculated entropy and the observed entropy for each of the plaque types. The region is labeled with a given plaque type if its equation produces the minimum absolute difference between the calculated and observed entropy. If this difference is larger than the observed entropy, the region is labeled as an outlier.

IV. RESULTS AND DISCUSSIONS

Image acquisition was performed using the C7XR FD-OCT system (LightLab Imaging, Inc, Westford, Massachusetts). It provides $15\mu m$ radial resolution and $20-40\mu m$ angular resolution (depending on the radial position). The acquisition frame rate of the system is 100 frames/s (500 lines/frame) and its pullback speed is $20mm/s$.

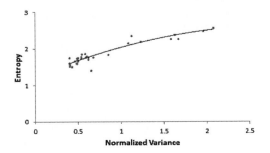

Figure 5.   Lipid Plaque.

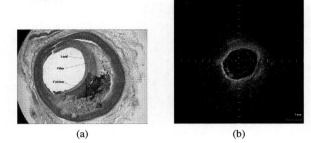

(a)   (b)

Figure 6.   Sample histology and its corresponding OCT image.

The three major atherosclerosis plaque types (fiber, calcium, and lipid) can be identified on OCT images by comparison to histology from the visual properties suggested by Yabushita et al. [1]. Fibrous plaque is generally identified as homogeneous signal rich region. In contrast, calcified plaque appears as signal poor region with sharp upper and/or lower borders. Lipid rich regions are also recognized as signal poor regions but with diffused borders as shown in figure 6.

Figures 3-5 show the results from the learning phase. Second degree polynomials were fitted to the data. The quadratic equations 4, 5 and 6 represent the results of the fit for fiberous, calcified, and lipid plaque, respectively, where E is the entropy and v is the normalized variance.

Approximately, 100 different regions were manually selected for characterization from each of the three plaque types. Due to the relatively moderate size of our data set, we implemented 30-fold cross-validation [20] to better assess the characterization performance of the model. Our data set were randomly partitioned into 30 subsets where a single subset was retained as the validation set and the remaining 29 sets were used to build the parametric model. The cross-validation process was repeated 30 times where each of the 30 subsets were used once as the validation set. The resulting parameters and performance measures were then averaged to produce the final results.

In addition to the validation set, about 30 regions were selected from the catheter, background, and randomly generated patterns to test the performance of the method in the presence of outliers. This set was used in the validation at each of the 30 repetitions.

The characterization performance of the method estimated from a 30-fold cross-validation demonstrated mean sensitivity of 100% for fiber, 76% for calcium, and 53% for lipid with specificity of 97%, 94%, and 93% respectively. This is a considerable improvement over the currently available intravascular ultrasound (IVUS) commercial system offering the virtual histology (VH) feature. The sensitivity of IVUS-VH for the detection of fibrous, fibro-fatty, and necrotic core tissue has been shown [21] to be 76.1%, 46%, and 41.1% respectively with poor specificity. Todate, tissue characterization has not yet been offered by any commercial OCT systems.

$$E = -0.0002v^2 + 0.0446v + 4.2934 \qquad (4)$$

$$E = -0.003v^2 + 0.168v + 2.758 \qquad (5)$$

$$E = -0.426v^2 + 1.596v + 0.969 \qquad (6)$$

V. Conclusion

We have presented a new method for characterizing atherosclerosis plaque in intravascular OCT images. The method has demonstrated high characterization performance and stability in the presence of outliers. The proposed method is practical and easy to implement, as well as fast enough for real time systems.

References

[1] H. Yabushita, B. E. Bouma, S. L. Houser, H. T. Aretz, I.-K. Jang, and et al., "Characterization of human atherosclerosis by optical coherence tomography," *Circulation*, vol. 106, pp. 1640–1645, 2002.

[2] J. Narula and J. Willerson, "Prologue: Detection of Vulnerable Plaque," *Journal of the American College of Cardiology*, vol. 47, no. 8, pp. C1–C1, 2006.

[3] M. Cilingiroglu, J. H. Oh, B. Sugunan, and et al., "Detection of vulnerable plaque in a murine model of atherosclerosis with optical coherence tomography," *Catheterization and Cardiovascular Interventions*, vol. 67, no. 6, pp. 915–923, 2006.

[4] D. Stamper, N. J. Weissman, and M. Brezinski, "Plaque characterization with optical coherence tomography," *Journal of the American College of Cardiology*, vol. 47, pp. 69–79, 2006.

[5] T. Kubo, T. Imanishi, and et al., "Assessment of culprit lesion morphology in acute myocardial infarction: Ability of optical coherence tomography compared with intravascular ultrasound and coronary angioscopy," *Journal of the American College of Cardiology*, vol. 50, no. 10, pp. 933–939, 2007.

[6] P. Barlis, P. Serruys, N. Gonzalo, W. van der Giessen, P. de Jaegere, and E. Regar, "Assessment of culprit and remote coronary narrowings using optical coherence tomography with long-term outcomes," *The American journal of cardiology*, vol. 102, no. 4, pp. 391–395, 2008.

[7] A. Tanaka, T. Imanishi, H. Kitabata, and et al., "Distribution and frequency of thin-capped fibroatheromas and ruptured plaques in the entire culprit coronary artery in patients with acute coronary syndrome as determined by optical coherence tomography," *The American journal of cardiology*, vol. 102, no. 8, pp. 975–979, 2008.

[8] P. Barlis, P. W. Serruys, A. DeVries, and E. Regar, "Optical coherence tomography assessment of vulnerable plaque rupture: predilection for the plaque shoulder," *European Heart Journal Advance*, vol. 29, no. 16, p. 2023, 2008.

[9] C. H. Chen, L. F. Pau, and P. S. P. W. (eds.), *The Handbook of Pattern Recognition and Computer Vision (2nd Edition).* World Scientific Publishing Co., 1998.

[10] J. W. Goodman, *Speckle phenomena in optics theory and application.* Roberts & Company, 2007.

[11] K. Gossage, T. Tkaczyk, J. Rodriguez, and J. Barton, "Texture analysis of optical coherence tomography images: feasibility for tissue classification." *Journal of biomedical optics*, vol. 8, no. 3, pp. 570–5, 2003.

[12] K. W. Gossage, C. M. Smith, E. M. Kanter, L. P. Hariri, A. L. Stone, J. J. Rodriguez, S. K. Williams, and J. K. Barton, "Texture analysis of speckle in optical coherence tomography images of tissue phantoms," *Physics in Medicine and Biology*, vol. 51, no. 6, pp. 1563–1575, 2006. [Online]. Available: http://stacks.iop.org/0031-9155/51/1563

[13] X. Qi, J. Sivak, M.V., D. Wilson, and A. Rollins, "Processing of endoscopic optical coherence tomography images for quantitative diagnosis of dysplasia," June 2003, pp. 3 pp.–.

[14] X. Qi, J. Michael V. Sivak, G. Isenberg, J. E. Willis, and A. M. Rollins, "Computer-aided diagnosis of dysplasia in barrett's esophagus using endoscopic optical coherence tomography," *Journal of Biomedical Optics*, vol. 11, no. 4, p. 044010, 2006. [Online]. Available: http://link.aip.org/link/?JBO/11/044010/1

[15] G. J. Tearney, H. Yabushita, S. L. Houser, H. T. Aretz, I.-K. Jang, and et al., "Quantification of macrophage content in atherosclerotic plaques by optical coherence tomography," *Circulation*, vol. 107, pp. 113–119, 2003.

[16] B. D. MacNeill, I.-K. Jang, B. E. Bouma, N. Iftimia, and et al., "Focal and multi-focal plaque macrophage distributions in patients with acute and stable presentations of coronary artery disease," *Journal of the American College of Cardiology*, vol. 44, pp. 972–979, 2004.

[17] M. Baroni, S. Diciotti, A. Evangelisti, P. Fortunato, and A. L. Torre, "Texture classification of retinal layers in optical coherence tomography," vol. 16, 2007, pp. 847–850.

[18] C. A. Lingley-Papadopoulos, M. H. Loew, M. J. Manyak, and J. M. Zara, "Computer recognition of cancer in the urinary bladder using optical coherence tomography and texture analysis." *Journal of biomedical optics*, vol. 13, no. 2, 2008. [Online]. Available: http://dx.doi.org/10.1117/1.2904987

[19] C. Pitris, A. Kartakoulis, and P. Ioannides, "Spectral analysis of optical coherence tomography images," Sept. 2008, pp. 60–63.

[20] R. Kohavi, "A study of cross-validation and bootstrap for accuracy estimation and model selection." Morgan Kaufmann, 1995, pp. 1137–1143.

[21] J. F. Granada, D. Wallace-Bradley, H. K. Win, C. L. Alviar, A. Builes, E. I. Lev, R. Barrios, D. G. Schulz, A. E. Raizner, and G. L. Kaluza, "In vivo plaque characterization using intravascular ultrasound-virtual histology in a porcine model of complex coronary lesions," *Arterioscler Thromb Vasc Biol*, vol. 27, no. 2, pp. 387–393, 2007. [Online]. Available: http://atvb.ahajournals.org/cgi/content/abstract/27/2/387

Multidimensional Visualization Techniques for Microarray Data

Urška Cvek[1,2], Marjan Trutschl[1,2], Phillip C. Kilgore[1], Randolph Stone II[2], John L. Clifford[2]

[1] Department of Computer Science, LSU Shreveport, USA

[2] Center for Molecular and Tumor Virology, LSU Health Sciences Center, Shreveport, USA

[3] Department of Biochemistry, LSU Health Sciences Center, Shreveport, USA

{ucvek, mtrutsch, kilgorep54}@lsus.edu, {rstone, jcliff}@lsuhsc.edu

Abstract

Analysis of high-dimensional microarray expression data is based mostly on the statistical approaches that are indispensable for the study of biological systems. To aid the analysis and exploration of such data, the process of analyzing such data is often enhanced with visual, data mining and other computational techniques. We utilize a set of tools for the visual analysis of data aimed at generating the hypotheses. We show the usability of classic and novel multi-dimensional visualization tools in life sciences. Additionally, we survey and show a few multidimensional visualization tools applied to the process of data exploration using a urothelial cell carcinoma of the bladder time course. These tools have the potential of uncovering non-trivial relationships and structures in the data.

1. Introduction

Microarrays have become the norm for simultaneous measurement of expression levels of thousands of genes. The "current/next generation" platforms have enormous promise in revealing functions of genes, cell populations, tumor classifications [1], understanding cellular pathways, drug target identification, just to name a few [2]-[3]. Biological conclusions as well as the methods applied to the signal data can be roughly divided into preprocessing and data analysis, which is further divided into data mining and visualization exploration. A variety of data mining algorithms are at hand for the subsequent task: from self-organizing maps (SOMs) [4] to hierarchical clustering - one of the most utilized data mining methods. Visualization tools range from scatter plots to dendrograms, line plots, histograms, and box plots. Modern visualization tools and techniques targeted towards high-dimensional data remain heavily underutilized. A quick survey of the publications applying multidimensional visualizations in bioinformatics indicates that manuscripts using such tools are mostly published in the information visualization and scientific visualization rather than life

science domain. In 2004, Saraiya et al. evaluated the use of visualization tools by biologists and discovered that there is an overwhelming variety of tools to chose from, causing confusion [5]. A similar survey has been recently completed by Gehlenborg et al. [6]

Novel multidimensional visualization techniques enable display of large, high-dimensional datasets in a meaningful, more descriptive manner. They have been shown to have a very high intrinsic dimensionality [7] and the ability to uncover non-trivial patterns and relationships in the data. We combine these visualizations with the topology-preserving neural network and projection technique, the SOM [8], enabling the discovery of previously unknown relationships.

We are using a dataset of the urothelial cell carcinoma (UCC) of the bladder generated by the Clifford Lab at LSUHSC-S to illustrate these novel data analysis techniques [9]. In Section 2, we discuss the setup and processing of the UCC dataset. We continue with the description of multidimensional visualizations, including parallel coordinates and Radviz, and their intrinsic dimensionality in Section 3. Section 4 is a discussion of SOMs, their extensions and combination with multidimensional visualization techniques. In Section 5 we combine the techniques and apply them to the UCC dataset.

2. Urothelial cell carcinoma dataset

Urothelial cell carcinoma of the bladder (UCC) ranks 4th in incidence of all cancers in the developed world, yet the mechanisms of its origin and progression remain poorly understood. The transgenic mice, UPII-SV40T [10], develop a condition closely resembling human carcinoma *in situ* (CIS) starting as early as 6 weeks of age, progressing to invasive UCC from 6 months onward. We determined the relative expression level on a set of duplicated microarrays for two factors: mouse genotype (WT or SV40T) and week (3, 6, 20, 30) creating eight targets [9].

We characterized the histologic progression of premalignant, carcinoma in-situ, early invasive UCC and more advanced invasive UCC occurring at 3, 6, 20 and

1550-6037/11 $26.00 © 2011 IEEE

DOI 10.1109/IV.2011.37

30 weeks of age, respectively, in the UPII-SV40T mice [17]. Preliminary analysis using the Ingenuity Pathways Analysis software package (Ingenuity Systems Inc.) revealed that cell cycle regulatory, DNA replication, and cancer related genes were more strongly expressed in the SV40T bladder urothelium at the highest proportion, even at the 3-week point.

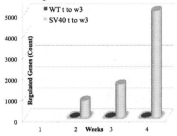

Figure 1 Gene regulation at 6, 20 and 30 weeks for the WT and SV40T lines.

We identified genes that are differentially expressed between the bladders of SV40T mice and their age-matched wild type (WT) littermates at 3, 6, 20 and 30 weeks of age. Figure 1 shows the counts of up and down regulated genes for each of the lines, when compared to the first time point for the WT. As expected, virtually no regulation is present in the WT. An exponential increase in regulation for the SV40T line from approximately 1,300 to 2,100 and 4,400 at time points 6, 20 and 30 is observed (Fig. 2).

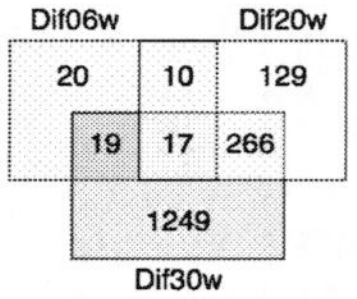

Figure 2 Two-way analysis confirms the increased regulation in the SV40T line.

We further analyzed the set of 585 genes that are differentially expressed at the early stages, namely weeks 6 and 20 (Fig. 2). We tested several of the genes upregulated in SV40T urothelium, including hyaluronan mediated motility receptor (RHAMM), RacGAP1, PCNA and others as biomarkers for premalignancy, in urine samples from a completed chemoprevention trial.

3. Multidimensional visualizations

It is difficult to display datasets of four or more dimensions on a two-dimensional (2D) screen, or a piece of paper, with no loss of insight. Two of the dimensions of the data can be represented as x and y coordinates while the other dimensions map to the color, texture, size, and shape of a record. With human perceptual ability limited to three to four dimensions tracked on a visual display [18], our goal is to identify multidimensional tools that can accommodate medium and large datasets to aid the process of visual knowledge exploration.

We can divide the multidimensional techniques into three sets. The first set of techniques is focused on the reduction of the data size and preservation of its significant features. Pixel level visualization schemes allow for the display of a large number of records are not scalable and depend on the size of the display area [19]. The second set of techniques is based on matrices [20-22] as one of the techniques first utilized to address this problem. A scatter plot matrix, for example, shows all pairwise scatterplots, mirrored across the diagonal. The problem with this approach is the growth of the scatter plot matrix as the number of dimensions increases. The third set of techniques is the group of line-based (i.e., parallel coordinates) and point projections (i.e., Radviz). Parallel coordinates use parallel axes instead of perpendicular axes for mapping of dimensional values [23-24]. Radviz [25] positions dimensional anchors around the perimeter of a circle using Hooke's law. Visual effectiveness of these visualizations can be measured to determine their benefits.

3.1. Parallel coordinates

The parallel coordinates (PC) [23-24] algorithm has been applied to a wide range of data analysis tasks. They can display a large number of dimensions of a dataset, but suffer from the disadvantage that the number of records that can be displayed is limited. Visualizing a medium or larger size dataset usually results in over-plotting or clutter, a featureless blob, which hides the underlying data structure. Regardless of their application, we can group existing techniques based on their topology into 2D and 3D techniques.

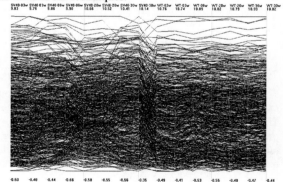

Figure 3 Parallel coordinates of the 585 early changing genes of the UCC data.

PCs can be augmented with information displays or interactive tools such as histograms, frequency or density information, glyphs, etc. Average shifted histograms visualize density plots with PCs [26-27] aiming to remove the problem of dimension's bins or frequency intervals. This approach is extended by painting pixels of polylines with intensity proportional to the pixel's record overlap [28]. Artero et al. [29] create an interactive PCs frequency and density plot. Visual data mining displays [30] use cluster centroids placed on top of the PCs and tracked statistical measures displayed as static or animated glyphs in a separate coordinate system. SpringView [31] explores coupled multiple views of Radviz and PCs and applies brushing, color and data clustering. PCs have also been interactively linked with star glyphs, scatter plots and dimensional stacking [32]-[25], among others.

In Figure 3 we show the over-plotting or occlusion that occurs when visualizing the set of 585 unique UCC genes that are differentially expressed in SV40T line at week 6 and/or week 20. We display all of the 15 dimensions of this dataset and order them by first listing the SV40T lines followed by the WT lines. We cannot notice any significant differences across the dimensions, although we can detect that majority of the records have low to mid values. There are only a few records with high signal values. We notice a dip in the expressions in the center of the display, which is due to the switch from the SV40T dimensions to the WT dimensions and is not a true pattern in the dataset.

3.2. Radviz

Figure 4 Example of Radviz spring forces of an 8-dimensional record.

Radviz (radial visualization) is a radial display technique places dimensional anchors (dimensions) around the perimeter of a circle and utilizes spring constants to represent relational values among points. The record in Figure 4 has 8 dimensions ordered on the circle in counter-clockwise equidistant fashion. Each position vector points from (0,0) to the corresponding fixed point on the perimeter of a unit circle. The values of each dimension are usually normalized to a 0 to 1 range to eliminate any effects of the variable minimum and maximum values in the range. Each data point is displayed at the point where the sum of all spring forces equals zero and the stiffness of each spring is proportional to the value of the corresponding dimension. The point ends up at the position where the spring forces are in equilibrium. The position of the data point depends largely on the arrangement of dimensions around the circle; however, vectors with similar dimensional values are always placed close together. The technique has been complemented by dimension ordering approaches, where the dimension order is determined by the structure of the data or the inherent class separation [31], [36-37] and 3D extensions [38].

One of the major disadvantages of Radviz is the overlap of points that occurs not only when the records have identical values on the displayed dimensions, but also when the records are scaled. For example, records (1,1,1,1,1,1) and (10,10,10,10,10,10) would appear at the same location in the center of the circle (they are pulled by all dimensions equally). Dimension ordering and placement of dimensions away from the radial layout minimizes this problem, but does not completely solve it. We developed an approach that utilizes the third dimension to organize the data when overlap occurs.

Upon the examination of the Radviz display of the SV40T line on the 585 early differentially expressed genes of the UCC dataset (Fig. 5), we noticed that majority of them are either in the center (pulled equally by all dimensions) or positioned towards the bottom of the visualization. We can conclude that the signal values at the 30-week time point are relatively large and that our genes are more likely up-regulated. When we show the UP or DOWN regulation for the genes as the record color, we can confirm this.

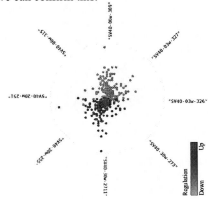

Figure 5 Radviz display of the 585 early changing genes of the UCC data.

4. Self-Organizing Map

The SOM is an unsupervised neural network that facilitates mapping of a set of n-dimensional vectors to a two-dimensional grid [8]. Training of the unsupervised neural network is data-driven, without a target condition; therefore, the output of a SOM algorithm represents the relationships among the input vectors. SOM is a great summarization technique, effectively reducing the complexity of the dataset by displaying clusters of the data in a grid. Its widespread use is attributed to its simplicity.

The learning of the SOM is the process in which a nonlinear projection of the records onto a map is performed. The self-organizing grid or map consists of an array of output nodes (neurons), each of them associated with an n-dimensional weight vector n_i (corresponding to the n dimensions of the input dataset). Initial values of n_i may be randomly selected, preferably based on the values in the dataset. Each randomly selected record is positioned on the map, one by one, until the dataset is exhausted. The process is repeated to achieve convergence.

A record is mapped onto the SOM by calculating the similarity between the input vector and node i's weight vector n_i. Each node i receives the same input vector and produces a single similarity value. The input record maps onto the best-matching (winning) node w, based on the largest similarity coefficient or the smallest distance (depending on the implementation). The weight vectors of nodes topologically close to the winning node (up to a certain geometric distance) adjust their weight vectors, learning about the current input. The adjustment depends on the size of the neighborhood, the value of the neighboring function and the learning function. This process is repeated until the output map converges to a stable or organized state when the average error falls below a pre-specified value or a certain number of iterations have been reached.

Most SOMs are visualized on a rectangular display of output nodes, although hexagonal and irregular grids are also used. Numerous SOM algorithms and extensions have been developed in a multitude of fields, which include biomedical applications. One of the seminal applications of SOMs in the biomedical arena was the work by Tamayo et al. [4] in which SOMs were used to find the classes in 828 genes of the Yeast cell cycle.

5. Combining SOM with multidimensional visualizations

5.1. 3D PC and 3D Radviz algorithms

The original SOM algorithm only has one mapping step at which the output node for the record is determined. Our algorithm consists of primary and secondary mapping steps in the effort to merge the SOM and a multidimensional visualization. For the 3D *parallel coordinates,* we first start by replacing the original dimensional axes by grids of output nodes and then proceed with a two-step mapping process (Fig. 6).

Primary mapping determines the location for a record on the dimensional axis, just as in the original step, but mapping to a primary bin that has been created by the grid in the y dimension. The *secondary mapping* replaces the single grid cell is by the single-dimensional set of SOM output nodes to which the record can map. The output node is chosen based on the Euclidean distance between the record and representative weight vectors of the output grid (Fig. 6). Records with similar dimensional values are placed closer together in three dimensions through the repetition of the two mapping steps using the neighborhood and learning function.

The organization of records into the three PC dimensions provides a larger surface on which the records' polylines can be organized onto, which helps remove the overlap/occlusion, but does not completely eliminate it. One of the options we provide to resolve these is *bundling* of records. We represent the records plotted in a 3D PC plot mathematically in the form of Bezier curves (replacing polylines) grouping similar records together. To set the number of bundles in the y and z directions, we implemented partitioning of the

plane into a number of partitions. The second option we provide is *force-directed record placement.* This approach utilizes weight vectors used for self-organization along the grids. Using these weights, nodes are either pushed apart or pulled together, depending upon their similarity.

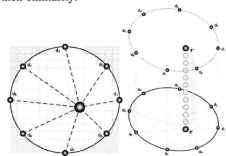

Figure 6 Binned Radviz surface and secondary mapping into the third dimension.

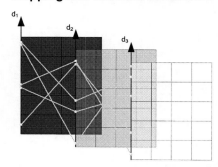

Figure 7 Primary and secondary mapping steps of our 3D PC algorithm.

For the 3D *Radviz* we first start by placing the records based on the original Radviz algorithm. The main difference is that instead of positioning it in by the original algorithm, we grid the Radviz surface and position the record into its primary bin (Fig. 7). The position is then augmented in the *secondary mapping* step, where we build a single-dimensional SOM at each Radviz grid cell into the third dimension. The same process is repeated for all of the records, adjusting based on the neighborhood and learning function and stopping after no learning takes place (or it falls below a certain threshold). The neighborhood affects the three dimensions (x, y, z) as all of the neighboring output nodes are adjusted.

5.2. Application to the UCC dataset

Figure 8 shows the binned parallel coordinates plot of the 585 records that are differentially expressed early (weeks 6 and 20). We are displaying one replicate at the 3, 6, 20 and 30-week points (in order from left to right) of the SV40T line. The data is colored by the 30-week time point (the dimension furthest to the right). If we compare it to the original parallel coordinates plot, it is less cluttered, as the records have been collapsed into the bins (10 bins were created for each dimension). The points appear to distribute evenly on each dimension.

There is a lot of occlusion and the only way that structure like this can be explored further is by utilizing brushing, selection, filtering and similar interaction techniques.

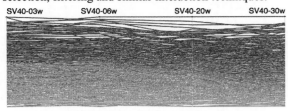

Figure 8 585 records of the SV40T set, 4 time points, and colored by regulation in week 30.

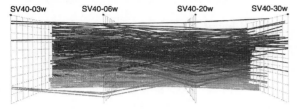

Figure 9 Records move along the *z*-axis based on their dimensional values.

Our next step was to explore the projection using the 3D PC, which position a grid of 10x10 output nodes at each of the dimensional axes (Fig. 9). We can start discovering more structure – not all the records that have the same dimensional values continue to stay together in the third dimension. We can observe that while some of the records have higher dimensional values, most of them do not stay at the high value across all dimensions but rather project onto the low or medium dimensional values in majority of the dimensions.

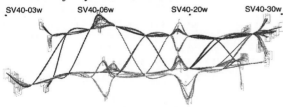

Figure 10 Force-directed record placement and bundling of the 585 UCC records.

A bundling approach is applied to the data (Fig. 10). Records with similar expression values are bundled together thus reducing clutter. To create an even more descriptive display, we apply a force-directed placement of records. Output nodes associated with a grid at each dimension are pulled together whenever the output nodes contain similar weight vectors or repelled when the values in the neighboring output nodes are dissimilar. This helps to further reduce clutter and provide for a cleaner set of data patterns to be explored interactively. Moreover, this process separates related records into distinct groups. Each of the 585 records belongs to one of the clusters associated with each dimension. There are four such clusters associated with SV40-03w, five with SV40-06w and so on. We provide a sample cross-eye

stereo pair of the 3D Parallel Coordinates visualization from Figure 10 [39].

The 3D Radviz approach moves the 585 record set into the third dimension based on all or a subset of dimensional values (Fig. 11). The pull is driven by the self-organization of the data. We color the records by the regulation, creating a color map from red (up-regulated) to green (down-regulated). The distribution of signal values of the data is not uniform, with more values at the lower end of the range. It is important to note that we do not only provide for self-organization of the data within a classic visualization, in this case Radviz, but at the same time also address and virtually eliminate the effect of occlusion. Records that continue to overlap are either the same or have similar dimensional values.

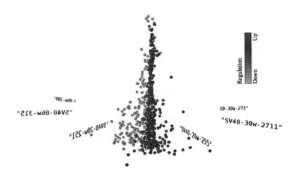

Figure 11 3D Radviz projection of all 8 dimensions of the SV40T line.

Conclusions

We emphasize the importance of multidimensional visualization tools in the knowledge discovery process of microarray and other life science data. We discuss the details of two visualization techniques: parallel coordinates and Radviz, which we combine with the self-organizing map projection to showcase novel data exploration methods. We examine the UCC dataset from which we already obtained meaningful leads that have been confirmed in the laboratory setting.

Acknowledgements

The project was supported by NIH Grant Numbers P20RR016456 and P20RR018724 from the National Center for Research Resources. The content is solely the responsibility of the authors and does not necessarily represent the official views of the National Center for Research Resources or the National Institutes of Health.

References

[1]   T.R. Golub, D.K. Slonim, P. Tamayo, et al. Molecular classification of cancer: class discovery and class prediction by gene expression monitoring. *Science* 286(5439), pp. 531-537, 1999.

[2]   P.T. Spelman, G. Sherlock, M.Q. Zhang, V.R. Iyer, K. Anders, M.B. Eisen, P.O. Brown, D. Botstein, B. Fucher.

Comprehensive identification of cell-cycle regulated genes of the Yeast Saccharomyces Cerevisiae by Microarray Hybridization. *Molecular Biology of the Cell*, 9(12), pp. 3273-3297, 1998.

[3] T. Zhang, R. Ramakrishnan, M. Livny. Birch: an efficient data clustering method for very large databases. *Proc.Int. Conf. Management of Data,* pp. 103-114, 1996.

[4] P. Tamayo, D. Slonim, J. Mesirov, Q. Zhu, S. Kitareewan, E. Dmitrovsky, E.S. Lander, T.R. Golub. Interpreting patterns of gene expression with self-organizing maps: methods and application to hematopoietic differentiation. *Proc. Atl. Acad. Sci.,* 96(6), pp. 2907-2912, 1999.

[5] P. Saraiya, C. North, K. Duca. An evaluation of microarray visualization tools for biological insight. *Proc. Information Visualization 2004*, pp. 1-8, 2004.

[6] N. Gehlenborg, et al. Visualization of omics data for systems biology, Nature Methods, Vol. 7 (3), pp.S56-68.

[7] G. Grinstein, M. Trutschl, U. Cvek, High-dimensional visualizations. *7th ACM/SIGKDD Data mining Conference (KDD), 2001.*

[8] T. Kohonen, Self-organized formation of topologically correct feature maps. *Biological Cybernetics*, 1982.

[9] R. Stone, A.L. Sabichi, J. Gill, I-L Lee, R. Loganantharaj, M. Trutschl, U. Cvek, J.L. Clifford. Identification of genes involved in early stage bladder cancer progression, Cancer Prev. Res., 3:776-786, 2010.

[10] Z.T. Zhang, J. Pak, E. Shapiro, T.T. Sun, X.R. Wu. Urothelium-specific expression of an oncogene in transgenic mice induced the formation of carcinoma in situ and invasive transitional cell carcinoma. *Cancer Res.*, 59(14), pp. 3512-7, 1999.

[11] R. Gentleman, V. Carey, et al. (editors) *Bioinformatics and Computational Biology Solutions Using R and Bioconductor*, Springer, 2005.

[12] R. Gentleman, W. Huber. Working with Affymetrix data: estrogen, a 2x2 factorial design example. Practical Microarray Course, Heidelberg, 2003.

[13] R Development Core Team. *R: A Language and Environment for Statistical Computing*. R Foundation for Statistical Computing, Vienna Austria, 2008.

[14] R.C. Gentleman, V.J. Carey, D.M. Bates, B. Bolstad, M. Dettling, S. Dudoit S, et al. Bioconductor: open software development for computational biology and bioinformatics. *Genome Biology*, 5(10), R80, 2004.

[15] G.K. Smyth. Limma: Linear models for microarray data. *Bioinformatics and Computational Biology Solutions using R and Bioconductor.* R. Genleman, V. Carey, S. Dudoit, R. Irizarry, W. Huber (ed.), pp. 397-420, 2005.

[16] L. Gautier, L. Cope, B.M. Bolstad, R.A. Irizarry. affy--analysis of Affymetrix GeneChip data at the probe level. *Bioinformatics,* 12(3), pp. 307-315, 2004.

[17] R. Stone, A.L. Sabichi, J. Gill, I-L Lee, R. Loganantharaj, M. Trutschl, U. Cvek, J.L. Clifford. Identification of genes involved in early stage bladder cancer progression, Cancer Prev. Res., 3:776-786, 2010.

[18] J. Farrington, From the Research: Myths Worth Dispelling: Seven plus or minus two. Performance Improvement Quarterly 23(4) 113–116, 2011.

[19] D. Keim, H. Kriegel, M. Ankerst. Recursive pattern: a technique for visualizing very large amounts of data. *Proc. Visualization 1995*, pp. 279-286, 1995.

[20] D.F. Andrews. Plots of high-dimensional data. *Biometrics*, 29, pp. 125-136, 1972.

[21] J.M. Chambers, W.S. Cleveland, B. Kleiner, P.A. Tukey. *Graphical Methods for Data Analysis*, 1976.

[22] J. Bertin, *Semiology of Graphics: Diagrams, Networks, Maps.* University of Wisconsin, Madison, WI, 1983.

[23] A. Inselberg, The plane with parallel coordinates. *The Visual Computer*, pp. 69-92, 1985.

[24] A. Inselberg, B. Dimsdale, Parallel coordinates: A tool for visualizing multidimensional geometry. *Proc. IEEE Visualization*, pp. 361-378, 1990.

[25] P. Hoffman, G. Grinstein. Dimensional anchors: a graphic primitive for multidimensional multivariate information visualizations. Presented at NPIV 99, 1999.

[26] J.J. Miller, E.J. Wegman, Construction of line densities for parallel coordinate plots. Computational Statistics and Graphics, eds. A. Buja, P. Tukey, Springer-Verlag, pp. 107-123, 1990.

[27] E.J. Wegman, Hyperdimensional data analysis using parallel coordinates. Journal of American Statistical Association, 85 (411), pp. 664-675, 1990.

[28] E.J. Wegman, Q. Luo, High dimensional clustering using parallel coordinates and the grand tour. Proc. Conf. German Classification Society, Freiburg, 1996.

[29] A.O. Artero, M.C. Ferreira de Oliveira, H. Levkowitz, Uncovering Clusters in Crowded Parallel Coordinates Visualizations. Proc. IEEE Symposium on Information Visualization, pp. 81-88, 2004.

[30] D. Ericson, J. Johansson, M. Cooper, Visual data analysis using tracked statistical measures within parallel coordinate representations. Proc. 3rd IEEE Conference on Coordinated and Multiple Views in Exploratory Visualization, pp. 42-53, 2005.

[31] E. Bertini, L. Dell' Aquila, G. Santucci, Springview: cooperation of Radviz and parallel coordinates or view optimization and clutter reduction. Proc. 3rd IEEE International Conference on Coordinated & Multiple Views in Exploratory Visualization, pp. 22-29, 2005.

[32] P.C. Wong, R.D. Bergeron, Multivariate visualization using metric scaling. Proc. IEEE Vis., pp. 111-118, 1997.

[33] Y.-H. Fua, M.O. Ward, E.A. Rundensteiner, Hierarchical parallel coordinates for exploration of large datasets. *IEEE 5th Int. Conference on Info. Vis.*, 425-432, 2001.

[34] M.O. Ward, XmdvTool: Integrating multiple methods for visualizing multivariate data. *Proc. IEEE Visualization 1994*, pp. 326-333, 1994.

[35] J. Yang, A. Patro, S. Huang, N. Mehta, M.O. Ward, E.A. Rundensteiner, Value and relation display for interactive exploration of high dimensional datasets. Proc. IEEE Symp. on Information Visualization 2004, pp. 73-80.

[36] G. Leban, I. Bratko, U. Petrovic, T. Curk, B. Zupan. VizRank: finding informative data projections in functional genomics by machine learning. *Bioinformatics*, 21, 2005.

[37] P. Au, M. Carey, S. Sewraz, Y. Guo, S. Ruger. New paradigms in information visualization. *Proc. 23rd International ACM SIGIR Conf.*, Athens, Greece, 2000.

[38] L. Novakova, O. Stepankova, Multidimensional clusters in RadViz, Proc. WSEAS Int. Conf. on Sim., Modeling and Optimization, pp. 470-475, 2006.

[39] http://dl.dropbox.com/u/18739750/IVBI2011/3D-PC.png

Interactive Animated Visualizations of Breast, Ovarian Cancer and Other Health Indicator Data using Weave, an Interactive Web–based Analysis and Visualization Environment

Shweta Purushe, Georges Grinstein, Mary Beth Smrtic and Helen Lyons
Institute for Visualization and Perception Research, Department of Computer Science,
University of Massachusetts, Lowell
{shweta_purushe@student.uml.edu, grinstein@cs.uml.edu}

Abstract

Recent research in genomics and biomedical studies has shown a relationship between heredity, mutations in certain genes and the corresponding probabilities of developing certain cancers. In this study we looked at breast and ovarian cancer distributions across all states and counties in the United States over time. We describe briefly Weave, our Web–based Analysis and Visualization Environment and use it to explore these cancers and present interactive animated visualizations of family hereditary patterns and genetic distributions, not only for these cancers, but also for other life-threatening cancers and related health indicators. We also show how Weave can be used to integrate other diverse epidemiological data, in particular obesity, and explore its relationship with cancer data.

1. Introduction

Breast cancer and ovarian cancer are the leading life-threatening cancers in women today. Breast cancer has a lifetime risk of > 10% and ovarian cancer, although more rare, is also lethal with a lifetime risk of 1.71% Research in the past decade has attributed mutations in tumor suppressor genes to an increased predisposition to developing both these cancers. These genes are primarily BRCA1 and BRCA2. Based on breast cancer families with multiple and/or early-onset cases, estimates of the lifetime risk of breast cancer in carriers of BRCA1 or BRCA2 mutations may be as high as 85% and 54% for ovarian cancer [1, 2, 3 and 5].

Although some breast and ovarian cancers have a hereditary component, others seem to be sporadic (non–inherited) [5]. Such sporadic occurrences may be attributed to a number of environmental and/or lifestyle factors such as exposure to carcinogens, lifestyle preferences or addictions [1, 2]. To identify which environmental or life-style factors could be associated with increased risk of developing cancer is a daunting task as manual inspection of raw data is tedious, time consuming and error-prone. For this reason, visualization is used to allow researchers to quickly identify patterns of interest in large datasets. With interactive visualization and animation the researchers can explore data more quickly most often by selecting specific data or parameters on fly. Interactive visualizations have been used to study cancer data in a variety of ways.

In 2000 Carr used micromap plots of linked panel graphs [6] and in 2006 he used conditional choropleth maps supplementing an interactive visualization tool for displaying cancer statistics [7]. These tools enabled hypothesis generation and communicating patterns in statistical summaries. Robinson developed the Exploratory Spatio-Temporal Analysis Toolkit, a collection of geo-visualization tools for cancer spread data [8].

The National Cancer Institute (NCI) has funded a number of projects to map the spread of cancer incidence and mortality rates [8]. These have lead to a significant improvement in understanding the regional, environmental and socio-economic differences associated with cancer rates across the United States.

Most of the systems developed through these projects as well as many other commercial systems are not web-based, lack support for multiple visualizations and data sets and more importantly are difficult to extend.

We developed a web-based interactive visualization system, Weave, with the Open Indicators Consortium [www.openindicators.org]. Weave is a high-performance interactive visualization system (large datasets with high interaction response) providing a number of different visualizations tools including linegraphs, scatterplots, bargraphs, radial visualization and histograms for example. Visualization tools are linked so that actions on one tool are simultaneously reflected in all other visualizations. Data subset generation, subset visualization and linked highlighting throughout all the visualizations enable better user involvement and analysis.

1550-6037/11 $26.00 © 2011 IEEE
DOI 10.1109/IV.2011.108

Weave also includes statistical and mathematical calculation tools including an equation editor and an 'R-project text' editor. The former allows calculation of new metrics using the attributes from the datasets. The 'R-text' editor for script generation enables Weave to interact online with various R packages enabling quick on- the-fly statistical calculations that aid further analysis.

Weave supports visualizing several diverse and distributed datasets. For example rather than just visualizing breast cancer incidence rates across the United States , datasets on pollution, obesity or other socio-economic factors can also be tied into a single visualization in a single instance.

We used Weave to observe the trends of these cancers across the United States down to county level when possible. We explored visualizations of cancer statistics over a period of nearly ten years looking at the trends in incidence and death rates from both breast and ovarian cancers. The Weave visualizations were used to explore the data to identify possible relationships between the cancer data and other health indicators such as obesity. This same software was used to create presentations.

2. Motivation

Although a large number of research articles have been focused on understanding the causes, risk factors, heredity and occurrence of these cancers, additional studies are needed to understand the spread of the implicated heredity factors over given geographic locations. Data for this type of research is becoming more accessible as national organizations continue to accumulate cancer incidence and related data. To date, simple visualizations have been used to study these data sets, highlighting discernable statistics, however, there has not yet been a concerted effort to visualize, explore and link other variables to identify causalities involving socio-economic and environmental factors such as education, health standards, employment and life style preferences. Visualizing such relationships may help hint at specific suspected causes or new contributing factors currently not addressed by public health professionals.

3. Methods

Breast and ovarian cancer data and statistics at the U.S. state level was collected from the Center for Disease Control and Prevention (CDC) while county-level data was collected from Surveillance Epidemiology and End Results (SEER) [9, 10]. The state-level data, covered the years 1999 to 2006 while the county-level data covered the period from 2002 to 2006. As this was a preliminary study, only incidence and death rates were used. Other available data, including incidence population, incidence counts, death population and death counts were not considered since they were utilized in the calculation of the age-adjusted incidence and death rates.

In both cases (CDC and SEER data), the incidence rate was per 100,000 individuals and was age-adjusted to the 2000 U.S. standard population (19 age groups - Census P25-1130). Rates provided by both the CDC and SEER were suppressed in cases where there were fewer than 16 in any category (area, ethnicity etc) or when requested by a state or metropolitan area. The data obtained from CDC and from SEER includes only invasive cancer data and omits cancer reoccurrences.

The data collected from the CDC varies from that collected from the SEER program. The CDC provides annual incidence rates, while SEER provides a single rate for each state for the full four-year period from 2002-2006.

The data had to be cleaned by removing missing values and the additional statistics that had been reported for geographical regions within the U.S. were also removed. As a result only state and county level data remained in the final dataset.

The cancer statistics were used to find correlations if any, with other types of data. Percent obesity for each state was used to find a correlation with breast cancer.

4. Results

4.1. Visualization and Inferences

A number of different interactive visualizations and animated visualizations were created to study 10 years of cancer data. We present a few slides but these do not do justice to the interaction support for exploration or the interactive animations that can be generated with Weave [11]. A video which demonstrates the use of Weave to investigate this data is available at www.openindicators.org.

4.2. Hypothesis generation

In addition to identifying interesting patterns, visualizations can be used to find correlations with potential causes, which have not yet been discovered, although proving or disproving such correlations will still require corroborating scientific studies. We give a simple example of the use of Weave to generate a hypothesis between incidence of cancer and obesity.

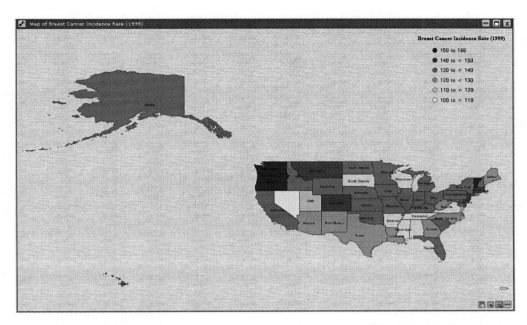

Figure 1: Incidence of Breast Cancer of the United States in 1999. States shown in the background color are those with missing data. This visualization shows an area of high incidence in the northwest and a generalized high incidence, ranging from 130-140 (number of individuals diagnosed with breast cancer per 1000,000 individuals), over most of the northern states.

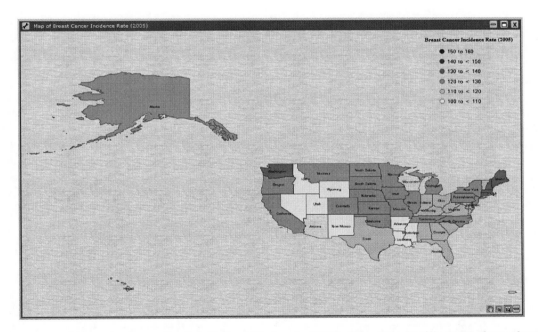

Figure 2: Incidence of Breast cancer in the United States in 2005. Compared with 1999 data shown in Figure 1, this visualization shows a marked decrease in the incidence of breast cancer with the rates of 130 or higher (dark pink) appearing in the far northwest and the far northeast.

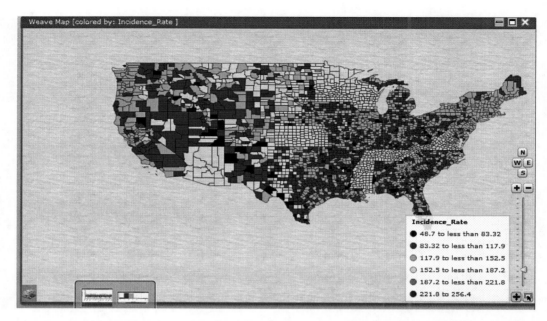

Figure 3: Incidence of Breast Cancer across United States counties from 2002-2006. The visualization shows a further decrease in breast cancer incidence. In this case the data is displaced at the county level. Those counties which display the background color (appear blank) are those for which data is missing or unavailable. The Shackelford, Hardeman and Cottles counties in Texas show the highest incidence rate (dark red and orange).

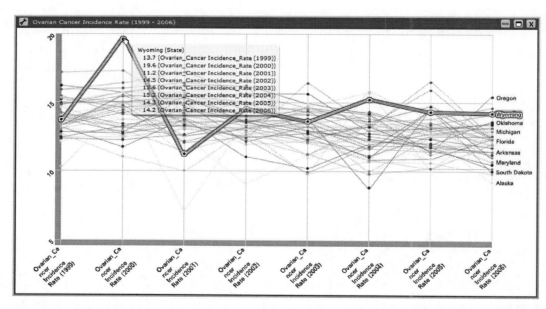

Figure 4: Profiles of death rates due to ovarian cancer in the United States from 1999 to 2006. Interaction allows users to observe the details of every state in a tooltip as seen above. Wyoming shows an undulation with an alternating increases and decreases in death rates.

250

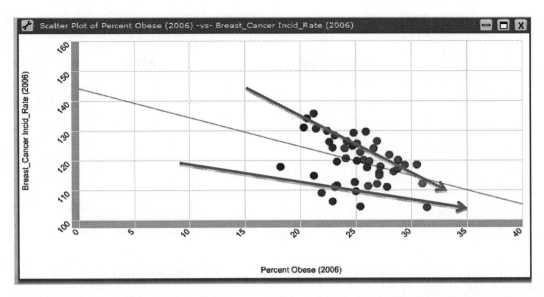

Figure 5: An attempt to visualize relatedness between different health indicators, percent obese and breast cancer in this case, in Weave. In this visualization, each point on the scatterplot represents one state. The points are positioned on the X-axis based on the percentage of the population within the state that is classified as obese (percent obese).

5. Discussion

Comparing Figures 1 and 2, at the end of 1999, we see that many of the states showed breast cancer rates of 130 or higher. By the mid 2000s, the incidence rates drop significantly across the country. Different factors could cause or explain this trend. Significantly increased disease awareness, more affordable health insurance plans or healthier changes in the population's lifestyle are possible factors. However it is also possible that another uninvestigated cause led to a significantly high incidence rate in 1999. Such investigations are time consuming and that's where Weave comes in.

The visualization shows a high incidence of breast cancer in the far northeast and in the far northwest. In addition, a higher incidence of cancer seems to prevail in the northern states whereas the southern states show a comparatively lower incidence rate. It would definitely be interesting to study why the northeast and the northwest show similar high rates. What do these two regions have in common and what factors are starkly different which nonetheless contribute to a similar high cancer incidence?

Figure 1 also shows that some states have missing data (displayed without any color). While collecting data from CDC and SEER, the data reported from some states did not match the publication requirements of the United States Cancer Statistics (USCS). Some states did not report data, although the CDC mentions that their data did meet publication standards. It would be worthwhile

to visualize the trend in the readiness of certain states to provide vital cancer statistics over time.

Figure 5 shows a negative correlation between percent obesity and the probability of developing breast cancer. One possible reason for this could be the difference in test populations contributing to the statistics. The entire population that was counted in the obesity study was not necessarily tested for breast or ovarian cancer. In addition the cancer study included only women whereas the obesity study included both men and women. This highlights the importance of using different visualization tools within Weave to gain quick insight on correlation between different datasets.

In addition it was observed that the groups of states on either side of the regression line map to different regions of the United States. The states below the regression line are mostly western states and the ones above eastern. Although the reason does not seem obvious it would be worthwhile to study further.

In this paper we cannot show Weave's interactive animated visualizations (see videos at [11]) which dramatically convey changes over a time period. By using a time or dimension slider, visualizations can show trends over time. Since the user can probe, query and thus interact with the data while the animation is progressing much insight can be gained and learned from the animations.

6. Conclusion

Weave was used not only to create interesting animated visualizations but also to visualize profiles of incidence and death rates of breast and ovarian cancers over a decade.

It would be incorrect to suggest that visualizations alone could identify the factors implicated in cancer spread. However with the plethora of cancer data and statistics available, Weave can help narrow the focus of experimentation to those factors which show a strong correlation. In addition any unexpected results could pave the way for further research studies. Weave provides a quick, efficient and comprehensive environment for clinicians, epidemiologists and heath care professionals to present important data and statistics to the general public.

7. Further Studies

We will continue to use Weave to study more and different types of cancers. We will study cancers across the globe and across different ethnicities and extrapolate the results to possible implicated genes. Our next focus of study is the occurrence of breast and ovarian cancers in the Ashkenazi Jewish population. The penetrance of the BRCA1 and BRCA2 genes is known to be significant in this community. We will map the epidemiological spread of hereditary breast and ovarian cancers across the United States and ultimately on a global level.

Interactive animated visualizations encourage hypothesis generation and experimentation. Visualization of relationships between cancers and lifestyle attributes such as obesity, education and pollution are possible by using other measure and indicator datasets. The early identification of such factors would definitely reduce the onus on scientists who are involved with exploratory studies.

References

[1]   Antoniou. A. et al "Average Risks of Breast and Ovarian Cancer Associated with BRCA1 or BRCA2 mutations Detected in Case Series Unselected for Family History: A Combined Analysis of 22 studies" Am. J. Hum. Genet. 72:1117-1130, 2003

[2]   Fodor. F. et al "Frequency and Cancer Risk associated with Common BRCA1 and BRCA2 Mutations in Ashkenazi Jewish Breast Cancer Patients" Am. J. Hum. Genet. 63:45-51, 1998

[3]   Claus. E. et al "Effect of BRCA1 and BRCA2 on the Association between Breast Cancer Risk and Family History" Journal of the National Cancer Institute 90: 23 1998

[4]   John.E.et al "The Breast Cancer Family Registry: an infrastructure for cooperative multinational, interdisciplinary and translational studies of the genetic epidemiology of breast cancer."Breast Cancer Research 6: R375 – R389 2004

[5]   King .M. et al "Breast and Ovarian Cancer Risks Due to Inherited Mutations in BRCA1 and BRCA2" Science 302 2003

[6]   Jim X. et al "Interactive Visualization of Multivariate Statistical Data" The International Journal of Virtual Reality, 5(3):67-73 2006

[7]   D. B. Carr, J. F. Wallin and D. A. Carr. Two New Templates for Epidemiology Applications: "Linked Micromap Plots and Conditioned Choropleth Maps", Statistics in Medicine, vol. 19, pp. 2521-2538, 2000.

[8]   Robinson A, et al "Human-Centered Design of Geovisualization Tools for Cancer Epidemiology", Proceedings of GIScience 2004, Adelphi, MD, p.314-316 2004

[9]   Center for Disease Control and Prevention (CDC): http://www.cdc.gov/

[10]   Surveillance Epidemiology and End Results (SEER): http://seer.cancer.gov/

[11]   The Open Indicator Consortium (OIC): www.openindicators.org

[12]   Baumann .A. et al "Exploratory to presentation visualization, and everything in-between: providing flexibility in aesthetics, interactions and visual layering"

[13]   Baumann, A., Grinstein, G.G., and Mass, W.: Collaborative Visual Analytics with Session Histories. Unpublished Research Paper. No. 2009-005,
University of Massachusetts Lowell, Dept. of Computer Science, Lowell,MA 01854. (http://teaching.cs.uml.edu/~heines/techrpts/details.jsp?Year=2009&SeqNo=005).

2. Visual Analytics

IV 2011

CoViz: cooperative visualization to facilitate sense making by groups of users

Bérenger Arnaud, Guillaume Artignan, Jérôme Cance, Gabriel Delmas, Mountaz Hascoët, Nancy Rodriguez
LIRMM, UMR 5506 CNRS
Univ. Montpellier II
Montpellier, France
{arnaud, artignan, mountaz, nancy.rodriguez}@lirmm.fr

Abstract

Coviz is a tool that uses visualization to support spontaneous construction, organization and exploration of collections. We use the term collection to identify a set of documents gathered for a given purpose by one or several individuals. Coviz facilitates creation, organization and update of collections by providing multi-scale visualization and interaction techniques. Coviz has been tested in several informative case studies involving small groups of users. In these situations, Coviz has fulfilled several important aspects of both groups and personal organization needs. Our initial experiments indicate that Coviz can even encourage unusual and interesting forms of cooperation among people.

Keywords--- **Visualization, collaborative sense making, spontaneous coordination**.

1. Introduction

Over the past few years numerous research efforts have been made to help people to search and organize the information they have to handle every day. Web search, web navigation, sense making, annotating, organizing, recommending and sharing have all been studied intensively. Advanced solutions have been proposed for each of these information management related activities. However, combining complementary yet separated approaches in a transparent and seamless way seems necessary to support knowledge emergence and is still a challenging problem.

Our objective with Coviz is to provide a tool supporting a broad range of information management activities. Based on advanced interaction and visualization techniques, Coviz integrates searching, bookmarking, annotating, harvesting, recommending, clustering, classification and sharing.

Coviz is designed for relatively small groups of users involved in cooperative sense making from web resources. Even though recent efforts have brought to the scene tools that support for collaborative web search, these approaches do not solve the problem of sense making and even sometimes they increase its complexity as noted by Paul and Morris [13] . Indeed, supporting collaborative sense making implies supporting very challenging issues such as group decision making, multiple search coordination, and merging of multiple personal information spaces, organization styles, and practices.

A key issue in organizing information spaces is to find a way of conciliating both group and personal perspectives that may differ widely. An interesting study by Abrams and Baecker [4] investigated the ideal organization of personal information spaces. Meanwhile, a huge literature has investigated group information organization. As noted by Halpin et al. [10] , "optimal means by which to organize information often pits formalized classification against distributed collaborative tagging systems". Group needs and especially consistency and stability over time is well embodied in formalized classification whereas distributed collaborative tagging systems are better suited to personal organization needs such as reactivity, spontaneity and rapidity. Our approach in Coviz consists in trying to conciliate both group and personal requirements for the organization of collections of documents and collaborative sense making.

The major contribution of this paper consists in (1) a transparent interaction model that combines different visual analytics techniques to facilitate creation, organization and update of collections and (2) informative experiments of the use of Coviz in real-world situations.

2. Coviz overview

Coviz handles textual data and metadata coming from heterogeneous sources (search engine, harvesters, personal web references, etc) and shared among a group of users involved in information management related tasks. Data handled in Coviz is mainly made of documents, uniquely identified by URLs. Coviz metadata is considered as a set of dimensions along which Coviz data can be annotated. Coviz is limited to a static set of dimensions to better focus on the design of the appropriate user interface for cooperatively handling several different dimensions. This has to be considered as an initial step necessary to reduce the complexity of the problem, but our longer term objective is to handle any arbitrary set of dimensions to represent any relevant metadata.

1550-6037/11 $26.00 © 2011 IEEE
DOI 10.1109/IV.2011.48

From the observation of user practices we have determined which initial dimensions could be chosen as mostly relevant. Amongst all possible dimensions, we chose dimensions that suit the following requirements: genericity, discrimination power, orthogonality, heterogeneity, simplicity and utility. The resulting set of preliminary chosen dimensions is (1) tags, (2) people, (3) collection, (4) quality ratings, (5) free text comments, (6) document kind. These dimensions are generic enough and were found useful for most data collections handled in Coviz experiments. The dimensions are very different in nature which makes them complementary to adequately annotate the data.

Tags can be seen as flat lists, or can be organized as hierarchies. Since all users handle their own tags personally, Coviz is designed to handle a set of hierarchies along which data can be annotated. This

People dimension is simpler since it is represented by a flat list of nominal values consisting of the name of commentators or authors referenced in the system.

Quality rating is a simple single-valued numerical dimension.

Free-text comment is a single-valued unstructured text dimension similar to description or people comments.

Document kind is a single valued categorical dimension similar to the content-type of mime metadata but while mime content-type describes low-level categories of documents, Coviz types of documents are higher-level categories such as research paper, talk, course, thesis, etc. As with other dimensions, the purpose of this dimension is to meet the requirements above for supporting the design of the user interface and in term to be replaceable by any other categorical dimension.

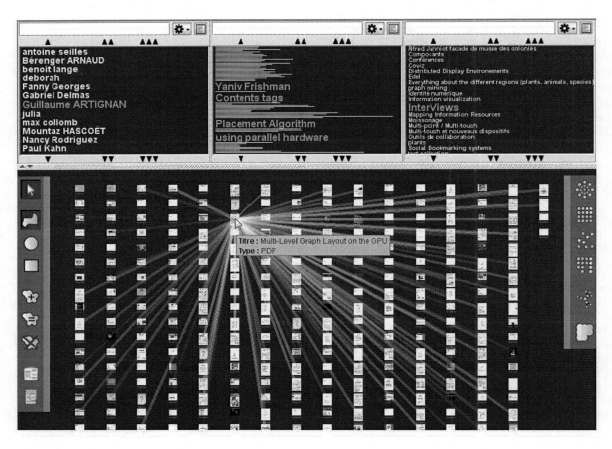

Figure 1: Coviz visualization and interaction window

dimension is also interesting because it is a multi-valued dimension. Several tags can be associated explicitly with documents or can be implicitly deduced. As a result the tag dimension is both multi-hierarchical and multi-valued.

Collection name can be considered as a multi-valued dimension that aims at providing direct access to the documents contained in collections. This dimension can be considered as an articulation or transversal dimension used to make it possible to support reuse of browsing results and combination of faceted browsing with other types of information gathering. The specificity of this dimension can be formally presented. First, let's recall how a set of data is defined. By extension it consists in enumerating the items in the data set. By intension it consists in exhibiting the set of features which are shared by the data contained in that set and that are sufficient to identify it. The specificity of the dimension collection is that it helps to define subsets of data both in extension, and in intension, whereas all other dimensions can only retrieve sets in intension. The experiments showed that this dimension was very useful for a user eager to merge subsets of "manually" selected documents with otherwise intentionally defined collections.

3. Graphical coding in Coviz

The visual representation of document is based on the graphical encoding of a multivariate clustered graph [3] . Nodes represent the Coviz documents, and edges represent a similarity relation between documents. Each node contains the following attributes: an identifier, a title, a URL, a date of insertion and a date of modification.

Edges are computed from the similarity between nodes – e.g. documents. Document are represented in a vector space using Term Frequency (TF) and Inverse Document Frequency (IDF) [13] to compute their coordinates in that space. TF corresponds to the frequency of apparition of a word in the document. IDF correspond to the frequency of apparition of a word in the entire corpus of documents. The TF-IDF measure corresponds to the ratio of these two measures. A Pearson's correlation is further computed between vectors representing documents in order to compute their similarity [14] .

Graphically, documents are represented by thumbnails. Links are represented by lines between documents. The more the color is opaque and the more similar are the documents. Links between documents are visible on mouse over. A bubble shape surrounding the documents represents the clusters. Mouse allows direct actions on documents while keys shortcuts help supporting interaction for sets.

The graphical encoding is further implemented using STOOG [3] , a graphical graph drawing API. The main originality of STOOG is the explicit declaration of style sheets for graph visualization. Fig. 1 illustrates the resultant visualization of documents in Coviz.

4. Tightly coupled fisheye lists for faceted metadata browsing

One important issue with faceted browsing [11] is the curse of dimensionality [7] . Coviz addresses this problem in three complementary ways: (1) a visualization of dimension values combined with advanced browsing and multi-level scrolling, (2) multi-scale visualization of documents, collections and relations and (3) tight coupling between (1) and (2).

Another important issue with faceted browsing is the exploration of the interrelations between dimensions. This type of exploration is quasi impossible for a user given the default user interfaces, like those found on most faceted based web site, for example. Rarely cited in the literature this apparently minor problem has, in fact, significant and negative impact on both exploration of data and overall sense making from it. Indeed, missing cues about how values are distributed and related across dimensions in a given data set constitutes a real hindrance in understanding what the content of a collection is. We call this problem the lack of *metadata insight*.

We have addressed the lack of metadata insight by combining two different modes of faceted browsing in Coviz. The first mode is similar to the default mode where the selection of items in the fisheye list views of dimension values filters the data in the document view (cf.Figure1) the item selected are displayed in purple. The selection of items on different dimensions is interpreted as a conjunction of disjunction when the dimensions are multi-valued and a simple conjunction when they are single-valued. We call this mode the selective mode that directly filters the data.

The second mode of browsing is called the highlight mode and was design to address the lack of metadata insight problem. It consists in highlighting related values in all dimensions when the user moves over items in the fisheye list. For example, if the mouse goes over a specific collection in the fisheye list displaying collections, all the tags found in the data of that collection will be highlighted in the fisheye list displaying tags whatever other selected criterions. As for tags, all other values appearing in the data will be highlighted in the other fisheye lists displaying other dimensions. This highlighting can be seen as a very simple type of brushing and was found so useful by users that one user asked to save these highlights. Enriching interaction in order to capture dynamic highlighting and transform it into a selection is in the roadmap of our future work.

5. Multi-scale visualization and clustering

Two kinds of clustering are proposed in Coviz, the interactive clustering and the automatic clustering.

The interactive clustering consists in letting the user construct its own clusters of documents. The documents must be selected from one or several groups. The selection is the result of a search or a manual selection. Fig.3 presents a sample of selection. The documents colored in blue, red and green are respectively in three selection groups. The execution of the clustering could transform these three groups of selection in three clusters. A cluster is considered as an element which can be moved or removed.

The automatic clustering takes the graph of documents and returns the clustered graph. We use the MCL algorithm [5] for clustering our weighted graph.

The algorithm is based on Markov chains and random walks [5] .

6. Architecture and implementation

Coviz system is implemented with Web technologies. The system is composed by (1) a server which providing services data storage, generation of dynamic pages and extra computation, and (2) a client part supporting visualization and interaction. In this section we present the system architectures and our implementation choices.

Architecture

The server has three components: database, web server and application server. The database enables data storage such as online documents, user account and tag hierarchies. It can be queried using the SQL relational language. The Web server provides generation of HTML pages and connection to database by the means of PHP language. The application server provides thumbnail generation and computes all necessary transformations on the data. This second server is powered over Java. Results are cached in database for future queries.

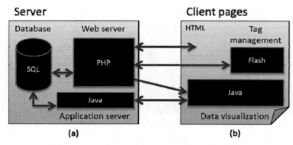

Figure 2: Overview of Coviz architecture

The client part consists mainly of HTML pages which is enough to do basic interaction and visualization. To avoid the basic limitation, web pages embedded two rich internet applications: (1) Flash modules, written with Adobe Flex language, for tag handling, and (2) a Java Applet for the multi-scale visualization of documents.

The figure 2.a presents the server architecture and 2.b the client architecture.

Implementation choices

Given the architecture properties, we made choices for implementing the user-oriented folksonomy approach and for keeping the user-centered context. Our choices impact features such as tags and documents meta-data.

An important issue concerns implicit tagging mechanism implementation, extracted from explicit tagging and sharing. We consider two options: (1) physically storing implicit tags or (2) computing implicit tag on-the-fly. The first option requires checking implicit tag integrity each time a tag is updated. The second

option is also costly because it requires processing each time a tag is selected. Finally, we choose the first option that favors fast response for visualization and data scaling.

7. Experiments and lessons learned

We have experimented Coviz in two different contexts: (1) a research project involving approximately 20 persons including researchers, engineers, designers, and PhD students, (2) a entire class of 30 undergraduate students. We describe the context, the objectives, the problems and lessons learned in this section.

In the first experiment, Coviz was used as an experimental tool and our objective was mainly to test very different user interfaces to best suit user needs. Several prototypes of the user interface based mainly on hierarchical list displays were initially designed to support sense making related tasks in a collection of documents coming from the social science community. These preliminary user interfaces were favored by people that were exposed to them, over alternative designs found in more popular systems. However, we found these preliminary user interfaces very frustrating because it did not meet two objectives: (1) a fast and fluid way to interact both at the item level and at the collection level and (2) a good way to conciliate visualization and interaction for groups and visualization and interaction for individuals. Clearly, even with advanced drag-and-drop based interaction, hierarchically displayed lists were far from meeting the challenges of handling both items and collections in a fluid interaction model. Secondly, another frustration came from the current state of the art of most frequently used default roles found in social systems that determine who is entitled to create/edit/delete what resource. Models that are based mainly on permission rights appeared as a real breaking point for the emergence of any significant spontaneous, fluid and cooperative interaction model useful for collaborative sense making related tasks.

Concerning the challenges of the visualization of both items and large collections, we designed the last version of Coviz (cf.Figure1) by combining of (1) graph visualization, (2) cluster visualization, (3) faceted browsing and (4) fisheye lists displays. This last version was used successfully and was way closer to meet the requirements we had than previous ones. However, it was obvious from usage that it still suffers from minor usability pitfalls mostly due to technological limitations and easy to fix in the future versions. Another lesson was learned from this experiment with the last version. The experiment raised interesting questions about the direct manipulation model of faceted based browsing. The combination of fisheye list display, multi-grain scrolling, highlighting and selecting modes of faceted browsing and the coupled graph based visualization was found to support fluid interaction pretty well according to our criteria. However, several filtering interaction strategies were tested and more experiments would be useful to adjust those strategies to better suits personal and group needs.

This version of Coviz was experimented to support resource gathering and annotating in a class. For this second experiment, students were undergrads and Coviz has provided help to them with their last and most important assignment. For this assignment students had to work in a both cooperative and competitive mode. The competitive mode was that they were asked to work by groups of two and each group had to perform the same project. The project consisted in creating a 3Dinteractive and graphic scene involving visual representations of Nao, a humanoid from Aldebaran [9] and reproducing in a virtual scene all the moves that Nao could perform for real. The cooperative mode consisted in using Coviz to gather and annotate all the resources necessary to achieve the projects. We made it clear from the beginning that both the administration and usage of Coviz were open to all students. Any student could add/remove/edit any resource. The only two simple guidelines were announced before they started: (1) if the system breaks you are all responsible and will have to fix it and (2) only high quality resources should be included and individuals are responsible for the quality of the resource they include in the system.

By using Coviz, and these very simple indications, the 30 students made an impressive job at collectively gathering high quality resources very rapidly. There was an impressive diversity in the ways that lead different students to different high quality resources. In less than one hour, a set of very highly relevant resources were collected and made available for all students at once. Our experiment with using other approaches in other classes is that this collaborative resource gathering takes several weeks without ever reaching that level of quality. This result was very encouraging and even beyond our initial expectations. Based on students comments and observations our speculation is that the next important step is to investigate how the editing and scaling factors should be adjusted. Indeed, one important problem was that no student dared comment the resources of the others. They spoke about them but did not write about them. We speculate that this is because the annotation tool was too formal and definitive to suit the need for politeness or solidarity among students. One student suggested that a forum be associated with Coviz so that casual discussion about the resources can be separated from the set of annotated resources.

8. Related work

Knowledge emergence from social networks
The emergence of knowledge from social networks either directly or after analysis is a very active field of research and has gained popularity with the apparition of social web sites such as Delicious, CiteUlike or others. In this area, systems, algorithms and studies have been proposed in a variety of domains including collaborative web search[7] , collaborative sense making [13]

collaborative tagging systems, recommendation systems [1] , etc. These research efforts have mainly focused on providing either the analysis of used systems and design recommendations for the next generation or systems that perform collaborative information and knowledge related tasks. Our focus in Coviz is very different from those approaches as our aim is to provide a transparent, consistent and flexible user interface that can handle most information or knowledge management tasks in a consistent and spontaneous way. As a consequence, Coviz features in terms of search features, bookmarking services or data analysis are minimal. At the same time, our experience with the inconsistency between systems that perform best in each area is maximal and the focus of Coviz is to help with conciliating the different approaches.

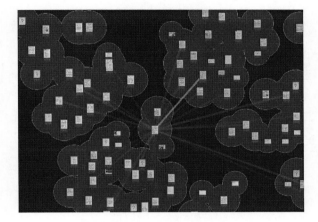

Figure 3: Clustering of data using Coviz

Faroog et al. [6] have analyzed two years of CiteUlike data and proposed 6 metrics for a better understanding of tagging behaviors. Their results indicate that (1) the number of tags used in CiteUlike is consistently growing as well as the number of new users. This model of tag growth is exactly the opposite of the results found by Marlow and David reporting a study with Flickr data. With Flickr data, tag growth is diminishing as time goes by. One speculation to conciliate these contradictory results is that tag growth is a consequence of growth of new users. This explanation would be consistent with the well-known vocabulary problem [8] , which states that the probability that two different users use the same label to describe the same concept is very low. The study of Farooq et al. brings to the scene very interesting questions and ends with recommendations for the next generation of social tagging systems. One of them is to facilitate tag reuse and our own study of user behavior corroborates this finding, so our approach in Coviz accounted for this recommendation carefully. Farooq et al. also insisted on recommending tags that are informationally powerful – e.g. with a high discrimination power and a high level of non-obviousness [6] . We found this recommendation more debatable considering our observations of users at work and their tagging motivations. We speculate that such a strategy would only result in creating a scale free network e.g. the distribution of tag usage would be a stabilized power law similar to what can be found in [10] . Our experiment in designing Coviz showed the importance of conciliating two conflicting usages of tags: the personal and the group perspectives. Conciliation of personal and group perspectives is achieved by supporting tag sharing over multiple personal tag hierarchies.

Social bookmarking and tagging systems

Social bookmarking principle can be described by a tripartite graph composed of users, bookmarks and web resources and links between those elements.

Since tagging in social bookmarking systems is central and has been extensively studied. Tagging is also included in every document oriented application, in which it is usually considered as one among others metadata. In [12] , three kinds of tagging are suggested (1) blind tagging where users do not know others user's tags, (2) visible tagging where the user can see the others user's tags and (3) suggested tagging where the system proposes tags to the user.

However, current social bookmarking systems have some important limitations. The vocabulary problem is one of them and was mentioned previously in this paper. Disambiguating tags when *polysemic tags* are used is another well-known challenging problem. Collaborative construction of consistent tag hierarchies to improve Folksonomies or tag-based ontologies is also very preliminary and often considered as an open issue [16] .

While most of the proposed approaches focus on system support of tag processing, our approach in Coviz is to integrate these processes in a visual system and to focus on interaction and cooperation among users. By first letting users construct their individual hierarchies of tags, shared hierarchies are further created progressively from individual ones. A direct benefit of our approach is to avoid the vocabulary problem since users can keep their own vocabulary, and share it explicitly with others while preserving the control over sharing processes. Similarly, multi-lingual tagging, as well as the polysemy problem can benefit from this visual analytics approach and the combination of interaction, visualization and automatic processing.

9. Conclusion

In this paper we have presented Coviz, a system to collaboratively visualize and interact with collections. We have reported lessons learned from real case studies that have shown that the combination of visualization and advanced interaction techniques was a difficult yet fruitful approach to collaborative sense making challenges. The experiments have also shown that meeting these challenges requires a deeper analysis and re-design of models of human cooperation that determines how people share things. Most frequent permission rights based models are clearly not suitable

for fruitful cooperation. The variety of alternative models that have been proposed so far is probably a good indicator of both the need for a change and the size of the challenge to find the next model.

Acknowledgements

Many thanks to Benoit, Antoine, Paul and all the people that provide fruitful comments and help in achieving this project. This work is partially funded by the TGE Adonis, from the French national research funding programs. Avec le Soutien du TGE Adonis.

References

[1]   Adomavicius, G.; Tuzhilin, A. "Toward the Next Generation of Recommender Systems: A Survey of the State-of-the-Art and Possible Extensions", IEEE Transactions on Knowledge and Data Engineering 17 (6): 734–749, 2005.

[2]   Amershi, S. and Morris, M.R. CoSearch: A System for Co-located Collaborative Web Search. Proceedings of ACM CHI, ACMPress 2008.

[3]   Artignan, G., Hascoët, M.: STOOG - Style-Sheets-based Toolkit for Graph Visualization. ICEIS'10, Portugal. 2010.

[4]   David Abrams, Ron Baecker, and Mark Chignell. 1998. Information archiving with bookmarks: personal Web space construction and organization. In Proceedings of the SIGCHI conference on Human factors in computing systems (CHI '98).

[5]   Dongen, S. V. Graph Clustering by Flow Simulation. PhD thesis, University of Utrecht. 2000.

[6]   Farooq, U., Kannampallil, T. G., Song, Y., Ganoe, C. H., Carroll, J. M., and Giles, L. 2007. Evaluating tagging behavior in social bookmarking systems: metrics and design heuristics. In Proceedings of the 2007 international ACM GROUP '07, 351-360, 2007.

[7]   Freyne, J. and Smyth, B. Cooperating search communities. In Proc. Adaptive Hypermedia and Adaptive Web-based Systems 2006, 1--10.

[8]   Furnas, G. W., Landauer, T. K., Gomez, L. M., and Dumais, S. T. The vocabulary problem in human-system communication. Commun. ACM 30, 11 1987.

[9]   Gouaillier David, Hugel Vincent, Blazevic Pierre, Kilner Chris, Monceaux Jérôme, Lafourcade Pascal, Marnier Brice, Serre Julien, Maisonnier Bruno: Mechatronic design of NAO humanoid. ICRA 2009

[10]   Halpin, H., Robu, V., and Shepherd, H. The complex dynamics of collaborative tagging. WWW '07. ACM, New York, NY, 211-220. 2007.

[11]   Ka-Ping Yee, Kirsten Swearingen, Kevin Li, and Marti Hearst. Faceted metadata for image search and browsing. CHI '03. ACM, 2003

[12]   Marlow, C., Naaman, M., Boyd, D., and Davis, M. HT06, tagging paper, taxonomy, Flickr, academic article, to read. In Proceedings of the Seventeenth Conference on Hypertext and Hypermedia (Odense, Denmark, August 22 - 25, 2006). HYPERTEXT '06. ACM, 2006

[13]   Paul, S.A., and Morris, M.R. (2009). CoSense: Enhancing Sensemaking for Collaborative Web Search. In Proceedings of the Conference on Human Factors in Computing Systems (CHI 2009), Boston, MA.

[14]   Pearson, K. Mathematical contributions to the theory of evolution. Regression, heredity and panmixia. Philos. Trans. Roy. Soc. London Ser. 1896.

[15]   Sparck Jones, K. A statistical interpretation of term specificity and its application in retrieval. In Document Retrieval Systems. P. Willett, Ed. Taylor Graham Series In Foundations Of Information Science.1988

[16]   Wu, X., Zhang, L., and Yu, Y. 2006. Exploring social annotations for the semantic web. WWW '06. ACM, 2006

Extracting and Visualising Tree-like Structures from Concept Lattices

Cassio Melo[1], Bénédicte Le-Grand[2], Marie-Aude Aufaure[1] and Anastasia Bezerianos[1]
[1]École Centrale Paris – MAS Laboratoire, [2]Laboratoire d'Informatique 6 – LIP6
{cassio.melo, marie-aude.aufaure, anastasia.bezerianos}@ecp.fr, benedicte.le-grand@lip6.fr

Abstract

Traditional software in Formal Concept Analysis makes little use of visualization techniques, producing poorly readable concept lattice representations when the number of concepts exceeds a few dozens. This is problematic as the number of concepts in such lattices grows significantly with the size of the data and the number of its dimensions. In this work we propose several methods to enhance the readability of concept lattices firstly though colouring and distortion techniques, and secondly by extracting and visualizing trees derived from concept lattice structures. These contributions represent an important step in the visual analysis of conceptual structures, as domain experts may visually explore larger datasets that traditional visualizations of concept lattice cannot represent effectively.

Keywords--- **Concept Lattices, Formal Concept Analysis, Tree Extraction**.

1. Introduction

The vast amount of data generated over the last decades has brought new challenges to the analytics science. Visual data analysis and knowledge representation employ methods such as Formal Concept Analysis (FCA) in order to identify groupings of patterns from the analysis process [26]. FCA provides an intuitive understanding of generalization and specialization relationships among objects and their attributes in a structure known as a *concept lattice*. A concept lattice is traditionally represented by a *Hasse diagram* illustrating the groupings of objects described by common attributes. A Hasse diagram is a graph where concepts appear as vertices on the plane connected by line segments or curves. The layout of the partially ordered set may be seen as a layered diagram [2]. Lattices visualization becomes a problem as the number of clusters grows significantly with the number of objects and attributes. Interpreting the lattice through a direct visualization of the line diagram rapidly becomes impossible and more synthetic representations are needed.

In this work we propose alternatives to the traditional lattice representation, firstly by enhancing the readability of concept lattices though colouring and distortion techniques; secondly by extracting and visualizing trees derived from the lattices structure. The tree extraction from the original lattice has some unique advantages: it eliminates all edges crossing and the resulting hierarchy is also easier to interpret and to represent. Moreover, this representation still provides an overview of the dataset, highlighting significant properties of the lattice. In order to extract trees from lattices, we define a set of parent concept selection criteria, including the *stability* and *support* indexes [1,4] provided by FCA literature, *confidence* index as well as topological features of the lattice.

The paper is organized as follows. Section 2 provides background on lattice representations; Section 3 proposes a set of criteria for transforming concept lattices into trees; Section 4 discusses colouring and distortion techniques for enhancing interpretations of lattices. Section 5 presents instantiations of the suggested criteria and visualizations in the biology domain, followed by a discussion in section 6. Section 7 finally concludes and presents perspectives for future work.

2. Visual Representation of Concept Lattices

As mentioned above, FCA analysis produces lattices, usually represented as layered directed acyclic graph graphs, named Hasse diagrams, that illustrate the groupings of objects described by common attributes. Hasse diagrams display the *partially ordered sets (posets)* between concepts in a hierarchical fashion, where each concept may have several parent concepts. In the following example about animal's features, the formal context in table 1 generated the concept lattice illustrated in figure 1. The partial order among concepts of the lattice is materialized through the generalization and specialization relationships: for instance Concept 4 (representing the set of *flying birds,* containing *Finch* and *Eagle* objects), is more specific than Concept 1 (which contains all *birds* –flying or not-), and thus contains a smaller number of objects (Concept 1 has an extra one, the *ostrich*). This partial order provides different levels of abstraction and native navigation links from a given concept.

As mentioned earlier, such diagrams are usually layered graphs, where concept vertices are assigned to horizontal layers according of the number of common attributes, and are ordered within each layer to reduce edge crossings. FCA lattices in particular suffer from considerable edge crossings, especially if the number of concepts exceeds a few dozen as is the case in more real word applications [13], which leads to reduced graph readability and aesthetics [3].

To reduce the complexity of lattices, simplified diagrams can be produced by condensing or clustering concepts according to similarity [4]. Visualisations can also be restricted to portions of the data [5], and concept size reduction is possible by incorporating conditions into the data mining process [6]. Finally, conceptual measures can be applied to identify the most relevant concepts and filter outliers [7].

To deal specifically with the visual complexity of *Hasse* diagrams, several approaches allow users to dynamically explore and reveal specific parts of the diagram, using visual query languages [8-10]. However these techniques do not provide a clear view of the entire lattice.

Other FCA visualization approaches map the distances between concepts to visual variables, in order to highlight patterns. For example in [11] similar concepts are represented as similarly coloured pixels placed in the 2D space along a *Peano-Hilbert curve*, so that similar concepts are placed close from one another. Nevertheless in these representations detailed relationships between concepts are lost. Finally, systems often provide users with hybrid/combined lattice visualization, e.g. showing both a general *Hasse* diagram and a tag cloud for representing the neighbours of a specific concept (for a review see [12]).

Our approach consists in representing lattices not as *Hasse* diagrams, but as trees. We use different criteria to extract trees from lattices, and visualize the resulting trees. Trees are inherently simpler hierarchical structures than *Hasse* diagrams and due to their applicability in many domains, there is a plethora of tree representations. These include: indented outline trees, sometimes called a "tree list" (common in file browsers such as windows Explorer), traditional layered node-link diagrams in 2D or 3D (e.g. *ConeTrees* [14]), spatially transformed tree diagrams (e.g. *Radial* [15]) as well as several space optimization (*Space Optimized trees* [16]) and space-filling tree visualization techniques (e.g. *TreeMaps* [17]).

Table 1. A formal context of animals.

Animal	Preying	Mammal	Flying	Bird
Lion	X	X		
Finch			X	X
Eagle	X		X	X
Hare		X		
Ostrich				X

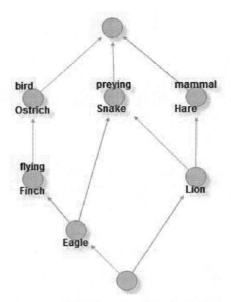

Figure 1. Generated concept lattice for the animal's context in table 1.

3. Tree Extraction from Concept Lattices

Trees are a common and easily understandable visual representation. We consider them as a visualization alternative to large cluttered concept lattices, which preserves all lattice entities and some of its structure. In order for a tree visualization to be an effective alternative to a lattice, the extraction of the tree from the lattice needs to preserve the most essential features of the original structure.

The present approach consists in extracting a tree from a concept lattice by choosing one single parent concept for each concept of the lattice. We start from the most specific concepts i.e. the parent concepts of the lower bound of the lattice, at the bottom of the *Hasse* diagram (concepts 5 and 6 in Figure 1) and select a single parent concept for each of them, and reproduce this recursively. Choosing a single parent concept at each step leads to an information loss. Our goal is to minimize this loss by selecting parents using the most relevant criteria according to the kind of analysis performed by the analyst. Before proceeding, we briefly recall the FCA terminology [18]. Given a (*formal*) *context* $K = (G, M, I)$, where G is called a set of *objects or extent*, M is called a set of *attributes or intent*, and the binary relation $I \subseteq G \times M$ specifies which objects have which attributes, the *derivation* operators $(\cdot)'$ are defined for $A \subseteq G$ and $B \subseteq M$:

$$A' = \{m \in M \mid \forall g \in A : gIm\};$$
$$B' = \{g \in G \mid \forall m \in B : gIm\}.$$

In the following sections we consider various strategies for selecting parent concepts, including the *stability* and *support* indexes from FCA literature, *confidence*, as well as topological features of the lattice.

3.1. Parent Selection based on the highest Stability or Support

The stability index measures the proportion of subsets of *objects* of a given concept whose derivation is equal to the *intent* of this concept [1]. In other words, the *stability* indicates the probability of preserving a concept *intent* while removing some objects of its *extent*. We recall the definition of stability:

Definition 1. *Let K = (G,M,I) be a formal context and (A,B) be a formal concept of K. Card is a cardinality function. The stability index of (A,B) is defined as:*

$$\sigma(A,B) = \frac{Card(\{C \subseteq A \mid C' = B\})}{2^{Card(A)}}$$

Using the context in table 1 as an example, we calculate the *stability* for concepts 2 and 4 in order to select a parent for concept 5 (0.25 and 0.5 respectively); we keep the one with highest *stability*, in this case we therefore remove the edge between concepts 2 and 5. The idea behind the choice of the parent concept with the highest *stability* is that we expect to keep parent concept's meaning even if some of the objects or attributes are removed.

On the other hand, the support measure is the relation between the *intent* closure and the number of total of objects [4]:

Definition 2. *Let B ⊂ M. The support count of the attribute set B in K is:*

$$\varphi(B) = \frac{Card(B')}{Card(G)}$$

The use of support as parent selection criteria may lead to trees containing concepts that have fewer specialization levels since in general, generic concepts have higher support values than their most specific counterparts [4]. Concept *stability* and *support* measures have been widely used in FCA and their combination has been promising [1] in reducing the lattice.

3.2. Parent Selection Based on Shared Attributes and Objects

This approach relies on clustering parent and child concepts which share most of their attributes or objects. Parent and child having a great number of attributes in common are supposed to be grouped together following the principle of similarity clustering and local predictability [19]. Its definition is:

Definition 3. *Let ConceptParent (A,B) be such that A ⊂ G and B ⊂ M. Let ConceptChild (C,D) be C ⊂ G and D ⊂ M. The shared attribute index of an edge E (C,D)•(A,B):*

$$\phi(E) = \frac{Card(B \cap D)}{Card(M)}$$

In the same animal's context in table 1, we have potential parent concepts 2 and 4 sharing the same number of objects with concept 5, but concept 4 has more attributes in common with 5, so it should be chosen as the unique parent of concept 5.

3.3. Parent Selection Based on Confidence

The *confidence* value of a concept estimates how likely an object which has an attribute set A, also has an attribute set C [18]. In other words, it tries to measure how strong the *implication* of the parent attributes in the child objects is. For instance, considering the formal context in table 1, what is the probability of a given object that is {*Bird, Flying*} to be also {*Bird, Flying, Preying*}? The following paragraph formalizes its definition.

Definition 4. *Let ConceptParent (A,B) be such that A ⊂ G and B ⊂ M. Let ConceptChild (C,D) be C ⊂ G and D ⊂ M. The confidence of an edge E (C,D)•(A,B):*

$$\delta(E) = \frac{Card(C)}{Card(A)}$$

An advantage of this method is its consistency with the interpretation of concept lattices. Taking our animals context as example, there is a 50% probability that an animal that is a *flying bird* is also a *flying* and *preying bird*. By contrast, an animal that is *preying* has only 33% of chance to be also a *flying bird*.

3.4. Tree Transformation Based on the Minimum Spanning Tree

This topological-driven approach seeks to choose the tree configuration on the graph which has the shortest paths among all concepts. A detailed definition of the algorithm can be found in [20]. In this case, we choose the parent concept which minimizes the number of steps needed to reach the top of the lattice, and therefore most generic parents (closer to the top) will be preferred rather than the specialized ones. This is the only proposed strategy that takes into account the topology of a lattice, and it yields concepts with similar depth (*specialization*) levels.

4. Using extraction criteria to enhance Lattice and Tree Interpretation through Drawing, Sizing and Shaping

Common graph drawing techniques include the assignment of different colours, shapes and sizes to nodes and edges, according to different dimensions or properties. This approach is underused in traditional lattice visualizations, where the main visual variable used is node/link colour to reflect user selections or node size to indicate the immediate presence of an extent or intent as displayed in *ConExp*[1].

In our work we use these as well as other visual variables in a *Hasse* diagram to represent possible tree extraction criteria. This provides several benefits to lattice and extracted tree understanding. First, it enables users to rapidly associate the dimension/criteria in question (e.g. *stability*, *support* in Figure 2 with concepts, thus justifying the choices made during the tree extraction process. Second, visualizing different extraction criteria using various visual variables, allows users to compare these criteria in order to choose the one that better fits their needs. Third, irrespective of the tree extraction process, matching visual attributes to concept attributes establishes a benchmark/comparison among concepts, making it possible to compare at a glance different concepts, even if they do not have a link in common, as well as gain insights on the whole lattice itself. Finally, prominent features of the lattice like specialization and generalization can be better understood: for instance the power of *implications* of different concepts can be rendered by edge thickness. The concept node itself can be a visual metaphor for the intent and extent. In the example of figure 2, a pie chart replaces the traditional box representation to depict the proportion of *objects* (blue) and *attributes* (yellow). In this way users can be guided in understanding and choosing criteria for extracting trees to simplify the lattice representation.

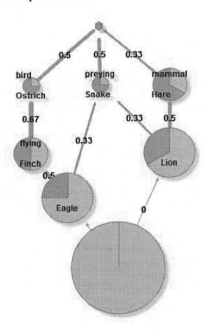

Figure 2. Animal lattice with nodes as pie charts sized by stability, and edge thickness by confidence. Pie charts indicate the ratio intent/extent of the concept.

---

[1] *ConceptExplorer*. http://conexp.sourceforge.net/

5. A Qualitative Analysis of the Proposed Parent Selection Criteria

In this section we discuss a case study of a concept lattice to qualitatively examine the nature of the trees resulting from different criteria. The techniques for lattice transformation and drawing were implemented in a visual analytics tool called *CUBIST Analytics* and applied to a dataset[2] containing 8 animals and 9 attributes which produced a lattice with 19 concepts (figure 3). Each of the measures proposed revealed particular aspects on the analysis of a lattice, illustrated in table 2.

Table 2 a) shows the tree generated with *stability* as parent selection criterion. In practice, it resulted in a tree with very stable concepts more likely to retain their subsequent children. For instance, the concept {*lives in land*} was the preferred parent of the concept that holds our notion for amphibians: {*lives on land, lives in water*} because it is more stable than its counterparts.

The measure of *shared objects* was the criterion that generated the tree in table 2 b). Parent concepts sharing most objects with child concept were the preferred candidates. As an example, the concept {*lives on land*} shares more objects with {*lives on land, needs chlorophyll*} than concept {*needs chlorophyll*} does, therefore it was the chosen parent in this case.

Table 2 c) the tree was generated from *confidence* criterion, therefore children nodes are associated with the parent with which the relationship of confidence is the highest among the candidates. As a result, the relation {*can move, has limbs*} has a stronger implication in {*lives on land*} than {*lives on land*} has for {*can move, has limbs*}, for example.

Table 2 d) depicts the tree generated by the minimum spanning tree criterion. In this configuration, concepts are arranged in a way that they are closer semantically from the rest of lattice and hence it features a more symmetric structure in comparison with previous approaches.

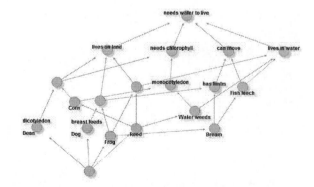

Figure 3. Concept lattice of the biology domain.

---

[2] The "Needs water to live" dataset is available at http://www.upriss.org.uk/fca/examples.html

6. Discussion

Some may argue that due to the tree construction, the present approach breaks the original lattice meaning, and therefore subsequent mathematical models based on this structure. It is noteworthy to observe however, that only the links in the lattice graph structure are removed and the lattice structure remains semantically valid, since there is no need to take out the attributes or objects that concepts have in common with their parents.

Table 2. Trees generated from the lattice in figure 4 for each one of the proposed measure.

	Example
a) Stability	
b) Shared objects	
c) Confidence	
d) MST	

The choice of parent selection criteria for tree transformation corresponds to a classification problem to some extent. Deciding if a Lion is more "mammal" than it is "preying" it's not always straightforward, hence we rely on the measures that attempt to keep the context semantics when looking at the entire concept lattice. For instance, if we have more objects described by mammal which are "closer" to Lion than other concepts, then it may reasonable to be chosen as its parent. As general recommendations, one should use the criteria that best fits to their analysis task (table 3).

In addition to the tree-extraction strategies, the use of colours, size, shaping and thickness for both nodes and edges in the original lattice to represent the criteria metrics (such as *stability*, *support*, *specialization* or *implication*) can enhance the interpretation of a concept lattice, and aid users in their choice and interpretation of the created trees.

The labelling strategy for identifying concepts should be taken into account as well. Merely placing attributes and objects names on concepts may be cumbersome for large lattice analysis (used in most FCA visualizations). In this case, it is recommended to represent the concept's *intent* and *extent* with visual metaphors like the *pie chart* shown in figure 2.

Conclusions and Future Work

Traditional software in FCA makes little use of visualization techniques, producing poorly readable lattice graphs when the number of concepts exceeds a few dozens. In this work we have presented a transformation approach to extract trees from concept lattices, attempting to minimize both semantic and conceptual loss in favour of readability and interpretation. We have also presented ways to visually show the extraction criteria in the original lattice. This is an important step in the visual analysis of conceptual structures, as the resulting tree structures are visually easier to understand than cluttered lattice graphs. Domain experts can thus visually explore larger datasets that traditional visualizations of concept lattice cannot represent effectively. Each of the tree construction measures proposed in our work provides particular insights valuable to different analysis tasks, identified in our paper as recommendations.

In the future we plan to combine two or more criteria for parent selection with other lattice reduction techniques (e.g. *icebergs* lattices [4]). We also plan to conduct user experiments to understand when users want to have full lattice views *vs.* tree views, which metrics for creating trees are of most interest to them and under which circumstances, and assess if our visual indications allow users to understand the extraction tree process.

Acknowledgements

This work is partly funded by the CUBIST project ("Combining and Uniting Business Intelligence with Semantic Technologies"), funded by the European Commission's 7th Framework Programme of ICT, under topic 4.3: Intelligent Information Management.'

Table 3. General guidelines on the usage of the proposed metrics.

Criteria	Description	Rationale	Suitable for
Stability	It measures how likely a concept is to change if some of their attributes or objects are removed.	Stable concepts are less impacted by noise and usually represent strong correlation with real world entities (e.g.: a concept that encapsulates our notion of "mammal").	Observing real world analogies
Support	It measures the frequency of the concept itemset.	Frequent concepts are usually generic concepts since they aggregate a larger number of objects than the specialized ones.	Frequent pattern analysis
Shared objects / attributes	It represents the degree of similarity between parent and child nodes.	Concepts that share most attributes or objects should be linked together because they are similar.	Similarity analysis
Confidence	It measures how strong the implication is between a parent concept in a child concept.	Implication is one of the desired interpretation of a concept lattice.	Confidence analysis
MST	It extracts a minimum spanning tree from the concept lattice.	It looks at concepts that have some degree of similarity with all other concepts.	Topological analysis

References

[1] Kuznetsov, S.O.: Stability as an estimate of the degree of substantiation of hypotheses derived on the basis of operational similarity. Nauchn. Tekh. Inf., Ser.2 (Automat. Document. Math. Linguist.) 12 (1990) 21–29

[2] Di Battista, G.; Tamassia, R. (1988), "Algorithms for plane representation of acyclic digraphs", Theoretical Computer Science 61: 175–178.

[3] C. Ware, H. Purchase, L. Colpoys, and M. McGill. Cognitive measurements of graph aesthetics. Information Visualization, 1(2):103–110, 2002.

[4] Stumme, G., Taouil, R., Bastide, Y., Pasquier, N., and Lakhal, L. Computing iceberg concept lattices with Titanic. In Data & Knowledge Engineering, Volume 42, Issue 2, pp. 189-222, 2002.

[5] Ducrou, J., Eklund, P., and Wilson, T. An Intelligent User Interface for Browsing and Searching MPEG-7 Images Using Concept Lattices. In S. Ben Yahia et al. (Eds.): CLA 2006, LNAI 4923, pp. 1–21, Springer-Verlag Berlin Heidelberg 2008.

[6] Zaki, M.J., Hsiao, C-J. Efficient Algorithms for Mining Closed Itemsets and Their Lattice Structure. In IEEE Transactions on Knowledge and Data Mining, Vol. 17, No. 4, IEE Computer Soc., 2005.

[7] Le Grand, B., Soto, M., Aufaure, M.-A. (2009) "Conceptual and Spatial Footprints for Complex systems Analysis: Application to the Semantic Web", in 20th International Conference on Database and Expert Systems Applications 2009, pp.114-127.

[8] Blau, H., Immerman, N.,and Jensen, D.. A Visual Language for Querying and Updating Graphs. University of Massachusetts Amherst, Computer Science Department Tech: Report 2002-037. 2002.

[9] Cruz, I. F., Mendelzon, A. O., and Wood, P. T.. A Graphical Query Language Supporting Recursion. In Proc. of the Association for Computing Machinery Special Interest Group on Management of Data, pages 323–330. ACM Press, May 1987.

[10] Consens, M., and Mendelzon, A. Hy+: a Hygraph-based query and visualization system. SIGMOD Record, 22(2):511–516, 1993.

[11] Michel Soto, Benedicte Le Grand, Marie-Aude Aufaure, "Spatial Visualisation of Conceptual Data," International Conference Information Visualisation, pp. 57-61, 2009.

[12] Eklund, Peter, Villerd, Jean. A Survey of Hybrid Representations of Concept Lattices in Conceptual Knowledge Processing Formal Concept Analysis. Lecture Notes in Computer Science 2010, Springer Berlin/Heidelberg, pp. 296- 311

[13] C. Roth, S. Obiedkov, D. G. Kourie. "Towards Concise Representation for Taxonomies of Epistemic Communities", CLA 4th Intl Conf on Concept Lattices and their Applications. 2006.

[14] George Robertson, Jock D. Mackinlay, Stuart Card. Cone Trees: Animated 3D Visualizations of Hierarchical Information. In Proceedings of the ACM CHI 91 Human Factors in Computing Systems Conference, pages 189--194, Association for Computing Machinery. 1991.

[15] P. D. Eades. Drawing free trees. Bulletin of the Institute for Combinatorics and its Applications, 5:10–36, 1992.

[16] Quang Vinh Nguyen; Mao Lin Huang. A space-optimized tree visualization, Information Visualization, 2002. INFOVIS 2002, pp. 85- 92, 2002

[17] B. Johnson, B. Shneiderman: Tree maps: A Space-Filling Approach to Visualization of Hierarchical Information Structures. IEEE Visualization 1991: 284-291

[18] Ganter, B., Wille, R.: Formal Concept Analysis: Mathematical Foundations. Springer, Berlin (1999)

[19] Hannan, T., Pogel, A.: Spring-based lattice drawing highlighting conceptual similarity. In: Proceedings of the International Conference on Formal Concept Analysis, ICFCA 2006, Berlin. LNCS, vol. 3974, pp. 264–279. Springer, Heidelberg (2006)

[20] Gallager, R.G., Humblet, P.A., and Spira, P.M. 1983. A Distributed Algorithm for Minimum-Weight Spanning Trees. ACM Trans. Program. Lang. Syst. 5, 1 (Jan. 1983), 66-77.

Nugget Browser: Visual Subgroup Mining and Statistical Significance Discovery in Multivariate Datasets

Zhenyu Guo, Matthew O. Ward, Elke A. Rundensteiner
Worcester Polytechnic Institute, Worcester Polytechnic Institute, Worcester Polytechnic Institute
zyguo@cs.wpi.edu, matt@cs.wpi.edu, rundenst@cs.wpi.edu

Abstract

Discovering interesting patterns in datasets is a very important data mining task. Subgroup patterns are local findings identifying the subgroups of a population with some unusual, unexpected, or deviating distribution of a target attribute. However, this pattern discovery task poses several compelling challenges. First, computational data mining techniques can generally only discover and extract pre-defined patterns. Second, since the extracted patterns are typically multi-dimensional arbitrary-shaped regions, it is very difficult to convey in an easily interpretable manner. Finally, in order to assist analysts in exploring their discoveries and understanding the relationships among patterns, as well as connections between patterns and the underlying data instances, an integrated visualization system is greatly needed. In this paper, we present a novel subgroup pattern extraction and visualization system, called the Nugget Browser, that takes advantage of both data mining methods and interactive visual exploration. The system accepts analysts' mining queries interactively, converts the query results into an understandable form, builds visual representations, and supports navigation and exploration for further analyses.

1 Introduction

Subgroup discovery [3] is a method to discover interesting subgroups of individuals, such as "the subgroup of students who study in small public high schools are significantly more likely to be accepted by the top 10 universities than students in the overall population". Subgroups are described by relations between independent (explaining) variables and a dependent (target) variable, as well as a certain interestingness measure. There are many application areas of subgroup discovery. For example, the extracted subgroups can be used for exploration and description, as well as understanding the relations between a target attribute and a set of independent attributes. Each subgroup or a set of subgroups is a pattern, i.e., a sub-region in the independent space. Detailed examination of such regions can be useful to improve understanding of the process that result in the pattern.

The subgroup discovery poses many challenges:

First, since the analysts may not know in advance what kind of interesting features the data contains, they may have to repeatedly re-submit queries and explore the results in multiple passes. For example, when the user submits a mining query, they need to specify the target attribute range of interest, such as the top 10 universities mentioned before. However, for different datasets and different application scenarios, the number of the top universities may be different, so they might have to try several times to find an appropriate range. This makes the mining process tedious and inefficient. Thus, we need an interactive mining process that allows analysts to submit queries dynamically and explore the results in an interactive manner.

Second, without visual support, users can only examine the mining results in text or tables. This makes it very hard to understand the relationships among different subgroups and how they are distributed in the feature space. Besides, when the user explores the mining results, the results are often in a descriptive or a abstracted form, such as summaries of the sub-regions. However, the examination of the instances in the region is also very important for understanding the data point distribution. Thus, without a visualization of the mining results, Users cannot build connections between the patterns and the instances.

Finally, adjacent subgroups should be aggregated and clustered when they are of the same interesting type. For example, given there are two subgroups of students, both of which have significantly higher acceptance rates than the population, and they are adjacent to each other in one independent attribute, such as the groups with medium and high income. Then the two subgroups should be aggregated, and reported or treated as a whole subgroup. One benefit is that this aggregate representation is more compact, which provides the users a smaller report list for easy examination. Another benefit is that the compact representation can be more efficiently stored in a file and loaded in computer memory. However, the clustered mining results generally tend to be multi-dimensional arbitrary-shaped regions, which are difficult to understand, report and visual-

1550-6037/11 $26.00 © 2011 IEEE
DOI 10.1109/IV.2011.21

ize. Therefore, conveying the pattern in a compact, easily understandable, and visualizable form is desirable.

Focusing on these challenges, our main goal is to design a visual interface allowing users to interactively submit subgroup mining queries for discovering interesting patterns. Generally, the main users of our system are analysts who want to perform subgroup mining tasks but have difficulties in understanding the mining results. Without a visual representation of the results, analysts are have difficulties determining if the mining results are interesting, if there are any patterns in the results, and how to refine their queries. Another type of user for our system are analysts who have difficulties specifying queries. Like other types of mining queries and tasks, such as clustering and association rule mining, some parameters are needed to form the query, such as how to define subgroups and what is the target share range. Therefore, an exploratory process is strongly needed that supports analysts in examining mining results and refining queries. Specifically, our system can accept mining queries dynamically, extract a set of hyper-box shaped regions called *Nuggets* for easy understandability and visualization, and allow users to navigate in multiple views for exploring the query results. While navigating in the spaces, users can specify which level of abstraction they prefer to view. Meanwhile, the linkages between the entities in different levels and the corresponding data points in the data space are highlighted.

The primary contributions of this paper include:

- A novel subgroup mining system: we design a visual subgroup mining system where users can conduct a closed loop analysis involving both subgroup discovery and visual analysis into one process.

- An understandable knowledge representation: we propose a strategy for representing the mining results in an understandable form. In addition to storage benefits, this representation is easy for analysts to understand, and can be directly displayed using common multivariate visualization approaches.

- A 4-level structure model: we designed a layered model that allows users to explore the data space at different levels of abstraction: instances, cells, nuggets, and clusters.

- Visual representation for the nugget space: for each level, we design a view in which users are able to explore and select items to visualize. The connections between the adjacent layers are shown based on the user's cursor position.

- We implemented the above techniques in an integrated system called *Nugget Browser* in XmdvTool [21], a freeware multivariate data visualization tool.

- Case studies suggest that our visualization techniques are effective in discovering patterns in multivariate datasets.

2 Related work

Visual data mining techniques aim to combine information visualization with data mining [22, 17, 13]. A powerful data mining strategy should involve users in the visual analytics process. The users should be allowed to explore the discoveries and specify what they are looking for. The mining results should also be easily understandable. Recently, numerous visual analytics based systems have been presented to solve knowledge discovery tasks. Hao et al. [9] presented the Intelligent Visual Analytics Query (IVQuery) concept that combines visual interactions with automated analytical methods to support analysts in discovering the special properties and relations of the identified patterns. Yang et al. [23] presented the Nugget Management System (NMS) that allows users to extract patterns via interactive range queries and provided several mechanisms for users to manage their discoveries, such as filtering out similar nuggets and refining the discoveries. Guo et al. [8] presented a model space visualization system that assists users in discovering linear patterns in a dataset. The system can reveal multiple coexisting linear trends and provides users the flexibility to tune the discovered trends. uchs et al. [7] proposed a system that integrates interactive visual analysis and machine learning to support insight generation. Yu et al. [25] also proposed a closed loop between visual analysis of discoveries and data mining processes. They showed how this system can be effectively applied to multimedia datasets and continuous time series data. This paper follows these visual mining technique concepts allowing the analysts to interactively submit mining queries to discover interesting multi-dimensional patterns. In this paper, we focus on a specific data mining method, i.e., subgroup mining, to assist the users in discovering statistical significance in multivariate datasets.

Subgroup pattern mining is a very popular and simple form of knowledge extraction and representation [14]. In [15], an advanced subgroup mining system called "SubgroupMiner" is proposed, which allows the analysts discovering spatial subgroups of interest and visualize the mining results in a Geographic Information System (GIS). In [2], it is shown that the subgroup discovery methods benefit from the utilization of user background knowledge. In this paper, we not only allow the users to perform the subgroup mining in an interactive manner, but also visualize the mining results in different coordinated views, assisting the users in examining the patterns and understanding the multi-dimensional relationships among the patterns.

Since usually the extracted features in multivariate datasets are high-dimensional, a major problem is the difficulty in effectively visualizing such high-dimensional patterns and their relationships. There are several techniques that map high-dimensional patterns to a lower dimensional space. A linear mapping method takes the first two principal components obtained from Principal Component Analysis (PCA) [12] and maps the dataset to a 2 dimensional space. Multidimensional Scaling (MDS) [5] and Kohonens Self Organizing Maps (SOM) [16] are non-linear variants, requiring the minimization of a cost function of the distances. Somorjai et al. [18] proposed a relative distance plane method. $2N - 3$ of the $N(N-1)/2$ interpattern distances are preserved in terms of two reference points. Radviz [10] is a radial visualization with dimensions assigned to points called dimensional anchors (DAs) placed on the circumference of a circle. We apply the layout strategies in our system for different views to reveal the relationships between multiple patterns and query results.

3 Visual Subgroup Mining and a Proposed 4-Level Layered Model

As mentioned in Sec. 1, a subgroup discovery problem can be defined in three main features: subgroup description, a target attribute, and a interestingness measure function.

A subgroup in a multivariate dataset is described as a sub-region in the independent attribute space, i.e., range selections on domains of independent attributes. For example, "male Ph.D. student in computer science department whose age is large (larger than 25)" is a subgroup with constraints in the 4 independent attribute space, i.e., *gender*, *degree program*, *department* and *age*. The sub-groups can be initialized by partitioning the independent attribute space. Given a multivariate dataset, pre-processing partitions the data space into small cells by binning each independent attribute into several adjacent subranges, such as low, median and high ranges. Each cell is a description of one subgroup element.

For the target attribute, based on the application and the cardinality, it can be continuous or discrete. The quality functions are different for these two target attribute types.

As a standard quality function, we uses the classical binomial test to verify if the target share is significantly different in a subgroup. The z-score is calculated as:

$$\frac{p - p_0}{\sqrt{p_0(1 - p_0)}} \sqrt{n} \sqrt{\frac{N}{N - n}}$$

This z-score quality function compares the target group share in the sub-group (p) with the share in its complementary subset. n and N are subgroup size and total population size. p_0 is the level of target share in the total population and ($p - p_0$) means the difference of that target shares. For continuous target attributes and the deviating

mean patterns, the quality function is similar, using mean and variance instead of share p and $p_0(1 - p_0)$.

Users can submit queries on the target attribute to specify target range or a significant level to measure the interestingness of each group. The subgroups with high quality measures are query results, i.e., discovered patterns. Users can visually explore the extracted patterns and furthermore, can adjust the previous query and perform a new loop of query processing.

Intuitively, we use color to represent the mining result in the cell level. The cells (subgroups) are colored gray if their quality measure don't satisfy the significance level (usually 0.05). If the z-score is larger than zero and the p-value is less than 0.05, the cells are colored red. This means that the target attribute share or the average target attribute value are significantly larger than the population. Similarly, for the cells whose z-score is less than zero and the p-value is less than 0.05, the cells are colored blue. This means that the target attribute share or the average target attribute value are significantly lower than the population. We say two subgroups are *of the same type* if they both satisfy the same query, i.e., both of them are significant and their z-scores are both larger than the positive critical value (1.96) or smaller than negative critical value (-1.96). we use different colors to represent different subgroup types.

A direct way to report the mining results is to return all the colored cells. Notice that the number of cells is exponential in the number of independent attributes. The query result can be very large, which makes it hard for the user to explore and understand. Specifically, a large set of unrelated cells may not be desired, because: 1. Users may only care about large homogeneous regions (subgroups of the same type) rather than a set of unrelated cells. 2. Users may want to know how many connected regions there are and what the sizes are. 3. The result should be in a compact manner for ease of understanding.

Towards these goals, we computationally extract two higher level of abstractions of the mining result, i.e., the nugget level and the cluster level.

In the cluster level, we aggregate neighbor cells of the same type to form a cluster i.e., a connected region (Fig. 1 (a)). The clustering results can be used to answer questions, such as how many connected regions there are and what the sizes (number of instances or cells) are. There are two benefits for the result in the cluster level besides to ease exploration. The first one is that the number of clusters can reveal the distribution of the mining result, such as a single continuous large cluster or a set of discontinuous small clusters scattered in the space. This can assist the users to better understand how the independent attributes influence the target share.

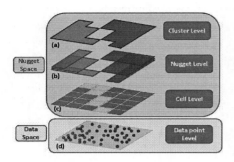

Figure 1: The proposed 4-level layered model. User can explore the data space in different levels in the nugget space.

Second, since the subgroups of the same type are generally treated as a whole set, the same treatment can be applied to all individuals in one cluster rather than each single cell. Since users might be only concerned with the large clusters, we can further filter out the small clusters, based on a user-specified threshold. This idea of clustering cells is similar to grid-based clustering and more benefits are discussed in[20, 1]. The difference is that we cluster the cells of the same type in terms of their interestingness based on the significance level for a target attribute, while most of the grid-based clustering techniques only consider the densities of each cell.

Although there are some benefits to representing the result as clusters, the largest problem is that the clusters are generally arbitrarily-shaped sub-regions in multi-dimensional space. This makes it very difficult for the users to understand the shape of a cluster and visually represent a cluster. To deal with these problems, we propose another level between the cell level and the cluster level, i.e., the nugget level. Specifically, we aggregate neighbor cells to form larger block-structured hyper-boxes for compact representation and easier perception. This aggregation of a set of adjacent cells is called a *nugget*. A nugget can be unambiguously specified and compactly stored by two cells, i.e., a starting cell and an ending cell, which are two corners of the corresponding hyper-box. A nugget has two important properties: *irreducibility* and *maximality*.

irreducibility: any sub-region of a nugget, also in the cell form, is still of the user's interest and meets the interestingness measure function requirement.

maximality: a nugget cannot be extended in any direction in any dimension to collect more cells to form a larger one.

The concepts of irreducibility and maximality were proposed by [4]. We extend this idea to a multi-dimensional space to generate a set of largest hyper-rectangular regions that satisfy the query.

The proposed 4-level layered model is shown Fig. 1. As shown in Fig. 1 (a), assume that the whole feature space is two dimensional (the gray plane) and the target dimension values (binary) are represented as the point color. In this example, assume the blue and red points are from two classes, e.g., USA cars and Japanese cars. Assume the user's query is requesting to find the subgroups where the target share (origin is USA) of the cars are significantly higher or lower than the population. To answer this, we first color the cells based on z-score: color the cell blue (red) if the percentage of cars from USA is significantly higher (lower) than the whole of the population. The partitioning and coloring results are shown in Fig. 1 (c). A gray cell means no significance is detected or are empty cells.

4 Nugget Extraction

In this section, we describe our proposed nugget representation and extraction method. Assume there are D dimensions in the feature space. As the discretization mentioned before, each dimension is partitioned into several bins. Assume there are B_k bins for dimension k. The cut points for dimension k are $C_{k,1}$ (*min*) $< C_{k,2} < \cdots < C_{k,B_k+1}$ (*max*). Here $C_{k,j}$ means the value of the jth cut point in dimension k, assuming the first cut point is the minimum in this dimension.

For any cell x, we assign an index (entry) based on its value position in each dimension: [$I_{x,1}$, $I_{x,2}$, $\cdots$, $I_{x,D}$] ($1 \leq I_{x,k} \leq B_k$, for $1 \leq k \leq D$). For example, if the first dimension value lies between the minimum and the second cut point, i.e., $C_{1,1} \leq v < C_{1,2}$, the index value of the first dimension of this instance is 1.

Definitions and the nugget extraction algorithm are introduced below:

Sort all cells: we define a cell c_a as *ahead of* another cell c_b if for a dimension k, $I_{c_a,k} < I_{c_b,k}$, and for the previous indices, they are all the same, i.e., $I_{c_a,t} = I_{c_b,t}$ for $1 \leq t < k$. We sort all the cells according to this order. We call the sorted list *CellList*. Some positions could be missing if the cell with that index is empty.

Of the same type: two cells are *of the same type* if they both satisfy the same query. This means they have the same color.

Previous cell: c_a is the *previous cell* of cell c_b in dimension k if $I_{c_a,k} = I_{c_b,k}$ - 1, and for the other indexes, they are the same, i.e., $I_{c_a,k} = I_{c_b,k}$ for $1 \leq j \leq D$ and $j \neq k$. So usually one cell has D previous cells in terms of all the dimensions.

Between two cells: cell c_x is *between* c_a and c_b if for each dimension, the index of c_x is larger than or equal to c_a, and smaller than or equal to c_b, i.e., $I_{c_a,k} \leq I_{c_x,k} \leq I_{c_b,k}$, for $1 \leq k \leq D$. If cell c_x is between c_a and c_b, it means c_x is covered by the hyper-box taking c_a and c_b as two corners. Note that here '*between*' does not mean the location in *CellList*.

Reachable: cell c_b is *reachable* from c_a if a) c_a and c_b are of the same type, and b) all the cells *between* these two cells are of the same type as c_a and c_b. If c_b is *reachable* by c_a, then that means the hyper-box, taking c_a and c_b as corners, is colored uniformly.

Algorithm Description: To find all the nuggets, for each cell c_x, we fill a list of cells, called *reachList*. If cell c_y is in the *reachList* of c_x, that means c_y is reachable from c_x. We fill this list from an empty list for each cell in the order in *CellList*. This is because when filling the *reachList* for cell c_x, we have finished the lists of the D (maybe fewer) *previous cells* of c_x. Due to the property of *irreducibility*, we only examine the cells in the list of *previous cells* for filling the list for the current cell. After getting the union of all the *reachList*s of all the *previous* cells, we check each cell in the unioned list and delete unreachable cells. For this purging process, again only the previous cells' *reachList* require access. To fulfill *maximality*, those surviving cells, which can reach the current cell, have to be removed from the *reachlists* of the previous cells. The area between cell c_x and c_y (a cell in the *reachlists* of c_x) is a nugget.

5 Nugget Browser System

In this section, we introduce the system components, views, and the interactions. The overall mining and exploring procedure is as follows. Users start from a data space view and submit mining queries in this view interactively, such as changing the subgroup definition (the cutting point positions) and target share range. The mining results will be shown in real-time in both the data space view (Section 5.1) and the nugget space view (Section 5.2). Users can explore the visually represented mining results in different coordinated views, and then adjust their queries until an interesting pattern is found. Therefore, a closed loop is formed to guide users in fining interesting subgroups by refining their queries.

5.1 Data Space

We employ Parallel Coordinates (PC), a common visualization method for multivariate datasets [11], to visualize the data points and nuggets. In parallel coordinates, each data point is drawn as a poly-line and each nugget is drawn as a colored translucent band (Fig. 6), whose boundaries indicate the values of the lower range (starting cell) and upper range (ending cell) for each dimension. The color blue and red indicate the sign of the z-score and darker color means higher significance is discovered for the subgroup. We provide interactions in the nugget navigation space view so that users can select which data points to view in the cell, nugget and cluster level. The last dimension (axis) is the target attribute that guides the user in submitting queries and changing the target share ranges. The

query ranges are shown during adjustment (vertical colored bars on the last axis). To assist users filtering out uninteresting nuggets, a brush interaction is provided. Users can submit a certain query range in the independent attribute space and all the nuggets that don't fully in the query range will be hidden in the nugget view. An example of a query is to select all the subgroups within a certain age range.

5.2 Nugget Space

In the nugget space view, three coordinated views, i.e., cluster view, nugget view, and cell view are shown in different 2D planes (Fig. 7). The linkages show the connections between adjacent views [6].

Cluster View. In the cluster view (Fig. 7 left), we employ a small "thumbnail" of a parallel coordinate view to represent each cluster. The size of each thumbnail is proportional to the number of instances each cluster contains, so that large clusters attract the user's attention. When the user moves the cursor onto a cluster, the parallel coordinate icon is enlarged and the connections are shown from this cluster to all the nuggets in the nugget view that comprise this cluster. Meanwhile, the corresponding instances are shown in the data space view.

Since the clusters consist of the data points in a high-dimensional space, to preserve the high-dimensional distances among the clusters we employ an MDS layout [5] to reveal latent patterns. The question is how to measure the similarity of two clusters. A commonly used and relatively accurate method for measuring the distance between two groups of instances is to average all the Euclidean distances of each instance pair from different groups. The problem is that for large clusters, the computational cost is high. We therefore calculate the distance in a upper level of the proposed 4-level model, i.e., using the average Euclidean distances between all cell pairs. As a result, the cost reduces as it depends on the number of cells, which is much smaller. The cell distance is calculated as the Euclidean distance between two cell centroids.

Nugget View. As mentioned before, each nugget is a hyper-rectangular shape. A single star glyph with a band, as proposed in [24], can thus be used to represent a nugget (Fig. 7 middle). The star glyph lines show the center of the nugget, and the band fades from the center to the boundaries. Similar to the cluster view, connections between the nugget view and the cell view are displayed according to the user's cursor position. The corresponding data points are also highlighted.

We again use an MDS layout for the nugget view, but the distance metrics are calculated differently from the cluster view. This is because any two nuggets could overlap in space, thus an instance could be covered by multiple nuggets. To reveal the distance between two nuggets, we designed two different distance measurements: one for overlapping nuggets and one for non-overlapping nuggets.

When the two nuggets have common cells, the distance metric indicates how much they overlap:

$$Dis(Nugget_A, Nugget_B) = \frac{|A| + |B| - 2|A \cap B|}{|A| + |B|}$$

Here $|A|$ means the number of cells that cluster A includes. When the two cells have a very small overlapping area, i.e., almost non-overlap, the distance is near 1. When the two cells almost fully overlap on each other, the distance is near 0.

When the two nuggets do not have any common cells, we use the Manhattan distance as the measurement. For each dimension, the distance is measured by using a grid as a single unit, called *grid distance*. For example, the grid distance for dimension k is 0 if on that dimension the two nuggets' boundaries meet without any gaps, or the two nuggets have overlapping bins (note that the two nuggets do not overlap in space, but may overlap in certain dimensions). The grid distance of dimension k is 1 if there is a one-bin gap between the two nuggets on that dimension. The distance in any dimension is the cell distance $+1$ indicating how many steps they are away from each other:

$$Dis(Nugget_A, Nugget_B) = \sum_{k=1}^{D} (GridDistance_k(A, B) + 1)$$

Note that the minimal distance is 1 for two non-overlapping nuggets, which is also the maximal distance for two overlapping nuggets. Hence in the MDS layout view, the nuggets in a cluster will tend to stay together to help reveal patterns.

Cell View. In the cell view (7 right), each cell is represented as a square. The cell colors are consistent with the colors in other views. The cell is highlighted when the user is hovering the cursor on it. Meanwhile, all the data points in this cell are shown in the data space view. The curves indicating connections between the cell level and the nugget level are also shown for the cells the cursor points to. Instead of a single curve, multiple ones are shown as a cell could be included in multiple nuggets.

6 Case Studies

In this section, we discuss a case study showing the effectiveness of our system. The dataset was obtained from the UCI Machine Learning Repository called "Mammographic Mass Dataset" [19]. Mammography is the most effective method for breast cancer screening. The dataset size is 961 (830 after removing instances with missing values). 5 independent attributes, such as the *age* of the patient and the *density* of the mass, are extracted and the target attribute is *Severity* (benign or malignant).

There are two main goals for analyzing the dataset. The first one is to understand how the independent attributes influence the target. This can help the doctors find the important attributes impacting the diagnosis results. The second goal is to discover the subgroups that the benign (malignant) rate is significantly higher or lower than the population. For a future diagnosis, if a patient is discovered in those groups, more attention should be paid or some conclusion about the diagnosis result could be drawn.

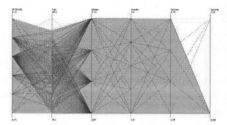

Figure 2: This is the data space view (parallel coordinate). The red poly-lines are brushed benign instances. The pink region is the brushed area.

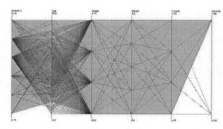

Figure 3: Similar to Fig. 2: the red poly-lines are brushed malignant instances.

To show the difficulty of finding how the independent attributes influence the target attribute using common multivariate data visualization techniques and interactions, we first display the dataset using Parallel Coordinates in XmdvTool. As shown in Fig. 2 and 3, the highlighted instances are selected using the brush technique (range query) on the target attribute. Fig. 2 shows the query result on all the benign instances (red color poly-lines) and Fig. 3 shows the query result on all the malignant instances. The pink area shows the bounding box of all the instances in the query. It can be observed that for each query, the instances cover almost the whole attribute ranges and all different values in different dimensions. This shows the common visualization technique, even with interactive range queries, can hardly reveal the relationship between the independent attributes and the target attribute.

We then show the insufficiency of the traditional subgroup mining technique without visualization in providing a compact and easily understandable mining results. We performed the mining as follows. The target share value is benign in the target attribute. This query examines the subgroups with significantly higher benign rate and significantly lower benign rate. Note that significantly lower benign rate does not necessarily mean significantly higher malignant rate, which can be examined by specifying another mining query that takes share value as malignant in the target attribute.

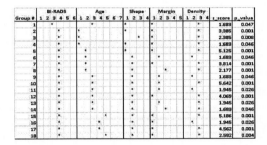

Figure 4: The mining results are represented in a table before aggregating neighbor subgroups. Each row is one subgroup and each subgroup is described using stars.

The independent attribute space is portioned by binning each attribute. Specifically, for the attribute whose cardinality is smaller than 7, the bin number is the same as the cardinality, such as *density*. For numerical attribute (*age*), the bin number is set to 7. We chose 7 because for lower values, the patterns are very similar, but less clear. While higher number of bins results in a lower number of instances in each group, which reduces the reliability of significance due to the small sample size. After the binning, the whole dataset is partitioned into a set of subgroups. Each subgroup consists of a group of individuals whose attribute values are similar or the same in all dimensions. Each subgroup is examined using the p-value and z-score of the statistical test as the interestingness measure.

Parts of the mining results are shown in Fig. 4 as a table. The star means the description of each subgroup in each dimension. 18 subgroups have the benign rate significantly larger than the population. It is clear that without the visualization, analysts cannot understand how the subgroups are distributed in the space and the relationships between the subgroups. Also, for some subgroups, such as number 12, 13, and 14, they are adjacent to each other and can be reported as a single group for a compact representation.

From the previous discussions, we can observe several difficulties: 1. it is hard to understand how the independent attributes influence the target using common visualization techniques, and 2. it is hard to understand the distribution of the subgroups, and 3. the mining results are not reported as a compact knowledge representation form. Next we will show how to use the Nugget Browser system to better solve the subgroup mining problem. Fig. 5 shows the higher level, i.e., the nugget level representation of the mining result in a table form. 8 nuggets are reported in a more compact manner, compared to the result of traditional subgroup mining, i.e., a list of subgroups. Fig. 6 shows all the nuggets (translucent bands) extracted in the data space view. Color blue means a significantly higher benign rate and color red means a significantly lower benign rate.

It is very clear that subgroups with high benign rates can be differentiated from the low benign rate subgroups in most of the dimensions, which indicates that the independent attributes have a strong impact on the target. However, this influence can hardly be discovered in traditional multivariate data visualization techniques, even with range queries. Specifically, the high benign rate subgroups have lower values for attributes *BI-RADS*, *Age*, *Shape* and *Margin*, compared to the low benign rate subgroups. Most of the subgroups with significance discovered have *Density* value 3 (means low). More details of how the independent attributes influence the target will be discussed later.

Nugget #	BI-RADS 1	2	3	4	5	6	Age 1	2	3	4	5	6	7	Shape 1	2	3	4	Margin 1	2	3	4	5	Density 1	2	3	4
1		*	*						*							*		*							*	
2			*				*	*						*	*			*						*	*	
3			*						*							*		*	*	*					*	
4			*				*	*	*	*	*			*	*			*							*	
5			*				*	*	*	*	*	*			*			*							*	
6			*					*	*	*				*				*						*	*	
7			*					*	*						*			*							*	
8			*				*							*	*	*		*							*	

Figure 5: The mining results are represented in a table after aggregating neighbour subgroups. This representation is more compact.

Although the nugget representation, shown in Fig. 5, is more compact than the cell representation, without the visual representation, users still have difficulties understanding the distribution of the nuggets and build connections between the pattern and the instances. To better understand the mining results and further explore them, analysts can open the nugget space view (Fig. 7). Based on the distribution in the nugget view and the cluster view, the high benign rate cluster and the low benign rate cluster are separated from each other in the attribute space, indicating that the target is influenced by the independent attributes. We can also discover that a large red cluster and a large blue cluster are extracted. It is shown that the higher benign rate regions and low benign rate regions are continuous in the independent attribute space. More discoveries found during the exploration in the nugget space are as follows:

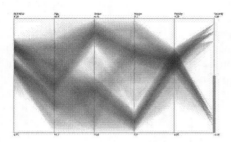

Figure 6: The data space view shows all the nuggets as the translucent bands. The rightmost dimension is the target attribute. The blue vertical region on the target dimension indicates the target range of the subgroup mining query.

1. For the low benign rate subgroups, there are two outliers outside the main cluster. By hovering the cursor and selecting on the two outliers, we can discover what causes the two outliers to differ from the main cluster: the *Shape* values of the main cluster (red) are 3 and 4, while the two outliers have *Shape* value 1. When showing these two outlier subgroup instances in the data space view, we can observe that no instances are benign and the group sizes are small. Thus, the doctors can consider that they are not typical and ignore these two outlier subgroups during analysis.

2. The shape value 4 is more important for the low benign rate. This can be discovered when displaying all the instances in the red cluster: the shape values are either 3 (means lobular) or 4 (means irregular), while for the value 4 , higher significance is found, which can be recognized by a darker color.

3. For lower age patients, higher benign rate tend to be discovered. This can be verified by the distribution of the interesting subgroups: no higher benign rate groups are in age bin 6 and 7; no lower benign rage groups are in age bin 1 and 2.

4. Attribute *BI-RADS* has a negative effect for higher benign rate, i.e., lower *BI-RADS* values tend to have higher benign rate. This can be discovered according to the distribution of subgroups with significance on this attribute. For the higher benign rate subgroups most of them have *BI-RADS* value 4. For low benign rate subgroup: most of them have *BI-RADS* value 5. The analysts can understand this trend better if the know the meaning of this attribute: each instance has an associated BI-RADS assessment. The low-

est value means definitely benign and highest value means highly suggestive of malignancy.

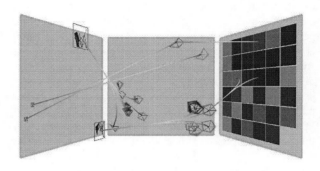

Figure 7: The nugget space view shows the mining result in 3 level of abstractions. The connecting curves indicate the connection between adjacent levels.

Conclusions

In this paper, we describe a novel visual subgroup mining system, called *Nugget Browser*, to support users in discovering patterns in multivariate datasets. We proposed a 4-level layered model that allows users to explore the mining result in different levels of abstraction. The nugget level mining results are represented as regular hyper-box shaped regions, which can be easily understood, visualized, and compactly stored. The layout strategies help users understand the relationships among extracted patterns. Interactions are supported in multiple related nugget space views to help users navigate and explore. The case studies show how our system can be used to reveal patterns and solve real life application problems.

In the future, we plan to extend our system to support more types of mining queries and pattern extraction methods. Furthermore, more complex mechanisms for managing the user's discoveries will be supported, such as adjusting nugget boundaries with domain knowledge and removing highly overlapping nuggets without reducing much accuracy. In addition, building an evidence pool that allows users to create a structured pattern graph with extracted nuggets is also one of our future goals. To better evaluate this system, we plan to conduct a formal user study to confirm how easy it is to learn this system, what types of users can benefit from using this system, what types of visual representations of the nugget space are better, pseudo-3D or purely 2D, and what interesting patterns analysts can have difficulty finding without a visual exploration.

Acknowledgements

This work is supported under NSF grant IIS-0812027.

References

[1] Rakesh Agrawal, Johannes Gehrke, Dimitrios Gunopulos, and Prabhakar Raghavan. Automatic subspace clustering of high dimensional data for data mining applications. In *SIGMOD '98*, pages 94–105. ACM, 1998.

[2] Martin Atzmueller. Exploiting background knowledge for knowledge-intensive subgroup discovery. In *In: Proc. 19th Intl. Joint Conference on Artificial Intelligence (IJCAI-05*, pages 647–652, 2005.

[3] Martin Atzmueller. Subgroup discovery. In *Künstliche Intelligenz*, volume 4, pages 52–53, 2005.

[4] Yonatan Aumann and Yehuda Lindell. A statistical theory for quantitative association rules. *J. Intell. Inf. Syst.*, 20(3):255–283, 2003.

[5] Ingwer Borg and Patrick Groenen. *Modern Multidimensional Scaling: Theory and Applications*. Springer, 1996.

[6] Christopher Collins and Sheelagh Carpendale. Vislink: revealing relationships amongst visualizations. *IEEE Trans Vis Comput Graph*, pages 1192–1199, 2007.

[7] Raphael Fuchs, Jürgen Waser, and Meister Eduard Groller. Visual human+machine learning. *IEEE Transactions on Visualization and Computer Graphics*, 15(6):1327–1334, 2009.

[8] Zhenyu Guo, Matthew O. Ward, and Elke A. Rundensteiner. Model space visualization for multivariate linear trend discovery. In *VAST '09*, pages 75–82. IEEE Computer Society, 2009.

[9] Ming C. Hao, Umeshwar Dayal, Daniel A. Keim, Dominik Morent, and Joern Schneidewind. Intelligent visual analytics queries. In *VAST '07*, pages 91–98. IEEE Computer Society, 2007.

[10] Patrick Hoffman, Georges Grinstein, Kenneth Marx, Ivo Grosse, and Eugene Stanley. Dna visual and analytic data mining. In *VIS '97*, pages 437–441. IEEE Computer Society Press, 1997.

[11] Alfred Inselberg and Bernard Dimsdale. Parallel coordinates: a tool for visualizing multi-dimensional geometry. In *VIS '90*, pages 361–378. IEEE Computer Society Press, 1990.

[12] J. Edward Jackson. *A User's Guide to Principal Components*. Wiley-Interscience, 2003.

[13] Daniel A. Keim. Information visualization and visual data mining. *IEEE Transactions on Visualization and Computer Graphics*, 8(1):1–8, 2002.

[14] Willi Klösgen and Jan M. Zytkow, editors. *Handbook of data mining and knowledge discovery, chapter 16.3: Subgroup discovery*. Oxford University Press, Inc., New York, NY, USA, 2002.

[15] Willi Klsgen and Michael May. Spatial subgroup mining integrated in an object-relational spatial database. In *PKDD, T. Elomaa, H. Mannila and H. Toivonen, eds, 6th European Conference*, pages 275–286, 2002.

[16] Teuvo Kohonen. *Self-Organizing Maps*. Springer, 2000.

[17] Ben Shneiderman. Inventing discovery tools: combining information visualization with data mining. *Information Visualization*, 1:5–12, 2002.

[18] R. L. Somorjai, B. Dolenko, A. Demko, M. Mandelzweig, A. E. Nikulin, R. Baumgartner, and N. J. Pizzi. Mapping high-dimensional data onto a relative distance plane: an exact method for visualizing and characterizing high-dimensional patterns. *J. of Biomedical Informatics*, 37(5):366–379, 2004.

[19] UC Irvine Machine Learning Repository. Mammographic Mass Data Set. http://archive.ics.uci.edu/ml/datasets/Mammographic +Mass.

[20] Wei Wang, Jiong Yang, and Richard R. Muntz. Sting: A statistical information grid approach to spatial data mining. In *VLDB '97*, pages 186–195. Morgan Kaufmann Publishers Inc., 1997.

[21] M. Ward. Xmdvtool: Integrating multiple methods for visualizing multivariate data. *Proc. IEEE Visualization*, pages 326–333, 1994.

[22] Pak Chung Wong. Guest editor's introduction: Visual data mining. *IEEE Computer Graphics and Applications*, 19(5):20–21, 1999.

[23] Di Yang, Elke A. Rundensteiner, and Matthew O. Ward. Analysis guided visual exploration of multivariate data. In *VAST '07*, pages 83–90, 2007.

[24] J. Yang, M. Ward, and E. Rundensteiner. Hierarchical exploration of large multivariate data sets. *Data Visualization: The State of the Art 2003*, pages 201–212, 2003.

[25] Chen Yu, Yiwen Zhong, Thomas Smith, Ikhyun Park, and Weixia Huang. Visual data mining of multimedia data for social and behavioral studies. *Information Visualization*, 8(1):56–70, 2009.

CyBiS: A novel Interface for Searching Scientific Documents

Gennaro Costagliola, Vittorio Fuccella
Department of Informatics
University of Salerno
{gencos,vfuccella}@unisa.it

Abstract

Although textual interfaces for browsing scientific papers have several drawbacks, they are still the most used in digital libraries. Several visual approaches have been proposed in recent years in order to provide the user with a deeper insight of the search context and to allow him/her to quickly gather a collection of documents judged as useful for his/her research. This paper presents CyBiS, a novel 3D analytical interface for a Bibliographic Visualization Tool with the objective of improving scientific paper search. The design choices are justified on the basis of previous experiences described in literature and its effectiveness is shown through the description of an example session.

1. Introduction

One of the key tasks of scientific research is the study and management of existing work in a given field of inquiry [9]. Researchers have been spending many efforts in the definition of visual interfaces for document search in the last fifteen years. Nevertheless, most digital libraries still employ textual interfaces. In these interfaces the results are generally presented as a list of items sorted by relevance, each of them being a preview of the document. Textual visualizations can be ineffective from several points of view [13, 19]. As reported by Nguyen and Zhang [19], it is difficult for users to group results that are relevant to particular topics or their current subjects of interest, with a linear way of presenting Web search results. Other drawbacks are the limited number of shown items, the lack of adequate means for evaluating paper chronology, influence on future work, relevance to given terms of the query.

Information Visualization (IV) can be useful to overcome the above drawbacks. Several visual interfaces for *Bibliographic Visualization Tools* (BVTs) have already been proposed. At present there are no standards in this field and there is not even a well established terminology. Nevertheless, some principles gained from the experience of the researchers can be considered valid. For instance, a credited principle is the *Visual Information-Seeking Mantra* [17] also known simply as *the mantra*, which describes a general behavior for visual interfaces: "Overview first, zoom and filter, then details-on-demand".

In order to evaluate if a document meets his/her needs, the seeker should evaluate different features, including its relevance with respect to the query terms, influence over the field, "age" and relation with other documents. Many visual tools described in literature can display one or more of the above. Nevertheless, it is rare that all of them are shown in a single view at the same time: e.g., some systems [13, 9] use different views to show relevance to terms and citation relations. In this paper we propose a novel interface, called *CyBiS*, acronym of *Cylindrical Biplot System*, which represents the salient data of searched documents in a single view. This way, the user is not compelled to switch between different visualizations thus loosing the focus on the current context. *CyBiS* shows document items as spheres embedded in a 3D cylinder placed horizontally on the screen. The relevance of a document to terms is given by height and depth of the item in the cylinder; the horizontal position, instead, represents document's publication year; the influence of the document is given by the color gradation of the item; citations are shown on-demand and are represented through connections.

Several operations are available in order to refine search. Firstly, the cylinder can rotate on the horizontal axis, in order to bring in the foreground the documents more related to a given term. It is also possible to *zoom*, which is equivalent to cut the cylinder along its horizontal axis, in order to select a time slice or to *filter*, for selecting a subset of items relevant to given terms. A prototypical implementation has been developed and used to produce an example session for evaluating the effectiveness of the proposed interface.

The rest of the paper is organized as follows: the next section contains a brief survey on BVTs; in section 3 the interface is described, with a particular reference to its objectives and main distinguishing features; the subsequent section presents the prototypical implementation, while section 5 describes the proposed example session; some final remarks and a brief discussion on possible future work conclude the paper.

2. Related Work

The main objectives of BVTs have been identified in [9]: though the main task is paper search, they can be also useful

1550-6037/11 $26.00 © 2011 IEEE
DOI 10.1109/IV.2011.95

for related tasks: finding authors or topics and tasks which give an overall picture of the research in a field, such as studying the citation network, chronology or collaboration. In this brief survey we only consider systems focused on search.

Following a model given in [18], we classify BVTs interfaces according to the way in which the results of a search query are presented:

- *analytical*: an information item represents a single document;

- *holistic*: information items represent groups of documents sharing the same value of a categorization attribute;

- *hybrid*: aggregated and detailed aspects of a search result are presented simultaneously.

The most commonly used *analytical* interfaces are those using a graph representation. An acyclic direct graph is a natural representation for a scientific paper citation network: the nodes generally represent documents, while connections encode a direct citation. A simple interface based on graph visualization is used in the BIVTECI [13]. More complex is the graph used in *Citespace II* [3], in which, among other features, the node color is used to convey information related to variations in the influence of the article over time. A co-citation network is represented in [5]: undirected arcs are drawn between two items representing documents that are co-cited. The *StarWalker* system [4] enables a 3D collaborative exploration of the graph. In the graph used in the *Lyberworld* system [1] both documents and terms are associated to graph nodes. The relevance of documents to terms is represented through distance.

Alternative to graph is the vector space-based visualization, in which attributes are associated to x, y and z axis: the position of the item in the space is informative about those attributes. On the other hand, with these interfaces it can be rather difficult to highlight the relations among the items. Generally, attributes are also associated to color and dimension of the item. Simple analytical vector space-based interfaces are presented in [18] and [19]. In the *Timeline View*, of the *CiteWiz* system [9] each article is visualized as an icon on a timeline, on the basis of its publication date: a more recent time slice is represented above the previous one, while an article citing a previous one is positioned just above it (if possible). Icons are scaled proportionally to the citation count of the represented article.

Pure *holistic* interfaces are not very spread, since *hybrid* interfaces can enable the same kind of analysis and also show the single documents. The *Interactive Concept Map* of the *CiteWiz* system adopts a graph-based interface in which every node represents a term. The dimension of a node is proportional to the weight of the represented term. Another example of pure *holistic* interface is presented in the *Periscope* system [18]. The information items are spheres split in sectors with different colors. A primary attribute (i.e. document language) is associated to a sphere, while a secondary attribute (i.e. document format) is associated to each sector. The dimension of the sectors allows the user to evaluate the number of documents for each attribute value.

Hybrid interfaces group the nodes on the basis of an attribute suitable for clustering. To this aim, they generally use geometrical figures embedded in other figures. Real world metaphors, such as a plant and its flowers in the *Knowledge Garden* [6], a library with books in the *Docu-World* [8] system, a soil with mountains [7] in the *VxInsight* system are employed rather frequently to represent a group and its articles, respectively. Another real world metaphore is the butterfly used in [12]. The body of the butterfly represents an article, while the two groups of its references and citers are associated to its left and right wing, respectively. A graph view is used in [15], where the articles are represented through small squares grouped in rectangular clusters. In a view of the *Periscope* system, [18] coaxial cylinders located on vertical axis represent a group of documents coming from the same domain (org, com, etc.), while bricks embedded in the cylinders represent single documents. Bricks of the same color represent documents coming from the same website.

3. The approach

CyBiS is the acronym of *Cylindrical Biplot System*. It is a 3D *analytical* interface for a BVT system. The interface is used for searching documents relevant to a given set of terms of interest, but it can help seekers in related tasks, such as: identifying the most influential documents in a set; identifying the most relevant topics in a field; analyzing the trends over time in a specific research field; filtering a set of documents according to specific criteria.

The above objectives are pursued by using a single visualization, thus alleviating the cognitive load required to the user to learn the use of the interface. The use of 3D is justified by the necessity of an additional dimension to help the user in perceiving all the informative attributes. In particular, the interface shows the following information:

- The relevance with respect to the search query and affine terms;

- The influence, given by the number of citations per year;

- The publication date;

- The relation with other documents, such as references and citations. These are available on-demand, upon the selection of the desired item.

3.1 The Interface

CyBiS uses a visive metaphor representing both documents and terms. The interface presents a cylinder located in the 3D euclidean space (see figure 1). The cylinder is drawn horizontally, i.e. its axis (height) is overlapped to

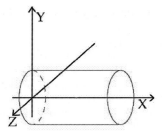

Figure 1. A cylinder located in the 3D euclidean space.

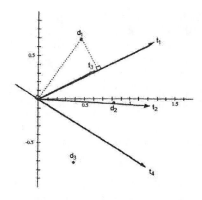

Figure 2. A biplot containing document and term vectors.

X-axis. A base of the cylinder is coplanar to the YOZ plane. Thus, the center of the base coincides with the origin. The cylinder is a container of documents represented through small spheres embedded in it. Each term is represented through a vector (y, z), i.e. located radially on the base of the cylinder. Besides being a familiar figure for humans, positioned in the space as described, the cylinder has a shape which immediately suggests the possibility of rotating around its axis.

The dimension of the spheres lets the user perceive their depth in the 3D space. More precisely, the spheres are scaled according to their position: those closer to the user's point of view are drawn bigger. If the user wants to bring in the foreground the farthest documents, s/he can opportunely rotate the cylinder around the X axis.

The X axis represents a timeline: documents are sorted by publication year increasingly from left to right. The Y and Z axes, instead, are used to represent the relevance of the item with respect to a number of terms. We obtain this effect by using the *biplot* graphical display of the matrix of the document-term weights. This process is clearly explained in [11]: summarizing, we have a matrix M with m rows and n columns corresponding to m documents and n terms, respectively. The element y_{ij} in M denotes the weight assigned to the j-th term t_j for document d_i. The matrix is graphically displayed through a *biplot* chart. The *biplot* is a type of chart largely used in statistics whose visual effect is to represent similarity in semantic space with proximity in the Euclidean space. In our case, the *biplot* contains two types of markers, representing document vectors and term vectors. Documents or terms which are strongly related to other documents or terms have a close direction of the corresponding marker vectors. In particular, as a rule of thumb, the relevance of a document to a term is visually noted by considering the size of the projection of the document marking vector on the term marking vector. Figure 2 shows an example of biplot containing 4 term and 3 document vectors. The document represented by the d_1 vector is very relevant to terms represented through t_1 and t_3 vectors. It also has a positive relevance to t_2.

In *CyBiS*, the *biplot* representation is used to obtain the y

and z coordinates of the documents, while the x coordinate is given by the publication year of the document. Furthermore, a mapping concept-color is used to represent the influence of a document: document items (simply referred to as *items*, in the sequel) are drawn with different levels of the red color. A darker red is for a greater number of citations per year.

The above described design choices have been inspired from previous experience in the field. In particular:

- The use of a single view instead of multiple views is advised by previous authors: as experienced by Klein et al. [10], switching between different visualizations confuses the users.

- The use of a timeline has been proved to be effective: as explained in [14], timelines "are a very effective method of displaying trends, building on the human perception of time as linear and taking advantage of the human ability to infer closeness of relation of two items from their spatial proximity". Spatial proximity is also exploited in the *biplot*, which itself is a well established visual method in statistics.

- Showing the relations with references and citers as soon as an item is selected is a way of interpreting the "details on demand" statement of the *mantra* and the possibility of seeing such details without loosing the focus on the paper and its context of relevance to the terms had been previously identified as an advisable choice in [2]. The support of zoom and filter operations, described in the sequel, also follows the *mantra*.

- The association of the influence of a document to item color is frequently adopted by other interfaces presented in literature. As remarked in [16], users take advantage from a concept-color mapping.

3.2 The Environment

The cylinder is displayed into a suitable environment which allows to launch queries and interpret their results.

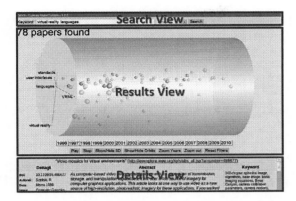

Figure 3. The three horizontal views of *CyBiS*.

The interface is horizontally divided into three views, as shown in figure 3.

- In the upper part there is the *Search View*, containing the search form to enter the search criteria. Besides the text field for the input of query terms, there is a combo box for choosing the maximum number of documents shown at the same time;

- In the center there is the *Results View* in which the cylinder is shown. It takes up most of the environment and most of the operations, except for *initialization*, are performed on it. Right below the cylinder there is a *toolbox* with buttons to perform specific operations;

- In the lower part there is the *Details View*, containing the details of a selected item, including title, authors, abstract, keywords, etc.

3.3 Operations

The users mainly interact with *CyBiS* through the mouse and the keyboard (only to enter the search query). The *initialization* of the interface occurs when the user fills the search form and submits the entered data. Once the system has initialized the interface by showing terms and documents, the following operations to browse the results are possible:

- *Rotation*: this operation rotates the cylinder around the *X* axis. The effect is to change the point of view for the visualized items, e.g. to put a given document in the foreground. This operation also entails a rotation of the term vectors. Thus, the rotation can also be interpreted as the will of the user to put one or more terms on top of the view, in order to have a closer view of the documents relevant to her/him. The rotation is performed by rotating the mouse wheel. Alternatively the cylinder can be animated by pressing the *Play* button in the toolbox;

- *Tooltip*: when the user hovers the cursor over an item without clicking it, a box appears containing title, venue and publication year of the item being hovered over;

- *Details*: further details are obtained when the user clicks over an item. The item is selected and the selection is highlighted through a yellow light surrounding the item. Details of the selected item are shown in the *details view* and include title, authors, venue, url, DOI, publication data, number of citations, abstract and keywords. Furthermore, the relations of the selected item to citers and references are shown through connectors. Due to the chronological ordering of the documents on the X-axis, the references and the citers will be shown on the left and on the right of the selected item, respectively.

- *Zoom*: this operation is useful when the user is interested in a shorter time interval than the one currently visualized, including only the documents published in one or more publication years. The interval of interest can be selected by dragging the mouse over a horizontal slice of the cylinder. The zoom on the selection is performed by pressing the provided *zoom-in* button in the *toolbox*. The operation cuts off the time intervals complementary to the selection and stretches the selected slice over the whole result view. The subset of items included in the selection is visualized with a larger spacing, thus allowing the user to have a more detailed view. Further *zoom* operations are possible on the selection. A *zoom out* operation, triggered by a suitable button in the *toolbox*, restores the original view.

- *Filter*: when the user performs a selection as explained at the previous point, without pressing the *zoom-in* button, the items not included in the selection are grayed. A similar filtering operation can be performed by clicking on a term marker. In this case, the items with a negative projection on the marker are grayed.

4 Implementation

A prototypical BVT with the *CyBiS* interface has been developed. The system is a Java Web application designed in compliance to the *Model 2* design paradigm, a variation of the classic *Model View Controller* (MVC) approach.

The *Model* principally manages the data contained in a relational DBMS. The main entities represented in the database are the *document* and the *term*. A local data set has been populated with data extracted from 5715 documents. The data set includes the papers published in the following venues: *IEEE Transactions on Visualization and Computer Graphics*, from 1995 to 2009; *IEEE Computer Graphics and Applications* from 1981 to 2009; *International Conference on Information Visualisation* (IV) from 1997 to 2009; *IEEE Symposium on Information Visualization* (INFOVIS) from 1995 to 2006; *IEEE Symposium on Visual Analytics Science and Technology* (VAST) from 2006 to 2009.

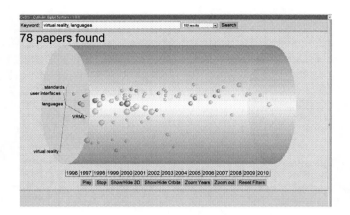

78 papers found

Figure 4. The CyBiS interface initialized with a query composed of the terms *virtual reality* **and** *languages*.

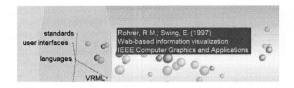

Figure 5. A tooltip with the details of a document.

"Web-based information visualization" (http://ieeexplore.ieee.org/xpls/abs_all.jsp?arnumber=595269)			
Details		**Abstract**	**Keywords**
Doi:	10.1109/38.595269	This article describes the Web as a fundamentally new medium for	World Wide Web, compli
Authors:	Rohrer, R.M.;	visualization that is changing the way visualization applications are	relational information,
	Swing, E.;	developed, delivered, and used. The authors briefly discuss Web-based	information visualization,
Date:	Jul/Aug 1997	development tools, Web-based information structures, and related work in	prototypes
Issue:	Computer Graphics	Web-based visualization. They then describe a number of Web-based	

Figure 6. The details of a document shown in the *Details View* **of the environment.**

The number of citations per paper has been obtained from *Google Scholar*. The *AlchemyAPI* library has been used to extract a set of *terms* from the documents and to determine their relevance with each of them. A many-to-many relation ties *documents* and *terms* and a weight assigned to each couple (document, term) represents the relevance of the document to the term.

The *Controller* is composed of Java servlets responsible for responding to user requests whenever an input operation is performed. Once a query is issued by the user, terms are extracted from the query and a set of relevant documents is selected from the database. Then, a document-term matrix is computed. The computation of the *biplot* data is performed through the *Java/R Interface* (JRI), which enables the execution of *R* commands inside Java applications. The query of the user can contain an arbitrary number of *terms*. In order to have an adequate number of them to create the *biplot*, the system puts additional terms in the matrix, when necessary. The chosen terms are those having the greatest average relevance to the selected documents.

The *View* is composed of the dynamically generated JSP pages. HTML5 and Javascript have been used to support the graphical display and operations. Many operations are handled through AJAX calls, to avoid page reload. The application is fully accessible with a Web Browser.

The prototypical BVT has been deployed on an *Apache Tomcat* server with a *MySQL* RDBMS.

5 An Example Session

With the objective of better clarifying the working and the characteristics of *CyBiS*, we report an example session. Let us consider the case of a user who wants to explore the research field of languages for virtual reality. The user has the necessity of:

- identifying the main topics and research trends;

- finding and scanning the most influential documents in order to go deeper into the field;

The view is initially void and the user can enter a search query, select the desired number of results and finally submit the form. In this example, the minimum number of displayed terms is set to 5. Figure 4 shows the cylinder after searching the query composed of the two terms *virtual reality* and *languages* separated by a comma. *CyBis* has returned 78 documents relevant to the query. The publication dates of the documents span a time interval from 1996 to 2010. Since the query is only composed of two terms, 3 more terms are added through the procedure outlined in section 4: *user interfaces*, *VRML*, and *standards*.

By observing the resulting view, the user can draw some initial considerations: i.e., by evaluating the density of the document markers, we can observe that the topic has a peak of interest in the late nineties and beginning of the past decade. The most influential papers are concentrated in that period, as inferred by the number of items with a darker color. At this point, the user can start exploring the result by interacting with the interface through the mouse pointer. The items representing the most influential documents, i.e. those with a darker red color, stand out against the lighter ones. The user can hover the pointer over them and obtain information through tooltips, as shown in figure 5.

Further details are shown on demand in the *Details View* of the environment as the user selects the item by clicking over it (see figure 6). This operation also shows the relations to other items already present in the view. A clearer view of the documents and its references is obtained by selecting a horizontal slice covering the 1996-1998 time interval and *zooming in*. E.g., the user can browse the references to search for possible interesting documents (see figure 7).

Lastly, the user may want to deepen on the documents more related to the *VRML* term, suggested by the system. By rotating the cylinder, the term can be placed in a more favorable position such that the items corresponding to the

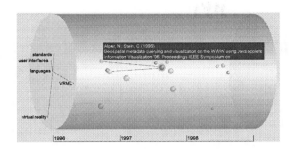

Figure 7. A zoom on the 1996-1998 interval. References of the selected item are shown.

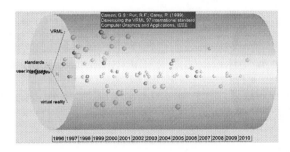

Figure 8. A rotation allows the user to see all the documents relevant to a given term.

documents relevant to it can stand out. With the cylinder rotated as in figure 8, all those items are shown in the upper part of it. If needed, a filter on the term marker can be used to exclude those not relevant to the term.

6 Conclusions and further research

Despite the effort spent by researchers to design visual interfaces, most of the scientific digital libraries still use textual interfaces to display the results of document search. The *CyBiS* interface, presented in this paper, has been designed bearing in mind many of the principles gained from the experience of the researchers in the last fifteen years. Its main distinguishing feature, rarely exploited in prior art, is the inclusion in a single view of the most important data of interest for a scientific paper. In *CyBiS*, they can be evaluated at the same time by the seeker without the need of switching among different views or changing the context.

A detailed example has been presented in order to show the potentiality of the interface. Future work will be aimed at evaluating the effectiveness and efficiency of the interface through targeted user studies. Besides relying on the opinion of users, we aim at obtain quantitative data for assessing the performances of the interface and compare them to those of other systems.

References

[1] M. , C. Kunkel, and A. Willett. Lyberworld—a visualization user interface supporting fulltext retrieval. In *Proceedings*

of ACM SIGIR'94, pages 249–259, New York, NY, USA, 1994. Springer-Verlag New York, Inc.

[2] P. Bergstrom and D. Atkinson. Augmenting the exploration of digital libraries with web-based visualizations. In *Proceedings of ICDIM'09*, pages 1 –7, nov. 2009.

[3] C. Chen. Citespace ii: Detecting and visualizing emerging trends and transient patterns in scientific literature. *J. Am. Soc. Inf. Sci. Technol.*, 57(3):359–377, 2006.

[4] C. Chen, L. Thomas, J. Cole, and C. Chennawasin. Representing the semantics of virtual spaces. *IEEE MultiMedia*, 6(2):54–63, 1999.

[5] T. T. Chen and L. C. Hsieh. On visualization of cocitation networks. In *Proceedings of IV'07*, pages 470–475, Washington, DC, USA, 2007. IEEE Computer Society.

[6] M. Crossley, N. J. Davies, A. J. McGrath, and M. A. Z. Rejman-Greene. The knowledge garden. *BT Technology Journal*, 17(1):76–84, 1999.

[7] G. S. Davidson, B. Hendrickson, D. K. Johnson, C. E. Meyers, and B. N. Wylie. Knowledge mining with vxinsight: Discovery through interaction. *J. Intell. Inf. Syst.*, 11(3):259–285, 1998.

[8] K. Einsfeld, S. Agne, M. Deller, A. Ebert, B. Klein, and C. Reuschling. Dynamic visualization and navigation of semantic virtual environments. In *Proceedings of IV'06*, pages 569–574, Washington, DC, USA, 2006.

[9] N. Elmqvist and P. Tsigas. Citewiz: a tool for the visualization of scientific citation networks. *Information Visualization*, 6(3):215–232, 2007.

[10] P. Klein, F. Muller, H. Reiterer, and M. Eibl. Visual information retrieval with the supertable + scatterplot. In *Proceedings of IV'02*, pages 70 – 75, 2002.

[11] U. Krohn. Vineta: navigation through virtual information spaces. In *Proceedings of AVI '96*, pages 49–58, New York, NY, USA, 1996. ACM.

[12] J. D. Mackinlay, R. Rao, and S. K. Card. An organic user interface for searching citation links. In *Proceedings of CHI'95*, pages 67–73, New York, NY, USA, 1995.

[13] D. Modjeska, V. Tzerpos, P. Faloutsos, and M. Faloutsos. Bivteci: a bibliographic visualization tool. In *Proceedings of CASCON '96*, page 28. IBM Press, 1996.

[14] S. A. Morris, G. Yen, Z. Wu, and B. Asnake. Time line visualization of research fronts. *J. Am. Soc. Inf. Sci. Technol.*, 54:413–422, March 2003.

[15] Q. V. Nguyen, M. L. Huang, and S. Simoff. Visualization of relational structure among scientific articles. In *Proceedings of VISUAL'07*, pages 415–425, Berlin, Heidelberg, 2007. Springer-Verlag.

[16] M. M. Sebrechts, J. V. Cugini, S. J. Laskowski, J. Vasilakis, and M. S. Miller. Visualization of search results: a comparative evaluation of text, 2d, and 3d interfaces. In *Proceedings of ACM SIGIR'99*, pages 3–10, New York, NY, USA, 1999.

[17] B. Shneiderman. The eyes have it: A task by data type taxonomy for information visualizations. In *Proceedings of VL'96*, pages 336–, Washington, DC, USA, 1996. IEEE Computer Society.

[18] W. Wiza, K. Walczak, and W. Cellary. Periscope: a system for adaptive 3d visualization of search results. In *Proceedings of Web3D '04*, pages 29–40, New York, NY, USA, 2004. ACM.

[19] J. Zhang. A novel visualization model for web search results. *IEEE Transactions on Visualization and Computer Graphics*, 12(5):981–988, 2006. Member-Nguyen, Tien.

Using Visual Analysis to Weight Multiple Signatures to Discriminate Complex Data

Renato Bueno[1], Daniel S. Kaster[2,4], Humberto L. Razente[3],
Maria Camila N. Barioni[3], Agma J. M. Traina[4] and Caetano Traina Jr.[4]

[1]*Federal University of São Carlos (UFSCar) – São Carlos, SP, Brazil – renato@dc.ufscar.br*
[2]*University of Londrina (UEL) – Londrina, PR, Brazil – dskaster@uel.br*
[3]*Federal University of ABC (UFABC) – Santo André, SP, Brazil – {humberto.razente, camila.barioni}@ufabc.edu.br*
[4]*University of São Paulo (USP) at São Carlos, SP, Brazil – {agma, caetano}@icmc.usp.br*

Abstract—Complex data is usually represented through signatures, which are sets of features describing the data content. Several kinds of complex data allow extracting different signatures from an object, representing complementary data characteristics. However, there is no ground truth of how balancing these signatures to reach an ideal similarity distribution. It depends on the analyst intent, that is, according to the job he/she is performing, a few signatures should have more impact in the data distribution than others. This work presents a new technique, called Visual Signature Weighting (ViSW), which allows interactively analyzing the impact of each signature in the similarity of complex data represented through multiple signatures. Our method provides means to explore the tradeoff of prioritizing signatures over the others, by dynamically changing their weight relation. We also present case studies showing that the technique is useful for global dataset analysis as well as for inspecting subspaces of interest.

Keywords-visual data analysis; multiple signature weighting; complex data similarity;

I. INTRODUCTION

Data visualization is a task of great importance in the data exploration process. Many works have addressed the development of visual data exploration environments, by adding interaction and analytical reasoning to one or more visual representations of data. From this integration emerged visual data mining, which relies on human visual processing channel and utilizes human cognition [1].

Several kinds of complex data can have a set of signatures extracted to describe its content. Each signature allows stating similarity relations between pairs of objects. When employed together, these signatures can enhance the data representation power, as they may provide complementary identifying information. However, stating the relative importance of each signature in the similarity distribution is a challenging task, as it depends on the analyst intent and background.

The work presented in this paper describes a new technique called Visual Signature Weighting (ViSW), which allows the user to visually interact with multiple visualizations of different signatures extracted from the same data,

tuning the weight associated with each signature in order to discover a reasonable tradeoff between them. It allows the comparison of several multidimensional mappings from the same dataset, using distinct sets of signatures and weights. Our goal is to help the user with an intuitive view of how to balance multiple signatures giving a view of the impact of varying the weight relation among them. The technique was implemented as an extension of the FastMapDB tool [2], allowing the interactive visualization of data stored in relational databases in 3D representations.

The paper is organized as follows. Section II surveys the concepts involved in similarity, multiple signature balancing and complex data visualization. Section III presents the proposed technique. Section IV shows case studies using the technique over real image datasets and Section V brings the conclusion of the paper.

II. FUNDAMENTAL CONCEPTS

A. Manipulation of Complex Data Through Similarity

Complex data are represented through signatures, or feature vectors, describing one or more object properties, which are generated by algorithms known as *feature extractors*. Classic feature extractors work on describing low-level data properties, covering a wide scope. For instance, images present three intrinsic low-level properties: color, texture and shape. Each of which has several feature extractors focused on it, such as the Normalized Histogram [3] for color, the Haralick's descriptors [4] for texture, and the Zernike Moments [5] for shape. To improve the semantics in the data representation, there have been developed several specific feature extractors, focused on particular domains, such as extractors for a given specialty of images of medical exams.

Representing complex data through signatures allows organizing the objects according to the *similarity* among them. This is usually done using *distance functions* to compute the dissimilarity between two signatures, such as the functions of the Minkowski family, the Quadratic distance and the Canberra distance [6]. The challenge is to identify the

1550-6037/11 $26.00 © 2011 IEEE
DOI 10.1109/IV.2011.59

components that form the similarity space, i.e. the signatures and distance functions, which best fit the user expectation.

One alternative is to employ more than one signature in the similarity, as distinct feature extractors can provide complementary information about the complex data content. The basic approach to combine several signatures is to concatenate every of them in a single "super-vector". One of the drawbacks of this approach is that the resulting similarity space is high dimensional, facing the *curse of dimensionality* problem, which drastically degrades the precision of the results as well as the performance of the analysis tasks. Several approaches involving either supervised or unsupervised techniques aim at fusing complementary signatures, considering the correlation among features, in order to reduce the dimensionality and enhance the representativeness of the features [7]. Despite of the improvements for dimensionality reduction, the super-vector approach does not allow employing extractors that do not generate dimensional signatures. Moreover, every signature that composes the super-vector are compared using the same distance function. However, it has shown that distinct signatures describing the same object can achieve better results using distinct distance functions [6]. Therefore, there are several works addressing alternative ways to combine multiple signatures.

B. Product Metrics and Multiple Signature Balancing

Another approach to combine multiple signatures is to aggregate the individual feature similarities, generating a value that measure the global similarity. This allows employing signatures that do not have a dimensionality defined as well as compare every individual signature using the best suited distance function. Most feature extractors produce signatures comparable through *metrics*, therefore they can be aggregated using a *product metric* [8]. A metric δ is a function defined over a data domain $\mathbb{S}$, that measures the distance, or dissimilarity, between elements in $\mathbb{S}$, satisfying the following properties, $\forall s_1, s_2, s_3 \in \mathbb{S}$: (1) symmetry: $\delta(s_1, s_2) = \delta(s_2, s_1)$; (2) non-negativity: $0 < \delta(s_1, s_2) < \infty$ if $s_1 \neq s_2$ and $\delta(s_1, s_1) = 0$; and (3) triangular inequality: $\delta(s_1, s_3) \leq \delta(s_1, s_2) + \delta(s_2, s_3)$. It is worth to notice that the most wide employed distance functions are metrics, such as the functions of the Minkowski family, the Canberra distance, and so on. Each pair $\langle \mathbb{S}, \delta \rangle$ forms a *metric space* $\mathbb{M}$. A product metric is a metric over the cartesian product of a set of metric spaces $\mathbb{M}_1 \times \mathbb{M}_2 \times ... \times \mathbb{M}_n$, which aggregates the metrics that form the metric spaces.

When individual similarities regarding multiple signatures are aggregated in a global similarity, it is crucial to balance them adequately. We call the *problem of multiple signature balacing* as how to weight each individual similarity in a way that they are neither underestimated nor overestimated in the global computation. Several works addressed this problem, relying either on supervised [9], or on unsupervised

techniques [8]. Although very useful, such approaches lack to give to the analyst a global view of the impact of variations in the balancing of the multiple features. Furthermore, real datasets usually have subspaces of interest, which can have conflicting parameters to define the most adequate similarity. Depending on the goal of the analyst, the balance of the multiple signatures may require a different adjust. Therefore, it must be provided mechanisms that allow users to explore similarity measure settings interactively, to figure out the impact of the variations available. This is the main goal of the work presented herein.

C. Visualization of Complex Data

Through data visualization techniques users may interact with large amounts of data at the same time. Colors allow users to immediately recognize the similarities of millions of data items and the data distribution can be arranged to express any relationship among them. The integration of visualization and automatic data mining algorithms in visual data mining techniques aim to use human perception to discover useful information, in order to help the user on many tasks such as data clustering [10], data classification [11], post-analysis of discovered rules [12], and trends and outliers detection [13].

An important issue for most algorithms is the embedded dimensionality of data. Dimensionality reduction techniques may be used to generate a new representation of data for the visualization in a 3D environment. A well known algorithm for dimensionality reduction is MDS (Multidimensional Scaling) [14], which allows performing data mappings from high dimensional or metric spaces to lower dimensional Euclidean spaces, preserving the characteristics of the original dataset through the distance computation among pairs of objects. However, MDS presents a computational cost of $O(n^2)$. An algorithm that provides an alternative for applications with real time needs, such as data visualization, is FastMap [15]. This algorithm also allows performing data mappings from high dimensional to lower dimensional Euclidean spaces, in linear computational time. The mappings performed by these algorithms try to preserve the distances among the data objects minimizing possible distortions caused by the mapping. The *FastMapDB* tool [2] aims at providing an environment for visual data mining. The input dataset from a relational database is seen as a collection of points in a complex data space, where each attribute represents a numeric value describing a given object property. In this sense, each tuple of the relation represent a complex object, and the user may try different distance functions. Thereafter, it uses the FastMap algorithm to map the original space into a 3-dimensional space, in which the visualization and interaction is performed. It allows the comparison of multiple mappings from the same dataset, using distinct subsets of features to visually identify correlations and perform feature selection. Distinct subsets of features generate mappings that may not maintain direct correspondence to each other in the mapped space, therefore we employed algorithms to superimpose them using a common spatial base, with regard to a set of carefully chosen tuples. This is achieved by computing the geometric transformations that best approximate the elements of the common base and appling such transformations to the remainder elements, as proposed in the techniques Topological Fit and Best Fit [16].

III. THE ViSW TECHNIQUE

This section presents the Visual Signature Weighting (ViSW) technique, developed to allow users to interactively vary the relative weight of signatures representing a complex object in the similarity evaluation based on a visualization of the induced space and also visually analyze the resulting data distribution.

In essence, a similarity space is defined by the dataset and the similarity measure employed. Therefore, any modification in such components induces an alternative similarity space instance. The FastMapDB, in which ViSW is implemented, treats features using a variation of the supervector approach for combining multiple vectorial signatures. The ViSW technique enhanced the FastMapDB to deal with multiple signatures using a product metric. The user loads a set of signatures and chooses one of the distance functions available in the system for each signature. Thereafter, he/she selects the product metric that will aggregate the partial similarities. The set of signatures and the product metric form a metric space, which is employed in the mapping algorithm to generate the 3D visualization.

After having the first 3D mapping, ViSW allows users to dynamically change the weight relation among the signatures and visually analyze the generated impact. The weight relation affects the product metric distance distribution, generating a new mapped space that is visually different from the original. To compare the mappings, ViSW approximate the spaces using a technique similar to the Best Fit. The main difference is that it is necessary to superimpose several mappings, instead of only two, as the user can vary the weights on-the-fly. This method selects six elements that are "in the border" of the mapping whose product metric has what we call the *fundamental weight relation*, i.e. when all partial similarities have weight equal to 1. These elements are the base pivots and compose axes that are as orthogonal to each other as possible, as datasets seldom have a set of elements that are far away from each other that allows tracing orthogonal axes. The base pivots are used to calculate the transformation matrix, which converts the original pairs of base pivots into these pivots in the weight modified mapping. Multiplying the transformation matrix and the base pivot matrix, generates the pivot matrix of the modified mapping. These matrixes are expanded generating a system of equations, whose linear approximation produces the errors $e(pivot_1)$, $e(pivot_2)$, ..., $e(pivot_n)$, where n is the number

of pivots. The sum of the individual squared errors is the minimum squared error E, as defined in Equation 1.

$$E = [e(pivot_1)]^2 + [e(pivot_2)]^2 + ... + [e(pivot_n)]^2 \quad (1)$$

Thereafter, the equation system is stated into the form $A \cdot x = b$, which is submitted to a Gaussian elimination procedure that is used by the least squared error method, returning the transformation matrix. This adjustment helps the users to visually state the relevance of individual similarities for each situation, comparing the generated mappings of several alternative weight relations.

As the visual weight tuning process provided by ViSW is interactive, it is important to provide the alternative mapping as fast as possible. In order to reduce the wait time, the technique pre-computes mappings in background, following a pre-defined weight relation step. Our hypothesis is that in general users experiment slight variations in a gradual way, to fine tune these parameters. At most, one or two abrupt weight changes can be performed, followed by several slight variations, which can take advantage of the pre-computed mappings.

IV. CASE STUDIES

This section shows case studies employing real datasets to illustrate the usefulness of the ViSW technique.

A. The ALOI Dataset

The first dataset discussed is the Amsterdam Library of Object Images (ALOI) [17]. It was built photographing small objects from several view angles and illumination color. We used a subset of 10 classes in this example, shown in Figure 1. As it is illustrated in the figure, each class is composed by the set of pictures of the same object, totalizing 84 images per class. To simplify the visual interpretation of the results, the aggregated similarity is given by the following linear product metric:

$$\Delta(x,y) = \sum_{i=1}^{n} w_i \cdot \frac{\delta_i(x_i, y_i)}{dmax_i} \quad (2)$$

where x and y are two images, each one with n signatures to be aggregated, δ_i is the distance function used for the i-th signature, w_i is the weight of this signature in the global similarity and $dmax_i$ is the maximum distance between two instances of this signature, which is used to normalize the values. In this example, we employed two signatures: a set of 140 Haralick descriptors (texture) and the 256 gray-level normalized histogram (color).

We generated several visualizations, varying the relative weight of the two signatures. In the visualizations in Figure 2a, the whole dataset is plotted, where each class is represented with a distinct color. It can be visually perceived that, in general, the classes are better separated from each other with a higher weight for the Haralick signature (the leftmost visualization), and when the Histogram signature

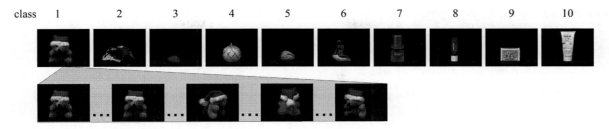

Figure 1. Sample images of the ALOI dataset. In the first line are pictures of the objects employed in this example. The second line shows that each class is composed by the set of images of the same object.

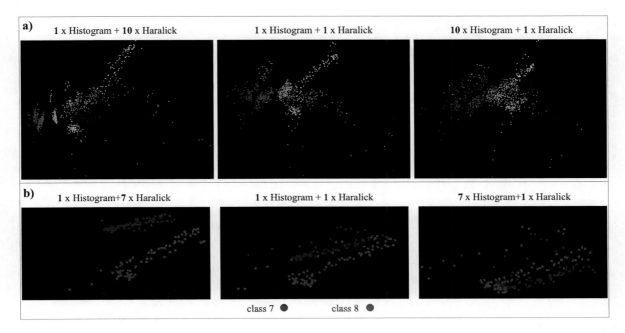

Figure 2. Visualizations of the ALOI dataset, with varying weight relations. a) Distribution of all classes. b) Zoom on the distribution of classes 7 and 8.

is assigned a higher weight the elements become more interleaved in the space (the rightmost visualization). In order to check this insight, we calculated the retrieval *average precisions* [18] of several weight combinations in the product metric, regarding the whole dataset, as well as two selected classes (7 and 8), generating the graph in Figure 3. This graph confirms the visual insight, showing that the best weight configuration, that is, the combination that yields the highest average precision, for all classes (the solid black line in the graph) prioritizes the Haralick signature in the similarity evaluation. With regard to the two selected classes, it can be noticed that their average precision curves, also shown in Figure 3 (the red dashed and the blue dotted lines), present a pattern similar to the average precision curve of the whole dataset. This behaviour can be clearly noticed in the visualizations in Figure 2b, which show zoomed views of the two classes. These classes are better separated with higher weights for the Haralick signature, even becoming

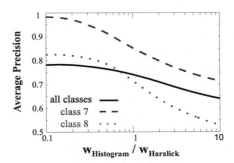

Figure 3. Average precision graph of the ALOI dataset.

totally disjoint in the space, as it can be seen in the leftmost visualization in Figure 2b.

B. The MRI_704 Dataset

The MRI_704 dataset is a collection of 704 images of Magnetic Resonance Imaging (MRI) exams, provided by the

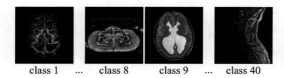

class 1 ... class 8 class 9 ... class 40

Figure 4. Sample images of the MRI_704 dataset.

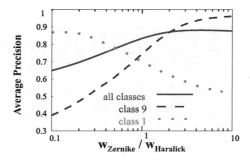

Figure 6. Average precision graph of the MRI_704 dataset.

Clinical Hospital of the Faculty of Medicine of Ribeirão Preto, University of São Paulo, Brazil. The images are classified into 40 classes, according to the body part and the scan plane, as illustrated in Figure 4. In this case study, we employed a texture versus shape tradeoff, using 140 Haralick descriptors for texture and the 256 first Zernike moments for shape. The product metric is the same of the previous example. However, instead of analyzing the global class behaviour, or comparing pairs of classes, in this experiment we focused on inspecting the behaviour of individual classes against the remainder of the dataset. This task is common in real complex data applications. For example, in a medical application the analyst could be interested in the best similarity evaluation settings to distinguish images that present a given type of lesion from all the remainder exams.

Figure 5 shows the effect of the weight variation, highlighting two classes with adverse behaviours. In Figure 5a, the class 9 is highlighted in the visualizations (the yellow points). Analyzing these visualizations from the left to the right, it is noticeable that the elements of this class are mixed with elements of other classes when the value for the Haralick signature is higher and become increasingly better separated when the weight of the Zernike signature domains the similarity. This behaviour is confirmed by the average precision curve of this class, which is the red dashed line of the graph in Figure 6. Moreover, this class follows the general behaviour of the dataset, whose average precision curve (the solid blue line) reaches the highest value with higher weights for the Zernike signature. Although it is not shown in the figure, usually there is a peak in the retrieval precision when the best weight combination is reached, and the retrieval precision drops after this point. Therefore, even if a signature is dominated by another in the similarity evaluation, it contributes to improve the precision of the results. Figure 5b shows visualizations highlighting the class 1. It can be seen in these visualizations that this class presents a behaviour that is the opposite to the behaviour of the whole dataset, being better distinguished assigning a higher weight for the Haralick signature. Again, this can be confirmed comparing the average precision curve of this class (green dotted line) to the other curves in the graph. Situations similar to the presented in this example are frequently faced in other real datasets. This makes visible that the signature weighting depends on the goal of the analysis being done, focusing on different aspects of the

data representation according to the situation. The proposed technique allows detecting such particularities, by selecting a specific class and analyzing the variation of its distribution on the space, regarding different similarity settings.

V. CONCLUSION

This paper presented the Visual Signature Weighting (ViSW) technique, which allows visually inspect the impact of varying the relative weight among multiple complex data signatures. The technique provides superimposed views of several mappings of different weight relations, which help users to analyze the effects both over the whole dataset and/or focusing on subspaces of interest. ViSW was implemented as an extension of the FastMapDB tool, allowing to handle large complex datasets identified through multiple signatures stored on relational databases, whose similarity is aggregated into a product metric. We also presented case studies showing the usefulness of the technique when performing visual analysis of real image datasets. Future work include adding knowledge in the signature balancing process, to try to reduce the iterations performed, while still being user-guided through the visualizations provided.

ACKNOWLEDGMENT

This work has been supported by CNPq, CAPES, FAPESP, STIC-AmSud and Microsoft Research.

REFERENCES

[1] S. J. Simoff, M. H. Böhlen, and A. Mazeika, "Visual data mining: An introduction and overview," in *Visual Data Mining*, ser. LNCS. Springer, 2008, vol. 4404, pp. 1–12.

[2] M. Barioni, E. Botelho, C. Faloutsos, H. Razente, A. Traina, and C. T. Jr., "Data visualization in RDBMS," in *IASTED ISDB*, 2002, pp. 264–269.

[3] R. C. Gonzalez and R. E. Woods, *Digital Image Processing (3rd Edition)*. Upper Saddle River, NJ, USA: Prentice-Hall, Inc., 2006.

[4] R. M. Haralick, "Statistical and structural approaches to texture," in *IEEE*, vol. 67, 1979, pp. 786–804.

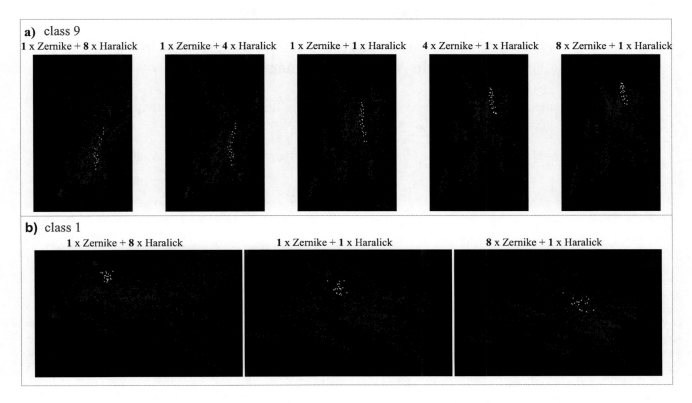

a) class 9

1 x Zernike + 8 x Haralick   1 x Zernike + 4 x Haralick   1 x Zernike + 1 x Haralick   4 x Zernike + 1 x Haralick   8 x Zernike + 1 x Haralick

b) class 1

1 x Zernike + 8 x Haralick   1 x Zernike + 1 x Haralick   8 x Zernike + 1 x Haralick

Figure 5. Visualizations of the MRI_704 dataset with varying signature weight relations, highlighting the classes 9 and 1.

[5] A. Khotanzad and Y. H. Hong, "Invariant image recognition by Zernike moments," *IEEE TPAMI*, vol. 12, no. 5, pp. 489–497, 1990.

[6] P. H. Bugatti, A. J. M. Traina, and C. Traina Jr., "Assessing the best integration between distance-function and image-feature to answer similarity queries," in *SAC*. Fortaleza, CE, Brazil: ACM, 2008, pp. 1225–1230.

[7] Y.-H. Yuan, Q.-S. Sun, Q. Zhou, and D.-S. Xia, "A novel multiset integrated canonical correlation analysis framework and its application in feature fusion," *Pattern Recogn.*, vol. 44, pp. 1031–1040, 2011.

[8] R. Bueno, D. S. Kaster, A. A. Paterlini, A. J. M. Traina, and C. T. Jr., "Unsupervised scaling of multi-descriptor similarity functions for medical image datasets," in *CBMS*. Albuquerque, New Mexico, USA: IEEE, 2009, pp. 1–8.

[9] B. Bustos, D. Keim, D. Saupe, T. Schreck, and D. Vranic, "Automatic selection and combination of descriptors for effective 3d similarity search," in *Multimedia Software Engineering*. Miami, FL, USA: IEEE, 2004, pp. 514–521.

[10] K. Chen and L. Liu, "iVIBRATE: Interactive visualization-based framework for clustering large datasets," *ACM Trans. Information Systems*, vol. 24, no. 2, pp. 245–294, 2006.

[11] J. Zhang, L. Gruenwald, and M. Gertz, "VDM-RS: A visual data mining system for exploring and classifying remotely sensed images," *Computers & Geosciences*, vol. 35, pp. 1827–1836, 2009.

[12] K. Zhao, B. Liu, T. M. Tirpak, and W. Xiao, "A visual data mining framework for convenient identification of useful knowledge," in *IEEE ICDM*, 2005, pp. 530–537.

[13] E. A. Rundensteiner, M. O. Ward, J. Yang, and P. R. Doshi, "XmdvTool: Visual interactive data exploration and trend discovery of high-dimensional data sets," in *SIGMOD Conf.*, 2002, p. 631.

[14] J. B. Kruskal and M. Wish, *Multidimensional Scaling*. SAGE Publications, 1978.

[15] C. Faloutsos and K.-I. Lin, "FastMap: A fast algorithm for indexing, data-mining and visualization of traditional and multimedia datasets," in *SIGMOD Conf.*, 1995, pp. 163–174.

[16] H. L. Razente, F. J. T. Chino, M. C. N. Barioni, A. J. M. Traina, and C. T. Jr., "Visual analysis of feature selection for data mining processes." in *Brazilian Database Symposium*, Brasilia, DF, 2004, pp. 33–47.

[17] J. M. Geusebroek, G. J. Burghouts, and A. W. M. Smeulders, "The Amsterdam library of object images," *International Journal of Computer Vision*, vol. 61, no. 1, pp. 103–112, 2005.

[18] R. A. Baeza-Yates and B. A. Ribeiro-Neto, *Modern Information Retrieval*. Wokingham, UK: Addison-Wesley, 1999.

Visualization of Automated and Manual Trajectories in Wide-Area Motion Imagery

Anoop Haridas, Rengarajan Pelapur, Joshua Fraser, Filiz Bunyak, Kannappan Palaniappan
Department of Computer Science, University of Missouri
Columbia, MO 65201 USA
{ahkrc,rvpnc4}@mail.mizzou.edu, jbfraser@gmail.com, {bunyak,palaniappank}@missouri.edu

Abstract

The task of automated object tracking and performance assessment in low frame rate, persistent, wide spatial coverage motion imagery is an emerging research domain. The collection of hundreds to tens of thousands of dense trajectories produced by such automatic algorithms along with the subset of manually verified tracks across several coordinate systems require new tools for effective human computer interfaces and exploratory trajectory visualization. We describe an interactive visualization system that supports very large gigapixel per frame video; facilitates rapid, intuitive monitoring and analysis of tracking algorithm execution; provides visual methods for the intercomparison of very long manual tracks with multi-segmented automatic tracker outputs; and a flexible KOLAM TrackingSimulator (KOLAM-TS) middleware that generates visualization data by automating the object tracker performance testing and benchmarking process.

I. INTRODUCTION

Tracking in wide-area motion imagery is a challenging research domain that is receiving a lot of current interest. The visualization of hundreds to thousands of tracks resulting from automated and manual tracking of objects offers new challenges in visualization and visual analytics. Even with standard video sequences, also known as full motion video (FMV), meaningful comparisons of tracking algorithm behavior with quantitative performance metrics were difficult to perform due to the paucity of standard video datasets with associated manual labeled ground truth. However, recent work has led to the creation of extensive, open repositories of *non-wide area* video datasets, tools and ground truth. Notable examples include open source tools such as the Video Performance Evaluation Resource (ViPER-GT) of scripts and Java programs [4], which allows for metadata viewing and editing, ground truth generation and annotation of video including a frame accurate MPEG-1 decoder; VIPER-PE a scriptable command-line based performance evaluation tool; VirtualDub for frame accurate capturing, playing back and filtering of video in AVI format; the Video Surveillance Online Repository (ViSOR) project [24], which comprises a web-based dynamic, shareable, open repository of surveillance video sequences and annotations using an event ontology; and the Scoring, Truthing And Registration Toolkit (START), for semi-automated ground truth generation using a keyframe approach [20]. Several workshops, such as the PETS series and

the VSSN series, and national-level projects, such as i-LIDS [7] and ETISEO [11], utilize the ViPER-XML annotation format in their video databases. Another important example is the ground truth motion database developed along with the layer segmentation and motion annotation tools at MIT CSAIL [9]. Since manual ground truth creation from real video is time consuming and error-prone an alternative approach using computer graphics tools to automatically create precise ground truth from realistic/synthetic video of virtual worlds using simulated cameras has also been studied [12], [18], [19]. The NGA coordinated Motion Imagery Standards Board (MISB) has been developing a metadata architecture and standards-based software interfaces for Video Moving Target Indicator (VMTI) systems to analyze and share activity-based GeoINT and tracking results for characterizing actions and interactions in a wide range of motion imagery including FMV and Large Volume Streaming Data (LVSD) [21].

The term LVSD is a NATO designation for a class of imagery also referred to as wide-area persistent surveillance (WAPS), wide-area aerial surveillance (WAAS), wide-area large format (WALF) and WAMI, which is an emerging area of interest, due to its large scale continuous coverage of geospatial regions for a variety of applications [16], [2], [17]. Given the established importance of FMV annotation ground truth databases and performance metrics, increasing attention is being focused on developing equivalent capability for WAMI. Working with WAMI data presents a unique set of challenges, distinct from standard video surveillance data, including interactive visualization of very large time-sequence imagery (100 Mpixels to 10 Gpixels per frame at rates of one Hz or faster using images from an array of smaller cameras with VIS, IR, MSI or HSI sensors), efficient algorithms for mosaicing, georegistration, stabilization, multi-target tracking, event and activity analysis [16] [17]. The difficulties of tracking vehicles in low frame rate aerial wide-area motion imagery are many, including large object displacements, parallax and occlusions from tall structures, low contrast, moving seams across camera boundaries, significant object appearance changes with viewing direction, shadows and are described in recent publications including [16], [13], [3], [17], [22], [8]. Unlike regular video surveillance databases, there are currently only a few WAMI datasets that are available in the public domain. One example is the PSS imagery described in this paper; another is the Columbus Large Image Format (CLIF) dataset, collected in a flyover of the Ohio

1550-6037/11 $26.00 © 2011 IEEE
DOI 10.1109/IV.2011.67

State University Campus in October 2007 [1]. Visualizing the statistical distribution of a dense set of automatically estimated tracks in a limited geographical region by overlaying a large number of trajectories is described in [8], [22].

The WAMI database utilized here for visualization, tracking and ground truth generation purposes, is from the Persistent Surveillance Systems (PSS) event management, law enforcement and emergency response collection. WAMI datasets were collected using an eight camera array on an airborne platform producing 256 megapixel mosaiced georegistered images. We used sample WAMI consisting of several thousand frames collected over Philadelphia (March 13, 2008) for this paper. Some of the features of the Philadelphia WAMI dataset are listed in Table I.

Frame Rate:	1 frame per second (fps)
Altitude:	3,500 – 12,500 ft.
Coverage:	4 square miles, 80°x 60°fov
GSD:	25 – 50 cm
Pixel Type:	Grayscale
Bandwidth:	1 TB/hr; 16K x 16K pixels / frame
File Format:	Tiled JPEG pyramids

TABLE I
WAMI NORTH PHILADELPHIA, PENNSYLVANIA DATASET
CHARACTERISTICS (DATASETS COURTESY OF PSS).

We have summarized some of the challenges in interactive visualization of WAMI datasets. The rest of the paper is organized as follows. First, we briefly describe our visualization platform KOLAM, followed by details about KOLAM-TS which automates tracker execution and performance evaluation. Then the different parser modules developed to handle the various ground truth formats are explained and the need for a standard format for ground truth described followed by conclusions.

II. KOLAM INTERACTIVE VISUALIZATION TOOL

The KOLAM (K-tiles for Optimized muLtiresolution Access with coMpression) application was developed using C++ and the Qt 4.x SDK to provide cross-platform (Windows, Mac OS X, Linux) interactive visualization of extremely large, time-varying image datasets, on the order of hundreds of gigabytes to terabytes in size. KOLAM achieves smooth interactive display, navigation and analysis of massive datasets through a combination of pyramidal out-of-core data structures, efficient application-level paging, and concurrent I/O and processing [14], [15]. An early motivation for developing KOLAM was to extend linked multiple window visualization tools [5], [6], [23] to support extremely large datasets. Other tools for visualization of WAMI datasets include Persistent Surveillance Systems (PSS) iView and MIT Lincoln Laboratory Advanced Persistent Image eXploitation (APIX) Viewer and processing system.

The pyramidal data structure used for organizing the image into spatially coherent multiresolution tiles using a hierarchical scale–and–tile architecture is shown in Figure 1. Each successive image layer is scaled by one-fourth of the prior

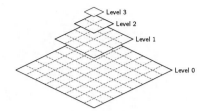

Fig. 1. Multiresolution tiled image pyramid data structure using the scale–and–tile approach for supporting interactive access to datasets much larger than main memory.

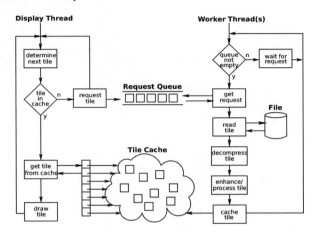

Fig. 2. Multithreading and priority caching system using a tile request queue in KOLAM for parallel reads overlapped with non-blocking interactive visualization.

level (one-half in each dimension) to create a multiresolution structure which is then reorganized into fixed-size tiles [14], [15]. Each tile is individually compressed to create a self-contained subimage. KOLAM can display this tile organization by drawing grid lines to depict the scaled tiles being drawn from the appropriate layer of the pyramid as the user zooms in and out.

In addition to the native pyramid storage format, the open architecture of KOLAM allows for the support of different multiresolution, hierarchical data types. The PSS file format is organized using a scale–and–tile pyramidal structure similar to the native KOLAM datasets and utilize per-tile JPEG compression. Extensions to support JPEG2000 and NCSA HDF5 access are being explored.

In order to provide interactive display updates, KOLAM fetches and displays only those tiles required for the view into the data. In order to display images much larger than primary memory, tiles are cached and paged according to a distance-based metric. The reading and decompression of tiles is accomplished asynchronously using a safe multithreaded architecture. Tile visibility determination for display is managed in a separate thread from those servicing I/O and decompression requests in order to keep the display interactive. A single thread manages the display while multiple read (worker) threads fulfill the tile requests.

KOLAM utilizes a workpile concurrent model by creating

Fig. 3. The KOLAM user interface, showing the various subsystem widgets during a sample session for tracking moving and stationary objects, the lat-long position readout panel in the lower left, filename, ROI and zoom information in the status bar, interactive animation panel, assisted multi-object tracking panel on the right that also controls the display parameters for multiple trajectories and the original and stabilized trajectories trailing behind the two tracked objects.

a queue in which pending operations are enqueued, to be then dequeued by worker threads. KOLAM takes advantage of the manner in which the operating system scheduler manages the blocking and yielding of thread execution for load balancing. The workpile model is used in the KOLAM multithreaded environment by inclusion of the POSIX *pread()* functionality (under Mac OS X and Linux), which ensures that all read operations are atomic (combined seek and read) with respect to the files being handled and ensures that the operations are threadsafe with multiple reader threads. Under the Windows operating system a fully functional *pread()* is not available so KOLAM uses a single reader thread. Figure 2 illustrates the primary display and read/worker threads architecture of KOLAM.

An important theme in the KOLAM GUI design, has been to minimize the number of interaction steps needed for a specific functionality to maximize productivity – such as single-click manual/assisted tracking. The interface components needed for ground truth generation and output visualization from KOLAM-TS are explored below.

A. KOLAM Display Interface

Figure 3 shows the KOLAM user interface along with three subsystem tool interfaces. The KOLAM user interface was designed so that user dialogs can be freely moved and do not occupy a fixed subregion of the main window area. This maximizes the main window region available for motion video visualization. This design choice is useful when multiple monitors are available, in which case the entire display area of the primary monitor can be devoted to visualization, and all dialogs can be positioned on the other display devices in an appropriate user-preferred configuration. Standard functionality such as panning and zooming within large gigapixel imagery is efficiently implemented to provide a smooth interaction user experience. This enables rapid navigation to any region

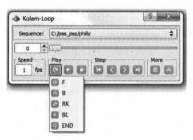

Fig. 4. Animation playback interface in KOLAM supporting forward and backward temporal access, adjustable framerate, random frame access, scrub bar, etc.

of interest at any zoom factor like a virtual light table. An overlay system provides multiple, transparent layers tiered above the actual display area, which serves the dual purpose of presenting additional information superimposed on the display, and enabling marking and annotation of the data. The overlay feature enables the ground truth creation and trajectory display either interactively or using KOLAM-TS.

B. Video Playback/Animation Interface

The KOLAM animation GUI panel in Figure 4 is compact, with an expandable detail tab that provides access to commonly used functionality for seamless playback of multiple WAMI sequences as well as a sequence of (same-sized) image frames in popular formats like TIFF, PNG, JPEG, etc. Bidirectional playback with or without looping is supported, at varying frame rates and stride sizes. It is also possible to single-step forward or backward one frame at a time, or jump to an arbitrary frame in the sequence. Rock (RK) cycles between playing the sequence forward then in reverse order. Blink (BK) animates two adjacent frames that may be separated by an arbitrary stride (step) size. A drop down list shows a selectable playlist of active sequences currently loaded by the user.

C. KOLAM Tracking Interface

The assisted tracking interface in KOLAM is a versatile GUI front-end that interfaces in an open architecture manner to multiple tracking algorithms and allowing tracker specific configuration. These may be grouped as follows: (a) Tracker properties: Creating instances for objects that need to be tracked, selecting a tracker algorithm, switching between automatic (algorithm invocation) and manual (ground truth generation) tracking modes, and invoking the selected tracker on a selected object. (b) Track properties: Setting track visibility, color, and thickness; whether the display dynamically centers itself on the current object, saving to and loading from an archive of previously generated track data, and deleting data for a particular object. Figure 5 shows the KOLAM tracker interface providing real-time feedback via messages whenever any of the above properties are modified, updating the user about tracker initialization, and normal or abnormal tracker termination.

III. KOLAM-TS MIDDLEWARE

The KOLAM-TrackingSimulator (KOLAM-TS) middleware provides a set of utilities and tools for creating, evaluating and visualizing object trajectories for assisted tracking in WAMI. KOLAM-TS automates the process of tracker algorithm performance testing and benchmarking, as a faster alternative compared to manual target reacquisition by restarting the tracker on the exact frame where it fails, using the ground truth information. The program is also used to determine performance characteristics of a tracker. One key function is to provide the tracker with an accurate template (bounding box) of the object that is being tracked when restarts are needed by taking into account occlusions, similar to how assisted tracking is done.

KOLAM-TS uses several different output processing modules for visualization as well as for performance assessment. These modules allow us to combine ground truth centroids and polygons, visibility/occlusion status, and tracker outputs in a unified framework in order to assess tracker behavior post-simulation. This combined information is visualized using KOLAM. The block diagram in Figure 7 describes the overall KOLAM-TS system.

KOLAM-TS has evolved over a period of time to accommodate a variety of trajectory ground truth and WAMI file formats. It currently reads ground truth in XML (structured), KOLAM (flat file), iView (flat file) formats. The initialization of the tracker needs a parameter input file which also acts as one of the inputs to the main harness/simulator module. KOLAM-TS provides flexibility by allowing the user to select partial or complete input from any of the listed sources. The XML structured format is produced by the MIT Layer Annotation Tool [9] as output from ground truth annotation; an example of the MIT LAT GUI is shown in Figure 6. We transitioned from using only centroid information for the target to using both polygon and centroid XML structured tags in order to facilitate automatically restarting trackers during performance testing with accurate, oriented and scaled bounding-box information for the target (vehicle).

Fig. 6. MIT Layer Annotation Tool [9] for ground truthing showing polygon boundaries around several moving objects and the tracked vehicle highlighted in green.

The MU-Harness component of KOLAM-TS shown in Figure 7, outputs two main types of files – MATLAB files needed for tracker performance evaluation as well as computing bounding box information helpful for static visualization, and KOLAM track files for dynamic trajectory visualization. A high level description of MU-Harness functionality is shown in pseudocode form in Algorithm 1. There are three different parser modules that are embedded within the MU-Harness. The XML parser mainly extracts data from a structured XML file format. It reads the object shape information represented as a polygon and calculates the geometric center of the object (i.e. centroid) using Simpson's method. The other two parsers within the MU-Harness are for reading visibility occlusion status and for target initialization (non-oriented bounding box and frame filename) from flat files. In addition to the

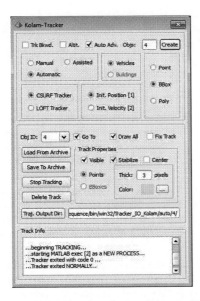

Fig. 5. KOLAM-Tracker interface for specifying tracking parameters: manual vs automatic vs assisted tracking, type of tracker (i.e. LOFT), type of trajectories to display (stabilized and unstabilized) and text feedback showing the state of the automatic tracker.

parsers embedded within the MU-Harness, we also have five different parsers for conversion between the different file formats shown in purple in Figure 7. This gives us the freedom to collect ground truth using a host of different tools. The XML2KOLAM converter was mainly designed to facilitate the visualization of polygons in KOLAM. The XML2iView and iView2KOLAM essentially perform the same task but they do not include the polygon information while outputting to the KOLAM output trajectory format.

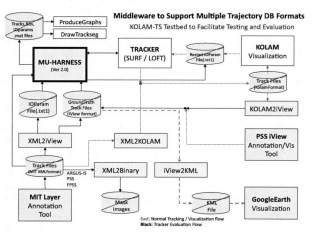

Fig. 7. KOLAM-TS middleware system diagram with external interactions showing the MU-Harness in cyan, track file conversion parsers (MATLAB programs) in purple, the interactive tools in yellow, and the flow of information as directed edges.

Algorithm 1 MU-Harness (MATLAB)

Input: $GTList$ // Centroids, polygons, start & end frame, etc.
Output: $TrackList, BBoxList$
1: //Initialize total number of tracker segments and target object
2: $count \leftarrow 0, Target = [\ ]$
3: **for each** $(GT \in GTList)$ **do**
4:     $fr \leftarrow GT.start\_frame$
5:     **while** $(fr < GT.end\_frame)$ **do**
6:         // Update Target information
7:         $Target.start\_frame = fr$
8:         $Target.start\_bbox = GT[fr].bbox$
9:         // Start Tracker
10:         $Track \leftarrow$ **Tracker**$(Target)$
11:         // Tracker returns when $(fr > GT.end\_frame)$ .OR.
12:         // $(||Track[fr].xy - GT[fr].xy|| > max\_dist)$
13:         $count \leftarrow count + 1$
14:         $TrackList[count] \leftarrow Track$
15:         $BBoxList[count] \leftarrow Target.start\_bbox$
16:         $fr \leftarrow Track.end\_frame + 1$
17:         // Re-acquire target only when it is fully visible
18:         **while** $(\ (fr < GT.end\_frame)$ .AND.
            $(GT[fr].visible == false)\ )$ **do**
19:            $fr \leftarrow fr + 1$
20:         **end while**
21:     **end while**
22: **end for**

The need for multiple parsers (eight so far in the KOLAM-TS) points out the benefits of developing a common XML-based Ground-truth Tracking Markup Language (GTML).

These parsers were required to convert between and combine different trajectory, meta-data and supporting information file formats. The tools shown in Figure 7 all have their advantages and disadvantages for collecting and managing ground truth information but output metadata in different formats. KOLAM-TS needs to interface with all these formats in order for us to be able to evaluate our tracking algorithm given multiple ground truth sources and dataset formats. The need for a standard format for ground truth has thus become essential in order to effectively share data and results. We propose the use of GTML, as an extension of the XML formats used in ViPER-XML [4] and the MIT Layer Annotation Tool [9]. ViPER and MIT LAT do not support wide-area imagery, ViPER does not provide general polygon shape drawing and MIT LAT does not support marking occlusions. GTML is still in its nascent phase and currently incorporates occlusion status for every frame, bounding polygon information as well as other metadata. The GTML file can further interface with a database for managing a large collection of experiments similar to the ViSOR system [24]. Key-Length-Value (KLV) representation established by the Society of Motion Picture and Television Engineers (SMPTE) is an alternative to XML based metadata that is being adapted by the MISB for WAMI and consists of a 16-byte SMPTE administered universal label (Key), followed by length of the data (Length) then the payload of bytes (Value). KLV coding is very efficient for streaming and high performance applications and is generally more backwards compatible as metadata standards evolve [10].

Figure 8 shows the visualization of tracker produced segments (computed tracks in cyan) along with the ground truth (target tracks) using KOLAM. The yellow trajectory shows the stabilized ground truth or target track and the cyan trajectory segments show the automated tracker output or computed tracks. The marked area shows the location where the tracker failed and was restarted by MU-Harness (Algorithm 1). KOLAM provides dynamic visualization of the trajectory evolution compared to ground truth within the spatial context of occlusions and scene complexity.

IV. CONCLUSIONS

The KOLAM environment provides an integrated toolset for: (i) interactive visualization of WAMI datasets (ii) manual ground truth generation of moving and stationary objects (iii) an efficient assisted tracking mode to increase user productivity and (iv) KOLAM-TS to facilitate automated evaluation of tracking algorithms. KOLAM allows the user to interactively step through and view tracked frames, compare trajectories or segments with ground truth. KOLAM-TS uses ground truth information to evaluate the tracker algorithm performance and visualize the track segments, making it convenient to view the image region in the failed frame and/or the restarted frame for debugging and improving the tracker. Together, these tools provide a comprehensive interface for visualization, evaluation and benchmarking of automated object tracking performance versus manual ground truth in wide-area motion imagery.

Fig. 8. Visualization of tracking results (Car2, Philly) showing manual ground truth (unstabilized in red and stabilized in yellow) and several stabilized automatic tracker segments (in cyan). One location where MU-Harness restarted the tracker after it failed is shown inside the white box (detailed zoomed view in lower left inset). The red triangles mark the failed frames.

ACKNOWLEDGEMENTS

The PSS database is a WAMI repository collected and maintained by Persistent Surveillance Systems Inc. kindly made available to us by Ross McNutt. Ilker Ersoy provided feedback on improvements to KOLAM and KOLAM-TS and worked on the tracking algorithms. Ariel Abrams-Kundan and Koyeli Ganguli assisted with ground truth creation and parts of KOLAM-TS middleware. This research was partially supported by grants from the U.S. Air Force Research Laboratory (AFRL) under agreement FA8750-11-1-0073 and Leonard Wood Institute (LWI 181223) in cooperation with the U.S. Army Research Laboratory (ARL) under Cooperative Agreement Number W911NF-07-2-0062. The views and conclusions contained in this document are those of the authors and should not be interpreted as representing the official policies, either expressed or implied of AFRL, LWI, ARL, or the U.S. Government. The U.S. Government is authorized to reproduce and distribute reprints for Government purposes notwithstanding any copyright notation thereon.

REFERENCES

[1] Air Force Research Laboratory. Columbus Large Image Format (CLIF) 2007 dataset. *https://www.sdms.afrl.af.mil/datasets/clif2007/*.

[2] C.J. Carrano. Ultra-scale vehicle tracking in low spatial resolution and low frame-rate overhead video. In O.E. Drummon and R. D. Teichgraeber, editors, *SPIE Proc. Signal and Data Processing of Small Targets*, volume 7445, 2009.

[3] N.P. Cuntoor, A. Basharat, A.G.A. Perera, and A. Hoogs. Track initialization in low frame rate and low resolution videos. In *Int. Conf. Pattern Recognition*, pages 3640–3644. IEEE, 2010.

[4] D. Doermann and D. Mihalcik. Tools and techniques for video performance evaluation. In *15th Int. Conf. Pattern Recognition*, volume 4, pages 167–170. http://viper-toolkit.sourceforge.net, 2000.

[5] A. F. Hasler, D. Chesters, M. Jentoft-Nilsen, and K. Palaniappan. High performance animation of GOES weather images. In *SPIE Proc. on GOES-8 and Beyond*, volume 2812, pages 80–83. 1996.

[6] A. F. Hasler, K. Palaniappan, M. Manyin, and J. Dodge. A high performance interactive image spreadsheet (IISS). *Computers in Physics*, 8(4):325–342, 1994.

[7] Home Office Scientific Development Branch. Imagery library for intelligent detection systems i-LIDS. In *IET Conf. Crime and Security*, pages 445–448. http://www.ilids.co.uk/, 2006.

[8] X. Jiangjian, C. Hui, H. Sawhney, and H. Feng. Vehicle detection and tracking in wide field-of-view aerial video. In *IEEE Conf. Computer Vision and Pattern Recognition*, pages 679 – 684, 2010.

[9] C. Liu, W.T. Freeman, E.H. Adelson, and Y. Weiss. Human-assisted motion annotation. In *IEEE Conf. Computer Vision and Pattern Recognition*. IEEE, 2008.

[10] NGA Motion Imagery Standards Board. Profile 2: KLV for LVSD Applications (MISB EG 0810.2). http://www.gwg.nga.mil/misb/docs/eg/EG081002.pdf.

[11] A.T. Nghiem, F. Bremond, M. Thonnat, and V. Valentin. ETISEO: Performance evaluation for video surveillance systems. In *IEEE 5th Int. Conf. Advanced Video and Signal Based Surveillance*, 2007.

[12] Object Video. Virtual Video Tool: A Half-Life 2 Mod. *http://development.objectvideo.com/*.

[13] K. Palaniappan, F. Bunyak, P. Kumar, I. Ersoy, S. Jaeger, K. Ganguli, A. Haridas, J. Fraser, R. Rao, and G. Seetharaman. Efficient feature extraction and likelihood fusion for vehicle tracking in low frame rate airborne video. In *13th Int. Conf. Information Fusion*, 2010.

[14] K. Palaniappan and J.B. Fraser. Multiresolution tiling for interactive viewing of large datasets. In *17th Int. Conf. on Interactive Information and Processing Systems (IIPS) for Meteorology, Oceanography and Hydrology*, pages 338–342. American Meteorological Society, 2001.

[15] K. Palaniappan, A.F. Hasler, J.B. Fraser, and M. Manyin. Network-based visualization using the distributed image spreadsheet (DISS). In *17th Int. Conf. on Interactive Information and Processing Systems (IIPS) for Meteorology, Oceanography and Hydrology*, pages 399–403, 2001.

[16] K. Palaniappan, R. Rao, and G. Seetharaman. Wide-area persistent airborne video: Architecture and challenges. In B. Banhu, C. V. Ravishankar, A. K. Roy-Chowdhury, H. Aghajan, and D. Terzopoulos, editors, *Distributed Video Sensor Networks: Research Challenges and Future Directions*, chapter 24, pages 349–371. Springer, 2011.

[17] R. Porter, A.M. Fraser, and D. Hush. Wide-area motion imagery. *IEEE Signal Processing Magazine*, 27(5):56–65, 2010.

[18] F.Z. Qureshi and D. Terzopoulos. Surveillance camera scheduling: A virtual vision approach. *Multimedia Systems*, 12(3):269–283, 2006.

[19] F.Z. Qureshi and D. Terzopoulos. Smart camera networks in virtual reality. *Proceedings IEEE*, 96(10):1640–1656, 2008.

[20] S.K. Ralph, J. Irvine, M.R. Stevens, M. Snorrason, and D. Gwilt. Assessing the performance of an automated video ground truthing application. In *33rd IEEE Workshop Applied Imagery Pattern Recognition*, pages 202–207, 2004.

[21] S. Randall and J. Antonisse. The standard exchange of motion indicators by image-based trackers. In *Proc. SPIE on Geospatial InfoFusion Systems and Solutions for Defense and Security Applications*, volume 8053, 2011.

[22] V. Reilly, H. Idrees, and M. Shah. Detection and tracking of large number of targets in wide area surveillance. In *11th European Conf. Computer Vision*, pages 186–199. Springer-Verlag, 2010.

[23] Jonathan C. Roberts. State of the Art: Coordinated & Multiple Views in Exploratory Visualization. In Gennady Andrienko, Jonathan C. Roberts, and Chris Weaver, editors, *Proc. 5th Int. Conf. Coordinated & Multiple Views in Exploratory Visualization*, July 2007.

[24] R. Vezzani and R. Cucchiara. Annotation collection and online performance evaluation for video surveillance: The ViSOR project. In *IEEE 5th Int. Conf. Advanced Video and Signal Based Surveillance (AVSS)*, pages 227–234, 2008.

Prisma Maps – A Geovisualization Support for Prisma Multiple Coordinated View Information Visualization Tool

Edson Koiti Kudo Yasojima, Bianchi Serique
Meiguins, Nikolas Carneiro, Rafael Veras
Universidade Federal do Pará - UFPA
Belém-PA, Brazil
koitiyasojima@gmail.com, bianchi.serique@terra.com.br,
nikolas.carneiro@gmail.com, rafaveguim@gmail.com

Aruanda Simões Meiguins
Centro Universitário do Pará - CESUPA
Rede Informática Ltda.
Belém-PA, Brazil
aruanda@redeinformatica.com.br

Abstract— This paper presents a new view for PRISMA information visualization tool; this new visualization will provide support for analyzing data on maps. The use of maps will provide a way for geographical data analysis by using coordinates. Geographic analysis becomes important when it comes to verification of database that uses the location as a key factor to create contexts. This paper will describe the new integrated view and main features of the map.

Keywords- Information Visualization; Geographical Analysis; Map View

I. INTRODUCTION

A. Abbreviations and Acronyms

Geovisualization can be described as a combination of geographical information systems, information and scientific visualization, virtual environments and data analysis. [1]

As the result of technology evolution, manipulation of data through maps has become a very important factor in making decisions through the analysis of cartographic data. Geospatial data are relevant to a large number of applications. Examples include weather measurements such as temperature, rainfall, wind-speed, etc., measured at a large number of locations, use of connecting nodes in telephone business, load of a large number of Internet nodes at different locations, air pollution in cities, etc. [2] [3]

According to [2], Map interaction techniques can be categorized based upon the effects they have on the display. Navigation techniques focus on modifying the projection of the data onto the screen, using either manual or automated methods. View enhancement methods allow users to adjust the level of detail on part or all of the visualization, or modify the mapping to emphasize some subset of the data. Selection techniques provide users with the ability to isolate a subset of the displayed data for operations such as highlighting, filtering, and quantitative analysis. Selection can be done directly on the visualization (direct manipulation) or via dialog boxes or other query mechanisms (indirect manipulation).

B. Information Visualization (IV)

As well as information data grows up, IV provide ways to organize and create views that show a context about this data accordingly to the user interaction. Information visualization takes advantage of the human cognitive capacity to isolate and show data in visual presentations. [4]

Human interactions and views can be extended to various techniques, IV already quite advanced and is now possible to find and use various techniques to manipulate data. [5] Identified a start point of what is essential for interactions that must exist in a visualization tool: overview, zoom, filter, and details-on-demand.

C. Equations

PRISMA is an information visualization tool based on multiple coordinated views to explore multidimensional datasets using the following techniques: treemap, pie, graph, scatterplot and parallel coordinates. It is extensible, portable and easy to maintain since it has been developed in Java using design patterns. [4] [6]

Users may analyze data in each view individually or simultaneously in all views. Data can be modified and reflected to the others views. [6]

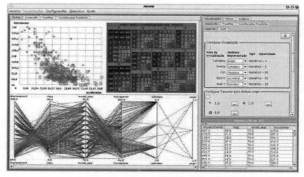

Figure 1 PRISMA Multiple Views

II. Related Works

An application using tag maps and tag clouds was developed by [7]. By using text and maps, they combine geography and text to create and plot geo-referenced text strings on the map.

Also, [8] have developed the GeoDDupe an application for reconciling and treatment of multiple location references on a map, to resolve similar data positions.

III. Architecture

The application, in a global context, dock with PRISMA and it is divided in three layers that cooperate to each other. It was developed to be a module that can easily attach to it.

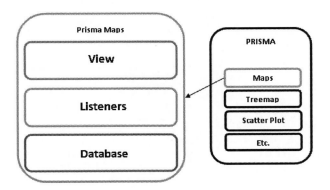

Figure 2 Prisma Maps module overview

PRISMA will provide synchronization between an modification on a different view.

Also, it is possible to reuse instances of the map, to other applications that support this kind of view. For example, if we want to create a web or desktop application that uses geographical data like longitude and latitude, the module can be used to retrieve this data and return a view of the map as an image to be used on these applications.

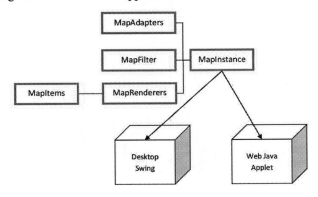

Figure 3 Module Reuse

IV. Prisma maps and State of Art

A. Overview

The application module provides all the operations cited by [5]. On the main screen, it's possible to see the summary of all the data of the database, like how many tuples the base has, how many distinct values each column has. The map support dynamic zoom.

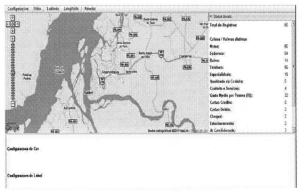

Figure 4 Main screen of the module

First of all, it is possible to select the column of the database that will represent the coordinates on the map, only double valuable columns are possible to select.

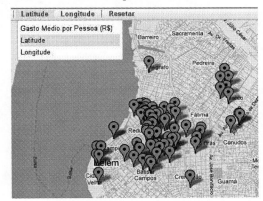

Figure 5 Latitude and Longitude selection

B. Configuration

After the markers were put on the map, it's possible to manipulate the data such as color or label selection. Each value can represent a color previously selected by the user.

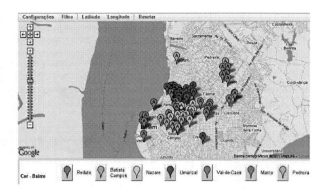

Figure 6 Color configuration

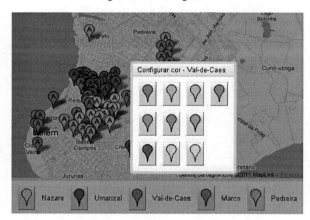

Figure 7 Color selection

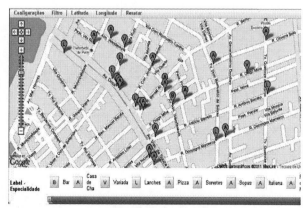

Figure 8 Label configuration

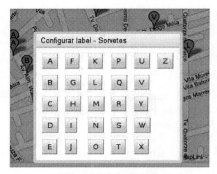

Figure 9 Label selection

C. Filtering

The module supports multiple filters; it's possible to select more than one value that will be filtered from the map. Users can select the values they want to show on the map, other values will be hidden after the operation.

Figure 10 Filter operations

D. Details on demand

It is possible to see the details of each item on the map, as well as configure the visible columns that will appear in the details pop-up. This feature helps if there are too many columns in the database.

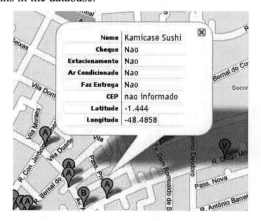

Figure 11 Details on demand

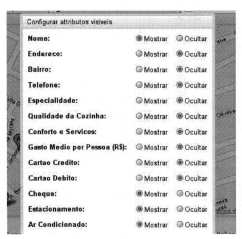

Figure 12 Selecting visible columns

V. GOOGLE WEB TOOLKIT (GWT) AND GOOGLE MAPS API

GWT is a toolkit for Java developers, it provide various pre-made components that can be used to build web applications using the Google infra-structure. It is possible to use other google Gadgets as well. When Java code is compiled in GWT, Javascript code is generated, creating the webpage with standardized code. [11]

The Google Maps API library provides a way to access the Google Maps API from a GWT project without having to write additional JavaScript code. The library gives full control using the standard Maps components such as InfoWindows, Markers, MapTypes, and Geocoding. [12]

Also, it's possible to create custom components to be used or attached to the map, like videos, other webpages etc.

VI. TEST CASES

As shown by [6] and [10] it will be used pre-defined tasks, and analysis of some characteristics such as:

- User profile: users will have a little or none knowledge in information visualization.

- Evaluation procedures: users will have some time to study and get familiarized with the application.

- Dataset: the dataset selected will be compatible with a geographical context.

- Tasks: users will have to accomplish some tasks that will evolve identification, visualization, comparison, inference, configuration and location.

By analyzing the results, any interaction on the map module will be rated based on the case study evaluated by [9].

CONCLUSIONS

This paper presented a new module for PRISMA, based on geographic visualization, using Google Maps and GWT support.

Maps are very useful in many knowledge areas, based on the study made [9] and the test that will be applied [6] [10]. We'll aim to provide an even better interaction for the user and getting better results.

For future works we aim to:

- Provide a better color configuration, like using a color pallete.

- Provide the possibility to create custom label for markers.

- Be able to load more than one dataset at the same time.

- Make a route system between two or more selected markers.

- Comparative case study with other geographical information visualization systems.

REFERENCES

[1] Faeth, Adam.; Oren, Michael.; Harding, Chris. Combining 3-D geovisualization with force feedback driven user interaction. Proceedings of the 16th ACM SIGSPATIAL international conference on Advances in geographic information systems, 2008.

[2] Dykes, Jason.; Maceachren, M. Alan.; Kraak, Menno-Jan. Exploring Geovisualization. Elsevier Inc. 1º Edition. 2005.

[3] Haug, Dan.; MacEachren, A.M.; Hardisty, Frank. The challenge of analyzing geovisualization tool use: Taking a visual approach. 20th International Cartographic Conference. 2001.

[4] Meiguins, Bianchi Serique.; Gonçalves, Aruanda Simões. Multiple Coordinated Views Supporting Visual Analytics. IEEE ICDM Workshop on Visual Analytics and Knowledge Discovery – VAKD. 2009.

[5] Shneiderman, B.; "The eyes have it: a task by data type taxonomy for Information Visualizations", Proceedings IEEE Symposium on Visual Languages. 2006.

[6] Godinho, Paulo I.; Meiguins, Bianchi S.; Gonçalves, Aruanda.; Casseb do Carmo, Ricardo.; Garcia, M.; Almeida, Leandro.; Lourenço, Rodrigo. PRISMA – A Multidimensional Information Visualization Tool Using Multiple Coordinated Views. 11th International Conference Information Visualization (IV '07). 2007.

[7] Slingsby, Aidan.; Dykes, Jason.; Wood, Jo.; Clarke, Keith. Interactive Tag Maps and Tag Clouds for the Multiscale Exploration of Large Spatio-temporal Datasets. 11th International Conference Information Visualization (IV '07). 2007.

[8] Kang, Hyunmo.; Sehgal, Vivek.; Getoor, Lise. GeoDDupe: A Novel Interface For Interactive Entity Resolution in Geospatial Data. 11th International Conference Information Visualization (IV '07). 2007.

[9] Wisniewski, P.K.; Pala, Okan.; Lipford, H.R.; Wilson, D.C. Grounding geovisualization interface design: a study of interactive map use. Proceedings of the 27th international conference extended abstracts on Human factors in computing systems. 2009.

[10] Pillat, R. M.; Valiati, E. R. A.; Freitas, C. D. S. Experimental Study on Evaluation of Multidimensional Information Visualization Techniques. Proceedings of the 2005 Latin American conference on Human-computer interaction (ACM). pp. 20-30. Cuernavaca, Mexico. 2005.

[11] Google Web Toolkit url: http://code.google.com/intl/pt-BR/webtoolkit/overview.html

[12] Google Maps url: http://code.google.com/p/gwt-google-apis/wiki/MapsGettingStarted.

Information Visualization in Climate Research

Christian Tominski[1]
[1]University of Rostock
Rostock, Germany
ct@informatik.uni-rostock.de

Jonathan F. Donges[2,3]
[2]Humboldt University
Berlin, Germany
donges@pik-potsdam.de

Thomas Nocke[3]
[3]Potsdam Institute for Climate Impact Research
Potsdam, Germany
nocke@pik-potsdam.de

Abstract—Much of the work conducted in climate research involves large and heterogeneous datasets with spatial and temporal references. This makes climate research an interesting application area for visualization. However, the application of interactive visual methods to assist in gaining insight into climate data is still hampered for climate research scientists, who are usually not visualization experts.

In this paper, we report on a survey that we conducted to evaluate the application of interactive visualization methods and to identify the problems related to establishing such methods in scientific practice. The feedback from 76 participants shows clearly that state-of-the-art techniques are rarely applied and that integrating existing solutions smoothly into the scientists workflow is problematic. We have begun to change this and present first results that illustrate how interactive visualization tools can be successfully applied to accomplish climate research tasks. As a concrete example, we describe the visualization of climate networks and its benefits for climate impact research.

Index Terms—Information Visualization, Climate Research, Climate Networks, Graph Visualization, Geo-Visualization

I. INTRODUCTION

Climate research involves many different scientific activities, among which data analysis and exploration play an important role. Interactive visualization methods aim to ease the interpretation of countless data tables filled with large quantities of numbers by providing an interactively steerable mapping process that transforms data into more easily interpretable visual representations.

When climate researchers visually analyze data, the typical procedure is to reduce or aggregate the data by analytical means and then to visualize them in a rather straightforward way as a static image. The consequence is that only little or no interaction is possible. For the purpose of presenting research results, the scientists use online portals such as the Climate Wizard (http://www.climatewizard.org), which provide access to a large number of climate-related maps, but these maps are also limited in terms of interaction and analysis facilities.

On the other hand, advances in the field of information visualization have yielded a number of innovative and promising solutions (see for example [1], [2], [3]). However, an interactive visual exploration of heterogenous climate data with multiple coordinated interactive visual representations has not yet become common practice in this field.

In order to better understand the current situation of application of visualization in climate research, we conducted a survey among 76 scientists at the Potsdam Institute for Climate Impact Research (PIK). Our major interest was in getting to know:

- Which visual, interactive, and analytical tools are applied by the scientists?
- Which tasks are accomplished with the help of these tools?
- What are the reasons for the low pervasion of state-of-the-art visualization tools?

In Section II, we summarize the feedback that we got with regard to these questions and discuss possible interpretations of the results. Based on the feedback from the questionnaires we launched an effort to convince the scientists of the advantages of interactive visual analysis and exploration. In this effort, PIK has begun to incorporate visual methods into the research workflow.

In this paper, we present a concrete application of information visualization to the exploration and analysis of climate networks. As we will see in Section III, analyzing climate networks is a recent movement that has already yielded promising results in climate research.

How this new branch of climate research can be supported with interactive visualization will be explained in Section IV. We describe the specific requirements of the application background and how interactive visualization was utilized to accomplish climate research tasks, including visual exploration for hypothesis generation and visual confirmation for hypothesis evaluation. We also include the scientists' feedback and indicate where they saw shortcomings and disadvantages. Section V will summarize our work and suggest possible directions for future work.

II. SCIENTIST INTERVIEWS ON VISUALIZATION IN CLIMATE RESEARCH PRACTICE

To gain an overview of the requirements in the heterogeneous field of climate and climate impact research, we informally interviewed researchers at the Potsdam Institute for Climate Impact Research (PIK). We took notes of the interviews and collected answers to key questions in a questionnaire for later investigation. In total, we had 76 participants including senior researchers, researchers, post-docs, PhD students, and student assistants. The participants had a wide range of scientific backgrounds: 24 participants classified themselves as meteorologists, climatologists, oceanographers & hydrologists, 30 as economists & sociologists, 27 as ecologists & biologists,

1550-6037/11 $26.00 © 2011 IEEE
DOI 10.1109/IV.2011.12

14 as physicists, 14 as geo-statisticians & geographers, and others (multiple disciplines were possible).

As our interest is mainly in scientists who have already applied visualization tools and in those who could potentially use such tools in the future, we filtered out 5 participants for whom this was not the case.

For the remaining 71 interviewees, we analyzed the questionnaire in more detail. We sought answers to the following questions: (1) Which visualization techniques are used? (2) For which tasks are visualization techniques applied? (3) Which systems and tools are utilized to generate visual representations? (4) Which are important features of visualization software?

In the following, we summarize the main results from the questionnaire:

Visualization techniques – The majority of participants apply classic visualization techniques. Time charts are applied most of the time (90%) followed by bar charts (77%), basic maps (66%), and scatter plots (56%). There is a clear preference for 2D techniques. Visualization techniques that generate 2.5D and 3D presentations are of minor relevance: Only 18% of the participants mentioned the use of height fields and 37% of them apply 3D techniques.

Tasks accomplished with visualization – 93% of the participants use visualization mainly for the purpose of presenting results in a scientific context (e.g., publications and conference talks). The evaluation of models and the verification of hypotheses are also quite relevant: 76% and 70% of the participants use visualization to accomplish these tasks. Even 69% of the participants said that they use visualization for data exploration in order to find unknown patterns and structures. The communication of scientific results in a comprehensible manner for decision makers, stakeholders & public media has been mentioned by 58% of the participants.

Applied systems & tools – Office suites (spreadsheets, diagramming, presentation) are the most frequently applied software for generating visual representations. Such tools are applied by 75% of the participants. In the shared second place follow script-based systems (e.g., R, Ferret, Grads and GMT) and commercial mathematical packages (e.g., Matlab, Mathematica), where each group of software is used by 44% of the participants. Unsurprisingly, 38% of the participants apply geographic information systems (GIS) (e.g., ArcGIS) to accomplish climate research tasks. Special purpose systems (Ocean Data View, Vis5D) were mentioned in only 20% of the questionnaires. Sophisticated visualization systems and toolkits (e.g., OpenDX, AVS/Express, IDL, Spotfire, InfoVis Toolkit, prefuse) are only marginally used (7%) or are even unknown.

Important features of visualization software – Appropriate labeling was mentioned as an important feature in 81% of the questionnaires. The ability to faithfully represent geo-spatial aspects of the data (e.g., different geographic projections) was mentioned as important by 56% of the participants. Surprisingly, a high degree of interactivity is important to a minority of only 14% of the participants.

With our survey, we found that there is a lack of utilization of visualization as an interactive analysis tool in the routine work of these scientists. The major task accomplished with the help of visualization is to transform data and analysis results into classic static visual representations for scientific publications (often called "plotting").

Possible reasons for this are manifold. First, the advantages of sophisticated visualization methods and tools are hardly known. Second, data heterogeneity due to different types of data, different scales, and different climate scenarios is not easily resolvable by scientists because there is no system that covers all of these aspects. Third, managing the volumes of data to be queried interactively requires elaborate data structures and caching mechanisms, so the scientists tend to believe that a large dataset can not be handled by an interactive analysis system at all.

Data size and heterogeneity are most challenging in this context, because they burden climate researchers with the task of making an appropriate choice for the methods or tools to be applied. In practice however, climate researchers are familiar with one visualization system and hardly know alternatives. Thus, the users' flexibility of using interactive visualization techniques is strongly restricted, and therefore they tend to resort to basic "plotting" solutions.

Furthermore, discussions with the scientists revealed that there is a kind of mistrust in interactivity in general. They fear the arbitrariness of visual representations that have been generated by interactive adjustments of thresholds or visualization parameters. In (natural) sciences, the comparability of visual representations is very important. Therefore, script-based visualization systems that generate reproducible representations are favored over interactive solutions where it is often unclear which parameter settings are required to generate a certain view on the data.

However, in recent years, new technologies such as "Google Maps", "Gapminder", and other web-based visualization services serve as a kind of starter. Many young scientists are very accustomed to utilizing the interactive features that such tools offer. So, nowadays, there is a rising acceptance of interactive visualization, however, mainly for the purpose of presentation.

Using this "new wave", we have started to go beyond presentation and to provide researchers with interactive visual tools for data exploration and analysis. Our goal is to incorporate such tools into the researchers' typical workflows. This also includes raising the awareness of well-accepted interactive visualization concepts such as multiple coordinated views, brushing and linking, or dynamic queries. Although not queried in the questionnaire, our experience was that climate researchers hardly use such concepts. After introductory lessons and demonstrations of tools that support these features, the feedbacks have been very encouraging and first successes were achieved with the help of such tools.

In the next sections, we describe this in more detail with the example of visual exploration and analysis of climate networks.

III. CLIMATE NETWORKS: BACKGROUND & DATA

Climate researchers are investigating the impact of natural phenomena and human society on the earth's climate and vice versa. These investigations involve a variety of data sources as well as complex models, which in turn produce an enormous amount of data. Linear statistical analysis is currently the main means to gain insight into such data.

In this context, the analysis of climate data from the point of view of complex network theory is a very recent and powerful approach for studying the rich data available to researchers today. In this novel approach, which has become known as climate network analysis, the idea is to construct a network or graph $G = (V, E)$ representing the structure of significant pairwise statistical relationships present within a spatiotemporally resolved data set [4]. Here V and E denote the sets of vertices and edges, respectively. This method is complementary to the by now classical and exclusively linear principle component analysis of climate data fields [5], which is commonly used in climate science [6]. Climate network analysis has been successfully applied to detect the signature of El-Niño Southern Oscillation (ENSO) variability in climate data [7] even if only data from the Arctic is considered [8], and a backbone structure carrying a considerable amount of matter, energy and dynamical information flow was uncovered in the global surface air temperature field [9], [10]. More recently, a well pronounced community structure was detected in climate networks constructed from various climate observables and exploited to improve statistical predictions of future climate variability [11]. Furthermore the method has been generalized to coupled climate network analysis allowing to study the cross-correlation structure between two or more distinct fields of climate variables which already provided some interesting insights into the Earth's atmosphere's general circulation structure [12].

The *vertices* $i \in V$ of a climate network represent measurement stations or grid points, where data like temperature or precipitation is available in the form of time series $x_i(t)$. An *edge* is introduced between pairs of vertices (i, j) iff the value of a particular measure of statistical association C_{ij} between time series $x_i(t), x_j(t)$ (e.g., linear Pearson correlation or nonlinear mutual information [10]) exceeds a threshold T_{ij}. Hence, the network's adjacency matrix A_{ij} [13] is given by

$$A_{ij} = \Theta \left(C_{ij} - T_{ij} \right) - \delta_{ij},$$

with $\Theta(\cdot)$ the Heaviside function and δ_{ij} Kronecker's delta introduced to avoid artificial self-loops. Usually a global threshold T is prescribed such that $T_{ij} = T$ for all (i, j) [9], [10], [12], [4], [7], [8], but the threshold may also be chosen adaptively for each pair based on suitable statistical significance tests of time series analysis [11].

The so obtained climate network is then subjected to a detailed statistical analysis using the tools of complex network theory [13], where the choice of particular methods and network theoretical measures depends on the questions to be asked about the data at hand.

The types of data studied by means of climate network analysis range from purely observational such as raw data collected by the Deutscher Wetterdienst (engl: German weather service), which are the basis for refinement by scientists at PIK, to processed reanalysis data sets relying on observations, e.g., the one provided by the NCEP/NCAR Reanalysis 1 project [14], to pure model output as generated by Atmospheric and Oceanic General Circulation Models (AOGCMs), e.g., the WCRP CMIP3 Multimodel Dataset [15].

The main aim of climate network analysis is to serve as an explorative technique for investigating the wealth of information contained in the data's spatial correlation structure. Its validity may be confirmed by showing that known statistical relationships and structures are picked up by the method in a way that is consistent with physical expectations and the network theoretical interpretation of specific network measures under study. Moreover, the above cited studies demonstrate that climate network analysis has the potential to uncover previously hidden or unexpected structures in the data which subsequently have to be put through a process of interpretation and careful analysis using complementary methods to answer relevant questions of interest and to generate new insights into the climate system's functioning.

IV. VISUALIZATION OF CLIMATE NETWORKS

In the following, we describe first successful applications of interactive visualization to climate network analysis. As described in Section III climate networks are complex multivariate structures. They typically contain $|V| = \mathcal{O}(10^4)$ vertices and $|E| = \mathcal{O}(10^6)$ edges rendering any attempt to extract useful information from a direct and unprocessed visualization (plot) of the network structure unfeasible. Hence, researchers applying climate network analysis have so far relied on static visualizations of statistical results such as degree and edge length distributions [7], time series of the number of edges $|E(t)|$ for time-dependent climate networks [8], global maps and scatter plots of local network measures such as degree, closeness and betweenness centrality and local clustering coefficient [9], [10], or line plots showing the evolution of global network measures such as average path length or transitivity with height [12]. This static approach is not unique to climate network analysis, but appears to be common practice in the modern analysis of general complex networks which is guided by quantitative ideas from physics (most prominently statistical mechanics), mathematics and social science [16], [13], [17].

However, the plethora of different metrics provided by complex network theory complicates the process of gaining an overall picture and, hence, a deeper understanding of climate network structure when following the static approach. This is particularly true since the spatial embedding as well as a possible time dependence of climate networks add additional dimensions to the problem. Given this challenging situation, interactive visualization promises to provide an intuitive way of combining information from the actual network structure, the network's spatial embedding and several statistical network

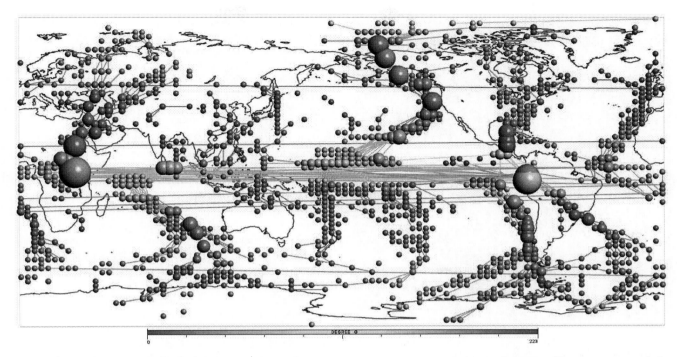

Fig. 1. The global SAT climate network visualized on a two-dimensional map, where vertex color and size encode degree and betweenness, respectively. The network has been filtered dynamically based on vertex and edge betweenness in order to reduce edge clutter. This revealed the backbone of the network.

quantifiers, e.g., degree and (edge-) betweenness centrality [13], to generate and test hypotheses ultimately based on the underlying climate data set.

Before going into detail with concrete visualization examples, let us first briefly summarize the requirements that have been derived from the interviews with the climate impact researchers:

- Climate networks with $|V| = \mathcal{O}(10^4)$ vertices and $|E| = \mathcal{O}(10^6)$ edges must be handled efficiently.
- Due to the size of the data, dynamic filtering mechanisms are mandatory. The filtering must be flexible in order to account for various data attributes and analysis tasks, and it must be reproducible (e.g., re-apply stored filters).
- The visual encoding of vertex and edge attributes should be interactively adjustable. However, this should be possible only within reasonable limits to tackle the arbitrariness of visual representations.
- The geographical frame of reference of the network is of utmost importance for the interpretation the data. Visualizing networks on two dimensional maps as well as on three dimensional globes is important, whereas graph layout algorithms are less relevant.
- To address the demand for comparability of visual representations, views must show data consistently. So, linking and coordination of views is required.
- Because network vertices have fixed geographical positions, the layout cannot be modified to reduce edge crossings. Therefore, other means are required to tackle edge congestion.

There are a number of graph visualization tools and systems, including Pajek [18], ASK-GraphView [19], GUESS [20], and Gephi [21]. However, only a few systems fulfill the requirements stated before: Tulip [22] and CGV [23]. While Tulip offers fully-fledged visual graph analysis functionality, CGV focuses on interactive exploration. Moreover, CGV is able to run in a web browser, a feature that matches with the scientists' common practice of making research results publicly available on web sites.

Next, we present two examples of applying the CGV system to interactive visualization of climate networks and discuss some first experiences as well as advantages and disadvantages with respect to this approach. The climate networks to be visualized are provided in the DOT or GraphML file format with precalculated vertex-based and edge-based network measures of interest included in the network as vertex and edge attributes, respectively.

A. Visualizing global climate networks

In this example, we study a climate network derived from the monthly averaged global surface air temperature (SAT) field taken from a 20th century reference run (20c3m, as defined in the IPCC AR4) by the Hadley Centre HadCM3 model [15] covering the time span January 1860 to December 1999. Consistently with [9], [10], we choose a global threshold T such that 0.5 % of all theoretically possible edges associated to the largest values of linear Pearson correlation between pairs of time series are included in the SAT climate network. The networks contains about 6k vertices and 115k edges.

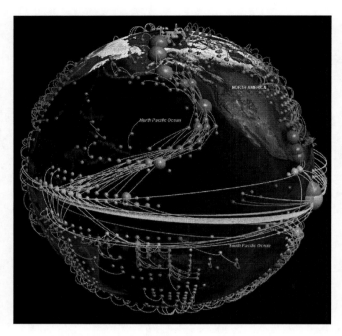

Fig. 2. Spherical three-dimensional globe representation of the SAT network. The visual encoding and filtering is the same as in Fig. 1.

The climate network of a selected time point is visualized as a node-link diagram, where the positions of vertices are fixed, and where vertex color and size encode the vertex attributes degree and betweenness, respectively. Using CGV's dynamic filtering facilities, we interactively filtered for vertices and edges with high vertex and edge betweenness, therefore highlighting structures with particular importance for hypothetical communication following shortest paths within the network.

A two dimensional lat-lon-projection of the filtered network (see Figure 1) reveals patterns consistent with the backbone of significantly increased vertex betweenness discussed in [9]. Moreover, this visualization contains additional information on edge betweenness, highlighting that high betweenness edges tend to fall into two categories: very short and very long edges. This fact becomes particularly clear in a spherical representation of the same filtered climate network (see Figure 2) which shows less visual clutter than the two dimensional projection, but on the downside restricts the view to one hemisphere only.

Based on both views we may formulate the hypothesis that certain short range as well as long range processes are particularly important for coupling the dynamics of the surface air temperature field. While the important short range edges may represent advection of heat by strong surface ocean currents, the long range connections appear to correspond to known teleconnection patterns, e.g., the long range edges in the tropical Pacific ocean seen in Figure 2 are consistent with teleconnections induced by ENSO. Interactively varying the filters one can easily evaluate the robustness of such patterns, which is particularly important when testing hypotheses.

One disadvantage with respect to this approach is that filter settings are not derived from quantitative criteria, thereby rendering the results arbitrary to some degree. However, it should be noted that visualizations such as the one presented in Figure 2 have already proven highly valuable and successful in intuitively conveying the basic ideas and results of climate network analysis to scientific audiences at international conferences (see [24]).

B. Visualizing regional climate networks

Our second example concerns a regional climate network constructed from daily mean surface air temperature time series covering the years 1951 to 2006 measured at climate stations scattered across Germany. While the raw data is provided by the Deutscher Wetterdienst, the scientists at the Potsdam Institute for Climate Impact Research have processed the data to improve its quality and consistency before compiling the climate network. A global threshold T was chosen to include 1% of all maximally possible edges corresponding to the largest values of Pearson correlation. The resulting network contains 2k vertices and 27k edges.

A two-dimensional node-link visualization as provided by the CGV system at first glance highlights a pronounced community structure being particularly prevalent in the northeast of Germany (see Figure 3). Furthermore, one clearly sees that vertices of high degree tend to have a small betweenness, while those of high betweenness have a small degree. This behavior is typical for networks with an organized, non-random structure [13].

But what factors could be essential for organizing the network and, hence, the underlying temperature field's correlation structure in the observed way? We may hypothesize that geographic features, e.g., orographic structure such as hills or mountain ranges play a major role as one would expect from physical considerations.

This hypothesis could be tested interactively by adding information from a digital elevation model to the CGV system. If visual support were to be found, the next step would be to test the hypothesis in a statistically rigorous way. In this spirit, our second example illustrates how interactive visualization can aid in formulating and testing hypotheses on network structure and the underlying data, particularly if few a priori knowledge and expectations are present.

Although the visualization has been considered useful for exploring the climate network in general, the scientists also raised concern about the heavy clutter of edges in the node-link representation. One way to alleviate this problem is to dynamically filter out edges based on edge attributes. As an alternative, the edges can be routed into bundles. To this end, we adapted Boyandin's implementation [25] of the force-directed edge bundling approach of Holten and van Wijk [26].

The edge bundling was generally perceived as a suitable and aesthetically pleasing solution. However, as shown in Figure 4, there is a tradeoff between using straight edges and bundled edges. While bundled edges are quite useful for reducing edge clutter, individual edges can be best identified when using straight edges. This indicates that there is no visual representation that suits all of the different tasks that climate researchers

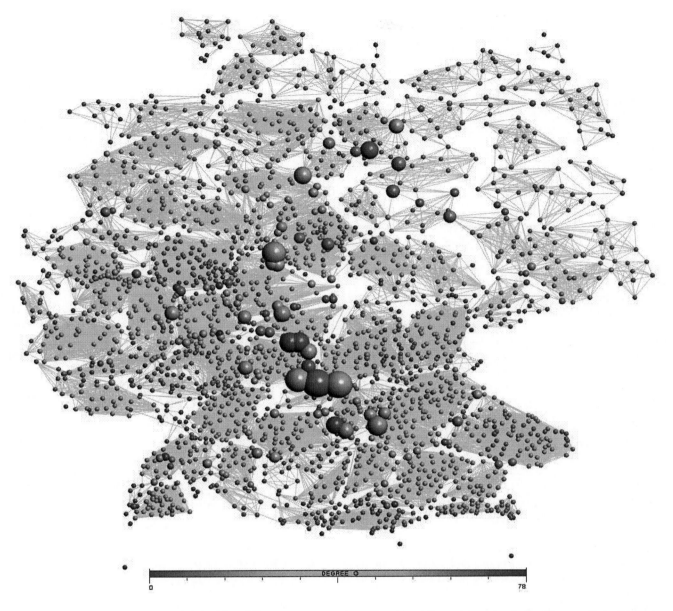

Fig. 3. Visualization of a climate network derived from daily mean temperature data collected at weather stations scattered across Germany. Vertex betweeness and degree are visualized with varying sizes and colors, respectively. The visual representation clearly reveals the network's strong community structure.

might have to accomplish. Therefore, interactive and task-dependent parametrization of the visualization is important in order to arrive at appropriate visual representations. So besides making climate scientists aware of new innovative information visualization approaches such as edge bundling, we also have to provide information about the approaches' usefulness for different data, tasks, and application scenarios.

V. DISCUSSION & FUTURE WORK

The examples presented in the previous paragraphs indicate that climate researchers have begun to recognize information

visualization as a valuable tool. Based on a list of requirements, we were able to provide solutions that enable the scientists not only to present their research results, but also to evaluate hypotheses, and in particular to generate hypotheses through visual exploration. These first successes are very promising and motivate us to continue our work.

But still it is too early to claim that climate researchers would be *using* information visualization tools, and we feel that there is still more trust in statistics and analytical computations, rather than in visual representations, the interpretation of which may vary. In order to accomplish the ambitious goal

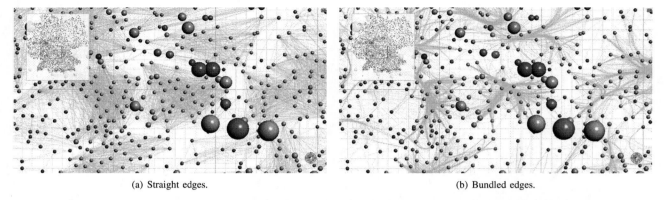

(a) Straight edges.   (b) Bundled edges.

Fig. 4. Rendering edges as straight lines better suits the task of identifying connections between vertices, but visual clutter is a problem. Bundling edges reduces clutter, however discerning individual edges becomes more difficult.

of really making information visualization common practice in climate research, further hurdles have to be taken.

As we learned from the questionnaire, the interactivity is not always appreciated because the options for different visual encodings and different perspectives on the data are sometimes experienced as indiscriminate. Additional methods are required to support the users in finding good views on the data and in determining appropriate parametrizations of visualization techniques. As researchers begin to integrate visualization systems in their daily work, there are a number of practical aspects to consider: Undo and redo mechanisms must be integrated, ongoing work must be storable on disk for later continuation, and derived findings must be annotatable, to name only a few (see [27], [28]).

Secondly, there is the pressing issue of time-dependency of climate networks. In general, time-dependency implies additional conceptual and technical challenges because the dimension of time can be structured in a number of different ways and because the data size is multiplied by the number of time steps [29]. Up to now, individual time steps have to be loaded separately, which hinders the exploration of temporal trends and patterns in the data. New visualization views have to be integrated to address this problem.

In future analysis scenarios, the climate networks' geographical frame of reference will not be restricted to latitude and longitude, but may also contain depth (oceanographic models) or height (atmospheric models). Additionally, uncertainty of model structure and hence of the generated data will play an increasingly important role. As a result, we have to consider the 3D visualization of uncertain graph structures with uncertain attributes, which we think is a formidable challenge.

In order to arrive at user-centered solutions for these issues, we will continue the close collaboration between our institutions, applying recent developments in the field of visualization to problems in climate impact research and non-linear analysis. We plan to extend existing solutions and to integrate additional tools (see Figure 5) into the researchers' workflows much like in the spirit of visual analytics [30].

ACKNOWLEDGMENT

We acknowledge financial support by the German National Academic Foundation, the Leibniz association (project ECONS), the Federal Ministry for Education and Research via the Potsdam Research Cluster for Georisk Analysis, Environmental Change and Sustainability (PROGRESS), and the DFG Graduate School (GRK 1539 "Sichtbarkeit und Sichtbarmachung"). The work presented in this paper has been partly conducted in the context of the EU coordination project "VisMaster".

REFERENCES

[1] T. Nocke, U. Heyder, S. Petri, K. Vohland, M. Wrobel, and W. Lucht, "Visualization of Biosphere Changes in the Context of Climate Change," in *Information Technology and Climate Change – 2nd International Conference IT for empowerment*, V. Wohlgemuth, Ed.   trafo Wissenschaftsverlag, 2009, pp. 29–36.

[2] J. Kehrer, P. Filzmoser, and H. Hauser, "Brushing Moments in Interactive Visual Analysis," *Computer Graphics Forum*, vol. 29, no. 3, pp. 813–822, 2010. [Online]. Available: http://dx.doi.org/10.1111/j.1467-8659.2009.01697.x

[3] F. Ladstädter, A. K. Steiner, B. C. Lackner, B. Pirscher, G. Kirchengast, J. Kehrer, H. Hauser, P. Muigg, and H. Doleisch, "Exploration of Climate Data Using Interactive Visualization," *Journal of Atmospheric and Oceanic Technology*, vol. 27, no. 4, pp. 667–679, 2010. [Online]. Available: http://dx.doi.org/10.1175/2009JTECHA1374.1

[4] A. A. Tsonis and P. J. Roebber, "The Architecture of the Climate Network," *Physica A*, vol. 333, pp. 497–504, 2004. [Online]. Available: http://dx.doi.org/10.1016/j.physa.2003.10.045

[5] J. Wallace and D. Gutzler, "Teleconnections in the Geopotential Height Field During the Northern Hemisphere Winter," *Monthly Weather Review*, vol. 109, no. 4, pp. 784–812, 1981. [Online]. Available: http://journals.ametsoc.org/doi/abs/10.1175/1520-0493%281981%29109%3C0784%3ATITGHF%3E2.0.CO%3B2

[6] H. von Storch and F. W. Zwiers, *Statistical Analysis in Climate Research*. Cambridge University Press, 1999.

[7] A. A. Tsonis and K. L. Swanson, "Topology and Predictability of El Niño and La Niña Networks," *Physical Review Letters*, vol. 100, no. 22, p. 228502, 2008. [Online]. Available: http://dx.doi.org/10.1103/PhysRevLett.100.228502

[8] K. Yamasaki, A. Gozolchiani, and S. Havlin, "Climate Networks Around the Globe are Significantly Affected by El Niño," *Physical Review Letters*, vol. 100, no. 22, p. 228501, 2008. [Online]. Available: http://dx.doi.org/10.1103/PhysRevLett.100.228501

[9] J. F. Donges, Y. Zou, N. Marwan, and J. Kurths, "The Backbone of the Climate Network," *Europhysics Letters*, vol. 87, no. 4, p. 48007, 2009. [Online]. Available: http://stacks.iop.org/0295-5075/87/i=4/a=48007

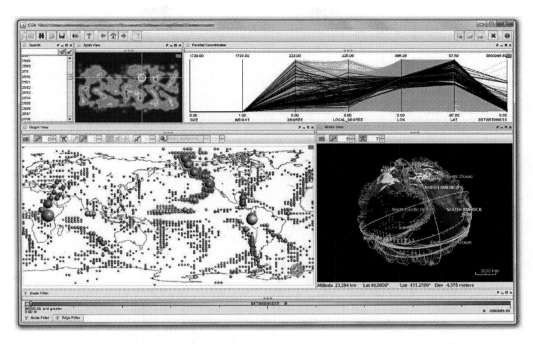

Fig. 5. Multiple coordinated views as provided by the system CGV to support the interactive visual exploration of climate networks.

[10] ——, "Complex Networks in Climate Dynamics," *European Physical Journal Special Topics*, vol. 174, no. 1, pp. 157–179, 2009. [Online]. Available: http://dx.doi.org/10.1140/epjst/e2009-01098-2

[11] K. Steinhaeuser, N. V. Chawla, and A. R. Ganguly, "Complex Networks as a Unified Framework for Descriptive Analysis and Predictive Modeling in Climate Science," *Statistical Analysis and Data Mining*, 2011, to appear. [Online]. Available: http://dx.doi.org/10.1002/sam.10100

[12] J. F. Donges, H. C. H. Schultz, N. Marwan, Y. Zou, and J. Kurths, "Investigating the Topology of Interacting Networks – Theory and Application to Coupled Climate Subnetworks," *European Physical Journal B*, 2011, to appear. [Online]. Available: http://dx.doi.org/10.1140/epjb/e2011-10795-8

[13] M. E. J. Newman, "The Structure and Function of Complex Networks," *SIAM Review*, vol. 45, no. 2, pp. 167–256, 2003. [Online]. Available: http://dx.doi.org/10.1137/S003614450342480

[14] R. Kistler, E. Kalnay, W. Collins, S. Saha, G. White, J. Woollen, M. Chelliah, W. Ebisuzaki, M. Kanamitsu, V. Kousky, H. V. D. Dool, R. Jenne, and M. Fiorino, "The NCEP–NCAR 50-Year Reanalysis: Monthly Means CD–ROM and Documentation," *Bulletin of the American Meteorological Society*, vol. 82, no. 2, pp. 247–268, 2001. [Online]. Available: http://dx.doi.org/10.1175/1520-0477(2001)082%3C0247:TNNYRM%3E2.3.CO;2

[15] G. A. Meehl, C. Covey, T. Delworth, M. Latif, B. McAvaney, J. F. B. Mitchell, R. J. Stouffer, and K. E. Taylor, "THE WCRP CMIP3 Multimodel Dataset: A New Era in Climate Change Research," *Bulletin of the American Meteorological Society*, vol. 88, no. 9, p. 1383, 2007. [Online]. Available: http://dx.doi.org/10.1175/BAMS-88-9-1383

[16] R. Albert and A. L. Barabasi, "Statistical Mechanics of Complex Networks," *Reviews of Modern Physics*, vol. 74, no. 1, pp. 47–97, 2002. [Online]. Available: http://dx.doi.org/10.1103/RevModPhys.74.47

[17] S. Boccaletti, V. Latora, Y. Moreno, M. Chavez, and D. U. Hwang, "Complex Networks: Structure and Dynamics," *Physics Reports*, vol. 424, no. 4–5, pp. 175–308, 2006. [Online]. Available: http://dx.doi.org/doi:10.1016/j.physrep.2005.10.009

[18] W. de Nooy, A. Mrvar, and V. Batagelj, *Exploratory Social Network Analysis with Pajek*. Cambridge University Press, 2005.

[19] J. Abello, F. van Ham, and N. Krishnan, "ASK-GraphView: A Large Scale Graph Visualization System," *IEEE Transactions on Visualization and Computer Graphics*, vol. 12, no. 5, 2006. [Online]. Available: http://doi.ieeecomputersociety.org/10.1109/TVCG.2006.120

[20] E. Adar, "GUESS: A Language and Interface for Graph Exploration," in *Proceedings of the SIGCHI Conference on Human Factors in Computing Systems (CHI)*. ACM, 2006. [Online]. Available: http://dx.doi.org/10.1145/1124772.1124889

[21] M. Bastian, S. Heymann, and M. Jacomy, "Gephi: An Open Source Software for Exploring and Manipulating Networks," in *International AAAI Conference on Weblogs and Social Media*, 2009.

[22] D. Auber, "Tulip : A Huge Graph Visualisation Framework," in *Graph Drawing Softwares*, ser. Mathematics and Visualization, P. Mutzel and M. Jünger, Eds. Springer-Verlag, 2003.

[23] C. Tominski, J. Abello, and H. Schumann, "CGV – An Interactive Graph Visualization System," *Computers & Graphics*, vol. 33, no. 6, pp. 660–678, 2009. [Online]. Available: http://dx.doi.org/10.1016/j.cag.2009.06.002

[24] Y. Zou, J. F. Donges, and J. Kurths, "Recent advances in complex climate network analysis," *Complex Systems and Complexity Science*, vol. 8, no. 1, pp. 27–38, 2011, in Chinese.

[25] I. Boyandin, E. Bertini, and D. Lalanne, "Using Flow Maps to Explore Migrations Over Time," Workshop GeoVA(t) - Geospatial Visual Analytics: Focus on Time at the AGILE International Conference on Geographic Information Science, 2010.

[26] D. Holten and J. J. van Wijk, "Force-Directed Edge Bundling for Graph Visualization," *Computer Graphics Forum*, vol. 28, no. 3, pp. 983–990, 2009. [Online]. Available: http://dx.doi.org/10.1111/j.1467-8659.2009.01450.x

[27] M. Kreuseler, T. Nocke, and H. Schumann, "A History Mechanism for Visual Data Mining," in *Proceedings of the IEEE Symposium on Information Visualization (InfoVis)*, 2004, pp. 49–56. [Online]. Available: http://doi.ieeecomputersociety.org/10.1109/INFOVIS.2004.2

[28] C. T. Silva, E. W. Anderson, E. Santos, and J. Freire, "Using VisTrails and Provenance for Teaching Scientific Visualization," *Computer Graphics Forum*, vol. 30, no. 1, pp. 75–84, 2011. [Online]. Available: http://dx.doi.org/10.1111/j.1467-8659.2010.01830.x

[29] W. Aigner, S. Miksch, W. Müller, H. Schumann, and C. Tominski, "Visualizing Time-Oriented Data – A Systematic View," *Computers & Graphics*, vol. 31, no. 3, pp. 401–409, 2007. [Online]. Available: http://dx.doi.org/10.1016/j.cag.2007.01.030

[30] D. Keim, J. Kohlhammer, G. Ellis, and F. Mansmann, Eds., *Mastering The Information Age – Solving Problems with Visual Analytics*. Geneve, Switzerland: Eurographics Association, 2010.

Exploratory Visualization for Weather Data Verification

Patrik Lundblad*, Hanna Löfving[†], Annika Elovsson[†] and Jimmy Johansson[†]

*Swedish Meteorological and Hydrological Institute, Sweden

[†]C-Research, Linköping University, Sweden

patrik.lundblad@smhi.se, {hanlo184,annel047}@student.liu.se, jimmy.johansson@liu.se

Abstract

Today weather forecasts assist in the preparation of roads during the winter season to avoid accidents resulting from snow, rain and slipperiness. As with any weather forecast there is always a search for improvement. One way to do this is by verifying the forecasted parameters with the actual weather observed in the forecasted area.

To facilitate identification of significant trends and patterns within weather data we have developed an application based on interactive information visualization techniques. The application was created in close collaboration with domain experts from the Swedish Meteorological and Hydrological Institute and initial feedback from a performed user study shows that interactive visualization speeds up the analysis process as well as increases flexibility compared to currently used manual methods.

Keywords— **Information visualization, verification of weather data, exploratory analysis**

1 Introduction

The Swedish infrastructure is vulnerable to unexpected weather events that can result in severe traffic accidents. This creates a demand for both accurate as well as long time forecasts so that preparations for the effects of weather may be taken to improve personal safety. One area of particular interest is road safety during the winter season. Every year roads are affected by rain, snow and ice that make them dangerous for driving unless preventive actions are taken. The decreasing regard for bad weather conditions, due to modern aids such as anti-lock and anti-spin systems, is another factor that contributes to many accidents during the winter season. Inaccurate weather forecasts can also mean unnecessary costs for municipalities sending out snow ploughs when the forecasts wrongfully indicate snow. Preventive methods are taken using forecasts provided by meteorologists specifically assigned to the task of making forecasts and warnings within this domain. Verification is needed to improve the forecast models and help meteorologists find specific scenarios that will aid them in their work. Consequently, it is important that

these forecasts are as accurate as possible.

In this paper we present a web-enabled application for interactive exploration of weather data verification for analysis of road weather conditions. The application has been developed in close collaboration with domain experts from the Swedish Meteorological and Hydrological Institute (SMHI). The input for the application consists of hourly measured observations along Swedish roads together with daily forecasts for the observation points.

The interface consists of visual representations that allow both overview as well as detailed analyses. The overview components are used to analyze the full season and enable searching for systematical errors that occur over long time periods. These components can also be used to investigate the accuracy of forecasts for different geographical areas. With the aid of a Self-Organizing Map (SOM) the multivariate data is projected to a lower dimension to facilitate analyses. The detail components are used to explore specific scenarios during the season.

The web-based application, figure 1, has been developed to support the following major exploratory tasks:

- Investigation of significant trends and patterns for verification of the underlying forecast model.

- Communication of accuracy measurements for competitive comparisons.

- Visual analysis on multiple levels of detail; from the full winter season down to individual hours.

The remainder of this paper is structured as follows. Related work is provided in section 2. General description of attributes in the input data and events in section 3. In section 4 the application is described followed by an application scenario in section 5. Section 6 contains a user study and finally the paper is concluded with the general results and a discussion in section 7.

2 Related Work

Analysis of large, multivariate and spatial data is a very active research area within the information visualization

1550-6037/11 $26.00 © 2011 IEEE

DOI 10.1109/IV.2011.79

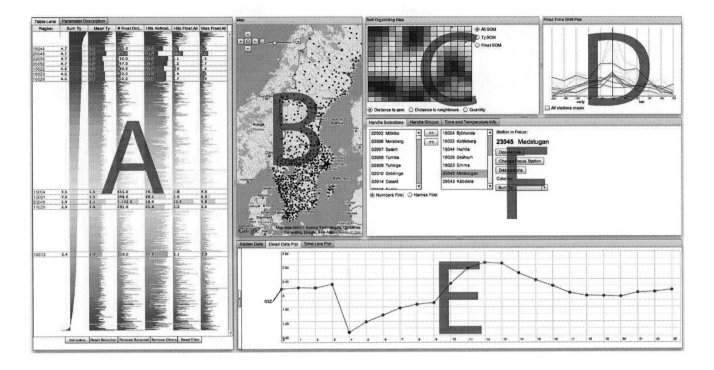

Figure 1: The application is developed to assist the weather forecast verification work at SMHI. Weather data can be examined in different components and on different levels of detail. The application consists of four overview components: table lens (a), glyph map (b), SOM (c) and frost time shift plot (d), and two detail components: detail data plot (e) and time line plot (in the second tab, next to e). In f, three tabs contain extra information about the selected stations.

and geo-visualization communities. Several tools for multivariate data analysis are available today, some of which are Protovis [2], Improvise [21], Prefuse [8], GAV Flash [9], InfoVis Toolkit [4], CommonGIS [3], GeoVista Studio [6], VIS-STAMP [7] and CGV [19]. As discussed in Ho et al. [9], it has been a challenge to adapt many of these tools to the Internet. They propose that web-enabled tools are needed for applications with the purpose of communicating analyses of large spatial-temporal and multivariate data. GAV Flash has been adapted for Internet usage through Adobe Flash and is "designed with the intention to significantly shorten the time and effort needed to develop sophisticated and dynamic Web-enabled Geovisual Analytics applications" [5].

RoadVis [14], introduced by Lundblad et al., is a web-enabled application created for road weather visualization. It is a tool for deploying real-time weather forecasts and observations for the winter roads for selected attributes. The tool calculates present and forecasted scenarios for the coming 24 hours and alert the user of risks on the roads, using information visualization components.

Koonar et al. [11] present a road weather information network built to provide a safer and more sustainable road

system in Canada. A network of sensors collect weather data which is used to determine when hazardous road condition occurs. The paper does not, however, describe how the data can be visualized.

Exploratory analysis of multivariate, time-varying and spatial data for weather forecast verification requires specialized visualization and interaction components not readily available in the tools described above. Our proposed solution is influenced by several of these tools and also adopts the concept of coordinated and multiple linked views.

The review of multiple linked view tools, methodologies and models provided by Roberts [15] presents that linking and relating information between views will assist the user's exploration process and provide additional insight to the underlying information. Multiple views can also help stimulate the visual thinking process [13]. Wang Baldonado et al. have developed a set of guidelines for when and how to use multiple views in information visualization [1] to avoid unnecessary complexity of the system. According to Kosara et al. [12] the usage of multiple views on the same data is trivial, but it is not as easy to implement it right and to provide it with the necessary interaction.

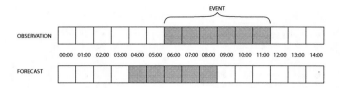

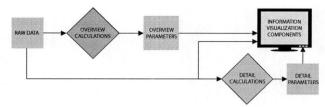

Figure 2: Forecast and observation data is collected for each hour, which is called a time tag. One or more coherent time tags are described as an event. In the figure, two events partly overlap. The forecast event starts two hours before the observation event and ends three hours early.

3 Weather Forecasts and Observations

This section describes the data provided by SMHI and the Swedish Transport Administration which is used as input to the application, and introduces the concept of events which is used to describe a snowfall or a frost occasion.

SMHI produces several different forecasts on a daily basis, covering weather information from one hour up to ten days in advance, based on models and calculations. Four times a day, the numerical model HIRLAM (High Resolution Limited Area Model) forecasts the weather for 24 hours [20]. This means that for any given hour there are four forecasts, hereinafter referred to as model runs, predicting a number of weather parameters for that hour. The model runs are called 03Z, 09Z, 15Z and 21Z where the number indicates when (in UTC) the forecast was made.

The Swedish Transport Administration provides SMHI with observations from over 760 weather stations that are located at roads with a high risk of slipperiness [18]. The stations monitor the weather conditions and measure air temperature, road temperature, air humidity, precipitation, wind speed and wind direction. The forecasts can be compared to the observations to verify their accuracy.

The majority of the weather stations have an associated environment description. This information can be interesting to examine and compare between different stations since patterns in these descriptions can be found between stations with similar values.

For both the forecasts and the observations, data for an entire winter season is collected at hourly intervals, hereinafter referred to as a time tag. Each time tag contains values for the observation and the four forecast model runs, for all parameters.

3.1 Parameters

The weather parameters focused on in this work are road temperature, frost and snowfall. Surface temperature and snowfall are both forecasted with calculations from HIRLAM and observed by the weather stations. However, frost cannot be measured by the weather stations, but the

Figure 3: The raw forecast and observation data is used to calculate the overview parameters used as input to the visualization. When a station is in focus, the data for the specified station is read and both shown in its raw format as well as used to calculate detail parameters.

formation of frost can be calculated from other parameters. Frost is formed when solid surfaces are cooled to below the dewpoint temperature of the adjacent air as well as below the freezing point of water (formula 1).

$$\begin{cases} \text{road temperature} < \text{dewpoint temperature} \\ \text{road temperature} < 0°\text{C} \end{cases} \quad (1)$$

The road temperature is difficult to forecast and can also occasionally be observed incorrectly, e.g. if snow is covering the observation location. In these cases the forecast and observation can differ significantly and needs to be taken into account when examining the data.

3.2 Event

When measuring the difference between for example road temperatures, the observation value has been subtracted from the forecast value. However when verifying parameters such as frost or snowfall different methods for non numerical values need to be used.

One or more coherent time tags are described as an event. If a forecast event and an observation event fully overlap, the forecast is perfect regarding time. However, if they only partly overlap, see figure 2, it is unclear how to measure the accuracy of the forecast. The values can be compared for each time tag and give a hit/miss value that can be used to calculate different hit rates, but they do not indicate whether the forecast was on time or not. A time shift is calculated by comparing the start for the observation and forecast, regarding time. The difference between the start times can range between -5 to 5 hours (chosen as a limit by the domain experts), where a value of zero indicates that the forecast and the observation frost events usually start at the same time and a negative value represents that the forecast events usually are too early.

4 Application

The following section describes the functionality and interactivity of the application (figure 1). The application

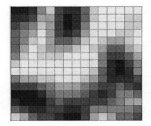
(a) All parameters

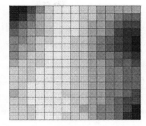
(b) Surface temperature

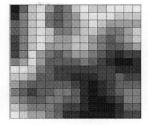
(c) Frost

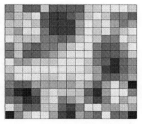
(d) Distance to neighbours

Figure 4: In this application three different SOMs are calculated. In (a) the map is calculated from all parameters, in (b) it is based on the road temperature parameters and in (c) the frost parameters. In (d) colour is used to convey similarities between neighbouring nodes, from green (small values) to brown (large values).

contains two component categories: overview components and detail components. Multiple stations can be selected in the overview components and the first selected station, hereinafter referred to as the station in focus, is presented in the detail components.

4.1 Pre-processing

The raw input data is pre-processed into overview and detail parameters, see figure 3. The following section gives a short description of the calculated parameter categories.

- The road temperature is examined in two ways. Sum Ty indicates if forecasts for a station tend to be too warm or cold and Mean Ty describes the mean error between the forecast and the observation.

- A root mean square value of the frost time shift distribution is calculated to indicate the deviation of the start for the frost event.

- For the frost forecasts accuracy a number of hit rates (hit, miss, false alarm) are calculated.

For all parameters global values are calculated for an entire season, as well as local values for the different months during the season. Also an hourly average is calculated for each hour of the day for the entire season. The global parameters can be used as a starting point when examining the data to find stations with interesting values for further analysis, and to give an overview of the stations.

4.2 Overview Components

The overview components are used to analyze the full winter season and consists of a table lens, a glyph map, a SOM and a frost time shift plot.

4.2.1 Table Lens

A table lens is a graphical spreadsheet that can be used when examining multivariate data sets. It combines overview and detail, can manage both categorical and quantitative data and has the advantage that many people are familiar with tables [17].

The table lens, figure 1a, is central in the application. The rows represent the stations and the columns represent the overview parameters. Using this component, stations with high or low values can be found, the rows can be reordered to find correlations between parameters and a number of interesting stations can be selected for further examination. The user can edit the visible parameters to adjust the view for easier examination. The colours of the stations represent the values for a specified parameter and can be changed so that further relationships can be found.

4.2.2 Glyph Map

The geographical position of a weather station can affect its values, and to be able to extract geographical patterns the application contains a glyph map, see figure 1b. The map consists of a Google Map with an associated glyph layer, where the weather stations are represented by black glyphs. Selected stations are represented by purple glyphs, and to distinguish the station in focus from the rest it is represented by a red glyph. The map is zoomable and a level of detail function controls the size of the glyphs so they are visible on all zoom levels without overlapping.

4.2.3 Self-Organizing Map

To examine and find patterns in multivariate data, the data is often projected to a lower dimension using reduction methods [7]. A SOM is an artificial neural network that represents a multidimensional data set with a low-dimensional map [10]. The visual representation of the multivariate data becomes easier to understand since the data is represented with spatial clustering which facilitates exploratory analyses [13]. The link between the attribute space visualization tools and maps in multiple views can provide multiple perspectives for exploration, evaluation and interpretation of patterns and ultimately support for knowledge construction.

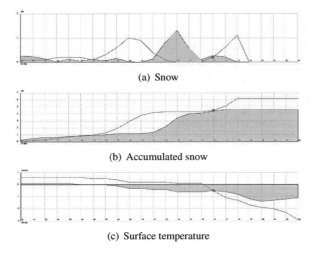

(a) Snow

(b) Accumulated snow

(c) Surface temperature

Figure 5: The raw data of the forecast and observation is shown in the time line plot. For a specified range of dates the snow (a), accumulated snow (b) or road temperature (c) can be examined. The green line represents the 15Z model run and the dot indicates the first hour of the forecast. The observed values are represented by the blue surface.

The SOM (figure 1c) consists of 15 x 15 nodes, which can be adjusted if the number of stations change. There are three different maps in this application: all parameters (figure 4a), road temperature parameters (figure 4b), frost parameters (figure 4c). This enables the user to examine clusters using a specific parameter category. Initially the colours of the nodes represent the distance between the weight vector and a zero vector. The brown nodes are further away from zero than the green nodes. The nodes can also be coloured using the distance between the weight vectors and its neighbours (figure 4d), or coloured by the station quantity in each node. If one or more, but not all, stations in a node are selected the node is marked with a red rectangle in the upper left corner. If all stations in a node are selected it is indicated with a red bounding box.

4.2.4 Frost Time Shift Plot

In the frost time shift plot (figure 1d) each selected station is represented by a line in the plot. The x-axis represents the number of hours the forecast event is shifted in time compared to the observation, from -5 to 5 hours, and the y-axis represents the number of times each case has happened. To match the selected stations with the lines in the plot, the lines have the same colour as the stations in the table lens. The black line represents the mean value of all the stations to indicate the trend of the frost forecast accuracy.

4.3 Detail Components

A detail data plot and a time line plot are used to explore specific scenarios.

4.3.1 Detail Data Plot

The detail data plot distributes the overview parameters over the 24 hours of the day (figure 1e). Each measurement represents a mean value for the specific hour for the whole season. The plot allows the user to further examine the parameters and find if the accuracy of the weather forecasts differ during certain parts or hours of the day.

The parameters can be examined separately in the plot, where the x-axis concern the time and the y-axis the actual values. The model runs can be examined separately or all at the same time. It is also possible to view a line showing the merged values from all the model runs for comparisons between the overall trend and a specified model run.

4.3.2 Time Line Plot

While the overview components can provide the user with an image of what the data looks like, there are times when the data needs to be examined in very high detail. The plot displays the raw data and is generated by selecting a time span and one of the parameters road temperature, snowfall or accumulated snowfall (figure 5). The model runs are presented as lines and the observation values are shown as a blue surface. The dots represent the first hours of the forecasts.

4.4 Implementation

The application has been developed using GAV Flash [5] which includes visual components, analytic algorithms, data providers and other tools for developing web based interactive systems. A pre-processing programme was written in C# to process the raw data and calculate the overview parameters. The SOM was calculated in MATLAB using the function package SOM Toolbox [16].

5 Application Scenario

The following is a typical application scenario where a meteorologist explores the data on different levels of detail to find areas where the model may be improved.

The meteorologist starts exploring the data in the table lens and selects the station with the highest mean road temperature error, Mean Ty (figure 6, left), to examine possible reasons to why the forecasts for this station are less accurate than for other stations. The geographical position of this station can be seen in the glyph map (figure 6, middle). To find stations with similar values for the road temperature parameters, the user selects the node belonging to the selected station in the Ty SOM (figure 6, right). These stations are now also selected in the glyph map (figure 7) and since all three stations are located in the northern part of Sweden the user can suspect a possible correlation between geographical position and a high value for Mean

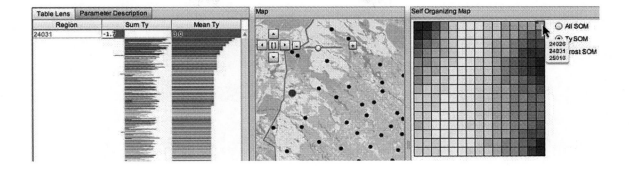

Figure 6: When a station is selected in the table lens (left) it is also selected in the glyph map (middle) and the SOM (right). The cell containing the selected station is marked in the SOM, which contains two additional stations with similar values for the road temperature parameters.

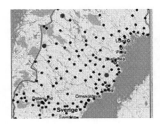

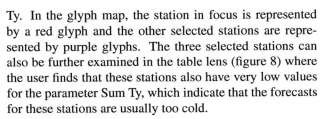

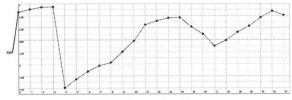

(a) Mean Ty - the mean road temperature error.

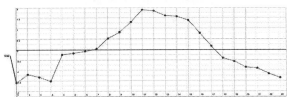

(b) Sum Ty - the sum of the road temperature error.

Figure 7: Three selected stations in the glyph map. The red glyph represents the station in focus.

Figure 8: Detailed information about the three selected stations in the table lens.

Figure 9: The station in focus in the detail data plot, showing the overview parameters distributed over the 24 hours of the day.

Ty. In the glyph map, the station in focus is represented by a red glyph and the other selected stations are represented by purple glyphs. The three selected stations can also be further examined in the table lens (figure 8) where the user finds that these stations also have very low values for the parameter Sum Ty, which indicate that the forecasts for these stations are usually too cold.

The detail data plot is used to examine the road temperature for a station on a detailed level. In the plot for Mean Ty (figure 9a), the user can see that the 03Z forecast is better during the first hours from when the forecast was made and also better during the afternoon. In the plot for Sum Ty (figure 9b), the user can see that the forecasts are usually too cold during the night and too warm during the day. These conclusions can be subject to further analysis.

To see if the found results have any correlation with other parameters, the user examines the starts of the frost events in the frost time shift plot (figure 10). The three selected stations are represented with three lines in the plot and the user can draw conclusions whether the frost forecasts are early or late.

Another examination possibility could be if the user knew that the forecasts had difficulties during a particular time period. This period can be selected in the time line plot where the raw data is graphically represented and the user can study the data in very high detail. Figure 11 shows the snow forecast for the Christmas Day 2009 and reveals that the 03Z forecast was approximately correct in amount but incorrect with respect of time.

6 User Study

A preliminary user study was performed as a first attempt to evaluate the application. The main purpose was to get feedback on the functionality, interface, and the overall navigation of the application.

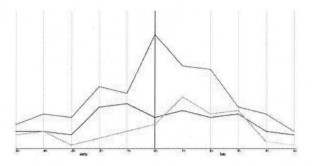

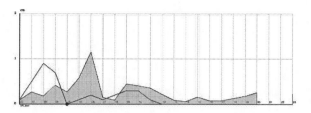

Figure 11: The time line plot shows the 03Z snow forecast for Christmas Day in 2009. The forecast is approximately correct in amount but incorrect with respect of time.

Figure 10: The distribution of occurrences of frost forecasts that are early or late, from -5 to 5 hours, compared to the observations. The station with a peak value at 0 (blue line), indicates that the forecasts often are on time, while the station with a peak value at +1 (yellow line), indicates that the forecasts often are one hour late. For the station represented by the red line a significant peak is missing and thus the forecasts are usually both early and late.

6.1 Procedure

The user study was conducted with two meteorologists and four master students, all performing the same tasks. The meteorologists, who had been involved in the requirement and design phase, had domain knowledge but were less experienced with visualization. The students were familiar with information visualization, but had no previous experience with meteorological data.

According to Koua and Kraak [13] a user-based evaluation is the most suitable approach to assess usability and usefulness of geovisual environments. Their presented performance-oriented approach was however replaced with a more satisfaction-oriented test. Since no one in the test group was familiar with both the weather data and the visualization techniques, the focus lay on whether the components and user interface felt intuitive and easy to use.

To begin with, the application was demonstrated and explained, and the users were provided with a parameter and component description. Two test leaders were present to answer questions and document the result. The users were asked to complete a number of tasks, which were designed to encourage them to try all the visualization components.

Some representative tasks were as follows:

- "Identify one station with more than 800 frost hours that is not located in the northern part of Sweden."

- "Is there any correlation between the nodes in the SOM and the geographical position of stations?"

- "When during the Christmas weekend was there most precipitation for the station MS4 SMHI?"

When the tasks were completed the test ended with a discussion about the overall experience of using the application, which tasks had been difficult to complete and why, and what improvements could be made.

6.2 Result

Most of the tasks were completed by the test group with little or no difficulty and the general opinion was that the applications feels intuitive and easy to use after the given introduction. The test group pointed out suggestions for concept design improvements and changes in the layout.

In the time line plot, one of the participants wanted to be able to adjust the time span with a slider in addition to the calendars. This would make the creation of weather data plots easier and more intuitive, and would help improve the interactivity and efficiency of the component.

Some of the participants confused the overview and detail parameters and tried to change the parameter for the detail data plot component in the table lens.

Since many stations are represented in the table lens it is hard to examine them in a time-efficient manner, but as one of the participants pointed out a fish-eye feature could make the searching in the table lens more efficient.

7 Conclusions and Future Work

In this paper we describe a web-based interactive application for exploration of weather data, focusing on verification and analysis of road weather conditions. The application has been developed together with meteorologists from the Swedish Meteorological and Hydrological Institute. It was designed to simplify the process of finding spatial and temporal regions where weather forecasts models needs to be improved and to identify inaccurate weather stations.

The results from an informal user study with meteorologists showed that the application has great potential to help them in their verification work. The use of interactive visualization was a new way of working with weather data verification which was seen as a good compliment to the traditional manual methods currently used.

The presented application was designed as a proof of concept to demonstrate interactive visualization and its possibility to assist the process of finding patterns and relationships in weather data. Possible future work includes investigating the usability of more advanced information visualization components as well as further evaluation of the existing application. Furthermore, the user study showed that additional interaction, allowing even more detailed exploration, were highly desired by the meteorologists.

Acknowledgements

This work was partly supported by the Swedish Research Council in the Linnaeus Centre CADICS and by funding from the Visualization Programme coordinated by the Swedish Knowledge Foundation. The authors wishes to thank the involved meteorologists at SMHI for their feedback during the project and their dedicated contribution that made this project possible.

References

[1] M. Q. Wang Baldonado, A. Woodruff, and A. Kuchinsky. Guidelines for using multiple views in information visualization. In *Proceedings of the working conference on Advanced visual interface*, 2000.

[2] M. Bostock and J. Heer. Protovis: A graphical toolkit for visualization. *IEEE Transactions on Visualization and Computer Graphics*, 15:1121–1128, 2009.

[3] CommonGis. url: http://www.commongis.de.

[4] J.-D. Fekete. The infovis toolkit. In *Third International Conference on Information Technology and Applications*, pages 167–174, 2005.

[5] GAV Flash. url: http://ncva.itn.liu.se/tools.

[6] Geovista. url: http://www.geovista.psu.edu.

[7] D. Guo, J. Chen, A. M. MacEachren, and K. Liao. A visualization system for space-time and multivariate patterns (vis-stamp). *IEEE Transactions on Visualization and Computer Graphics*, 12(6):1461–1474, 2006.

[8] J. Heer. Prefuse: a toolkit for interactive information visualization. In *In CHI 05: Proceedings of the SIGCHI conference on Human factors in computing systems*, pages 421–430. ACM Press, 2005.

[9] Q. Ho, P. Lundblad, T. Åström, and M. Jern. A web-enabled visualization toolkit for geovisual analytics. In *SPIE: Electronic Imaging Science and Technology, Visualization and Data Analysis, Proceedings of SPIE, San Francisco*, 2011.

[10] T. Kohonen. *Self-Organizing Maps*. Springer; 3rd edition, 2000.

[11] A. Koonar, P. Delannoy, and D. Denault. Building a road weather information network for integrating data from heterogeneous sources. In *Third International Conference on Information Technology and Applications*, pages 501–507, 2005.

[12] R. Kosara, H. Hauser, and D. L. Gresh. An interaction view on information visualization. In *Eurographics*, pages 123–138, 2003.

[13] E. L. Koua and M-J Kraak. A usability framework for the design and evaluation of an exploratory geovisualization environment. In *Proceedings of the Eighth International Conference on Information Visualisation*, pages 153–158, 2004.

[14] P. Lundblad, J. Thoursie, and M. Jern. Swedish road weather visualization. In *Information Visualisation, International Conference on*, volume 0, pages 313–321, Los Alamitos, CA, USA, 2010. IEEE Computer Society.

[15] J. C. Roberts. Exploratory visualization with multiple linked views. In *Exploring Geovisualization*, pages 150–170. Amsterdam: Elseviers, 2004.

[16] Self-Organizing Map Toolbox for Matlab. url: http://www.cis.hut.fi/somtoolbox.

[17] R. Spence. *Information visualization design for interaction*. Prentice Hall, Harlow, second edition, 2007.

[18] The Swedish Road Administration's brochure about Road Weather Information Systems (VViS). url: http://publikationswebbutik.vv.se/upload/5455/89370_vagvaderinformationssystem_vvis.pdf.

[19] C. Tominski, J. Abello, and H. Schumann. CGV - An Interactive Graph Visualization System. *Computers & Graphics*, 33(6):660–678, 2009.

[20] P. Unden, L. Rontu, H. Järvinen, P. Lynch, J. Calvo, G. Cats, J. Cuxart, K. Eerola, C. Fortelius, J. A. Garcia-Moya, C. Jones, G. Lenderlink, A. Mcdonald, R. Mcgrath, B. Navascues, N. Woetman Nielsen, V. Degaard, E. Rodriguez, M. Rummukainen, K. Sattler, B. Hansen Sass, H. Savijarvi, B. Wichers Schreur, R. Sigg, and H. The. Hirlam-5 scientific documentation. Technical report, 2002.

[21] C. Weaver. Building highly-coordinated visualizations in improvise. *Information Visualization, IEEE Symposium on*, 0:159–166, 2004.

3. Knowledge Visualisation

IV 2011

Using Visualization for Exploring Relationships between Concepts in Ontologies

Isabel Cristina Siqueira da Silva
Instituto de Informática
Universidade Federal do Rio Grande do Sul
Faculdade de Informática
Centro Universitário Ritter dos Reis
Porto Alegre, RS, Brasil
isabels@inf.ufrgs.br

Carla Maria Dal Sasso Freitas
Instituto de Informática
Universidade Federal do Rio Grande do Sul
Porto Alegre, RS, Brasil
carla@inf.ufrgs.br

Abstract—Usually, ontologies are represented as static 2D graphs, being the relationships exhibited as overlapping edges, which may cause a cognitive overload. On the other hand, 3D representations can also lead to confusion in terms of navigation due to occlusion. Moreover, as the ontologies grow, incorporating new concepts (and their relationships), the visualization complexity increases either in 2D or in 3D. In this paper, we discuss a visualization tool for exploring relationships between ontology concepts. We employ linked tree structures that capture the hierarchical feature of parts of the ontology while preserving the different categories of relationships between concepts. Ontologies are displayed as trees on a plane, representing only the hierarchical relationships between concepts, allowing the user to explore other connections by creating projections of nodes (concepts) in another plane and linking them according to the relationships to be analyzed.

Keywords-Visualization; Ontology; Interaction

I. INTRODUCTION

A large volume of information, originated from many sources and represented in different formats, is available, and efficient methods for information retrieval are needed for allowing networks of cooperation and interoperability between different systems. Data semantics is the more traditional approach for data integration because it focuses on the relationships between data. As such, ontologies define concepts and ensure interoperability between systems. In his work, Sowa [21] points out that ontology is the study of the categories of things that exist or may exist in some domain, i.e., it is a catalogue of the types of things that are assumed to exist in a domain of interest D from the perspective of a person who uses a language L for the purpose of talking about D.

Gruber [10] states that ontology is a formal and explicit specification of a conceptualization; the conceptualization refers to the way people think and the explicit specification relates concepts and relationships which must be supplied in accordance with specific and well defined terms. In computational context, Noy and McGuiness [17] discuss that ontology share common understanding of the structure of information among people or software agents. Ontologies separate domain knowledge from the operational knowledge, make domain assumptions explicit and enabling reuse of this.

However, due to the specificities of the concepts expressed in an ontology, the analysis of individual relationships between them is complex. Thus, the ontology visualization and the quality of interaction provided must be efficient. Katifori [11] confirms that it is not simple to create a visualization that will display effectively all this information and, at the same time, allows the user to perform easily various operations on the ontology. Then, the challenge is to define the best way to represent relationships between categorized concepts, mainly because each concept can have a number of related attributes.

This work discusses the use of a visualization tool for exploring relationships between concepts in ontologies. In a previous work [20] we performed a requirements analysis based on interviews with experts who work with conceptual modeling and ontologies in a specific domain, and proposed a 2.5D ontology visualization tool that aims at systematizing and transmitting knowledge more efficiently. In this paper we present our tool and compare it with another one also used for modeling and visualization of ontologies. The text is organized as follows. Section 2 briefly reviews related work. Section 3 summarizes the requirement analysis and presents our visualization method, while evaluation and results are discussed in Section 4. Finally, some conclusions are drawn in Section 5.

II. RELATED WORKS

Different authors propose alternatives for visualization and interaction with ontologies.

Katifori [11] discusses different techniques that could be adapted for ontology representation, such as indented lists, trees and graphs, zooming, space subdivision (treemaps, information slices), focus+context and landscapes. Besides that, tools for ontology visualization and interaction are discussed. Fluit et al. [8] present the cluster map technique as a simple and intuitive method for visualizing complex ontologies.

The OntoSphere tool [4] uses two techniques - 3D and focus+context – for providing overview and details according to user needs. Baehrecke [3] and Babaria [2] proposed the use of treemaps to visualize GO (Gene Ontologies Consortium). In a treemap, color, size and grouping are used in order to facilitate user interaction and information extraction.

1550-6037/11 $26.00 © 2011 IEEE
DOI 10.1109/IV.2011.40

Mostly, researchers use Protégé [16] for the creation and visualization of ontologies. Protégé's main visualization for the ontology hierarchy is a tree view (Class Browser). However, different visualization techniques have been proposed: Katifori [12] presents a comparative study of four visualization techniques available in past versions of Protégé: Class Browser, Jambalaya (discontinued), TGVizTab (discontinued) and OntoViz (discontinued). The information retrieval provided by these tools was also evaluated.

The works by Samper et al. [18] and Amaral [1] address semantics aspects. Amaral [1] proposes a semantics-based framework for visualizing descriptions of concepts in OWL. The framework aims at allowing users to obtain deep insights about the meaning of such descriptions, thereby preventing design errors or misconceptions. Icons and symbols are used in diagrams to characterize classes that represent concepts descriptions. One can combine information visualization techniques, as in the work by Schevers et al. [19], where the user interacts with the ontology in the Protégé tool. Classes representing spatial information (like polygons, points, etc.) are presented in a second graphical interface that is used to mimic the functionality of a GIS (Geographic Information System).

Erdmann et al. [6] presents the NeOn Toolkit, an open-source multi-platform ontology engineering environment, which provides comprehensive support for the ontology engineering life-cycle. The toolkit is based on the Eclipse platform, and provides an extensive set of plug-ins (currently 45 plug-ins are available) covering a variety of ontology engineering activities. Catenazzi et al. [5] presents a study about tools for ontologies visualization and proposes the OWLeasyViz tool. It combines textual and graphical representations for displaying the class hierarchy, relationships and data properties. Interaction techniques such as zooming, filtering and search are available. Lanzenberger et al. [14] discuss the visualization of ontology alignment as well as solutions for dealing with the complexity of large ontologies. The techniques are compared in order to point out their advantages and disadvantages.

Kriglstein and Wallner [13] present Knoocks, a visualization tool focused on the interconnections within the ontology and the instances. This tool employs the overview + details approach, and was evaluated against another tools, although three of these tools are not available in Protégé last versions (TGVizTab, OntoViz and Jambalaya).

III. 2.5D VISUALIZATION TOOL

Visualization systems should consider two main issues: the mapping of information to a graphical representation in order to facilitate its interpretation by the users, and means to limit the amount of information that users receive, while keeping them "aware" of the total information space and reducing cognitive effort. When we analyze an image, we activate our perceptual mechanisms to identify patterns and perform segmentation of elements. The user must perceive the information presented in the display, and the understanding involves cognitive processes. An image can

be ambiguous due to lack of relevant information or by excess of irrelevant information.

As presented in section 2, many studies have addressed the importance of ontology visualization in creation, manipulation and inference processes. Different visualization methods have been proposed, but there are still many gaps to be filled in by efficient methods of visualization and interaction. The solution for these problems may be the use of different techniques. Information visualization and concepts of human computer interaction can optimize the comprehension of ontologies. The searched information can be placed in focus, distinguishing it from the unnecessary information and facilitating the understanding of correlated data.

Our study started with interviews with four users, all experts in the creation and manipulation of ontologies. Due to the low number of participants, quantitative measurements were not taken, but the qualitative notes were found very interesting, following Nielsen [15]. The following questions were posed to the experts:

1)   When an ontology is created, which aspects could be improved with visualization?

2)   After the ontology was created, which information is searched more often and how this information could be displayed in order to make understanding more efficient?

3)   When and why a visualization is better than another?

From the results of the interviews (more details in [20]), we reached the following requirements for an ontology visualization tool:

- Provide overview of the ontology hierarchy, with the possibility of detailing some parts;
- Avoid presenting the different aspects of an ontology (classes, description, object properties, data properties, individuals) together in a unique visualization;
- Optimize the results from the ontology validation;
- Explore the use of visual attributes such as color, transparency, and shapes;
- Provide display filters based on different techniques of focus+context and/or overview+detail, zoom, pan and rotation of the image;
- Allow rapid and simple inclusion of visual elements in the visualization, as well as their removal;
- Allow printing the entire ontology in paper sizes commonly used, such as A4.

These requirements were considered the starting point to propose our tool described below.

Graphs are the most intuitive form of visualizing the relationships between concepts of ontologies by their both hierarchical and relational characteristics. However, the relationships are displayed as edges, which often overlap and cause cognitive overload. An interactive graph or tree solves part of the problem, allowing the user to highlight the information in focus through selection, but the overlapping edges are still a problem. We studied the hypothesis of representing ontologies in a 3D space, allowing the user to navigate through in-depth visual representations, rotating, expanding and selecting the desired items. However, such views require user immersion and depth perception is crucial.

Considering these aspects, we propose a visualization method that fits the requirements pointed out by users as well the tasks from Katifori [11]. In this study, we have chosen to focus on visualizing the hierarchy of the ontology and the relationships between concepts employing multiple views. For the hierarchy, we employ the 2D hyperbolic tree which reduces the cognitive overload and the user disorientation that might happen during the interaction with the nodes, expanding and contracting it, especially in ontologies with many concepts (Figure 1a).

However, besides the class hierarchy (relationship "is a"), users of ontologies need to analyze, in an integrated way, the other relationships. Thus, we use a third dimension to display one or more relationships (object properties) selected by the user in a second view. To view them, we take the plane where the tree is displayed and perform a 90° rotation around the X-axis (Figure 1b). The rotated plane, positioned in 3D as an XZ-plane, displays the hyperbolic tree, and selected relationships are represented as curved lines in space, connecting the related concepts, without interfering with the display of the hierarchical relationship.

Figure 1c shows the proposed 2.5D scheme applied to an ontology hierarchy/graph. The main aspects of visualization and interaction are:

- Nodes are displayed with different geometric forms according with the type (root, sub tree and leaf);
- Edges of hierarchy are displayed with solid lines and edges of relationships are displayed with dashed curves where the colors are related to relationships;
- In 2D hyperbolic tree view, the user can choose which nodes will be in focus on image, hiding the other nodes;
- Both 2D and 2.5D views can be displayed together, side by side - the user remains "aware" of the ontology hierarchy and visualizes one or more relationships in a separate spatial dimension;
- The user can choose to display one or more relationships at the same time or hide them;
- In 3D space, the user can choose which levels of the tree view or hide, reducing the cognitive overload;
- In addition to rotations around the X-axis, rotations around the axes Y and Z, zoom and pan are also allowed, providing full 3D navigation;
- The background color can be changed;
- Tooltips are displayed over nodes and edges as additional information.
- Such usability features aimed at reducing the cognitive effort of the user in analyzing the image and, at the same time, add functionality to the tool.

IV. EVALUATION AND RESULTS

In order to evaluate our 2.5D visualization method, we have chosen to compare it with Ontograf [7], a 2D tool for visualizing hierarchy and relationships of ontologies. Ontograf is available on the current version of Protégé software (4.1).

Ontograf presents seven visualization possibilities: alphabetical grid, radial and spring graphs, and four implementations of tree visualization: vertical, horizontal, directed vertical and horizontal. Figures 2(a) and 2(b) show two Ontograf visualizations examples.

The four specialists interviewed in the first phase of our study (as described in Section 3) were invited again to perform evaluations of our 2.5D visualization and Ontograf. Moreover, we invited two other specialists in ontology specification to participate, so we had a sample of 6 specialists.

For the evaluations we used two ontologies: a large ontology, related to Stratigraphy concepts, and a smaller one, representing cities' urban performance. Before the participants started with the tasks, we shortly introduced them to the important functionalities of the tools and they explored the visualization in many ways. After the subjects had finished their training, we started the evaluation process.

The tools were presented in different order for users. For each tool, they were asked to perform an analysis based on four questions that were defined in order to evaluate the requirements listed in Section 3. The questions are listed below:

1) Is the initial layout clear?

2) Is it possible to clearly separate the concepts' hierarchy from the other relationships between these concepts?

3) Does the possibility of rotating the ontology representation improve the analysis of relationships?

4) Do the pruning and expansion of the ontology levels help the understanding of hierarchical relationships?

Three possibilities of answers were defined: Yes; Partially; No. Figure 3 summarizes the users' answers for these questions.

Regarding question (1), the majority of users (67%) responded that the initial 2.5D layout is clear compared with Ontograf. Among the reasons for that, users pointed out the large amount of information displayed at the same time (nodes overlap) in the image of Ontograf. This is a problem of scale versus amount of information, and causes user disorientation. In our 2.5D method, this problem is solved due the nature of the hyperbolic tree.

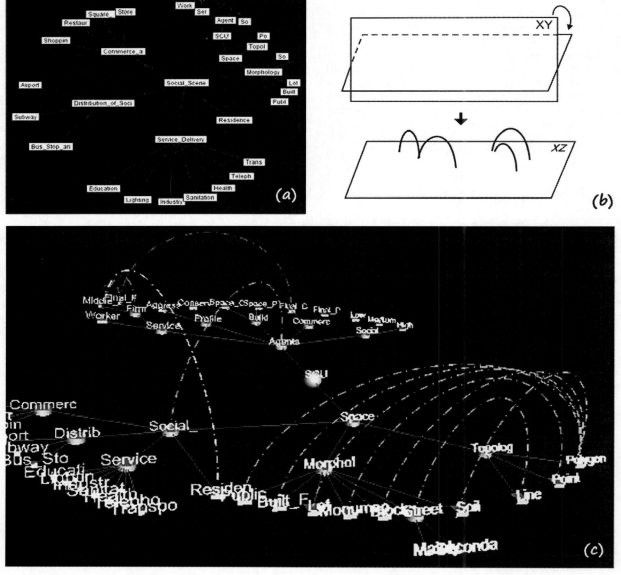

Figure 1. Ontology visualization. (a) 2D hierarchy visualization; (b) 2.5D Visualization scheme; (c) hierarchy and relationships in 2.5D.

In relation to question (2), users were divided (50%) between "Partially" and "No" answers for Ontograf, because nodes and edges overlapping. Usually, users do not want to see relationships simultaneously, due to the cognitive overload it would arise. Thus, the possibility of analyzing the "is a" (hierarchy) and other relationships in different dimensions helps the user to understand the ontology. Another problem indicated in Ontograf is that the user needs to change the positions of nodes in order to reveal the relationships occluded by them.

An important positive aspect noticed by users in both tools is the presence of tooltips when the mouse is over the nodes or relationships. According to Gurr [9], visual representations can be constructed in order to express the properties of a concept. The use of tooltip texts can help in the encoding of the displayed information, because they contain high loads of information, and are presented selectively as the user explores the visualization of the ontology.

Users approved different colors for different types of relationships. According to Ware [22], colors are mainly a resource for information categorization. Also in accordance with Ware [22], graphical elements like shapes and location of elements in the space help the user in mapping the concepts, and these features are present in our 2.5D method.

Regarding question (3), this functionality is not present in Ontograf, and the users considered it an important interaction mode. In our 2.5D method, rotations around the three axes

(X, Y and Z) are possible, and complemented by zoom and pan. To prevent from user disorientation during the interaction with the visualization in 3D space, we implemented the reset functionality, which resets the visualization to its initial state. Thus, users have more freedom to interact with the visualization. One of the users reported that when interacting with the 2.5D view, he did not feel claustrophobia, which is common in other tools, including Ontograf.

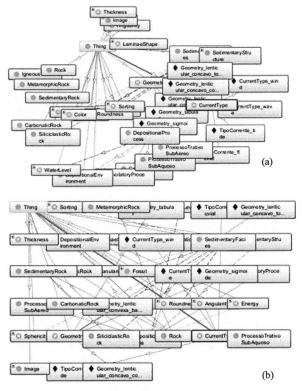

Figure 2.   Ontograf views (a) Radial; (b) Alphabetical grid

Finally, in relation to question (4), while 100% of users answered "Yes", for the 2.5D view, for Ontograf, most users (83%) answered "Partially" and "No". This result is due to the feature of Ontograf related to the repositioning of nodes when it is pruned or expanded -this fact causing disorientation on users. On the other hand, the 2.5D allows pruning and expansion in two ways: by the hyperbolic tree functionality of repositioning nodes, and by hiding or showing levels of the hierarchy.

These results indicate that our studies about the proposed 2.5D visualization of ontology concepts and relationships are progressing. The use of 2.5D visualization might be a solution to common problems presented by 2D and 3D ontology visualization tools, mainly cognitive overload and user disorientation. For sure, we need to perform further studies to find alternatives to display instances and semantic concepts of ontologies. Icons, symbols and transparency are being studied in addition to other information visualization techniques.

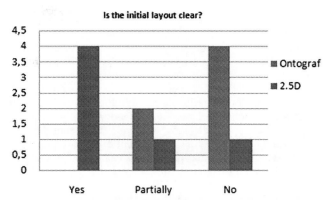

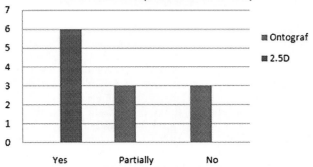

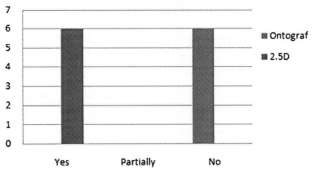

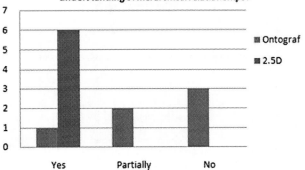

Figure 3.   Evaluation results.

V. 5. CONCLUSIONS

Ontologies tend to grow, incorporating new concepts and relationships, therefore increasing the visualization complexity. Static graphs, commonly used for ontology representation, are not the best alternative for such visualizations. Thus, we need efficient visualization and interaction methods tailored to ontologies. Information visualization techniques amplify cognition and reduce the exploration time of data sets, allowing the recognition of patterns and facilitating inferences about different concepts.

In this work, we have designed a visual and interactive method for exploring ontologies, improving the process of insight from such data. For this, we started with the definition of requirements for visualization and interaction with ontologies in order to support our approach for helping users to perform different operations on ontologies more easily and efficiently.

Our 2.5D visualization tool combines aspects of both 2D and 3D techniques. During its design we have taken into account the aspects pointed out by expert users. The main idea is to provide a representation that is intuitive and allows efficient analysis of the concepts displayed in the ontology visualization.

We evaluated the 2.5D visualization proposal by comparing it with the Ontograf tool, available in the version 4.1 of Protégé. The results of the comparative study reinforced the importance of usability and functionality in tools dedicated to ontology visualization.

This study represents an initial step in the development of an ontology visualization tool. Future work involves the investigation of alternative ways to display properties and instances of the ontologies.Acknowledgement

We would like to thank the users that participated in the interviews and evaluation process.

ACKNOWLEDGEMENTS

We would like to thank the users that participated in the interviews and evaluation process.

REFERENCES

[1] Amaral, F. Visualizing the semantics (not the syntax) of concept descriptions. In *VI Workshop em Tecnologia da Informação e da Linguagem Humana (TIL 2008), Vila Velha, ES*, 2008.

[2] Babaria, K. *Using Treemaps to Visualize Gene Ontologies*, Human Computer Interaction Lab and Institute for Systems Research, University of Maryland, College Park, MD USA, 2004.

[3] Baehrecke, E. H., Dang, N., Babaria, K. Shneiderman, B. *Visualization and analysis of microarray and gene ontology data with treemaps*. BMC Bioinformatics. 2004.

[4] Bosca, A., Bomino, D., Pellegrino, P. OntoSphere: more than a 3D ontology visualization tool. *In Proceedings of SWAP, the 2nd Italian Semantic Web Workshop*, Trento, Italy, December 14-16, CEUR, Workshop Proceedings, ISSN 1613-0073, Vol-166, 2005.

[5] Catenazzi, N., Sommaruga, L., Mazza, R. User-friendly ontology editing and visualization tools: the OWLeasyViz approach. In: *Proceedings of the 13th IEEE International Conference on Information Visualisation. Barcellona*, Spain. 14-17 July 2009. pp. 283-288. IEEE. ISBN: 978-0-7695-3733-7.

[6] Erdmann, M., Peter, H., Holger, L, Studer, R. *NeOn – Ontology Enggenering and Plug-in Development with the NeOn Toolkit.* Url: http://www.neon-toolkit.org/images/tutorials/tutorial%20eswc08.pdf.

[7] Falconer, S. *OntoGraf.* URL: http://protegewiki.stanford.edu/wiki/OntoGraf. Last access in 2010 october.

[8] Fluit, C., Sabou, M., Harmelen, F. Ontology-based Information Visualisation: Towards Semantic Web Applications. *International Symposium of Visualisation of the Semantic Web (VSW'05)*. 2005.

[9] Gurr, C. Effective Diagrammatic Communication: Syntatic, Semantic and Pragmatic Issues, Journal of Visual Languages and Computing, 10, 317-342, 1999.

[10] Gruber, T. (1996). *What is an ontology?* [S.l.: s.n.], 1996. Url: http://www-ksl.stanford.edu/ ksl/ what-is-an-ontology.html.

[11] Katifori, A.; Halatsis, C.; Lepouras, G.; Vassilakis, C.; Giannopoulou, E. *Ontology visualization methods - a survey.* ACM Comput. Surv. 39, 4 (Nov. 2007), 10.

[12] Katifori A, Torou E, Vassilakis C, Lepouras G, Halatsis C: Selected results of a comparative study of four ontology visualization methods for information retrieval tasks. *In: Research Challenges in Information Science, 2008 RCIS* 2008 Second International Conference on: 2008; 2008: 133-140.

[13] Kriglstein, S. Wallner, G. Development Process and Evaluation of the Ontology Visualization Tool Knoocks - A case study. In: *International Conference on Information Visualization Theory and Applications IVAPP, 2011,* Vilamoura-Algarve. Proceedings of the International Conference on Imaging Theory and Applications and International Conference on Information Visualization Theory and Applications. Portugal: SciTePress Science and Technology Publications, 2011. p. 187-197.

[14] Lanzenberger, M., Sampson, J., Rester, M. Visualization in Ontology Tools. Ontology Visualization: Tools and Techniques for Visual Representation of Semi-Structured Meta-Data. *Journal of Universal Computer Science,* vol. 16, no. 7 (2010), 1036-1054.

[15] Nielsen, J. Usability Inspection Methods. *Proceedings of Conference on Human Factors in Computing Systems* (CHI'95). 1994. Colorado, USA.

[16] Noy, N., Fergerson, R., Musen, M. The knowledge model of Protege-2000: Combining interoperability and flexibility. *In Proceedings of 2nd International Conference on Knowledge Engineering and Knowledge Management (EKAW'2000),* Juanles-Pins, France, 2000.

[17] Noy, N.; McGuiness, D. *Ontology Development 101 – A guide to creating your first ontology.* KSL Technical Report, Standford University, 2001.

[18] Samper, J., Tomás, V., Carrillo, E., Nascimento, R. Visualization of ontologies to specify semantic descriptions of services. *IEEE Transactions on Knowledge and Data Engineering.* 20(1): p. 130-134. 2008.

[19] Schevers, H.A.J., Trinidad, G.; Drogemuller, R.M. *Towards Integrated Assessments for Urban Development.* Journal of Information Technology in Construction (ITcon), Vol. 11, Special Issue Decision Support Systems for Infrastructure Management, pg. 225-236. Url: http://www.itcon.org/2006/17.

[20] Silva, I.; Freitas, C. Requirements for Interactive Ontology Visualization - Using Hypertree+2.5D Visualization for Exploring Relationships between Concepts. In: *International Conference on Information Visualization Theory and Applications IVAPP, 2011, Vilamoura-Algarve.* Proceedings of the International Conference on Imaging Theory and Applications and International Conference on Information Visualization Theory and Applications. Portugal : SciTePress Science and Technology Publications, 2011. p. 242-248.

[21] Sowa, J.F. *Guided Tour of Ontology,* 2005. Url: http://www.jfsowa.com/ontology/guided.htm.

[22] Ware, Colin. Visual Thinking for Design. Morgan Kaufmann, Burlington, MA, 2008.

A Knowledge Visualization of Database Content Created By A Database Taxonomy

H. Paul Zellweger
ArborWay Labs, Rochester MN
{pz@arborwaylabs.com}

Abstract

The synergy between information visualization and knowledge visualization is explored using the "Database Taxonomy" to guide the way. Drawing extensively on Burgin's mathematical theory of named sets, this new knowledge visualization treats all database content as if it were scientific data, regardless of the database application. This mathematical tool penetrates deep into the logical structure of data and data relations, enabling a single algorithm to generate a conceptual knowledge structure, which pre-structures raw data in the database into a list of nested data-topic lists that works like a book index. For end-users, this visualization is familiar, convenient and precise. For the research community, this knowledge structure and the techniques used to build it offer an empirical tool for investigating the underlying properties of data, information, and knowledge on a computing device. The transformation from data to information to knowledge is automatic and seamless, thanks to a novel analysis of the logical structure of the symbols on these mechanical devices, one which reveals meta-symbols consisting of physical-values (v) and constructed-types (t). The Database Taxonomy also provides a first glimpse into how navigating this structure can generate a predicate logic expression, an outcome which the author believes promises to advance our theoretical understanding of knowledge visualization and of the influence of a digital media on symbolic logic.

.

Keywords--- Database navigation, knowledge visualization, RDBMS interface.

1. Introduction

A recent argument seeking synergies between information and knowledge visualizations calls for cooperation between these two fields, since "in order to make large amounts of information easily accessible, information has to be pre-structured" [1, p. 1]. Such an appeal is valid because all technologies have an underlying mathematical core [2], which eventually can be condensed when the underlying structures are recognized. But, information visualization and knowledge visualization developed independently of each other—although both started off in the same medium, static images on paper, and then both leapt into the same new medium, the digital world. Information visualization, briefly stated, focuses on *assigning* meaning to raw data [1] and on the use of computer-supported representations of abstract data to amplify cognition [3], while, knowledge visualization, as Burkhardt argues, places an emphasis on a more encompassing phenomenon, namely *interaction* with the receiver [4]. These two research areas, like the field of computer science itself, are multidisciplinary—drawing on mathematics, physics, engineering, etc.—and both are still in an early stage. Knowledge visualization is the more recent newcomer of the two to the computer science community, and, as Bertschi reminds us, it still lacks a rigorous theoretical foundation [5].

In order to find a common ground for these two different types of visualization, the author begins with one particular technical shortcoming that both share in the digital medium. When one is trying to support information retrieval using an information visualization approach, the screen display itself can be a problem; for the larger the data set on a screen, the more difficult it is to visualize its abstract data [6]. The same problem holds true when one is trying to use concept mapping technology to visualize knowledge, or when one uses this structure to navigate a database, because it relies on a single visual plane [7]. In each case, the method used to pre-structure the data for the visual metaphor falls short.

Two recent studies in information visualization highlight the single most important challenge in pre-structuring database content; it centers on aligning the pre-structuring technique to the logical structure of the database. In one study, the mSpace *data structure* organizes the logical branching of data in a database table for a faceted search [8]. But it can only accommodate a fixed number of properties or attributes and their values on the screen at any given time [9]. In another study, SNAPP encourages end-users to trace out data relations and to create value-based "paths"which can flow from one table to another [10]. However, these paths are not seamlessly integrated into SNAPP; they need to be configured before hand. Together, these two studies suggest that the logical space of relational data has two dimensions: *breadth* and *depth*, or data branching and paths, which are difficult to display on the computer screen at the same time.

The aim of the current paper is to offer a simple account explaining how the Database Taxonomy pre-structures relational data in the database at a deep logical level of the database. By employing Burgin's theory of named sets (BNS) [11], the author is able to go well beyond today's set-theoretical understanding of the relational database and thus is able to model the logical space of data and data relations in a more abstract fashion. This model, in turn, enables the graphics used in the visualization to display the full breadth and depth of this logical space, regardless of the screen size. The paper also seeks to provide a rough sketch of the underlying logical structure of the data itself, by introducing the concept of "meta-symbols," which, the author argues, enables symbols to self reference—mechanically—and to express recursion. Lastly, the paper tries to show how this new visualization technique uses recursion to transform raw data into information and then into knowledge in one continuous flow of program logic, thereby enabling the research community to carefully investigate these three concepts—data, information, and knowledge—in a more precise way from an computational perspective.

An entirely new type of knowledge visualization is presented here. Unlike Chen's technique used to visualize a knowledge domain managed by the database, such as [12] or [13], the Database Taxonomy treats all database content as if it were scientific data, transforming this data into an end-user interface, which functions like a book index, regardless of the database application (see Fig. 1 below). The graphics which can be used to display this taxonomy include industry standard interfaces, such as nested list menus and tree views, as well as custom-built displays. Recent advances to this interface include hybrid navigation structures which display menu data files that were *compiled* ahead of time as well as ones that were generated at *run-time*.

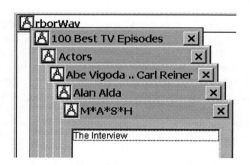

Fig. 1 The Database Taxonomy

2. The Database Taxonomy

The software components used to build this new visualization were first described by Zellweger in [14]. The architecture consists of an authoring system, menu data files generated by the authoring system, and a client browser which displays them as the Database Taxonomy. The authoring system consists of a comprehensive set of interactive tools and utilities to model data relations in the database and to generate menu data files algorithmically, according to BNS. To improve the readability of these menus, developers can add topics to this taxonomy structure by hand. To address scalability issues, for very large data sets, say 1.5M records, bottom-up tab structures can be generated which enable end-users to pinpoint an individual record in this set within a depth of 4 list menus. The authoring system also includes WYSIWYG editors for designing information windows which are linked to the end of every menu path.

3. Burgin's Theory of Named Sets

The mathematical concept of "named sets" was introduced by Burgin in the 1990's [11]. The essence of this new concept is that there exists a mathematical structure more basic than the set: it is the fundamental triad. It assumes that within any given system two components are bound together by a third element, a consistent set of "rules." This idea goes back to Aristotle's syllogism—the original "premise-rules-conclusion" triad—and ascends right up to Wittgenstein's emphasis on the *rules* in learning a language, making it ideally suited to the challenges of the Knowledge Age and its flood of information.

In set theory, the metaphor articulates inclusion/exclusion to shed light on classes and categories of things, an activity generally associated with the information age. In contrast, the BNS triad and its metaphor express a figure/ground visualization, where the objects and their mapping are viewed from the perspective of a system. Using triangulation, a spotlight can be directed on any one of the elements in the triad to clarify or analyze its logical relationship to the others, because BNS relaxes the rules on mapping to include M:M and M:1. BNS assumes that by naming something, humans are capable of perceiving something logical about it, something which warrants a name. Within a precise and tightly integrated system, like a digital computer, BNS provides an opportunity to unify a collection of parts into a whole and give it a name. Like language itself, BNS uses context to overcome ambiguity. But unlike set theory, it is fully capable of modeling self-referencing. By combining the fundamental strengths and weaknesses of language with the precision of mathematical thought, the BNS mathematical primitive provides a powerful new way to simplify complexity by unifying individual parts into a new composition to form new concepts.

An example of a BNS triad may be taken from set theory, where the elements of a set constitute one component, their property another; and the set's name completes the triad by showing that all its elements conform to their property. This triad can be modeled using a diagram, which displays each component and its elements, and the mapping between the two, or it can be modeled algebraically, by referring to each component by a name or label. Building on this simple idea, one named set can relate to another by "chaining," to show how this logical mapping holds a system together, for example, when two sets undergo an AND operation and one employs a BNS chain to model the steps in this operation and to analyze the results for any contradictions.

According to BNS, when modelling data relations in a data table, a pair of attributes forms a "binary attribute relation" or BAR[1]. In formal BNS notation, the BAR would be "(A, r , B)," where r are the rules which bind these two attributes together, and which express data branching. In this case, r is a BAR query, or a SQL SELECT statement having a single input and output attribute. In simplified notation, this query is "$\sigma(A_{input}= v, B_{output}) = d$," where A and B are attributes, v represents an input condition, and d represents data output or the branching which would be consistent with the one or more data symbols extracted from B_{output}.

At first, the data mapping between v and d in a BAR query is difficult to view as a pattern, because it can be either simple (1:1) like a in Fig. 2, or complex (1:M) like b. This ambiguity has kept these data relations hidden from view. But, BNS, which relaxes the mapping rules between source and destination objects—conventionally limited to *mathematical* functions (M:1 and 1:1)—can model both mathematical functions and logical relations (M:M and 1:M). Furthermore, it can represent this pattern of data relations in an abstraction, by referring to attribute labels in a new compact form '(SIZE, SHAPE),' which refers to their data relations and which also serves as meta-query data for an SQL SELECT.

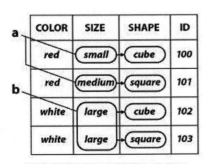

Fig. 2 A Sample Data Table

In a chain of interrelated BARs, such as ((A, A), (A,B), (B, C)), one can model any data relations supported by a relational database [16], including ones which link to related tables. One can also view this chain

algebraically, in which case the actual notation becomes a visual aid for studying the properties of attributes and their data from a BAR query. These properties lay the foundation for identifying the rules on how each link contributes to the chain, including having a primary key in its final link. By isolating these rules, the author identifies a well-formed formula (WFF) here as a named set chain, which, when viewed from the navigation interface, represents a network of menu paths.

4. Meta-Symbols: A Look At The Deeper Logic of Digital Symbols

The notation in the BAR query also serves as a visual aid for exposing the deeper logical nature of relational data, in fact, of all data. The appearance of the input clause '$A_i=v$', as opposed to the simpler output A_o, offers the first clue to a mechanical division of labor which exists in this simple query, one which treats data differently according to its role as input or output. Like the general-purpose *search*, input to a retrieval operation employs pattern matching on physical strings of 0's and 1's to differentiate one data symbol from another. The author argues that this <u>physical-value or v</u> is universal for all digital symbols, a position somewhat implied by data transformations in information visualization [17]. He also contends that these physical-values are meta-symbols, possessing a property even more fundamental than variable types. He asserts this claim for two reasons: 1) each symbolic representation has its own numeric identity, and 2) this identity forms the basis for all data retrieval, including the way digital symbols mechanically self-reference.

The BAR query also highlights another property of data symbols, namely that all data symbols are logically contained within pools of data. Output from the BAR query makes this clear by referring to one of these pools of data by name – A_o, an attribute label in the data table. The author believes that this notion of pools of data can be generalized and thus can refer to a wide range of pools of data serving a wide range of—often overlapping—functions, like data types, variables, knowledge representations and so on. However, unlike physical-values, these <u>constructed-types or t</u> are strictly symbol-based constructs, which have their roots in hardware addresses, and which rise upwards in a mathematical fashion to create multiple, overlapping pools of symbols. Within the context of a database system, each attribute is a very high-level constructed-type which distinguishes one identical data symbol from another, i.e. 'NY' the City, from 'NY' the State.

5. Recursion And A Tight Level of Integration and Logical Alignment

The visualization algorithm at (1) uses recursion to transform raw data into the K2h conceptual knowledge structure displayed in Fig. 3 below. At first, K2h

---

[1]It is important to note that Codd, the seminal figure who invented the relational model, actually argued against binary atomization as he considered each database table to be a "minimal meaningful unit," at least in the design process [14, p.413]. Since then, however, no one has considered the BAR in terms of the BAR query, and so the logical space of data and data relations in the relational table has remained unexplored until now.

organized all menu data for the Database Taxonomy. This allowed the entire collection of data-topics it to be compiled into a series of files, where each file represented a mutually exclusive segment of K2h. Over time, K2h came to represent a conceptual framework for viewing data in the database as lists of data, which, from the perspective of BNS, could be viewed algebraically as meta-query data. Thanks to this possibility, the Database Taxonomy was able to generate run-time menu data and intersperse it with compiled lists of data still using K2h in the process.

$$K2h(chain,d,cmd) \quad \sum_{chain \neg \emptyset} \quad \begin{array}{l} A_i, A_o = CAR(chain); v = CAR(d) \\ cmd = 'A_i = v' \& 'AND' \& cmd \\ \sigma(cmd, A_o) = d \\ addBranching(v,d) \\ K2h(CDR(chain), CDR(d), cmd) \end{array} \quad (1)$$

Data in the table form of Fig. 2, along with the BNS chain '((COLOR, COLOR),(COLOR,SIZE), (SIZE,SHAPE),(SHAPE,ID))', can be used to demonstrate how the recursive algorithm at (1) builds K2h. It is important to note that this BNS chain both *models* the data and data relations in Fig. 2 as a network of menu paths in Fig. 3 as well as *programs* the recursive steps taken by 1. At the core of this algorithm is an *applied* BAR query or $\sigma(input\_conditions, A_o) = d$ which extracts a list of data from a database table on each iteration. It is followed by a call to addBranching, which adds each new list to a leaf node in K2h in a ***depth-first tree-growing*** method [18].

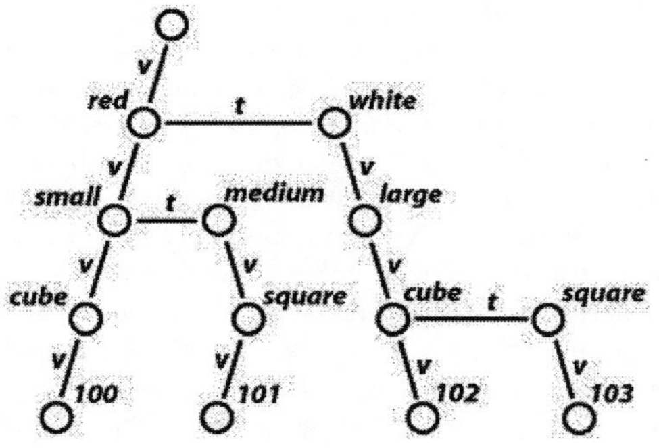

Fig. 3 The K2h Structure

The structure of K2h is very similar to the LEFT-child, RIGHT-sibling digraph described by Knuth [18]. Both are composed of a set of nodes ordered by two edges: child and sibling pointers. But its branching nodes are labelled with *data-topics* and its leafs with *primary keys*. In addition, with an interactive authoring system which enables a developer to add topics to the K2h by hand, as well as to generate complete network segments automatically, this data structure goes well beyond Knuth's simple memory management tool.

The algorithms used to build K2h and its source material, relation data, contribute more than just symbolic values to the K2h structure. Each K2h level

corresponds to a link in a chain of named sets, giving this structure its <u>depth</u> and all of its *pathways* an equal length. In each link, the output attribute is represented at each level by sibling lists which show how each domain is logically partitioned, giving each branching level in this structure its <u>breadth</u>. While the derivation of these dimensions from a data table is not entirely new to visualization research, as per [8], the chain of named sets amplifies the logical elements here, making them easy to see and to investigate.

When K2h's construction is taken into consideration, one can see how the meta-symbols introduced earlier in Section 4, contribute to the syntax and semantics of this structure. The physical-value of each digital symbol or v anchors a child pointer to a branching node, with the constructed-type or t using sibling pointers to form a list of data-topics. The fact that each level in K2h expresses a well-formed logical partition of an attribute domain, gives rise to the idea that a very fundamental <u>semantic</u> grounding occurs on computing devices, one which is entirely based on logical constructions and containment. When the child and sibling pointers are labelled by v and t, this digraph also furnishes visual evidence that K2h has a consistent and well defined <u>syntax</u>. More importantly, this labelling reveals that each data symbol is composed of both v and t, since each node in a sibling list *unifies* them. This unification not only clarifies the semantic nature of data symbols, as each labelled node is an element of the larger taxonomy, but it also expresses the fact that each data symbol in this knowledge structure has a pure logical <u>identity</u>, one of the three classical laws of logic, when $t = v$. This is a significant discovery because it signifies that these meta-symbols are *invariant*.

The K2h digraph also embodies <u>rules of inference.</u> Its root-to-leaf flow demonstrates a precise logical progression which takes every domain in the Universe of Discourse into consideration. Each new level implies $v \rightarrow t_d$, where t_d represents a logical partition of A_o or the t domain. The progression from one domain to the next is deductive and takes the form of forward chaining. This too is very significant, because it suggests that the logical alignment in this transformation from data to knowledge is tightly integrated and absolute, in a mathematical sense, according to K2h as a picture proof, constructed by the exacting rigour and precision of an algorithm. This form of a visual proof goes back in time to Euclid. Yet, it has only recently been show to be sound and complete with objects like Euler's circles, which have a syntax, semantics, and rules of inference [20, p. 69-82], and which should be seen as an independent logical system in its own right [21, p. 135].

6. A Visualization Where Knowledge Complements Information

When the K2h structure is displayed in a graphic user interface, like a list of nested list menus, its practical utility becomes self-evident. The visual metaphor invoked here, a book index, is both familiar and convenient. End-users can browse and explore data and data relations in the database, and they can navigate down its paths to pinpoint information managed by the database. At the end of each menu path, a window object displays information which is based on a unique record in a primary table and all its related fields in others.

On the computer screen, each individual list menu in this graphical user interface represents an information visualization. Each list of data-topics is presented within its own meaningful context, consisting of a header title which represents a prior selection followed by this grouping. The dependency between the current display of data-topics and its header title *assigns* both a semantic and logical meaning to the raw data in this list, with the former conveying an IS-A-TYPE-OF condition with the title, and with the latter actually representing the list of data-topics as a logical subset of the prior selection.

When the end-user navigates from one list menu to the next, the Database Taxonomy *engages* him or her in a logical pursuit of information. The setting is interactive and the user actively participates in what happens next. Each new selection *transforms* an old set of options into new ones, and his/ her selected data-topics form a menu path which has a one-to-one correspondence with raw data associated with a specific database table record. Thus each menu path represents a logical progression which is purposeful and illuminating. Each list menu presents raw data as information, and the path from one list to another reveals an overarching presence of knowledge. In this regard, the graphic structure of Database Taxonomy interface combines elements of both Information Visualization and Knowledge Visualization, with the two approaches complementing each other.

This user interface also provides another way of looking at the mechanical workings of the database and its retrieval operations. Each time a data-topic is selected from one of these list menus, this system, technically speaking[2], instantiates a term for a logical condition, $A = v,$ where A represents the name for an attribute or a domain associated with the list menu and v represents the data topic just selected. This mechanical process of pairing a domain value with an attribute type, such as "COLOR IS *red*", forms a predicate. When

((COLOR = 'red') AND (SHAPE = 'cube') AND (SIZE = 'small'))

Fig. 4 An Expression of Predicate Calculus

[2]While the current technology is able to generate such queries, they were found to be less efficient then the process described in the paper. However, this particular technique is now deployed in a variation of this technology which generates SQL queries for a controlled vocabulary.

navigating from one list menu to the next, each new predicate is added to any previous ones, enabling this progression to create a symbolic expression whose formality and semantic precision closely resembles that of predicate logic, i.e., "... $(A_1 = v_1)$ AND $(A_2 = v_2)$ ...", see Fig. 4 for the details.

This expressive capability of the Database Taxonomy interface suggests that the relational database, which has traditionally been viewed as a mathematically based "information" system, may be in fact be a far richer system altogether, as a tool for studying the digital mechanisms of knowledge and symbolic logic on the computer.

Conclusion

By pre-structuring database content at a deep logical level of the relational model, the Database Taxonomy represents an entirely new type of knowledge visualization which combines aspects of both Information and Knowledge Visualizations. Raw data is displayed in menu lists, which link to other data lists to narrow the context or which link to a window which displays information found at the end of each path. The visual metaphor here is a book index that enables its users to browse and explore the database and to pinpoint the exact information they need. This ability to penetrate deep into the database's logical structure is owing to the mathematical rigor of Burgin's theory of named sets. The power of this mathematical tool can be demonstrated by a single algorithm which transforms raw data seamlessly into a conceptual knowledge structure identified here as K2h. Only a brief overview of this visualization and its underlying techniques can be given here, but it is worth noting that the results have already raised a series of far-reaching questions and conjectures. For instance, if digital symbols do rely on meta-symbols to self-reference, and its physical-value v can be reduced to single bit and its constructed-type t to an address, could this axiomatic view develop into a formal theory of digital symbols, something which AI has been attempting to do for decades? Furthermore, if one can formally demonstrate that K2h has its own syntax, semantics, and rules of inference, would this construct be a suitable setting for studying the flow of data to information and then to knowledge in a formal and theoretically satisfying manner? One might also ask how users' selections in the K2h interface can produce a symbolic query which closely resembles predicate logic and, more importantly, how this digital expression differs from symbolic logic on paper? And could this question re-ignite interest in Russel's logicism and, hopefully, redirect it away from the paper-based thinking of the past, like his PM, the Turing machine, etc., to today's classical computing devices? These questions can go full circle, particularly when we recall that each new database schema undergoes a rigorous "pre-structuring" itself, which relies extensively on data normalization to avoid any unwanted update or search anomalies. When this design phase is fully taken into consideration, new questions arise about the data relations it creates, and about the knowledge visualization which portrays them. This is an important matter, because both relational data and the visualization which portray them are scripted like a story, which has a beginning, a middle and an end, and both depend upon transformations to make the story meaningful. If this is the case, then one should consider the possibility that the theoretical foundation of Knowledge Visualization may be far more mathematically complex than that of its slightly older fraternal twin, Information Visualization.

Acknowledgements

The author thanks Mark Burgin for his generous support over the years.

References

[1] Tergan, Sigar-Olaf and Tanja Keller. Visualizing Knowldege and Information: An Introduction. In *Knowledge and Information Visualization, Searching for Synergies*. Sigar-Olaf Tergan and Tanja Keller, Eds. Berlin: Springer Lecture Notes in Computer Science. 2005. 1-23.

[2] Mark Burgin. How We Know What Technology Can Do. In *Communications of the ACM* 44(11). 2001. 82-88.

[3] Card, Stuart, Jock Machinlay, and Ben Shneiderman. "Readings in Information Visualization, Using Vision to Think." San Francisco, CA: Morgan Kaufman Publishers, Inc. 1999. 7.

[4] Remo Burkhard. Knowledge Visualization: The Use of Complementary Visual Representations for the Transfer of Knowledge. A Model, a Framework, and Four New Approaches. D.Sc. Thesis. Swiss Federal Institute of Technology (ETH Zurich). 2005.

[5] Stefan Bertschi. Without Knowledge Visualization? Proposing a Deconstructionist Approach to Metaphor, Meaning and Perception. In *The Proceedings of the 11th International Conference Information Visualization (IV'07)*. IEEE Computer Science Press. July 2007. 342-347.

[6] Ivan Herman, Guy Melançon and M. Scott Marshall. Graph Visualization and Navigation in Information Visualization: A Survey. In *IEEE Transactions on Visualization and Computer Graphics* 6(1). January 2000. 24-43.

[7] Alberto J.Cañas, R. Carff, G. Hill, M. Carvalho, M. Arguedas, T. C. Eskridge, J. Lott, R. Carvajal. Concept Maps: Integrating Knowledge and Information Visualization. In *Knowledge and Information Visualization: Searching for Synergies*. Sigar-Olaf Tergan & Tanja Keller, Eds. Berlin: Springer Lecture Notes in Computer Science. 2005. 205-219.

[8] Michael J. McGuffin and M.C. Schraefel. A Comparison of Hyperstructures: zzstructures, mSpace, and Polyarchies. In *Proceedings of the Fifteenth ACM Conference on Hypertext and Hypermedia (HYPERTEXT'04)*. Santa Cruz, California. August 2004. 153-162.

[9] M. C. Schraefel, Max Wilson, Alistair Russell, Daniel A. Smith. mSpace: improving information access to multimedia domains with multimodal exploratory search. In *Communications of the ACM* 49(4). April 2006. 47-49.

[10] N. Polys, C. North, D. Bowman, M. Moldenhauer, A. Ray, C. Dandekar. Snap2Diverse: Coordinating Information Visualizations and Virtual Environments. In *Proceedings of SPIE Visualization and Data Analysis (VDA)*. January 2004. 189-200.

[11] Mark Burgin. Theory of Named Sets as a Foundational Basis for Mathematics. In *Structures in Mathematical Theories*, San Sebastian. 1990. 417-420.

[12] Chaomei Chen, Il-Yeol Song, Xiaojun Yuan and Jian Zhang. The thematic and citation landscape of Data and Knowledge Engineering (1985-2007). In *Data & Knowledge Engineering* 67(2). November, 2008. 234-259.

[13] Bruce Herr, Weimao Ke, Elisha Hardy, Katy Borner. Movies and Actors: Mapping the Internet Movie Database. In *The Proceedings of the 11th International Conference Information Visualization (IV'07)*. Zurich, July 2007. IEEE Computer Science Press. 465-469.

[14] Paul Zellweger. A Database Taxonomy Based on Data-driven Knowledge Modeling. In *Integration of Knowledge Intensive Multi-Agent Systems (KIMAS'05)*. IEEE Catalog Number 05EX1033. Waltham, MA. April 2005. 469-474.

[15] Edgar F. Codd. Extending the database relational model to capture more meaning. In *ACM Transactions on Database Systems* 4(4). December 1979. 397-433.

[16] Edgar F. Codd. A Relational Model of Data for Large Shared Data Banks. In *Communications of the ACM* 13(6). 1970. 377-387.

[17] Lisa Tweedle. Characterizing Interactive Externalization. In *Conference on Human factors in Computing Systems (CHI'97)*. March 1997. Atlanta, Georgia. 375-382.

[18] Norman Briggs. Discrete Mathematics. Oxford, United Kingdom: Oxford University Press. 1996. 193-195.
[19] Donald Knuth. The Art of Computer Programming, Vol. 1 Fundamental Algorithms. Reading, Massachusetts: Addison-Wesley. 1997. 348.

[19] Donald Knuth. The Art of Computer Programming, Vol. 1 Fundamental Algorithms. Reading, Massachusetts: Addison-Wesley. 1997. 348.

[20] Eric Hammer. Logic and Visual Information. Stanford, California: CSLI Publications. 1995.

[21] Mark Greaves. The Philosophical Status of Diagrams. Stanford, California: CSLI Publications. 2001.

What is Knowledge Visualization? Perspectives on an Emerging Discipline

Stefan Bertschi,[1] Sabrina Bresciani,[2] Tom Crawford,[3] Randy Goebel,[4] Wolfgang Kienreich,[5] Martin Lindner,[6] Vedran Sabol,[5] Andrew Vande Moere[7]

[1]*loginb consulting, {knowledge}@loginb.com,* [2]*Università della Svizzera italiana (USI),* *{bresciani.sabrina}@gmail.com,* [3]*VizNetwork, {tom}@viznetwork.com,* [4]*University of Alberta,* *{rgoebel}@ualberta.ca,* [5]*Know-Center, {wkien, vsabol}@know-center.at,* [6]*MicroWeb,* *{martin.lindner}@gmail.com,* [7]*KU Leuven, {andrew.vandemoere}@asro.kuleuven.be*

Abstract

This paper collates eight expert opinions about Knowledge Visualization; what it is and what it should be. An average of 581 words long, topics span from representation, storytelling and criticizing the lack of theory, to communication, analytics for the masses and reasoning, to trendy Visual Thinking and creativity beyond PowerPoint. These individual views provide a picture of the present and the future of a discipline that could not be more timely, aiming for a common understanding of the visualization of knowledge.

Knowledge Visualization is…

The International Symposium on Knowledge Visualization and Visual Thinking is now in its seventh year, and it is about time to assemble a selection of expert opinions on where we are today and where the discipline should be heading.

Therefore, members of the Advisory and Review Committee were invited to participate in a joint paper, and seven co-authors have accepted the invitation. The requirements were: to contribute a personal view of no more than 625 words, with no illustrations allowed, using a few references if needed. The topical requirement stated that these personal opinions had to reflect on the current and/or future state of what the authors consider to be Knowledge Visualization.

The result is a set of individual vistas on a multifaceted discipline. Each view sheds a different perspective on the notion of knowledge visualization and highlights specific theoretical or practical aspects. As a whole, they lead beyond the diversity of visualization.

Stefan Bertschi

…about communication – fundamentally (Tom Crawford)

While classically, the word communication implies that it is from one person to at least one other, it can also be communicating to yourself as a way of understanding and remembering what you have learned.

The process of Knowledge Visualization contains steps such as gathering, interpreting, developing an understanding, organizing, designing, and communicating the information. While the previous sentence implies a linear flow, it is hardly a linear process. In fact, any step can link to any other step in any number of iterations until a "final" representation is created. Of course, it never is quite final. Even if we were able to come up with the perfect visualization, our knowledge changes and with it changes the visual. In fact the visual often provides so much insight that our knowledge changes and thus the visual needs to change creating a fascinating recursive loop.

Strangely, while we have learned much about Knowledge Visualization over the last 100 years, we still have yet to re-think and redesign some of the most common forms of communication. For example, the lowly recipe, which has been around and largely unchanged for over 3,600 years, is a form of communication from one person to another. The original assumption of the recipe designer was that anyone who needed to read it shared a specialized language and process, which often now is learned either as an apprentice or in culinary school. However, that language breaks down when the same information design goes from chef to home cook. The assumptions of terminology and process break down when the home cook has not had the same education or experience as the professional chef.

So, what would happen if we were to re-think the design of the recipe and apply Knowledge Visualization techniques to the problem?

During the early stages of Knowledge Visualization we would conclude that the recipe contains four basic types of information: ingredients, process, and equipment which are combined in particular ways via a series of techniques. In analyzing the current recipes, we would find that the design mixes the four types of information somewhat randomly which leads to the possibility of mistakes.

For example, the list of ingredients also contains process steps (e.g. 200 grams onion, diced). These are two different pieces of information. An ingredient list is essential for making sure that what is needed to make the recipe is present. However, what you do with those ingredients should all be handled in one place. It becomes even more complex when understanding that "dicing" an onion is not one but actually five steps (cut in half, top, peel, plus at least two cuts).

Knowledge Visualization would not only make it clear what kind of onion, but also what then needs to be done with it. No longer would cloves be confused with garlic cloves because they look nothing alike. Photos could be used to show what a ripe banana looks like in comparison to one that is past its prime to help the home cook choose not only the right ingredient, but the freshest and best ingredients. The same idea could be applied to the equipment which is rarely, if ever, shown in a recipe. Food mills, reamers, mandolines and many other infrequent, but valuable tools could not only be shown, but demonstrated directly in the context of the recipe.

The recipe is only one of the common forms of communication that could use a much closer look. By using the tools and process of Knowledge Visualization, we can begin looking deeply at the recipe's components, who it is used by, and what they are using it for, and therefore create more effective tools that reduce errors and increase satisfaction. That is Knowledge Visualization.

...storytelling (Andrew Vande Moere)

Knowledge is information that has been made part of a specific context. In order for information to transform into knowledge, one must share some context, some meaning, in order to become encoded and connected to preexisting experience. In that sense, Knowledge Visualization can be considered as data visualization "in context". While Knowledge Visualization facilitates people to explore trends, patterns and outliers in data, it does not necessarily aim to discover them, but rather attempts to unravel the driving principles that influence these data phenomena. With such

knowledge, data trends can be explained, rather than simply discerned. Knowledge, therefore, is not about knowing the facts, but knowing the causal factors and context in which the facts have come about.

Stories are a powerful means of providing context. Not surprisingly, knowledge is often shared and communicated through the process of storytelling [1]. Storytelling tends to place information (e.g. activities, events, facts) within a commonly accepted contextual framework, often by exploiting the qualities of internalization and socialization. While a story aims to convey a series of specific truths, it is the narrative that provides a context in interpreting the overarching meaning, which potentially transforms it into actionable knowledge.

While Knowledge Visualization is recognized as an independent scientific discipline [2], the relevance of storytelling towards its scientific goals is still relatively unexplored. Early research proposed some simple "actions" like animation, mood and place as particularly effective storytelling techniques in data visualization [3]. A more recent study has investigated several design dimensions like genre and visual or narrative structure to categorize the existing methods of visual storytelling in the domains of online journalism, graphic design, comics, business, art, and visualization research [4]. In the context of Knowledge Visualization research, the emerging popularity of online visual storytelling [5] presents at least two new challenges.

First, the use of storytelling in visualization has been primarily considered on a phenomenological level, as a set of design techniques that have the ability to direct a viewer's attention through a sequential narrative, or a series of visual transitions. This experiential viewpoint seems to miss the role of context in the visualization practice, and how providing rich context can augment the visual sense-making process from observing eventual data patterns and trends into reasoning about the meaning of their occurrence. If context drives data-driven knowledge acquisition, then how is it best represented? Second, it might be equally revealing to analyze visual storytelling techniques in the context of Knowledge Visualization, or vice versa, investigate Knowledge Visualization design methods. Such wide analysis should at least provide a better understanding in successful design strategies. Alternatively, one might discover promising but under-explored approaches to Knowledge Visualization.

While Knowledge Visualization might be less entertaining and eye-catching than most popular forms of currently existing visual storytelling, both approaches focus on conveying context, and therefore a form of knowledge, to an increasingly information-hungry audience. What might make data visualization different from other types of visual storytelling is the complexity and scale of the content that needs to be communicated [3]. However, with the emerging popularity of data visualization in current online media, expectations will inevitably shift from simply delivering information to conveying the causally influencing factors that drive the events in our world today.

...inductive transformation from data to visual space (Randy Goebel)

Current – The current state of the art in Knowledge Visualization is pretty well represented by the distribution of papers in [6], which I claim shows a healthy diversity of ideas on how to transform data into pictures. There is balance between the development of new ideas for rendering objects in a visual space, and on the application of existing methods to a variety of application specific data, including health, bioinformatics, geography, and a broad spectrum of web data. There remains opportunity for the articulation of insight into visualization semantics and the role of cognitive science in drawing inferences from pictures; I suggest these aspects should be stronger, because, after all, visualization is about how the human visual system can be inferentially amplified by rendering data in appropriate visual spaces.

The overall scientific interest in visualization is also growing, for example, by the seven years of the Science Visualization Challenge [7, 8], which has brought the role of visualization into the scientific mainstream. The continued problem here, however, is that while the Science challenge raises awareness and interest in visualization, it still has the flavor of a kind of "beauty contest," instead of a disciplined assessment of the quality of visualization techniques. The question should always be about *how well* a particular visualization technique supports visual inference.

Future – With respect to the future of visualization, I think an appropriate approach is captured by Alan Kay's assertion that "The best way to predict the future is to invent it." [9] One strong personal motivation for inventing the future of visualization arises from an assertion I recently read in a paper I was refereeing, which wrote "...as the theory of visualization tells us...." I balked, as there is no theory of visualization. But there should be.

To invent the future of visualization is not to abandon the current state in pursuit of some fundamentally different paradigm, but just to bring a little more scientific thinking to what a theory of visualization should be? If the simply stated goal of visualization is to amplify the human visual system's ability to draw inference from complex data, then we need much more work on *what kinds* of inferences can be made, and *how well* they can be made.

Again from my own viewpoint, not uniformly shared, I believe that it is scientifically useful to view pictures as inductive inferences about the data and data relationships from which they arose. Within that framework, we can not only design experiments that evaluate the quality of inference that a visualization method provides, but can also reflect on how easy it is for humans to reach conclusions intended by visualization methods application.

So, take Alan Kay's generic advice to heart, and invent the future of visualization. This requires a stronger role for good scientific reasoning to guide the connection of visualization research components: clever graphics, scientifically justified "art," innovative multi-dimensional rendering, all *coupled* with evaluation with respect to the efficacy of making insightful inferences.

Prognosis – Perhaps Knowledge Visualization is a kind of maturing teenager, slowly emerging out of the eclectic chaos of graphics cleverness, scientific modeling art, and overly specific multi-dimensional rendering? I think the best evidence is the continued diversity of visualization ideas, coupled with an increasing volume of work on visualization evaluation. After all, if the goal of visualization is to amplify our visual systems' ability to draw inferences from visual representation of data, then we need to develop scientific discipline about how to assess alternative visualization methods. From that will emerge aspects of a theory of visualization, and the future will be invented.

...expressing concepts through meaningful graphical mapping (Sabrina Bresciani)

Visualizing knowledge means mapping concepts graphically, by structuring text and visuals in a meaningful way. Visual representations are used to organize information and concepts in order to convey knowledge, to amplify cognition and to enhance communication. Examples include conceptual diagrams, knowledge maps, visual metaphors and sketches.

Knowledge Visualization can overcome the limitations of textual/verbal communication and of visual representations alone. Through the use of spatial distribution, it leverages on both the textual and the visual abilities of the brain to express meaning (Dual Coding Theory [10]). Knowledge Visualization can provide the big picture, give an overview and show the relationships between concepts. It structures conceptual knowledge [11, p. 7] and provides salience, thereby facilitating the focus on certain information at the expense of other. Images have an impact also on the emotional attitude of the user, by providing engagement and motivation. Visualizing knowledge is useful for collaborative work: mapping the group dialogue can facilitate the integration of knowledge and it can surface misunderstandings more prominently than text.

A relevant aspect is the relationship between Knowledge Visualization and Information Visualization. The two concepts overlap in their common aim to offer insights to the user [12]: "Knowledge visualization [...] designates all graphic means that can be used to construct and convey complex insights." [13, p. 551] Yet the uniqueness of Knowledge Visualization lies in the content that is being mapped, posing a stronger emphasis on knowledge and experiences rather than on numerical information. Adopting the definition of Chaomei Chen, "[t]he term *information visualization* refers to computer generated interactive graphical representations of information." [12, p. 387] By contrast, Knowledge Visualization is not necessarily computer generated, nor interactive. A mind map drawn with pen and paper is a common example of Knowledge Visualization which is not computer generated. However, recent developments in Information and Communication Technology (ICT) enable a widespread use of Knowledge Visualization by empowering any user with limited drawing skills to easily create conceptual visualizations.

Visualizing knowledge is not without risks. Typical challenges and mistakes committed while creating or using knowledge visualizations include, for example, oversimplification and ambiguity of meaning.

In recent years, reflecting a trend in society, we witness a growing number of case studies and theoretical conceptualization, and thus the emergence of Knowledge Visualization as a new discipline. Yet, the lack of a solid theoretical background is a significant limitation for the development of this particular field.

Future directions of development for Knowledge Visualization and its potentials are seen along the following three main paths. Firstly, the discipline would benefit from rigorously studying and measuring the impact of visualizations, especially in emerging forms of collaborative interactions, including visual groupware, Group Support Systems and social media. Secondly, the diffusion of innovative input devices such as (multi-)touch screens is enabling new ways of interaction with software and particularly in groups. The field of Knowledge Visualization could benefit from understanding the implications of these fluid forms of interaction. Finally, it could expand its horizon of applications by introducing and testing knowledge visualizations in new domains, including for instance intercultural communication, a context where visual representations can be particularly useful to overcome linguistic and cultural barriers.

...the link between visualization and information overload (Wolfgang Kienreich)

Knowledge Visualization is the missing link between the expert tools developed in the thriving field of Visual Analytics and the frantic demand of the general public for intuitive ways to cope with increasingly large and complex personal digital universes.

Visual Analytics, the science of analytical reasoning facilitated by interactive visual interfaces, combines automated analysis, visual representation and user interaction in a closed loop intended to provide users with new insights [14]. This approach has been successfully applied in domains like business intelligence or genetics. Visual Analytics emphasizes the use of visual abstractions to represent aggregated information and facilitate the formulation and validation of hypothesis by expert analysts.

Knowledge Visualization utilizes visual representations to foster the communication of knowledge between two or more people. Clear benefits of this approach have been demonstrated for common situations like presentations and discussions [15]. Knowledge Visualization emphasizes the use of visual metaphors to represent relevant information and facilitates collaborative dissemination and decision making by domain experts.

Phenomena like the advent of social and consumer generated media or the prevalence of personal imaging devices have vastly increased the size and complexity of personal digital universes. As a consequence, many analytical tasks which have traditionally been performed by experts have become a concern for the general public: When a private photo collection is comprised of many gigabytes of image data, locating relevant images requires facetted multimedia search and retrieval techniques. When a personal social network is comprised of hundreds of individuals, identifying who could contribute to a problem or benefit from a piece of information requires methods of social network analysis. A plethora of services and applications enables users to share content and media and to build networks. However, simple, accessible means for analyzing, evaluating and, ultimately, utilizing the wealth of knowledge thus created are sadly lacking.

We propose that Visual Analytics and Knowledge Visualization join forces in order to tackle this problem. Visual Analytics could contribute techniques for the automated analysis of large amounts of information and the closed loop approach which integrates analysis, visualization and interaction. For instance, consumer-generated media could automatically be analyzed for sentiment and quality. User feedback provided through a visual interface could adapt the model of what constitutes sentiment and quality on a personal level.

Knowledge Visualization could contribute the practices and methods required to design domain and user specific visual representations. Such representations would be comprehensible for users with limited visual literacy. For instance, media analysis results could be presented using a map, meter or aquarium metaphor. Appropriate knowledge visualizations have already been proposed for supporting discussions. In the outlined scenario, they would be backed by aggregated information computed from massive repositories.

Multi-touch surfaces could turn out to be a driving technological factor for a closer integration of Visual Analytics and Knowledge Visualization. Recent applications of Visual Analytics acknowledge the benefits of collaborative approaches and utilize multi-touch tables to support joint analysis of complex problems by groups of experts [16]. Knowledge Visualization already has accumulated a wealth of experiences and findings on how to visually support such group situations. Both disciplines could only benefit from a closer exchange of ideas and of an integration of approaches in applications to solve real world problems.

...the crucial stage in knowledge processes (Vedran Sabol)

To define Knowledge Visualization, it is important to agree on a definition of knowledge: knowledge is an acquired, established set of facts, recognized to be valid and valuable within a specific domain. It can be represented by a formal model consisting of concepts, relationships and logical conditions. Knowledge Visualization deals with creating and applying visual representations with the purpose of constructing and communicating useful knowledge [17]. Knowledge Visualization includes both static visual representations, such as panels or posters, as well as interactive visualizations, offering possibilities for exploration of visualized knowledge depending on users' needs. Knowledge in visual form not only facilitates remembering and transfer, it also provides the fuel for reasoning processes where new knowledge is derived and created from previously acquired knowledge.

Knowledge Visualization is contrasted by the fields of Information Visualization and, more recently, Visual Analytics. Both disciplines operate at a lower level of abstraction than Knowledge Visualization, focusing mainly on raw data and information. In this context, data is understood as sequences of numbers or characters, representing qualitative or quantitative attributes of specific variables. To obtain information data is processed and brought into a context within which it gains a specific meaning and becomes understandable to users. Information Visualization makes use of human visual perception capabilities for recognition of patterns and extraction of knowledge from raw data and information. Visual Analytics builds upon Information Visualization to facilitate analytical reasoning by combining automated discovery and interactive visualization [18, 19].

While Visual Analytics focuses on discovery of new knowledge from raw data and information, and targets analysts in application domains such as business intelligence, Knowledge Visualization deals with expression and creation of knowledge, targeting areas such as knowledge management and strategic management in general. Although different in their conception and areas of application, both fields share several common properties: they breed new knowledge, deliver support for decision making, and provide a common basis for collaboration.

Knowledge Visualization is a powerful resource which could be used outside of its traditional application domains. Knowledge Discovery is a data processing chain consisting of, roughly speaking, data selection, transformation, and mining and presentation steps, where at the end of the process new knowledge arises from raw data [20]. Visual Analytics has been successfully applied in the context of Knowledge Discovery, where it serves as the final stage of the process chain, supporting users in visually identifying patterns and extracting new knowledge. Because knowledge is the final product of the process, it appears as a compelling idea to integrate Knowledge Visualization as the final stage of the Knowledge Discovery process chain. Moreover, in this final stage Knowledge Visualization could build upon and be combined with Visual Analytics. Therefore, a unified process would be created where visual interfaces are used for discovery, creation and communication of knowledge. Management support, which is provided by Knowledge Visualization, would now be closely integrated with analysts' output, which is supported by Visual Analytics.

Many questions remain open though, for example: How could findings provided by Visual Analytics be incorporated in Knowledge Visualization representations? How could Knowledge Visualization and Visual Analytics be combined to generate synergies in a Knowledge Discovery process which not only provides means for unveiling hidden facts, but also delivers knowledge as its final product including all its accompanying facets such as experiences, attitudes, perspectives and opinions?

...the doodle revolution (Martin Lindner)

Visual Thinking is a big trend, particularly in the age of the "micro-web". Its main exponents are Dave Gray (CEO of consulting firm XPLANE, co-author of "Gamestorming" [21]), Dan Roam (author of "Back of the Napkin" [22]), Lee LeFever (creator of the simple explanation videos "…in Plain English" that became popular via YouTube) or Sunni Brown who coined the term "Doodle Revolution" (book forthcoming, cf. [23]). "Enterprise 2.0" consultancies like XPLANE or the more mainstream Root Learning use visualizations collaboratively created by workshop participants for change management processes [24].

The wider context, I think, is a new wave of visualizations and Visual Thinking that was started in the 1990s. Of course we had revolutions in visual language before: Otto Neurath invented modern "infographics" around 1930, and Quentin Fiore, who collaborated with Marshall McLuhan in the 1960s, may also stand for early revolutions. However, this wave reached new heights in the 1990s: digital data, Apple-driven graphic engines and, finally, the Web 2.0 have changed the game.

We have discovered whole new possibilities to collect, organize and manipulate digital data, but this has opened the view on new abstract facts, new complex realities. Meanwhile, human understanding is still stuck in the primary world of physical objects, face-to-face communication and people doing things to each other in direct ways. In a world of massively mediated interaction and communication this cognitive model must fail. As mass "macro-media" become grassroots "micro-media", they reach beyond entertainment and pop culture. What we see emerging is a new mode for new ways of collective thinking, networked conversations and knowledge creation.

Certainly, there are a lot of trends in visualization that run back to the "Big Bang" caused by personal computing and digital networking. A presentation by designer Peter Morville gives a good and visual overview of Visual Thinking [25]. On the "richer" side, we have Hans Rosling's famous performances explaining the world through statistical visualizations (see the stunning BBC Four video "200 Countries, 200 Years, 4 Minutes"). This is in line with Al Gore's effort to visualize the ungraspable reality of Global Warming in his "illustrated talk" that was finally turned into a movie.

Back in 2000, Al Gore was basically using PowerPoint as visualization tool, which then was criticized by Edward Tufte in 2003 for its inherent tendency towards "Stalinist" visual New Speak: corporate salespeople silencing their audience with a power play of curves, bullets and pies. But at the same time, artist David Byrne introduced new ways of using PowerPoint. In the last five years, this has become the mainstream: A bunch of Web 2.0 pioneers has developed a new style of well-designed Visual Thinking (although most are using Keynote, the presentation software for Macs).

All in all, new visual languages and new cognitive styles are emerging. This has many facets. I am especially interested in new formats that can be discovered and observed in the World Wide Web: simple visual objects that can be produced with little effort by almost anyone, like a doodle or a napkin sketch. They are part of what Lev Manovich called "micro-media" in 2000, and what is now the evolving trend towards "micro-media convergence". Because they only require a small attention span to get their ideas and messages, these simple user-generated objects can be easily circulated in the cloud: in blogs, via flickr, SlideShare or YouTube.

This is part of a paradigm shift from "published ideas" to "circulating ideas". What people formerly did on their desks is now part of collaborative thinking processes enabled by the Web 2.0 ecosystem. It was web intellectual Steven Johnson who described this ecosystem in some detail. He even made a fascinating animated "graphic recording"-video to promote his book quite successfully [26]. It is 4:07 minutes, the length of a pop song. Possibly, this is not mere coincidence. It just may be the natural format for the hive mind.

…visualization beyond PowerPoint (Stefan Bertschi)

The roots of Knowledge Visualization, as it is presented annually at the International Conference Information Visualization, are in business and management. Therefore, we learn from research into visualization that strategic and operational processes rely on communication and interaction. Visualization of any kind significantly improves communication and therefore business processes. Knowledge Visualization caters for refined and aggregated information commonly used in planning and implementation practices as well as projects and change processes [2]. Though not solely confined to business, Knowledge Visualization aims to understand how the sender's intended meaning can be transferred in such a way that it is not distorted in the recipient's perception, therefore allowing effective and efficient communication to take place.

The human mind is a strange thing, however, for most people we may state that complex dependencies and interactions can more easily be understood when illustrated: an intelligent process flow chart makes more sense than a numbered list describing the same process in words, a project (Gantt) chart showing timelines and interdependencies allows for better understanding than a project scope, even if structured. The difficulties are to be found in how to make best use of the understanding of others, their intentions and perceptions, simply because there is no direct way to look inside their heads. Visualization and Visual Thinking subsequently allow us to reveal these "understandings" because they provoke discussion, allowing the alignment of opinions and arguments.

If organizations in need of successful transfer of knowledge are to ensure they benefit most from current knowledge, then the single most important advice would be: "listen", but also "listen with your eyes". Think of illustrations and visualizations beyond PowerPoint and Project; think why "pencil selling" just using pen and paper is so much more effective than words alone in selling anything, ranging from goods to projects. Do not be afraid to draw and sketch in front of a live audience, or even better, sketch collaboratively and experience how much better ideas are being generated, ideas that stick in all participants' heads.

Speaking and listening with your eyes also means making full use of the available methods (see the Periodic Table of Visualization Methods [27]). Knowledge that can be seen can be used effectively and efficiently. It is important to keep a critical mind, if used incorrectly visualizations can be risky [28]. Furthermore, the activities of knowledge workers (like attorneys, marketers, scientists and senior executives) are "too variable or even idiosyncratic to be modeled or structured with a defined process". Basically, their need for access to knowledge sources, ranging from online databases and social media to spreadsheets, presentation tools and business intelligence analytics "is presumed to be equally eclectic and unpredictable." [29, p. 90f.] The range of tools used does not ease the knowledge process.

Does this mean the complexity of some of the tools and software available is a barrier to creating visuals? I would not necessarily blame the complexity of software but the lack of complexity or willingness for creativity in creating these visuals. I have personally had great experiences with visual co-creation both in strategy and in operational processes. Visuals stimulate discussion, and discussion creates knowledge. Arguing this way, full use of methods does not mean to use them all at once, but to use and combine them as necessary. Less is many times more because the average human brain can process far less information than we anticipate: four complex arguments in one go are too many, rather make your three points, but make them right and sustainably. Transparency and simplicity are the answer – visibly and visualized for business purposes and far beyond.

What is Knowledge Visualization?

By reading "only" eight opinions on Knowledge Visualization, it seems difficult to find a unifying definition that says it all about Knowledge Visualization and Visual Thinking. The aim of this joint paper was to span the discipline by provoking a range of individual vistas. Therefore, let us revisit what we can learn through the eyes of others.

Tom Crawford highlights the communicative function of Knowledge Visualization; in his opinion, the non-linear process of representing knowledge is a recipe for success, if handled correctly and by using visuals as an effective tool.

Andrew Vande Moere identifies the importance of storytelling and meaning. In his opinion, Knowledge Visualization allows to explore patterns by putting them close to their context. The "story" is the perfect visual carrier for knowledge, rendering it actionable.

Randy Goebel offers a reflection on the theoretical and methodological foundation of visualization. In his opinion, the strength is in the diversity to achieve insightful inferences. He criticizes the lack of a theory of visualization and argues for inventing the future.

Sabrina Bresciani organizes her insights around the need to amplify cognition and to enhance communication; visuals should also consider emotions and experiences. Knowledge Visualization has to question the actual impact of visualizations across all methods.

Wolfgang Kienreich promotes Visual Analytics as a way of managing the complex digital universe of today's knowledge and network society. Driven by the closed loop of representation and interaction, he pleads for analytical means for the masses.

Vedran Sabol sees Knowledge Visualization as the most important stage of knowledge processes. In his opinion, it not only provides fuel for reasoning but operates at the highest level of abstraction, allowing sound perspectives, effective decisions and valuable synergies.

Martin Lindner introduces Visual Thinking as the main trend of Enterprise 2.0. Whilst visual revolutions are nothing new, we see new efforts to overcome the failing cognitive model of objects and physical interaction, promoting collective thinking in the cloud.

What can be learned from all contributions is that visualization improves communication, in particular the interaction around cognitive processes. Knowledge Visualization and Visual Thinking fabricate the necessary understanding of these processes because knowledge needs to be "seen". If there is one common truth contained in all eight perspectives, then it would be: without successful and sustainable transfer, knowledge is meaningless.

Beyond the diversity of visualization and of these views, it becomes apparent how all eight contributions (at least implicitly) emphasize a process-driven concept of visualization. The act of visualizing is more important than the image itself: medium > message.

Stefan Bertschi

References

[1] Swap W., Leonard D., Shields M. and Abrahams L. (2001), Using Mentoring and Storytelling to Transfer Knowledge in the Workplace, *Journal of Management Information Systems* 18 (1), 95-114.

[2] Burkhard R. (2005), Knowledge Visualization: The Use of Complementary Visual Representations for the Transfer of Knowledge – A Model, a Framework, and Four New Approaches, D.Sc. thesis, Swiss Federal Institute of Technology (ETH Zurich).

[3] Wojtkowski W. and Wojtkowski W. G. (2002), Storytelling: Its Role in Information Visualization, *Res-Systemica* 2, Proceedings of the Fifth European Systems Science Congress, Crete, 16-19 October 2002, http://www.afscet.asso.fr/resSystemica/Crete02/Wojtkowski.pdf.

[4] Segel E. and Heer J. (2010), Narrative Visualization: Telling Stories with Data, *IEEE Transactions on Visualization and Computer Graphics* 16 (6), 1139-1148.

[5] Schmitt G. (2009), Data Visualization is Reinventing Online Storytelling – And Building Brands in Bits and Bytes, *AdvertisingAge*, 19 March, http://adage.com/digitalnext/post?article_id=135313.

[6] Banissi E. et al. (eds) (2009), Proceedings of the 13th International Conference Information Visualisation, Barcelona, 15-17 July 2009, Los Alamitos, CA: IEEE Computer Society Press.

[7] Griggs J. (2010), Visualization Challenge: Prizewinning Pictures, *NewScientist*, 18 February, http://www.newscientist.com/article/dn18548-visualization-challenge-prizewinning-pictures.html.

[8] Nesbit J. and Bradford M. (2010), Visualization Challenge 2009, *Science* 327, 19 February, 945-953.

[9] Kay A. C. (1989), Predicting the Future, *Stanford Engineering* 1 (1), 1-6.

[10] Paivio A. (1969), Mental Imagery in Associative Learning and Memory, *Psychological Review* 76 (3), 241-263.

[11] Keller T. and Tergan S.-O. (2005), Visualizing Knowledge and Information: An Introduction, In Tergan S.-O. and Keller T. (eds), *Knowledge and Information Visualization: Searching for Synergies*, Lecture Notes in Computer Science, Berlin: Springer, 1-23.

[12] Chen C. (2010), Overview: Information Visualization, *Wiley Interdisciplinary Reviews: Computational Statistics* 2 (4), 387-403.

[13] Eppler M. J. and Burkhard R. (2006), Knowledge Visualization, In Schwartz D. G. (ed), *Encyclopedia of Knowledge Management*, Hershey, PA: Idea Group Reference, 551-560.

[14] Thomas J. J. and Cook K. A. (2006), A Visual Analytics Agenda, *IEEE Computer Graphics and Applications* 26 (1), 10-13.

[15] Bresciani S. and Eppler M. (2009), The Benefits of Synchronous Collaborative Information Visualization: Evidence from an Experimental Evaluation, *IEEE Transactions on Visualization and Computer Graphics* 15 (6), 1073-1080.

[16] Burkhard R., Schneider C. and Meier M. (2009), The ETH Value Lab and Two Software Tools for Knowledge Creation in Teams, Proceedings of the 13th International Conference Information Visualisation, Barcelona, 15-17 July 2009, Los Alamitos, CA: IEEE Computer Society Press, 469-473.

[17] Eppler M. J. and Burkhard R. A. (2004), Knowledge Visualization – Towards a New Discipline and its Fields of Application, ICA Working Paper 2/2004, Institute for Corporate Communication, Università della Svizzera italiana.

[18] Thomas J. J. and Cook K. A. (eds) (2005), *Illuminating the Path: The Research and Development Agenda for Visual Analytics*, Richland, WA: National Visualization and Analytics Center. http://nvac.pnl.gov/agenda.stm.

[19] Keim D. A., Mansmann F., Oelke D. and Ziegler H. (2008), Visual Analytics: Combining Automated Discovery with Interactive Visualizations, *Lecture Notes in Computer Science*, No 5255, Proceedings of the 11th International Conference Discovery Science, Budapest, 13-16 October 2008, 2-14.

[20] Fayyad U. M., Piatetsky-Shapiro G. and Smyth P. (1996), From Data Mining to Knowledge Discovery in Databases, *AI Magazine* 17, 37-54.

[21] Gray D., Brown S. and Macanufo J. (2010), *Gamestorming: A Playbook for Innovators, Rulebreakers, and Changemakers*, Sebastopol, CA: O'Reilly.

[22] Roam D. (2008), *The Back of the Napkin: Solving Problems and Selling Ideas with Pictures*, New York: Portfolio.

[23] Brown S. (2011), The Miseducation of the Doodle, *A List Apart Magazine*, 25 January, http://www.alistapart.com/articles/the-miseducation-of-the-doodle.

[24] Eppler M. J. (2011), Change Images for the Head, Heart and Hand: What Visual Thinking Can Do for Change Communication. An Interview with Dave Gray, *OrganisationsEntwicklung* 1/2011, 16-22.

[25] Morville P. (2010), Experience Maps: KM and Visual Thinking, Presentation, http://www.slideshare.net/morville/xmaps-upload.

[26] Johnson S. (2010), *Where Good Ideas Come From: The Natural History of Innovation*, New York: Riverhead Books. Promotional video: http://www.youtube.com/watch?v=NugRZGDbPFU.

[27] Lengler R. and Eppler M. J. (2007), Towards A Periodic Table of Visualization Methods for Management, Proceedings of the IASTED International Conference on Graphics and Visualization in Engineering (GVE'07), 83-88. http://www.visual-literacy.org/periodic_table/periodic_table.html.

[28] Bresciani S. and Eppler M. J. (2008), The Risks of Visualization: A Classification of Disadvantages Associated with Graphic Representations of Information, ICA Working Paper 1/2008, Institute for Corporate Communication, Università della Svizzera italiana.

[29] Davenport T. H. (2011), Rethinking Knowledge Work: A Strategic Approach, *McKinsey Quarterly*, Number 1, 89-99.

Contract Clarity through Visualization

Preliminary Observations and Experiments

Helena Haapio

Lexpert Ltd

Helsinki, Finland

helena.haapio@lexpert.com

Abstract— In the crafting of commercial contracts, many participants are involved, often professionals from different countries and backgrounds. The challenge, then, is to achieve a balance between the business and legal requirements and to facilitate communication and coordination. While some contracts may need to work as evidence in court, most contracts do not. Instead, they need to work as business tools for the parties so they get the results they want to accomplish. This paper presents preliminary observations of research work in progress, aimed at developing new methods to improve the clarity and usability of commercial contracts. It proposes a new field of research and practice, contract visualization, and invites cross-professional dialogue to explore the opportunities that exist for industry-changing innovations in this area.

Keywords-commercial contracting; contract visualization; invisible terms; legal risk; visualizing legal information

I. CONTRACTS IN THE COMMERCIAL WORLD

When hearing the word "contract," people have a tendency to think of formal, legal documents. Many tend to categorize "contracts" under "law" and think that contracts are best left for lawyers. Traditional management literature seems to have a rather legalistic view of contracts also. Up until recently, most managers and researchers outside the legal field have ignored contracts, despite the fact that the ability to understand and use contracts is increasingly important in today's business.

In every collaborative venture where two or more companies work together, a contract is present. It may be written or unwritten, formal or informal. In manufacturing industries, the move from goods to services and solutions makes contracting increasingly complex and time consuming. At the same time, the current business climate requires companies to act quickly. Opportunities are lost if contract creation and negotiation take too long or if contracts are hard to interpret and to implement.

This paper draws from the early results of a recently started research project where contracts are seen as an important part of collaborating companies' value creation. It builds on research that proves the growing importance of contracts and contracting capabilities for today's interconnected enterprises [1, p. 1061] and competitive advantage [2, p. 667–668]. It looks into the many different functions of contracts, of which only a small fraction seems to be related to the law. Instead of "contracts in court" or "contract law in the books", we explore "contracts in action", as they appear in the commercial world, from both business and legal perspectives. Here, when used *proactively*, contracts communicate crucial information inside and between organizations; they help share, minimize and manage cost and risk; and, in case of a dispute, contracts work as a record and evidence of what has been agreed and provide a means to resolve the dispute. Further, when used *preventively*, contracts communicate the deal and its terms clearly so as to avoid future disputes over their meaning. [3, p. 111]

II. CONTRACT PUZZLE: IT TAKES A TEAM

Contracts are expected to provide businesses with predictable outcomes. Still contract interpretation remains the largest single source of contract litigation between business firms [4]. While empirical research is needed to enhance our understanding about the reasons for this, one thing is clear: Contracts do not make things happen – *people* do.

After negotiating and signing, the parties must follow their contract. Understandability is a prerequisite in order for users to perform any task. For a vast majority of contracts, courts, arbitrators, and lawyers are not the primary readers and users – people in the operational and delivery teams implementing the contracts are. These people are seldom lawyers. They need information contained in contracts to coordinate in-house and outsourced functions, manage budget, scope, schedule, resources, and so on.

Today's commercial contracts can be viewed through the analogy of a jigsaw puzzle. With a complex project in mind, Fig. 1 shows a contract as a puzzle of 1) technical and contextual, 2) performance and delivery, 3) business and financial, and 4) legal and risk management related parts, with 5) project and contract management as the center piece. If correctly assembled – and only if correctly assembled – the pieces of the puzzle form a complete, synchronized picture. Ideally, the supplied solution will then meet the customer's requirements, while the project will satisfy the supplier's needs in respect of profitability and risk management. [3, p. 124; 5, p. 121–123]

1550-6037/11 $26.00 © 2011 IEEE

DOI 10.1109/IV.2011.70

Figure 1.   The Contract Puzzle [3, p. 124; 5, p. 122]

Such contracts are seldom planned or crafted by one person. Rather, they are put together by a team. Research into high-technology firms' contract design capabilities confirms the fact that the input of managers and engineers is needed in key areas, in order to lay the foundation for the deal and construct operationally efficient contracts. [1] Interaction and cross-communication are required, as each stakeholder only has a fragmented understanding of the issues involved [6, p. 6].

Even if the contract is as clear as it can be, major issues can arise from a disconnect between the pre-contract sales or procurement process and post-contract implementation and management. One reason for this is that people are reluctant to read contracts [7, p. 133]. Few managers have formal training in *how* to read contracts or *why* they should do so [7; 8].

Yet many people are *expected* to read contracts and work with them. The buyer's solicitation team and the supplier's proposal team may consist of people different from those on the contract negotiation team, none of whom may be part of the operational or delivery team. The teams may not meet, they may just "inherit" from their predecessors the contract documents that they are expected to master and work with.

Without guidance, delivering on the promises made in such documents is not easy. On the sell-side, the operational team may not only need to implement the supply contract but also pass on to subcontractors the applicable terms (and risks) of that contract. Things get even more complicated when dealing under global umbrella agreements – framework agreements made between group parent companies designed to be implemented at local level in several countries, all with their own jurisdictional, language, and other requirements.

III.   RESEARCH GOALS AND EARLY OBSERVATIONS

The initial theoretical aim of the research in progress is to review existing literature related to designing, organizing and communicating complex business and legal information, with an emphasis on potential solutions offered by visualization. Through the literature review and by exploring and prototyping approaches towards visualizing contracting processes and documents, the goal is to provide conceptual clarity to the subject. Working together with corporate case owners, the information designer and contract lawyer of the core research team will use the findings to determine the framework for empirical case study research that will follow. In addition to the expected theoretical contributions, the goal

of the research is to strengthen participating companies' contracting capabilities and to enhance their ease of doing business.

The first months into this research have shown some major challenges: on the business side, the way contracts are perceived and often ignored, and on the lawyers' side, unease in working with other than text or "tested language" (often meaning language tested in court).

The early results of our literature review confirm the preliminary findings from our interviews with participating companies: visualizations have an impact on attitude and behavior, and they can be used in business to leverage both the *emotional* response of the readers and to enhance their *cognitive* abilities to understand the content [9; 10, p. 2].

Contracts seek to regulate future conduct. To work as intended, as privately-made rules, contracts need to be read, understood, and followed. Our early experiments and preliminary discussions with participating companies suggest that the use of images can lead to better access to and understandability of the rules, making complex information easier to find, more interesting, and easier to work with. The early examples discussed in the following Sections suggest that visualizations have the potential to bring clarity and beyond: when the chosen visualizations are right for the context and audience, they can also lead to better rules and better rulemaking, both in commercial contracting and in public lawmaking.

To gain wider acceptance among business and legal professionals, more examples are needed, from both publicly-made rules (administrative and legal codes) and privately-made rules (commercial contracts). Research is required into what kinds of visualizations are most helpful for different audiences, contexts and goals; what tools are available to convert text into images; and what principles should guide the selection of the tools and visualizations.

IV.   CLARITY THROUGH VISUALIZATION: EXAMPLE

Clarity in communication requires clarity of thought. To achieve desired results, the results should be clear. If they are not clear, how can they be shared, articulated in a contract, or achieved? The path to *results* begins from clarity of thought and expression and, then, ideally, flows as follows [11]:

Clarity → Understanding → Fast decisions → Action → Results

The following example illustrates lack of clarity and how visualization could have helped to prevent it. This is a real-life case where the text of a single clause in a contract cost the parties a bitter 18 months' dispute, with more than a Million Canadian Dollars at stake [12; 13]:

In 2002, Rogers entered into a contract with Aliant, in which Aliant gave Rogers access to around 91,000 poles that carried its cables to homes across Canada. In order to raise the rates in 2005, Aliant gave Rogers one year's notice to terminate the contract. Rogers objected, stating that the contract could not be terminated before it had been in force for five years. The misunderstanding revolved around a single clause:

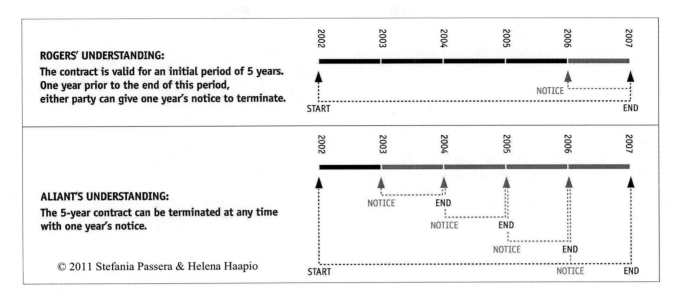

Figure 2. Different understandings of a contract clause. Visualizations courtesy of Stefania Passera, Aalto University [13].

"This agreement shall be effective from the date it is made and shall continue in force for a period of five (5) years from the date it is made, and thereafter for successive five (5) year terms, unless and until terminated by one year prior notice in writing by either party."

As regards the initial term of the contract, Rogers thought that it had a five-year deal. Aliant was of the view that even within this initial term, the contract could be terminated at any time with one year's notice. The validity of the contract and the money at stake all came down to one point: the final comma. In 2006, the Canadian authority CRTC (Canadian Radio-television and Telecommunications Commission) sided with Aliant: "Based on the rules of punctuation," the comma in question "allows for the termination of the contract at any time, without cause, upon one-year's written notice." [14]

However, the dispute did not end there. In response to Rogers' appeal, the CRTC later reviewed the French-language version of the contract, which provided a different solution. In 2007, the CRTC sided with Rogers: the contract ran for the full five-year initial term, until May 2007, and could not be terminated. [13; 15]

If during the pre-contract phase, the parties would have used visualization to share and double-check their view on the duration of the deal, this could have resulted in mutual clarification. Simple timelines, as in Fig. 2, could have shown the parties' different understandings and made abstract terms visible and easier to compare. Using visualization during their negotiations, the parties would have had a chance to work out a mutually acceptable solution and, when drafting the deal documents, they could have included the selected picture so as to avoid ambiguity in future interpretation. [13]

In this case, a simple timeline could have prevented the dispute and saved the parties from spending management time and legal fees on solving it. In the words of Louis M. Brown, known as the Father of Preventive Law: "It usually costs less to avoid getting into trouble than to pay for getting out of trouble" [16, p. 3].

V. VISUALIZING LEGAL INFORMATION

In Central Europe, *visualizing legal information* has developed into a research field in its own right. In the German-speaking countries, the terms *legal visualization* (Rechtsvisualisierung), *visual legal communication* (Visuelle Rechtskommunikation), *visual law* (Visuelles Recht) and *multisensory law* (Multisensorisches Recht) have been used to describe this field of growing research and practice. [17; 18] So far, while some aspects of contract law (publicly-made rules and court cases) have attracted this field's researchers' attention, commercial contracts (privately-made rules) do not seem to have done so. One of the reasons may be the latter's focus on business aspects (such as scope, deliverables, schedule, and pricing) rather than legal aspects.

In the United States, the use of visualizations has been studied, for instance, in the context of improving the comprehension of jury instructions [19; 20] and facilitating the making of complex decisions related to dispute resolution [21, p. 154–161; 22]. Visualization has also been noted to play a role as a persuasion tool in various settings, from the court room [23; 24] to the board room.

In Canada, recognizing the need for new ways to inspire public access to the law, the Government commissioned a White Paper in 2000 proposing a new format for legislation. The White Paper [25] by David Berman, a communication designer, also introduced the concept of using diagrams to help describe laws, stating that this concept is "revolutionary, and likely the most innovative information design feature in the new design" [25, p. 23]. Among the people who would find diagrams useful the author mentions individuals needing to know if the general provisions of a piece of legislation apply to them and senior government officials who need to gain a quick appreciation of a particular piece of legislation. In the process of creating a flow chart diagram Berman's team also discovered inconsistencies that were not accounted for in the legislation, suggesting that if rendering laws into diagrams was part of the process of drafting, the resulting legislation would in some instances be substantively improved. [25, p. 24]

Another example of visualizing the law is the work of the Street Vendor Project carried out by Candy Chang, a designer, urban planner and artist, in collaboration with the Center for Urban Pedagogy in New York. Having noted that the "rulebook [of legal code] is intimidating and hard to understand by anyone, let alone someone whose first language isn't English", they prepared a visual Street Vendor Guide called "Vendor Power!" that makes city regulations and rights accessible and understandable. The Guide features diagrams of vendors' rights and the most commonly violated rules along with some text. [26] Fig. 3 ("Before") and Fig. 4 ("After") illustrate the difference between text and visual guidance.

In the Wolfram Demonstration Project, the use of visualizations has been explored in the area of legal rules applicable in a Battle of the Forms situation. Such a Battle arises in the not uncommon situation in which one company makes an offer or bid using a pre-printed form which contains its standard terms, and the other party responds with

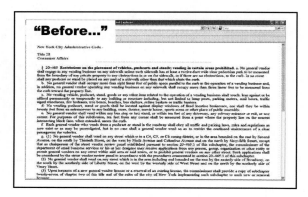

Figure 3.   Typical page from New York City Administrative Code [27]

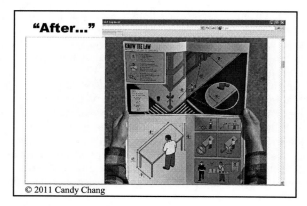

Figure 4.   Street Vendor Guide. Accessible City Regulations.
Visualization courtesy of Candy Chang [26]

its own form and standard terms. Both parties then hope that a contract will be based on *their* terms rather than those of the other party. The applicable law may lead to a negative surprise to one party or both, including the possibility of no contract being formed. The visual demonstration contributed by Seth J. Chandler illustrates Article 2 of the Uniform Commercial Code that governs domestic sales of goods in the United States. The user can choose various details, and the output shows the most likely judicial finding as to whether a contract exists and the terms of that contract, along with a graph that explains the argument that will be advanced in support of the judicial finding. [28]

VI.   VISUALIZING CONTRACTS: EARLY EXPERIMENTS

Unlike visualizing legal information, visualizing contracts (or the *visual communication of contracts*) remains an almost unexplored research area. Research related to legal risks in the context of contracts offers an exception: In a recent case study, a group of lawyers, managers, and engineers were asked to analyze the risks related to a contract proposal using a method based on graphical language and diagrams. The case study showed that graphical language was helpful in communicating risk amongst the case study participants. However, the need for simplicity and usability also led to some limitations and the need for a combination of graphical and natural language for improved decision-making. [29, p. 237–262]

Knowledge visualization in the context of risk management in itself is not new. It has been researched, for instance, at the University of St Gallen Institute for Media Communications and Management. Their research findings related to risk communication and communication of knowledge between experts and decision makers [30] are likely to prove highly relevant for our continued research, where ways to enhance communication between managers and their legal advisors and managerial-legal decision making are focus areas.

A noteworthy example of using visuals to guide the use and interpretation of complex contracts comes from the UK: the NEC family of contracts. This family consists of several contracts designed for procuring a diverse range of works, services and supply and their associated guidance notes and flow charts. The latter two are not part of the contract documents but assist in their understanding. Originally launched in 1993, and then known as the "New Engineering Contract", the NEC has been praised for its collaborative and integrated working approach to procurement. It has been said that the implementation of NEC3 contracts has resulted in major benefits for projects both nationally and internationally in terms of time, cost savings and improved quality. [31; 32]

The findings of legal and business practitioners, too, show that flowcharts and other non-textual tools can add value and improve productivity and efficiency in the corporate contracting process [33; 34; 35]. Published examples include the Outsourcing Contract Dashboard developed by DLA Piper's UK Office: a web-based contract assessment and reporting tool designed to help provide a simple, visual answer to the question "how good is this contract?" [36].

When teaching cross-border contract law to business managers and students, the Author has experimented with visualizations and visual metaphors, with the aim of curing *contract phobia,* changing attitudes, and making contracts' *invisible terms* visible [37; 38; 39; 22]. Here, the concept *invisible terms* is used to refer to terms (such as implied terms, implied warranties, and statutory default rules) that do not appear in the contract but become part of it, unless they are expressly excluded or amended. A lawyer familiar with the context knows and "sees" the *invisible terms,* while a non-lawyer does not. [37; 38; 22] Many legal problems could probably be prevented, if visualizations would show the presence and impact of such terms. Especially in international dealings, problems are often encountered not because of what the contract *says,* but because of what it *does not say.* Such gaps can be risky, especially for a supplier who wants to balance risk with reward and avoid excessive, unlimited liability exposure. [38, p. 32–33]

Not all tools need to be sophisticated. Let us use task allocation as an example: an important area that needs to be captured and articulated in a contract. The Author's simple "hand tool" (Fig. 5) lists the trivial-sounding but crucial questions that must be answered when creating or reviewing contractual rights, responsibilities, and remedies: who/which party shall do – what – where – when – how – and, last but not least, what if/what if not. Often it is also worthwhile to ask who bears the risk and cost of doing things.

Like the contract puzzle (Fig. 1), the "hand tool" illustrates that risk and contingencies are not what contracts are made for; contracts are made to help get things done and establish a framework for success. While it is important to have safeguards and minimize the negative consequences of failure, a contract can not and should not be developed in isolation from the overall scope, business deal, and relationship. Success requires managerial-legal collaboration and communication. Future research will show how visualization can help in this endeavor.

The "hand tool" (Fig. 5) lacks professional polish. It confirms the fact that lawyers (like the Author) need partners, tools, and guidance in order to create visualizations. With few exceptions, lawyers are typically accustomed to conveying their thoughts and ideas using words only. [5, p. 146] If our research in progress reaches its goals, this may start to change. The early findings from our experiments suggest that many benefits can follow, both for the legal profession and for its clients.

Figure 5.   Hand Tool for Better Contracts [3, p. 135; 5, p. 114]

VII.   CONCLUSION

Contrary to common belief, *contracts* are not taught at law school; *contract law* is. Contracts do not equal contract law. Contract-related issues do not end at the boundaries between academic disciplines or industrial professions. This is even more true in the context of communicating contractual information.

What works for judges or other lawyers may not work for business and project managers, or vice versa. The goal of this paper is to present and test *contract visualization* as an emerging topic for research and practice and to initiate discussion with scholars in related fields to explore and develop the topic further. In addition to management, legal, and information design scholars, cognitive psychologists and communication experts will be needed to assure that the visual representations of contractual information provide optimal communication and decision support for the different users and messages. User studies will also be needed in order to recognize the opportunities and challenges and to establish good practices. Before this can happen, many researchers', business managers', and lawyers' attitudes towards contracts need to be changed. Visualization seems to offer tools for this purpose also.

In contract visualization, questions are likely to arise that have not been asked before. Our research in progress is a first step towards asking those questions and providing some early answers. This paper invites new questions, suggestions and insights from the field of knowledge visualization.

REFERENCES

[1]   N. Argyres and K. J. Mayer, "Contract Design as a Firm Capability: An Integration of Learning and Transaction Cost Perspectives," Academy of Management Review, vol. 32, issue 4, 2007, pp. 1060–1077.

[2]   G. J. Siedel and H. Haapio, "Using Proactive Law for Competitive Advantage," American Business Law Journal, vol. 47, issue 4, Winter 2010, pp. 641–686. Available as a Working Paper at http://ssrn.com/abstract=1664561, 4.5.2011.

[3]   H. Haapio, "Innovative Contracting," in A Proactive Approach to Contracting and Law, H. Haapio, Ed., Turku: International Association for Contract and Commercial Management & Turku University of Applied Sciences, 2008, pp. 105–152.

[4]   A. Schwartz and R. E. Scott, "Contract Interpretation Redux," Yale Law Journal, vol. 119, issue 5, March 2010, pp. 926–965, http://ssrn.com/abstract=1504223, 4.5.2011.

[5]   G. Siedel and H. Haapio, Proactive Law for Managers: A Hidden Source of Competitive Advantage. Farnham: Gower Publishing, 2011.

[6]   M. J. Eppler, "Knowledge communication problems between experts and managers. An analysis of knowledge transfer in decision processes." Paper 1/2004, May 2004, University of Lugano, Faculty of Communication Sciences, Institute for Corporate Communication, unpublished, http://doc.rero.ch/lm.php?url=1000,42,6,20051020101 029-UL/1_wpca0401.pdf, 4.5.2011.

[7]   S. J. Burnham, "How to Read a Contract," Arizona Law Review, vol. 45, no. 1, 2003, pp. 133–172.

[8]   G. Berger-Walliser and H. Haapio, "Promoting Business Success through Proactive Contracting and Visualization," Acad. Legal Stud. In Bus. Nat'l Proc., vol. 41, 2010, http://alsb.roundtablelive.org/Resources/Documents/NP%202010%20 Berger-Walliser_Haapio.pdf, 4.5.2011.

[9] J. H. Larkin and H. A. Simon, "Why a Diagram is (Sometimes) Worth Ten Thousand Words," Cognitive Science, vol. 11, 1987, pp. 65–99.

[10] S. Bresciani, M. Tan and M. J. Eppler, "Augmenting communication with visualization: Effects on emotional and cognitive response." Paper for IADIS ICT, Society and Human Beings 2011 (ICT 2011) Conference, 20.–26.7.2011, Rome, Italy, unpublished.

[11] M. Eppler, "Why care about Clarity? Because it leads to results" in his presentation How to be CLEAR in Complex Corporate Communication at Aalto University Business School on 24 January 2011, citing Xplane, Inc.

[12] I. Austen, "The Comma That Costs 1 Million Dollars," New York Times, 25 October 2006, http://www.nytimes.com/2006/10/25/business/worldbusiness/25comma.html?_r=1, 4.5.2011.

[13] S. Passera and H. Haapio, "Facilitating Collaboration through Contract Visualization and Modularization." Paper for the European Conference on Cognitive Ergonomics ECCE 2011, 24.–26.8.2011, Rostock, Germany, unpublished.

[14] Costly Drafting Errors, Part 1—Rogers Communications and Aliant. AdamsDrafting, 7 August 2006, http://www.adamsdrafting.com/2006/08/07/costly-drafting-errors-part-1/, 4.5.2011

[15] Rogers Victory in the Comma Case, AdamsDrafting, 20 August 2007, http://www.adamsdrafting.com/2007/08/20/rogers-victory-in-the-comma-case/, 4.5.2011

[16] L. M. Brown, Preventive Law. New York, NY: Prentice-Hall, Inc., 1950.

[17] C. R. Brunschwig, Visualisierung von Rechtsnormen – Legal Design [Visualization of Legal Norms]. Doctoral Thesis. Zürcher Studien zur Rechtsgeschichte, vol. 45. Rechtswissenschaftliche Fakultät d. Universität Zürich. Zürich: Schulthess Juristische Medien, 2001.

[18] C. R. Brunschwig, "Multisensory Law and Legal Informatics – A Comparison of How these Legal Disciplines Relate to Visual Law," Jusletter IT, 22 February 2011, http://jusletter-it.weblaw.ch/_104?lang=de, 4.5.2011.

[19] C. Semmler and N. Brewer, "Using a Flow-Chart to Improve Comprehension of Jury Instructions," Psychiatry, Psychology and Law, vol. 9, no. 2, 2002, pp. 262–270.

[20] F. Dattu, "Illustrated Jury Instructions: A Proposal," Law & Psychology Review, vol. 22, 1998, pp. 67–102.

[21] G. J. Siedel, "Interdisciplinary Approaches to Alternative Dispute Resolution," The Journal of Legal Studies Education, vol. 10, Summer/Fall 1992, pp. 141–169.

[22] G. Berger-Walliser, Gerlinde, R. C. Bird, and H. Haapio, "Promoting Business Success through Contract Visualisation," The Journal of Law, Business & Ethics, vol. 17, Winter 2011, pp. 55–75. Available as a Working Paper at http://ssrn.com/abstract=1744096, 4.5.2011.

[23] N. Feigenson and C. Spiesel, Law on Display. The Digital Transformation of Legal Persuasion and Judgment. New York, NY: New York University Press, 2009.

[24] S. H. Solomon, "Visuals and Visualisation: Penetrating the Heart and Soul of Persuasion." DOAR Litigation Consulting, October 2006, http://tillers.net/solomon.pdf, 4.5.2011.

[25] D. Berman, "Toward a new format for Canadian legislation – Using graphic design principles and methods to improve public access to the law." Human Resources Development Canada and Justice Canada Project Paper, 30 November 2000, http://www.davidberman.com/NewFormatForCanadianLegislation.pdf, 4.5.2011.

[26] Candy Chang, Street Vendor Guide. Accessible city regulations, http://candychang.com/street-vendor-guide, 4.5.2011.

[27] New York City Administrative Code § 20–465 Restrictions on the placement of vehicles, pushcarts and stands; vending in certain areas prohibited, http://24.97.137.100/nyc/AdCode/Title20_20-465.asp, 4.5.2011.

[28] Visualizing Legal Rules: Battle of the Forms. The Wolfram Demonstrations Project, http://demonstrations.wolfram.com/VisualizingLegalRulesBattleOfTheForms, 4.5.2011.

[29] T. Mahler, Legal Risk Management – Developing and Evaluating Elements of a Method for Proactive Legal Analyses, With a Particular Focus on Contracts. Doctoral Thesis. Oslo: Faculty of Law, University of Oslo 2010.

[30] USI HSG Knowledge Communication – Publications, http://www.knowledge-communication.org/publications.html, 4.5.2011.

[31] What is the NEC? Achieving excellence in the procurement of Works, Services and Supply. Promoting best practice procurement, http://www.neccontract.com/documents/WhatistheNEC.pdf, 4.5.2011.

[32] NEC Products, http://www.neccontract.com/products/index.asp, 4.5.2011.

[33] H. W. Jones and M. Oswald, "Doing deals with flowcharts," ACCA Docket, vol. 19, no. 9, October 2001, pp. 94–108.

[34] H. W. Jones III, "Envisioning visual contracting: why non-textual tools will improve your contracting," Contracting Excellence, August/September 2009, pp. 27–31, http://www.iaccm.com/userfiles/file/CE_2_6_press_new.pdf, 4.5.2011.

[35] K. Rekola and H. Haapio, "Better business through proactive productization and visualization of contracts," Contracting Excellence, June/July 2009, pp. 17–19, http://www.iaccm.com/userfiles/file/CE_2_5_press_C2(1).pdf, 4.5.2011.

[36] Outsourcing Contract Dashboard, DLA Piper, http://www.dlapiper.com/uk/content/onlineservices/outsourcing_contract_dashboard, 4.5.2011.

[37] H. Haapio, "Invisible Terms in International Contracts and What to Do about Them," Contract Management, July 2004, pp. 32–35. National Contract Management Association NCMA, http://www.ncmahq.org/files/Articles/81EEB_cm_July04_32.pdf, 4.5.2011.

[38] H. Haapio, "Invisible Terms & Creative Silence: What You Don't See Can Help or Hurt You," Contract Management, September 2009, pp. 24–35. National Contract Management Association NCMA, http://www.ncmahq.org/files/Articles/CM0909%20-%2024-35.pdf, 4.5.2011.

[39] Visualization, Lexpert Ltd, http://www.lexpert.com/en/visualisation/index.htm, 4.5.2011.

Listening to Managers:
a Study about Visualizations in Corporate Presentations

Wibke Weber, Ralph Tille
Stuttgart Media University
{weber@hdm-stuttgart.de, tille@hdm-stuttgart}

Abstract

This paper presents a study about the use of visualizations in corporate presentations. We interviewed nine executive managers of a leading technology company about how they create business presentations for different meetings and different audiences. Thereby, we focused on which visualization types they normally use and whether they would accept new forms of visualizations such as information graphics, which are currently very popular. Due to the explorative character of the study, we used the grounded theory approach.

Results show that design principles or effective visualizations are not known to the most interviewees. The interviewees rated corporate design, use of master layout, and templates higher than individually designed slides. The most popular visualization types managers use in presentations are bar and pie charts. The term "information graphic" was not known. Our conclusion leads to the following hypothesis: If a company wants to change or improve its communication, it will have to become aware of the power of visual storytelling and start an "iconic turn".

Keywords: **corporate presentation, business visualization, information graphic, design process, corporate design, visual language, visual storytelling**

1. Introduction

Starting point for our research was a question of a senior manager who wanted to know why all the presentations in the company are so sterile, unemotional, not appealing, overloaded with information, and therefore difficult to understand (especially the presentations with technical topics). He asked whether the new visual form of information graphics he had seen in many newspapers might be an adequate visualization tool for presentations. Indeed, information graphics become more and more popular. Whether printed in newspapers, interactive on news sites, or animated on TV – information graphics are increasingly used to

explain complex information clearly and in an intelligible manner. They have the potential to summarize amounts of data comprehensible, point out causal relationships, and engage the readers by telling an appealing story.

In media science the term "information graphic" is defined differently. In our previous study [1] we define information graphic (1) as a visual representation of information or knowledge. Each graphic intends to tell a story with one topic. The value of an information graphic is to display complex information, which is difficult to be told verbally, in a visual way. (2) An information graphic is a hybrid presentation of different modalities: Verbal elements (texts, audios, typography) and visual elements (photos, illustrations, diagrams, maps, symbols, icons, pictograms, videos, moving images) are combined. A line chart or a scatter plot can be a significant part of an information graphic, but does not represent an information graphic by itself. (3) Interactivity, hypertextuality, and multimedia are main characteristics of an interactive or animated information graphic. [cf. 1, p. 361] In the words of the information graphic designer Alberto Cairo, "An information graphic is an aid to thinking and understanding." [2] An example what we mean by information graphic is shown in Figure 1: an online information graphic published by the New York Times with video, verbal explanations and an exploded diagram about the oil rig Deepwater Horizon and how the rig crew responded to the blowout [3].

What in journalism has proved to be successful might also be an option for communication purposes in companies and organizations. Conveying sales figures, showing how a new technology works, communicating a new marketing strategy, convincing stakeholders to fund a research project – these are relevant business issues managers have to communicate. Would an information graphic be an appropriate visualization type in a presentation instead of the common charts in a PowerPoint slideshow? There is no question: The ubiquitous tool in organizations *is* PowerPoint and its templates for visualizations, e.g. pie, bar, line, area charts, – ready-made, easy to use, and therefore well

1550-6037/11 $26.00 © 2011 IEEE
DOI 10.1109/IV.2011.28

accepted as a standard for presentations [4]. On the one hand, the vividness of an information graphic might attract more interest than standardized PowerPoint slides and enhance better understanding of the presented facts; on the other hand, employing information graphics in a business presentation might be understood as a breach of the corporate communication standards in a company.

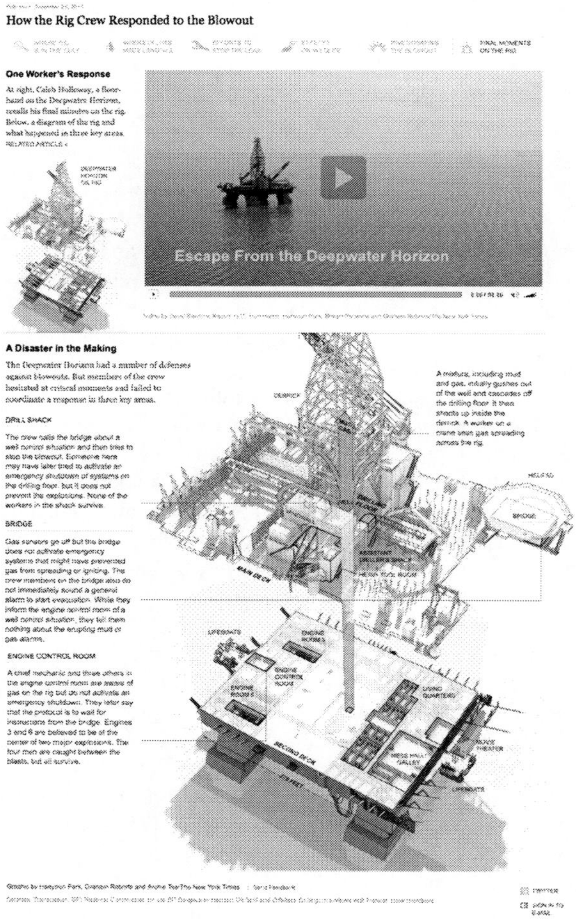

Figure 1: The information graphic shows the final moments of the Deepwater Horizon oil rig and explains the disaster in the making

Starting from these considerations we wanted to find out: Do managers and marketing consultants know at all what information graphics are and what they are useful for? What do they know about visualizations in general? How do they employ visualizations in a presentation? And would they be open for the new visualization type information graphic? In order to investigate these questions, we interviewed executive managers of a leading technology company in Germany about the creation process of their presentations.

In the following chapters we first link our study to related work and former research, then we describe the methodology and finally present the results followed by a conclusion with discussion and possible future steps.

2. Related Work

Information graphics as defined above are particularly employed in newspapers and news sites, manuals, scientific literature, public relations, and in the field of education (e.g. school books, museums). However, information graphics in business presentations represent a rather new form of visualizations.

For printed information graphics, we find an extensive body of literature: from books that provide outstanding examples and rules for designing information graphics [5, 6, 7, 8] through to perception and knowledge acquisition with information graphics [9]. Especially Tufte provides good examples for the connection between visual thinking and decision-making [10]. For interactive information graphics – a relatively new form of visual storytelling – the research is at its very beginning [1].

An immense body of literature deals also with the use of PowerPoint and how to perform a first-class presentation, but only a few studies and publications focus on visual thinking in the business world or on visualizations in PowerPoint presentations or on presentations generally [4, 11, 12, 13]. Lengler and Eppler [14] selected 100 visualization methods via five criteria; the result shows a periodic table of visualization methods, which gives an overview of how to choose the appropriate method. Bertschi [15] described the importance of visual metaphors in the field of knowledge visualization. Burkhard [16] developed a decision framework model with three categories to arrange the various problems in visualizing business issues. Bresciani and Eppler [17] have started to study the use of qualitative information visualization in the business world; they provide a first overview of how familiar managers are with different visualization types.

3. Methodology

Following up the research of Bresciani and Eppler we wanted to investigate, which visual representations managers currently use in corporate presentations, for which target groups and for which purposes, and what the design process of a corporate presentation looks like. In addition, we wanted to gain insights about the corporate culture, the corporate design and whether there are constraints on the part of the company regarding visualization types, layout and visual templates. Due to the explorative character of our study, we chose a qualitative research approach: the grounded theory [19]. In contrast to traditional scientific research the grounded theory method does not start with a hypothesis, but ends with a hypothesis developed from the collected data.

Strauss and Corbin describe the grounded theory as a qualitative research method "that uses a systematic set of procedures to develop an inductively derived grounded theory about a phenomenon". [19, p. 24] Important steps of grounded theory comprise:

- *Data collection* directed by *theoretical samplings*, which means: not representative sampling, but „sampling on the basis of concepts that have proven theoretical relevance to the evolving theory". [19, p. 176] Sampling stops only when theoretical saturation is achieved.
- *Data coding* (open, axial, selective coding)
- *Memo writing* (written records and notes of the researchers' thinking about data)
- *Conceptualizing* and *categorizing* (grouping the data into concepts and the concepts into categories) with the aim of:
- *Theory building*

For the data collection process we conducted so-called expert interviews in a leading technology company in Germany, which has more than 250.000 employees and is a global supplier for automotive and industrial technology. We interviewed nine experts chosen by the company: top managers (development managers, heads of department, sales managers, marketing managers) who regularly have to prepare presentations for strategy meetings, board meetings, and customer presentations. The interviews were based on an interview guide specially developed for the research questions of our study. We focused on four main aspects in terms of company presentations: (1) content and target groups, (2) design process, (3) corporate culture and corporate design, (4) employment of visualizations and acceptance of new visualization types such as information graphics. The questions were asked open-ended, that means, the interviewees could not answer with a simple "yes" or "no". Each interview took about one hour and was recorded as audio file. Afterwards the interviews were transcribed, anonymized, and qualitatively evaluated with the grounded theory method. We analyzed the data during the whole research process by constantly comparing one interview to another, identifying concepts on different levels of abstraction and integrating the concepts into categories (Figure 2).

Nr.	Interview	Frage	Textsegment	Stelle	Kommentar	Thema	Kategorie
1	ND 3	WU 2	Weil dann doch gerade in Sachen Templates, die so weltweit jetzt Anwendung finden, man doch merkt, dass da in den vergangenen Jahren viel passiert ist und das es einfach jetzt weltweit einheitliche Standards dann gibt, die jetzt auch schon in den Regionen verwendet werden, zumindest zum Teil	00:00:13	In den letzten Jahren wurden Templates und Standards entwickelt, die weltweit Anwendung finden sollen. Diese haben sich aber noch nicht in allen Regionen durchgesetzt. [Anmerkung: Zu den formalen Vorgaben gehört z.B. auch die Festgebung.]	Internationale/ Einsatz von Templates und formalen Vorgaben	Templates Formale Vorgaben
2	ND 3	WU 2	Das erleichtert eben einfach auch die, man kann sich eben, wenn man das Standard verwendet, dann kann man sich eben als Außenstehender deutlich schneller mit den Inhalten vertraut machen; weil man nicht anfangt überhaupt die Art des ersten mal zu sehen und dann erst mal anfangen muss zu lesen, „was steht den da alles drauf?", sondern man blickt da drauf und sagt, „ah ja, ok, hab ich verstanden".	00:00:13	Der Einsatz internationaler Standards und Templates erleichtert es Kollegen anderer Standorte sich schnell mit Inhalten vertraut zu machen, da diese auf bereits bekannte Art und Weise aufbereitet bzw. dargestellt sind.	Vorteile Internationaler Standards	Templates Standards
3	ND 3	WU 2	Einfach die Lesbarkeit, die schnellere Lesbarkeit. Das ist eigentlich für mich so der hauptsächliche Vorteil, dass ich also nicht ewig brauche bei ich das verstanden habe was da auf dem Chart steht sondern dass ich mit einem Blick eigentlich recht gut erkennen kann was es ist und dann sage ich mal, die Kerninhalte mit auch besser abspeichern kann, ich kann mich mehr darauf konzentrieren was der Inhalt ist als darum was wird da überhaupt dargestellt.	00:01:56	Im Vergleich zu älteren Templates hat sich vor allem die Lesbarkeit und damit auch die Verständlichkeit der Präsentationsfolien verbessert. Kernhalte können heute schneller erfasst und behalten werden. So bleibt mehr Zeit um sich mit den eigentlich wichtigen Inhalten zu beschäftigen. [Anmerkung: Die Verbesserungen beziehen sich speziell auf Diagramme, aber auch auf die Textgestaltung.]	Verbesserungen gegenüber älteren Templates Vorteile dieser Verbesserungen	Templates
4	ND 3	WU 2	Das eine waren so Kuchendiagramme wo es um Marktanteile ging. Das war von der Farbgebung her sehr angenehm, von der Schriftgröße her auch und das ist einfach gut hängen geblieben.	00:02:37	Besonders positiv sind Kuchendiagramme in Erinnerung geblieben, bei denen z.B. Farbgebung und Schriftgröße verbessert wurden.	Verbesserungen gegenüber älteren Templates	Templates

Figure 2: Data coding of the interviews according to the grounded theory method

The following concepts have been developed from the data: context and conditions of creating a presentation, content and preparation, design process, effort required for a presentation with visualizations, types of visualizations, tools and work techniques, corporate design and templates, corporate culture and corporate identity, expectations of the different target groups, consequences and suggestions by the managers. The concepts were grouped into five more general and abstract categories:

1. Conditions of creating presentations

2. Target groups

3. Design process

4. Corporate identity

5. Visualizations

These categories and their relationship with each other form the basis to develop a hypothesis about managers' visual literacy and the visual language in a company.

4. Results

The five categories as described and sketched above display the results of the study: They summarize what managers know about visualizations and how they deal with them in presentations.

4.1 Conditions for Creating Presentations

Creating presentations belongs to the main tasks of the interviewed persons. They often have to present for different target groups, in different settings, at different levels. All interviewees emphasize that they attach great importance to presentations, particularly for crucial meetings such as strategy meetings. For these crucial meetings they calculate enough time and invest a lot of diligence in the preparation of their PowerPoint slideshow starting several months before up to six months. One manager said, "The higher a meeting is ranked the more time the preparation takes. Sometimes, the slides are fine-tuned and refined again and again."

Even though managers often start their presentations with a sketch on paper, all interviewees agreed that PowerPoint is the undisputed tool for running a presentation. Furthermore, the corporate communication department has created over 250 templates for presentations and visualizations to ensure the corporate design of the company. A problem mentioned in the interviews is the time management – not to prepare a presentation, but to present a compelling story in a few slides. Often the managers underestimate how much time their presentations will take, and after a long introduction they have to run through the slides and miss the main point of the story.

4.2 Target Groups

The target groups differ in internal and external target groups. Every target group determines the content, the objectives, and the style of a presentation. Whereas in external customer presentations the managers want to show a high performance and competence and endeavor to convey their message emotionally und attractively as much as possible, the internal presentations require a rational and unemotional style. The heterogeneity of the target groups makes it so difficult for managers to use the same templates and the same visualizations in different settings and to engage the audience by presenting the suitable topics and facts. Custom-tailored or standardized slides? This question remains unsolved for the interviewees.

4.3 Design Process

Design principles or rules for making good design or effective visualizations are not known to the most interviewees. They decide on the basis of a gut feeling: "looks good or I don't like it". Admittedly, the company offers trainings for effective business presentations, but those trainings do not address visualizations or how to convey ideas with pictures.

One important factor for the design process is efficiency. The interviewed persons told that as often as possible they reuse and adjust their "old" slides to accelerate the design process. They consider this strategy as efficient. The disadvantage of the strategy is that they use only those visual representations they are familiar with (e.g. pie, bar, line charts). Consequently they run the risk that all their PowerPoint presentations look similar and boring.

Another crucial factor that has much impact on the design process are the many templates predefined by the company and the master layout with the corporate design elements. Design guidelines, master layout and templates were assessed differently. On one side, the interviewees appreciate a standardized design of the slides, because in a global acting company a uniform design fosters the corporate identity; in addition, one interviewee mentioned that the templates support her in creating slides. On the other side, the managers feel overwhelmed by so many templates. They do not have the time to check over 250 templates for selecting an adequate visualization type, nor do they know every visualization type and its usefulness. In the managers' opinion, templates and the "overproduced" master layout cost a lot of time, because they have to adjust pictures and diagrams, correct typography to get the same font on every slide, they have to choose the right colors and to align headlines and subheadings (in case of copy and paste to transfer text or data from an old slide to a new one). An interviewee stated, "With all these adjustments I waste a lot of time." That is why most interviewees deem templates and master layout less efficient. Moreover, the interviewees regard the templates as a strict limitation in terms of presentations, because (1) especially external target groups (e.g. customers) demand for a custom-tailored slide show, (2) the employees do not feel encouraged by the company to visualize or present in other ways or to try something new.

4.4 Corporate Identity

Most interviewees believe that the heads of department and the board of directors expect presentations according to the corporate guidelines. That means: avoid emotions, present in an objective style, fact-orientated, try to communicate concisely in only a few slides. It seems that for the managers it is more important to give a short presentation than to look what the data or the content requires. That implicates that the managers overload a minimum of slides with a maximum of text, figures, and facts. In the interviews we also received the impression that the managers value the corporate design (CD), the use of master layout and the templates (given by the company) higher than individually designed slides. A manager said, "Slides that are too much elaborated could be regarded as negative."

4.5 Visualizations

The most popular visualization types the interviewed managers use in presentations are bar and column charts, and for marketing purposes pie charts. In addition, the managers also employ maps (to depict the sites of the company), tables, roadmaps, and technical drawings. "We use the things we are familiar with and we can master" – this statement was confirmed in all interviews. The managers do not know very well the usefulness of the different visual forms. A manager admitted, "Sometimes we use trial and error to find out what visual form fits best." The interviewees are not aware either of the strength and weakness of the visual presentations or the wide range of visualization types.

Surprisingly, the interviewees express that they would like to use more photos, illustrations, animations, and videos, particularly for sales presentations. However, for these visualization types the company offers no templates, image database or digital asset management, what would be appreciated by the interviewees. As a consequence the presenters would have to search for photos or produce videos and animations by themselves, and this would cost a lot of time they do not have.

When we asked about information graphics the interviewed persons did not know what we mean by this; the term was unknown. It was only when we showed examples of information graphics that they recognized this visualization type they have already seen in newspapers. However, information graphics would be a new visual form, the employment of information graphics in a presentation was deemed positive due to the power of an information graphic: to explain complex things in a simple and compelling way. In contrast, the acceptance for information graphics in presentation was evaluated differently: from "too cheerful, not factual enough" through to "why not". The interviewees view information graphics as an appropriate visual form for marketing or customer presentations; however, in internal business meetings they would not risk to use this visual form. Since the company itself does not have the capability to develop information graphics in-house, the effort to produce an information graphic by an external agency would be too high.

In sum, the interviewed persons prefer vivid visualizations to those, which are less abstract, sterile, and unemotional. They would like to shape presentations along attractive stories to improve emotional appeal and the impact of visualizations.

4.6 Hypothesis

"What are the causes of the dreaded Engineering by PowerPoint?" Tufte asks and surmises among other things, "Designer guidelines and bureaucratic norms that insist on PP for all presentations regardless of content?" [4, p. 28]. Our results seem to confirm Tufte's surmise.

The relations between the five categories (1) conditions of creating presentations, (2) target groups, (3) design process, (4) corporate identity, and (5) visualization lead to the following theses: Organizations have an (unwritten) code how a presentation should look like, especially when the target group belongs to the top management of an organization. PowerPoint, master layout built on the corporate design guidelines of the company, and templates for diagrams are the default basis for every presentation – this fact is not questioned by the managers; other visual forms like information graphics, animated graphics, visual metaphors do not seem to play a significant role. Managers, who often have to present, perceive templates, master layout and corporate design more as a corset that constricts visual thinking than a support to create slides and convey the message efficiently. This corresponds to Tufte's statement that the PowerPoint design style "uses only about 40% to 60% of the space available on a slide to show unique content, with all remaining space devoted to Phluff, bullets, frames and branding" [4, p. 15]; the result is that all presentations look similar and boring.

The reason for that might be that the adherence to corporate design and predefined visualization templates is regarded as a more successful strategy in business meetings than to present unconventional and individually designed visualization types such as information graphics.

We assume that in organizations only little awareness of visual storytelling exists; the power of visual representations to convey a message is unknown or even ignored as well as the correct usage of visuals and design principles. Therefore, our *hypothesis* based on the study is: If a company wants to change or improve its presentation culture, it will have to start an "iconic turn". That means: to foster all aspects of visual thinking and to develop a *visual corporate language,* which includes not only a style guide for the corporate design (e.g. logo), but also how to communicate a story or a message visually. A first step towards this "iconic turn" could be a manual with guiding principles for visuals (e.g. charts, graphs, illustrations, photographs, information graphics, animations, videos); in addition an organization should have an interest in improving the visual literacy of the employees, regardless of their profession. A second step might be to discuss and relax the corporate design restrictions. A helpful tool would be a digital asset management, as proposed by the interviewees.

5. Conclusion and Future Work

Whereas in newspapers and on the Web information graphics and visualizations play an important role meanwhile, in the business world the visual communication is at its very beginning. Whereas journalists try to tell a story verbally <u>and</u> visually, organizations still seem to focus on text and corporate design. The "iconic turn" [18] that is taking place in the world of media convergence has not yet arrived in the world of corporate communications, particularly in the internal communication (e.g. business presentations). Managers would highly appreciate to communicate their messages via more attractive visual forms such as information graphics, animated graphics, or videos. But for this, the communication culture of an organization has to change, and the attitude towards visualizations that are unusual in the managerial world, too. Similar to the corporate language, which refers to the verbal communication, a company should develop a *visual corporate language*, that means: to develop guiding principles how to use visuals, namely not only business charts, but also visual representations that might be unusual for the managerial world, e.g. information graphics or animations – with the aim to enrich corporate identity. That is a qualitative conclusion of our study in terms of the company that has been investigated.

A quantitative conclusion cannot be drawn. Since our study had an explorative character, we decided for the grounded theory approach. The grounded theory approach always generates only qualitative data, not quantitative. That is a limitation of our study. Another critical question concerning the grounded theory approach is: When is the theoretical sampling finished? According to Strauss and Corbin "sampling continues until theoretical saturation of categories is achieved" [19, p. 193]; that is the point where new data from further interviews has no more implications for the theory. Even though the number of the interviews in our study might seem very small, we received the impression that the theoretical saturation was achieved by nine interviews. To ensure the point of theoretical saturation we evaluated the interviews independently from each other, reexamined the interview guide and discussed our insights and memos constantly in order to develop concepts, categories and finally formulate the hypothesis.

We consider our hypothesis as a useful step for further research. In order to verify our hypothesis, more studies in different companies, different branches, and different countries (cultures) should be carried out. This could also be done in the form of quantitative studies with questionnaires. Additionally, we would like to interview the external and internal target groups, especially the different departments and different levels of corporate hierarchy (e.g. board of directors), how they perceive visualizations in corporate presentations. A further step would be to analyze the visual language in corporate publishing (e.g. custom media, employee magazines) to find out whether the trend of information graphics has already reached the world of corporate communication – whether in printed form, animated, or as an interactive visualization.

6. References

[1]   M. Burmester, M. Mast, R. Tille, W. Weber. How Users Perceive and Use Interactive Information Graphics: an Exploratory Study. In: IEEE Proceedings of the 14th International Conference Information Visualization (IV 10). London 2010. 361-368.

[2]   N. Paul, L. Ruel. Animated infographics and online storytelling: Words form the wise. (An interview with Alberto Cairo, May 23, 2007). http://www.ojr.org/ojr/stories/070523ruel/ (retrieved Feb 25, 2011).

[3]   How the Rig Crew Responded to the Blowout. http://www.nytimes.com/interactive/2010/12/26/us/2010122 6-deepwater-horizon-rig-video-diagram.html?ref= multimedia, retrieved Feb 19, 2011). Interactive Feature.

[4]   E. R. Tufte. The Cognitive Style of Power Point. Cheshire, CT, Graphics Press. 2003.

[5]   E. R. Tufte. Envisioning Information. Cheshire, CT, Graphics Press. 1990.

[6]   P. Wildbur, M. Burke. Information Graphics. Mainz: Schmidt. 1998.

[7]   D. M. Wong: The Wall Street Journal Guide to Information Graphics: The Dos and Don'ts of Presenting Data, Facts, and Figures. New York, Norton. 2010.

[8]   A. Cairo. Infografía 2.0. Visualización interactive de información en la prensa. Madrid, Alamut. 2008.

[9]   K. Foster, S. Stiermling, T. Knieper: Wissensvermittlung durch animierte Infographiken: Ein Experiment. In: C. Thimm (Hrsg.): Netz-Bildung. Frankfurt a. M., Peter Lang. 2005. 75-100.

[10]   E. R. Tufte. Visual Explanations. Cheshire, CT, Graphics Press. 1997.

[11]   S. Kernbach, M. J. Eppler. The use of visualization in the context of business strategies. In: IEEE Proceedings of the 14th International Conference on Information Visualization IV10. London. 349-354.

[12]   N. H. Lurie, C.H. Mason. Visual Representation: Implications for Decision Making. Journal of Marketing, 71 (January). 160-177. 2007.

[13]   M. J. Eppler, K. Platts. Classifying visualization methods for management: results of card sorting experiments with managers and students. In: Proceedings of the International Conference on Information Visualization: IEEE Press, 2007. IV07. – Zürich. 335-341.

[14]   R. Lengler, M. J. Eppler. Towards a Periodic Table of Visualization Methods for Management. In: Proceedings of the IASTED International Conference on Graphics and Visualization in Engineering. ACTA Press. Anaheim, CA. 2007. 1-6.

[15]   S. Bertschi. Linguistic Learning. A New Conceptual Focus in Knowledge Visualization. In: Proceedings of the Ninth International Conference on Information Visualisation. Los Alamitos, CA. IEEE Computer Society Press, London. 2005. 383-389.

[16]   R. Burkhard. Visual Knowledge Transfer between Planners and Business Decision Makers. In: Van Leeuwen, J. P. (Hrsg.) ; Timmermans, H. J. P. (Hrsg.): Developments in Design & Decision Support Systems in Architecture and Urban Planning. Eindhoven: Eindhoven University of Technology, 2004.

[17]   S. Bresciani, M. J. Eppler. Choosing Knowledge Visualizations to Augment Cognition: the Manager's View in. In: Banissi, E. et al. (Eds.): IEEE Proceedings of the International Conference on Information Visualization IV10. London. 355-360.

[18]   G. Boehm (Hrsg.). Was ist ein Bild? München, Fink. 1994

[19]   A. Strauss, J. Corbin. Basics of Qualitative Research. Grounded Theory, Procedures and Techniques. Newbury Park, CA, Sage. 1990.

7. Acknowledgement

We would like to thank the research assistants Daniela Vey and Nadine Draksler for their support in carrying out this study.

What is an Effective Knowledge Visualization?
Insights from a Review of Seminal Concepts

Martin J. Eppler
University of St. Gallen
mcm *institute*
St. Gallen, Switzerland
e-mail: martin.eppler@unisg.ch

Abstract— The domain of knowledge visualization focuses on the collaborative use of interactive graphics to create, integrate and apply knowledge. This emerging approach nevertheless builds on decades of research on using images collaboratively for sense making and knowledge sharing. In this paper, we review seminal concepts from different disciplines that help to explain how visualizations can effectively act as collaboration catalysts and knowledge integrators. Our review makes it apparent that many different labels and conceptions exist in very different domains to explain the same phenomenon: the integrative power of visuals for knowledge-intensive collaboration processes. These concepts can be used to compile a list of the requirements of an effective knowledge visualization. We conclude the paper by showing the theoretical and practical implications of this review.. *(Abstract)*

Keywords- knowledge visualization, knowledge integration, key concepts, collaboration, boundary object, conscription device, confection, artifact of knowing, transitional object, immutable mobile

I. INTRODUCTION

The domain of knowledge visualization is a relatively young discipline that focuses on the collaborative use of interactive graphics to create, integrate and apply knowledge – particularly in the management context. This young field nevertheless builds on decades of research on using images collaboratively for sense making and knowledge sharing.

The objective of the current paper is to make this rich legacy of the knowledge domain field visible and use it to inform the practice visualizing knowledge. In this paper, we will thus review seminal concepts from different disciplines that help to explain how visualizations can act as collaboration catalysts and support the elicitation, integration, and application of knowledge on a team or group level. The review will make it apparent that many different labels exist in various domains to explain the basically same phenomenon: the integrative power of visuals for knowledge-intensive collaboration. Our review of key concepts, however, will also reveal that visuals must meet certain criteria to achieve this integration function effectively.

The paper is structured as follows: First, we provide an example of a knowledge visualization and discuss the already identified attributes of such epistemic (knowledge-intensive) images in section 2. Then, we describe the rationale behind our review of key concepts that can inform knowledge visualization conceptions in section 3, where we also discuss seminal, highly cited constructs from disciplines as diverse as sociology, art history, e-learning, psychology, epistemology, or design. We cluster these constructs according to their emphasis on visualization or collaboration respectively. As a main contribution we identify similarities among the concepts and summarize them in five derived knowledge visualization principles. To illustrate these principles, we focus on a few seminal concepts in more depth in section 4. In the subsequent section 5, we derive implications from the reviewed constructs for the theory and practice of knowledge visualization. The final section 6 of this paper consists of a short conclusion and an outlook on future research in this area.

II. THE REALM OF KNOWLEDGE VISUALIZATION

We define knowledge visualization (in contrast to the mostly data-driven information visualization field) as follows: Knowledge visualization designates all (interactive) graphic means that can be used to develop or convey insights, experiences, methods, or skills [1, 2]. This definition implies that the realm of knowledge visualization is not limited to computer-based images and that the main purpose of knowledge visualization is to support the (inherently social) processes of creating and sharing knowledge with others.

The following figure provides a simple example of this approach. Figure 1 represents the completed analysis conducted by a management team regarding the service quality problems in their call center. Starting with the empty iceberg metaphor (as a discussion template) and its tip containing the label "service quality low", the team went to probe its root causes and mapped the main issues or problem drivers in a reverse causal chain backwards to the less visible problems (in the lower part of the iceberg). In doing so, the group elicited the team members' different insights regarding the current challenges in the call center. The graphic iceberg template and corresponding facilitation method enabled the team to pool these insights and relate them to each other, as well as devise adequate improvement actions.

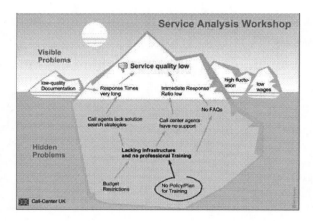

Figure 1. An example of a knowledge visualization

The resulting image can then be used in subsequent meetings to explain the problem to other staff members and to help in the implementation of improvement measures. The image contains knowledge on a detail level, such as the impact of budget restrictions on the available infrastructure, as well as one overall insight, namely that the service quality level is just the tip of the iceberg of a much larger problem. The image in Figure 1 is a typical knowledge representation in the sense that it contains various types of images, such as the visual metaphor of an iceberg, sketchmarks for highlighting (the blue circle) as well as diagrammatic elements (text elements and arrows). It also indicates a process of how to discuss the problem analysis, namely in an overview to detail, top-to-bottom process.

A knowledge visualization, such as the simple one depicted above, consequently has to fulfill the following criteria to merit the label in our (group-level) application context:

1. It has to be able to *capture* and *depict knowledge*, that is to say (valid and current) insights, experiences, concepts, perspectives, opinions arguments etc. of informed participants.
2. Ideally, it contains *insights* from more than one *person* alone and *relates* these ideas to one another.
3. It has to be *visual* in the sense that the knowledge mapped in the image is spatially positioned within a diagram, visual metaphor (as above), sketch, map, or photograph, or combinations thereof.
4. It has to support the (group) *process* of knowledge integration among various people. It should in other words *facilitate (synchronous or asynchronous) conversations*.
5. To achieve this, the visualization has to be *revisable* or flexible, so as to be able to react to changing insights in a group over the course of time.

6. It has to be *communicable* in the sense that the image can be communicated to others (of different professional background) who have not been present during its creation process (this is for example a common problem with the use of mind maps).
7. Ideally, its use leads to *new discoveries* or insights that were previously unknown and that are *useful* to viewers of the visualization.

These criteria are derived from the cognitive [14] and collaborative dimensions of visualization research [17] and from the practical use of knowledge visualizations in management [1, 2]. However, requirements for knowledge visualization may go beyond this straight forward list of attributes. Are there other key characteristics that knowledge visualizations should exhibit to support knowledge processes? Are these seven attributes confirmed by approaches in other domains?

To answer these questions, we have reviewed seminal concepts related to 'collaboration through artifacts' (the larger subject domain). These concepts are shortly presented and compared in the next section.

III. A REVIEW OF SEMINAL CONCEPTS

Having described the goal and rationale of reviewing concepts related to knowledge visualization and more broadly working with artifacts to share knowledge, we now proceed to a concise overview of closely related constructs from different domains.

Altogether, we have been able to identify the following concepts that describe the key notion of using visualization as a catalyst for knowledge sharing. Each one contains a profound insight into the nature of images as collaboration platforms. We will briefly discuss these insights below.

The selection criteria for these concepts were that a) they have to be highly cited, i.e., have achieved more than at least one hundred citations (in Google scholar), b) they have to specifically address (at least partly) images as knowledge exchange mechanisms and c) relate them to collaboration contexts (to a lesser or greater extent).

We were also interested in concepts from radically different domains, so that different kinds of insights into collaborative visualization could be fruitfully integrated.

To select highly influential concepts, we have counted the total amount of citations reported on Google Scholar for the first three articles (in terms of citations) employing the concept in the article title or abstract. This has lead to the following list of seminal concepts:

TABLE I.   KEY CONCEPTS RELATED TO KNOWLEDGE VISUALIZATION FROM DIFFERENT DOMAINS

Concept	Concept Domain	Originator	Citations (Σ top 3)
Boundary Object	Sociology	Star et al. [3]	2083
Epistemic object	Epistemology	Knorr-Cetina [5]	1919
Dynamic affordance	Management	Cook & Brown [11]	1523
Transitional object	Management	Eden & Ackermann [8, 9]	1200
Notation criteria	Philosophy (of Art)	Goodman [15]	1120
Cognitive dimensions of notation	Computer Science	Green [14]	110
Confection	Information Design	Tufte [13]	924
Immutable mobile	Sociology	Latour [16]	860
Visual language	Instruction	Horn [12]	499
Conscription Device	Sociology	Henderson [4]	366
Representational Guidance	e-learning	Suthers [10]	324
Diagrammatic reasoning	Logic	Peirce [7]	283
Visual hybrids	Art history	Elkins [6]	113
Visuospatial reasoning	Psychology	Tversky [18]	100

These concepts not only differ with regard to their disciplinary background, but also with regard to their respective focus.

As we have shown in Figure 2, the concepts can be distinguished regarding their emphasis on the role of images or on the actual collaboration that (graphic) artifacts can support.

The resulting segmentation shows two main groups of concepts, namely those focusing on *visualization* (represented by visualization scholars such as Edward Tufte, James Elkins, or Barbara Tversky), and those focusing primarily on *collaboration* (visualized as empty bubbles in the matrix, such as the ethnographic work of Barbara Knorr-Cetina in the context of scientific discovery or of Kathryn Henderson in the area of design engineering).

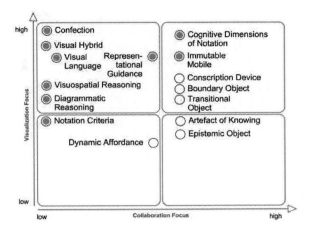

Figure 2.   A segmented overview of key concepts for knowledge visualization

More important than their differences, however, are the at times astonishing (given their radically different backgrounds) similarities among these concepts. In the following table, we have articulated key requirements for knowledge visualizations (KV) directly deduced from these seminal concepts.

TABLE II.   REQUIREMENTS DERIVED FROM THE CONCEPTS

Derived KV principle	Base Concepts	Main Insight of the Concepts
Visual Variety	Confection; Visual Hybrids; Visual Language; Boundary Object; Notation Criteria; Cognitive Dimensions of Notation	An image that is able to capture and convey the knowledge of different people requires different ways of expression, ranging from simple sketched marks to complex rich visual metaphors contained in a single image.
Visual Unfreezing	Immutable Mobile; Boundary Object; Conscription Device; Notation Criteria; Cognitive Dimension of Notation; Transitional Object	To be useful for knowledge sharing and collaboration, a visualization must be able to be switched from a fixed mode to a flexible, modifiable mode and back.
Visual Discovery	Diagrammatic Reasoning; Visuospatial Reasoning; Dynamic Affordance; Representational Guidance; Conscription Device; Cognitive Dimensions of Notation	A visualization for collaboration must provide assistance for reasoning, reflection, and linking items in new ways so as to facilitate new discoveries from the shared insights.

Visual Play-fulness	Representational Guidance; Diagrammatic Reasoning; Transitional Object; Conscription Device	In order to overcome rigid assumptions or role definitions and narrow perspectives, the visual should provide playful mechanisms to reframe issues and cajole participants into a different mindset and thus generate new insights and intensify collaboration.
Visual Gui-dance	Representational guidance; Transitional Object; Boundary Object; Diagrammatic Reasoning; Dynamic Affordance	The visual has to fulfill a dual role of not only capturing and structuring contributions, but also of providing a process of doing so in a useful sequence of actions.

Compared to the original list of knowledge visualization attributes presented earlier, we notice that visual playfulness is a new item, while visual variety, visual unfreezing, and visual discovery, as well as visual guidance are existing ones that are confirmed. Based on these attributes we can now provide a normative definition of what a knowledge visualization should amount to, namely a communicable image, consisting of various visual notations, that is interactively annotated in a playful yet systematic manner and leads to new discoveries while remaining flexible to incorporate future revisions and insights.

In the next section, we present a few of the above listed seminal concepts in more detail to show how they contribute to the emerging principles of knowledge visualization.

IV. SELECT SEMINAL CONCEPTS IN DETAIL

To illustrate the principle of *Visual Variety*, we can use Elkin's idea of Visual Hybrids, Tufte's concept of Confection and Latour's notion of Immutable Mobile:

A *visual hybrid*, according to Elkins [6] is a graphic notation system that not only relies on one image genre, but combines two or more visualization formats (such as graphs, charts, tables, diagrams, genealogical trees, etc.). According to Elkin "Especially given the hurtling development of new image technologies, mixed images can be said to be the norm rather than the marginal exception" [6, p. 91].

Very close to this notion is the idea of a visual confection. A *Confection* according to Tufte "is an assembly of *many visual events*, selected from various streams of a story, then brought together [....] Confections illustrate an argument, present and enforce visual comparisons, combine the real and the imagined, and tell us yet another story" [13, p. 121]. "Confections are not direct representations of pre-existing scenes, nor are they the result of placing data into

conventional formats such as statistical charts, tables, or maps" [13, p.122]. Tufte himself thus envisions that there are other visualizations than simple data or information representations.

Also Latour's concept of Immutable Mobiles emphasizes the need for visual variety defining such artifacts as consisting of "*figures, diagrams, plates, texts, silhouettes.*" [16, p. 37].

Latour's concept can also be used to explain the concept of *Visual Unfreezing*. Inscriptions are mobile as their elements can easily move, but these inscriptions become immutable and fixed on paper, once they have been confirmed by all participants.

Star and Griesemer's concept of a *Boundary Object* also emphasizes this dual nature of collaborative artifacts. Boundary Objects, according to Star and Griesemer [3], are "both *plastic* enough to adapt to local needs and constraints of the several parties employing them, yet *robust* enough to maintain a common identity across sites." Boundary objects are weakly structured in common use, and become strongly structured in personal use. They may be abstract and conceptual or concrete and specific. They have different meanings in different social or professional contexts, but their structure is common enough to more than one professional community to make them recognizable means of translation.

The principle of *Visual Discovery* is not unique to the domain of knowledge visualization, as detecting new patterns is also the main aim of the field of information visualization. In the knowledge visualization context, the pursue of novel insights takes on a different form, as they are generated not out of the analysis and mapping of mass data, but rather visualized individual and collective views, opinions, assessments, and analyses.

This notion of insight through a process of interacting with a visual is probably best captured in the concept of *Diagrammatic Reasoning* that was first introduced by Charles Peirce [7]. The visualization becomes a think tool with which an individual or a group tackles a difficult problem. A simple example of diagrammatic reasoning is the positioning of elements according to their similarities in overlapping or containment circles, as in a Euler or Venn diagram. From this positioning, new insights can emerge, for example groups with many versus groups with few members.

The principle of *Visual Guidance* is a particularly important concept for knowledge visualization, as images in this context are not only used as representations of data but as catalysts for a collaboration process. Images act as signposts to what should be discussed and in what order. We find this attribute in Suthers' concept of

Representational Guidance [10] in the context of e-learning and in Cook and Brown's concept of Dynamic Affordance in the management context [11]. An image used in collaboration can act as a representational guidance, according to Suthers, by providing certain constraints to a discussion, by stimulating certain actions in a group, and by drawing attention to certain discussion topics (that are made salient graphically). Dynamic affordance, according to Cook and Brown's perspective, is what becomes possible when knowledge is used as a tool in the context of situated activity [11, p. 392]. These situated activities can be influenced through artifacts that invite participants to do one thing rather than another. Visuals thus provide affordances to steer the discussion in a particular direction.

Regarding the new principle of *Visual Playfulness*, we can – for instance – use Eden and Ackermann's notion of *Transitional Objects*: In their book on strategic management [8, p.71], Eden and Ackermann state that to do something enjoyable together can make collaboration easier; for example tinkering with a strategy visualization used as a transitional object. Used in this provisional, exploratory or playful way, the visualization encourages an open dialogue and is capable of change by the group in real-time (ibid.). According to Eden and Ackermann, the participants who interact in this way waste less energy in impression management and are more immersed in their knowledge exchange than they would otherwise be. In this way playfulness can be conducive to productive collaboration.

V. IMPLICATIONS

In terms of *practical implications*, the principles derived from the review of seminal concepts can be used as a checklist for group facilitators in the preparation stage of their work. They can use the identified attributes to evaluate or improve their discussion templates and thus make them more conducive to knowledge elicitation, integration and application. More specifically, the five principles derived above can be used as check questions before knowledge creation, sharing or application session, as exemplified below:

- **Visual Variety**: Have you provided a sufficiently rich visual vocabulary that enables participants to express their ideas through various ways, such as through diagrams, sketches, metaphors, or simple text additions?
- **Visual Unfreezing**: Have you incorporated ways in which certain states of a collaboratively drawn visualization can be captured and 'frozen' for later reference? Are there clear criteria when a frozen visual can be re-elaborated and changed again?

- **Visual Discovery**: Does the visual template provide affordances to connect elements in a new way or look at the big picture and detect new patterns?
- **Visual Playfulness**: Does the visual invite participants to change perspectives, assume new roles, immerse in the collaborative effort, let go of assumptions or otherwise reframe issues creatively?
- **Visual Guidance**: Does the visual offer a clear 'roadmap' of how it should be iteratively populated or completed? Is it clear where to start in the visualization and how to proceed?

In terms of *theoretical implications*, we have seen that in spite of their great differences in background, the examined concepts have an astonishing congruence with regard to the underlying mechanisms that they discuss. Anyone working on a future theory of collaborative knowledge visualization is thus well advised to venture outside the realm of his or her own discipline and make use of the insights generated in such diverse disciplines as design, instruction, sociology, psychology, or art history. In this way the domain of knowledge visualization could also make this often dispersed knowledge accessible to scholars and practitioners alike.

VI. CONCLUSION

In this paper, we have made an attempt to define the requirements of a knowledge visualization that deserves the label. We have done so based on our practical experience [1, 2], the cognitive and collaborative dimensions framework [14, 17] and based on seminal concepts in the literature on collaborating with artifacts [3-16]. This has resulted in an extended list of requirements for knowledge visualizations that we captured in five knowledge visualization principles. These principles can be used to assess or improve knowledge visualization templates used in knowledge sharing tasks of teams.

In future research, we would like to see which of these requirements are in a trade-off relationship with one another and how they can be achieved through the help of interactive visualization software and adequate facilitation interventions.

REFERENCES

[1] M.J. Eppler, R.A.Burkard (2004) "Knowledge Visualization. Towards a New Discipline and its Fields of Application" Schwartz, D.G. (Ed.) *Encyclopedia of Knowledge Management*. Idea Group.

[2] M.J. Eppler, & R. Burkhard, (2007) "Visual Representations in Knowledge Management: framework and cases" *Journal of Knowledge Management,* 4(11), 112-122

[3] *SL Star & JR Griesemer (1989) "Institutional Ecology, 'Translations' and Boundary Objects: Amateurs and Professionals in Berkeley's Museum of Vertebrate Zoology" Social Studies of Science 19(4), 387–420.*

[4] K. Henderson (1991) "Flexible Sketches and Inflexible Data Bases: Visual Communication, Conscription Devices, and Boundary Objects in Design Engineering" *Science, Technology & Human Values,* vol. 16, 448-473.

[5] K. Knorr-Cetina (2003) *Epistemic Cultures. How the Sciences Make Knowledge,* [1999]. Cambridge: Harvard University Press Cambridge.

[6] J. Elkins (1999) *The Domain of Images*. Ithaca and London: Cornell University Press.

[7] H.G. Michael Hoffmann (2003) "Peirce's "Diagrammatic Reasoning" as a Solution of the Learning Paradox" *Process Pragmatism: Essays on a Quiet Philosophical Revolution.* Ed. Guy Debrock. Amsterdam: Rodopi, 121-143.

[8] C. Eden, F. Ackermann (1998) *Making Strategy, The Journey of Strategic Management.* London: SAGE Publications.

[9] C. Eden, F. Ackermann (2006). "Where Next for Problem Structuring Methods". *Journal of the Operational Research Society* 57(7): 766-768.

[10] D.D. Suthers (2001) Towards a Systematic Study of Representational Guidance for Collaborative Learning Discourse. *Journal of Universal Computer Science (J.UCS),* 7(3), 254-277.

[11] S. D. N. Cook, J. S. Brown (1999). "Bridging epistemologies: the generative dance between organizational knowledge and organizational knowing." *Organization Science* 10(4): 381-400.

[12] RE Horn (1998) *Visual Language: Global Communication for the 21st Century.* Bainbridge Island (WA): MacroVU Press.

[13] E.R. Tufte (1997) *Visual Explanations*. Cheshire, CT: Graphics Press.

[14] TRG Green (1996) Usability Analysis of Visual Programming Environments: A Cognitive Dimensions Framework. Journal of Visual Languages and Computing, 1996

[15] N. Goodman (1969) Languages of Art. London: Oxford University Press.

[16] B. Latour (1990) "Visualisation and Cognition: Drawing Things Together" Michael Lynch and Steve Woolgar (Eds.) *Representation in Scientific Activity*, Cambridge Mass: MIT Press, , 19-68.

[17] S. Bresciani, A.F. Blackwell M. J. Eppler (2008) "A Collaborative Dimensions Framework: Understanding the Mediating Role of Conceptual Visualizations in Collaborative Knowledge Work" *Proceedings of the 41st Hawaii International Conference on System Sciences (HICSS 2008).* Hawaii: IEEE Press.

[18] B. Tversky (2005) "Visuospatial Reasoning" *The Cambridge Handbook of Thinking and Reasoning.* Eds. K. Holyoak and R. Morrison, Chapter 10. Cambridge: Cambridge University Press.

Distributed Group Collaboration in Interactive Applications

Serge Gebhardt[1], Christine Meixner[1], Remo Aslak Burkhard[2]
[1]ETH Zurich, Chair for Information Architecture, Zurich, Switzerland
[2]vasp datatecture GmbH, Zurich, Switzerland
gebhardt@arch.ethz.ch, meixner@arch.ethz.ch, Remo.Burkhard@vasp.ch

Abstract

This paper describes approaches for near-realtime collaboration over distance in interactive applications. It presents approaches to tackling most of the encountered challenges by using our interactive risk management tool as an illustrative example. In particular it focuses on browser-based bi-directional client-server network communication, concurrent object manipulations, and data synchronization.

Keywords: Collaborative computing, web-based interaction, synchronous/concurrent interaction, risk management, multi-touch collaboration, evaluation/methodology.

1. Introduction

This paper describes approaches for near-realtime collaboration over distance in interactive applications. The innovation focus lays on technical challenges, but we will use our risk management tool as an illustrative example to expose the difficulties. For this we first introduce the environment.

The ETH Value Lab (Figure 1) is an attractive space with daylight and high ceilings. It is equipped with three large wall-mounted multi-touch screens, two large table-mounted multi-touch screens, three video projectors and a video conferencing system. The concept is described in [7].

We found out that the ETH Value Lab is an ideal environment for collaborative workshops [6]. We then developed a novel software-based approach for a wide range of management tasks such as risk, strategy or project management, which leverage the capabilities of the ETH Value Lab in the context of collaborative workshops.

In order to bring collaboration a step further, we envisioned approaches to overcome social and technical challenges, and developed a tool that enables collaboration over distance.

Implementing this near-realtime distributed collaboration posed some challenges, such as browser-based bi-directional client-server network

Figure 1. ETH Value Lab with five multi-touch displays (Source: Chair for Information Architecture, ETH Zurich).

communication, concurrent object manipulations at different locations, and data synchronization.

In this article we describe approaches to tackling most of these challenges, using our risk management tool as an illustrative example.

2. Risk Management Tool

To illustrate our technical research contribution we first introduce the application context, which is risk management.

The responsibility of enterprise risk management lies in the hands of the board management. They are responsible for identifying, evaluating, and assessing the risks, as well as deriving actions to reduce these risks. We identified three main challenges in current quantitative risk management approaches:

Getting the big picture: Risk management systems become increasingly detailed and complex. Monthly risk reports easily exceed 100 pages and decision-makers quickly lose the overview. How can a software tool provide such an overview?

Risk assessment with multiple stakeholders: More and more stakeholders become involved in the risk assessment process, such as the board of management, the executive board, the auditing firm and team leaders. They all have diverging backgrounds, risk perceptions and professional experiences. How can the quality and involvement in a risk assessment meeting be increased, while assisting decision-making? Research has shown that visualization techniques are very useful for group coordination and group decision-making [5,9,10,11,12].

Creating risk evaluation reports: To comply with legal regulations companies must provide a risk evaluation, e.g. as part of their annual report. However, there are no established best practices on how to create such risk evaluation reports.

We devised an ideal approach to overcome these three challenges [2] and developed the interactive risk management tool (Figure 2).

We introduced the application context of our research contribution, which is a distributed collaborative system. In the next section we will describe the software aspects in more details.

3. Approach to Interaction over distance

The risk management tool is built with ease of use in mind: users simply connect to the website and instantly run it in the browser. Alternatively, they can choose to install the software as a native application in the operating system. The installation process is as easy as a right-click and choosing "Install".

Two modes of operation are available: an online mode and an offline one.

When used in offline mode the application behaves autonomously and is completely separate from the server. This mode obviously offers no support for distributed collaboration.

When used in online mode the application registers with the server by sending the user-provided username and password. Upon successful authentication it loads the initial data from the server. Every subsequent data modification is sent from the editing client to the server,

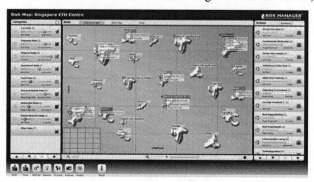

**Figure 2. Risk management tool
(Source: Chair for Information Architecture,
ETH Zurich).**

which broadcasts the modification to all registered clients. Changes are thus synchronously sent to all remote parties at the same time and the tool is ready for distributed collaboration.

3.1. Client Application Architecture

Our tool is written in Microsoft Silverlight 4 using C#, making it instantly runnable as embedded object in any widespread browser that supports the Silverlight plug-in, or as native application on Windows, Mac OS X and Linux. The tool itself consists of a custom-developed component-based toolkit, on top of which we built the actual risk module.

The toolkit comprises generic and reusable components, such as support for touch inputs and gestures, drag&drop handling, generation of PDF and Excel reports, shared graphical elements and helper utilities.

The risk module is built on top of the toolkit, thereby inheriting all its functionality, and implements the logic specific to risk management.

This decoupling allows for reusability and extensibility, while clearly separating each part's concerns. Based on this architecture it is possible to develop additional modules for distributed collaboration in other specific areas.

3.2. Server Architecture

The server part of our tool consists of a web service written in C# using the Windows Communication Foundation (WCF). Behind the service-oriented interface runs the server logic that is responsible for user authentication and data synchronization across all the connected clients. All data is persisted to a backend SQL database.

After an initial deployment on our own dedicated server we moved to the hosted cloud infrastructure on Microsoft Windows Azure.

The distributed nature of the cloud infrastructure is a good fit with our tool's context of distributed collaboration. Furthermore the cloud's absence of maintenance overhead and its seamless scalability contribute to the overall stability of the tool.

4. Challenges with Distributed Collaboration

Collaboration over distance inherently poses new challenges not found in standalone applications. This section focuses on two of them: (1) browser-based client-server network communication; and (2) concurrent object manipulations.

4.1. Browser-Based Client-Server Network Communication

For security reasons applications running in a web-browser are generally not allowed to open generic network sockets.

Browser applications are therefore bound to exclusively use the standard HTTP protocol. This has three added benefits: (1) easily passes through corporate firewalls, which usually block generic socket connections; (2) solves authentication, which is already defined for HTTP; and (3) solves privacy issues because HTTP can be encrypted with the industry-standard SSL encryption protocol (HTTPS protocol).

But by specification the HTTP protocol requires the web-client to open a connection to the server and request a given document. The client can also pass arguments to the query. The server replies with the requested document. In our context of distributed collaboration this implies that only the client application can open a connection to the server, never the other way around. How can data modifications then be pushed from the server to the registered clients?

Furthermore the HTTP protocol was not designed for messages going indefinitely back and forth between clients and server, but rather for a single request-response dialog. In our context of distributed collaboration this poses a challenge to keep connections open and active between the server and all its registered clients.

To solve these issues we implemented the *HTTP Duplex Channel* technique. It has partly been integrated into Microsoft Silverlight 4. It enables the browser application to overload the HTTP connection to the server with the illusion of a bi-directional channel, likewise to a generic socket.

The client connects to the server without requesting a document, but leaving the connection open as long as possible. When the server has data modifications to push to all its registered clients, it first queues the messages locally and sends them to the clients as soon as they become available. The client re-opens the channel to the server upon disconnection. This provides the illusion of a bi-directional channel supporting near-realtime message pushing between a HTTP server and multiple clients.

This technique is quite error-prone when implemented incorrectly. It then results in seemingly random behavior and debugging network channels is always cumbersome.

4.2. Concurrent Object Manipulations

In the context of collaboration over distance attention must be given to concurrent operations. Two users at different locations may not manipulate the same object at the same time.

Our approach introduces a token per object. When a client wants to modify an object, it requests the token for that object. If no token is assigned to it, the server provides a token to the client and registers the association. When the client has finished modifying the object and transmitted the changes back to the server, it requests the release of the token. The server then unregisters the token from the object, hence deleting the association between client and object. The object is now free for other clients to request its token.

In case a client requests the token for an object that is already associated with a token, the server declines the requests with a "has token" message. The client must then display an error message to the user and retry the token request at a later time.

The client, in which the workshop manager is logged in, benefits from higher privileges than all the other clients. He has the power to revoke other clients' tokens and can reclaim them for himself at any time. This serves two purposes: (1) he can revoke writing privileges from misbehaving clients; and (2) he can return locked objects to all other clients. The latter reason need not be with bad intentions; it could result from network problems, or a client forgetting to confirm a dialog box.

This token-based approach does not take fairness into account. Hence resource starvation is possible if a client always requests all tokens on all objects. The tools are used in the context of distributed collaboration, as opposed to distributed sabotage; hence we do not consider this a drawback. The workshop manager always has the power to exclude a misbehaving client and thus restore fair resource allocation.

5. Further enhancements

The presented material is work-in-progress and we are currently expanding it further, especially regarding support for mobile devices, synchronization of the user interface, and three-way data synchronization.

5.1. Mobile Devices

We plan to port our planning tools to a wider range of mobile devices, beyond the laptop. Some problems remain to be solved, especially concerning the execution environment: our frameworks and applications are developed in Microsoft Silverlight, which is not (yet) available for most mobile devices. Furthermore we must develop an interaction logic specific to small screens.

5.2. User Interface Synchronization

We discovered that workshop participants connected from a remote location easily lose track of data modifications done by other participants. The best approach to tackle this challenge is to give each participant a distinct color and highlight his modifications with the color. Ideally the user interface is synchronized across all participants.

Depending of the infrastructure, some participants may choose to open different views of the application simultaneously on different screens. How can then the user interface be synchronized? Furthermore we may need to introduce a token-based locking mechanism as detailed above.

5.3. Three-Way Data Synchronization

Currently collaboration is only possible either fully online or fully offline; a mixed mode is not supported. We plan to overcome this limitation and implement three-way data synchronization.

Then a user could participate in the workshop or download the workshop data to his laptop. While on the go, s/he could work on the data, e.g. re-assess risks or update progress. Once back online, the changes would be matched and differentially updated on the server. Furthermore multiple users could work offline on the same data in parallel and all changes would be synchronized. How to handle conflicting changes is still an unsolved issue.

Conclusions

We presented approaches for near-realtime collaboration over distance in interactive applications. We described approaches to tackling most of the encountered challenges by using our interactive risk management tool as an illustrative example.

These approaches are stable and being used in productive software. We are currently working on the discussed enhancements to further improve collaboration over distance.

Acknowledgements

We would like to thank KTI/CTI[1] for supporting this research project.

References

[1] Åhlberg, M.: "Varieties of Concept Mapping". In Proc. 1st Intl. Conference on Concept Mapping 2004.

[2] Burkhard, R. and Merz, T.: "A Visually Supported Interactive Risk Assessment Approach for Group Meetings". In Proc. I-KNOW 2009.

[3] Cart, SK., Mackinlay, JD., Shneiderman, B.: "Readings in Information Visualization: Using Vision to think". Morgan Kaufmann Publishers Inc., 1999.

[4] Chen, C.: "Mapping Scientific Frontiers: The Quest for Knowledge Visualization". Springer London, 2003.

[5] Eppler, M. and Burkhard, R.: "Visual Representations in Knowledge Management". In Journal of Knowledge Management, 11, 4 (2007), 112-122.

[6] Halatsch, J. and Kunze, A.: "Value Lab: Collaboration in Space". In Proc. 11th International Conference Information Visualization 2007 (IV'07), IEEE, Switzerland, Zurich, 376 - 381.

[7] Halatsch, J., Kunze, A., Burkhard, R. and Schmitt, G.: "ETH Value Lab - A Framework for Managing Large-Scale Urban Projects". In 7th China Urban Housing Conference, Faculty of Architecture and Urban Planning, Chongqing University, Chongqing (2008).

[8] Horn, RE.: "Visual Language: Global Communication for the 21st Century". MacroVU Press, 1998.

[9] Jacobi, M., Halatsch J., Kunze A., Schmitt G., Turkienicz, B.: "A grammar-based system for the participatory design of urban structures". SIGraDi, 2009.

[10] Kaplan, RS. and Norton, DP.: "Having Trouble with Your Strategy? Then Map It". In Harvard Business Review, 2000.

[11] Kaplan, RS. and Norton, DP.: "Strategy Maps: Converting Intangible Assets into Tangible Outcomes". In Harvard Business School Press, 2004.

[12] Tergan, SO., Keller, T.: "Visualizing Knowledge and Information. An Introduction". In Knowledge and Information Visualization: Searching for Synergies. LNCS 3426, Tergan SO. and Keller T., Springer-Verlag Heidelberg, 2005.

[13] Vande Moere, A., Mieusset, KH. and Gross, M.: "Visualizing Abstract Information using Motion Properties of Data-Driven Particles". In Conference on Visualization and Data Analysis 2004.

---

[1] KTI/CTI: http://www.kti.admin.ch/index.html?lang=en

Visualizing Service Contracts – The Case of an Equipment Manufacturer

Katri Rekola, Ph. D. (Econ.), M. Sc. (Tech.)
Rekola Design, Finland
Kerttuli Boucht, M. Sc. (Tech)
Bredantie 34 b, 02700 Helsinki, Finland

Abstract

This paper presents the case of an industrial equipment manufacturer facing the challenge of selling services. The main source for confusion was the complexity of the services and the multiplicity of options offered to the customers. It was hard to have a clear picture of what entitlements or responsibilities followed from the choices, and draft a contract accordingly. The company decided to try visualization to facilitate communication and to clarify the service content. The experiment provided valuable insight into the possibilities and limitations of contract visualization in the context of industrial service contracts. The conclusion was that visuals can help but are not the answer to all communication problems. It is for example essential to fit the visual content to the targeted audience and to make sure that the text that is going to be visualized is understood correctly in the first place.

1. Introduction

The shift from products towards services with the 'servitization' [29] of the manufacturing industry has made it necessary to find new ways to cope with the situation, for example through adopting a service-dominant logic which means a more service-oriented way of thinking and operating [30], or service productization which means giving services product-like features [18, 19, 20]. The transition from product manufacturer into service provider constitutes a major managerial challenge. Manufacturing companies must learn to value services and how to sell, deliver and bill them. Services require new organizational principles, structures, and processes, and the emphasis of the business model changes from transaction- to relationship-based. [15] In addition, recent organizational, economic, and legal research shows the importance of contracts for inter-firm relationships [2]. Does this mean that as well as becoming more service-oriented manufacturing companies should increase their contracting capabilities and legal expertise? In practice, legal matters are often left to legal professionals for various reasons. Recently, legal visualization has emerged as a new research field and a potential tool to increase interest in contracts among non-lawyers.

In this paper we describe the way towards what might one day become 'contract visualization', the challenges encountered along the way, and the lessons learned. We present the case of an equipment manufacturer trying to sell more and better services with the aid of service contract visualization. To provide background for the case, we first discuss the role of contracts and contracting capabilities in manufacturing companies, and explore the potential of visualization.

2. Goals and Methods

The case study was conducted in spring/summer 2010 in a globally operating equipment manufacturing company in Finland. The case provides insights into legal visualization in practice in the context of service contracts: what works, what does not, and what the challenges are. Obviously, one case study does not provide sufficient grounds for generalization of the conclusions. However, the goal of this paper is to initiate a discussion on service contract visualization and its potential benefits, pitfalls, and challenges.

1550-6037/11 $26.00 © 2011 IEEE
DOI 10.1109/IV.2011.35

First, to provide background for the case study, we discuss the role of contracts and the possibilities of visualization based on literature and present qualitative findings from 21 interviews in 4 companies that are good representatives of globally operating manufacturing companies with different levels of service focus. Those interviewed were different professionals that come into contact with contracts in their daily work. They were asked about contracting practices and potential ways to enhance the contracting process, including visualization. We conclude the paper with a discussion on the topic of contract visualization, initial conclusions based on the case as well as remarks on future research.

3. Background

Our interviews support the view that many non-lawyers consider contracts a real pain and prefer to leave all law-related matters to legal professionals. Contracts are seen as risk management tools that are needed if something goes wrong. Few consider contracts management tools that work as road maps for business relationships. One reason might be that contracts contain concepts and language that non-lawyers can find incomprehensible. However, the complicated language of law is seldom the fundamental reason for a reluctance to deal with legal matters; non-lawyers just do not see why they should be bothered. After all, a business organization has specialized experts, including legal professionals, for a reason. Non-lawyers need a valid incentive to add legal understanding to their expertise.

Research suggests that law [4, 25] and contracts [26], can add value to an organization, and emphasizes the importance of legal astuteness for managers [3] as well as legal knowledge as a company's capability [25]. Crafting business contracts requires both subject matter and legal expertise. Argyres and Mayer [1] show that much of the knowledge needed to craft successful contracts resides in managers and engineers, rather than legal professionals. These economic implications of good contracting capabilities might provide non-lawyers with a reason to not ignore contracts. Could something be done to further facilitate this change in behavior and make contracts more usable in practice? Can for example visualization techniques be of use here?

Using images as part of a collaborative conversation seems to be a practice that is both rich in practical relevance and in unresolved research questions [10]. Research on visualization is fragmented and needs to be collected from many fields such as knowledge management, organization studies, human-computer interaction, diagram research, anthropology, small group research, cognitive psychology, information visualization, design studies, and architecture [10]. Legal visualization research has its origins in Central European legal informatics [7] and the doctoral thesis by C. R. Brunschwig on "Visualization of Legal Norms" [6]. Existing literature outside Europe addresses cognitive and linguistic reasons for common difficulties in comprehending law focusing on pedagogical aspects, but does not address business relationships [23]. In the U.S., research on legal visualization mainly relates to using visualization in court [12, 13, 27]. Some articles on contract visualization have been published in professional publications [21].

A visual perspective on collaboration offers tremendous potential even for areas where drawings do not necessarily represent tangible objects, like strategic planning or process management [10]. Visualization has been successfully used to make understanding easier and to combat information overload [9]. Words can have different meanings to different people, even if they are supposedly speaking the same language. Visuals don't necessarily depend on the language and can help communication in global contexts and between people with different backgrounds [22]. In their framework, Eppler and Platts [11] emphasize a process view of visualization: the actual act of visualizing rather than the final outcome is the vital sense-making activity. Their framework also stresses the situated use of visualization that is targeted to a specific content, step or goal, and benefit. Used in this systematic way, visualization can become a powerful, analytic business language [11].

Our interviews show that there are some road blocks in the way of contract visualization. In the words of an interviewed sales manager: 'Contracts are much too important and serious to be visualized. Are we supposed to draw pictures in them?' The danger is that if contracts are too visual they do not seem official any more to those used to lengthy legal text. There are also cultural differences in how contracts are regarded. Global business requires contracts that are accepted globally, and too much visualization might get a negative reaction from potential business partners. Offering a visual contract might seem like not taking the deal seriously or not respecting the ability of the other party to understand contract language. Visualization is a tool that has to be approached with caution.

Bresciani and Eppler [5] note that despite the notable number of publications on the benefits of using visualization in a variety of fields, few studies have so far investigated the possible pitfalls of graphic depictions used for communication or reasoning, even though there are several caveats that need to be considered in the application of visualization [11]. They provide valuable insights into the pitfalls of graphic representations [5]: i.e. the cause of a visualization disadvantage can be the designer(s) or the user(s) and their interpretation [28]. The effect of visualization drawbacks can be classified for example into cognitive, emotional, and social effects [8, 24, 5].

The way people understand visual images is embedded in their cultural and professional backgrounds. If visuals differ from the generally understood forms, icons, and symbols, the practical purpose of visualization is defeated. Instead of demystifying, it will create more complexity. Even though icons, unlike symbols that are based on a general agreement of their meaning, are based on images of concrete objects, even they can be misleading if one does not have the right background. For example the image of a computer disc used to mean 'save' has no meaning as such for those who have never come into contact with one. [22]

The challenge is to use visuals in a way that removes complexity instead of adding confusion. It is most likely impossible to create a visual language that would immediately be understood by all without any additional information. When visualizing contracts an important guideline is to first understand the context and the people that are going to need to understand the information we plan to visualize. [21]

To be able to fully benefit from contract visualization we need to learn another skill in addition to contract literacy: visual literacy. Learning to read and write using visuals, being visually literate, enables us to communicate accurately and appreciate and accept diversity of culture and visual expression [16]. Visual literacy which has been widely ignored as a concept [17] can be defined as the learned ability to interpret visual messages accurately and to create such messages [14].

4. The Case

The case company is a high-technology machine manufacturer with worldwide business activities and representation in more than 130 countries. Its strengths are leading technological expertise in three primary areas and insight into customer processes. The company has 44,000 employees and sales of approximately EUR 8 billion (2009). It has successfully embraced the servitization challenge with open arms and is now trying to do even better: to sell more services, to sell better

services, to sell more services better. The goal is to make selling service contracts or add-on modules to service contracts safer and easier and to facilitate conflict resolution, collaboration, and communication, both internally and with customers. The service offering is modularized and packaged into products according to the principles of service productization. One of the sources of confusion is trying to make sense of what follows when customers make choices between available options in the service products: what is it that they are actually entitled to and what that means to the service delivery organization.

Visualization comes up as one possible way to clarify the contracts and the entitlement dilemma. The idea is to create for example flowcharts as a complementary element to the text – no way as a replacement to the contract text – and to clarify the main elements of a service contract in a more simple chart and the details in separate charts. The goal is to first create a visual sales tool to help explain the service content to customers and eventually somehow make it easy to connect corresponding contract modules and service modules thus facilitating crafting better contracts faster and with better results. Here, better is understood to mean more manageable and more understandable, indeed contracts that would possibly have the potential to work as some kind of road maps for the service relationship. Another goal is to facilitate communicating the content of the contracts to all concerned. So far, so good, the goal has been agreed on. Or has it?

The first misunderstanding concerns the concept of a contract. Is it a legal document including all appendices etc? After much discussion it appears that with a service contract the company representatives mean the productized service product: a package of service modules with some options for the customer to customize the service product for their particular requirements. The 'legal stuff' should be left alone and visualization applied to the service description and related documents with the goal of making it easier to craft the final contract document by putting together the customer's choices (mostly affecting the service description) and the 'legal stuff', meaning terms and conditions, limitations of liability etc.

The visualization team sets to work, armed with contract templates (80 pages), appendices, service descriptions, and product specifications. Many of the internal documents are already visual: flowcharts are used to describe the service process including everything the service personnel is supposed to do. However, these documents are not to be shown to the customers since they contain a lot of information that is irrelevant to them. Tables and matrices are used to describe the service content, outcomes, and deliverables. The first task is to understand the service products in order to be able to visualize them. And here comes the first really major problem. In spite of their prior knowledge and experience of the company and its products as well as extensive engineering expertise, the visualization team is completely puzzled by a couple of sentences in the descriptions. Reading through all the available documents does not help, this is just something 'everybody knows'. After several false interpretations they finally get it (almost) right – but not quite, as it turns out after the visual tool has been finalized.

The result of the visualization effort is a combination of drawings, charts, text, and photographs that describes the service process. The 'legal stuff' comes in as connections to another document that contains 'legal alerts', as in contractual matters that concern certain actions in the service process, for example the responsibilities and accountabilities of the customer and what happens if those are not fulfilled satisfactorily. There are also different views of the visual document, some to be used internally and some to be shown to customers.

5. Discussion

What can we learn from the visualization experiment? The first lesson is that to construct a meaningful visualization of a text one first needs to really understand the message of that text. Before text can be visualized successfully it has to be clear and understandable. In this case one reason for the unclear text was probably that the documents had been written by multilingual teams whose first language was not English. Another reason was that the documents described something that the service engineers and sales people were very familiar with, and consequently did not need to read any documents to know what was to be done.

The second lesson is that it is essential to consider and understand the target audience and the goal of visualization. The engineers liked the idea of showing service levels in graph form and were of course very familiar with flowcharts but found the simplest form of the sales tool too simple. After all, the buyers are mostly also engineers and can be insulted if their ability to understand complex matters in relation to a product they know well is put to question. If, on the other hand, the goal is to illustrate marketing material, the visualization needs are very different.

The third lesson is that the process of visualization can be much more useful than the final visualized result. To create meaningful visuals the visualizers need to truly understand the text they are visualizing and analyze its meaning. Thus the process can lead to for example new understanding of what a service contract should include or how the service process could be improved. Visuals can be effective communication tools especially when language fails, as was sometimes the case here. Drawing things can clarify thought processes and thus promote understanding and communicating that understanding to others.

The fourth lesson is that it is still unclear what contract visualization actually means and should mean in practice. At one point the visualization team considered turning the actual contract text into a flowchart but in the end that did not seem to add clarity. Some things just need to be spelled out and putting text in boxes that are connected to each other by arrows does not necessarily help. The idea of using an 80-page document as a practical management tool in its entirety is slightly absurd; different groups need different parts of the contract and for example service descriptions – in many cases including flowcharts and service level graphs - are already used to guide the service process.

Finally, the case supports the belief that attitudes need to change a lot before non-lawyers start reading contracts and finding them even remotely interesting or useful in practice. No legal professionals participated in the visualization project. The consensus among all participants was that it was best to leave legal matters to lawyers and get on with real business without them; the best contract being the kind of contract that never needed to be looked at after signing.

If we assume that non-lawyers in a business organization should adopt a new mindset towards contracts, the question is how to motivate them. All experts have their own professional pride and if someone – in this case a lawyer – comes up and suggests that they are somehow lacking – in this case lacking legal understanding – that is bound to lead to immense resistance. Most business professionals need a reason that can be translated into money to be convinced. The argument that increased legal understanding promotes better business and successful long-term business relationships could be a valid reason. Visualization can help communication and make contracts less off-putting for visual thinkers and could thus be one way to promote an increased interest in contracts. In a global company visuals might serve as the common language that all understand, if created with care and an understanding of the company and its employees. However, it is necessary to keep in mind that in a business organization also non-lawyers are experts in their own fields and in no way illiterate or intellectually challenged and can be insulted if their ability to understand contracts is automatically put to question.

6. Conclusions and Further Research

The goal of this paper was to provide material for further discussion on the topic of legal and contract visualization. As a starting point, we offer five points based on conclusions drawn from the case as well as the interviews and literature review: (1) The ultimate goal should be a clear message, whether textual or visual, (2) You should make sure you understand what you are visualizing, to what purpose and to what audience, (3) The process of visualization can be more useful than the final result, (4) Much research into what contract visualization means in practice is still needed, and (5) Increasing the legal expertise of non-lawyers entails a huge attitude change. Admittedly, the paper would have benefited from the inclusion of concrete examples of the created visual tools. However, the case company did not agree to have the results published and altering the visuals enough to satisfy their wishes would have defeated the purpose of providing a concrete example.

Further research into legal and contract visualization should be constructive of nature and geared towards more practical applications in business contexts, including the concrete analysis of the visuals created during the research. It is necessary to turn theory into practice, in a way that can actually benefit real business organizations in the real world. A question that needs further research is whether it is necessary to increase legal knowledge among non-lawyers and to what extent - and how to overcome the resistance that gets in the way of adopting a new mindset.

7. References

1.   Argyres, N. and Mayer, K. J. [2004]. Learning to contract: Evidence from the personal computer iIndustry, Organization Science, 15, *pp*. 394–410.

2.   Argyres, N. and Mayer, K. J. [2007]. Contract design as a firm capability: An integration of learning and transaction cost perspectives, Academy of Management Review, 32, pp. 1060-1077.

3.   Bagley, C. E. [2008]. Winning legally: The value of legal astuteness, Academy of Management Review, 33, pp. 378–390.

4.   Bird, R. C. [2010]. The many futures of legal strategy, American Business Law Journal, 47, pp. 575-586.

5.   Bresciani S. and Eppler M. [2009]. The Risks of Visualization: a Classification of Disadvantages Associated with Graphic Representations of Information. In: Schulz, P.J., Hartung, U., Keller, S. (Eds.), Identität und Vielfalt der Kommunikations-wissenschaft, UVK Verlagsgesellschaft mbH, Konstanz (Germany).

6.   Brunschwig, C. R.   [2001]. Visualisierung von Rechtsnormen – Legal design [Visualization of legal norms]. Doctoral Thesis. Zürcher Studien zur Rechtsgeschichte, Vol. 45. Rechtswissenschaftliche Fakultät d. Universität Zürich. Schulthess Juristische Medien, Zürich.

7.   Brunschwig, C. R.   [2006], Visualising legal information: Mind maps and E-government, Electronic Government, an International Journal, 3, pp. 386–403.

8.   Buergi, P. and Roos, J. [2003]. Images of strategy. European Management Journal 21(1), pp. 69-78.

9.   Eppler, M. J. and Mengis, J. [2004]. The concept of information overload: A review of literature from organization science, marketing, accounting, MIS, and related disciplines. The Information Society - an International Journal, 20, 5, pp. 1-20.

10.   Eppler, M. J. [2007]. Toward a visual turn in collaboration analysis ?, Building Research & Information, 35, pp. 584-587.

11.   Eppler, M. J. and Platts [2009]. Visual strategizing The systematic use of visualization in the strategic-planning process, Long Range Planning, 42, pp. 42-74.

12.   Feigenson, N. and Dunn, M.A. [2003]. New visual technologies in court: Directions for research, Law and Human Behavior, 27, pp. 109–126.

13.   Feigenson, N. and   Spiesel, C. [2009]. Law on Display. The digital transformation of legal persuasion and judgment. New York [USA], New York University Press.

14.   Heinich, R., Molenda, M. and Russell, J. [1982] Instructional media and the new technologies of instruction. John Wiley, New York .

15.   Oliva, R. and Kallenberg, R. [2003]. Managing the transition from products to services. International Journal of Service Industry Management, Vol. 14(2), pp. 160-172.

16.   Pettersson, R. [2009] Visual literacy and message design', TechTrends, Vol. 53, No. 2, March/April, pp. 38–40.

17.   Rezabek, L.L. [2004] 'Why visual literacy: Consciousness and convention', TechTrends, Vol. 49, No. 3, pp. 19–20.

18.   Rekola, K. [2007a] Service design as a basis for successful contracting, Contracting   Excellence,   December.   [Online]   Available   at: http://www.iaccm.com//contractingexcellence.php?storyid=374.

19.   Rekola, K. [2007b] Service design as a basis for successful commercial contracting, IACCM EMEA Conference proceedings.

20.   Rekola, K. [2008] Service design as a basis for successful commercial contracting in Corporate contracting capabilities; Conference proceeding and other writings, Joensuun yliopisto.

21.   Rekola, K. and Haapio, H.   [2009]. Better business through proactive productization and visualization of contracts. Contracting Excellence, June/July, pp. 17–19. Available at http://www.iaccm.com/userfiles/file/CE_2_5_press_C2 [1].pdf

22.   Rekola, K. and Haapio, H. [2011] Proactive contracting + service design = success! International Journal of Services, Economics and Management, forthcoming

23.   Robinson, P. [2009]. Graphic and symbolic representation of law: Lessons from cross-disciplinary research, Murdoch university electronic journal of law, 16, 1, pp. 53-83.

24.   Roos, J., V. Bart, et al. [2004]. Playing seriously with strategy, Long range planning 37, pp. 549-568.

25.   Roquilly, C. [2010], From legal monitoring to legal core competency: How to integrate the legal dimension into strategic management. In Legal Strategies: How Corporations Use Law to Improve Performance, edited by A. Masson and M. J. Shariff. Berlin Heidelberg: Springer.

26.   Siedel, G. J. and Haapio, H. [2010]. Using proactive law for competitive advantage, 47 American Business Law Journal, 4, pp. 641–686.

27.   Taiti, D. [2007]. Rethinking the role of the image in justice: Visual evidence and science in the trial process, Law, Probability and Risk, 6, pp. 311–318.

28.   Tufte, E. R. [1986]. The visual display of quantitative information. Cheshire, Connecticut, Graphic Press.

29.   Vandermerwe, S. and Rada, J. [1988] 'Servitization of business: Adding value by adding services', European Management Journal, Vol. 6, No. 4, pp. 314–324.

30.   Vargo, S.L. and Lusch, R.F. [2004] Evolving into a new dominant logic for marketing, Journal of Marketing, Vol. 68, No. 1, pp. 1–17.

The Effectiveness of Knowledge Visualization for Organizational Communication in Europe and India

Sabrina Bresciani[1], Martin Eppler[2], Asha Kaul[3], Riina Ylinen[4]

[1]Università della Svizzera italiana (Switzerland), [2]University of St. Gallen (Switzerland),
[3]Indian Institute of Management Ahmedabad, (India), [4]Aalto University (Finland)
{[1]bresciani.sabrina@gmail.com, [2]mjeppler@gmail.com,
[3]ashakaul@iimahd.ernet.in, [4]riina.ylinen@aalto.fi}

Abstract

In recent years we are witnessing a growing interest and use of knowledge visualization for communicating ideas and insights. Companies are deploying diagrams and knowledge maps to convey crucial business concepts. Scholars are reporting successful company cases, theorizing on the topic and compiling classifications and best practices. Yet few studies have attempted to prove the effectiveness of visualization, nor have they based their hypotheses on theories with predictive power. We aim to provide a contribution for the advancement of the field of knowledge visualization by testing the effects of different visualizations on the attitude toward its content. Second, we assess if visualization effectiveness is universal or culturally-bounded. We have conducted an experimental study, comparing text and two knowledge visualization types. The results of 231 subjects in Europe and India demonstrate that knowledge visualization has the power to increase the effectives of the message compared to text, and that these benefits replicate across different cultures.

Keywords--- Knowledge visualization, business communication, attitude, cross-cultural experiment, India, strategy communication.

1. Introduction

With this study we aim to provide a contribution toward the understanding of the effects of knowledge visualization for organizational communication. We observe a general trend in organizations toward an increasing use of visualization for communicating knowledge. The benefits of visualization are extensively discussed in various academic fields, ranging from psychology [1] to education [2], and business [3-4] to logical reasoning [5]. Academic studies specifically in knowledge visualization have provided descriptions of successful cases, as well as classifications and conceptualizations of these phenomena. At this stage of development of the field we identify the need to provide a testing of the observed benefits of visualization through rigorous empirical studies.

Thus we have set up and conducted a controlled experiment in which we have assessed the effects of knowledge visualization compared to text. As a specific application context for the study we have selected a common and often problematic communication task in organizations: the communication of a company's strategy [6].

The second aim of the study is to evaluate if the effect of knowledge visualization is universal or dependent on a specific cultural background. While Asia is gaining more and more relevance in the economic sphere, it is not clear if communication messages created in the Western world are equally effective in Asia, or vice versa.

Visualization is often conceived as a universal language, globally understood and able to overcome language barriers. Yet there is evidence that cultural differences in thought patterns can affect the reception of any kind of communication, including visual messages [7]. Based on theories of cultural differences in views of the world between Westerners and Asians [8-9] we have developed two different visualizations, of which one is more suitable for Westerners and one more suitable for Asians.

We have conducted an experiment with three conditions: a control condition with text and two treatment conditions with knowledge visualization types suitable for Westerners (a linear diagram) and Asians (a holistic visual metaphor), respectively. We have replicated the experiment in two very different cultural contexts, Europe and India. The results show that knowledge visualization has a significant positive effect on the attitude towards the content, compared to text, across the two cultures. Second, we find confirmation of cultural preferences for different visualization types (diagrammatic and metaphorical), as predicted by theory.

1550-6037/11 $26.00 © 2011 IEEE
DOI 10.1109/IV.2011.29

These results demonstrate that a suitable knowledge visualization has the power to improve the communication of business concepts, such as a strategy. Organizations can therefore deploy knowledge visualization for improving the effectiveness of their strategy communication.

The novelty of this study is to be found in the development of a model based on solid theories and on a rigorous theory testing process. Although conceptual visualization is commonly considered helpful for improving communication, and several studies and speculated on its usefulness and possible reasons, very few studies have thus far measured the truth of these claims and the extent of the effects. This paper provides a first demonstration of the actual positive effects of knowledge visualization.

In the following sections, we provide a review of the relevant literature, followed by a description of the experimental methodology employed, sample description and results. In the fifth section implications for theory and practice are given and in the conclusion we consider the limitations of the study and provide suggestions for future research directions.

2. Selective Literature Review

Visualizing knowledge means mapping concepts graphically, by structuring text and visuals in a meaningful way. Visualizations are used in organizations for enhancing both the *cognitive and emotional* response to the presented content.

Scholars in various fields [1-5, 10] posit that when visual representations are used, *cognitive* abilities are enhanced, thanks to the ability of visualization to structure information [11] and to "reduce cognitive load, enhance representation of relationships among complex constructs, provide multiple retrieval paths for accessing knowledge" [2: page 71]. Second, visualization can affect the *emotional* response by creating involvement [12] and engaging employees [13].

As the world is becoming more and more flat [14], companies are expanding worldwide and conducting business across national borders. Thus they have an ever increasing need to communicate to employees of different cultures. Visual representation can be particularly helpful for conveying information across cultures, for its inherent ability to be understood despite language differences. Well known examples are the pictograms found in airports or used at the Olympic Games. Knowledge visualization can provide further benefits for conveying knowledge across cultures, as it can lower the ambiguity of verbal and written communication by making concepts more tangible and concrete.

Yet, cultural differences in traditions and conventions can affect the interpretation of visual representations, as for instance in the meaning of colors, the understanding of symbols and metaphors (for an extensive review and references see [15]). On a deeper level, cultural background can affect thought patterns. The concept of the Geography of Thought, developed by Nisbett [9] and in line with previous studies [7], suggests that Westerners are more comfortable with an analytic and liner reasoning style, while Asians prefer storytelling and holistic reasoning. Specifically for the context of Europe and India, it has been proposed [8] that the differences we observe today in behavior and communication style can be traced back to differences in Mythical heroes of India over two thousand years ago (i.e., Ram) and in ancient Greece (i.e., Achilles). Hence, the interpretation of visual metaphors and analogies are likely to be shaped by exposure to diverse traditions and educational systems of these two cultural regions.

3. Methodology

3.1. Experiment Design

To address the proposed research question of demonstrating if knowledge visualization leads to more positive results (in terms of its perception) than textual communication, we have set up a controlled experiment. This methodology is considered the most appropriate for our aim of conducting theory testing and be able to generalize on the findings. The application context is the communication of a business strategy. A typical company strategy in text format is compared to visual formats of the same content, displayed on a letter-sized paper. As reviewed in the previous section, visualization can affect people's cognitive and emotional response to content: the dependent variables of the study are thus *cognitive* and *emotional response* toward the content of the strategy, assessed through scales of 3 items each and collected via a questionnaire.

The second aim of the study is to assess if there are *cross-cultural differences* in the reception of visualization in Europe and India. Thus, based on the theoretical background discussed in the previous section, two types of knowledge visualizations have been developed: One which is most suitable for Westerners (emphasizing linear and analytical thinking), and one which is suitable for Asians (emphasizing storytelling and holistic thinking). The selection of these graphic formats is a somewhat arbitrary process due to the lack of specific and concrete guidelines. The authors have analyzed existing literature and business practices for strategy communication, and have brainstormed with researchers in Europe and Asia to develop culturally appropriate visualizations. The outcome of this process is the selection of the 'timeline' as possibly the most appropriate strategy representation for Westerners [16], and of the 'mountain trail' visual metaphor for Asians [17].

The mountain metaphor carries the meaning of adventure and goal of reaching the peak in both cultures. It emphasizes a holistic cognitive process and metaphorical associations, thus we hypothesize that its effect is stronger in Asia, where it can also be associated with pilgrimage to holy places which are often located at the top of mountains. Pilgrimages are collective experiences, which emphasize the sense of traveling together to a holy destination and supporting each other; each "stop" along the way is not only a means to an end, but an important experience in itself.

The timeline is a rather standard visual format with time depicted on the x axes, from left to right in both cultural regions. It is an abstract and analytic visualization, hence we hypothesize that it is more suitable for westerners which prefer systematic and analytic thinking.

OUR BUSINESS STRATEGY

50% growth by 2012

- *Sub-goal 1: 20% growth in mature business areas*
  - Manage customer relationships
  - Provide high quality services
  - Unique understanding of customers to sell them more related products
  - Increase customer retention
  Problem: competition

- *Sub-goal 2: 30% growth through international expansion*
  - Get distribution deal in foreign countries
  Problem: legal issues (Patent etc.) ➔ Sign cooperation contract with local dealer
  Problem: low brand recognition ➔ Brand campaign
  - Stabilize distribution
  Problem: dealer commitment ➔ Sales incentives

Success factors:
Long term vision
Cost control
Competition monitoring
Internal communication
Spot future opportunities

Figure 1 Control Condition: Textual

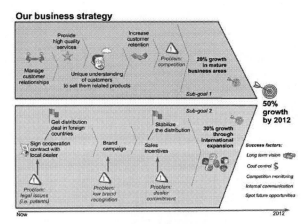

Figure 2 Treatment Condition: Timeline

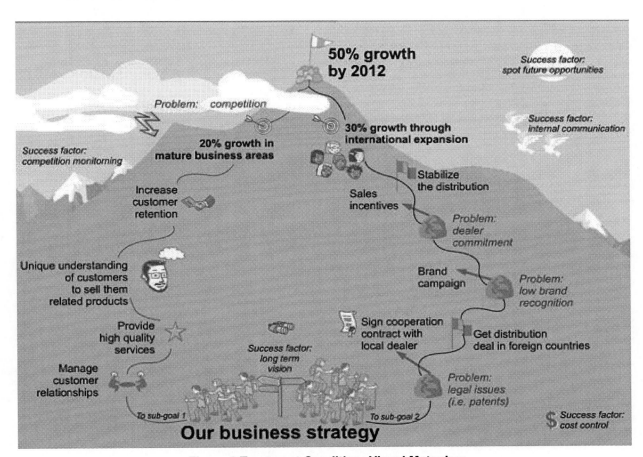

Figure 3 Treatment Condition: Visual Metaphor

The experiment is a 3-condition between-subjects design. We compare three formats of the strategy, with exactly the same content in terms of words: (1) a control condition with bullet-points on a PowerPoint slide, simulating the usual format for communicating a strategy in an organization (Figure 1), to (2) a treatment condition with a sequential diagram in the form of a timeline (Figure 2), and (3) a treatment condition with a visual metaphor in the form of a mountain trail (Figure 3). It should be emphasized that the content remains exactly the same across the three conditions, and that the difference is found in the inclusion of the background images for the treatment conditions, and – accordingly – the mapping of the content on the page.

3.2. Procedure

The subjects have been randomly assigned to one of the three conditions, as suitable in controlled experiment, for having a random distribution of subjects' characteristics [18]. Each participant has received one of the three representations of the strategy (on a color letter-size paper sheet) and a questionnaire. Subjects have been given instructions to read the strategy carefully and answer the questions in the given order. In the questionnaire they have been asked about the dependent variables of cognitive and emotional response through self-developed scales of three items each, rated on 7 point Likert scales. They have also been asked to explain their understanding of the represented strategy. We have also included questions regarding potentially confounding variables, i.e. demographic characteristic, familiarity with the topic and with the representation etc., and about their cultural background for manipulation checking.

4. Results

4.1. Sample Description

The subjects who have participated in the experiment are 231 graduate students with work experience, attending management courses in Europe (N=87) and in India (N=144). All the subjects are enrolled in programs held in English.

The median age is 24, and they have 3 years of work experience (median); 164 are males and 67 are females. Sample characteristics are fairly distributed across cultures.

4.2. Analysis

First, a principal component analysis (p.c.a.) is conducted on the scales of cognitive and emotional response, which are composed of 3 items each. The p.c.a. results are satisfactory, with all items loading on the expected factors, and having factors loadings above the recommended value of .6. Then reliability analysis is performed: the cognitive response scale returns a

Cronbach's Alpha of .736, and the emotional response scale gives a Cronbach's Alpha of .876, hence both values are well above the recommended threshold (of .6).

The mean of the experiment results are reported in Table 1, with Standard Deviation values (S.D.). A visual representation of the results is reported in Figure 4 for the cognitive response and in Figure 5 for the emotional response.

	Cognitive Response		Emotional Response	
	Mean	(S.D)	Mean	(S.D)
Control:				
Europe	3.84	1.34	2.80	1.08
India	4.48	1.14	4.01	1.24
Timeline:				
Europe	5.12	1.21	4.17	1.14
India	4.97	1.01	4.11	1.16
Metaphor:				
Europe	4.56	1.06	3.96	1.26
India	5.24	1.03	4.94	1.06

Table 1 Experiment Results: Means by Treatment Condition

A first inspection of the results already suggests that the data follow the direction hypothesized, with the treatment conditions having higher values than the textual condition, in both cultures. To test the significance of these differences, Analysis of Variance (ANOVA) is performed, with planned comparison contrasting the control condition to each of the two (visual) treatment conditions.

For both the European and Indian sample ANOVA indicates a significant positive value for the cognitive (p<.5) and for the emotional response (p<.5). This means that the treatment has a significant positive effect compared to the control condition on the cognitive response toward the content: the subjects judge the strategy as more convincing (i.e. "This strategy makes sense") when it is conveyed with the visual representations. Subjects also have a more positive attitude toward the strategy (i.e. "This strategy is engaging") when it is conveyed with the visualizations, compared to when it is conveyed with text.

In particular, contrasting the effects of the two visual representations, European subjects have more positive responses when exposed to the timeline linear diagram compared to the mountain metaphor, while Indians have more positive responses when exposed to the mountain visual metaphor compared to the timeline diagram.

These results confirm both hypotheses of the study: communicating a business strategy with knowledge visualization, compared to text, has a significant positive impact on the cognitive and on the emotional response of the subjects. Secondly, there is evidence of cultural difference in the preferences for different visualizations. As predicted by theory, the European sample has more positive results with the timeline, while the Indian sample displays more positive results with the visual metaphor.

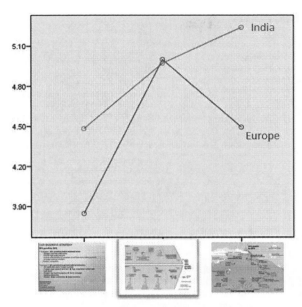

Figure 4 Results: Cognitive Response

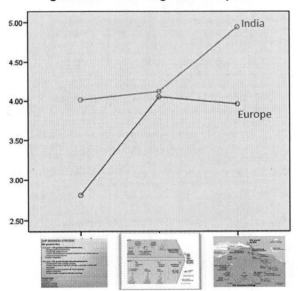

Figure 5 Results: Emotional Response

5. Implications

5.1. Theoretical Implications

The results of the study indicate that knowledge visualization can have a positive impact on the emotional and cognitive response toward the content of a message, compared to text. Implications of these findings are relevant on a theoretical level as they show that visualization is not a mere "nice to have" or decorative element in communicating and conveying knowledge, but truly makes a substantial difference, improving the attitude of the reader toward the content, both cognitively

and emotionally. These results confirm the theoretical work reviewed in the second section, as expressed by [1, 4, 5, 12, 13], and it is innovative as it provides a testing of the theories with rigorous assessment. Furthermore it successfully combines different and complementary theoretical perspectives: this study provides innovative insights by extending the concept of the Geography of Thought [9] and of cross-cultural mythology [8] and philosophy [19] to knowledge visualization. It is the first study of this kind, at best of our knowledge. The study also shows that the positive effect of visualization is found across cultures, but that there are cultural preferences for certain types of visualizations. Hence when a culturally appropriate visualization is employed, the advantages of knowledge visualization can be enhanced.

5.2. Practical Implications

Organizational communication has the power to attract and solicit compliance from employees at all rungs, provided it is well communicated. Increasing business opportunities across countries and cultures has created a need for communicating strategy in different languages and formats. While the overarching goal remains the same, the mode for communication is often given a local hue for easy and quick comprehension and implementation. Organizations can, to their advantage, exploit the benefit of visual representation for sustained and improved communication of information and insights across cultures. This study shows that visualizing knowledge is a very effective way to communicate, with the potential to secure the attention and buy-in of employees toward the content, for example a company's strategy. These positive effects are found across cultures; therefore companies that operate internationally can safely deploy visualization with a changed patterning for maximum effect in Western countries and Asia. However, for enhancing the effect of the communication, they should use visual representations which are specifically adapted to the local culture. In particular, when communicating strategic goals to Europeans, a sequential and abstract diagram, as for example the timeline, might be suitable. When communicating to Indians, a holistic and metaphorical representation, as for example a mountain trail metaphor, seems more appropriate.

In addition, this study provides first rigorous empirical evidence regarding the potential advantages of knowledge visualization – specifically in the form of timeline and mountain visual metaphor – compared to text alone (of the same content) for communicating strategy. Thus organization can exploit knowledge visualization to potentially improve the response to their strategy communication programs and organization's change management. The commitment of employees to implement the strategy and their buy-in is fundamental for the strategy success. Several scholars [3, 6] have mentioned communication as the number one cause of failure of strategy implementation.

This study shows that knowledge visualization can offer an effective and easy to implement tool for organizations: creating a suitable conceptual visualizations (as Figure 2-3) requires a very small effort, and can substantially improve employees attitude toward the strategy: the return on investment (for creating the visualization) is thus very high.

The results suggest that the rare use of visualization nowadays in business communication might be a missed opportunity for organizations, as they are not exploiting the full potential of communication tools available.

6. Limitations and Conclusion

This study has limitations typical of experimental works: by emphasizing internal validity and rigorous evaluation, the experimental task is somewhat artificial, and therefore has problems regarding external validity. Futures studies could address the issue for instance by conducting the study in a real organizational setting. A second limitation regards the choice of the experimental treatments: due to the lack of guidelines for designing and selective effective visualizations for specific tasks and cultures, the choice of the visual representations was somewhat arbitrary. The translation of theories of cross-cultural psychology and anthropology to specific visualization forms is not free of problems. We would like to encourage more research in this direction, given the pragmatic relevance and the corresponding scarce amount of guidelines on the topic.

Only one type of textual representation, in the form of bullet points, has been tested. This format was selected to be able to have the exact content in the same form for all three conditions. Similarly, other visualization types might lead to different results. We have limited the number of conditions to three, in order to be able to have an adequate number of subjects per condition and thus make it likely to have sufficient statistical power to be able to generalize the findings. Further research is needed to understand how different textual and visual formats affect the results.

In this study we have hypothesized and demonstrated that knowledge visualization can have a significant positive impact, compared to text, on the cognitive and emotional response of the subjects toward the presented content. The results show that theories of cross-cultural differences in reasoning patterns apply as well to conceptual visual representations. We find that visualization is more effective than text across cultures (specifically Europe and India), and when a culturally appropriate visualization is deployed, its perception can be improved.

References

[1] B. Tversky. Visuospatial reasoning. In: K. Holyoak and R. Morrison (Eds.), *Handbook of Reasoning*. Cambridge, UK: Cambridge University Press, pp. 209-249. 2005.

[2] A.M. O'Donnell, D.F. Dansereau and R.H. Hall. Knowledge Maps as Scaffolds for Cognitive Processing. *Educational Psychology Review*. 14 (1), 71-86. 2002.

[3] H. Mintzberg. Strategic Thinking as "Seeing". In: H. Mintzberg, B. Ahlstrand and L. Lampel (Eds.) *Strategy Bites Back*. London: Financial Times Prentice Hall, pp. 133-138. 2005.

[4] M.J. Eppler and R.A. Burkhard. Visual Representations in Knowledge Management: Framework and Cases. *Journal of Knowledge Management*, 4 (11), 112-122. 2007.

[5] J.H. Larkin and H. Simon. Why a Diagram is (Sometimes) Worth Ten Thousand Words. *Cognitive Science*, 11, 65-99. 1987.

[6] L.D. Alexander. Successfully Implementing Strategic Decisions. *Long Range Planning*, 18: 91-97. 1985.

[7] M.H. Segall, D.T. Campbell and M.J. Herskovits. *The Influence of Culture on Visual Perception*. Indianapolis: Bobbs-Merrill Co. 1966.

[8] D. Pattanaik. Myth = Mithya A Handbook of Hindu Mythology. Penguin. 2008.

[9] R.E. Nisbett. *The Geography of Thought*. Bookwell: New York. 2003.

[10] A. Okada, S. Buckingham Shum and T. Sherborne (Eds.). *Knowledge Cartography. Software Tools and Mapping Techniques*. London: Springer. 2008.

[11] D.D. Suthers and C. Hundhausen. An empirical study of the effects of representational guidance on collaborative learning. *Journal of the Learning Sciences*, 12(2): 183-219. 2003.

[12] T. Buzan. *The Mind Map Book: How to Use Radiant Thinking to Maximize Your Brain's Untapped Potential*. Plume. 1996.

[13] A.S. Huff. *Mapping Strategic Thought*. Chichester, New York: John Wiley & Sons Inc. 1990.

[14] T.L. Friedman. *The World is Flat*. London: Penguin Books. 2006.

[15] S. Bresciani and M.J. Eppler, M.J. Glocalizing Visual Communication in Organizations. In: B. Bertagni, M. La Rosa M. and F. Salvetti (Eds.), *Glocal working*. Milan: Franco Angeli, pp. 233-251. 2010.

[16] E.K. Yakura. Charting Time: Timelines as Temporal Boundary Objects. *Academy of Management Journal*; 45 (5), 956-970. 2002.

[17] M. Useem, J. Useem and P. Asel. *Upward Bound: Nine Original Accounts of How Business Leaders Reached Their Summits*. Crown Business. 2003.

[18] D.T. Campbell and C.J. Stanley. *Experimental and quasi-experimental design for research*. Chicago, USA: Rand McNally College Pub. Co. 1966.

[19] E. Holenstein. *Philosophie-Atlas: Orte und Wege des Denkens*. Zürich: Ammann. 2004.

Knowledge Visualization in Qualitative Methods – or how can I see what I say?

Nicole Bischof
University of St. Gallen
=mcm institute
St. Gallen, Switzerland
nicole.bischof@unisg.ch

Alice Comi
Università della Svizzera italiana
IMCA Institute
Lugano, Switzerland
alice.comi@usi.ch

Martin J. Eppler
University of St. Gallen
=mcm institute
St. Gallen, Switzerland
martin.eppler@unisg.ch

Abstract: In several research fields, qualitative interviewing (i.e., face-to-face individual interviews and focus groups) is an essential approach to gather high-quality, and deep data about a wide range of subjective experiences. Although being a well-established research method, qualitative interviewing is fraught with various shortcomings such as difficulties in initiating the interview process, in eliciting tacit knowledge and in avoiding information redundancies. In this paper, we propose the use of visual tools (e.g., visualization software) as a support to facilitate the interview process and to gather sound qualitative data. Visual representations provide structure, context and explicitness, and thus foster knowledge elicitation and sharing in interviews. Our contribution is two-fold: First, we provide a methodological extension of qualitative interviewing. Second, we suggest a practical approach to use visuals in interviews, presenting concrete examples from the research field. We conclude our paper by discussing the limitations of our approach, and by suggesting directions for future research on visualization-based interviewing.

Keywords - Qualitative interviewing; one-to-one interviews; focus groups; projective techniques; visual aids; visual facilitation.

1. INTRODUCTION

Qualitative interviewing is a valuable research method for gathering data on people's attitudes, opinions, and life experiences [1]. The aim of qualitative interviews is thus to address questions of *how* and *why*, not *how much* or *how many* [2]. Usually, the researcher lets data emerge from the interviewees' accounts and inductively reconstructs clusters of meaning and action [3]. Qualitative interviewing can take a wide variety of forms, being "not a research method, but a family of research approaches that have only one thing in common – conversation between people in which one person has the role of the researcher" [1, p. 2]. While one-to-one interview is most commonly used, qualitative interviewing can also be conducted in larger groups, as in focus groups [4].

Even though interviewing has been the subject of a large body of literature [5, 6] many practical difficulties in conducting interviews have not yet been solved. Visual aids (e.g., cards, maps, photographs) are often used as *projective techniques* to encourage participants to share their innermost feelings or thoughts [7, 8]. In projective techniques, interviewees are asked to freely express their thoughts, by making associations between the visual stimuli and the concept with which they are being presented [14]. In essence, projective techniques evoke reactions to a familiar stimulus (i.e., an image) in order to aid partici-

pants elaborate their perceptions about a novel stimulus (i.e., concept).

In this paper, we propose an approach where visuals are used not only as stimuli to elicit comments from participants, but also as instruments to facilitate the interview process. In this *facilitation approach*, visuals are used not as static objects, but rather are drawn simultaneously by the interviewer and the participants. As explained in the next sections, visual facilitation can bring cognitive and communicative advantages to qualitative interviewing, such as enhancing knowledge sharing [9], focusing attention and fostering common understanding [10, 7]. We structure our paper as follows: First, we focus on qualitative interviewing by paying particular attention to the shortcomings of both one-to-one interviews and focus groups. Subsequently, we review the current literature on projective techniques in the attempt to explain the use of visual objects as stimuli in qualitative interviewing. Finally, we describe the advantages of using visuals as facilitation techniques for qualitative interviewing, while also introducing real examples of visual interviews and visual focus groups. We conclude by outlining the limitations of our approach, and by suggesting directions for future research on the use of visual methods in qualitative research.

2. QUALITATIVE INTERVIEWING: CHARACTERISTICS, ADVANTAGES AND SHORTCOMINGS

2.1. One-to-One Interviews

One-to-one (or individual) interviews are as old as mankind, and had already been used by the Ancient Egyptians for demographic investigations [11]. For individual interviews to be a research method, one of the participants should act as a researcher, and conduct the interview with the objective to answer a research question. Individual interviews can take a large variety of formats, ranging from structured (or close-ended) to unstructured (or ethnographic): While the first gives little room for variation in the answers [11] the latter is closer to observation and leads to open-ended data [12]. In between these two extremes, semi-structured interviews allow for long and in-depth accounts, while also providing guidance on the interview topic.

There are several advantages of one-to-one, face-to-face interviews: First, qualitative interviewing enables the researcher to gain deep insights into the respondents' perspectives [8]. Second, qualitative interviews are relatively inexpensive and allow collection of very rich data, enabling the researcher to notice and correct the respondents' misunderstandings, to probe vague answers, as well as to clarify doubts or concerns. Compared to other research methods, face-to-face interviews allow to monitor the order in which the questions are answered, and to control the context of the interview, thereby avoiding the possible biasing presence of other people [8]. Finally, the interviewing methodology is easily adjustable and can be combined with quantitative methods [3].

2.2. Focus groups

The focus group is an interview technique where the researcher collects data by creating a group interactive discussion [13, 14, 15]. This definition deliberately excludes groups or research methods that have inappropriately been called focus groups: First, focus groups should be distinguished from groups set up for purposes other than data collection (e.g., decision making, product development, project management groups). Second, focus groups should be set apart from procedures that involve multiple participants but do not allow interactive discussions, such as nominal and Delphi groups. Finally, focus groups should be distinguished from methods to collect data in naturally occurring discussions where no one acts as an interviewer [15]. Frey and Fontana [4] further suggest to draw a dividing line between group interviews and focus groups: Group interviews cannot be considered as focus groups if they (i) are conducted in informal settings; (ii) use nondirective interviewing; or (iii) use unstructured question formats. To this definition, marketing scholars [16, 14] add another criterion, suggesting that focus groups consist of structured discussions "among 6 to 10 homogeneous strangers in a formal setting" [15, p. 131] As explained by Hoyle et al. [8, p. 401], "Fewer than 6 makes it less likely that the desired diversity of opinions will be elicited, more than 10 makes it difficult for everyone to express their opinions fully … Lack of familiarity promotes free expressions of ideas and opinions that may not be forthcoming if members feel constrained by what they have said in the past to others in the group". Given the breadth of their possible applications, focus groups are used across a variety of academic fields, such as communication studies, education, and public health. Outside of academia, focus groups are popular in marketing research, where they are used to collect consumer's opinions about products, or to estimate the impact of advertising campaigns [17].

Focus groups are low in costs, produce results relatively quickly, and can increase the sample size of a study. However, the main advantage of focus groups lies in the ability to generate *collective data*, as the interviewer asks participants to build on each other, rather than aggregating individual data in search for general patterns. In the words of Morgan [15]: "What makes the discussion in focus groups more than the sum of separate individual interviews is the fact that the participants both query each other and explain themselves to each other". Moreover, the interaction in focus groups – i.e., the "group effect" – enables the investigation of complex phenomena, that are more difficult to uncover in one-to-interviews. Morgan and Krueger [18] have also underscored that such group

interaction provides valuable data on the extent, and the nature of consensus and diversity among participants.

2.3. Shortcomings of Qualitative Interviewing

There are several challenges in qualitative interviewing, such as getting the interviewee to speak freely, and gathering high-quality and valuable data. During the interview process, one of the greatest challenges is managing information, which means eliciting tacit knowledge, and at the same time avoiding information redundancy. Fontana and Frey [11, p. 361] describe the process-related difficulties of qualitative interviewing in a vivid and concrete way: "Asking questions and getting answers is a much harder task than it may seem at first. The spoken or written word has always a residue of ambiguity, no matter how carefully we word the questions and report or code the answers". Besides issues of wording and language choice, the phenomenon of *knowledge asymmetry* often threatens to disrupt the interview flow. In some instances, the knowledge of the interviewee – especially if she is an expert in her field – is much larger than the foreknowledge of the interviewer. This discrepancy leads to misunderstandings which usually are not detected prior to analyzing the data. At this stage, contacting the interviewee for further clarifications or questions may be practically unfeasible. The problem of knowledge asymmetry may occur also in the other direction, when the interviewer – because of her confidence with the interview topic – uses an expert language which is too elaborated for the counterpart to understand. If the interviewee is unable to fully understand the question, she may fear to lose her status when probing the question, and thus may provide inaccurate or vague answers.

Another difficulty lies in building up trust with the interviewee, and gaining access to deep and high quality data. If the interviewer fails to build a personal chemistry with the counterpart, for example by appearing unprofessional, the respondent may hide information. Furthermore, *interviewer effects* may interfere in the rapport between the interviewer and the respondent: The interviewer's expectations or personal characteristics, such as ethnicity, physical appearance and sex, can bias the responses. Since a strong interpersonal rapport is created in face-to-face interviews, respondents often tend to please the interviewer by providing socially desirable, yet invalid answers [8].

In focus groups, the moderator is faced with further challenges, such as encouraging participants to build on each other, avoiding overlaps in turn taking, and preventing individuals from dominating the conversation. In addition, there may be *conformity pressure* operating in a focus group: In this case, the moderator should identify nonverbal signs that indicate that a participant disagrees with what is being said. Besides, it is undeniable that group members affect each other in their answers [15, 19]. Sussman et al. [19] found a *polarization effect* related to group interaction – i.e., the attitudes of participants become more extreme after the group discussion. Moreover, the *mutual exposure* of participants limits the range of topics that can be effectively investigated in focus groups.

Since group interaction requires self-disclosure, some participants may find certain topics unacceptable for discussion [15].

Given the inherent challenges of qualitative interviews, the skillfulness of the interviewer / moderator has important consequences for the quality of the data collected. In focus groups, the moderation role is particularly difficult, since the facilitator is required to guide a multilateral conversation and at the same time to carefully process what is being said. Finally, a common challenge in both focus groups and interviews is to organize, and analyze the data gathered in order to identify recurrent patterns of meaning [8].

In the next sections, we make an attempt to explain how visual aids may help to overcome the multiple challenges of qualitative interviewing. We start by reviewing the current literature on projective techniques, and outline the advantages and the limitations of using visuals as stimuli in qualitative interviews. We then argue for a paradigm shift in the role of visuals, suggesting that the use of visual facilitation may improve qualitative interviewing, and increase the quality of data collection.

3. VISUALS AS STIMULI IN QUALITATIVE INTERVIEWS

Visual aids, such as drawings, pictures and maps, can be used during the qualitative interviewing as projective techniques to elicit comments from the participants [8]. Visual aids remove respondents' natural inhibitions, reveal less conscious and deeply-seated feelings, while also allowing to add affective evaluations to rational evaluations. As illustrated by Anastas [21], visuals jump-start respondents' imaginations and verbal responsiveness: "When asked a question like 'what are your feelings when you use this product?', some respondents become tense and anxious … When asked 'select a picture and tell how it shows your feelings when you use the product', they relax and jump into complex stories". By engaging interviewees, visuals enable better access to the participants' thoughts, energize the interview process and in turn lead to high-quality data [20]. Moreover, visuals act as *boundary objects* [22], i.e. as objects that facilitate the sharing of tacit knowledge, and reduce knowledge barriers between the interviewer and the participants. In reviewing the current literature on projective techniques [14, 23], we have identified four typologies of visual-based stimuli:

- *Association.* In the association technique, photographs are used to stimulate the participants' thinking, and to help them articulate their feelings about the discussion topic. In general, the interviewees are asked to express their impressions about pictures portraying people (personality associations), or situations (situational associations) that are connected to the discussion topic. In alternative, the participants may be invited to indicate which of several photographs in a stack most closely relate to the subject under discussion (forced associations). This technique enables the interviewer to uncover deep insights, as the partic-

ipants tend to project their feelings of the discussion topic onto the pictures stack.

- *Expression.* In expressive drawing, participants are asked to provide their reaction to a discussion topic by drawing a picture of how they feel about it. At the end of the task, the interviewer asks the respondent to comment on the meaning of her picture, and to elaborate on the relationship with the discussion topic. In focus groups, the moderator can involve the entire group in developing interpretations of each other's drawings, and hence of the discussion topic. Expressive drawing can be very useful to elicit information that otherwise might not be generated with traditional techniques, and at times can also motivate respondents.

- *Completion.* Another type of projective technique used in qualitative interviews is picture completion. In this technique, the participants are presented with an incomplete comic-strip story and are asked to add statements into the empty balloons. Like other projectives, picture completion helps the interviewer delve into the participants' minds, and learn more about their inner feelings.

- *Grouping.* In the grouping technique, participants are asked to collect, and to group a number of images that relate to the topic being discussed. The interviewees – either individually or in group – are given a pile of newspapers, scissors, glue and a blank piece of paper onto they can make a collage of pictures to represent the discussion topic. At the end of the task, the interviewees are asked to comment on the collage, and to explain the rationale behind their image choices. Often used in marketing research, this technique has proven useful to elicit the values, typical users, and purchasing motives associated to new products.

Although providing high-quality and deep data, the visual projectives described above fail to fully address the multiple challenges normally encountered in qualitative interviewing. In the following section, we explain how a paradigm shift from visuals as *projective techniques* towards visuals as *facilitation techniques* may enhance qualitative research, by enabling interviewers to fully exploit the potential of visual language.

4. VISUALS AS FACILITATION TECHNIQUES IN QUALITATIVE INTERVIEWING

As mentioned above, visuals can be introduced into qualitative interviews not only to elicit comments from participants (i.e., content support), but also to improve the research methodology (i.e., process support). In the facilitation approach, visuals are drawn simultaneously by the researcher and the participants during the qualitative interview. The visual language is thus integrated into the research process, and shifts from being an external stimulus to prompt answers, to becoming an integral component of the research method. As an example, the facilitator in focus groups may use visualization tools such as visual templates, sticky walls, and e-moderation software to lead the discussion, and at the same time enable participants to write and/or draw out their thoughts. In particular, visual templates – printed on a large poster support – provide a structured canvas where participants can document the discussion with post-it notes.

In comparison to purely text-based facilitation (e.g., flipchart handwriting), visual facilitation enables greater visibility of discussion threads, while also providing a more engaging experience for participants. Moreover, visual representations play a crucial role in the sense-making of individuals and groups, by bringing the advantage of *representational guidance*. In fact, the notations on a visual template may constrain what is expressed, and at the same time make certain aspects more salient. Thus, visual representations may support qualitative interviewing by providing an overarching structure which organizes information, coordinates the conversation, and highlights key aspects [24]. As suggested by Kuchenmüller and Stifel [25, p. 394], by filling visual templates the individual and / or the group "answers important questions while respecting definite rules".

By drawing attention on central themes, visual facilitation helps both the researcher and the interviewee to keep track of the conversation threads. In focus groups, this leads to the constitution of a *group memory*, which reduces the participants' difficulties in following the conversation, and building on each other's contributions. This advantage is present also in *online interviews* and *focus groups*, where visual techniques enable participants to make more fitting contributions, by providing tangible orientation and signposts during the conversation.

Furthermore, visualization techniques have been proven to facilitate balanced participation of group members, and to reduce the potential for interpersonal conflict. This is the case, since the target of the conflict shifts away from the person, to the concept being mapped onto the visual canvas. The *de-personalization effect* of visuals is particularly beneficial in focus groups, for reducing social pressure and encouraging participants to freely express their dissent with the rest of the group. When the conversation is mediated by visuals, participants are not pointing directly at each other, but rather express their agreement or disagreement towards impersonal objects, such as notes on a visual template [26]. In a study of business meetings, Kuchenmüller and Stifel [25, p. 388] consistently noticed that "it is easier to offend and attack using words than images". At the end of the qualitative interview, showing the filled template to the participants offers the possibility to gather further data, by asking probing questions, delving into important aspects, and commenting on the main findings.

As regards the final stage of data analysis, the use of prefabricated templates facilitates the *aggregation*, and the *comparability of data* collected across multiple interviews or focus groups. Thus, the use of visual templates leads to more reliable results, while also reducing the risk of gathering highly idiosyncratic data that cannot be easily inserted into the broader framework of the research theme.

Based on our literature review, as well as on our experience in qualitative interviewing, we suggest a four-stage method for visual-based research in one-to-one interviews and focus groups:

1. Preparing visual templates: Before the qualitative interview, the researcher should carefully choose visual templates based on the topic under investigation. As an example, a visual template for expectation inquiry may be useful in the initial phase of a focus group, to explore participants' expectations, experiences, perplexities, and questions on the subject at hand. For the selection of visual templates, the extant literature on knowledge visualization may provide a useful reference [27].

2. Filling visual templates: During the qualitative interview, the researcher fills the visual template by prompting answers from the interviewee(s). As regards group interviews, guiding and at the same time visualizing the conversation may be exceptionally difficult, and it is therefore advisable to have two facilitators acting in combination, one to moderate and the other one to visualize on her behalf [25].

3. Wrapping-up with visual templates. At the end of the qualitative interview, the researcher can summarize the main points emerged in the interview process by showing the filled template to the interviewees. By wrapping up the qualitative interview with visual representations, the interviewer may stimulate respondents to further delve into relevant topics, or to clarify misunderstandings in the documentation process.

4. Analyzing visual data. The researcher may look for consistent patterns by integrating the visual data reported on multiple templates. If necessary, she may explore group differences by comparing the visual templates filled out by different categories of interviewees and participants. In a way, the availability of standard templates replicates the rigor of quantitative procedures for data collection, although without trading away the richness and deepness of qualitative data.

In the next section, we present a few examples from our research experience, to better illustrate the use of visual facilitation in one-to-one interviews and focus groups.

5. EXAMPLES FROM THE FIELD

In two large research projects, we have facilitated qualitative interviewing situations with a total of more than 60 participants. In all of these face-to-face interviews (one-to-one and focus groups) we have been using visualizations for three purposes: First, to stimulate respondents and thus to initiate the interview process; Second, to sharpen the quality of data by eliciting deeper information; and third, to moderate the interview process with considerable improvements from a methodological perspective. In the following sections, we will present examples and discuss results from both interview situations.

5.1. Visualizations in One-to-One Interviews

In the first research project, we have conducted qualitative interviews for the purposes of gathering expert information on the use of software applications for monitoring natural hazards in Switzerland. Challenges at the very beginning of one-to-one interviews, such as establishing rapport, gaining trust, and understanding the language of respondents, could be overcome by using an association stimulus, i.e. a sketch about the interview process (Fig. 1). This sketching was used not only as an 'ice-breaker' at the beginning of the interview, but also as a reference to structure the interview content, and to ensure coverage of all the discussion topics (e.g., problems in software appropriation).

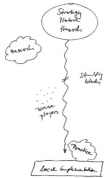

Figure 1: A sketch used as stimuli for expert interviews.

During the interview process another visual tool was used, namely a visual timeline loaded on a graphic facilitation software (Fig. 2). The respondents were asked to fill out the empty template by indicating how they perceived the evolution of their work domain including events, laws, and directives. This completion stimulus addresses the challenge of gathering high-quality data, by literally bringing tacit knowledge, experiences and opinions to the table. All of the participants liked the template completion, and provided positive feedback without being asked. Often, there was a moment of surprise in the beginning, which then turned into 'fun' and an ambition to fully complete the sheet. While filling out the visual, the interviewees kept on talking, what we consider as 'thinking aloud'. This phenomenon is reminiscent of ethnographic interviewing [11].

Based on our experience, we observed three main advantages of using visualization in one-to-one interviews: First, the respondents shared insights, experiences and memories which probably would have been hidden or forgotten without the template. Second, the template use allowed deep insights into the opinions and world views of the respondent and thus generated high-quality data. Third, the visuals enabled us to note side information mentioned incidentally by the interviewee, and in turn to elicit nuances that often lead to highly important and unexpected findings. Last but not least, the interviewer using visuals appeared to be more reliable and was regarded as being professional, objective and clear in her communication.

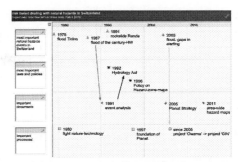

Figure 2: Timeline used as visual facilitation during the interview and for data analysis in retrospect.

5.2. Visualizations in Focus Groups

In a second research project, we have investigated the use of software applications for supporting decision-making in inter-organizational settings. In terms of research design, we have used randomized experiments as a primary method, and introduced focus groups as a follow-up method. In particular, we have used focus groups with the purpose to clarify unexpected experiment findings, while also gathering richer and deeper data on the research topic (see [15, 17] on the use of focus group in combination with other research methods). The experimental subjects served as focus group participants and were asked to reflect on their experience in the experiment.

In conducting the focus group, the facilitator used a visualization software (let's focus) connected to a video projector. For each interview question, the facilitator filled a visual template with contribution from the focus group participants (an example is shown in Fig. 3). In this regard, visual templates were used for real-time documentation of the focus group discussion. The visual facilitation enabled focus group participants to keep track of the discussion, and to build on each other's contributions with greater ease. Furthermore, the use of visual templates ensured consistency and comparability of data collected across different focus group sessions. As regards the data analysis, the availability of standard templates facilitated the comparisons, and aggregation of qualitative data. In this regard, the researchers elaborated an aggregated visual template summarizing the common patterns that emerged across the focus group sessions.

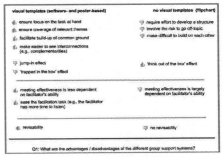

Figure 3: Visual template used for real-time documentation in focus group

6. DISCUSSIONS AND CONCLUSIONS

Although providing considerable advantages, qualitative interviewing is fraught with methodological shortcomings. The major difficulties are situated in initiating the interview process, capturing valuable data, and preventing respondents to go off topics. In this article, we have proposed an interdisciplinary procedure, suggesting to use visual methods in qualitative interviews to obtain deeper insights. The visuals, used both as stimuli and facilitation, work as 'boundary objects' [22] and therefore enhance discussions, debates or consensus during the interview situation. This allows for more awareness of the respondents' perceptions, and thus permits to draw more rigorous conclusions. However, some limitations exist in the use of visuals for qualitative interviews and focus groups, as for example:

- The productivity of the interview is highly dependent on the visual literacy of the interviewer or moderator.
- Given the difficulty of simultaneously conducting and visualizing the interview, it is advisable to have two facilitators or interviewers working together. Nevertheless, the coordination among the two researchers may be difficult, or bias the interview process.
- The respondents may be 'locked' into the visual templates, and neglect discussing relevant issues that are not pointed out on the visual structure. This is the negative side of the representational guidance provided by visual representations [24].
- The visuals may 'cajole' the respondents, and lead to overly positive attitudes towards the interview topic [28].

Moreover, the mentioned strengths of visualization methods in qualitative interviews need to be substantiated with further empirical evidence. In future studies, for example, researchers could assess the added value of visualization-based interviewing through an experimental methodology, i.e. by comparing the quality of data gathered in intervention (visualization-based interviewing) versus control (pure verbal interviewing) groups. Also, our practical methodology for using visualizations in one-to-one interviews and focus groups has to be further tested, evaluated and discussed in academia. Nevertheless, it should be mentioned that our preliminary experiences make it evident that the real-time use of visualization enables people to better see what they say and mean.

REFERENCES

[1] H. Arksey and P. Knight, Interviewing for social scientists. London: Sage, 1999.

[2] C.A.B. Warren, "Qualitative Interviewing", in Handbook of Interview Research, J.F. Gubrium and J.A. Holstein, Eds. London: Sage, 2002, pp. 83-101.

[3] T. Brüsemeister, Qualitative Forschung ein Überblick. Wiesbaden: Westdt. Verl., 2000.

[4] J.H. Frey and A. Fontana, "The group interview in social research," Social Science Journal, vol. 28, 1991, pp. 175-197.

[5] A.L. Cunliffe, "Crafting Qualitative Research: Morgan and Smircich 30 Years on, " Org. Research Methods, vol. 00, 2010, pp. 1-27.

[6] N.K. Denzin and Y.S. Lincoln, Handbook of qualitative research. Thousand Oaks, CA: Sage, 1994.

[7] N. Crilly, A. Blackwell, and P.J. Clarkson, "Graphic elicitation: using research diagrams as interview stimuli," Qualitative Research, vol. 6, 2006, pp. 341-366.

[8] H.R. Hoyle, M.J. Harris, and C.M. Judd, Research methods in social relations. US: Wadsworth, 2002.

[9] S. Bresciani, A.F. Blackwell, and M.J. Eppler, "A Collaborative Dimensions Framework: Understanding the Mediating Role of Conceptual Visualizations in Collaborative Knowledge Work," Proc. ICSS 2008.

[10] M. Banks, Using visual data in qualitative research. London: Sage, 2007.

[11] A. Fontana and J. Frey, "Interviewing. The art of science," in Handbook of qualitative Research, N. K. Denzin and Y. S. Lincoln, Eds. Thousand Oaks, CA: Sage, 1994, pp. 361-376.

[12] J. v. Maanen, Tales of the field. On writing ethnography. Chicago: The University of Chicago Press, 1988.

[13] R. Barbour, Doing focus groups. Thousand Oaks, CA: Sage, 2007.

[14] T.L. Greenbaum, Moderating focus groups: A practical guide for Group Facilitation. London: Sage, 2000.

[15] D.L. Morgan, "Focus Groups," Annual Review of Sociology, vol. 22, 1996, pp.129-152.

[16] B.J. Calder, "Focus groups and the nature of qualitative marketing research," J. of Marketing Research, vol. 14, 1977, pp. 353-364.

[17] D.L. Morgan, Focus Groups as Qualitative Research. Qualitative Research Methods Series. Thousand Oaks, CA: Sage, 1997.

[18] D.L. Morgan and R.A. Krueger, "When to use focus groups and why," in Successful Focus Groups, D.L. Morgan, Ed. London: Sage, 1993, pp. 3-19.

[19] S. Sussman, D. Burton, C.W. Dent, A.W. Stacy, and B.R. Flay, "Use of focus groups in developing an adolescent tobacco use cessation program: collective norm effects," J. Appl. Soc. Psychol. vol. 21, 1991, pp. 1772-82.

[20] C.B.M. van Riel, N.E. Stroeker, and O.J.M. Maathuis, "Measuring Corporate Images," Corporate Reputation Review, vol. 1, 1998, pp. 313-326.

[21] M. Anastas, "Visuals stimulate richer response in focus groups and individuals interviews," Quirk's Marketing research review, 1994.

[22] P.R. Carlile, "A Pragmatic View of Knowledge and Boundaries: Boundary Objects in New Product Development," Organization Science, vol. 13, 2002, pp. 442-455.

[23] R.A. Krueger and M.A. Casey, Focus groups: a practical guide for applied research, 4th ed., London: Sage, 2000.

[24] D.D. Suthers, "Toward a Systematic Study of Representational Guidance for Collaborative Learning Discourse," Journal of Universal Computer Science, vol. 7, 2001, pp. 254-277.

[25] R. Kuchenmüller and M. Stifel, "Quality without a name," in The IAF Handbook of Group Facilitation, S. Schuman, Ed. San Francisco, CA: Jossey-Bass, 2005, pp. 381-420.

[26] A. Comi and M.J. Eppler, "Assessing the Impact of Visual Facilitation on Interorganizational Collaboration: an Experimental Study," Journal of Universal Computer Science, forthcoming.

[27] M.J. Eppler and R.A. Burkhard, "Visual representations in knowledge management: Framework and cases," Journal of Knowledge Management, vol. 11, 2007, pp. 112-122.

[28] S. Bresciani and M.J. Eppler "The risks of visualization: A classification of disadvantages associated with graphic representations of information," in Identität und vielfalt der kommunikations-wissenschaft, P.J. Schulz, U. Hartung, and S. Keller, Eds. Konstanz: UVK Verlagsgesellschaft mbH, 2009, pp. 165-178.

4. Design Visualisation
IV 2011

Memory, Difference, and Information: Generative Architectures Latent to Material & Perceptual Plasticity

Andrew P. Lucia[1,2], Jenny E. Sabin[1,2,4], Peter Lloyd Jones[1,2,3,4]

Sabin+Jones LabStudio[1], School of Design[2], School of Medicine[3], Institute for Medicine and Engineering[4]; University of Pennsylvania

{palucia@design.upenn.edu, js@jennysabin.com, jonespl@mail.med.upenn.edu}

Abstract

Stemming from ongoing research between architecture and the biological sciences, this paper explores dynamic organizations of matter in both a multi-dimensional, microscopic scale human cellular system and a human-scaled perceptual environment from an information theoretical framework. This research examines latent virtual diagrams residing within real dynamic material systems whose generative potential emerges from difference, history, and ultimately the structural information content of spatiotemporal data arrays. Through the development of a design tool, we offer a method for visualizing the underlying formal structures of these data arrays. Currently this method is being developed and deployed in the biomedical sciences as a means of analyzing dynamic biological data sets for purposes of determining unique spatiotemporal behavioral signatures in different cell types within unique cellular environments. From a design standpoint, a parallel aim of this research deploys these same information theoretical principles as an analytic technique, specifically in areas of generative design, materiality, and affect as they pertain to organizations of data arrays generated from objects within their environments with and without perceiving subjects, or what we call relative observers.

Keywords: architectural models, information theory, geometry, computational design, spatiotemporal order, difference, memory, perception, material phenomena

1. Introduction

The work presented herein stems from an inquiry rooted in architecture and design. The questions posed are raised in relation to how we conceive of (to design) and construct (to build) the world about ourselves. Furthermore, the research and design described was conducted through a systemic approach to material systems of which we are a part, thereby allowing its applications to extend to other pertinent areas of inquiry. Here, one such area is explored in the biological sciences through the examination of cellular motility in relation to its surrounding architecture or extracellular matrix environment.

Education, technology and traditions of the trade, frequently predispose architects and designers to approach the world via descriptive and projective geometric principles. There are, however, alternate mathematical formal abstractions and representations to investigate under the topics of materiality and affect. In setting aside these geometric predispositions, how else might we approach these issues from a design standpoint? We ask:

1.) Can a dynamic material system's characteristics be understood in terms of spatiotemporal order, *difference*, and *information* rather than through descriptive or projective geometric terms?

2.) To what extent do humans identify with an object's curvature or rates of change (or environmental curvatures), over that object's morphological symbolism? In this regard, what are the underlying formal structural diagrams residing beneath actual morphologies or perceptions of morphologies? How could these diagrams be represented and characterized in architectural design?

Taken as an architectural design inquiry, this investigation is at the root of questions pertaining to how we identify with material aggregations (i.e. their relationship to us, and our perception and sensations of them within our environments). While aspects of the initial discussion which center on human perception could revolve around several human sensorial systems, we

1550-6037/11 $26.00 © 2011 IEEE

DOI 10.1109/IV.2011.54

direct our focus to the visual realm given the nature of light-based data analyzed for our case studies; the *information* that is said to arise from these examples is generated from the advent of *difference* in light intensities within multidimensional dynamic data arrays.

This paper explores the roles of *difference*, history, and framing upon the *information content* inherent to data arrays generated within dynamic micro cellular and macro material systems; here, *information* is defined as a function of temporal *difference* within a particular signal, or set of signals, within a specific spatial neighborhood. Considered from an *information theoretical* standpoint, this paper ultimately underscores a fundamental shift away from a description of environments in descriptive and projective geometric terms to one based on spatiotemporal order and disorder, and ultimately the *structural information content*. Here, environmental perception is a generative function of the variant or invariant elements of a given data set which give rise to the perception of material plasticity. Simply put, if one is to perceive, there must be *information* generated between an observer and their surrounding environment. Furthermore, the current research offers a new method for characterizing the underlying formal structure of these multidimensional data arrays and the objects and material environments of which they are borne, be it through analyzing the pure *difference* or *information* generated within.

This way of "seeing" *difference* suggests a fundamental shift in the way we relate to objects within our spatial environments. The detection or study of objects is not undertaken in this research. Rather, our work posits that all objects or entities arising out of dynamic processes generate a continuum of constantly fluctuating *potential information* arrays. These *information* arrays, or *events of interest,* are field-based and favored over object-based analyses of systems. For example, when moving through space the term "parallax" is frequently used to describe the greater relative displacement of objects in the foreground as opposed to those in the background. This parallax depends upon a geometric understanding of the world about us. However, this paper does not presuppose a Cartesian 3-dimensional world. In other words, we do not constrain the "geometry" of objects or environments by limiting them through a description of their breadth, width and depth. Rather, we focus upon the *difference* between and within the objects and material in a given environment, which give rise to multidimensional observational data about that specific environment. These data would have greater or lesser associated rates of change within particular

spatially structured neighborhoods. Thus, as it would still hold true that the matter nearer to a person in motion would generate a *differenced* data array with a corresponding rate of change higher than matter farther away, this suggests the *information* generated between an observer and the environment is not a geometric problem, but rather is one of *structural information* which is therefore capable of being understood solely in terms of spatiotemporal order and disorder.

Of primary importance to the research presented is the *difference* arising within dynamic datasets. While the merits of examining pure *difference* within data are worthy in and of themselves, we have extended this inquiry to probabilities of *difference* in the form of *information* calculations for 2 reasons: 1.) By involving the probability of change (*information*) within a dataset, we are able to weight the likelihood of temporal events for visualization and classification purposes, as is the case in the biological data presented here, and 2.) Psychologists and neuroscientists have demonstrated that human perception arises ultimately through the generation of *information,* not merely the *difference,* inherent in perceptual datasets. As such, designers of environments and perceptual phenomena might take into consideration the instantaneous causal relationships inherent to the generation of affects, and furthermore examine the potential loci of their productions within environments and material systems.

While the paper initially centers around 2 distinct visually-based data mapping case studies relating to: 1.) Behavioral signatures of biological systems, and 2.) The human perceptions of moving through space, our extended studies broach more fundamental questions about the loci of *information* production within systems and our relationship to them. We ask, "What are the implications of *information* generated: 1.) Extrinsically to a system [produced internally within a system and observed autonomously], or 2.) Intrinsically within a system?" Here, the ramifications of dynamic material interactions upon a system's *information* content are considered from the standpoint of digital mechanisms, though from two conceptually different framing references: 1.) From a scientifically "objective" standpoint of cellular behavior within a specific microenvironment under a microscope, and 2.) A camera tracked through a hallway, essentially mimicking/recording how a human moves through a specific space or environment (Figure 1).

Following our studies of the acquisition of biological and perceptual data generated within these dynamic systems in Sections 3 and 4, we introduce a method for visualizing the distribution of spatial intensities inherent to both the pure *difference* and *information* generated from these dynamic datasets and others (i.e. images of paintings and an autonomous object) for comparison and proof of principle in Sections 5 and 6. By further examining neighborhoods surrounding discreet locations within a given dataset, spatial intensities may be extracted from their metric neighborhoods and remapped to a vector space devoid of their "real" spatial distributions/representations. First, we present this method in context of the perceptual datasets from our initial case studies (Section 5), and then further extend these concepts to autonomous objects and environments thereby establishing intensity distribution signatures based upon the rates of curvature intrinsic to the objects/environments in question (Section 6). These diagrams may then be further characterized in terms of their organization or disorganization.

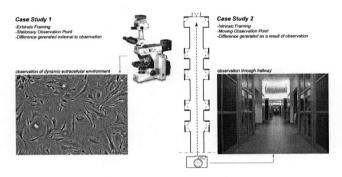

Figure 1: Extrinsic Framing (Case Study 1, left) and Intrinsic Framing (Case Study 2, right) for data acquisition. (Cellular images courtesy of Peter Lloyd Jones Lab, University of Pennsylvania)

2. Background

2.1. Information Theory

Within our trans-disciplinary research, which spans biological science and architectural design, *information* is taken as a measure of non-linguistic content or the communicative artifact of dynamic material systems. In these terms *information* is the medium of communicative exchange for relative observing bodies, be they organic or inorganic. These bodies are said to be relative in that each distinct observer possesses a unique memory or history that has an impact on the instantaneous perception about its environment. Often termed "*information entropy,*" this approach to the measurement of

information quantifies the likeliness of events within a signal. More specifically, this measurement is a function of the probability of those unique events. As stated by neuroscientist Kenneth Norwich,

"*Information theory* provides a way of quantifying the initial uncertainty and, therefore, quantifying the information received. The uncertainty preceding the occurrence of an event is usually termed entropy, so that the quantity of information received is equal to the reduction in *entropy* [1]."

Here, the more unlikely an event is to occur the more information is said to be associated with that event's actual occurrence.

2.2. Spatial Perception, Art, and *Information*

As proposed by Norwich, human perception ultimately arises through the production of *information,* not merely the *difference,* inherent in perceptual datasets. Given that architects and designers are interested in the roles of materiality in the production of perceptual phenomena, it is increasingly important to revisit this discussion in the context of contemporary advancements in digital architectural design and computation, permitting us to consider the possibility and importance of the roles of *information* and *difference* upon the perception of environments and material systems. The following section provides an introductory overview of a sampling of the nuanced ideas surrounding *information's* role in perception and its usefulness in artistic debate (for a more complete discussion, readers are strongly encouraged to see the sources cited below). Of course, *information's* role in these arenas is not new nor are the references cited herein. Therefore, this research should be viewed as a revision of these ideas, which certainly deserves consideration given advances in computational design and an evolving architectural discourse which questions the role of symbolic metaphor in favor of one which has the capacity to position issues of memory and material phenomena in a non-rhetorical manner.

Additionally, Norwich suggests, if one is to perceive, *information* must be present with respect to an observer. This sounds simple enough, but a *signal* and *information* should not be confused, for uncertainty is a necessary requisite for there to be *information* present within a signal. Put another way, there must be *difference* within a signal in order for it to contain *information.* From an entropy-based approach to perception, Norwich states "when our uncertainty vanishes...so do our perceptions

[2]." This ultimately suggests that even in the presence of a signal, the perception of the data within that signal is only available through differentiation, either in the signal itself or in the relation of an observer to that signal.

Compared to Norwich's entropy-based theory of perception, which is rooted in uncertainty and *difference* within perceptual channels, psychologist James J. Gibson developed a novel theory of perception based upon *ambient information* arrays, specifically visual arrays of disparity, which must have structure in order to be perceived. Ultimately it is both Gibson's and Norwich's insistence upon *difference* as a requisite factor of *information* which merits discussion within this paper. As Gibson states,

"Only insofar as ambient light has *structure* does it specify the environment. I mean by this that the light at the point of observation has to be different in different directions (or there have to be *differences* in different directions) in order for it to contain any information. The differences are principally differences of intensity [3]."

In order to be perceived, these arrays must be heterogeneous, or contain *difference*. Specifically, Gibson focuses on what aspects of these *information* arrays remain variant or invariant under transformation with respect to an observer [4]. It should be noted, however, that Gibson strongly distinguishes his idea of "information" from its use in *information theory*. Gibson's *Ecological Approach to Visual Perception* posits an understanding whereby the world is "specified" by *information*, and opposed an approach to *information* as it existed in signal processing and communication theory because he believed "the environment does not communicate with the observers who inhabit it...The concept of stimuli as signals to be interpreted implies some such nonsense as a world-soul trying to get through to us [5]." More importantly, Gibson's "direct perception" of the external environment favors a view that is not mediated through higher order man-made constructs, such as symbols. If we set aside the notion of a transcendental communicating world, however, there are complementary ideas put forth by Norwich and Gibson which suggests that perception can be approached as a function of *differenced* arrays (signals) of data present to our person.

Last but not least, our research also addresses another issue surrounding the artistic merits of *information theory* questioned by psychologist Rudolf Arnheim. Also taking issue with signal processing and communication theory in the essay *Entropy and Art: an Essay on Order and Disorder*, Arnheim confronted the field of *information theory* for its ambivalence towards spatial structure [6]. Our research, however, posits that such concern for metric spatial structure can be accounted for if one takes into consideration (and holds true) the spatial aspects of data within an array of *potential information*. Arnheim may be correct in originally considering this neglect from a communication theoretic approach, but only because he critiqued an approach which utilizes single sources of data transfer (i.e. singular data arrays through communication systems), which do not inherently possess multidimensional spatial attributes. Essentially, Arnheim and Gibson failed to or chose not to take into consideration the actual possibility of multiple, discrete, spatially structured data arrays from an *information theoretical* standpoint. Taken as our starting point, we have generated and developed unique digital design tools for the analysis of spatiotemporal *information* arrays comprised of discrete signals that possess a unique spatial structure.

3. Methods for Establishing *Difference* and the Generation of *Information*

3.1. Difference

Dynamic processes are governed and marked by *difference*, i.e. fluxes of matter and energy which are the essential driving mechanisms governing the emergence of events within physical systems. As an outcome or byproduct of emergent events, *potential information* is also generated as an artifact of the dynamic processes in consideration. These emergent events create potential perceptual stimuli possessing an uncertainty and which we suggest are comparable to Gibson's *ambient information arrays*. Norwich has "termed an absolute entropy or an uncertainty, as the *potential* of the perceiving system to acquire information. *Potential information is transformed gradually into information as the perceptual act proceeds* [7]." At its inception, this *information* is generated through *difference* within dynamic spatiotemporal data arrays. Within the case studies presented here *difference* in pixel brightness (intensity) is considered to be generated in 2 ways: 1.) External to an observing mechanism (video microscopy), and 2.) As a function of an interacting observing mechanism and its environment (i.e. video camera moving through a hallway).

Case Study 1 is an account of observation by a stationary mechanism (video microscopy) examining distinct dynamic extracellular environments (Figure 1).

Difference in this system's associated data array is generated solely within the dynamic cellular environment, and captured externally by an observing mechanism (video camera); *difference* is determined between discrete pixel intensities across all time states within a video (Figure 2).

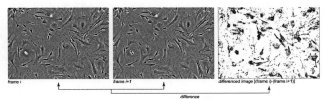

Figure 2: Case Study 2-Extrinsic Framing. Contrast difference in consecutive cell images under microscope (captured with video microscopy). (Cellular images courtesy of Peter Lloyd Jones Lab, University of Pennsylvania)

When one turns the data-capturing mechanism away from a scientifically "objective" scenario, however, to one in which an observer operates, a new set of issues arise as to the "objectivity" or "subjectivity" of the data being captured. Our second case study relies on the relative *difference* generated between a non-stationary observer and the environment within which the observer moves; here, *difference* is neither solely a product of external or internal references but exists simultaneously between the two. In this example, the observing mechanism (video camera) is tracked through a hallway in order to generate *difference* in intensities for pixel arrays between time frames (Figures 1 & 3).

Figure 3: Case Study 2-Intrinsic Framing. Contrast difference in consecutive images while moving through hallway (captured with video camera).

3.2. History/Memory

Thus far, *difference* has been understood in terms of change within a system and an observer to/within that system. As an example, we have implicated this change to arise out of: 1.) Plastic morphologies between a population of dynamic cells within a physically associated and extremely plastic extracellular environment at a micro-scale, and 2.) From the acquisition of data about the surface variation within a hallway by means of movement through that environment at a macro-scale. Both approaches rely upon a particular framing (extrinsic or intrinsic) for *differences* to arise.

Until now, only *differences* within each system have been considered. The production of *information*, however, relies upon the history or memory of change that is internal to the systems in question. As stated above, the *information* of a system is reliant upon the uncertainty or likelihood of an event's occurrence. In our studies, we consider an event-space to be each discrete pixel within the spatial array of the viewing frame. To consider that an event has occurred we merely ask "Has this pixel changed?" To determine a probability of occurrence we could have chosen a fixed *a priori* probability of change for each pixel. However, we consider our systems to be naïve, having no "knowledge" of their expected behaviors. As such, they require their own history to be queried in order to determine the probabilities of events within (Figure 4).

The outcomes of these studies are represented in the form of *information* maps that do not consider short term memory and adaptation; rather they take into consideration total histories of the systems. As such, we disregard the ramifications of short-term, long-term, or floating durations of probability in the particular examples presented here.

4. Case Studies

4.1. A Note on Data Acquisition

The mappings presented in Case Studies 1 and 2 represent the cumulative *information* accrued over all time states. Pixel intensities represent the moments of what we consider the "common, moderate and rare-events" within the respective systems (Figures 5 & 7). Events occur only within each discrete pixel across a temporal array with spatial structures and coordinate positions remaining constant. Though only discrete pixels are taken into consideration temporally, the ordinal spatial structure of the pixels is considered to be absolute and unalterable, thus taking into consideration the likelihood of events within discrete signals (individual pixel states through time) and spatial structure of the overall pixel arrays on each discrete picture frame. Given this pixel-based approach, the fidelity of spatial measurement of any array in question will be governed by the resolution of the associated pixel array, while temporal fidelity is taken to be the duration between each captured frame (Figure 4).

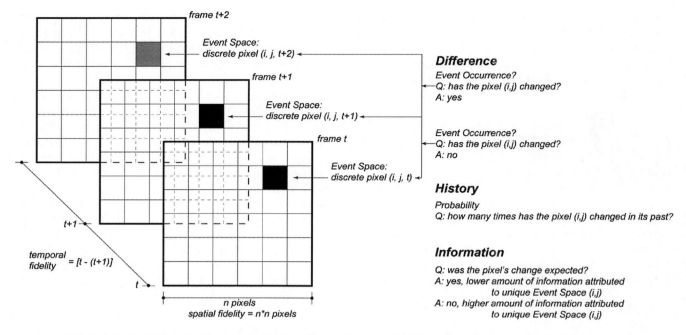

frame t+2

Event Space:
discrete pixel (i, j, t+2)

frame t+1

Event Space:
discrete pixel (i, j, t+1)

frame t

Event Space:
discrete pixel (i, j, t)

t+1

$$\text{temporal fidelity} = [t - (t+1)]$$

t

n pixels
spatial fidelity = n*n pixels

Difference

Event Occurrence?
Q: has the pixel (i,j) changed?
A: yes

Event Occurrence?
Q: has the pixel (i,j) changed?
A: no

History

Probability
Q: how many times has the pixel (i,j) changed in its past?

Information

Q: was the pixel's change expected?
A: yes, lower amount of information attributed
   to unique Event Space (i,j)
A: no, higher amount of information attributed
   to unique Event Space (i,j)

Figure 4: Schematic diagram of Pixel Event Space, Difference, History, and Information.

4.2. Case Study I: *Information* Mapping of Biological Behaviors

We originally developed the Case Study 1 as a way of detecting and measuring subtle, yet biologically important, differences as to how identical human cell types behave within different external environments, be it a petri-dish or an artificially generated, self-assembling, extracellular protein-based network of one type or another. A major goal of this biological research was to detect distinct spatiotemporal behavioral signatures between cell types or their environments. These signatures will ultimately be used to produce non-invasive tools designed to diagnose, prognosticate, and to determine responses to new and existing therapeutics on a patient-to-patient basis. Current means of capturing and understanding behavioral differences in cell behavior involves classifying individual cells as discrete objects with each possessing a distinct boundary. These methods of object detection, however, have inherent philosophical, logical and technical limitations. Therefore, in order to derive cell behavioral signatures, we do not rely upon object detection, but rather employ a technique which distinguishes regions of difference between 2 consecutive images. This technique, known as "image difference analysis," relies upon the recognition of abstract change over an entire data field, regardless of the objects contained within (Figure 4).

Figure 5: Cumulative summation values for information maps derived from the same video that demonstrate weighted "standard" [(p)log₂(p)] (left), "moderate" [log₂(p)] (middle), and "rare" [(1/p)log₂(p)] (right) event occurrence information for smooth muscle cells in the same non-native environment.

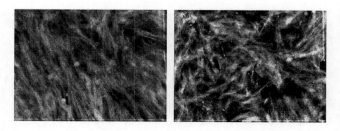

Figure 6: "Moderate" information maps for smooth muscle cells in 2 unique environments, native (left) and non-native (right).

Next, the information content is measured by calculating the probability of *difference* events across a data array through time. In this case, the primary parameter is contrast variation in pixel brightness values between temporally consecutive images of human vascular smooth muscle cells within different microenvironments over time (Figures 4, 5, 6, & 7).

Consequently, upon the advent of change within a pixel array between two time points, the spatiotemporal sequence of events (i.e. pixel brightness change) is catalogued for further analysis. Already, as a measure of total change through time, our preliminary studies have succeeded in providing a means to distinguish statistically significant differences in smooth muscle cell motility within the different interacting extracellular microenvironments. Similarly, the information mappings of these same studies have further revealed distinct spatiotemporal patterns of event probabilities arising from these different and physiologically relevant microenvironments (Figure 6).

4.3. Case Study II: *Information* Mapping and Spatial Perception

Using the same techniques and tools outlined in Case Study 1, Case Study 2 begins to speculate upon a *difference* based approach to environmental sensorial data acquisition, whereby *difference* is generated not solely as a function of objects and environments external to an observer but rather as a function of the intrinsic *difference* between an observer and their environment.

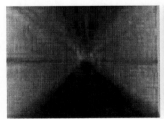

Figure 7: "Moderate" (left), and "rare" (right) event information maps for an observer through a hallway.

Presented as end-state total *information* mappings, the visualizations presented in Figure 7 do not mark a 1:1 correspondence between their production and our actual perception of the selected environments. Nonetheless, these mappings reveal insights to those data (*potential information*) present in our environments that are capable of giving rise to perceptions and sensations about that environment. Such *information* maps and our comprehension of the surroundings in which we exist and interact are ultimately generated by the same concepts of *difference* and history/memory. This dependence also suggests uniqueness to an observer's understanding of a system (of which they are a part) based upon their memory of and history within that system (Figure 7). In other words, *information* generated from 2 distinct observers traversing an identical environment will bear similar, though different information signatures because the generation of *information* is linked to the probability of events that have occurred in the history of a system (for a more complete discussion of perception and *information theory*, please see *Information, Sensation, and Perception* by Kenneth Norwich, 2003 [8]).

5. Method for Developing Intensity Distribution Signatures of Perceptual Data

5.1. Overview

So far, we have considered a basis for establishing the *difference* and ultimately the generation of *information* inherent within dynamic multi-dimensional data arrays. How would/could one further visualize the underlying formal structures of these arrays removed from their original metric neighborhoods or "real" representations? We posit that production of such a diagram would enable designers to study the affectual attributes associated with a particular aggregation of matter (i.e. environment or object) devoid of the burden associated with their symbolic legacy.

The qualities of interest inherent in these *information* mappings do contain an overall ordered structure, namely in the form of adjacent intensities. Given a field of these adjacencies, a macro pattern begins to emerge. At the time that Arnheim presented his critique on *information theory* and perception, the ability to take these macro patterns and structures into consideration was absent or lacking. By using a rigorous local and global approach to the data acquisition and *information* calculations, however, we have adequately addressed Arnheim's critiques, which were likely philosophically limited due to technological constraints during his time [9]. Given this, a method for the extraction of the structural qualities from their metric space of representation is presented--a transform which allows better understanding of the relational qualities underlying the formal diagrams of these data arrays.

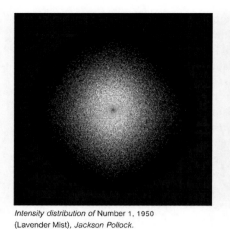 

Intensity distribution of Number 1, 1950 (Lavender Mist), *Jackson Pollock.*

Intensity distribution of Composition A, 1923, *Piet Mondrian.*

Intensity distribution Arcs From Four Corners, 1971, *Sol Lewitt.*

Figure 10: Spatial intensity distribution signatures mapped to polar coordinate system for 3 paintings.

5.2. Method of Intensity Extraction and Mapping

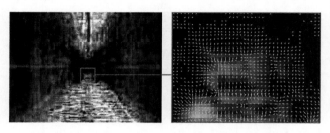

Figure 8: Information content displayed as an array of pixel brightness (left). Vector field derived from intensity and direction of information in pixel array (right).

In order to visualize the *structural information* distribution signatures thus far generated, pixel intensity is again considered to be the main parameter of interest. While a histogram generating approach could have been used to characterize the distributions of each pixel intensity value throughout the image, such a limited analysis would ultimately provide no useful knowledge with respect to the spatial structures of the intensity distribution in relationship to the given image as a whole (dataset). Therefore, a method was developed whereby the intensity at each discrete pixel is compared against its nearest neighbors. This method does not inherently measure *information* content per se, but rather the spatial distribution of intensities across any given image. Therefore, this method may be used to determine any brightness intensity distributions within an image, be it an *information* mapping or the difference in pixel intensities across an actual image as are the cases presented in Figure 10.

First, the intensity of each pixel (i,j) within an image is compared to each of its surrounding neighbors. The difference of each of these 8 values is scaled and assigned a vector. Next, each of these 8 vectors is summed and this sum is again normalized in order to determine a single resultant vector representing the intensity difference of each pixel (i,j) with its surrounding neighbors (Figure 9). This new resultant vector describes how much and in what dominant spatial direction pixel (i,j) is different from its neighbors (Figure 9).

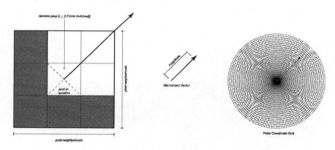

Figure 9: Difference in brightness between each pixel (i, j) and its nearest neighbors (left) is assigned an intensity vector, normalized, and mapped to a polar coordinate system using the resultant vector's intensity and direction (right).

Next, each resultant vector within a given image's pixel space (Figure 8) is plotted to a unit polar coordinate grid comprised of 360 radial divisions and 256 concentric divisions (one for each possible pixel value given a 256 value working pixel space) (Figure 9). For visualization and quantification purposes, each resultant vector is assigned to its corresponding location in one of these 360 x 256 (direction & magnitude) divisions, defined as a "bin," within the polar coordinate grid.

The number of resultant vectors falling within each of these polar bins is summed. This sum is then assigned a pixel brightness value between 1 and 256.

A demonstration of this method's visualization potential in Figure 10 illustrates the distribution mappings of nearest neighbor difference vectors calculated for 3 paintings using the above method: Jackson Pollock's *Number 1, (Lavender Mist)*; Piet Mondrian's *Compostition A, 1923*; and Sol Lewitt's *Arcs from Four Corners*.

6. Method for Developing Intensity Distribution Signatures for Autonomous Objects and Environments

6.1. Overview

In the previous sections, *information* was a function of the *difference* in data arrays arising from variant or invariant data structures borne between an observer and their environment. Complementary to that inquiry, this methodology is extended to objects and environments whose *difference* or change is internal to their makeup; this method relies solely on autonomous internal rates of change to local neighborhoods regardless of an implied observational mechanism. Similar to the former method of visualizing intensity distributions, the underlying formal structure of objects and environments is examined by way of extracting the rates of change (curvatures) associated within local neighborhoods. This is not, however, a description of that entity's *information* content, rather a classification of its underlying formal attributes (i.e. how similar or dissimilar is the object/environment to itself?). Whereas the method presented in Section 5 is not a method for calculating *information* but rather a method to visualize spatial intensities in perceptual data, the method presented here is similarly not a determinant of *information* but rather a method for visualizing spatial intensities intrinsic to objects and environments. Similar to the study in Section 5, this method would also produce a diagram that would enable designers the ability to study the characteristic curvatures inherent to morphologies devoid of the burden associated with their symbolic legacy. Once extracted, this type of abstract formal diagram of material organization may subsequently be used as a productive device enabling designers the ability to generate new, yet familiar, objects and environments without necessarily working through projective geometric means as a description of shape.

6.2. Method of Intensity Mapping

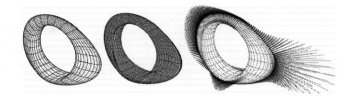

Figure 11: Original object/environment under question (left). Gaussian curvature analysis (middle). Curvature intensities translated to vectors using Gaussian values as magnitude and surface normal as direction (right).

Much like the previous studies, whereby the amount of change surrounding a discrete pixel is taken in its local neighborhood, here the Gaussian curvature values are taken at each (u,v) parameter upon a given surface. By taking the Gaussian curvature values, external observations are not inherently presumed nor is determination of curvature projected upon the object or environment in question. For the Gaussian value at each (u,v) point in question, a vector is assigned whose magnitude and direction are taken to be the Gaussian curvature value and normal to the surface at that point respectively (Figure 11; Note: the vector magnitudes in Figure 11 are amplified for visualization purposes).

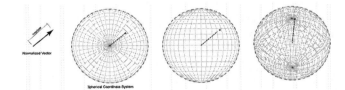

Figure 12: Each curvature vector is normalized and mapped to a spherical coordinate system using the vector's intensity and direction.

Similar to the previous studies, where distributions are made about a polar coordinate system, here each new resultant vector characterizing the intensity and direction of curvature at each point about an actual surface is mapped to a spherical coordinate system accordingly (Figure 12). The point cloud represented in 2 views in Figure 13 corresponds to the distribution of vectors extracted from the (u,v) space about the deformed torus shown in Figure 11. As the measured (u,v) density of the actual environment in question approaches infinity, so too does the density of the point data mapped to spherical space, ultimately approximating a surface (Figure 13).

Conclusion and Discussion

Should designers and architects limit themselves to being merely actors in a world of objects external to their persons, or is it possible to expand this perspective towards a continuum of fluctuating entities (persistent and non-persistent) whose identities are a product of our relational difference with them? If we accept the latter, this would suggest a fundamental shift in how we conceive of and approach designing objects, environments, and affects. The studies presented, rooted in *difference* and *information*, serve to demonstrate a shift in thinking from the construction and production of objects and environments in solely descriptive and projective geometric terms to one which places emphasis upon thinking organizationally though time about the aggregation of material systems and their phenomenal affects. While descriptive and projective geometric principles continue to serve the architecture community, they are burdened by the remnants of an idealized transcendental world. Furthermore, these geometric principles and abstractions also offer an *ex post facto* description and simplification of the world about us which also requires a qualitative description to be ascribed to the entities within that world. As an alternative, an approach rooted in *information* production inherently suggests an instantaneous perceptual construction of the world through which we traverse. This latter direction also takes into account the affectual attributes of the material organizations with which we interact as participating agents. While various approaches have been rhetorically discussed within architectural design, this paper provides a framework and rigorous methodology in support of a discourse by which we may approach a set of design problems surrounding actual material phenomena removed from their symbolic inheritance. Furthermore, the methods presented offer a means by which we may study latent formal diagrams underlying the identity of metric morphologies and affects of actual entities. Not only could these diagrams be harnessed as productive devices for the production of new-yet-familiar material organizations, they also offer an approach to discuss the underlying similarities and differences inherent to the formal make-up of such spatiotemporal material aggregates while allowing the potential for a dialogue beyond morphological symbolism. This approach necessitates considering the actual parameters at play in the production of material organizations and affects by examining the much larger implications of *difference*, history, and *information* upon our perception of systemic environments as we shift away from an object oriented approach to the analysis, comprehension, and construction of the world in which we are actively a part.

Acknowledgements

Special thanks to Alexandra Klinger, Christopher Lee, Shawn M. Sweeney, & Mathieu Tamby.

References

[1] Norwich, Kenneth H. *Information, Sensation, and Perception.* Originally published, San Diego, CA: Academic Press. Published on the Internet by Biopsychology.org, 9. 2003.

[2] *Ibid.* 13.

[3] Gibson, James J. *The Ecological Approach to Visual Perception.* Hillsdale, NJ: Lawrence Erlbaum Associates, 51. 1986.

[4] *Ibid.* 13, 73-75, 89-91, 122-123, 310-311.

[5] *Ibid.* 62-63.

[6] Arnheim, Rudolf. *Entropy and Art, an Essay on Disorder and Order.* Berkeley: University of California Press, 15-20. 1971.

[7] Norwich. 93. 2003.

[8] Norwich. 2003.

[9] Arnheim. 1971.

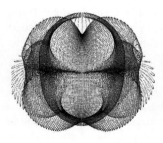 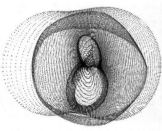 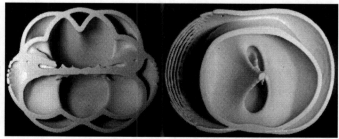

Figure 13: Vector data derived from a deformed torus and mapped to a spherical coordinate system (left). Rapid prototyped (printed) sectional model of an approximated surface from vector data (right).

Practice of using virtual reconstruction in the restoration of monumental painting of the Church of the Transfiguration of Our Saviour on Nereditsa Hill

Petrova, Yulia Anatolievna; Tsimbal, Irina Valerievna; Laska, Tatiana Vladimirovna; Golubkov, Sergey Vitalievich

Faculty of Arts
Saint-Petersburg State University
St.-Petersburg, Russian Federation
e-mail: office@inform.pu.ru

Abstract— There are many architectural monuments and old relics, the restoration of which is an unrealizable task. This may be due to the great amount of hard work to be done, complexity of the work, lack of information about the object and other reasons. In such cases, the virtual reconstruction is an effective tool.

Saint-Petersburg State University developed a method of restoration of partially or completely lost monumental paintings. As an example and a practical application of new technology there was completed the virtual reconstruction of fresco paintings of the Church of the Transfiguration of Our Savior on Nereditsa Hill.

The church was almost completely destroyed during the Second World War. It appeared to be possible to reconstruct an architectural view of the church according to the old drawings, but rare frescos of the XIIth century had been irretrievably lost. The extant parts of frescoes consist of 325,000 pieces. Although they are being on restoration now, but this work is still far from completion. In this case the method of computer-based reconstruction is much more efficient, it helps us to avoid mistakes and find a compromise decision on the issue of reconstruction or restoration of the object.

As a result of the project, a fairly accurate reconstruction of the object has been produced and a method of reconstruction of the lost fresco painting has been developed. The basis and sources of virtual reconstruction were archaeological materials, archival and contemporary historical, architectural and art papers, scientific research in this field.

In the process of virtual reconstruction there were used two main methods: a technology of computer graphics as well as analog pictorial reconstruction. The first method makes it possible to complete the work of reconstruction with complete fidelity, whereas the second method helps us to convey the artist's style, to reproduce the form, direction and strength of the artist's touch and texture of the frescos.

The results of the project can be used for further practical work for the restoration of the object. The methodology, developed by authors of the project, may open new possibilities for the restoration of other fresco ensembles.

Keywords-virtual, reconstruction, restoration, monumental, painting, architectural, cultural, heritage

I. RECONSTRUCTION OF ART AND CULTURAL MONUMEMENTS

Historical sites of the Russian monumental art, due to their centuries-long life, undergo inevitable changes in color and structure of frescoes, destruction or alteration of the original architecture. Numerous natural, climatic and anthropogenic reasons bring about significant changes, partial or complete destruction of works of art. Despite the fact that it has been 65 years since the end of the Second World War, many ancient Russian art masterpieces still have not been restored to an acceptable display state. A considerable amount of materials is stored in museums waiting to be reinstalled in interiors of churches.

Nowadays wide experience in the exploration and restoration of monuments, as well as modern technologies allow to integrate the information in specific areas of knowledge, making it easily accessible to the public. In our case, we refer to architectural monuments of ancient Russia. Information about this objects is dispersed across many sources: books, articles, drawings and sketches, located in different storage locations, and sometimes even in different countries. An integrated information database will enable the use of all currently available information. Creation of a single source of information based on reconstruction of a monument will help to understand the historical context and conditions under which the object was built, to reproduce the lost and missing data on each monument, and to update the existing traditional art databases. With enough data it becomes possible to present a monument at various stages of its construction and development, to analyze and demonstrate options for its reconstruction, to illustrate the features and history of its painting. The method of sequential computer reconstruction allows not just to review the virtual model of the monument, but also to get details, associated with the whole life of the object.

Creation and demonstration of historical reconstructions, as a progressive method of presentation of ancient exhibits, makes it possible to achieve a new level of preservation and transmission of cultural heritage.

1550-6037/11 $26.00 © 2011 IEEE
DOI 10.1109/IV.2011.33

II. ABOUT THE NEREDITSA PROJECT

The "Nereditsa. Link of Times" research project currently takes place under development in the St. Petersburg State University.

Major museums and cultural institutions, such as: the State Russian Museum, the State Historical and Architectural Reserve-Museum of Novgorod the Great, the Institute of History of Material Culture of RAS, and Ilya Repin St. Petersburg State Academic Institute Of Fine Arts, Sculpture and Architecture take part in this research.

The project is dedicated to a unique monument of ancient architecture and art, the Church of the Transfiguration of Our Saviour on Nereditsa Hill. In 1992 the Church of the Transfiguration of Our Saviour on Nereditsa Hill was included into the UNESCO World Heritage List, along with several other monuments of Novgorod the Great and its surroundings[1].

The Church of the Transfiguration of Our Saviour on Nereditsa Hill is one of the most famous monuments of ancient Russian culture. The church was built by Prince Yaroslav Vladimirovich's order in 1198 and a year later, in 1199, its interior was decorated with fresco paintings. Exceptional art value, unusual unique iconography of the monument have earned it a worldwide fame.

Like the Saint Sophia Cathedral, representing the XI century, and the St. George Cathedral of the St. George's Monastery, representing the early XII century, the Church on Nereditsa Hill is considered to be a typological and stylistic architectural standard of the late XII century[2].

During the Second World War, the temple was almost destroyed. Only half of masonry and 15% of frescoes were preserved. According to old drawings it was possible to restore an upper part of walls, arches and dome, but the rare frescos which had covered the entire church until the twentieth century, have been irretrievably lost[3].

Archival material contains of: preserved fragments of frescoes, photos interior of the temple, detailed descriptions of the monument, made by experts from the State Historical and Architectural Reserve-Museum of Novgorod the Great and historians from Saint-Petersburg State University, copies of frescos, carefully preserved in the State Russian Museum, in combination with modern technologies provide a unique opportunity for a virtual revival of the lost masterpieces of ancient art - frescoes of the Nereditsa Church.

The Church of the Transfiguration of Our Saviour on Nereditsa Hill has been an object of scientific art research at St. Petersburg State University for many years. As a result, a lot of research materials about the history of the church, it's architectural features and frescos has been collected. Scientific research of this monument has been provided at the St. Petersburg State University, Novgorod State Museum, State Russian Museum for several years.

The first expedition was organized by the Saint-Petersburg University and the Russian Archaeological Society in 1910. After the architectural restoration in 1903-1904, a number of scholars, including M.I. Artamonov[4], turned to studying its paintings. After being almost destroyed by the Nazis, the Church was restored in 1958, and researcher's attention was again focused mostly on the architecture[5].

Many thousands of fragments of frescos has been collected during restoration, architectural and archaeological work. At present, they are kept in museum collections. It does not seem possible to restore the fresco decoration in its original form[6]. But using methods of virtual restoration, we can achieve significant results in solving this problem. Three-dimensional graphics technology, art modeling and virtual reality provide artistic reconstruction of the lost (partially or completely) cultural heritage with any specific scientific precision.

III. VIRTUAL RECONSTRUCTION OF THE CHURCH OF THE TRANSFIGURATION OF OUR SAVIOUR ON NEREDITSA HILL

In 2008 the materials describing the history of the Church, stored in various museums and archives, were collected and investigated under the "Nereditsa. Link of Times" project.

In 2009 the main publications on the history of the Church were collected and digitized, its frescos were analyzed and its restoration history was described.

In 2009 a three-dimensional model of the Nereditsa Church as well as artifacts and household objects associated with the history of the Church of Our Saviour on Nereditsa Hill were produced "Fig. 1".

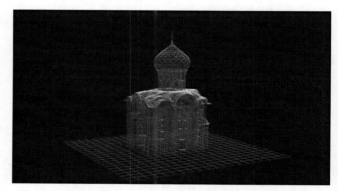

Figure 1. A three-dimensional model of the church Spas-na-Nereditse.

At the present time the frescos are being restored. Restoration of this paintings is a serious problem. The extant parts of frescos are strengthened and preserved. Many thousands of fragments, which were collected in the course of restoration, architectural and archaeological works are kept in museum's collections.

The survived parts of painting consist of 325,000 fragments, and now they are being on restoration, which is still far not complete "Fig. 2".

According to enormous complexity and lack of effectiveness of the "manual" method of search and selection of fragments, it was decided to use a computer reconstruction of the fresco. This method allows to avoid mistakes and find a compromise decision on the issue of reconstruction or restoration of the object.

Figure 2. The process of fresco's restoration.

The choice of virtual reconstruction answers the practical needs of science and education. One of the most important points of the whole research is the question of choosing the method of reconstruction - analogue or computer reconstruction.

A. 1-st method - a documentary historical reconstruction (virtual restoration).

In this case, reconstruction is the creation of a virtual object model, based only on extant fragments. This model can be completed with some objects (fragments of frescos, interior objects stored in museum's funds and collections), if they are mentioned in archival documents.

This method provides keeping historical accuracy, and it abandons reconstruction of the lost fragments by analogy.

B. 2-nd method - analog reconstruction.

The monuments of culture which survived to our time, are often partially lost. Because of a lack of documentary evidence their recovery is a problem, that could be solved only through art and historical analysis. This ensures the authenticity of reconstruction. But in this case, the result can not pretend to be absolute reproduction of the original.

Moreover, it should be clear that, based on various documentary sources of information, we can reach several possible versions of the analog reconstruction, and all of them will be grounded on theory at the same way.

The practical implementation of the analog reconstruction requires the involvement of experts in different fields of knowledge – not only specialists in computer graphics, but, first of all, artists, architects and archaeologists. This is due to the fact that without deep understanding of architecture and proportions of the object, it's authentic virtual analogue can not be created.

This work requires high professional theoretical and practical knowledge of all project developers.

Starting working on restoration of the murals, you need to develop a methodology for recovery of losses, combining two methods - using of documentary materials and restoration of color and form, based on the study of analogues.

Specialists are attempting to determine the role of reconstruction in preservation and promotion of monuments. It is important to develop main principles of virtual reconstruction, such as:

- Applying the method of complex restoration, when the monument is taken as a system of architectural, painting, interior and exterior spaces.
- Development of main theoretical principles of admissibility and limits of application of modern technologies in recreating monuments of historical and cultural heritage in terms of ethical, legal and aesthetic aspects of reconstruction;.
- Providing further reconstruction in accordance with these formulated principles on the basis of archival, historical, design, technical, literary, scientific, restoration, art, copied and other materials using computer technology;

This main principles are being tested on the example of reconstruction of the lost paintings of the Church of the Transfiguration on Nereditsa in Novgorod the Great.

IV. RECONSTRUCTION METHOD FOR THE CHURCH OF THE TRANSFIGURATION OF OUR SAVIOUR ON NEREDITSA HILL

A. Collecting the supporting information for the project:

Searching, analyzing, structuring of archival, historical, technical, literary, scientific, art and other documents which contain any information (photos, drawings, pictures, descriptions) about the frescos of the church.

Basic historical materials of the Nereditsa Church are kept at the State Russian Museum, the Novgorod State Museum, the Institute of History of Material Culture Sciences, methodological foundation of the State Academic Institute of Painting, Sculpture and Architecture named after I.E. Repin. The leading experts are: historians, art historians, restorers, muralists, keepers of these organizations have assisted authors of the project and helped to find, analyze and collect a lot of important information.

At the stage of collecting information about the object it is very important to find as much facts about the monument as possible, to make the fullest possible description. Qualitative archival photographic and illustrative material, knowledge of the exact coloring of paintings, permanent free access to all fragments of the frescos make the process of reconstruction more accurate, correct and fast.

Over a thousand archival photos of the church were investigated. Most of them are stored in the Novgorod State Museum. These photos capture all stages of restoration of the temple, which took place at the beginning of XX century.

Collections of unique architectural details and structural elements of the temple, such as plinfy, brick, stone, etc. were analyzed in the Novgorod State Museum. According to the curvilinear shape of the wall surface, these materials are needed for correct scaling of photos and liquidation of distortions. Also this information is important to analyze the character of wall surface as a basis for painting.

Authors have carefully studied unique materials - fragments of frescoes, collected in the restoration workshops of the Novgorod Museum, which present the process of actual restoration of the frescos of the church.

Archival material stored at the Institute of History of Material Culture of the Russian Academy of Sciences were also studied by authors – this material consists of negatives and photographs taken in the church before the Second World War.

The main source of information about the coloring of paintings were watercolors that have been stored in collections of the Russian Museum. These images are in fact the copies of frescoes, made before the war.

Copies of frescoes, created in various Russian churches, are stored in the methodological foundation of St. Petersburg State Academic Institute of Painting, Sculpture and Architecture. These materials are also necessary for recreation of color palette of fresco painting.

B. Measurements and photographing images of the existing interior condition and images from museum collections.

Before starting any restoration it is required to measure the object and to make various photographic images from different sides.

The church was measured, the drawings were presented. The whole interior of the church and fragments of frescos were photographed. Elements of paintings, which were kept in museum's collections were also studied and photographed.

It is important to take all photos frontally, using the same scale. All pictures were made in two versions: with lighting similar to interior's lighting of the church, and with lighting which helped to introduce the most accurate reproduction of frescos.

C. Making a single tone image based on archival photographs

The next stage of the process is making a single image of the wall, using archival documents.

Figure 3.   Monochrome image of the wall.

On the basis of few extant paintings on the walls of the church and archival black-and-white photographs, completed

before 1941, a single monochrome image of the wall was produced "Fig. 3", "Fig. 4".

Figure 4.   Monochrome image of the wall, completed witn pictures from archival photographs.

Images obtained from the photographs were corrected according to the saved fragments of frescos.

Efficiency of this stage depends on the number of fragments remaining on the wall (reference points). In practice, it turned out that the main photographs taken before the war, were not frontal, and they had distortions, so it made the work more difficult.

The exact place of every fragment was defined according to concerned author's drawing. It is necessary to emphasize that at this stage there is no artistic interference. Created materials may help the restorers to project the image on the wall and to draw the contour of the lost mural, so that it would be a base for collecting separated fragments of frescoes.

The monochrome image, completed with fragments from photographs is the documentary base for further reconstruction of color and pattern of lost parts. From this moment all the activities can be called the analog reconstruction.

D. Producing a coloristic painting process map.

The next important stage is the producing of technological coloristic map of murals. The color system of paintings was deeply studied and a palette was created, and it became a basis for further reconstruction, and then restoration.

E. Producing of linear patterns at a scale 1:1 (performed only in artistic reconstruction, as the basis for paintings)

After this stage we begin an analog reconstruction of frescos, which is actually a process of painting of all lost fragments, based on archive materials and analogues. We create several templates with outlines, produced at a scale 1:1. These templates repeat the expected author's drawing, based on previous computer reconstruction.

F. Producing of artistic coloured cardboards the same size as real frescos or smaller (working models)

The task of this stage is to find appropriate technology of painting, artistic manner, drawing system. It is very important to draw complicated parts (faces, hands, clothes) as well as more simple parts (backgrounds, ornaments) very precisely "Fig. 5", "Fig. 6".

Figure 5.   Fragment of analog reconstruction.

G. Making sweeps of walls

After the reconstruction of frescos it was made a sweep of the western wall of the church "Fig. 7". Lost elements of the interior were also reconstructed "Fig. 8". The basis for the reconstruction was results of scientific research and archival material.

Figure 6.   Fragment of analog reconstruction.

H. Visualisation, producing of three-dimensional colour modelling

The final stage of work is three-dimensional color modeling. In future static images, video, interactive models, which allow a user to choose the viewing angle of architecture and frescos are planned to be made up.

So, step by step, we have accurately recreate the frescos of the Church on Nereditsa Hill, which seemed to be lost forever.

Figure 7.   A sweep of the western wall of the church (analog reconstruction).

Two main methods of reconstruction: a technology of computer graphics and analog pictorial reconstruction are used at the same time. Both of them have its advantages and disadvantages. The method of computer reconstruction provides maximum documentary accuracy - all manipulations with shapes and colors are made strictly in accordance with historical documents. In addition, each operation can be fixed at any stage of work. At the same time this method can't help us to convey the artist's style, to reproduce the form, direction and strength of the artist's touch and texture of the frescos.

So, especially when we deal with completely lost fragments of frescos, it is better to use the method of pictorial reconstruction. The main disadvantage of this method is its complexity. It is very difficult to provide exact documental accuracy and to find appropriate author's stylistic manner at the same time. Painting has become cyclic: some fragments were redrawn several times according to produced template until reaching expected result.

Virtual reconstruction may be used as the basis for making in future: for producing static images, videos, interactive models enabling users to choose a camera and viewing angles when browsing through architecture and artistic decorations.

Figure 8.   Western wall of the church (result of reconstruction).

In contrast to the widespread practice of relative approach to documentary materials, a specific feature of the project is maximum approximation of the model to the actual original appearance of the monument. Documentary precision of the material provide usage of the results in practical work for the restoration of the object in future. Moreover, the method used in the project may open new possibilities to solve restoration problems of other fresco ensembles of the medieval Novgorod, also lost during the War.

The results of the project can be used for further practical work for the restoration of Nereditsa Church.

Virtual model of the church may be used in future as a basis for producing virtual exhibition. Using modern technologies, such as multi-projection systems, holograms, and augmented reality systems, information about the monument can be produced in interesting interactive form. Such information center can be organised in the Nereditsa Church, the Novgorod State Museum or any other complex.

The results of the work are presented at the educational portal of St. Petersburg State University http://sakai.spbu.ru/portal/site/169dd5df-93bd-4150-9a01-86f567045218 or http://www.nereditsa.ru in the form of educational resource Nereditsa.

REFERENCES

[1] http://whc.unesco.org/en/list/604/multiple=1&unique_number=716.

[2] Komech, A.I. Novgorod architecture of XII century // Actes du XVe Congres International d'Etudes Byzantines. Athenes, 1991. Part 2.

[3] Bulkin, V.A. Two episodes from the history of Novgorod architecture of XII century / Monuments of Medieval Culture: inventions and versions. St. Petersburg, 1994.

[4] M.I. Artamonov. Craftsmen of Nereditsa // Novgorod Architectural Collection. Issued in Novgorod the Great, 1939. P. 33–47.

[5] G.M. Shtender. Restoration of Nereditsa // Novgorod Historical Collection. Issue 10. Novgorod the Great, 1962. P. 169–205.

[6] Lutsiy S.A., Jaworski, L.A. Review of methods of icons recognition applied to problems of compilation of the fresco fragments - Dep. VINITI № 1159-V2004 on 07/06/2004.

[7] Pivovarova, N.V. Frescos of the church Spas-na-Nereditse in Novgorod. St. Petersburg, 2002.

[8] The church Spas-na-Nereditse: From Byzantium to Russia. Moskow, 2005.

Exploring the Origins of Tables for Information Visualization

Francis T. Marchese
Computer Science Department
Pace University
NY, NY 10038 USA
e-mail: fmarchese@pace.edu

Abstract— **This paper considers the deep history of tables as visualization modalities. It covers four kinds of tables that have appeared between 1900 BCE and 1300 CE: Sumerian accounting tables, chronicles, canon tables, and medieval calendars as representations of some of the earliest milestones in information visualization. Analysis of these tables demonstrates as early as 1300 BCE the need to visualize information had driven the invention of representations that transformed the way information has been communicated and used.**

Keywords - information visualization, tables, computus, calendars, medieval art.

I. INTRODUCTION

This paper considers the deep history of tables as visualization media. The organizational constructs of the tabular format are ubiquitous, as may be seen in contemporary artifacts such as calendars, agendas, and time tables; as the foundation for spreadsheets; and for their subsequent support of other information visualization methods [1 - 10]. It is well understood that tables are important data visualization tools and the first stage in the information visualization pipeline, organizing raw data into a form that may be translated into graphics. The table's strength as a visualization medium derives from its compactly organized, gridded structure; a format that promotes associations among diverse data elements, and facilitates exploration of relationships among them.

Recently, I have explored the history of the design of chemical tables [11], particularly the periodic table, demonstrating how its design has evolved over time to meet the changing needs of chemists and their increased understanding of chemical combination. This paper proceeds in the same way, but steps back in time to focus on the early history of tables and their uses for the organization of information. It is concerned with exposing the visualization community to the kinds of tabular visualizations that appeared between 1900 BCE and 1300 CE. People throughout time have needed to extract, reorganize, and reconnect information, not only for documentation and communication, but also for usability. As such, the problems faced were computational in nature, requiring invention of

algorithms and visual representations as interfaces to their information.

This paper will discuss four kinds of tables from history: Sumerian accounting tables, chronicles, canon tables, and medieval calendars. These tables have been selected because they represent some of the earliest milestones in information visualization, and provide a starting point for expanding the historical narrative. With the exception of mathematical tables, historians have paid little attention to tables in general as a mode of information communication [12], mostly focusing on the history of the periodic table [13]. But, like the periodic table, the tables covered herein have transformed the way information has been communicated and used.

The following section presents a brief introduction to the gridding of data and the origins of written language. The four subsequent sections cover the nature and importance of Sumerian accounting tables, chronicles, canon tables, and medieval calendars as information visualization modalities. Finally, these tables are considered from within Wainer's analysis framework for table design and use [14][15].

II. BACKGROUND

The history of graphical representation and analysis of information begins with the grid. The grid is a metric by which we establish distance and direction of any position relative to a reference point, line, or plane. It is latitude and longitude, or the perpendicular x and y axes. It is the American football gridiron, and Manhattan's east-west streets and north-south avenues. Twenty-five thousand year old representations of the grid are found on the walls of Lascaux cave in southern France. There is an hieroglyphic symbol resembling an orthogonal grid, which was used to designate districts of towns. Ancient Egyptian surveyors used the grid to lay out land. About 140 BCE Hipparchus employed latitude and longitude to locate celestial and terrestrial positions. Ptolemy, an astronomer and geographer, utilized these methods to map the known world in a standardized and consistent way. By the second century CE Ptolmey published his *Geographia*, a collection of 25 geographical maps, along with methods for constructing and using grids [16]. First century CE Chinese cartographers used grids to map the country. The Romans employed a grid system called the centuration, which, according to David Turnbull, turned "all Europe into one vast sheet of graph paper" [17]. The ancients

1550-6037/11 $26.00 © 2011 IEEE
DOI 10.1109/IV.2011.36

created charts and maps to organize their geographical knowledge. Today, maps and charts have evolved into general graphic representations designed to facilitate a spatial understanding of objects, concepts, processes, and events. Their purpose of ordering knowledge remains central to their utility.

The gridding of space creates containers – locations that may hold a variety of information. The contents of elemental positions within the periodic table and spreadsheet cells are just two examples. It appears as well that the creation of containers through gridding was important to the Mesopotamian origins of written language. With the agricultural revolution approximately 10,000 years ago came the need to document and manage economic transactions related to farming, livestock, fisheries, and the division of labor of a complex society. This was particularly the case for the powerful fourth millennium BCE Mesopotamian cities who traded agricultural and animal products for metals and luxury goods with geographically distant kingdoms. Documentary evidence for these accounting practices is found in over five thousand clay tablets recovered from the ancient Sumerian city of Uruk and its surroundings dating to the mid-fourth millennium BCE [18]. The inscribed grid on these clay tablets created boxes, each of which represented one accounting unit. Contained within a box was an ideogram, a symbol that represented a word or idea, and a numerical value representing a quantity.

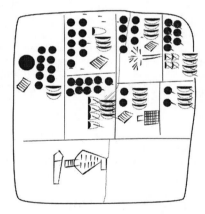

Figure 1: Uruk III Tablet, (MSVO 3, 51, Louvre Museum, Paris, France). Drawing courtesy of R. Englund.

Figure 1 shows a drawing of a tablet from the Uruk III period (ca. 3200-3000 BCE) containing an accounting of deliveries of barley and malt from two individuals for the production of beer. The bottom row bears the name of the official in charge. The table is read from right-to-left and top-down. Each row corresponds to an individual, with the first two columns containing entries for malt, followed by a column for barley. Subtotals are given in the third column (barley groats (top) and malt (bottom)). The left-most box displays the grand total [19]. No formal language was used to express the relationship between the signs and symbols in the tablet. Instead, the grid structure provided that syntax [20].

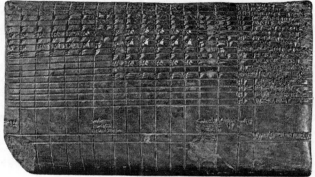

Figure 2: Cuneiform tablet, temple of Enlil at Nippur, (CBS 3323, University of Pennsylvania). Reproduced from [22].

III. SUMERIAN ACCOUNTING TABLES

The first systematically structured tables (see e.g. Figure 2) originated in Mesopotamia about 1850 BCE [21]. The evolution of cuneiform from a pictographic into a symbolic language that supported the phonetics of spoken Sumerian created a compact language that facilitated accounting practice as well. In an analysis of Mesopotamian tables from this period, Eleanor Robson has found striking similarities with contemporary counterparts [21]. These similarities may be seen in Figure 2, which shows both the obverse and reverse sides of a cuneiform tablet from the temple of Enlil at Nippur. It is a record of sources of revenue and monthly disbursements to forty-six temple personnel by its bursar Ḫunabi for the year 1295 BCE [22]. There are column headings and row titles. Column headings at the top of the table specify month names. Names and professions are shown in the right-hand column (e.g. seeress, weaver, overseer, temple servant). Eighteen of the individuals listed receive no payment for all or half the year. (Notice the blank "smooth" cells along rows.) These individuals are classified as either dead or fugitive. Grid locations within the table contain numerical information that are part of calculations, flowing first down a column, and then across a row. Subtotals for each individual are given every six months, culminating with a yearly total adjacent to row labels. The table is annotated with explanatory interpolations under columns containing totals, and a summary column at the table's end.

The utility of this tabular format was cemented with the invention of the sexagesimal (base 60) place value system of arithmetic that provided a means for each table *cell* to be quantitatively linked in a formal mathematical way. As Robson has observed, "the new format enabled numerical data and relationships to be seen and explored in ways hitherto unimaginable," creating "conceptual advances in quantitative thinking" [21].

IV. CHRONOLOGIES

A chronology is a record of events in the order of occurrence. One of the earliest extant historical records is the Parian Marble, a Greek chronological table covering the years from 1581 BCE to 264 BCE, inscribed on a stela (now at Oxford's Ashmolean Museum) [23]. A later example decorated the Emperor Augustus's arch in the Roman Forum. Known today as the *Fasti Capitolini Consulares,* it is a collection of marble plaques listing in tabular format all the chief magistrates of Rome since the Republic's foundation, and the victorious leaders from Romulus onward [24]. Although the ancient world had many chroniclers such as Herodotus, Pliny the Elder, and Josephus, only fragmentary records exist of attempts to create a synchronous chronology encompassing all cultures of the known Western world [25]. This was to change with Eusebius of Caesarea.

Eusebius of Caesarea (c. 263 – 339/340 CE), also known as Eusebius Pamphili, was Bishop of Caesarea in Palestine, scholar, friend and biographer of the Emperor Constantine I, and historian who wrote *Historia Ecclesiastica,* an early history of the Church [26]. But before he wrote his Church history Eusebius wrote his *Chronicles* (ca. 311 CE), a universal history of the nations from Abraham through Constantine I [27]. The *Chronicles* are divided into two parts. The first part, the *Annals,* summarizes the history of each nation individually. The second, the *Chronological Canons,* synchronized the historical records of all the nations.

The challenge Eusebius faced in creating the *Chronological Canons* was not only how to link together chronographical information from Hebrew, Greek, Persian, and other sources, but also how to translate the relative chronology of each kingdom or empire into a universal time line to produce a synchronized succession of events. Universal dating did not exist during Eusebius's time. The Anno Domini (A.D./B.C.) system of dating used today was not created until 525 CE, and not widely used until 800 CE [28]. Exacerbating Eusebius's problem was that different cultures based their chronologies on different reckoning schemes. Ancient Greeks dated years according to Olympiads, which were on four year cycles. The Hebrew calendar follows a solar schedule segmented by lunar cycles. The Macedonian calendar followed a lunar cycle - a year has only 354 days. And the information reported by early historians and commentators could be just plain inaccurate!

Eusebius's eventual solution to his problem began with the codex, the forerunner of the contemporary book. Invented by the Romans, the codex was originally constructed by binding together waxed wooden writing tablets, and eventually papyrus and parchment sheets [29]. The codex is more practical than a scroll, given that it allows random information access, as opposed to a scroll's sequential access; and unlike the scroll, both sides of a sheet may be used for writing.

Eusebius began his process of correlation by drawing a multi-column table on a codex page. Each column corresponded to a kingdom, and each row to a year in a king's reign [30]. The leftmost column represented the dominant empire during a historical time period. It began with the Assyrians. The Persians took their place, and eventually the Romans occupied this column. The total number of columns varied as kingdoms came and went. There were as many as nine columns, for which Eusebius used a double-page spread. Eusebius left a space in the middle of each page to allow for commentary. Finally, Eusebius decided to set the starting date for his universal history with the earliest date he felt he could reasonably compute, that being the birth of Abraham. He marked off every tenth row with the number of years since Abraham's birth.

He filled his table by finding correlations between loosely connected regional years, linking them together by placing them on the same row of the table. For example, he determined that Darius of Persia and Alexander the Great of Macedonia lived at the same time, since the latter overthrew the former. This linked the Greek and Persian lists. He linked Jewish and Persian events by noting that the Bible recorded the second temple in Jerusalem was built in the second year of the Persian king Darius' reign.

Clearly this was an arduous task, something that could be easily handled today with computer intervention. But as Eusebius must have realized, one strength of tables is that all data are visible, thus making the viewing of inconsistencies or inaccuracies easily apparent. And there were many errors! Eusebius dealt with this problem by drawing a line under the periods of confusion to highlight these errors for future resolution.

Eusebius's own *Chronicle* in the original Greek no longer exists, but a Latin translation by St. Jerome does. This bishop and Church scholar translated Eusebius's tables, adding dates from 325 – 379 CE; publishing his *Chronicon* in 380 CE [31]. Figure 3 shows a page from Jerome's *Chronicon,* taken from a ninth century CE copy of the manuscript (MS. 315 fol. 96r, Merton College, Oxford University). The page is arranged in four columns – Persia, Rome, and Macedonia, with a column of commentary. Three ink colors (black, red, and green) were used as a means to distinguish dynasty lists. Eusebius specified the use of color to enhance legibility, and Jerome carried this through with his own version. In the far right column (in red) the rise of Alexander as King of the Macedonians is noted. To its left, Eusebius/Jerome recorded that Pythagoras died in the sixth year of Alexander's rule. On the table's far left column are two small red roman numerals (MDX and MDXX) designating the time lapsed in years since the birth of Abraham. Olympiads are shown in red, preceded by green roman numerals specifying the 69th, 70th, etc in the sequence.

Finally, at the top of the Persian column, the roman numerals mark the 15th and subsequent years of Darius's 36 year reign.

Eusebius recorded all aspects of culture in his *Chronicle*, including the real and fictitious: inventions, wars, lives of poets and scholars, lifespans of gods and politicians, to name but a few. As such it became a comprehensive cultural compendium that inspired the creation of future chronicles and itself lasting until the Protestant Reformation.

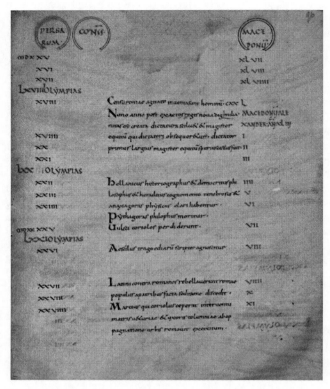

Figure 3: Jerome's *Chronicon*, (Merton MS 315, fol. 96r). Reproduced by permission of the Warden and Fellows of Merton College, Oxford.

V. CANON TABLES

A gospel is a New Testament book that describes the life and works of Jesus. There are four Canonical Gospels that were written by the evangelists Matthew, Mark, Luke, and John sometime between the years 60 and 80 CE. During the early Middle Ages these four gospels were often assembled into their own volume, a gospel book, and used as a teaching or evangelical tool. The most famous book of this kind is the *Book of Kells* created by Celtic monks around the year 800 CE.

Christian Bibles and gospel books had already taken the form of the codex by the second half of the first century CE [29]. The codex's design strength of random access facilitated preaching by providing unfettered access to all evangelical content. But one significant problem remained. All four gospels possess many passages in common. Analysis of the four gospels from nearly all Greek and Latin manuscripts reveals about 1165 self-contained passages distributed across Matthew (355), Mark (235), Luke (343),

and John (232) [32]. The challenge faced by a student of the gospels is not only how to find those passages that are in common among the gospels, but also those passages that are attributable to a subset of the authors or just an individual author.

Ammonius of Alexandria, an early Church Father, attempted a correlation around the year 220 CE as part of his *Harmony of the Gospels* (now lost) [33]. Taking Matthew's gospel as a referent, because it was the most comprehensive, Ammonius placed the corresponding passages of the remaining gospels adjacent to Matthew's text. This arrangement allowed the verbatim gospel commentaries to be compared in parallel. It was the method's strength. Its weakness was that it completely destroyed the narrative structure of the other three gospels.

The first successful attempt at creating a tool that cross-correlated gospel passages was made by Eusebius of Caesarea. He saw the power of Ammonius's method, but wanted to preserve the whole of all the texts, not just the Gospel of St. Matthew. His solution was to create a kind of tabular index called a canon table, containing information about where to locate gospel passages that shared content. Eusebius began his process by numbering all gospel passages, writing a reference number at the beginning of each. For example, there are 355 passages in the Gospel of St. Mathew, so passages were numbered in black ink from 1 to 355 in the gospel margins. Tables were then constructed that correlated these passages. Four column tables related those passages shared by all four authors. Three column tables contained pointers to passages that were shared by only three evangelists; tables with two column tabular correlations followed. Finally, a single column table was created that contained references to passages unique to each gospel. There were ten tables in all. And they were placed at the beginning of the gospel book with a description of how they were to be used.

A representative example of a Eusebian canon table is exhibited in Figure 4 (MS. Egerton 608, fol. 11, British Library). It is drawn from a gospel book that originated at the Monastery of St Willibrord, Echternach, Germany; produced during the 2nd or 3rd quarter of the 11th century. This is Canon Table IV, a three column table enclosed within an architectural arcade. Each column is labeled in Latin with the abbreviated name of an author (MAT (Matthew), MAR (Mark), and JOH (John)). Each table row contains the numbers of three correlated gospel passages. For example, the first row of this canon table records passage numbers XVIII, VIII, and XXVI. A reader would interpret this line as meaning that the passages numbered XVIII in Matthew, VIII in Mark, and XXVI in John all share commentary about a particular event in Jesus's life. The reader would then look up those numbered passages in each of the gospels to study the commentary.

Now suppose that someone upon reading a passage in one of the four gospels, say John CXXI, wished to discover whether other gospels contained similar presentations. The reader would find a number written in red ink below the passage number of this text placed there by Eusebius to indicate in which canon table a correlation could be found. The reader would then proceed to the designated canon table, here table IV, read down John's column until arriving at the row containing John's passage number, and then read along that row to find the numbers of the correlated passages.

In the year 331, by the order of the Emperor Constantine, Eusebius sent fifty copies of the gospels to Constantinople, the new capital of the Roman Empire, for use in its churches. By the fifth century they were in common use. In all probability, Eusebius's seeding of the Roman Empire with his canon tables ensured their success as a visualization tool. Indeed, they may be found in nearly all surviving copies of the gospels up to c. 1200, including gospel books written in Greek, Latin, Syriac, Gothic, Armenian, Georgian, and Ethiopian [34].

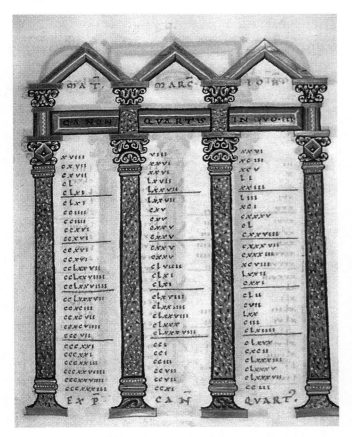

Figure 4: Eusebian canon table for Matthew, Mark, and John, © British Library Board (MS. Egerton 608, fol. 11, British Library).

VI. MEDIEVAL CALENDARS

Keeping track of time was important to medieval agriculture, and even more so for the Christian clergy [35]. The Church's liturgical practices involved a complex cycle of rituals and feasts that were celebrated in varying ways depending on the calendar day of the event. Since prayer was an intrinsic part of these celebrations, calendars were integrated into religious manuscripts such as psalters, breviaries, books of hours, missals, and almanacs.

Figure 5 shows a typical medieval calendar for the month of November, taken from an English psalter produced during the first quarter of the thirteenth century (MS. Royal 1DX, fol. 14, British Library). There are two roundels: a lower roundel indicating November's zodiac sign - Sagittarius, and an upper roundel designating the "Labour of the Month" - here a man slaughtering a pig. The term "Labours of the Months" refers to yearly cycles in Medieval art depicting common rural activities. The contents of cycles varied with date, location, and the kinds of work. For example, April was a time of sowing and July was a month for reaping so images would reflect these labors.

The column to the left of the roundels lists the feast days, with major feasts written in red. The illuminated "KL" initials at the table's top stand for the Latin word kalends, which marks the first day of the month in the Roman calendar. Below it in blue letters are initials marking in Latin the nones (5th day), ides (13th day), and remaining days until the next month's kalends. This column is augmented by a column of Roman numerals to its left containing a countdown from November's kalends, to nones, ides, and finally December's kalends. The calendar's format carries forth the structure of ancient Roman calendars (e.g. *Fasti Antiates Maiores*), including its use of red to highlight important events (red letter days) [24].

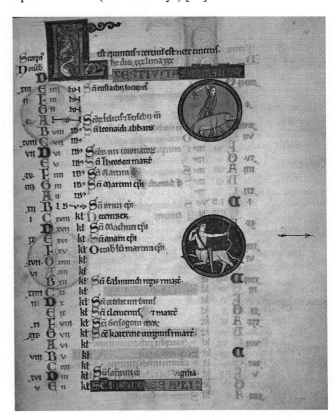

Figure 5: Calendar, November, English Psalter, © British Library Board (MS. Royal 1DX, fol. 14, British Library).

The calendar's first two columns contain roman numerals and letters respectively. These are related to the computus, a collection of algorithms for determining the date of Easter in the Christian calendar that were developed during the early Middle Ages [36][37]. Easter is the holiest feast day in Christendom, making the correct computation of its date one of the most important computations of the early Middle Ages. The Christian calendar contains two kinds of feast days – immovable, feast days that remain unchanged from year to year; and movable, feasts, such as Easter, that are linked to lunar and solar cycles.

Setting a yearly date for Easter was a source of controversy in the Church as early as the 3rd century. Although originally linked to the Jewish calendar through its relation to the Paschal (or Passover) celebration, various schools of thought within the Church, particularly Rome and Alexandria, had already developed their own methods of reckoning. They argued for Easter to be liberated from the Jewish calender because in some years the Jewish calender placed Easter's date either before the vernal equinox or not on Sunday. The First Council of Nicaea in 325 decreed that Christians should use a common method to establish the date of Easter independent of the Jewish method, but did not suggest a mode of computation. It would take several centuries before a common method was accepted throughout Christianity.

The problem that Church computists needed to solve was to find the date of Easter given the requirement that it is to be celebrated on the first Sunday after the 14th day of the lunar month that falls on or after the day of the vernal equinox. Their solutions to this problem were table-based, incorporating calculations of the cycles of the sun and moon. Figure 6 displays a sample computistical table known as the table of Dionysius Exiguus (MS. 17, fol. 30r, St. John's College, Oxford University) from the *Thorney Computus*, a manuscript produced in the first decade of the 12th century at Thorney Abbey in Cambridgeshire, England. It is a perpetual table of the great Paschal cycle of 532 years constructed from a Paschal lunar cycle of 19 years for the repeat of a full moon (columns) and a 28 year solar cycle of recurrent weekdays (rows). When the lunar and solar cycles are combined (19 x 28), a perpetual Great Paschal Cycle of 532 years results. With this table it is possible to predict the date of Easter up to 532 years in the future.

The Paschal table is set between the two inner margins (dark boarders) of Figure 6. Color flags designate cells marking the beginning of solar cycles (yellow), and cells which signal the beginning of *indictions* (green) [38]. Indictions is a Roman bureaucratic cycle of 15 years, established for taxation purposes during the reigns of Diocletian and Constantine that began on September 1st, the start of the fiscal year. Justinian made indictions part of the official dating style for government documents. They were included in the Alexandrian Paschal tables, migrating via Dionysius Exiguus into the standard Paschal tables used in the medieval west [38].

Numerous symbols and encodings envelope this table. They were intended to be used in concert with mnemonics, either memory or rhyming schemes, that described how the table was to be utilized; and with computation employing a

variation of medieval finger reckoning [39]. The complexity of Medieval computus meant that calendar reckoning could only be performed by individuals with appropriate training, such as that received in a medieval monastery. Indeed, many calenders were expanded to include additional columns for predicting phases and eclipses of the moon, and for supporting astrological prognosticatications. But even medieval monks found many of these computations too complex. As a result, simplified versions were designed to make calendars easier to use (see again Figure 5). By employing only the first two columns of the table in Figure 5, it became possible for an average monk to calculate the date of Easter for a given year. This simplification also made it possible for educated laity to own calendars. Such examples have been found in books of hours of rich individuals. One of the most famous is the *Très Riches Heures du Duc de Berry* (c. 1410) by the Limbourg Brothers.

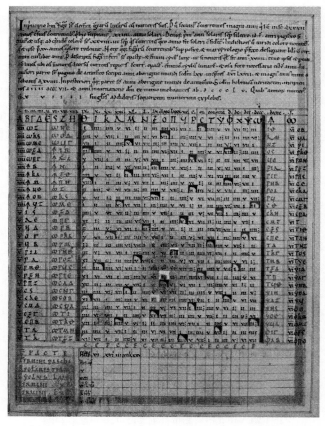

Figure 6: Computus Table, (MS. 17, fol. 30r, St. John's College, Oxford). Reproduced by permission of the President and Fellows of St John's College, Oxford.

VII. ANALYSIS

Wainer has set forth rationales for table usage and design: exploration, communication, storage, and illustration [14][15]. As part of exploration, tables help answer questions about data. As exemplars of communication, tables provide effective means for presenting data - each table has a story or stories to tell. Storage archives data, supporting a historical context, and aiding in data retrieval. As illustration, tables are used as graphics in support of narrative.

All tables described herein support exploration. The gridded, spreadsheet-like format of the Sumerian table makes it easy to ask questions about individuals and their monthly wages. Eusebius's chronologies and medieval calendars are arranged to make it easy to find important dates and events. While the canon table's structure logically organizes the gospel texts.

If longevity is an effective measure of the communication capability of these tables, then they are all highly effective. The Sumerian table structure is used in spreadsheets today. The structure of Eusebius's *Chronicles* remains a standard format for historians. And the medieval calendar's layout is a standard structure for contemporary agendas. In addition, the structure of each table supports the creation of narratives. The temporal structure of Eusebius's *Chronicles* and medieval calendars sets forth clear narrative paths. The correlated index structure of canon tables provides a means for communicating parallel and intersecting Gospel narrative threads. And the Sumerian table allows the creation of stories about the temple's yearly disbursements to its workers throughout the year.

These tables support ease of information storage and accessibility. The 532 year Easter cycle of the computus table, the myriad feast days of the medieval calendar, and Eusebius's *Chronology* all imbue these tables with a deep sense of history as well. Indeed, the Roman bureaucratic cycle that became embedded within the computus table (Figure 6), demonstrates the historical evolution of a table from a purely liturgical tool to a secular tool as well.

Finally, in Wainer's rationale of illustration for table usage, tables are viewed as graphical objects in support of narrative. All tables discussed are coherent graphical entities consistent with Bertin's rules for visual encoding [40]. For example, color was an important design component clearly specified by early designers. Eusebius and Jerome dictated the colors to be used, and how to use them. The accompanying text to the computistical table shown in Figure 6 explains a color coding scheme attributed to Abbo of Fleury (c. 945 – 1004) [38]. Table cells associated with solar and bureaucratic cycles were highlighted with yellow and green respectively, in order to highlight their temporal patterns for ease of visualization. And the specification of important medieval calendar dates in red, which became known as red letter days, is traceable as far back as the Romans.

VIII. CONCLUSION

The five tables investigated here appeared between 1300 BCE and 1300 CE. Sumerian accounting tables, chronicles, canon tables, medieval computus, and calendars, may be considered early milestones in the history of information visualization. Analysis of these tables demonstrates that as early as 1300 BCE the need to visualize information had driven the invention of structured visual representations for information. Ancient Sumerian scribes invented a table structure that anticipated the spreadsheet by nearly 4000

years. During the late Roman empire, Eusebius of Caesarea invented respectively, a new representational structure for a chronology, and the concept of the canon table in order to organize and access both historical and liturgical texts. The need to compute a yearly date for the Christian feast of Easter led early medieval scholars to develop computational algorithms for reckoning the date of Easter. Expressed as tables, these algorithms provided a theoretical foundation for the Roman calendar's temporal structure, and eventually furnished a means for the integration of computus with calendral information of a social and religious nature.

Finally, an analysis of these tables employing Wainer's rationales has shown them to be exemplars of table design. Their usability has most assuredly secured each of these table's place in visualization history, ultimately transforming the way information has been used, stored, and communicated.

ACKNOLEDGEMENTS

I would like to thank Professor Robert K. Englund of the Cuneiform Digital Library Initiative for providing the drawing of the Uruk III tablet. The assistance of the following individuals in securing image permissions is greatly appreciated: Dr. Julia Walworth, Fellow Librarian of Merton College, Oxford; Stewart Tiley, Librarian, St John's College, Oxford; and Sandra Powlette, British Library.

REFERENCES

[1] E. H.-H. Chi, P. Barry, J. Riedl, and J. Konstan, "A spreadsheet approach to information visualization," In Proceedings of the 10th annual ACM symposium on User interface software and technology (UIST '97). ACM, New York, NY, USA, 1997, pp. 79-80.

[2] F.T. Marchese, "Teaching computer graphics with spreadsheets," In ACM SIGGRAPH 98 Conference Abstracts and Applications, ACM SIGGRAPH, 1998, pp. 84-87.

[3] E. H-H. Chi, J. Riedl, P. Barry, and J. Konstan, "Principles for information visualization spreadsheets," IEEE Comput. Graph. Appl., vol. 18, 4, 1998, pp. 30-38.

[4] F. Nunez and E. H. Blake, "ViSSH: A data visualization spreadsheet," In Proceedings of the Second Joint Eurographics-IEEE TCVG Symposium on Visualization, Amsterdam, The Netherlands, May 29-31, 2000, pp. 209-218.

[5] H.-W. Hsieh and F.M. Shipman, III, "VITE: a visual interface supporting the direct manipulation of structured data using two-way mappings," In Proceedings of the 5th international conference on Intelligent user interfaces (IUI '00). ACM, New York, NY, USA, 2000, pp. 141-148.

[6] S. Sarni, A. Maciel, and D. Thalmann, "A spreadsheet framework for visual exploration of biomedical datasets," In Proceedings of the 18th IEEE Symposium on Computer-Based Medical Systems (CBMS '05). IEEE Computer Society, Washington, DC, USA, 2005, pp.159-164.

[7] R. Brath and M. Peters, "Excel visualizer: one click WYSIWYG spreadsheet visualization," In Proceedings of the conference on Information Visualization (IV '06). IEEE Computer Society, Washington, DC, USA, 2006, pp. 68-73.

[8] M. Itoh, J. Fujima, M. Ohigashi, and Y. Tanaka, "Spreadsheet-based framework for interactive 3D visualization of web resources," In Proceedings of the 11th International Conference Information Visualization (IV '07). IEEE Computer Society, Washington, DC, USA, 2007, pp. 65-73.

[9] A.Streit, B. Pham, and R. Brown, "A spreadsheet approach to facilitate visualization of uncertainty in Information," IEEE

Transactions on Visualization and Computer Graphics, vol. 14, 1, 2008, pp. 61-72.

[10] S. Kandel, A. Paepcke, M. Theobald, H. Garcia-Molina, and E. Abelson, "Photospread: a spreadsheet for managing photos. In Proceeding of the twenty-sixth annual SIGCHI conference on Human factors in computing systems (CHI '08). ACM, New York, NY, USA, 2008, pp. 1749-1758.

[11] F.T. Marchese, "The chemical table: an open dialog between visualization and design," In Proceedings of the 12th International Conference on Information Visualization: IV'08. IEEE Computer Society, Washington, DC, 2008, pp. 75-81.

[12] M. Campbell-Kelly, M. Croarken, R.G. Flood, and E. Robson (eds.), The History of Mathematical Tables from Sumer to Spreadsheets. Oxford: Oxford University Press, 2003.

[13] E.R. Scerri, The Periodic Table: Its Story and Its Significance, Oxford: Oxford University Press, 2007.

[14] H. Wainer, "Understanding graphs and tables," Educational Researcher, vol. 21, 1, 1992, pp. 12-23.

[15] H. Wainer, "Improving tabular displays, with NAEP: tables as examples and inspirations," Journal of Educational and Behavioral Statistics, vol. 22, 1, 1997, pp. 1-30.

[16] J. L. Berggren and A. Jones, Ptolemy's Geography: An Annotated Translation of the Theoretical Chapters. Princeton and Oxford: Princeton University Press, 2000.

[17] D. Turnbull, Maps are Territories. Science is an Atlas. Chicago: University of Chicago Press, 1994.

[18] R. K. Englund, "Texts from the Uruk period," in Späturuk-Zeit und Frühdynastische Zeit (ed. P. Attinger and C. Uelinger), Freiburg and Göttingen, 1998, pp. 15–233.

[19] N. Veldhuis, "The archaic lexical corpus, digital corpus of cuneiform lexical texts," University of California, Berkeley. Retrieved April 29, 2011 from http://oracc.museum.upenn.edu/dcclt.

[20] M.W. Green, "The construction and implementation of the cuneiform writing system, " Visible Writing, vol. 15, 1981, pp. 345-72.

[21] E. Robson, "Tables and tabular formatting in Sumer, Babylonia, and Assyria, 2500-50 BCE," in M. Campbell-Kelly, M. Croarken, R.G. Flood, and E. Robson (eds.), The History of Mathematical Tables from Sumer to Spreadsheets. Oxford: Oxford University Press, 2003, pp. 18–47.

[22] A.T. Clay, Documents from the Temple Archives of Nippur Dated in the Reigns of the Cassite Rulers, 3 vols., The University Museum, Philadelphia, 1906, pls. 25–6.

[23] The Parian Marble, Ashmolean Museum of At and Archaeology. Retrieved April 29, 2011 from http://www.ashmolean.museum/ash/faqs/q004/.

[24] D. Feeney, Caesar's Calendar: Ancient Time and the Beginnings of History. University of California Press, 2007.

[25] B. Croke, The originality of Eusebius' chronicle," The American Journal of Philology, vol. 103, 2, 1982, pp. 195-200.

[26] F.J. Bacchus, "Eusebius of Cæsarea," In The Catholic Encyclopedia. New York: Robert Appleton Company, 1909. Retrieved February 24, 2011 from: http://www.newadvent.org/cathen/05617b.htm

[27] F.J. Bacchus, "Eusebius of Cæsarea," In The Catholic Encyclopedia. New York: Robert Appleton Company, 1909. Retrieved February 24, 2011 from: http://www.newadvent.org/cathen/05616a.htm

[28] G. Teres, "Time computations and Dionysius Exiguus," Journal for the History of Astronomy, vol. 15, 1984, pp. 177-188.

[29] C. Roberts and T. C. Skeat, The Birth of the Codex. British Academy, 1983.

[30] R. Pearse, "Jerome: the manuscripts of the 'Chronicon'," Retrieved April 29, 2011 from http://www.tertullian.org/rpearse/manuscripts/jerome_chronicon.htm.

[31] R. Pearse, et al., trans. "The chronicle of St. Jerome," in Early Church Fathers: Additional Texts, 2005. Preface to the Online Edition. Retrieved April 29, 2011 from http://rbedrosian.com/jerome_chronicle_00_eintro.htm .

[32] F. Bechtel, "Ammonian sections," In The Catholic Encyclopedia. New York: Robert Appleton Company, 1907. Retrieved February 23, 2011 from http://www.newadvent.org/cathen/01431a.htm

[33] H.H. Oliver, "The epistle of Eusebius to Carpianus. textual tradition and translation," Novum Testamentum, vol. 3, 1959, pp. 138-145.

[34] C. Nordenfalk, "Canon tables of papyrus," Dumbarton Oaks Papers, vol. 36, 1982, pp. 29-38.

[35] A. Borst, The Ordering of Time: From the Ancient Computus to the Modern Computer, Trans. by Andrew Winnard. Cambridge: Polity Press; Chicago: Univ. of Chicago Press, 1993.

[36] T. Morrison, "Computus digitorum for the calculation of Easter," Journal of the Australian Early Medieval Association, vol. 1, 2005, pp. 85-98.

[37] Bede, (translated by F. Wallis), Bede: The Reckoning of Time. Liverpool: Liverpool University Press, 2004.

[38] F. Wallis, "5. Computus tables and texts II: 18. tabula Dionysii," The Calendar and the Cloister: Oxford, St John's College MS17. 2007. McGill University Library. Digital Collections Program. Retrieved April 29, 2011 from http://digital.library.mcgill.ca/ms-17.

[39] B.P. Williams and R.S. Williams, "Finger numbers in the Greco-Roman world and the early middle ages," Isis, vol. 86, 4 , 1995, pp. 587-608

[40] J. Bertin, Semiology of Graphics (translated by W.J. Berg). University of Wisconsin Press, 1983.

Showing Action in Pictures

Yvonne Eriksson, Peter Johansson
Division of Information Design
Mälardalen University
Eskilstuna, Sweden
{Yvonne.Eriksson, Peter.Johansson}@mdh.se

Petra Björndal
Industrial Software Systems
ABB Corporate Research
Västerås, Sweden
Petra.Bjorndal@se.abb.com

Abstract— One challenge for the global market is to overcome communication problems of different kinds. The largest communication problem is language; people speak different languages and have limited knowledge in other languages. This problem is central in manuals and instructions for assembly and installations. One hopeful solution is that pictures can replace verbal instructions. In this paper we will discuss how illustrations in flat perspective can be useful for showing action in drawings.

Keywords - visual communication, instructions, sequential drawing, image style

I. Introduction

One challenge for the global market is to overcome communication problems of different kinds. The largest communication problem is language; people speak different languages and have limited knowledge in other languages. Therefore translations in different kinds of instructions are necessary. Since industries export to a widening range of countries, the instructions accompanying their products must be translated into several languages. Sometimes up to twenty different languages may be involved, which means that the instruction materials for a single product are often disproportionate to the information required. In many cases a small product is accompanied by a big instruction book that may weigh more than the product itself, which affects transportation costs. In order to reduce the costs for attached instructions, manufacturing industries are looking for alternatives to written instructions. The substitute for written instructions is visual instructions. However, to replace language with pictures is complex, since language and pictures belong to different symbol systems, and therefore demand different strategies from the designers of instructions.

In this paper we will present a suggestion for how to represent action in instructions for assembly and installation by using an example (See Fig. 1). The suggestion is based on the results from a research project made for a manufacturing company. The project is under a non-disclosure agreement and pictures used in this paper are therefore not the ones used in the pre-test or the following test. The pictures used in this paper have the style that was developed from the analysis and the tests but have another motif.

II. Replacing words with pictures

The project was initiated by a manufacturing company, and the objective for the company's partner in this study is twofold; firstly to explore the possibility of using pictures to a greater extent in installation instructions to achieve reduced translation and printing costs, and secondly to investigate the improvement potential for installation instructions per se.

Since language and pictures belong to different symbol systems, a different strategy has to be employed when changing from words to pictures. Writing can describe what to do, whereas pictures cannot. An activity can only be indicated in pictures; therefore the challenge for the project was to find a way to represent action in static pictures.

The objective of the research is to see if an alternative to the commonly used isometric line drawing can be used in installation instructions. The goal is to overcome differences in cultural traditions and to focus on the actual action rather than the object itself. The project's aim is also to see if a less detailed picture can be easier to interpret.

The research questions are:

- How can events/sequences connected to each other be visualized in an instruction?
- How does the image style affect how an instruction is perceived?
- How abstract/limited in amount of detail can a picture in an instruction be and still give information to the viewer?

III. Background

Language can be a communication obstacle for the global market on different levels — in business to business and in business to customer, and within individual companies. In manufacturing industries assembly is central, and many companies outsource that part. To avoid expensive assembly mistakes, it is necessary to disambiguate instructions. In manufacturing industries, pictures are used to clarify how assembly is performed and to show the appearance of the objects that are to be put together. However, the quality of the pictures is often very poor; they frequently consist of digital photos taken by the assemblers themselves. Such photos are often overloaded with information and hard to interpret for new workers who are not already familiar with the actual assembly process.

It is often pointed out that contemporary products are designed in CAD, and hence CAD files can be used as the

1550-6037/11 $26.00 © 2011 IEEE
DOI 10.1109/IV.2011.104

basis for assembly instructions. However, CAD files are complex and contain more details than necessary. For multifaceted products such as JAS airplanes with trained assemblers, it works [1]. In most industries the assemblers are not trained, nor are the installers of less complicated installations. Therefore the instructions have to be simple and clear, so they can be interpreted intuitively. This is easy to say but hard to realize, since there is no unambiguous definition of what is meant by a "simple" picture. Within engineering design there is a long tradition of using drawings for different purposes, e.g. for construction, for assembly and for installation [2]. Those drawings have their own taxonomy and can hardly be interpreted intuitively.

The heritage of contemporary engineering drawings is to be found in a French encyclopedia from the late 18th century. The French philosopher Roland Barthes has argued that the illustrations in Denis Diderot and d'Alemberts *Encyclopedia* were something radically new for 18th century readers. For the first time, French people saw objects represented in intersection and disassembly, piece by piece, on a plane surface [3]. The illustrations offered a new way of structuring understanding and knowledge. In the West this tradition is well established in scientific illustrations, engineering drawings and educational material. Studies indicate that the Western drawing traditions can be challenging to interpret by non-Western people, who often lack experience of the drawing style employed. Further research is needed to gain a deeper understanding of how different cultural backgrounds influence the ability to interpret traditional engineering drawings [4]. In addition, it is necessary to study the tradition of instrumental drawings (pictures for instructions, in teaching material or in scientific texts) in different cultures to learn more. For instance, China has a long tradition of using instrumental pictures that goes back to the 13th century [4]. In this paper we will present an alternative to the pictorial tradition that originates in the *Encyclopedia*.

IV. REPRESENTING ACTION IN DRAWINGS

One of the crucial points for picture-based instruction is, however, to interpret a static drawing as an intended action. Even though a drawing looks familiar, it is not obvious to everyone how it should be used, that is to perform a specific act. Action can be indicated in a series of pictures representing the change from one picture to the next. For example we see a person with long hair walking into a hairdresser, in the next picture we see the same person coming out from the hairdresser with shorter hair. From that we draw the conclusion that the person has had a haircut. It is the space between the pictures that makes sense for the viewer, not the pictures themselves, but this requires an experienced "reader". Otherwise the two pictures in this example will be interpreted as two separate pictures, not as one story. Research shows that illiterates often interpret comic strips as separate pictures, and not as a story that continues from picture to picture [5]. The action can also be indicated by arrows, but it is seldom obvious how to interpret an arrow; one reason is that it is hard to show its direction in a third dimension. Another reason is that the definition of arrow is not clear; does it include the line or not? [6].

There is a lack of research concerning how picture instructions work in different situations in general, and in an industrial context specifically. Scholars interested in picture instructions often study them from a cognitive or perceptual perspective. Our perspective is to combine the perceptual and cognitive processes that are involved in interpreting pictures with a picture theory. Others have done usability tests on picture instructions intended for consumers of such things as furniture or home-electronic equipment [7]. Only limited research has been done focusing on the use of pictures in manufacturing industries. One study concerning assembly in such industries has demonstrated the need for further research (Eriksson) [14].

Many scientific areas are dependent on visualizations, to illuminate their results or to prove them. Engineering drawings are central both for constructions and for communications [2]. Peter Galison, among others, has illustrated the importance of pictures in science from a scientific historical point of view, and the belief in photography as an objective medium for visualization in science [8]. In cognitive science, pedagogy and psychology research have shown the importance of pictures to clarify and to explain functions and appearances of objects. The cognitive scientist Barbara Tversky has emphasized that visualization is a cognitive tool, designed to augment human cognitive capacities [9, 10, 11]. She suggests that pictures aid memory by off-loading it from limited working memory or fallible long-term memory. By off-loading, visualizations relieve working memory of its memory functions, leaving more capacity for processing. In her research, Tversky shows the important and practical function of visualizations: to convey information [11]. Correctly designed pictures can clarify how to perform procedures such as assembly or installation. Correctly designed means pictures designed compatible with human perception and cognition [11]. Research has proved that illustrations are superior in assembly instructions because they show how to assemble without any further instructions. However, the research does not indicate, or make any concrete suggestions for, how to implement their results in assembly instructions for manufacturing industries, or for installations. And in addition they do not focus on the picture as such, that is as a meaningful entity that communicates independently in different contexts.

A. Traditions for visual representations

It is common to represent installations or assembly instructions by line drawings in an isometric perspective. This kind of drawing is often rich in detail. Drawings with many details can be hard to interpret, inasmuch as it can be difficult to understand the purpose of the picture. To be sure that the observer/reader of a picture will be able to understand the intended message, it is necessary to emphasize central parts in the drawing and omit details. This could be done by colors, or by the position of single objects on the surface, or by thicker lines, or by eliminating details around a specific part.

Reorganization is fundamental for pictures, because they are interchangeable. We recognize and identify objects by their shape, especially when we identify objects on a more general level. In pictures that represent objects in general, and not a specific element, the shape is often emphasized and details are eliminated. This might involve a clear shape contrasting against the background. To focus on an object as a whole is not always of interest; we often need to focus on single details. Details can be highlighted in different ways; one is to enlarge parts of the drawing. By oscillating between the object as a whole and enlarging parts we got a mixture of focus. This mixture helps us to represent an activity.

In an assembly instruction we have to focus on the object per se, in order to understand the expected outcome. Therefore we need to know the appearance of the actual thing we are to assemble. However, when we are to install something, it is the activity that has to be in focus, not the object itself. What shall be done? How shall we do it? The pictures should represent what? and How? But we must not ignore that it is fundamental to recognize the object that is to be installed, and the equipment that will be used for the installation.

B. Pictures for instructions in a global perspective

Today we have surprisingly poor knowledge about how visual communication works in different cultural, ethnic and language contexts. And we have only limited knowledge about the embedded codes in engineering drawings. On an everyday level there is no need for a definition of pictures [2, 12, 13, 14]. But to be able to use pictures in instructions in general and for installations specifically, it is necessary to define the concept. Pictures are a symbol system that differs from language, as mentioned before. Pictures contain symbols that are spatially organized, and in pictures it is possible to show things like appearance and relations. Pictures differ from other representations, such as text and music, because they can imitate. To imitate demands that essential elements in the visual representation correspond to the actual object [15]. A critical question concerning likeness is to what extent can a 2D picture represent a 3D object? What is required? In terms of installation instructions we have to ask ourselves: how do we represent objects and actions involved in installation processes?

Pictures are irreplaceable tools for showing appearance and relations of different kinds. Pictures can imitate, and therefore a common apprehension is that pictures are universal and can overcome language obstacles. As mentioned before, this is not true because pictures largely build on conventions that vary between cultures. Therefore, we have experimented with the style of pictures in instructions to try to find out if it is possible to identify a pictorial language that could satisfy the demand from industry for use in a global market. For art historians it is obvious that traditions of pictorial representations differ between cultures and from time to time. But in an industrial context this is rarely noticed. To be able to communicate via pictures there has to be a common understanding of how the pictures shall be interpreted. In Class, Codes and Control (1971), Basil Bernstein elucidates embedded codes in visual representations, and establishes that different viewers can read codes on different levels. According to Gestalt Theory, it is the shape that dominates in recognition of depicted objects, and this is universal. However, to be able to recognize an object from its shape, it is important that the object is depicted from an angle that shows its typical appearance. This is, more or less in front view. The discussion about the possibility to identify a specific object in a picture can be linked to the discussion about similarity. The ideas about pictures' mimetic qualities have a long history, and are strongly connected to the Western tradition. But if we accept the Gestalt Theory notions about shape identification as something universal, we should focus on shape in depictions when we are making instructions for the global market.

Visuals can be divided into different kinds, such as drawings, sketches, photos, and moving images. In an engineering context, the most common visual aids are drawings, but moving images are used for demonstrations and photographs for assembly. The technique and style used for visual representation affects the perception of the content. Drawings allow us to emphasize single parts, enlarge details and show several angles of an object at the same time, while photography can only represent one angle at a time. Therefore, it is only possible to focus on either details or the whole at the same time. However, photographic collage or montage offers other possibilities. In contradiction to moving images, it is complicated to show action in pictures, especially when it comes to instructions. It is one thing to look at a series of pictures and interpret a particular action, and another to follow an instruction and to fulfill a requested act.

However, pictures can be divided into two kinds: those that portray things that are essentially visuo-spatial, and those that represent things that are not inherently visual. Maps, molecules and architectural drawings belong to the first group; organization charts, flow diagrams and graphs belong to the second group [11]. Picture-based instructions can be defined as a mixture of the two, since they portray objects or parts of objects that should be installed or assembled, and at the same time provide instructions for the actual action. Arrows are fundamental for showing how to put different parts of an object together or to twist, bend or turn something upside down. Arrows are not inherently visual. Assembly or installations instructions are complex and they consist of both the appearance of the objects that are to be assembled or installed and representation of the action. Representation of an action is abstract since there are no conventions for showing how to do something. Interpreting pictorial instructions is a two- fold process: first one has to identify the object as such and its different parts; secondly one has to figure out how to act.

V. METHOD

A study involving 21 informants (9 Chinese, 2 Spanish, 3 Singaporean and 7 Swedish) was made to try to find an answer to the research questions: How can events/sequences connected to each other be visualized in an instruction? How does the image style affect how an instruction is perceived?

How abstract/limited in amount of detail can a picture in an instruction be and still give information to the viewer?

The work began with a survey and analysis of how drawings are used by the company that initiated the project. The analysis revealed what image style the drawings have and how they are used. An installation carried out by an experienced installer was filmed to understand how a professional conducts an installation. To compare how others in the same line of business use pictures, the observations from the analysis were compared with material from the company's subsidiaries. Instructions in other trades were also examined to get a better understanding of how drawings in instructions can look and how they are used.

When the analysis and survey of drawings in instructions was completed, a prototype of an instruction was drawn. The image style in the prototype was based on the observations in the analysis.

The image style in the prototype had a limited level of detail, and the drawings contained sequences that showed how to do an installation. The prototype had a twofold purpose. The main purpose was to test how the sequences worked – if it was possible to follow the steps and handle the drawings provided. The second purpose of the test was to see if a reduced level of detail affects how the drawings in an instruction are perceived.

The prototype was tested in Sweden with four informants who made installations guided by the prototype. The test was filmed and the informants answered a questionnaire about the instructions after the test. The test was also documented with a sound recording, and the result from the installations was photographed.

With the results from the prototype test, the sequences were redrawn to be more coherent. The test also gave hints for developing the image style. When the steps and handling in the sequences were refined, three different image styles were created. The image styles had a reduction of details in common. They differed in that one image style had a front view and contour lines, one image style had no lines and a front view, and one image style had no lines and an isometric perspective.

The instruction was now made in three versions: all versions had the same sequence but different image styles. Now the image style was tested. The test was performed with informants that work with installations. The test was carried out with professional installers in Sweden and in China. In China the test instruction was translated into Chinese, and two Spanish test informants in Sweden got the instructions in English. The Singaporean informants got their instructions in English. The Swedish informants did the tests in Swedish. The informants made the installations aided by the installation instruction. Each informant carried out one installation. No informant was allowed to do more than one installation. The test was documented with a video camera. The finished installation was photographed, and the informants answered a questionnaire about the installation instruction (the Singaporean informants did not answer the questionnaire but their results clearly showed high skills in installation).

We have chosen to discuss the results on a general level related to an industrial context, and therefore the example is an assembly instruction (see Fig.1). Because of the non-disclosure agreement the motif is not the same as in the tests.

VI. DISCUSSION

The instructions are represented in sequential order, from top to bottom. The picture elements are made on a gray background. Every illustration has a thin black frame and a white background. The frame and the white background focus the reader's attention on one picture at a time. Activities belonging together are linked by an arrow that goes from one picture to the next. The arrow goes from the lower part of the frame and points to the pictures below. Some of the illustrations show sequences with several pictures, since the appearance of a tool is established and how it shall be used. The instruction pictures are shown in a front view. And the picture elements are made as plain surfaces without contour lines. The tool has contour lines to emphasize action. The pictures do not have an accompanying text except from when size of tools and torque must be given.

The instruction starts with a picture frame that shows what kind of tool, which is needed to do the assembly and which part the installation will start with. Then the process is shown step by step. We will here discuss what we have found essential while composing the instructions.

A. Choosing central activities

The first step is to observe what is to be represented and analyze the situation. This could be done by asking an experienced worker to show what to do and taping the activity. From that one has to analyze the central activities and find out when one activity is replaced by another. In the pictures, it is important that the activity is represented step by step, one picture for one activity. The progress has to be represented in the following picture so a change can be interpreted. Showing new details or a change in perspective from an overall picture to close-ups could accomplish this.

B. Action indicated by tools

Key to installation is the use of tools. Therefore the actual tools can be used to indicate actions that should be performed, so the tool has to be linked to the activity that is expected to be done. In this example the screwdriver is close to the screw. The tool can be shown in action in e.g. a close-up picture.

C. Emphasis on shape and abstract pictures

The pictures are abstract, and therefore details are limited. This is because the focus is on the actual activity and not the appearance of the objects. Thus the instructions for using a screwdriver can be employed for different models of screw-drivers. We suggest that an abstract picture adds clarity concerning the actual activity, because unnecessary details are eliminated.

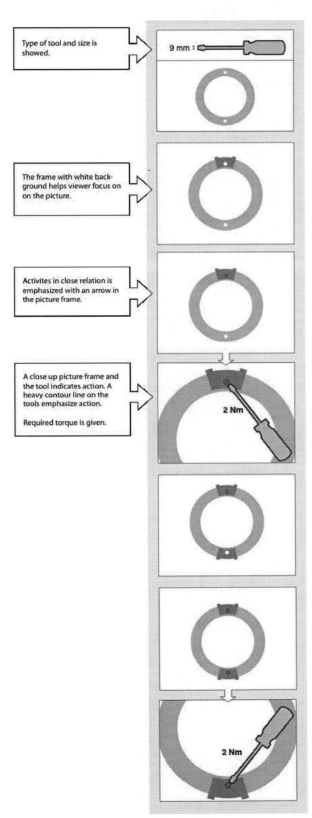

Figure 1. An example assembly instruction

VII. CONCLUSIONS

In this paper we have brought up questions concerning if and how it is possible to replace written instructions with pictorial ones for a global market. It is complex to represent activities in two-dimensional pictures. Therefore a strategy for how to focus on action rather than appearance is necessary. IKEA and other companies have developed assembly instructions for customers. However, it is hard to compare instructions for activities that take place once with those that are to be repeated many times, such as in professional installations or assembly in industry. For those contexts, the pictorial instructions should be useable for several purposes, including know-how and memory support. Information Design works in a tradition of human-centered design, which means that the design should meet the user's need. For a global market with limited knowledge of user needs, backgrounds, knowledge and experience from the field in question, it is a challenge to design with the individuals in focus. By combining theories about how human beings perceive visual representations with knowledge about culture and pictorial traditions, we suggest that it is possible to find new methods for pictorial representations that will work more effectively and efficiently. The pictures should be easier to draw and to work with – picture elements is easily reused by copy-paste instead of being redrawn from scratch. It should be less of an effort to update old material once the pictures have been drawn. We are striving to make the illustrations in the instructions clear with regard to identifying the represented objects. Therefore we concentrating on the shape and showing the objects in front view, and thereby propose an alternative to the traditional engineering drawings for installations and assembly for a global market.

REFERENCES

[1] K. Hendersson. On line and on paper. Visual Representations, Visual culture, and Computer Graphics in Design Engineering. Cambridge Mass. MIT Press. 1999.

[2] E.S. Ferguson. Engineering and the Mind's Eye. Cambridge Mass. MIT Press. 1994/2001.

[3] R. Barthes, "Image, Raison, Déraison", Ed. Barthes et al. L'universe de l'encyclopédie images d'une civilization. Les 135 plus belles planches de 'encyplocpédie de Diderot et d'Alambert. Paris: Les Libraires Assoiés. 1964.

[4] S. Han. A Chinese Word on Image – Zheng Qiao (1104-12) and his thought on images, diss., Göteborg: Acta Universitatis Gothoburgensis. 2008.

[5] F. Qarin. Bildval i alfabetiseringsundervisning- en fråga om synsätt. Rapporter om svenska som andrspråk ROSA 9. Institutet för svenska som andradraspråk, Göteborgs universitet. 2007.

[6] R. Krull and M. Sharp. Visual verbs: Using arrows to depict the direction of actions in procedural illustrations, Information design Journal, 14, 189–198.

[7] B. Tversky. Spatical schemas in depictions, Spatial schemas and abstract thoughts. Ed. M. Gattis, MIT Press, Cam. Mass. 2001.

[8] L. Daston, and P. Galison. Objectivity. New York: Zone Books. 2007.

[9] B. Tversky, Distortions in memory of maps. Cognition Psychology, 13, 407-433. 1991.

[10] B. Tversky. Some ways that graphics communicate, Mobile communication: Essays on cognition and community, Ed. K. Nyiri, Wien: Passagen Verlag. 2003.

[11] B. Tversky. Cognitive Design Principles for Automated Generation of Visualization. 2006.

[12] M. Twyman. Using Pictorial Language: A Discussion of the Dimensions of the Problem. In Designing Usable Texts, edited by Thomas M. Duffy and Robert Waller, 245-312. Orlando: Academic Press. 1985.

[13] J. Elkins. Into the Domaine of Images. Ithaca: Cornell University Press. 1999.

[14] Y. Eriksson. Bildens tysta budskap. Interaktion mellan bild och text. Stockholm: Norstedts Akademiska förlag. 2009.

[15] [15] R.L. Solso. Cognition and Visual Arts, MIT Press, Mass. Cambridge. 1994.

The Implications of David Hockney's Thesis for 3D computer graphics

Theodor Wyeld
Flinders University, Australia
{twyeld@gmail.com

Abstract

David Hockney's 2001 book Secret Knowledge of the Masters, *reignited the debate on the use of optical devices for constructing perspective images in the Renaissance. In it, he brings his insights as an artist to the debate. This paper explores his thesis in terms of its implications for 3D computer graphics. Just as technology informed the Renaissance artist on ways of seeing and representing natural phenomena, 3D computer graphics today uses algorithms to simulate these same phenomena. For both, various techniques are used to make the images produced seem real or at least real enough. In the case of the Renaissance artist, painterly techniques were used to generate the illusion of clarity. For 3D computer graphics, mathematical algorithms are used to simulate many of the same effects. Striving for realism is a common theme. However, while the Renaissance artist never lost site of their role in interpreting what they see, 3D computer graphics is supposed to be underpinned by the certainties of its apparent scientific veracity. But is this certainty deserved or is it merely that science and art are intertwined in ways that mean one is reliant on the other?*

Keywords--- **Hockney, Renaissance, 3D, Computer Graphics, Perspective.**

Introduction

In Hockney's [1] book, *Secret Knowledge, Rediscovering the Lost Techniques of the Old Masters*, he claims the Renaissance Masters transformed their art from Gothic symbolic spiritualism to a naturalistic realism using optical devices. This is not a new concept – it has been reported by others [2 - 7]. However, in a very practical way, Hockney recreates the conditions for optically projected images to apply his theories directly. What is interesting is how contemporary 3D computer graphics uses many of the Masters' terms.to describe their algorithmic corollary. It is the Masters' techniques for producing depth, light and shade that seems to inform the 3D computer algorithms used in creating computer generated realistic scenes today.

Hockney claims the projected image from mirrors and lenses allowed artists to capture fleeting expressions directly by tracing its projection thus accounting for what seems to be a dramatic shift to realism in the fifteenth century. It is this same realism that is captured in today's computer algorithms. But, how the algorithms are configured is subject to the same interpretations that the Renaissance Masters made of what they observed. Hence, scientific fact and artistic technique are conflated in the space of their mutual representation – each informing the other. Although not well documented, the terms used to describe the various 'realism' algorithms used in 3D computer graphics seems to confirm this connection.

The Projected Image

Da Vinci is perhaps the earliest clear link we have with the direct use of optics in the construction of Renaissance perspective images [1, 2, 13]. Da Vinci's lens-based system involved not just the technology available but an aspiration to a 'naturalism'. Conceptually, artistic representation was redefined as literal imitation. According to Hockney this was based on a developing culture that optical devices created images using the geometry of light to deliver a more objective imitation than the human eye could perceive. It provided a model for an 'objectification' of nature. In turn, Renaissance artists caused a profound change in the way the world was visually understood and organised – eventually influencing Galileo, Harvey, Descartes, and Newton's views [4].

While many authors [2, 4, 13-16] tend to agree that the availability of optics influenced the production of the perspective procedure in the Renaissance, Hockney goes further, claiming that studies of optics both provided a mechanism for, and the basis for establishing the rules of, its construction. Among other examples, as evidence for his thesis, Hockney points out how Jan van Eyck's Arnolfini Wedding of 1434 contains a convex mirror. This type of mirror, if silvered on the reverse side, would provide the very concave mirror required to generate the series of projected images necessary for the painting's production. Using a concave mirror, and its subsequent projection, each object in the scene could have been

1550-6037/11 $26.00 © 2011 IEEE
DOI 10.1109/IV.2011.98

individually rendered in a sharply realistic manner directly onto the canvas (see Figure 1).

Figure 1. Left: Arnolfini Wedding (1434) van Eyck [20]. Right: Detail of Jan van Eyck's Arnolfini Wedding (1434) [19].

Indeed, a number of devices can be used to mechanically construct a perspective: the camera obscura, the camera Lucida, a concave mirror, grids, screens, Brunelleschi's peephole, pinhole projections and so on. What they all tend to do is to map the world onto a flat plane. The interest in mapping space to the Renaissance artisan-engineer, coincided with its military and general surveying use.

This use of optical devices in the construction of perspectival pictures heralded a fundamental shift in artists' otherwise naive appreciation of the structure of their environments. In particular, they were able to represent the world in a more sophisticated way because of optics and its implied geometry. Using such optical devices artists would no longer just look at the world around them but represented a projected view of it.

The Photographic Image

Where perhaps Renaissance optics most informs today's 3D computer graphics methods is their common striving for a 'photographic' realism. These photographic qualities are evident, for example, in Cagnacci's The Death of Cleopatra (1658). If we reduce his painting to a black and white reproduction, its photographic-like qualities become more apparent (see Figure 2). The lighting is similar to that we associate with photography. Hockney's use of the analogy of a black-and-white photograph to demonstrate his point is further confirmed by Gombrich's [17, p91] assertion that using a black-and-white photograph-like reproduction of an artist's work helps "separate the code from the content" thus revealing, in this case, the overarching emphasis on reproducing the tonal quality of the projected image.

Perhaps just as computers today remove much of the drudgery in 'setting-up' a perspective, Renaissance artists simply used optical projections to overcome the difficult mathematical construction of their perspective compositions – an artist could merely trace a 'live' image and fill in the surfaces later. A tool which would have helped make images that were intensely realistic.

Figure 2. Left: The Death of Cleopatra (1658) Cagnacci [19]. Right: Cagnacci's The Death of Cleopatra reduced to black-and-white using Photoshop.

According to Edgerton [4, p17], constructed using a mirror or lens method, linear perspective made "metaphysical subject matter appear more tactile and therefore empirically believable,…[demanding that space should] be perceived as having the same physical properties and…[obey] the same geometric rules" as optics. In turn, this, would have furthered the notion of a rigorous scientific application to the 'observed' world. Today, the optical imitation of nature in the realm of 3D computer graphics, and in particular three-dimensional computer modelling follows the same perspective-construction algorithms. Pioneered in the 1960's, by Roberts and Cooms [18], their algorithms ushered in an era of efficient, human error free, perspective construction. The methodology, though digital, is essentially a re-configuration of the pre-existing renaissance-founded perspective paradigm.

While the advent of photography in the nineteenth-century meant the time consuming process of manually constructing perspectives was eliminated, the automation of perspectival imaging using 3D computer graphics algorithms has now completed the perspectival process first realised in the Renaissance. Computers which allow the projection of three-dimensional points in space onto a two-dimensional plane using perspective-generating mathematical algorithms reduce real objects to virtual objects consisting of Alberti's planes, surfaces and lines. The coordinates of each vertex is stored in computer memory. So too is the virtual camera, its point of view, direction of sight and relationship to a projection plane. Point by point a perspective image is generated by the frustum matrix. As colour was added in the 70's and 80's other algorithms were developed adding depth cues such as hidden line and surface removal, shading, texture, shadows, reflections, and so on.

3D Realism

How much of 3D computer graphics imagery algorithmically replicates natural phenomena and how much is artistic impression? For example, to project a decent image onto an adjacent wall in the Renaissance full sun was required. Nevertheless, the lack of contrast in such projected images meant the final painted production required interpretation of and reference to the actual scene. In a similar manner, many of the computer algorithms used to generate shading and highlighting in

3D computer graphics requires some interpretation as neither can approach the same level of light intensity as that reflected by real physical objects in full sun. Hence it follows that what is promoted as 'scientifically adduced as real' in 3D computer graphics is often merely interpreted as 'real enough'. However, unlike the sameness that pervades 3D computer graphics, the absolute subjectivity of vision is reflected in how painters made use of the Renaissance projected image. Velasquez, for example, used the rich colours and tones that a projected image does not provide (see Figure 3). Painters made choices like this consciously; hence, the differences between painters' subjective interpretation of what they saw in the projected image. And, Cotan's objects are almost super-real (much like the tonal accuracy and brilliance achieved in 3D computer graphics) (see Figure 3) – "the camera obscura does just that – making objects assume an uncanny look of concentrated 'real-ness'" [1, p245]. But what is this 'realness'? In painters' quest for a super-realism they used techniques which encourages one's perception to conceive a realness which does not exist. Tricks and techniques such as shading and highlights enter the artist's repertoire of representation to which over time we have become accustomed. They establish a metaphor for the seen thing. Similarly, in 3D computer graphics, the lens flare – something photographers try to avoid – is used to suggest a physical camera was used; raytraced or mapped shadows are used to indicate strong or soft light; fog is used to indicate depth; or, blur to introduce motion and so on – not things we consciously see in reality but merely metaphors or artistic techniques for generating a super-realism.

Figure 3. Left: Untitled (1618) Velazquez [20]. Middle: Still Life with Game Fowl, Fruit, and Vegetables (1602), Cotan [19]. Right: Computer generated architectural interior modelled by the author in 1999.

Highlights and tones are simplified by optical projection. The Hue, Saturation, and Volume (HSV) algorithms for lighting in a 3D computer graphics program are derived from a scientific analysis of how light behaves. Yet, despite claims that three-dimensional 3D computer graphics follow natural laws, the Masters' chiaroscuro techniques appear to have influenced how 3D computer graphics images are actually constructed. For example, wire-frame, point construction, primitives (cone, sphere, cube, cylinder) and carved solids are also the essential elements Alberti applied in his fifteenth-century treatise [8]. This suggests much is owed to the

Masters for defining the elements to be constructed algorithmically.

Where 3D computer graphics Emulates the Masters' Techniques

Just as the Renaissance painters "found ways to render effects of light on surfaces with increasing exactitude... da Vinci later made them seem quite naïve and unconvincing," and, in time, the algorithmically generated Lambert, Gourard, and Phong shaders will be supplanted by more powerful reality renderings [8, p161]. However, where 3D computer graphics and traditional art differs is in the complex dialogue implied by the artist's personal deviations from the computer's attempts at mathematically precise imitations of Nature. The artist's dialogue, by contrast, includes looking at, and representing Nature beyond, and in addition to, the scientifically adduced principles of optical devices. Unlike 3D computer graphic's mathematically constructed images, artists may not necessarily proceed in the same manner in every instance. For example, where Dutch realist painters, such as Van Eyck, relied on Nature reflected mirror-like to teach its perfect imitation, Italians like Piero della Francesca and others used precise geometrical rules for remaking Nature based on a scientific appreciation of 'natural law'. Van Eyck viewed humans' understanding of Nature by its expression as a surrogate reality created in his projected images [1]. Despite a lack of a singular geometric precision, Van Eyck saw mirrors as surrogate realities facilitating a conceptual shift to lens-based, mirror-based, or device-based naturalism. It is in this device-based naturalism that we find the paradigm which most closely informs 3D computer graphics today.

If we consider three-dimensional 3D computer graphics as simply an extension to a pre-existing representation of three-dimensional space on a two-dimensional surface (discounting developments in CAD-CAM, interactive games and so on) this produces the unsurprising result that many of the techniques of the Masters', and indeed photography, appear as discrete rendering algorithms. Algorithms used to generate shading, shadows, and so on, designed to look like their hand rendered chiaroscuro counterparts are hence, inherently not 'real' but rather appear to be literal referents to their traditional artistic metaphors –no more real, therefore, than the artistic metaphors they attempt to emulate.

A brief review of leading texts on 3D computer graphics [8 – 12, 20] confirms the assertion that, in relation to perspective, light, colour, surface, shade, reflection, and texture, most algorithms are indeed, typically derived from their traditional artistic equivalents.

Mitchell and McCullough [9] and Foley et al [10] discuss the 'visual effect' of perspective projection used in 3D computer graphics as similar to that of photographic systems, and the common 'hidden-line rendering' is referred to as being generated by the

'Painter's Algorithm'. The hidden-line algorithm follows Alberti's intellectual program, reconstructed in software, it mimics his descriptions of edge lines, outlines of surfaces and curvatures (see Figure 4).

Figure 4. Left: Hidden line rendering. Middle: Flat shaded rendering. Right: Shadow-mapped rendering (modelled by the author).

Even the application of perspectival composition informs the content of 3D computer graphics. Tufte [12] identifies the strength of Renaissance techniques in the construction of perspectival images in digital media such as the common tiled grid in a Renaissance perspective (see Figure 5). For example, in the case of a simulation of a cloud mass turning into a storm, the use of an exaggerated tiled grid as a perspectival cue is considered necessary to indicate its volumetric quality (see Figure 5).

Figure 5. Left: Nativity (1490), Fernando Gallego [12, p22]. Right: Study of a Numerically Modeled Severe Storm National Centre for Supercomputing Applications [12, p20].

To produce more painterly images, Mitchell and McCullough [9] claim a standard architectural convention is used whereby light appears to arrive from over the viewer's shoulder (see Figure 6). Where colour is used in both light source and on surfaces, Foley et al [10, p590] claim, the use of "Smith's HSV (hue, saturation, value) model...(also called the HSB model, with B for brightness) is user-oriented, being based on the intuitive appeal of the artist's tint, shade, and tone."

Mitchell and McCullough [9] extend this notion of a surface's artistic quality by referring to da Vinci's chiaroscuro techniques; Lambert's cosine shading is described as similar to old-fashioned drawing books which used tonal media such as charcoal and watercolour to demonstrate depth on a surface; and, successive rendering algorithms have attempted to emulate the artist's chiaroscuro techniques with increasing precision such as Gourard and Phong (see Figure 6).

While Lambert's eighteenth-century cosine law is now used as a scientific basis for its computer-graphic algorithmic corollary – specularity – it reduces to a precise formula a fact long known by painters regarding the, impossible to absolutely reproduce, incidental intensity of reflected light [9, 2].

Figure 6. Left: Lambert shading. Middle: Gourard shading. Right: Phong shading.

Where most of the authors discussed here define an achievable 'realism' in 3D computer graphics what they are actually describing is illusions in the creation of a conceptual pipeline [10] which generates an acceptable realism that we have become accustomed to through an acculturation to its conventions and metaphors since the Renaissance.

The dichotomy of both a reference to artistic quality and scientific fact is common among the exponents of 'realistic' 3D computer graphics. Indeed, most rendering packages approximate reality at best and positively fudge it at worst. Yet, the 'real' world is still typically described by 3D computer graphics programmers in terms of its ability to be simulated: "A fundamental difficulty in achieving total visual realism is the complexity of the real world. Observe the richness of your environment.... The computational costs of simulating these effects can be high" [10, p607]. Here it could be suggested that the deft stroke of a paint brush generates a greater complexity in both its visual quality and its quality as a tactile surface. This is something which a computer-graphic image is yet to achieve (neither should it necessarily). Indeed, while modern 3D computer graphics images may rely for their realism on the complexity of textures, often derived of photographic sources, the surfaces they are painted onto are ostensibly orthogonal hinting at the trade-off between visual complexity and operational performance. For example, if we compare the complexity of Rubens' work with that of a 3D computer graphics generated image, what is most striking about the painting is its organic tactility (though we cannot generate such a tactile surface in this document) this is in contrast to the more typical sterile and orthogonal (i.e. artificial) 3D computer graphics image (see Figure 7). Moreover, the space used to exposé 3D computer graphics tend to be orthogonal because of the perspective algorithms used for their generation.

Figure 7. Left: Adoration of the Magi (1618-19), Rubens [19]. Right: Computer-rendered

**traditional Japanese house using radiosity
[www.radiosity.tripod.co.jp, 10-10-2003].**

Conclusion

If we accept Hockney's assertions that the Renaissance Masters painted directly onto images projected on a two-dimensional surface from mirrors or other optical devices then what painters were illustrating was not always Nature directly but a projected vision of Nature – a Nature that could be observed and traced in detail. However, the quality of the image was by circumstance filtered and altered in ways that also affected the way artists approached the task of replicating and interpreting what they could see. By contrast, while 3D computer graphics technology appears to have borrowed from the lessons of the Masters in *its* representation and interpretation of Nature, it is underpinned by a scientific method. Yet, there also seems to be an accord between science and art in the construction of the 3D computer generated image. This lies at its code – where the underlying subjectivities of art should be anathema to the code's logical construction. Nonetheless, the terms used to describe the algorithms for constructing 3D images suggest that its art and technological invention coexist in a symbiotic relationship. The software engineer can claim to have constructed an algorithm which emulates the rules of natural phenomena, but when it is described in terms used by the quattrocento Masters then the net effect is something both less than its Nature-inspired corollary and more than its retinal impression. It becomes a convention we agree to use to describe that phenomenon. Indeed, in more general terms, it is from the symbiosis of Art and Science that emerge the conventions and rules we use to describe the natural world around us. Hence, once recognised as such, 3D computer graphics may finally be accepted as simply the contemporary artists' aide in the same manner that the lens was to the Renaissance artist.

References

[1] Hockney, D., Secret Knowledge, Rediscovering the Lost Techniques of the Old Masters, Thames & Hudson, UK, 2001.

[2] Kemp, M., The Science of Art: Optical Themes in Western Art from Brunelleschi to Seurat, Yale University Press, New Haven and London, 1990.

[21]

[3] Kemp, M., The Oxford History of Western Art, Oxford University Press, Oxford, New York, 2000.

[4] Edgerton, S. Y., The Heritage of Giotto's Geometry: Art and Science on the Eve of the Scientific Revolution, Cornell University Press, Ithaca, London, 1991.

[5] Ruskin, J., The Elements of Perspective, Routledge and Sons Ltd, London, 1907.

[6] Gombrich, E. H., The Image and the Eye: Further Studies in the Psychology of Pictorial Representation, Phaidon, Oxford, 1982.

[7] Gombrich, E. H., Art and Illusion: A Study in the Psychology of Pictorial Representation, Princeton University Press, Princeton and Oxford, 2000.

[8] Mitchell, W. J., The Reconfigured Eye: Visual Truth in the Post-photographic Era, MIT Press, London, 1994.

[9] Mitchell, W. J., and McCullough, M., Digital Design Media, Van Nostrand Reinhold, NY, 1995.

[10] Foley, J. D., van Dam, A., Feiner, S. K., and Hughes, J. F., 3D computer graphics: Principles and Practice, Addison-Wesley, NY, 2002.

[11] Woo M., Neider J., and Davis T., OpenGL Programming Guide, Second Edition, The Official Guide to Learning OpenGL, Version 1.1, Addison-Wesley, Massachusetts, 1997.

[12] Tufte, E. R., Visual Explanations: Images and Quantities, Evidence and Narrative, Graphics Press, Cheshire, Connecticut, 1997.

[13] Perez-Gomez, A. and Pelletier, L., Architectural Representation and the Perspective Hinge, MIT Press, Cambridge, Mass, London, England, 1997.

[14] Coyne, R., Designing Information Technology in the Postmodern Age, Cambridge, Massachusetts, The MIT Press, 1995.

[15] Lefebvre, H., The Production of Space, Blackwell, Oxford UK & Cambridge USA, 1991.

[16] Panofsky, E., Perspective as Symbolic Form, Wood, C., (Trans.), Zone Books, New York, 1991.

[17] Gombrich, E. H., Meditations on a Hobby Horse and other Essays on the Theory of Art, Phaidon, London and NY, 1978.

[18] Manovich, L., The Mapping of Space: Perspective, Radar, and 3-D 3D computer graphics, http://jupiter.ucsd.edu/~manovich/text/mapping.html, 1993, [05-06-2002].

[19] www.kfki.hu/~arthp [10-10-2003].

[20] Richens, P., Computer Aided Art Direction, in (eds.). F. Penz and M. Thomas, Cinema & Architecture: Méliès, Mallet-Stevens, Multimedia, British Film Institute, London, http://www.arct.cam.ac.uk/mc/cadlab/index.html, 1997, [05-06-2002].

Sculpture Meets Ecological Science: Marijana Tadić's *Wandering Albatross* Exhibitions & The Concept Of Philopatry

Christine Nicholls
Flinders University, Adelaide, Australia
{Christine.Nicholls@flinders.edu.au}

Abstract

The concept of philopatry is most often applied to animal, bird and insect populations. As such, it is closely connected to the disciplines of zoology, animal science, behavioural ecology and non-human genetics. Only rarely (in reality, almost never) is this concept deployed in relation to human population movement. Yet, as a result of colonisation, globalisation, intermarriage, wars, political unrest and other diasporic forces, increasing numbers of migrants and asylum seekers now settle in places far away from their countries of birth. Travel, often involving long distances back and forth between people's adoptive and natal homelands, and frequently taking place on a repetitive, seasonal, basis, has become a significant contemporary phenomenon. In the Yugoslav-born, Australian conceptual sculptor Marijana Tadić's recent installation and sculptural exhibitions, collectively titled Wandering Albatross, exhibited in South Australia February-March 2011, the artist has appropriated the concept of philopatry, applying it to ideas about contemporary patterns of migrancy with thrilling conceptual and aesthetic results.

Keywords--- **Sculpture; visual art; migrancy; philopatry; Wandering Albatross.**

Introduction

Australian conceptual artist Marijana Tadić's activities encompass the creative fields of sculpture, installation, public art and design. Born in Brcko, near the border of Croatia in the former Yugoslavia (now the Republic of Bosnia and Herzegovina), Tadić's childhood was spent in a house on the banks of the River Sava, a tribute of the Danube. That 'first place' – of deeply flowing water and movement – profoundly shaped Tadić's artistic consciousness. Today, ideas associated with the urgent energy of rapidly moving water inform Tadić's art making. Underpinning her artistic practice is an awareness of human population movement (migrancy, in the broadest sense of that word) as a metaphor for the human condition.

In 1969, as a teenager, Marijana Tadić migrated to Australia with her parents and younger brother. Initially the family stayed in a migrant hostel in New South Wales. When her father Joko found work at Chrysler's

Adelaide plant as a skilled tradesman, the Tadić family moved to South Australia, settling in Adelaide, for a while living near the beach at the Glenelg Migrant Hostel and later renting a bungalow at St Marys. After several years in Australia, the family returned to Yugoslavia, but their return was short-lived. Once back in Adelaide, Marijana Tadić took up office work, also taking on several other part-time jobs, mostly in the building industry. During that period she was awarded a Master Builder's certificate, the first woman in South Australia to do so. In 1983 she enrolled in the South Australian School of Art, majoring in sculpture. Whilst attending art school Tadić began seriously planning for an artistic future. After graduating in 1986 she began working as professional artist.

I Marijana Tadić's *Wandering Albatross* Exhibitions

Wandering Albatross, the umbrella title of Tadić's two Adelaide Fringe Festival 2011 exhibitions, on show more or less concurrently at South Australia's BMG Galleries (**BMG**Arts, 25 February – 19 March 2011) and AC Arts Gallery Light Square (16 February -10 March 2011), mark the culmination of Tadić's art-making thus far. In a career now spanning 25 years of uninterrupted practice, Tadić, who lives and breathes her artistic métier, has developed a distinctive body of work characterised by subject matter to which she keeps returning. Tadić's enduring themes and affiliations are clearly apparent in the titles that she bestows upon her artworks.

Tadić conceived *Wandering Albatross* as two interrelated exhibitions, distinct but connected spaces. These elegantly mounted, provocative art exhibitions were conceptualised as spaces between which audiences were encouraged to travel, like birds of passage. In these exhibitions the artist evoked, in visual terms, concepts relating to birds, flight, navigation, and the traversal of large stretches of water for the purpose of survival or simply that of seeking a better life. Balancing these ideas were artistic and thematic concerns about nesting and sanctuary.

The artworks in *Wandering Albatross* are analysable as visual metaphors relating to border crossing, the migration experience and its double, 'arrival'. Implicitly

1550-6037/11 $26.00 © 2011 IEEE
DOI 10.1109/IV.2011.105

posing questions about what might truly constitute a 'destination', Tadić also explores the connected concepts of 'destination' and 'destiny', words that share the same Latin root. (One may end up in an entirely different place in life's journey than the end point originally envisaged).

Poetic visual tropes about what old Chinese philosophers so tellingly described as 'crossing the great water' act as guiding metaphors in Tadić's work in another sense too, leading viewers towards understanding the tacit side of the emotions relating to the migration experience, since emotions also have a metaphoric structure. In part, Tadić expresses this affective dimension by means of the often rowdy, occasionally argumentative, but mostly joyous songfulness of Australian native birds, whose songs have been recorded in Australian backyards. Interspersed by meaningful silences, these sounds accompany the exhibition.

Figure 1. Marijana Tadić, Songlines, (detail, screens 13-16) 2011, recycled wood, computerised LED lighting, 24 screens, each 45 x 120 x 15 cm

Birdsong (*Bird Sounds*) was therefore an integral part of the AC Arts Light Square exhibition, as was its companion piece, *Songlines,* comprising 24 wall screens, all beautifully crafted from recycled Australian hardwood. Computerised lighting emanated from each separate panel, suggesting dawn or dusk – the times when birds are most communicative. They are also the times of day when early-morning or fading, crepuscular light flickers through nooks and crannies in the wooded areas. Each bird song is visually represented by its own unique sonogram pattern, which appears on an individual screen. Such visualisation of birdsong within a sculptural exhibition is original, powerful in affect and rich in metaphorical association, opening up possibilities for those working in both fields.

Included in this syncopated avian chatter are the idiosyncratic, musical sounds of various Australian native birds. Among those that can be heard are Australian magpies, three-wattled bellbirds, rainbow lorikeets, crimson rosellas and laughing kookaburras, intermixed with the distinctive twittering of various introduced species. These include an albatross and her chick, field sparrows, and a spotted turtledove, native to eastern Asia. All are talking nineteen to the dozen. Regardless of whether the birds are natives or introduced species, they are philopatric and migratory at certain points in their life cycle.

This exhibition entails a songful salute to Australia's unique environment and to our cultural diversity. Nowhere is this more apparent than in the occasionally quarrelsome and belligerent, but mostly joyful, cacophony of this sound installation.

The sound installations in *Wandering Albatross* are also significant insofar as Tadić deploys bird sounds and short silences as vehicles for explaining the short bursts of happiness and the convivial, familial chatter that is sometimes followed by a soundless lull of self-reflection on the part of those human beings who brave long, hazardous voyages across the sea, by plane or by boat.

Often they are traveling to destinations that are only partially known or even totally unknown. At various stages of such journeys different emotions will predominate; hope and fear will ebb and flow according to circumstance.

Figure 2. Marijana Tadić, 2011, Suspended Sanctuary (study) recycled hardwood, resin, steel cable, 190 cm diameter

Hanging from the AC Arts Light Square Gallery ceiling was *Suspended Sanctuary*, a large nest created from recycled hardwood and resin. This work speaks eloquently to the need for a place of respite from the ravages of journeying. It also speaks to the borderless world occupied by birds. Offering her art works as visual tropes, Marijana Tadić emphasises the interconnectedness of the human family and the importance of balanced, mutually respectful and reciprocal relations in all human interactions. Humans' relations with the natural environment were also highlighted.

The centrepiece of this exhibition was undoubtedly the eponymously named *Wandering Albatross* on display at the BMG Gallery. This minimalist, four-panelled exhibit is comprised of acrylic boxes and recycled acupuncture needles on MDF. The focal point of the work is an albatross, its distinctive shape delineated by her wingspan, extended in full flight. The bird's majestic form has been traced in outline using acupuncture needles, and the delicate patterning that results is an inspired touch. Tadić's 'needlepoint' albatross soars across waves, or perhaps mountains, or whatever the imagination can supply. Outlines of breakers or landforms cast delicate shadows over the stark white backdrop, lending this work a quality akin to that of fine lacework on patterned openwork fabric. Tadić's subtle use of skilfully arranged acupuncture needles to create pictorial representations affords this work – along with others in which she uses acupuncture needles – a calligraphic quality, especially when viewed from afar.

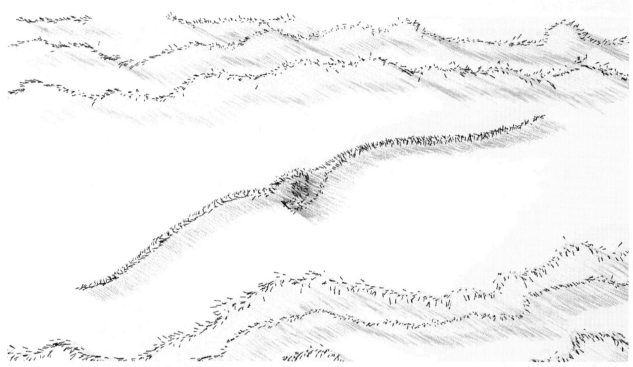

Figure 3. Marijana Tadić, 2011, Wandering Albatross (detail, Panel 2) recycled acupuncture needles on MDF, acrylic boxes, 4 panels, each 100 x 150 x 15 cm, BMG Gallery Adelaide. Photograph: Grant Hancock.

Marijana Tadić's refined visual patterning also provides viewers with a fresh narrative in relation to particular groups of recent émigrés who are less fortunate than many other Australians - including the artist and her immediate family members. Understanding *Wandering Albatross* simultaneously as something-in-itself and also as a coherent visual metaphor - which is precisely what Tadić asks of viewers - this work presents an important counterpoint to the largely populist, raucous and often ill-informed railing about asylum seekers that currently prevails on both sides of politics. The elaborate trans-Pacific and transatlantic networks traced in Tadić's artworks apply to those human beings who seek life and refuge (temporary or permanent) away from their own specific points of origin whilst at the same time needing to retain a concept of 'home' relating to their 'first place'.

II. Sculpture and Ecological Science: Applying the Concept of Philopatry to Human Migrant Groups

While philopatry is a concept most often associated with non-human animals, insects, and birds, and for which avian species are known to be neurologically hardwired, it can also be meaningfully applied as a trope to describe the behaviour of certain human populations. The notion is particularly relevant to those members of migrant groups living in Australia today, who regularly travel back and forth between their new home and their places of origin, where they retain strong, often inalienable, ties. That Australia's philopatric communities are marked by a high level of diversity is observable in the differing but complementary forms that Tadić has created for her *Philopatric Colony*, another work that functions as a potent visual metaphor. In titling this work Tadić has carefully chosen the word 'colony';

the concept's multivalency is purposeful. Formed from marble dust and white cement, standing erect on black granite, these distinctive abstract shapes suggest that notwithstanding the fact that there is considerable variation between humans, we nevertheless belong to the same larger family.

Like other birds, albatrosses demonstrate strong philopatry, returning to the same breeding and nesting sites for many years. Albatrosses are also colonial, most often nesting on remote islands free from natural predators.1. One aspect of Tadić's granite-based, cast bronze sculptures, *Sky-pointing ritual I & II,* is the specific allusion that these works make to the complex courtship rituals of particular albatross species, noisy events that involve honking, whistling, performing synchronised dances, bill-flanking, stretching their necks and pointing their bills vertically, skyward. The latter is described as 'sky-calling' or 'sky-pointing' [4, 6]. Following this display, the actual mating is a short-lived affair, but like (some) humans, albatrosses mate for life [4]. The sleek, quasi-avian forms that Tadić has created in her *Sky-pointing ritual* sculptures are influenced by the shapes of the fallen palm leaves that she loves to collect from the Arboretum at Urrbrae.

Sensing the Way, in which Tadić uses seagrass and resin, interwoven bowerbird-like, and related works *Staging the Way, Power of the Group* and *Reciprocity,* further extend this exhibition's *thématique* into the realms of the social and cultural, while expanding upon the concept of philopatry. Another sub-theme emerges in *Wandering Albatross*: that of the imperative to care about the welfare of our fellow human beings. Included in this equation, by implication, is the idea of caring for those asylum seekers who, in the hope of starting a new life on Australia's shores, venture out in rickety boats, some losing their lives, some arriving safely by sea (although the numbers who arrive by sea to Australia are very small compared with other destination countries [1,5].

Equally significant in terms of the *thématique* of this exhibition are the words 'RECIPROCITY', and 'Sanctuary', the only text-based elements in *Wandering Albatross*, sketched out with acupuncture needles that cast suggestive shadows. While it is overwhelmingly the concept of philopatry that ties these exhibitions together and affords them curatorial coherence, the latter are also key words and concepts in Marijana Tadić's artistic vocabulary. Indirectly they evoke the graffiti-word 'ETERNITY' written with chalk around Sydney last century by the reformed alcoholic Arthur Stace. For Stace, who continued writing that same, single word for a period of more than 35 years, it was a means of spreading the Christian gospel in which he so fervently believed. While Marijana Tadić's worldview is a secular one, like many others of similar persuasion she seeks an ethical and meaningful basis for co-existing with others in today's complex, highly mobile world. They are cornerstone word-concepts providing insight into Tadić's core values, especially with respect to the need to accept responsibility for less fortunate others – including those

others whose worldviews and life experiences that differ from one's own.

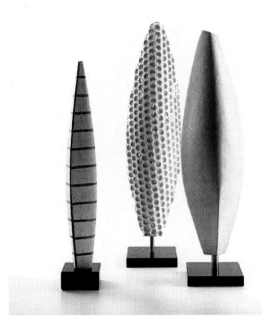

Figure 4. Marijana Tadić 2011, Philopatric Colony, marble dust and white cement, granite base, individual forms, 60 – 70 x 20 x 20 cm, BMG Gallery Adelaide. Photograph: Grant Hancock.

Such a philosophy also comes to mind with respect to Tadić's two *Subjective Destination* works (*Subjective Destination 1*, created from seagrass and resin, and *Subjective Destination 11*, sculpted from marble dust and white cement). *Subjective Destination 1* has been sculpted from seagrass washed up on Carrickalinga Beach to the south of Adelaide. The sea's strong currents twist and twirl the little sticks of seagrass, fashioning them into compact, interlocking balls. Tadić has re-shaped these into forms that are suggestive of, to use her own words, "circular migration patterns and navigation that takes place between the northern and southern hemispheres", (Personal Communication, Marijana Tadić to author, January 11th 2011) again suggesting philopatric cycles, whilst remaining redolent of natural processes. These semi-circular forms, balanced precariously like small rocking boats or cradles, seem to embody the expectations and anticipation that migrants bring with them as they embark on their journeying.

The key word here is 'anticipation', which can entail a range of emotions including expectation, doubt, hope and fear. When the judge and poet Barron Field (1786-1846), himself an English migrant, and the author of the first book of verse to be published in this country, claimed that in Australia "We've nothing left us except anticipation" [3] he might well have been describing the mixed feelings of today's migrants - especially asylum seekers, many of whom have endured firsthand the miseries of war and exile - as they make their way towards Australia.

III. Discussion of the Concept of Philopatry in Marijana Tadić's *Wandering Albatross*

While it is quite clear that the philopatric cycles of human beings do not exactly replicate those of other species, in any case the scientific literature pertaining to non-human species indicates that there is considerable variation between the philopatric migration patterns of different species [4, 6, 7, 8, 9]. What is perhaps surprising is that as far as I have been able to ascertain, there are no academic publications in Human Ecology, Sociology or other disciplines, either humanities- or scientifically-based, in which human behaviour is described as philopatric. Whilst the philopatric migration cycles may not constitute universal human behaviour, nevertheless, given the large number of migrants from other parts of the world who retain strong links with their countries of birth ('site fidelity') and even on occasion display 'natal philopatry', returning to their countries of birth to find a spouse or partner, this should be regarded as an interesting aporia.

One can only speculate on the reasons as to why the phenomenon of human philopatry (very much enabled by colonisation, which is also associated with non-human philopatry) and globalisation (something that has always defined bird behaviour) has not been researched nor found its way into the literature.

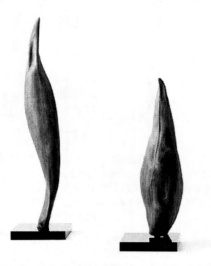 

Figure 5. Marijana Tadić 2011, Sky-Pointing Ritual I (right) and II, cast bronze, granite base, 125 x 20 x 20 cm.

Figure 6. Marijana Tadić 2011, Subjective Destination II, marble dust and white cement cast, 40 x 80 x 20 cm

As Stanley Benn quite openly declared in his 'Egalitarianism and Equal Consideration of Interest': "*...not to possess human shape is a disqualifying condition*" [2: 62 ff]. In other words Benn is only willing to afford 'equal consideration' to all human beings, and clearly does not extend this largesse to other species. It is possible that it is a function of humans' claim to a 'special status' as a species. Hence we stubbornly resist our behaviours being defined in terms of animals' or birds' behavioural characteristics. While a substantial literature exists that exhorts humans to accept other species as equals [see, for instance, 9], which, from our perspective involves an elevation of the current status of non-human species without relinquishing our own sovereign status, it is only comparatively rarely that the reverse applies. Humans seem ill-prepared and insufficiently humble to appraise ourselves honestly as just one animal species among many, and as, moreover, a species with many characteristics in common with the so-called 'lower species'.

The foregoing is, however, merely speculative and it is hoped that more research will take place in this field to determine the applicability of the concept of philopatry to contemporary post-migratory patterns of human behaviour. Nonetheless, it is time to begin to consider human behaviour in the wider field of animal and other non-human species ethology.

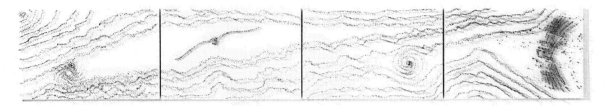

Figure 7. Marijana Tadić 2011, Wandering Albatross, recycled acupuncture needles on MDF, acrylic boxes 4 panels, each 100 x 150 x 15 cm, BMG Gallery Adelaide. Photograph: Grant Hancock.

Conclusion

To conclude, *Wandering Albatross* is a coherent visual arts exhibition of considerable aesthetic impact. The themes and issues that it raises are significant at this time in Australian history and also in our shared human history, (mostly) characterised as it is now by aesthetic and conceptual vacuity. Conceptually complex, rehearsing themes and ideas about migrancy, philopatry, belonging and 'unbelonging', navigation and the environment, nesting, home-making, kinesis and resting, the artworks in these two interrelated exhibitions contribute to our understanding of migrant Australians' lifeways while speaking eloquently to the extraordinarily generative effects of dislocation and relocation on cultures and identity.

In *Wandering Albatross* Tadić's complexities are provocative; evoking the flight of the migratory birds that daily ply their hazardous courses over strong ocean currents, eventually nesting in strange, distant lands. Tadić's evocation of the concept of philopatry is particularly challenging, if not confrontational, in terms of its more normative application to non-human species. This key concept also makes this pair of interconnected exhibitions extraordinarily thought provoking. Finally, this exhibition speaks to those migrants ('asylum seekers') who arrive on Australia's (and other) shores in small, leaky boats, seeking a good, or at least, a better life. That Tadić has the capacity to realise such subtly interconnected themes in visual terms is testament to her originality and artistic power.

Acknowledgements

The author would like to thank the artist, Marijana Tadić.

References

[1] Australian Senate, Senate Legal and Constitutional Affairs Committee, Answers to questions on notice, Immigration Portfolio, 20 October 2009, viewed 9th February 2011, http://www.aph.gov.au/senate/committee/legcon_ctte/estimates/sup_0910/diac/48_qon.pdf

[2] Benn, Stanley, 1996, "Egalitarianism and the Equal Consideration of Interests", Chapter13, in *Equality: Selected Readings*, (Ed. Louis P. Pojman), Oxford University Press, Australia and New Zealand.

[3] Field, Barron, 1823, 'On Reading the Controversy Between Lord Byron and Mr Bowles', in *First Fruits of Australian Poetry, The Kangaroo and Other Poems*, University of Sydney Library, prepared against the print edition published by Barn on the Hill, Sydney 1941, originally published 1819, Second Edition 1923, online version published 1998, viewed 14/2/11, http://setis.library.usyd.edu.au/ozlit/pdf/v00022.pdf.

[4] Fisher, H.I., 1976, "Some dynamics of a breeding colony of Laysan Albatrosses", in *The Wilson Bulletin* 88:121–142.

[5] Phillips, Janet and Spinks, Harriet, (Social Policy Section) 11 February 2011, "Boat Arrivals since 1976", Australian Parliamentary Library, Parliament of Australia, Department of Parliamentary Services, Canberra, viewed 11th February 2011, www.aph.gov.au/library/pubs/BN/sp/BoatArrivals.pdf

[6] Pickering, S.P.C. & S.D. Berrow, 2001, "COURTSHIP BEHAVIOUR OF THE WANDERING ALBATROSS *DIOMEDEA EXULANS* AT BIRD ISLAND, SOUTH GEORGIA", in *Marine Ornithology* 29: 29–37.

[7] Pomeroy, P.P., S. D. Twiss, and P. Redman, October 2000, "Philopatry, Site Fidelity and Local Kin Associations within Grey Seal Breeding Colonies", in Ethology, Volume 106, Issue 10, pages 899 –919

[8] Rabouam, C., Thibault, J.-C., Bretagnolle, V., 1998, "Natal Philopatry and Close Inbreeding in Cory's Shearwater (*Calonectris diomedea*)" in *Auk* 115 (2): 483–486.

[9] Singer, Peter, 2003, 'Not for Humans Only: The Place of Nonhumans in Environmental Issues', in *Environmental Ethics: an anthology*, (Eds. Andrew Light and Holmes Rolston III), Blackwell Publishing, Oxford, p 55-65.

[10] Wheelright, Nathaniel T. and Mauck, Robert A., April 1998, "PHILOPATRY, NATAL DISPERSAL, AND INBREEDING AVOIDANCE IN AN ISLAND OF POPULATION OF SAVANNAH SPARROWS", in Ecology Volume 79, Number 3: 755-767.

Colorscore - Visualization and Condensation of Structure of Classical Music

Aki Hayashi, Takayuki Itoh
Graduate School of Humanities and Sciences
Ochanomizu University
Tokyo, Japan
{aki, itot}@itolab.is.ocha.ac.jp

Masaki Matsubara
Graduate School of Science and Technology
Keio University
Kanagawa, Japan
masaki@nak.ics.keio.ac.jp

Abstract—It is not always easy to quickly understand musical structure of orchestral scores for classical music works, because these works contain many staves of instruments. This paper presents Colorscore, a technique for visualization and condensation of musical scores. Colorscore supports two requirements for composers, arrangers and players: overview and arrangement. Colorscore divides each track of the score into note-blocks, and determines their roles. Colorscore then displays all the note-blocks in one display space to provide the overview, so that novice people can quickly understand the musical structures. In addition, Colorscore supports vertical condensation which reduces the number of displayed tracks, and horizontal condensation which saves the display space. It is especially useful as hints to rearrange music for smaller bands.

Keywords-Visualization; Condensation; Classical music;

I. INTRODUCTION

Listening to the music necessarily takes time. Visualization of music information is very useful and powerful if we would like to understand the contents and story of the music in a short time. Many recent techniques on music visualization focus on representation of musical structures of musical works. We are focusing on visualization of structures of musical works composed for orchestras. Generally, it is not easy for beginner conductors, players, and composers, to read and/or write orchestral scores. We think one of the main reasons is that such scores line up many staves of instruments vertically in one page; therefore, readers must look at the many staves of instruments at one time, and turn over the pages frequently. In addition, it may be difficult for them to observe the overall structures and contexts of the musical works from the scores containing large number of pages. We think visualization is useful to solve the above problem; because it has the potential to provide overview of musical information, and interactive mechanisms to observe important parts of the works.

This paper presents "Colorscore", a technique for visualization and condensation of musical structures of MIDI-based classical music data. Colorscore consists of the following components: role determination, overview, and interactive condensation. Colorscore first divides notes of each track into blocks based on the rests of the tracks. It then determines the roles of blocks, by matching to predefined patterns of melodies and accompaniments. Colorscore draws

all the blocks into single display space, for the overview of musical structures, while it assigns independent colors to the blocks based on their roles. It also provides two mechanisms of interactive condensation to save the display spaces. One of the mechanisms is "vertical condensation", which reduces the number of displayed tracks, by remaining only note-blocks well matches to the predefined patterns. The other mechanism is "horizontal condensation", which shrinks the bars if no roles are changed at that time. We suppose Colorscore is especially useful for beginner or amateur players, composers, arrangers, and conductors. Score reading may be a hard task for junior high school or high school students who aim to enter the music departments of universities. Also, there have been more than a thousand of amateur orchestras at least in authors' country, and again, it may be a hard task for amateur players and conductors. They may need a long time to understand the whole structure of music by reading a score. We expect the overview provided by Colorscore will help to quickly understand it, because we can observe it by looking at single display space.

Also, we think that condensation of Colorscore will help to rearrange music. There have been many musical works that are arranged by various styles of bands. For example, "Pictures at an Exhibition" was originally composed for the piano by Mussorgsky, then arranged for orchestra by Ravel, and recently played by various bands including brass quintet (Canadian Brass) and 3-piece rock band (Emerson, Lake and Palmer). We expect condensation of Colorscore may suggest hints to such arranges for smaller bands, because it displays the structures of music as smaller number of tracks.

II. RELATED WORK

There have been many techniques on visualization of musical structures or scores. Many of such works [1], [2], [3] aim visualization of acoustic data, not MIDI data. Since audio source separation is still a difficult problem, such works did not visualize musical structures track-by-track. Some of early note-based music visualization works [4] were also simple representations, not detailed track-by-track visualization. Colorscore is quite different from these works because it aims to visualize roles of note-blocks of each track of orchestra separately into one display.

1550-6037/11 $26.00 © 2011 IEEE
DOI 10.1109/IV.2011.19

On the other hand, several recent works focus on visualization of track-by-track information of musical score. comp-i [5] visualizes musical structures of MIDI data in virtual 3D space. However, comp-i does not analyze roles of note-blocks. ScoreIlluminator [6] improves the readability of musical scores by assigning colors to phrases of tracks based on their similarities. However, ScoreIlluminator does not take the roles of the phrases into account for assigning colors. Moreover, comp-i and ScoreIlluminator do not support condensation of musical score. BRASS [7] realizes accordion-like interactive visualization, by partially expanding or shrinking the musical score, which looks similar to condensation of Colorscore. However, it does not take roles of phrases into account for expanding or shrinking. Against such related works, Colorscore realizes colored visualization and condensation of musical scores based on roles of note-blocks.

III. TECHNICAL COMPONENTS OF COLORSCORE

This section presents procedures and technical components of Colorscore. As a preprocessing, Colorscore analyzes musical structures to divide each track into multiple note-blocks, and determines their roles and transitions. Then, Colorscore displays the roles of note-blocks in multiple colors. Also, Colorscore can interactively condense scores by vertically or horizontally packing the displaying information.

A. Analysis of musical structure

Colorscore supports SMF (Standard MIDI file) as input data. It requires note information of MIDI, including pitch, strength, duration and timing. Colorscore firstly read the SMF file, and divides each track of the score into note-blocks. Then, Colorscore determines roles of note-blocks by matching their notes to patterns given by users.

1) Providing the patterns to decide the role: First of all, Colorscore requires the patterns used to determine the roles of the note-blocks. In this paper, "pattern" means a short set of notes which consists of just one track in MIDI format. Currently we assume that patterns are given by expert users. Colorscore determines whether each block plays melodies or accompaniments, as a "role." As regard to melodies, Colorscore supposes to input basic phrases of several main melodies. At the same time, Colorscore supposes to input only typical rhythms for the accompanying phrases such as harmonic or bass accompaniments: it does not analyze transition of intervals for accompaniments. We consider the accompaniments are often characterized by repeated rhythm rather than by transition of interval, and therefore we designed Colorscore to input patterns of accompaniments as rhythms.

2) Generating the initial note-blocks: After providing user-given patterns, Colorscore generates rough note-blocks,

called "initial note-blocks." Colorscore generates the initial note-blocks by the following:

1. Treat a track as a single block.
2. Scan a block, and divide it into two blocks at a whole note rest.
3. Repeat 2. for all blocks until all whole note rests are eliminated from the blocks.
4. Repeat 2. and 3. for all tracks.

3) Pattern-matching of the blocks with patterns: Colorscore matches each initial note-block (see Section III-A2) to user-given patterns (see Section III-A1). In this step, Colorscore calculates distances between the patterns and each note-block, and chooses the pattern closest to the note-block. It determines that the note-block has the role which is the same as the chosen pattern, if the distance between the note-block and the pattern is smaller than the predefined threshold. To calculate the distance between the i-th pattern and the j-th note-block, our implementation applies the following distance $D(i,j)$ [6] :

$$D(i,j) = w_1 D_{RA}(i,j) + w_2 D_{MA}(i,j) \qquad (1)$$

Here, w_1 and w_2 denote constant weights, $D_{RA}(i,j)$ is the cosine of timing which features the rhythm, and $D_{MA}(i,j)$ is the cosine of transition of the notes which features the melody. $D_{RA}(i,j)$ corresponds to the cosine of RA vectors between the i-th pattern and the j-th note-block. Here, RA vector is an n-dimensional vector denoting the timing of note-on events of note-blocks or patterns. To generate RA vector, Colorscore divides note-blocks into n pieces by the constant note. It then assigns positive number if there is the note-on event, otherwise assigns "0". Consequently, Colorscore generates the RA vector as an n-dimensional binary vector. $D_{MA}(i,j)$ corresponds to the cosine of MA vectors between the i-th pattern and the j-th note-block. Here, MA vector is an $(n-1)$-dimensional vector denoting the pitch transition of note-on events. To generate MA vector, Colorscore calculates the difference of pitches between k-th and $(k+1)$-th pieces as the k-th element value of the vector. Here, it takes a positive value if the pitch gets higher, otherwise a negative value. Figure 1(Left) shows an example of RA and MA vectors. Here, the bars in Figure 1(Left) are divided into nine pieces by quarter notes. Values of RA vector take 3 at the first beat, and 2 at the third beat. The MA value is calculated based on chromatic distances between two tones.

If the length of note-block is longer than that of pattern, it may often happens that the note-block partially matches to the pattern. Considering such situation, Colorscore first extracts parts of the note-block, where the lengths of the parts are equal to the pattern, and calculate $D(i,j)$ applying each part. If one of the parts matches to the pattern, Colorscore divides the note-blocks into two or three note-blocks, where one of them corresponds to the part matches

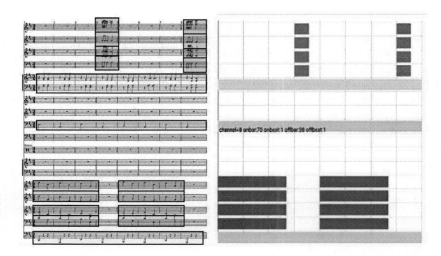

Figure 1. (Left) RA and MA vectors. (Center) Result of note-block generation and role determination. Pink blocks denote the main melody, yellow and flesh blocks denote accompaniments, and gray blocks denote decorations. (Right) Visualization by Colorscore.

to the pattern. Then, Colorscore applies the same process to the remaining note-blocks.

Colorscore applies the above-mentioned process to every note-block of every track. Here, Colorscore determines that a part of the j-th note-block matches to the i-th pattern, if the $D(i,j)$ is smaller than the predefined threshold D_0, where D_0 is a function of n.

The procedure to assign roles is as follows:

1. Calculate RA and MA vectors of the i-th pattern.
2. Calculate RA and MA vectors of the j-th note-block.
3. Extract a part of the note-block, where the length of the part is equal to the i-th pattern, and then calculate $D(i,j)$ between the part and the i-th pattern.
4. If $D(i,j)$ is smaller than D_0:
   a) Divide the j-th note-block if necessary.
   b) Assign the role of the i-th pattern to the matched note-block.
5. Repeat 3. and 4. for all possible parts of the j-th note-block.
6. Repeat 2. to 5. for all note-blocks.
7. Repeat 1. to 6. for all patterns.

B. Visualization of note-blocks

Colorscore visualizes the result of note-block generation and role determination. Figure 1(Center) shows the result of the analysis drawn on a traditional musical score, and Figure 1(Right) shows the result of visualization by Colorscore. It vertically draws the tracks, and horizontally draws the blocks in each track. It assigns colors to the note-blocks based on their roles. Our implementation assigns high-saturation colors to melodies, low-saturation colors to accompaniments, and gray to unmatched note-blocks.

C. Vertical condensation

Vertical condensation consists of the following two steps. The first step removes decoration note-blocks, then removes tracks which have no note-blocks to be drawn, and finally vertically packs the remaining note-blocks. The second step removes more note-blocks so that only the note-blocks especially similar to the given patterns remain in the visualization results. Our implementation remains only note-blocks whose $D(i,j)$ values are smaller than a predefined threshold D_1 ($D_1 < D_0$). This step eliminates harmonic melodies, and remains main themes. Above process is repeated until the tracks are reduced to the user-specified number. We think this functionality is especially useful while arranging orchestra music into smaller organization such as piano solo or chamber ensemble.

D. Horizontal condensation

Colorscore horizontally saves the display space based on transition of roles. It shrinks bars if no note-blocks end or change their roles, while it keeps other bars longer. For example, for Figure 1(Right) Colorscore shrinks the second and third bars because no note-blocks change their roles at that time. Also, it keeps the fourth bars longer, because new note-blocks start at that time.

IV. RESULTS

This section introduces examples of our visualization results applying the MIDI data of "Valse des fleurs" composed by Tchaikovsky.

A. Visualization

Figure 2(Upper) shows an example of visualization result of whole MIDI data which contains 16 tracks. Colorscore represents the musical structure in a single display space,

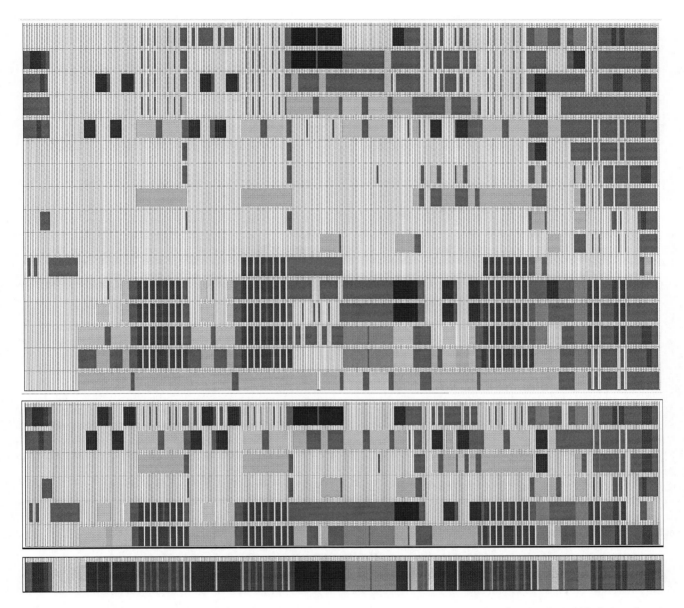

Figure 2. (Upper) Visualization result of "Valse des fleurs" by Tchaikovsky. (Center) Vertical condensation into 6 tracks. (Lower) Vertical condensation into 1 track.

even though a miniature score of "Valse des fleurs" we bought occupies 33 pages. Many traditional classical musical works have two themes, and forms musical structures while repeating and varying these two themes. Also, they may contain several additional melodies delivered from the themes. Considering such composition techniques, we prepared five melody patterns to visualize the music. We also prepared typical Waltz patterns for harmonic and bass accompaniments.

Also, we can observe various orchestration techniques from the visualization result. We can find that roles are switched across the tracks, or shared by several number of

tracks, along the variation of the music. We can also find combinations of multiple melodies at the same time.

B. Vertical condensation

Figure 2(Center)(Lower) shows the condensation of the visualization result shown in Figure 2(Upper). Figure 3(Left) shows a part of the visualization result shown in Figure 2, corresponding to 314 to 328 bars. It also shows a result of the second step of vertical condensation. It reduces the number of tracks from 16 to 1, 2, 4, or 6, and note-blocks from 29 to 4, 6, 11, or 13. This result shows that a melody drawn in pink are played two bars after a melody drawn

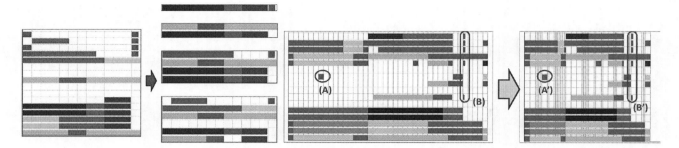

Figure 3. (Left) Vertical condensation into 1, 2, 4, or 6 tracks. Melodies drawn in purple and pink are preferentially remained when the number of tracks are fewer. (Right) Horizontal condensation. The bars (A) and (B) remained wider while other bars get narrower.

in purple. Colorscore remained this structure even in the 1-track condensation result. On the other hand, it remained bass patterns in the 2-tracks result, and other blocks in the 4- and 6-tracks results. The result shows that Colorscore adaptively realizes level-of-detail control of condensation.

C. Horizontal condensation

Figure 3(Right) shows a part of the visualization result in Figure 2, corresponding to 211 to 250 bars. It also shows a result of horizontal condensation. It reduces the width of the visualization space as approximately 60% of the original width. However, it does not shrink the timings when roles of note-blocks change: for example, it keeps the length of short note-blocks surrounded by circles (A) and (B) after the horizontal condensation, indicated as (A') and (B') in Figure 3(Right). With this functionality, Colorscore can draw longer music in limited display space, while preventing us from missing changes of roles. We think it is useful for various purposes of music understanding: for example, students majoring conduct can practice signs to players just before they have new roles.

V. EVALUATION

This section introduces our two kinds of evaluations to demonstrate effectiveness of Colorscore.

A. Understanding of novice examinees

We tested how novice people can understand the musical structure. First, we showed printed visualization result shown in Figure 2(Upper) to examinees. Then, we asked to mark bars to examinees, if they think that the bars can be separators. At the same time, three authors marked bars as examinees did, and treated a set of bars which two or more authors marked as correct answers. Consequently, we made 12 bars as correct answers.

We then calculated precision and recall of the answers of examinees. We tested with 27 university students, divided into two groups. "Group A" contained 18 of the examinees who had experiences of playing musical instruments and reading notes, but did not have experiences of reading scores. The other, "Group B" contained 9 of the examinees who did

not have such experiences. The experiment obtained precision of 0.8056 from Group A, and 0.6991 from Group B. Also, it obtained recall of 0.7870 from Group A, and 0.7037 from Group B. We think the result is totally good; however, differences between two groups were not ignorable. As future works, we would like to observe user tests more, and improve Colorscore reflecting these tests. Especially, we would like to carefully discuss how the visualization results are mistakable for non-experienced people.

B. Feedback from music computing researchers

We showed the visualization result shown in Figure 2 to music computing researchers and asked to give us feedbacks. We asked three researchers majoring music computing who are players in amateur orchestras, including authors of musical visualization techniques [5] [7]. This section summarizes their comments and suggestions.

[Discovery from the visualization result]
Answerers pointed that they discovered features of the music from the visualization result as follows:
1) Coloring is so effective that it is easy to understand the musical structures. For example, the theme indicated in pink appears three times, and finally arranged in the Coda. Other repetitions are also easy to understand.
2) Coloring is also effective to understand the roles of the musical instruments. Examples are as follows:, The theme indicated in pink is mostly played by the strings. Double Bass and Tuba do not play any melodies. Trombone and Percussions have long rests.
3) It is easy to visually compare the roles of specific track with others. For example, when horns play the theme, Violoncello and Double Bass play accompaniments in many bars. When horns play harmonies, strings play melodies, and wood winds play decorations.
4) It is easy to understand that the music gets more sensational in the latter part.

These discoveries were exactly what we expected, and we felt confident about the effectiveness of Colorscore.

[Possible applications]
Answerers pointed that Colorscore can be used as the following applications:

1) Additional musical information display for music player softwares or devices, or digital score softwares.
2) Education of music structure understanding.
3) Reference for staging, camera work, and choreography.

Actually we expect Colorscore can be used as above applications, and needs to develop more functions so that Colorscore can be used as above.

[Concerns]

Answerers pointed that they felt concerns about the visualization result and functionality of Colorscore as follows:
1) Since Colorscore horizontally shortens the musical score, beginners may feel that the first and the last bars are so close, and the top and the bottom tracks (usually piccolo and double bass) are so distant.
2) When we apply Colorscore to music much longer than "Valse des fleurs," it may be difficult to show the whole music in one display space. Authors need to test with such long music and discuss how to effectively show it.
3) Effectiveness of visualization results may depend on the number of patterns. It may be misunderstanding if the number is too small and therefore same colors are assigned to moderately similar note-blocks. On the other hand, it may be difficult to distinguish the roles of note-blocks if too many colors are used.

The first and second comments suggest that we need to have tests with more various users and music, and improve based on the results of the tests. The third comment suggests that we need to discuss what kinds of melody and accompaniment pattern definitions are effective for Colorscore. Also, it may be interesting to integrate Colorscore with automatic theme finding techniques.

[Potential future issues]

Answerers pointed that the following would be potential future issues:
1) Play of the music by clicking arbitrary points, or arbitrary tracks of the visualization result. .
2) Display of the specific tracks or note-blocks as staff notation.
3) Sound of harmonies or chords of arbitrary points.
4) Functions that when users click arbitrary note-blocks or interactively input melodies, it can jump to display the bars corresponding to the specified note-blocks or melodies.
5) Navigation for novice users to the most important parts of the score.
6) User interfaces and animations to smoothly control and display while condensation.

We have not developed the above interactive functions yet, but actually we think they are very important.

VI. CONCLUSION AND FUTURE WORK

This paper presented Colorscore, a visualization and condensation technique for MIDI-based classical music data. This paper introduced three components: role determination, overview visualization, and condensation. This paper also introduced user evaluations, and discussed its effectiveness and problems.

As short-term future works, we would like to develop additional functions discussed as potential future issues in Section V-B. Also, we would like to test Colorscore with more variety of users and music, to find more issues to improve Colorscore. Especially, we have not tested condensation functions with examinees yet, and therefore not discussed their issues well. Such additional tests will be helpful for our future enhancement.

Following are our long-term future issues. We are interested in more detailed information display of note-blocks. Especially, we would like to represent differences of note-blocks painted in the same colors, by assigning independent textures or glyphs. We are also interested in development of horizontal condensation so that it can detect repetition of note-blocks and shrink the repeated note-blocks.

As discussed in Section V-B, it may be an essential problem that we need to manually input melodies and accompaniment patterns, and therefore visualization result may strongly depends on the input. We would like to discuss how Colorscore can integrate with automatic theme or pattern discovery techniques, so that Colorscore can provide visualization results not depending on users' input.

REFERENCES

[1] J. Foote, Visualizing Music and Audio using Self-Similarity, 7th ACM International Conference on Multimedia, Part 1, pp. 77-80, 1999.

[2] M. Goto, SmartMusicKIOSK: Music Listening Station with Chorus-Search Function, 16th Annual ACM Symposium on User Interface Software and Technology, pp. 31-40, 2003.

[3] C. S. Sapp, Harmonic visualizations of tonal music, Proc. International Computer Music Conference (ICMC, Havana, Cuba, 2001), pp. 423-430, 2001.

[4] M. Wattenberg, Arc diagrams: Visualizing structure in strings, Proc. IEEE Symposium on Information Visualization 2002, pp. 110-116, 2002.

[5] R. Miyazaki, I. Fujishiro, and R. Hiraga, comp-i: A System for Visual Exploration of MIDI Datasets, Transactions of Information Processing Society of Japan, vol. 45, no. 3, pp. 739-742, 2004.

[6] M. Matsubara, H. Okamoto, T. Sano, and H. Susuki, Scoreilluminator: Automatic illumination of orchestra scores for readability improvement, International Computer Music Conference (ICMC 2009), 2009.

[7] F. Watanabe, I. Fujishiro, and R. Hiraga, Music Learning through Visualization, Second International Conference on WEB Delivering of Music (WEDELMUSIC'02), 2002.

MusiCube: A Visual Interface for Music Selection featuring Interactive Evolutionary Computing

Yuri Saito*   Takayuki Itoh*

∗Graduate School of Humanities and Sciences, Ochanomizu University

{yuri, itot}@itolab.is.ocha.ac.jp

Abstract

We often want to select tunes based on our purposes or situations. For example, we may want background music for particular spaces. We think interactive evolutionary computing is a good solution to adequately recommend tunes based on users' preferences. This paper presents MusiCube, a visual interface for music selection. It applies interactive genetic algorithm in a multi-dimensional musical feature space. MusiCube displays a set of tunes as colored icons in a 2D cubic space, and provides a user interface to intuitively select suggested tunes. This paper presents a user experience that MusiCube adequately represented clouds of icons corresponding to sets of users' preferable tunes in the 2D cubic space.

System Design of MusiCube

This section presents the processing flow and user interface design of MusiCube. Storing a lot of tunes, MusiCube firstly displays them as icons in a 2D musical feature space. It then randomly suggests several tunes to listen to, and expects users to evaluate them as "positive" or "negative" according to their purposes or situations.

The processing flow of MusiCube is as follows:

1. Calculate feature values of tunes.
2. Initialize the system.
3. Suggest several tunes by switching the colors of icons.
4. Receive user's evaluations, and switch the colors of icons of listened tunes.
5. Conduct the evolutionary computing to the next generation.
6. Repeat 3. to 5.

MusiCube displays icons corresponding to the tunes in a cubic space and three tabs corresponding user interface widgets: 1) play, stop and evaluation, 2) musical feature selection, and 3) playlist, as shown in Figure 1.

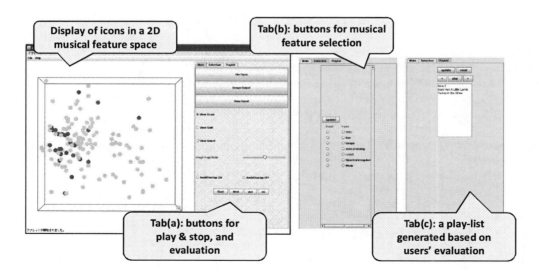

Figure 1: Window design of MusiCube. The left side of the window displays a set of colored icons corresponding to tunes. The right side of the window has three tabs.

1550-6037/11 $26.00 © 2011 IEEE

DOI 10.1109/IV.2011.78

5. Visualisation

IV 2011

A 3D molecular visualization system with mobile devices

Mariko Sasakura, Akira Kotaki, Junya Inada
Computer Science Department
Okayama University
Okayama, Japan
sasakura@momo.cs.okayama-u.ac.jp

Abstract—It is not very intuitive to manipulate objects visualized in 3-dimension by a mouse, because a mouse can only move in 2-dimension space. We propose an interaction technique to manipulate 3D objects by mobile devices with acceleration sensors. We have developed a 3D molecular visualization system which displays results of a simulation of the molecular dynamics method. In the system, we can rotate 3D objects by leaning a mobile device and change a viewing location by moving a mobile device. We discuss how we implement the interaction technique in this paper.

Keywords-Interaction technique; Mobile devices; Acceleration sensors; 3D objects;

I. INTRODUCTION

Since graphics workstations become widely used, computer graphics has improved a lot. Nowadays, we can see beautiful 3D computer graphics even on displays of personal computers. It is used for designing mechanical machine such as cars, amusing games, and visualizing many things. Technologies of computer graphics have also been improved. We can easily make a program of 3D computer graphics or animation by using free libraries such as OpenGL or Flash.

However, the major manipulation device for objects produced by computer graphics has never changed from the very beginning. It is a mouse. A mouse is an excellent and inexpensive device for 2D applications, but it is not enough intuitive to manipulate objects visualized in 3D, because it can move only in 2D space.

Therefore, many studies have been done for manipulating objects in 3D (for short 3D objects) intuitively. For example, data gloves for virtual reality, a 3D mouse, haptic devices, and an Wiimote are used to manipulate 3D objects. But all of them have a disadvantage. That is a user must buy the extra device.

In this paper, we propose a technique to manipulate 3D objects by mobile devices and develop a molecular visualization system in which we manipulate molecules by mobile devices. The advantage of using a mobile device, such as a mobile phone or mobile music player, is that almost of us usually take along.

We are developing an interaction technique using 3D acceleration sensors of mobile devices, such as iOS devices (iPhone / iPod touch / iPad). We are planning to detect a direction of lean or movement of an iOS device from its 3D acceleration sensors and using them as input of a computer.

3D acceleration sensors detect only acceleration. It means that they don't directly detect velocity or distance of movement of iOS device. Therefore, the direction of movement must be generated from value of 3D acceleration sensors. We are developing an algorithm and library by which we can get a direction of lean or movement from the values of 3D acceleration sensors. And we have developed a 3D molecular visualization system with mobile devices by using the library.

In section II, we review related works on 3D object manipulation. In section III, we describe how our library detects a direction of lean and movement from acceleration sensors of an iOS device. In section IV, we introduce our molecular visualization system using mobile devices, and we conclude in section V.

II. 3D OBJECTS MANIPULATION

Molecular simulation systems show chemical reactions usually obtained by simulating movements of molecules. Many Visualization techniques for the results of simulations represent each molecular as a 3D object and show temporal change of molecules as animations [6], [9].

To manipulate 3D objects, there have been many studies. The representable one may be virtual reality [1], [2], [5]. Virtual reality represents 3D objects in virtual 3D space, and typically manipulates them by using data gloves. But, we need big devices to construct a virtual reality system, such as big displays or a head-mounted display, data gloves, and complicated programs.

There are other works to manipulate 3D objects by cheaper and easily-obtainable devices, such as Wiimotes. The Wiimote has acceleration sensors and a CMOS sensor, and we can buy it at a low price. Some researches have used the Wiimote as a pointing device for a personal computer in place of a mouse [7], [10], [11]. Since the Wiimote can be moved in 3D space, it may be more intuitive than a mouse for manipulating 3D objects.

Similarly, mobile devices, especially mobile phones, are used to researches as input devices for computers. Nowadays, most people have their own mobile phone of which performance is as good as computers one generations ago.

Some mobile phones, such as iPhone, have acceleration sensors so that we can use them to manipulate 3D objects. Kim proposes a technique which uses the touch screen of an iOS device as an input device for CAVE which is a famous virtual reality system [4]. Some researches try to use mobile devices as an input/output device for computers [3], [8].

III. A LIBRARY FOR USING ACCELERATION SENSORS

iOS devices have 3D acceleration sensors. Figure 1 shows the three axes of acceleration sensors. Notice acceleration sensors detect acceleration, not speed. Therefore, we cannot know the exact distance of movement by acceleration sensors, but we can know the direction of movement.

The acceleration sensors always sense the gravity. Therefore, if we assume that the iOS device stays still, we can guess how the user hold it. For example, if we hold an iOS device as the home button is downside, like the leftside of figure of Figure 1, the y axes of the device senses gravity. Although the y axes of a device senses gravity, we cannot know whether the screen of the device faces the user or the back of the device faces the user, because in these two cases, the acceleration sensors show the same value. We suppose that a user always holds the device as its screen faces the user so that we can know how a user holds the iOS device from which axis detects the gravity.

When we know how a user holds an iOS device, we can achieve the detection of *orientation free direction of movement*. The detection of orientation free direction of movement is that we detect the direction of movement from the user's viewpoint regardless of how to hold the device. We show examples in Figure 2. The three figures in Figure 2 an iOS device in held in different way. The gravity is sensed by minus force of y axis in the left figure, plus force of x axis in the middle figure and plus force of y axis in the right figure. The force of the arrow in the figure is detected by plus force of x axis, plus force of y axis and minus force of x axis, respectively. But, we would like to detect the direction of movement is right in all cases.

Table I shows the relation of the axis which detects gravity, the axis which detects movement, and the orientation free direction of movement. In all cases, we suppose that the screen of the device faces the user. In the case of the gravity detected as z+ and z−, we suppose that the user holds the device as its home button stays below.

The judgment of direction is performed for each axis of acceleration sensors separately. For example, in the case of y− gravity, if we detect the change of plus value of x acceleration sensor, the direction is Right. If we detect the change of plus value of y acceleration sensor, the direction is Up. If both of x and y acceleration sensors make plus change, the library detects Right and Up.

We have found that we can distinguish between lean and movement because an acceleration sensor makes different pattern between the case of them. "Lean" means that we

don't change the position of the device but change the angle. "Movement" means that we change the position of the device without changing the angle of it. Our research shows the difference of the patterns are like in the Figure 3. The horizontal direction of the figure shows the time axis, and the vertical direction indicates the output value of the sensor. The pattern circled by red is appeared when a user moves an iOS device. The pattern circled by green is appeared when a user leans an iOS device.

We have developed a 3D acceleration library which can detects a direction of lean and movement of an iOS device based on Table I. The library has the following functions:

- Return the orientation free direction of moving.
- Return the orientation free direction of leaning.
- Return the observed value of acceleration sensors.
- Set the interval of measurement of acceleration sensors.

The library is provided for Objective-C programmers. They can use their original programs by using the library.

We discuss how many situations can be detected by the library. For moving, We have three axes and each axes can have three status : moving plus direction, moving minus direction and no moving. Therefore we can detect $3^3 - 1 = 26$ situations, in theory. But by our experience, it is difficult for users to make composition movement with the direction of front-back, such as forward-right, or forward-right-up and so on. Then, we can provide stable detection for 10 situations for moving: right, left, up, down, right-up, right-down, left-up, left-down, forward and backward.

For leaning, we also have three axes and each axes can have three status. But for leaning, we cannot detect the change of angle on the axis which detects gravity. And composition movement can hardly be imaged by users. Therefore we can use 4 situations practically: right, left, forward and backward.

Hence, we can use 14 situations by the library.

IV. A MOLECULAR VISUALIZATION SYSTEM

We have developed a molecular visualization system with mobile device by using the library. This system visualizes the result of simulation of molecular dynamics method (MD method). The system has features which are the same as typical molecular visualization systems:

- The input of the system is a file written by MFG which is an input format of AVS[1].
- The system visualizes a molecular as a sphere.
- The system can do standard 3D object manipulation : rotation, translation, scaling up/down and displaying cross-section.
- The system can present the result of simulation as an animation.

The original feature of the system is that we can manipulate 3D object by mobile devices. Figure 4 shows the

[1]http://www.avs.com

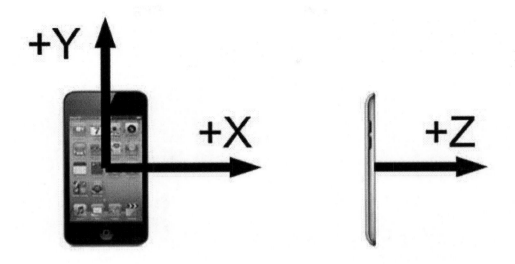

Figure 1. The three axes of acceleration sensors in the iOS device.

Figure 2. The detection of orientation free direction of movement.

architecture of the system. This system consists of a personal computer and several mobile devices. The personal computer works as a server. The result of simulation is visualized on the screen of the computer. One or more than one mobile devices can connect to the server and get data of the result of simulation. We can manipulate visualized 3D objects by moving or leaning one of the connected mobile device.

Figure 5 shows how we can manipulate 3D objects by a mobile device. The system displays the same 3D objects on the PC display and mobile device's screen so that a user can manipulate 3D objects, checking both of the screens. The leftside figure in Figure 5 shows the initial state. In the system, we adopt holding the device on z− gravity in the initial state, since we can match the direction of movement of the device and the 3D objects. When we lean the device on the y axis, that is right-left direction, 3D objects rotate to right-left direction. When we lean the device on the x

axis, that is forward-backward direction, 3D objects rotate to forward-backward direction. The right-upside figure in Figure 5 shows the case of right rotation, and the right-downside figure in Figure 5 shows the case of forward rotation.

V. CONCLUSIONS

We have developed an interaction technique using 3D acceleration sensors of mobile devices. We make a library for providing the technique to programmers and show a 3D molecular visualization system which uses the library. Our preliminary user testing shows positive results, that is users prefer our interaction technique using mobile device than the traditional mouse for its intuitive operations.

Future works are:

- Improve accuracy of detecting directions.
  In some cases, the library return different direction

Table I
THE DIRECTION DETECTED FROM THE VALUE OF ACCELERATION SENSORS.

Gravity	The value of acceleration sensor					
	x+	x−	y+	y−	z+	z−
x+	down	up	right	left	forward	backward
x−	up	down	left	right	forward	backward
y+	left	right	down	up	forward	backward
y−	right	left	up	down	forward	backward
z+	right	left	up	down	forward	backward
z−	right	left	up	down	forward	backward

Notes: In all cases, we suppose that the screen of the device faces the user. In the case of z+ and z− on gravity, we suppose that the user holds the device as its home button is on the downside.

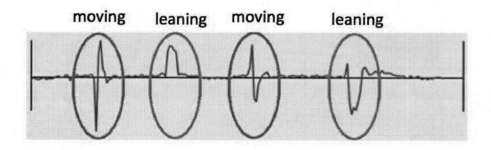

Figure 3. Patterns detected by an acceleration sensor.

from user's intension. We have to improve accuracy of detection for avoiding such cases.

- Improve response time of detection.

  Using the 3D molecular visualization system, users sometimes complain the response of interaction is slow. We have to improve the response time of detection for comfortable interaction.

- Evaluate the technique.

  We plan to evaluate the advantage and disadvantage of the proposed interaction technique compared with a mouse by usability testing.

REFERENCES

[1] Bryson, S.: *Virtual reality in scientific visualization* Communications of the ACM, vol. 39, no. 5, pp. 62–71, 1996.

[2] Cruz-Neira, C., Langley, R. and Bash, P. A.: *VIBE: a virtual biomolecular environment for interactive molecular modeling* Computer Chem. vol. 20, no. 4, pp. 469–477, 1996.

[3] Diehl, J., Kramer, J.-P. and Borchers, J.: *A framework for using the iPhone as a wireless input device for interactive systems*, UIST' 08, 2008.

[4] Kim, J.-S., Gracanin, D., Matkovic K. and Quek F.: *iPhone/iPod touch as input devices for navigation in immersive virtual environments*, IEEE Virtual Reality 2009, pp. 261–262, 2009.

[5] Nakano, A., Kalia, R. K. and Vashishta, P.: *Scalable molecular-dynamics, visualization, and data-management algorithms for materials simulations.*, Computing in Science & Engineering, vol.1, no.5, pp.39–47, 1999.

[6] Pettersen, E. F., Goddard, T. D., Huang, C. C., Couch, G. S., Greenblatt, D. M. Meng, E. C. and Ferrin, T. E.: *UCSF Chimera - a visualization system for exploratory research and analysis*, Journal of Computational Chemistry, vol. 25, no. 13, pp. 1605–1612, 2004.

[7] Santos B. S., Prada, B., Ribeiro, H., Dias, P., Silva, S. and Ferreira, C.: *Wiimote as an input device in Google Earth visualization and navigation: a user study comparing two alternatives*, 14th International Conference Information Visualisation, pp. 473–478 2010.

[8] Sasakura, M., Fujioka, S. and Yamasaki, S.: *Interaction with computers using mobile devices* Proceedings of 14th International Conference on Information Visualization(IV10), pp.122-127, July 27-29, 2010.

[9] Satoh, H., Aoki A. and Asaoka, H.: *ChemoJun: Open Source Chemical Graphics Library*, Journal of Computer Aided Chemistry, vol.7, pp.141–149, 2006.

[10] Sheridan, J. G., Price, S. and Pontual-Falcao, T.: *Wii remotes as tangible exertion interfaces for exploring action-representation relationships*, Whole Body Interaction 2009, A SIGCHI 2009 Workshop 2009.

[11] Wingrave, C. A., Williamson, N., Varcholik, P. D., Rose, J., Miller, A., Charbonneau, E., Bott, J. and LaVIola Jr., J. J.: *The Wiimote and beyond: spatially convenient devices for 3D user interfaces*, IEEE Computer Graphics and Applications, vol. 30, no. 2, pp. 71–85 2010.

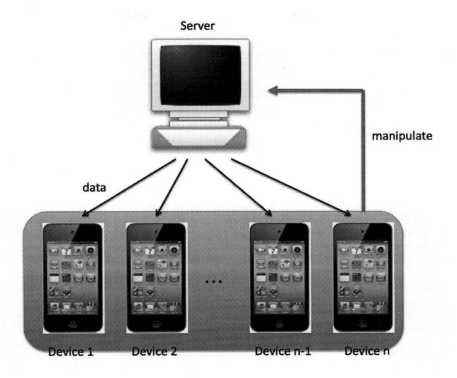

Figure 4.   The System architecture of the molecular visualization system with mobile devices.

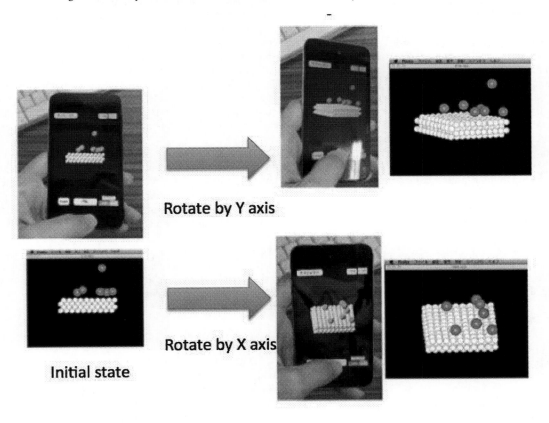

Figure 5.   Manipulating 3D objects in a computer by a mobile device.

Abstract Camera Controller for Three-Dimensional Visualizations

Adrian Rusu[1], Spence DiNicolantonio[1], Robert Russell[1], Eric Velte[2]
[1]Department of Computer Science, Rowan University, U.S.A.
[2]Mission Solutions Engineering, U.S.A.
rusu@rowan.edu, {dinico58, russel42}@students.rowan.edu, eric.velte@missionse.com

Abstract

In the realm of computer graphics, methods used to control a user's point of view in a three-dimensional world are rather convoluted and are often tightly coupled to the rendering system used. In response to this issue, we have developed a robust camera controller system that provides an intuitive interface for visualization and simulation programmers, while removing renderer dependencies completely. Our system follows common object oriented design principles to encapsulate the complex mathematics and computations involved in synthetic camera manipulation, providing a firm foundation for high-level camera features. We provide a use case where students with no graphics experience developed a visualization system using our camera controller.

1. Introduction

Proper manipulation of a user's viewpoint is essential to any visualization posed in three-dimensional space. If a 3D visualization system does not provide fluid movement and control in an intuitive manner, users may become distracted from the data or concepts being presented to them. Unfortunately, the current methods used in computer graphics programming for viewpoint manipulation do not provide an easy way to meet this need and, in fact, don't allow movement of the viewpoint at all.

According to the synthetic camera model adopted by most 3D graphics APIs, the virtual camera can be controlled only as far as defining the dimensions of its view frustum. This is the frustum (truncated pyramid) of viewable space extending from the front of the camera. Rather than allowing manipulation of the camera's position and orientation within respect to the world coordinate system, all objects in the world must be projected to the camera's local coordinate system [1], [15].

Our camera controller system acts as a façade between the counter-intuitive graphics API and the aspiring information visualization (IV) programmer, providing multiple conveniences and features. The controller stores camera state information internally and supplies a straightforward API to programmers for manipulation and queries. Essentially, the dynamic properties of a camera can be reduced to two characteristics: position and orientation. Position is represented as a three-dimensional vector, while orientation is represented as a rotation relative to a default camera orientation. IV programmers are free to query or apply rotations in a variety of forms: Euler angles, axis and angle notation, a unit quaternion, or a direction-cosine matrix (DCM). Our controller also contains a locking focus system and, in turn, automated orbital movement around the camera's point of focus.

From an integration point of view, our system requires only a few lines of code to be tied into any graphics API. A few queries must be made to get the camera's position and orientation information, which can then be applied to a graphics API of choice, as needed.

Extensive work has been done in the past to overcome obstacles in the field of graphics camera systems, but this research tends to focus on the design of high-level behavior concepts and is typically embedded in large-scale systems [18]. These systems often bring limitations to users with regard to input methods and offered behaviors. In contrast, our system places priority on simplicity, providing the basics of three-dimensional control and leaving all other aspects of camera behavior and input extraneous to the camera. Our system is an API for graphics and IV programmers. It is not tied to any graphical front-end and thus remains flexible for use in virtually any system. Because user input is extrinsic to our system, IV programmers are free to leverage the convenience of our system, without being limited in any way.

Another key benefit of our camera control system is the way in which it encourages the development of high-level automation and innovative viewpoint techniques. By hiding the intimidating complexities of simple camera manipulation, more advanced displays and front-end systems can be achieved.

Our paper is structured as follows: in section 2 we explain the architecture of our camera controller system, in section 3 we describe how our system benefited IV programmers through a use case, and in section 4 we explain future enhancements, followed by conclusions in Section 5.

2. Architecture

Our camera controller system has three distinct modules (see Figure 1). The first layer is the synthetic camera itself. Following the camera layer is a layer that encapsulates all geometric transformation logic needed to support the function and features of the synthetic camera. Finally, below the logic layer is a layer consisting of all non-primitive data types used in the system.

1550-6037/11 $26.00 © 2011 IEEE
DOI 10.1109/IV.2011.55

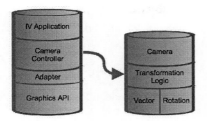

Figure 1. An IV application is built on top of the camera controller, which can then be integrated with any graphics API via a simple adapter.

2.1. Integration

Integration with any graphics API can be accomplished via a simple adapter. The adapter queries the camera system for information on its current state, including position, orientation, and optionally, clipping or field of view information. This queried data is then applied according to the graphics API in use. After the adapter has been created, IV developers are free to control all aspects of viewpoint manipulation via the camera controller's interface without worrying about the underlying graphics system.

By leveraging the adapter pattern [6], a user is able to change platforms and/or graphics API's as needed, with very few changes required to the actual application. Upon switching to a new graphics API, a developer can simply create a new adapter, applicable to the new API. All other aspects of the application, with regard to camera control, remain unaffected.

2.2. Data Types

The two fundamental elements of camera state are position and orientation. Position in 3D space can easily be represented as a three-dimensional vector, but defining orientation is more complex. One can inherently describe an orientation by the rotational variation from a given origination, or default orientation; however, there are many ways to define a 3D rotation mathematically and each has its advantages and disadvantages.

When first approaching the concept of rotation, the most intuitive, and thus desirable, representation is with the use of Euler angles (i.e., yaw, pitch, and roll). Unfortunately, when dealing with relative rotation, the use of Euler angles introduces a problem known as gimbal lock. In a three-gimbal system, bringing the axes of two gimbals into a parallel configuration results in the loss of one degree of freedom (see Figure 2) [9]. A three-gimbal system is analogous to a system based purely on Euler angles, thus gimbal lock poses a serious limitation. To avoid gimbal lock, one can use DCM matrices or unit quaternions to represent rotation [4], [13], [14], but these methods are rather abstract and specifying rotations explicitly in this manner is very difficult from a user's standpoint.

Figure 2. A three-gimbal system (left), providing three degrees of freedom. Gimbal lock (right): two axes are aligned, resulting in a loss of one degree of freedom.

In order to resolve this difficulty, we abstracted the concept of rotation from its underlying representation entirely and designed a Rotation class that can be defined using a variety of forms. Internally, a Rotation object is represented by a unit quaternion, because it avoids gimbal lock and requires less memory for storage than a DCM matrix. From an IV programmer's perspective, however, Rotation objects can be constructed using Euler angles, axis and angle notation, a unit quaternion, or a DCM matrix. In addition, Rotation objects can be queried for description in any notation desired following creation. This feature is made possible by a collection of conversion algorithms [10], [16], [17] hidden within the Rotation abstraction, which is convenient for IV programmers. Beyond the simple elegance of a unified abstraction, it allows the use of Euler angles, or any preferred notation, without the limitation of gimbal lock.

2.3. Conventions

Prior to development, certain conventions needed to be established for our system. First, the default orientation of the camera (represented by the identity matrix) must be defined. We chose to adopt the convention used in OpenGL, the industry standard graphics API, in which the camera faces the negative z-axis, with the positive y and x axes extending upward and to the right, respectively (see Figure 3) [15].

In addition, there must be an established convention for the application order of Euler angles, as variation will yield differing results. We chose to adopt the order used in the NASA standard airplane: yaw, pitch, and then roll [3]. It is important to note that while our chosen Euler order convention adheres to the NASA standard, our chosen coordinate system does not (see paragraph above). Therefore, with regard to our camera's coordinate system, yaw-pitch-roll equates to y-x-z, whereas the same ordering equates to y-z-x with using NASA's standard airplane system. From a user's standpoint, the difference is unnoticeable with regard to relative rotation and only visible when applying absolute rotation to the camera system (using the world coordinate system). Furthermore, this divergent behavior is invisible when thinking about camera control in terms of yaw, pitch, and roll (rather than coordinate axes), which is typically the case.

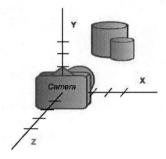

Figure 3. Our system follows the camera orientation convention established by OpenGL, in which the camera faces negative z-axis, with positive y and x axes extending upward and to the right, respectively.

2.4. Features

2.4.1. Basic Movement

Although movement is the simplest feature in a 3D camera system, it is also one of the most important. Fluid movement is key in the attempt to portray realism. Our camera control system not only gives the ability to get and set the position of the camera, but also provides an interface for both absolute and relative movement of the camera according to a given displacement vector. Absolute movement can be used in the event that the camera needs to be moved with respect to the world coordinate system, while relative movement is available in the event that movement relative the camera's local coordinate system is more desirable. For example, the movement in a first-person simulation will always be relative to the orientation of the viewer, thus relative movement is preferred. Alternatively, when a scripted movement track is involved with simultaneous user-controlled viewing, such as in a simulation of an amusement park ride, absolute movement is better suited in order to keep user-invoked orientation changes from altering the path of motion.

2.4.2. Orientation/Rotation

Using the Rotation class abstraction, achieving proper orientation and rotation of the viewpoint is straightforward. Querying the camera controller for orientation yields a Rotation object, which can then be queried for any form of rotational notation. Similarly, the orientation of the camera is set according to a given Rotation object, created via any desired notation.

Much like the provided movement support, a camera's orientation can be altered with respect to the world coordinate system, or to the camera's local coordinate system. By default, all rotation is performed

about viewpoint's origin; however, our system also supports rotation about any given point (see section 2.4.5).

2.4.3. Look At

Many graphics APIs support a "Look at" feature that will adjust the projection matrix in order to face a given point in 3D space [1], [15]. This feature, while convenient, may cause problems. When dealing with a graphics API directly to manipulate viewpoint, orientation is typically stored and updated manually when change is needed. In this situation, upon making a call to the graphics API's "Look at" function, the stored orientation is invalidated, as the resultant orientation will no longer match the stored orientation data. Within our system, this is not an issue because orientation is self-contained. Upon receiving a "Look at" invocation, our camera controller automatically updates all fields as needed.

2.4.4. Focus System

While designing our "look at" functionality, we began to recognize a certain amount of importance associated with the camera's focus point. This is the point in space at an arbitrary distance along the camera's view vector on which the camera is "focusing". In particular, we realized that in many situations, it is desirable to maintain the camera's focus on a given point regardless of movement. An example of this can be seen in our use case (see Section 3), in which the camera needed to focus on the center of a virtual Earth model while orbiting around to a desired vantage point. As a result, we chose to make the focus point of the camera persistent and developed a toggle-able locking mechanism. Our camera controller's interface allows a user to easily toggle a lock on the camera's current focus point. Doing so will prevent the camera from altering its focus. When the camera's focus is locked, modifications to the camera's state will cause its orientation to be subsequently rectified to view the locked focus point.

2.4.5. Orbital Movement

The locking focus system provides a foundation for a variety of new features, one of which being orbital movement. When the camera's focus is locked, yaw and pitch are restrained, but roll functionality is left unaffected, as it will not cause any alteration of the focus point. Movement, on the other hand, becomes rather different, depending on the approach used. Absolute movement will only be divergent with regard to a resetting of the camera's orientation after movement has been completed (in order to face the locked focus point). Relative movement forward and backward will not be at all different. However, any relative movement involving the x or y axes while the camera's focus is locked will be substantially different than while the focus is unlocked.

Consider an arbitrary point, *p*, located on the negative z-axis. Now consider a camera located at the world origin, with focus locked on *p*, undergoing a series of relative movements along the camera's local x-axis. Following the first movement, the camera will still be located on the world x-axis, but its orientation will have been consequently rectified to continue facing *p*. It can be easily seen that although each movement applied to the camera is in the same direction with regard to the camera's local coordinate system, the absolute direction of motion (in the world coordinate system) has changed and will be continuously changing with each subsequent movement. If we were to map this movement within the x/y plane, we would actually see a spiral around *p* (see Figure 4). The behavior we have just encountered is essentially orbital movement, but with some error based on the magnitude of displacement. In a perfect theoretical system, with an infinitesimal displacement per time quanta, no error would be present, resulting in perfect circular movement about the focus point

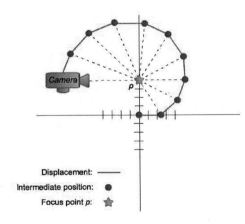

Figure 4. Illustration of spiral affect experienced during relative movement with locked focus, prior to orbital rotation fix.

We fix this spiral effect by implementing an orbital movement algorithm and integrating it into our relative movement algorithms for the specific case in which the camera's focus is locked. Because orbital movement is effectively rotation about an arbitrary point, we start by adding this functionality to our camera. Then, within our relative movement algorithm, we leverage orbital rotation in the event that focus is locked, using the given displacement vector's magnitude and direction as arc length and rotational tangent respectively. After the rotation has been performed, we simply adjust the camera's orientation to look at its initial focus point, thus achieving the desired results.

2.5. Programming Interface

As established in previous sections, our camera controller system encapsulates the complex computations involved in synthetic camera manipulation within a three-dimensional visualization. In this section, we establish how an IV programmer interacts with our system for a simple and intuitive experience. The interface is designed for ease and efficiency, as it promotes elegance and effectiveness within the production of IV applications.

2.5.1. Adapter

The following example describes the essential component of an adapter integrating our camera control system with JOGL, the Java bindings to OpenGL, a common graphics API (see Listing 1). The methods called will be discussed in Sections 2.5.2 and 2.5.3.

```java
/**
 * Called by the drawable to initiate OpenGL rendering
 */
public void display(GLAutoDrawable drawable) {

    // get rotation camera's current orientation
    Rotation orientation = camera.getOrientation();
    // inverse for application to Modelview matrix
    orientation = orientation.inverse();
    // get orientation in matrix form
    Matrix rotMatrix = orientation.toMatrix();

    // construct array containing matrix data
    double[] matData = rotMatrix.toArray(
        Matrix.ArrayOrder.COLUMN_MAJOR);

    // create double buffer of using rotation matrix data
    DoubleBuffer matrixBuffer =
        BufferUtil.newDoubleBuffer(matData.length);
    matBuffer.put(matData);
    matBuffer.rewind();

    // apply camera orientation to Modelview matrix
    gl.glMultMatrixd(matBuffer);

    // get camera position
    Vector3D pos = camera.getPosition();
    // inverse for application to Modelview matrix
    pos = pos.inverse();

    // apply camera position to Modelview matrix
    gl.glTranslated(pos.getX(), pos.getY(), pos.getZ());

    // graphics code
    ...
}
```

Listing 1. Example camera adapter, taken from "Reverie", an information visualization testing environment being developed at Rowan University.

At this point, the camera controller is completely wired to the graphics API. The bottom two layers of our IV application architecture (see Figure 1) have been completely established; therefore, the camera controller can be used exclusively for camera manipulation without consideration of the layers beneath.

2.5.2. Camera

Since we have established the foundation for an IV application, we now describe the interface available for manipulation and control of the synthetic camera. Our system follows the principles of information hiding, and thus all camera control methods are supplied within the Camera class itself, independent of the underlying logic.

The getPosition() and setPosition(Vector3D) methods are used to get and set the camera's position, respectively. The move(Vector3D, ...) method is used to move the camera according to a given displacement vector. Optionally, a boolean value can be supplied to explicitly specify whether absolute or relative movement should be applied to the camera; movement is relative by default.

The getOrientation() and setOrientation(Rotation) methods are used to get and set the camera's orientation, respectively, in the form of an abstract Rotation object. The rotate(Rotation, ...) method is used to rotate the camera about its origin. Similar to the move method, the rotate method can be given an optional boolean value, in order to explicitly specify absolute or relative rotation, relative rotation being the default. The rotate(Rotation, Vector3D, boolean) method is used for orbital rotation; i.e., rotation about a given point. As parameters, it takes the rotation to be applied, the point about which rotation will occur, and a boolean flag stating whether or not to alter the camera's orientation with the applied rotation. The lookAt(Vector3D, ...) method is used to rotate the camera to focus on a given point, changing the local y-axis (relative "up") as little as possible. Optionally, a desired local y-axis can be specified.

The following methods can be used to access information about the camera's focus. The getFocusPoint() method will return the point in 3D space on which the camera is focused, while getFocusDepth() will return the distance between the camera and the focus point. Another method called getFocusVector() is also provided, which will return a vector pointing from the camera's origin to its focus point. The getFocusedLocked() method is used to determine whether the camera's focus is currently locked. Furthermore, mutator methods are provided for each of these focus methods.

Information regarding the camera's local coordinate system can be queried using the getLocalXAxis(), getLocalYAxis(), and getLocalZAxis() methods. For convenience, the Camera class also provides storage and accessors/mutators for querying/setting near clipping distance, far clipping distance, and field of view angle. While these elements are not actually used intrinsically by the camera system, this added interface could be

useful when such information is dynamic and needed by the adapter.

2.5.3. Rotation

The Rotation class provides a variety of constructors and methods for creating, querying, and manipulating abstract rotations. The constructors available allow the creation of Rotation objects via Euler angles, an axis and angle of rotation, a DCM matrix, or a unit quaternion. Once created, methods such as getEulerAngles(), toMatrix(), and setPitch(double), among many others, can be used to query or alter information about the Rotation object with respect to any desired rotational formatting. The Rotation class provides an inverse() method, which computes and returns the inverse rotation, as well as an append(Rotation) method for concatenating a series of rotations. In addition, the slerp(Rotation, double) method can be used for computing the spherical linear interpolation across a given rotation, according to a given interpolation factor.

2.5.4. Vector3D

The Vector3D class encapsulates vector algebra logic, including addition, subtraction, scalar multiplication, dot and cross products, inverse computation, and linear interpolation. Many other query methods are supported such as isUnitVector(), which checks for a magnitude of 1, and isParallel(Vector3D) which determines if the vector is parallel to another given Vector3D object. The Vector3D class also contains a rotate(Rotation, Vector3D) method that rotates the vector by a given amount about a given point in 3D space.

3. Use Case

Our camera control system is currently being used at Rowan University. Undergraduate computer science students are required to take a course titled "Software Engineering I". In this course, students work on real-world projects with customers from large corporations.

One project given in a recent semester required the assigned group to develop a system that could display and track various data elements, which are represented as spheres, around Earth using a three-dimensional visualization (see Figure 5). This project required graphics programming to display the visualization as well as precise camera control, including movement and reorientation, within the 3D world to provide coherent following behaviors while tracking objects. None of the students in the group had any experience with computer graphics. By leveraging our camera control system, the group was able to successfully deliver the project to their customer with very little external guidance.

Overall, the use of our camera control system was a success. Undergraduate students, who had no prior experience with OpenGL or any other form of graphics programming, were able to develop an application that leverages advanced three-dimensional graphics. The movement of the camera and rendering of the world is completely decoupled from their application, which allows development of new functionality for either part of the system in the future. Information hiding is prevalent, as the students were not concerned with the mathematics and science associated with manipulating the camera. The students were only concerned with our supplied API and how these methods could be leveraged to accomplish their goals.

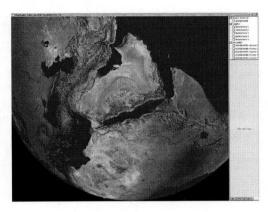

Figure 5. Students had to track elements around the Earth using our camera controller system.

4. Future Enhancements

Our camera controller can be expanded with other high-level features and automation. One of the planned developments includes an automated object-following algorithm and enhancement of our focus system. This expansion will provide the camera with the ability to focus on a collection of arbitrary focus points by computing the centroid of these points. In addition, the extended system will support any number of secondary focus points, which will stipulate additional points of interest. The camera system will be able to intelligently reorient and reposition itself in order to center viewing on the centroid of all primary focus points, while keeping all secondary focus points in view as well.

5. Conclusion

Our abstract camera controller system offers an intuitive and elegant replacement to an otherwise byzantine process. The system successfully encapsulates the complexities of the synthetic camera model, providing a comprehensible and pleasant experience for any IV developer or graphics programmer. Our system is currently in use within a variety of applications and visualization systems, and is even used as a learning tool within certain University courses. Students are provided with the opportunity to experience graphics and animation programming without the hurdle of learning low-level camera manipulation.

References

[1] Hearn Baker. Three-Dimensional Viewing. In *Computer Graphics with OpenGL, Third Edition*. Pearson Prentice Hall. 334-400. 2004.

[2] Frederick Brooks. Walkthough – A Dynamic Graphics Environment for Simulating Virtual Buildings. In *Proceedings of the 1986 Workshop on Interactive 3D Graphics*. 9–22. October 1986.

[3] Haim Baruh. Analytical Dynamics. Mcgraw Hill. 1999.

[4] Evangelos A. Coutsias and Louis Romero. The Quaternions with an application to Rigid Body Dynamics. February 1999.

[5] Steven M. Drucker and David Zeltzer. CamDroid: A System for Implementing Intelligent Camera Control. In *Proceedings of the 1995 symposium on Interactive 3D graphics*. ACM, 139-144. April 1995.

[6] Erich Gamma, Richard Helm, Ralph Johnson, and John Vlissides. *Design Patterns: Elements of Reusable Object-Oriented Software*. AddisonWesley. November 1994.

[7] Sundaram Ganapathy. Decomposition of transformation matrices for robot vision. In *International Conference on Robotics*. 130–139, March 1984.

[8] Michael Gleicher and Andrew Witkin. Through-the-lens camera control. In *Proceedings of the 19th annual conference on Computer graphics and interactive techniques* (SIGGRAPH '92), James J. Thomas (Ed.). ACM, 331-340. 1992.

[9] David Hoag. MIT Instrumentation Laboratory Document E-1344: Considerations of Apollo IMU Gimbal Lock. In *Apollo Guidance and Navigation*. April 1963.

[10] Noel H. Hughes. Quaternion to Euler Angle Conversion for Arbitrary Rotation Sequence Using Geometric Methods. url: http://www.euclideanspace.com/maths/geometry/rotations/conversions/quaternionToEuler/quat_2_euler_paper_ver2-1.pdf

[11] P. Karp and S. Feiner. Issues in the Automated Generation of Animated Presentations. Graphics Interface '90 Halifax, Nova Scotia. 1990.

[12] A. R. Klumpp. Singularity-free extraction of a quaternion from a direction-cosine matrix. In *Journal of Spacecraft and Rockets, vol. 13*. 754-755. Dec. 1976.

[13] E. E. L. Mitchell and A. E. Rogers. Quaternion Parameters in the Simulation of a Spinning Rigid Body. In *Simulation: the dynamic modeling of ideas and systems with computers. John McLeod*. 1988.

[14] Ken Shoemaker. Animating rotations with quaternion curves. *Computer Graphics*. 245–254. July 1985.

[15] Dave Shreiner and The Khronos OpenGL ARB Working Group. Viewing. In *OpenGL(R) Programming Guide: The Official Guide to Learning OpenGL, Version 3.0 and 3.1 (7th Edition)*.

[16] Arland Thompson. Euler Sequences. Advanced Technology Associates. url: http://www.atacolorado.com/eulersequences.doc

[17] Arland Thompson. Quaternion Simulation. Advanced Technology Associates. url: http://www.atacolorado.com/quaternionsimulation.doc

[18] Colin Ware and Steven Osborne. Exploration and virtual camera control in virtual three-dimensional environments. In *Proceedings 1990 Symposium on Interactive 3D Graphics*. 175–184. March 1990.

An Interactive Bio-Inspired Approach to Clustering and Visualizing Datasets

Ugo Erra
Dipartimento di Matematica e Informatica
Università della Basilicata
Potenza, Italy
Email: ugo.erra@unibas.it

Bernardino Frola, Vittorio Scarano
Dipartimento di Informatica
Università di Salerno
Fisciano, Italy
Email: frola@dia.unisa.it, vitsca@dia.unisa.it

Abstract—In this work, we present an interactive visual clustering approach for the exploration and analysis of datasets using the computational power of Graphics Processor Units (GPUs). The visualization is based on a collective behavioral model that enables cognitive amplification of information visualization. In this way, the workload of understanding the representation of information moves from the cognitive to the perceptual system. The results enable a more intuitive, interactive approach to the discovery of knowledge. The paper illustrates this behavioral model for clustering data, and applies it to the visualization of a number of real and synthetic datasets.

Keywords-visual clustering; behavioral model; GPU; high-dimensional datasets;

I. INTRODUCTION

The human perception system is the result of both evolution and experience of the environment. A direct consequence is the fact that humans have great ability to understand patterns in the natural environment through visual perception. Humans are physiologically receptive to natural shapes and behaviors and such patterns reach deep into our subconscious. For example, humans usually respond in a similar manner to the beauty of a sunset or to the shapes created by a flock of birds. Consequently, visualization of complex interrelationships may be better understood using natural analogues, producing visualizations that are motivated by metaphors inspired by nature. A methodology for the creation of effective visualizations based on our ability to immediately perceive complex information in nature is discussed in [1].

An approach that may be inspired by natural analogues is clustering. Clustering is essentially a data mining approach that addresses the problems of large amounts of data and the scarcity of human attention by discovering groups of similar objects. Each group, called a 'cluster', consists of objects that are similar to one another and dissimilar to objects of other groups. Based on given similarities, data is organized into clusters using an unsupervised learning approach that starts with an unlabeled dataset, from which the aim is to discover how the objects within that set are organized [2]. The main problem of clustering is in the visualization of vast volumes of data which is the first requirement for meaning to emerge and to be understood

effectively. Simplistic approaches to visualization lead to cluttered or confusing displays, which require a great deal of cognitive processing on behalf of the user in order to extract meaning from them.

This paper addresses the clustering of large high-dimensional datasets using a bio-inspired visualization technique that improves human understanding. The metaphor is based on a flock of birds. High-dimensional data is mapped as agents' features (we refer to autonomous agents using the word 'agent'). Each agent is assigned a local behavioral model and moves by coordinating its movement with the movement of other agents in a 3D environment. Our approach relies on the natural organization of groups that arises when agents with similar features interact using this local behavioral model.

In addition, we exploit the parallel architecture of Graphics Processor Units (GPUs) to guarantee interactive clustering. We illustrate the model and show how it enables agents to be organized into clusters with similar features. A significant advantage of the proposed approach is that it does not require the number of clusters as input, and data can be introduced interactively. Generally, our approach enables high-performance data analysis processing, and visualization based on an intuitive representation that avoids the projection of high-dimensional data in two- or three-dimensional space. Experimental results show a guaranteed quality of clustering from our algorithm, while implementation using the GPU architecture merely performs well.

The remainder of this paper is organized as follows: in section II, we review previous clustering approaches that are based on GPUs. In section III, we describe the behavioral model that inspired our clustering approach. In section IV, we illustrate our clustering algorithm. In section V, we present a brief description of the application. Section VI illustrates our results in terms of efficiency and performance scalability. Finally, section VII concludes and discusses directions for future work.

II. RELATED WORKS

An example of a system that uses visualization techniques for high-dimensional clustering is OPTICS [3]. The authors of OPTICS created a one-dimensional ordering of databases,

1550-6037/11 $26.00 © 2011 IEEE
DOI 10.1109/IV.2011.16

representing the density of clustering structures. Cluster points are close to each other in the one-dimensional ordering generated by OPTICS, and their reachability is found using a distance plot. This visualization system is valuable for understanding and guiding the clustering process. Another approach to high-dimensional clustering is the HD-Eye system [4]. HD-Eye considers clustering as a partitioning problem and enables the user to be directly involved in the clustering process - that is, in choosing the dimensions to be considered, in selecting the clustering paradigms, and in partitioning the datasets.

In the context of clustering, GPUs have demonstrated some interesting results. The k-means clustering algorithm is probably the algorithm most studied on GPUs. The first demonstrations of the use of GPUs to significantly accelerate k-means analysis are [5] [6]. Using an obsolete approach, based on shader languages, the authors of these studies exploit the computational capabilities of GPUs. Today, general purpose languages, like CUDA, offer better support to GPU architectures. The authors of [7] [8] tried to improve the efficiency of k-means using CUDA and optimizations directly targeted at parallel architectures. They obtained an increase in speed that is 14 and 13 times greater, respectively, than that of a CPU's sequential computation.

The authors of [9] used a shader language to implement hierarchical clustering. Their implementation speed was 2-4 times greater than that of a CPU. [10] explored parallel computation of hierarchical clustering with CUDA and obtained a 48-fold increase in speed.

The real-time simulation and visualization of large datasets using a GPU architecture has been proven to outperform CPU implementation in several past papers, for example [11]. In this work, the authors implement the proposed clustering approach using the BehaveRT framework [12]. This framework allows real-time simulation and visualization of large datasets. This enables developers to focus on the design and implementation of behavioral models that exploit the computational power of the GPU. We will show that this is a key aspect to obtaining interactive results.

III. THE BEHAVIORAL MODEL

Our clustering approach is inspired by the original behavioral models proposed by Reynolds [13]. In Reynold's model, each agent has a strictly local perception of the space it occupies. None of the group members have full knowledge of the entire group. Hence, agents must base their decisions on what they know of neighbors in their field of vision. Based on each agent's visibility, the synchronized aggregated motion of the group is achieved by calculating a weighted sum of *steering behaviors*. Reynolds defined three steering behaviors.

The first, *separation*, maintains a certain distance from neighbors. This is necessary to prevent collisions. A repulsive force $\vec{f_s}$ is calculated as the difference vector between

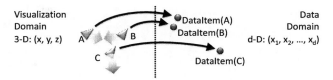

Figure 1: Each agent is associated with a data item in the dataset. Agents move in the 3D space while data items exist in the d-dimensional space. Data items affect the steering force of agents' behavior. For example, agents A and B represent similar data items (using a specific metric) and they move closer to each other. The data item of agent C is quite different to those of agents A and B, thus it moves away from them.

an agent's current position and the position of each of its neighbors, while the steering force is calculated as the average of all the repulsive force vectors. The second, *cohesion* moves the agent toward the center of his local neighborhood. This tends to aggregate the flock. The cohesion force $\vec{f_c}$ is obtained by computing the average position of neighbors. The third steering behavior, *alignment* tends to align the agent with other neighbors through group computing. The alignment force $\vec{f_a}$ is calculated as the difference between the average of the neighbors' forward vectors and the forward vector of the agent itself.

The overall steering force $\vec{f_r}$ of the Reynolds model, for the agent i, is achieved by summing the steering forces produced by all behaviors.

$$\vec{f_r} = w_s\vec{f_s} + w_c\vec{f_c} + w_a\vec{f_a}$$

where, w_s, w_c, and w_a are weights that manage the behavioral impact on the overall steering force.

IV. THE CLUSTERING MODEL APPROACH

In addition to the behaviors described in the model proposed by Reynolds, we defined two new behaviors called *Cluster-Cohesion* and *Cluster-Alignment*. These behaviors implement the agent-based clustering algorithm.

The cluster-cohesion force $\vec{f_{cc}}$, for a specific agent i, is computed as

$$\vec{f_{cc}} = \sum_{j \in Neighs(i)} sim_{ij}\vec{s_{ij}} + (1 - sim_{ij})\vec{f_{ij}}$$

where, $Neighs(i)$ are the nearest neighbors of the agent i. The vector $\vec{s_{ij}} = (\vec{p_j} - \vec{p_i}) - \vec{v_i}$ is the seeking force between agents i and j, while $\vec{f_{ij}} = -\vec{s_{ij}}$ is the fleeing force. The function sim_{ij} computes a similarity factor between the features vectors associated with agents i and j and must be between 0 and 1. The cluster-alignment force $\vec{f_{ca}}$, for a specific agent i, is computed as

$$\vec{f_{ca}} = \sum_{j \in Neighs(i)} sim_{ij}\vec{d_j}$$

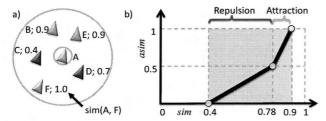

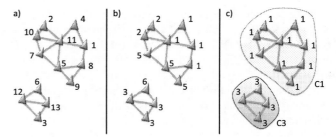

Figure 2: a) A group of 6 agents (triangles). Step I: Agent A computes the linear similarity (sim) of each neighbor. It also computes their minimum (0.4), maximum (0.9) and average (0.78) sim. Step II: Agent A computes the value of $asim$ for each of its neighbors, taking into account the minimum, maximum and average sim computed in the previous step. b) Adaptive vs. linear similarity. Agent A is repulsed by agents with $asim < 0.5$ (agents C and D) and attracted by those with $asim > 0.5$ (agents B, E and F).

Figure 3: Example of local label propagation for cluster identification (with *LPIterations* equal to 2). a) Step I: Assign a unique label to each agent. b) Step II, iteration 1: Propagate minimum values using neighborhood connections. c) Step II, iteration 2: Again, propagate minimum values. Agents with the same labels represent clusters.

The steering force $\vec{f}$ used in the flocking clustering algorithm is calculated by summing Reynold's steering forces and these two new forces

$$\vec{f} = \vec{f_r} + w_{cc}\vec{f_{cc}} + w_{ca}\vec{f_{ca}}$$

It should be noted that in this case, we use two weights w_{cc}, and w_{ca} to manage the impact of the clustering algorithm's behavior.

Similarity.: In our model, each agent represents an object in the data set, while the features vector associated with each object defines an agent's character (Figure 1). Agents move in a 3D environment where the most similar agents will be found and grouped. The overall effect is that when an agent finds another agent similar to itself, it stays near this agent but continues to explore the 3D environment, looking for groups of agents that are similar to its group. The purpose of using a 3D environment as the search space is twofold. First, the 3D environment enables clustering of high-dimensional datasets without feature loss. Second, the clustering process is visualized in an intuitive and natural fashion, irrespective of dataset dimensionality.

The similarity of two agents is computed using the values of their associated features. The implementation described in this paper defines the angular separation between agent i and j as

$$sim_{ij} = \frac{\vec{c_i} \cdot \vec{c_j}}{\sqrt{\|\vec{c_i}\| \|\vec{c_j}\|}}$$

where, $\vec{c}$ is the agent's features vector. The range of sim_{ij} is [0, 1] but it must be mapped in the range [-1, 1]. To achieve this, the similarity is recalculated as $sim_{ij} = (sim_{ij} + 1)/2$.

This similarity factor yields poor results when features vectors are not normalized, which is due to the mean value and variance of all the features vectors. This kind of normalization is unfeasible when data represents continuous streams. For this reason, we adopted a dynamic adjustment

of the similarity value, using the similarities between statistics for agents' neighbors.

At each step of our simulation, each agent collects information about the minimum value (s_{min}), maximum value (s_{max}) and average value (s_{avg}) of its neighbors' similarities. The adaptive similarity $asim$ is then computed as follows:

$$asim_{ij} = \begin{cases} lerp(sim_{ij}, s_{min}, 0.0, s_{avg}, 0.5) & \text{if } sim_{ij} \le s_{avg} \\ lerp(sim_{ij}, s_{avg}, 0.5, s_{max}, 1.0) & \text{else} \end{cases}$$

where, $lerp(val, x_a, y_a, x_b, y_b)$ represents the linear interpolation of val on the line whose vertexes are (x_a, y_a) and (x_b, y_b). Figure 2 shows the relationship between sim and $asim$.

Cluster Identification.: We implemented a simple local label propagation algorithm for cluster identification. The algorithm consists of two steps:

1) Assign a unique label to each agent.
2) Each agent examines each of its neighbors in turn. If its neighbor's label is smaller than its own label, then it replaces its own label with that of its neighbor. Repeat this step *LPIterations* times.

The value of *LPIterations* can be set at run-time by the user. Figure 3 shows an example of local label propagation.

V. THE APPLICATION

This model requires that in a large environment, neighbors can be identified - neighbors being all other agents that are within the field of view of a particular agent. This is fundamental because each agent must be able to make decisions based on its neighbors, therefore it must be able to pick out these agents efficiently. In order to guarantee interactive performances in clustering and visualization, we use a framework developed in a previous work called BehaveRT [12]. This framework exploits the computational power of modern GPUs and enables the parallel execution of

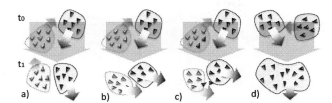

Figure 4: Common experimantal situations were: Collisions between flocks representing well-defined clusters (a). Similar clusters move towards each other (b). Movement of individuals between flocks (c). Flocks mixing (d).

a number of threads equal to the number of simulated agents. In addition, it offers an extensible architecture which enables an efficient implementation of the Reynolds model and of the Cluster-Cohesion and Cluster-Alignment behaviors on the GPU.

The GPU implementation of the proposed model enables the real-time introduction of agents into the 3D environment, using a sort of agent 'fountain' that eliminates the need to restart the algorithm when new data are available (Figure 5b). The objective is to maintain fast and consistently good clustering of the sequences so far observed. When the data stream of agents enters the environment, it naturally and immediately seeks similar clusters. This feature is implemented by preallocating buffer space in the GPU's memory and using these buffers whenever new data is available.

In the simulation, agents belonging to the same cluster may move together and form flocks. These flocks explore the 3D environment, looking for similar groups to join up with. When flocks (representing well-defined clusters) collide, they bounce off each other and follow different paths (Figure 4a). Flocks representing similar clusters move closer together but do not mix (Figure 4b). Some agents act as cluster bridges, moving between two flocks. These agents change flock membership, depending on whether the cluster of one flock matches its own features vector better than the cluster of its current flock (Figure 4c). Flocks representing the same cluster (according to the similarity function metric) merge into a bigger flock (Figure 4d). Our experiments showed that 2000 iterations were sufficient to reach a stable state, even for flocks consisting of thousands of agents.

Several parameters influence the formation of clusters. In addition to the weights of the model illustrated in Section IV, we use $worldRadius$, the size of the world; $searchRadius$, the range in question; $separationRadius$, the distance between agents; and $maxNeighbors$, the maximum number of neighbors an agent can have.

The visual interface (Figure 5a) supports the user in the process of classification and verification of output clusters, using the Visual Information Seeking Mantra "Overview, zoom and filter, details-on-demand" [14], described below:

- *Overview.* During cluster creation, the application sup-

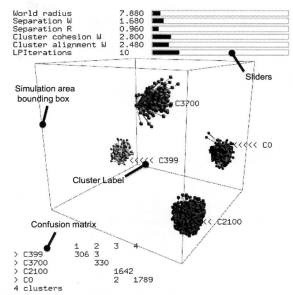

(a) The software Graphical User Interface (GUI)

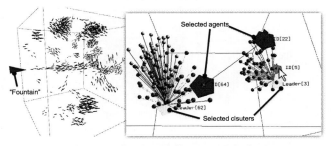

(b) Agents foutain and Cluster merge action

Figure 5: (a) Each agent is connected to the agent with the lowest label value (leader) amongst the agents that belong to the same cluster. (b) On the left, agents introduced on the fly in any place in a 3D environment. On the right, a screenshot of the merge action. Selected agents and cluster leaders are highlighted. Selected agents are connected with a line.

ports the visualization of the flocking approach. The overview provides the user with a visual summary of clustering results and allows a first evaluation of the number of clusters and relations between clusters. As described in Section IV, each agent is connected to the agent with the lowest unique index in its cluster. The name of the cluster is the label of the lowest unique index in that cluster. While clustering, the user can modify the simulation parameters at run-time, using several sliders. They can also change their point of view in the 3D environment, in order to explore one or more clusters from multiple angles.

- *Zoom and filter.* Because our approach can handle vast volumes of data, the visual interface allows the user

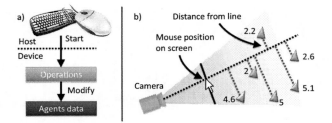

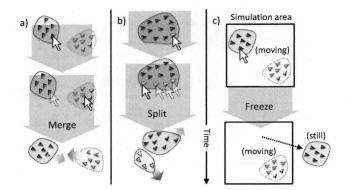

Figure 6: a) Interaction schema: The application forwards input events (generated by the CPU) to the GPU. b) Identification of the nearest agent to the position of the mouse on the screen. The solid line represents the screen. The dotted line indicates the position of the mouse pointer on the screen relative to the camera position. Each agent computes (in parallel) the distance to this line.

Figure 7: User interaction. The position of the mouse represents a mouse click on an agent. Three actions are possible: Merge (causes collision between clusters), Split (separates agents of the same cluster) and Freeze (moves the selected cluster out of the simulation area).

to zoom in from the initial overview, and filter information, refining the current view. If the user identifies clusters of interest in the overview, these clusters can be selected individually or removed from the clustering process.

- *Details-on-demand.* The user can select one or more agents and show their properties (position, class membership, etc.). Each input data is labeled with actual class membership, and the application shows detailed information about clusters, using the confusion matrix. Each row of the matrix represents the instances in a predicted class, while each column represents the instances in an actual class.

A. User Interaction

Our application allows the user to interactively modify the state of agents at run-time. The purpose of user interaction is to allow the user to improve the quality of the clustering result. Integrating user interaction into our application is not trivial as the data representing the state of agents (positions, directions, etc.) is stored in GPU memory, while the operating system generating input events uses the CPU.

With a large number of agents, we cannot transfer agents' data from GPU to CPU memory, because this operation is too expensive. The solution is to handle input events directly on the device (Figure 6a). This introduces some additional issues because computations are distributed across a number of threads equal to the number of simulated agents. Figure 6 illustrates how to calculate the nearest agent to the mouse position on screen.

The system computes the direction of the line l that starts from the camera position and passes through the 2D position of the mouse on the screen (the dotted line in Figure 6b). Each agent i computes in parallel the distance to l, $dist_i(l)$, that is the perpendicular component of l to the vector $\vec{v_i} = (p_{camera}, p_{agent_i})$ where p_{camera} is the 3D position of the camera and p_{agent_i} is the 3D position of the agent i. $dist_i(l)$

is the length of the dotted line joining the agent and the line l in Figure 6.

The index of the agent nearest to the mouse position on the screen is equal to the index j such that $dist_j(l) = min_i(dist_i(l))$. The system computes this minimum index performing a parallel reduction on GPU [15] of all the agents' distances in $O(log(n))$ steps.

The application allows the user to interact with agents in several ways. It is composed of two phases: selection and action. During the selection phase the user selects one or more agents by clicking on them with the mouse. Depending on which mode is currently active, the user can select a single agent or a cluster (e.g. when cluster selection is enabled, the user can select a cluster by picking any of its agents). The second phase allows one of the following three operations:

- The *Merge* action (Figure 7a and Figure 5b) causes a collision between two selected clusters. If these two cluster are similar, they merge as shown in Figure 4d.
- The *Split* action (Figure 7b) separates selected cluster agents from all other agents in the same cluster. The two separated clusters will move in opposite directions, and in order to force them to search for similar groups, they will not merged again for a certain number of iterations.
- The *Freeze* action (Figure 7c) moves the selected cluster out of the bounding box. The agents of a frozen cluster are immobilized and cannot interact with other agents.

VI. EXPERIMENTAL RESULTS

In this section, we show the results of two experiments. The first demonstrates the quality of our approach. The second is related to the efficiency of GPU, versus CPU, implementation. All tests were performed on an AMD Athlon 2800+ CPU, 2GB RAM and a NVIDIA GTX 470

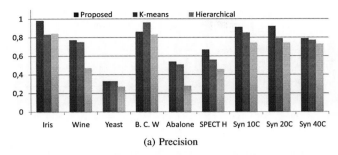

(a) Precision

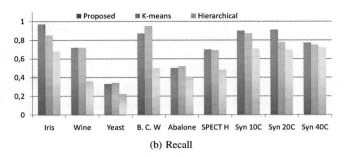

(b) Recall

Figure 8: Quality test results: average values after 500 iterations of (a) precision and (b) recall. The results of the proposed approach are compared with those of k-means and hierarchical clustering.

1280Mb RAM (CUDA compute capability 2.0). Software configuration: CUDA SDK v3.1, Windows 7. Clusters were rendered using OpenGL [16].

Quality.: For the quality tests, we selected six of the most popular datasets from UC Irvine's Machine Learning Repository [17]. The selected datasets are Iris, Wine, Yeast, Breast Cancer Wisconsin, Abalone and SPECT Heart. Below is a brief description of these datasets.

The *Iris* dataset contains information about Iris flowers. There are three classes of Iris flowers - Iris Setosa, Iris Versicolor and Iris Virginica. The Iris dataset consists of 150 examples of Irises that are classified according to 4 attributes. The *Wine* dataset is the result of a chemical analysis of wines grown in a region of Italy but derived from three different cultivars. There are three classes of wines. The dataset consists of 178 examples of wines. The *Yeast* data set contains 1484 records. The data determines the cellular localization sites of proteins. There are ten classes. The *Breast Cancer Wisconsin (B.C.W.)* dataset has 699 records of benign and malignant breast cancer tumors. The goal of this dataset is to explain the difference between the two diagnoses. The *Abalone* (sea snail) dataset has a total of 4177 records. Each record represent an abalone instance. The goal of this dataset is to determine the number of rings using various measurements. The number of rings ranges from 1 to 29. The aim of the Abalone dataset is to divide the number of rings into 3 classes. The *SPECT* Heart dataset has 267 records. In contrast to the other datasets, all of its attributes are binary. The goal of this dataset is to provide a diagnosis using 0 and 1.

In addition, we created three synthetic datasets using the Gaussian cluster generator proposed in [18]. Each contained 4000 records. The first has 10 classes (Synth. 10C), the second has 20 classes (Synth. 20C) and the third 40 classes (Synth. 40C). For each test we split the given dataset into two halves. One was used for training, the other for testing.

The parameters used for quality testing were set to $w_a = 0$, $w_c = 0$, $searchRadius = 4$, $separationRadius = 1.5$, $maxNeighbors = 32$. The training data was used to

Table I: Values of parameters

	Iris	Wine	Yeast	B.C.W.	Abalone	SPECT	Synth.
w_s	2.0	3.0	2.0	1.0	2.0	0.5	0.5
w_{cc}	3.0	4.0	4.8	2.0	4.0	1.0	3.0
w_{ca}	2.0	4.0	3.0	4.0	3.8	6.0	2.5

empirically determine the values of w_s, w_{cc}, and w_{ca} (shown in Table I). The value of $worldRadius$ is caluclated such that agent density in the 3D environment is always 0.05 world units per agent (in order to ensure a good level of interaction among agents).

For each dataset, we evaluated the correctness of classification results using *precision* (P) and *recall* (R). These measures are defined as:

$$P = \frac{tp}{tp + fp} \qquad R = \frac{tp}{tp + fn}$$

where, tp is the number of true positive patterns, fp the number of false positive patterns, and fn the number of false negative patterns.

Figure 8 shows average values of the proposed clustering algorithm after 500 iterations (these are subsequent to the 2000 iterations necessary to bring the simulation to a stable state). We also compared our results to those of k-means clustering [19] and hierarchical clustering (single-linkage) [20]. The k-means clustering algorithm was executed 500 times for each dataset. For all datasets, results were superior to the those achieved using hierarchical clustering. For Iris, Wine, and SPECT Heart, we achieved better results than with k-means. For Yeast and Abalone, the results were similar and, for Breast Cancer Wisconsin, slightly worse. Tests with the synthetic data show that datasets with high numbers of classes are properly classified.

Performance.: For performance tests, we used Gaussian-based synthetic datasets [18] with different number of instances, features and classes. Parameters are set to $w_s = 0.8$, $w_a = 0$, $w_c = 0$, $w_{cc} = 3.0$, $w_{ca} = 2.5$, $searchRadius = 4$, $separationRadius = 1.5$, $maxNeighbors = 32$, and $worldRadius = 0.05$.

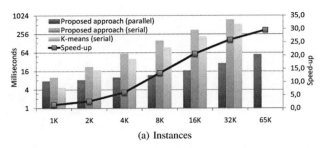

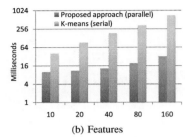

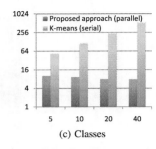

| (a) Instances | (b) Features | (c) Classes |

Figure 9: (a) Speed-up is seen between the CPU implementation (proposed approach - serial) and the GPU implementation (proposed approach - parallel). GPU implementation scales better than CPU implementation. GPU implementation is affected by an overhead that dominates overall performance in tests with a low number of instances (up to 1000). (b) The GPU implementation (proposed approach - parallel) does not scale as well as a classical clustering algorithm. This is due to the parallelization scheme chosen. Scalability improves with #instances, compared to #features. (c) The performance of the GPU implementation does not decrease with a high number of classes.

For the evaluation we developed a serial version of the application for the Opteron 252 2.6Ghz CPU with 2GB RAM and based on the OpenSteer steering library [21]. Performance was measured by comparing the number of milliseconds necessary for GPUs and CPUs to implement each algorithm iteration. We also compared the results of our GPU implementation with those of Matlab's k-means serial implementation, in order to have an idea of the results of a classical clustering approach. We executed the k-means clustering algorithm 500 times with each configuration and took the average elapsed time for a single execution.

Figure 9a compares results for GPU, CPU, and Matlab's k-means implementations, using various numbers of instances. With 1000 instances, CPU implementation is more efficient than GPU implementation (due to the data-reordering overhead, as described in [11]), though the latter scales better than the former. We achieved a 30-fold speed-up with a dataset of 65000 agent instances (or size of dataset). Figure 9a also shows that CPU implementation can run up to 2000 instances at interactive frame rates, while GPU implementation can run up to 32000 instances at interactive frame rates.

Figure 9b compares the results of the k-means implentatation with the results of the proposed GPU implementation. The performance of the proposed approach does not scale quite as well as the k-means. This is due the implementation used which launches a new thread for each of the agent's neighbors. This was done to ensure good performance with a high number of instances and a small number of features (up to 40). In future work, a new version of the kernel will address this problem of poor performance. A good solution would be to launch a new thread for each feature of each agent.

Figure 9c illustrates an interesting point. The computation time of the classical k-means implementation increases in proportion to the number of classes. The computation time of the GPU implementation decreases. This is because a large number of classes leads to high agent fragmentation in the 3D environment (one flock for each class). This in turn decreases the average size of the list of agents' neighbors. Thus, when the number of classes is high, the phase of searching for neighbors is slightly more efficient.

VII. CONCLUSIONS AND FUTURE WORKS

We proposed a biologically-inspired clustering model for large, high-dimensional datasets using GPUs. Each features vector is represented by an agent. The agent follows the rules developed by Reynolds and two new behaviors (Cluster-Cohesion and Cluster-Alignment) while moving in a 3D environment. Following these simple rules, similar agents gradually merge to form a cluster. GPU implementation is the key to obtaining an interactive visualization as it enables incoming data to cluster without the need to take into account all of the data already processed. Our approach is able to detect evolving input data. It can also detect new data, introduced into the 3D environment which must join old clusters or form new clusters.

Another advantage of our approach is that it does not require *a priori* knowledge of the number of clusters, or of the amount of data that will cluster. As the input data stream evolves during computation, the number of natural clusters changes. This enables the user to interactively introduce data streams into a user-defined 3D space. In addition, we implemented a local label propagation approach to automatically identify clusters. The detection and validation of our results was facilitated by the use of a visualization technique that relies on an interactive interface to improve data interpretation. The approach enables the user to perform several operations on clusters (such as merging, splitting and freezing). Experimental results show that our approach can improve the quality and performance of clustering.

ACKNOWLEDGE

We greatly acknowledge NVIDIA for providing us hardware used during the experiments.

REFERENCES

[1] P. K. Robertson, "A methodology for choosing data representations," *IEEE Comput. Graph. Appl.*, vol. 11, pp. 56–67, May 1991.

[2] A. K. Jain, M. N. Murty, and P. J. Flynn, "Data clustering: a review," *ACM Comput. Surv.*, vol. 31, no. 3, pp. 264–323, 1999.

[3] M. Ankerst, M. M. Breunig, H.-P. Kriegel, and J. Sander, "OPTICS - Ordering points to identify the clustering structure," *SIGMOD Rec.*, vol. 28, no. 2, pp. 49–60, 1999.

[4] A. Hinneburg, D. A. Keim, and M. Wawryniuk, "HD-Eye - Visual clustering of high dimensional data: A demonstration," *Data Engineering, International Conference on*, vol. 0, p. 753, 2003.

[5] J. D. Hall and J. C. Hart, "GPU acceleration of iterative clustering," in *ACM Workshop on General Purpose Computing on Graphics Processors*, August 2004.

[6] S. A. Shalom, M. Dash, and M. Tue, "Efficient k-means clustering using accelerated graphics processors," in *DaWaK '08: Proceedings of the 10th international conference on Data Warehousing and Knowledge Discovery*. Berlin, Heidelberg: Springer-Verlag, 2008, pp. 166–175.

[7] M. Zechner and M. Granitzer, "Accelerating k-means on the graphics processor via CUDA," *Intensive Applications and Services, International Conference on*, vol. 0, pp. 7–15, 2009.

[8] R. Farivar, D. Rebolledo, E. Chan, and R. H. Campbell, "A parallel implementation of k-means clustering on GPUs," in *PDPTA*, 2008, pp. 340–345.

[9] Q. Zhang and Y. Zhang, "Hierarchical clustering of gene expression profiles with graphics hardware acceleration," *Pattern Recogn. Lett.*, vol. 27, no. 6, pp. 676–681, 2006.

[10] D.-J. Chang, M. M. Kantardzic, and M. Ouyang, "Hierarchical clustering with CUDA/GPU." in *ISCA PDCCS*, J. H. Graham and A. Skjellum, Eds. ISCA, 2009, pp. 7–12.

[11] U. Erra, B. Frola, V. Scarano, and I. Couzin, "An efficient GPU implementation for large scale individual-based simulation of collective behavior," *High Performance Computational Systems Biology, International Workshop on*, vol. 0, pp. 51–58, 2009.

[12] U. Erra, B. Frola, and V. Scarano, "BehaveRT: A GPU-based library for autonomous characters," in *Motion in Games*, ser. Lecture Notes in Computer Science, R. Boulic, Y. Chrysanthou, and T. Komura, Eds., vol. 6459. Springer Berlin Heidelberg, 2010, pp. 194–205.

[13] C. W. Reynolds, "Flocks, herds and schools: A distributed behavioral model," in *SIGGRAPH '87: Proceedings of the 14th annual conference on Computer graphics and interactive techniques*. New York, NY, USA: ACM, 1987, pp. 25–34.

[14] B. Shneiderman, "The eyes have it: A task by data type taxonomy for information visualizations," in *Proceedings of the 1996 IEEE Symposium on Visual Languages*. Washington, DC, USA: IEEE Computer Society, 1996, pp. 336–.

[15] M. Pharr and R. Fernando, *Gpu gems 2: programming techniques for high-performance graphics and general-purpose computation*. Addison-Wesley Professional, 2005.

[16] OpenGL ARB, D. Shreiner, M. Woo, J. Neider, and T. Davis, *OpenGL(R) Programming Guide : The Official Guide to Learning OpenGL(R), Version 2 (5th Edition)*. Addison-Wesley Professional, August 2005.

[17] http://archive.ics.uci.edu/ml/datasets.html.

[18] http://dbkgroup.org/handl/generators/.

[19] J. B. MacQueen, "Some methods for classification and analysis of multivariate observations," in *Proc. of the fifth Berkeley Symposium on Mathematical Statistics and Probability*, L. M. L. Cam and J. Neyman, Eds., vol. 1. University of California Press, 1967, pp. 281–297.

[20] T. Hastie, R. Tibshirani, and J. Friedman, *The Elements of Statistical Learning*, ser. Springer Series in Statistics. New York, NY, USA: Springer New York Inc., 2001.

[21] C. W. Reynolds, "OpenSteer - steering behaviors for autonomous characters," 2004, http://opensteer.sourceforge.net/.

Visual Stimulation and Electroencephalogram under Scotopic Vision

Wuon-Shik Kim, Hye-Rim Oh, Hyoung-Min Choi, Ji-Soo Hwang, Seong Nam Park,
Hyun Kyoon Lim

Korea Research Institute of Standards and Science

209 Gajeong-ro, Yuseong-gu, Daejeon, Korea 305-340

wskim@kriss.re.kr, zcreame@naver.com, hmchoi78@gmail.com, jhwang@kriss.re.kr, snpark@kriss.re.kr, hlim@kriss.re.kr

Abstract— We tested the visual sensitivity of 15 healthy subjects under scotopic vision using flickering stimulus on the Liquid crystal display (LCD) with a light-emitting diode (LED) backlight (LED-LCD) panel. This test was made to know; 1) if LED-LCD panel might be used for the visual stimulation under scotopic vision, and 2) the minimum trials for ensemble average to get visually evoked potential (VEP). Green, Blue, and Red colors were tested in the darkroom. Electroencephalogram electrodes were used. The brightness of each color was degraded into 255 steps. All participants were asked to watch a circle with red, green, and blue color on the LED-LCD panel. As a result, VEP showed a well-known response pattern when the signals were ensemble averaged for 50 trials. The peak of VEP was not much changed after 25 trials. LED-LCD panel was simple and useful for the simple visual stimulation to test VEP.

Keywords-component; formatting; Scotopic vision, Light emission display, Visually evoked potential (VEP), Optimization

I. INTRODUCTION

At different light levels, the mechanisms of human vision are different. Under the typical during the day (photopic vision) cone cells in the eye are used to process light. Rod cells are used to see objects under very low light levels (scotopic vision) [1]. A combination between photopic vision and scotopic vision is known for mesopic vision which is not quite bright but not quite dark. In human eyes, luminance level of photopic, mesopic, and scotopic vision range from 1 to 10^6 cd/m², 10^{-2} to 1 cd/m², and 10^{-2} to 10^{-6} cd/m² each.

In 1924, CIE (International Commission on Illumination) defined the photopic spectral sensitivity function V (λ) of a human being. In 1951, CIE defined the scotopic efficiency function V'(λ) [2]. However, till now, no mesopic luminous efficiency function is defined officially [3-4]. In addition, functions defined before for photopic and scotopic vision were not objective but subjective.

In this study, we used electroencephalogram (EEG) to get objective data from the brain response to flickering visual stimulation. Before applying the idea using LED-LCD panel to mesopic vision, we tested this system for scotopic vision as a pilot study. Especially, EEG recording using simple test equipment such as a LED-LCD panel and computer program was very handy for the quantitative analysis for the

efficiency function. In this paper, we will show the pilot study results.

II. METHODS

All experiments were made at Korea Research Institute of Standards and Science with the help of participants who voluntarily contributed their time and effort to the study. Ease of Use

A. Participants

EEG was recorded from 15 healthy subjects (aged from 21 to 54: male = 8, female =7) who have no visual and mental problem on their clinical history. No one was color blind or night blind. All participants were asked not to drink and to sleep enough before the test. Five minutes were given before the main test in the dark room to make them adjust to the room after attaching EEG electrodes. The intra-individual difference and inter-individual difference were checked for visually evoked potential (VEP) patterns for the same color and different colors.

B. Electroencephalogram record

EEG electrodes were attached according to 10/20 international electrode system: Oz for active signal, A1 and A2 for reference, Fz for ground, and Fp1 and Fp2 for eye blink. The maximum impedance between electrodes was maintained less than 5 kΩ. Sampling rate was 512 samples per second.

C. Visual stimulation system

Visual stimulation system consisted of two parts: LED-LCD panel and a computer program for providing flickers to participants. The resolution of the LED-LCD panel (376 x 301 mm, 19″) was 1280 x 1024 pixels with 2 ms response time. The radiance and luminance ranged from 3×10^{-4} to 8×10^{-2} [W·sr⁻¹·m⁻²] and from 0.08 to 43.4 [cd·m⁻²] respectively. A computer program was made and used for flickering stimulation purpose. Each red, green, and blue color of the target was chosen selectively. The brightness of each color was degraded into 255 steps and the computer program displayed it on the LED-LCD monitor for each step. We found the optimized flickering time interval was 1 s for onset and 3 s for offset. Participants were asked to watch the LED-LCD monitor until a circle is appearing and to rest for three seconds for offset period. Two or three preliminary tests were made until a participant is getting used to the system before the main tests (Fig. 1).

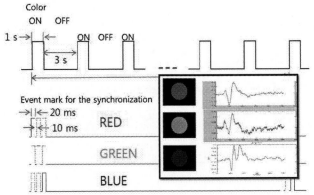

Figure 1. Color stimulation and the corresponding VEPs

III. RESULTS

A. Visually evoked potential (VEP)

VEP showed clearly a well-known response pattern when the signals were integrated for 50 trials (Fig. 2). Ensemble average showed the typical VEP patterns after 25 trials or more.

The intra-individual difference and inter-individual difference of VEP patterns for the same color and different colors were not always consistent. For an example, a participant showed that the peaks for red color and green were decreased when two records were compared few day time gap, but increased N1 and P1 for blue color (Table 1). In some cases, we could not get any consistent results from the same participants.

B. VEP difference between colors

There were no significant or distinguished pattern differences among colors for intra-individuals. However, the peak latency varies severely even for the same color and for the same observer. The VEP pattern varies severely among inter observer in the same color as well as in the different colors. VEP varied approximately from -10 μV to + 15 μV.

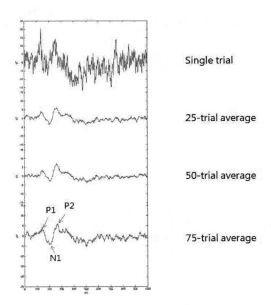

Figure 2 Visually evoked potential (VEP): single trial (top) and ensemble averaged signals (25, 50, and 75 trials). The vertical axis is for amplitude of VEP (μV) and horizontal axis is the latency of positive or negative peaks of VEP (ms)

TABLE I.   TEST-RETEST RESULTS FOR A PARTICIPANT

Color	Day	P1	N1	P2
RED	Day 1	117	164	223
	Day 2	111	162	221
Green	Day 1	117	160	207
	Day 2	86	129	176
Blue	Day 1	107	162	209
	Day 2	111	164	203

Please see the figure 2 for P1, N1, and P2.

IV. DISCUSSION

In this study, 15 participants were enrolled for the visually evoked potential using EEG system and LED-LCD monitor with a computer program.

Based on the traditional method of measuring light, to measure the photopic (or scotopic) luminous efficiency function of the human vision, a participant was supposed to using a button to press or made a sign to indicate the moment they recognized the color. We may collect objective data if we could consistent VEP results from the test.

For the moment, few participants showed consistent results and many of them did not show consistent results by stimulating colors on LED-LCD panel. Yet, the reason could not be explained from this pilot study. In addition, the patterns of VEP for the same color between trials within a participant were not showing any significant different patterns either. The variation may be caused by different viewing angle or ages.

The prediction of visual performance of a human is getting important matters to industries. To make a standardized testing protocol for the objective evaluation of the visual ability and sensitivity, further study should be made.

V. CONCLUSIONS

We recorded visually evoked potential from 15 participants. Ensemble average more than 25 trials may show typical VEP patterns. LED-LCD monitor may be used as a preliminary tool to get luminous efficiency function.

ACKNOWLEDGMENT

Authors thank all participants for their time and effort.

REFERENCES

[1] Y. Fu, Phototransduction in Rods and Cones. University of Utah Health Sciences Center, 1995.

[2] Wikipedia 2011 url: http://en wikipedia org/wiki/ CIE_1931_color_space

[3] H. C. Walkey, J. A. Harlow and J. L. Barbur, Changes in reaction time and search time with background luminance in the mesopic range. *Ophthalmic Physiol Opt* 26, 288-299, 2006.

[4] A. Stockman and L. T. Sharpe, Into the twilight zone: the complexities of mesopic vision and luminous efficiency. *Ophthalmic Physiol Opt* 26, 225-239 2006.

Art, Interaction and Engagement

Ernest Edmonds

Creativity and Cognition Studios, School of Software, FEIT, University of Technology, Sydney
{ernest@ernestedmonds.com}

Abstract

This paper reviews the development of frameworks for thinking and talking about interactive art in the context of my personal practice over the last forty years. It traces a number of paths taken, from an early simple direct notion of interaction through to communication between people through art systems and, more recently, interactive art for long-term engagement. The frameworks consist of an evolving set of concepts, over several dimensions, which are developing together with the practice of interactive art..

1. Introduction

A significant part of art making, for me, is the development of an understanding of the forms and material being used, what Cezanne called "a language and a logic" [7:17]. The language that the artist evolves is a language of form, of-course: shapes, colours, textures and so on. However, it is sometimes helpful to have a language of words to help one think about and discuss the art. For example, although the key issues about an understanding of colour are embodied in artworks exploring colour, it is also good to be able to name hue, saturation and intensity etc. This helps in the thinking about colour that provides the context for using it.

The practice discussed in this paper is concerned with developing and exploring interaction in the context of art. It is concerned with the form, language and logic, of interaction. The frameworks discussed are sets of words that help in the development of interactive art in the same way that words such as hue and saturation help with the painting of colour. So the frameworks help to frame the thinking and hence the practice of interactive art. It is not surprising, therefore, that they are always evolving.

2. Interaction and the computer

In the 1960s, although my art was primarily painting, I took an interest in 'happenings', in which direct and physical audience participation became, at times, an integral part of the artwork, such as in Allan Kaprow's Eat which, for example, included, amongst its props, fruit that the audience was invited to eat [14]. Artists devised situations in which the audience was meant to engage by actually taking part and so explicitly

shape or create the artwork. It seemed to me that involving audiences explicitly in the creative process of art making was 'in the air' at the time. Even in the case of the novel, B.S. Johnson published 'The Unfortunates", which consisted of 27 sections which, with the exception of the first and last, could be read in any order that the reader desired [13]. The visual artist Roy Ascott was working on a range of artworks that could be modified or re-arranged by the audience. He saw a potential for computers to enable the development of interaction in a number of ways, including what he termed 'telematic art' [1].

Thinking about audience engagement and interaction in the arts led to me also thinking about those ideas more generally. Cybernetics, and the closely related study of Systems Theory, seemed to me to provide a rich set of concepts that helped us to think about change, interaction and living systems [2,18]. Whilst my art has not been built directly on these scientific disciplines, many of the basic concepts, such as interactive systems and feedback, have influenced the development of the frameworks discussed below.

I first became interested in exploring interaction within my art practice in the late 1960s and, meeting with Stroud Cornock, I worked with him on an interactive artwork called *Datapack, which was shown in the CG70 exhibition at Brunel University in 1970. This was a very early computer-based interactive artwork. At the same time, we realised that we needed a conceptual framework for talking and thinking about such artworks. We presented a classification of interactive art systems, which we called "the matrix", at the CG70 conference [6]. We identified four situations, which we termed 'Static', 'Dynamic-Passive', 'Dynamic-Interactive' and 'Dynamic-Interactive (Varying)'. Briefly, 'Static' applied to works that do not change, 'Dynamic-Passive' to works that changed but were not influenced by the audience, 'Dynamic-Interactive' to works that changed as a result of audience actions and "Dynamic-Interactive (Varying)' applied to interactive works that were also influenced by other factors, so that their response varied. This was the initial framework that I worked with. As we will see, it did not cover all the cases that have turned out to be interesting in my practice, but it did provide a fairly robust starting point.

A useful explanation of the first Cornock and Edmonds framework was described as follows:-

1550-6037/11 $26.00 © 2011 IEEE
DOI 10.1109/IV.2011.73

"Static: The art object does not change and is viewed by a person. There is no interaction between the two that can be observed by someone else, although the viewer may be experiencing personal psychological or emotional reactions. The artwork itself does not respond to its context. This is familiar ground in art galleries and museums where art consumers look at a painting or print, listen to tape recordings and talk to one another about the art on the walls and, generally speaking, obey the command not to touch.

Dynamic-Passive: The art object has an internal mechanism that enables it to change or it may be modified by an environmental factor such as temperature, sound or light. The artist specifies the internal mechanism and any changes that take place are entirely predictable. Sculptures, such as George Rickey's kinetic pieces, that move according to internal mechanisms, and also, in response to atmospheric changes in the environment, fall into this category. The viewer is an observer of this activity performed by the artwork in response to the physical environment.

Dynamic-Interactive: All of the conditions of the dynamic passive category apply with the added factor that the human 'viewer' has an active role in influencing the changes in the art object. For example, by walking over a mat that contains sensors attached to lights operating in variable sequences, the viewer becomes a participant that influences the process of the work. Motion and sound capture techniques can be used to incorporate human activity into the way visual images and sounds are presented. The work 'performs' differently according to what the person does or says. There may be more than one participant and more than one art object. An example of this work is the Iamascope, a work which includes a camera looking at the viewers and is connected to a controlling computer. The work reacts to human movement in front of it by changing a kaleidoscope-like image and making music at the same time in direct response to the viewer's movements.

Dynamic-Interactive (Varying): The conditions for Dynamic-Interactive apply, with the addition of a modifying agent that changes the original specification of the art object. The agent could be a human or it could be a software program. Because of this, the process that takes place, or rather, the performance of the art system cannot be predictable. It will depend on the history of interactions with the work. In this case, either the artist from time to time updates the specification of the art object or a software agent that is learning from the experiences of interaction automatically modifies the specification. In this case, the performance of the art object varies, in addition to case 3, according to the history of its experiences." [5].

#Datapack was of the third kind, Dynamic-Interactive. By modern standards it was technologically very clumsy (this was a decade before the advent of the PC). However, it demonstrated the point. The participant sat at a 'tele-type' (keyboard and printer combined) and entered into a 'conversation' with the computer. This conversation was rather like the famous Eliza software [17] that spotted keywords and used various tricks to respond in ways that could be seen to be plausibly 'intelligent'. For example, when someone typed in "I feel sad", Eliza might respond with "Why do you feel sad?" As in our case, Eliza had no smart intelligent system that understood the user's remarks but rather presented a simulation of conversation that sounded (mostly) plausible.

As a result of the conversation, the computer software made certain decisions that determined what graphical output would result. This was in the form of a drawing executed on a plotter. The drawing identified a notional space around the Vickers Building next to the Tate Gallery (now the Tate Britain) in London. A package, including the drawing and a printed copy of the conversation (as produced by the teletype), was then handed to the participant as their artefact to take away. The key issue at this time was to find a way to explore interaction at all. The technical limitations made it difficult to match the theoretical goals, but *Datapack certainly was interactive and informal discussions with participants at the exhibition indicated that it was also engaging.

3. Interaction: from simple to complex

Working with the relative complexities of #Datapack, I wondered if it would be possible to make a very simple work that encompassed the same principles. I came up with JigSaw, which was just sixteen wooden pieces that could be fitted together, rather in the manner of a jigsaw puzzle. The key point was that they were so designed that there were hundreds of different ways of putting them together but each way was highly constrained. The participant could interact with the work by arranging or re-arranging it, but its internal logic constrained the result.

Having worked on an interactive and a re-arrangeable artwork, I started to explore the nature of interaction itself. I began to ask myself questions like: What was going on when a human interacted with the world around them? What motivated or limited those interactions? This led me to read about various psychological studies of human interaction with the world and with other humans. Current scientific studies of very young infants provided the clue that led to my next development. It seemed that right from birth a child interacts with its environment in a purposeful way: not just to obtain food and so on, but also to try to construct understandings about that world. "If I do this and that, will the world do some particular other thing?" This very early and basic form of interaction is conducted without a shared language, just by prodding the world and looking at what happens: trying to find patterns [4].

As a result of my reading about early infant behaviour I started to think about ways in which I might deal with such issues in an artwork. I did not want to build an imitation of an infant, but I tried to think of what might be essential elements of their situation in relation to interaction. As a result I started building what I came to call my Communication Game series of works . These interactive works were concerned with humans interacting with humans through technology (rather than humans interacting with technology). In part, they represented a realisation of Ascott's telematic art in that they transformed the viewer into an active participant in creating the artwork [8]. The key points about the work's intentions were to restrict communication between participant to a very low bandwidth, to provide no instructions or code and to add a certain amount of complexity. The complexity was injected by having what a participant saw controlled by two other participants, only one of whom saw the results of that participant's actions. We could say that the data that a participant was working with was incomplete or noisy, as tends to be the case in all real life situations.

After a few iterations of the Communication Games work, including the use of sound, I left it alone until about 2006, when I re-started the development of that series in the form of the Cities Tango works, of which more later on.

In my own art practice, I left interaction alone for some years. I was still interested, but I was not content with any of the technological methods that I found. However, I worked with PhD students and other artists on a number of approaches to making interactive art. Steve Bell, for example, looked in detail and different strategies. He concentrated himself on work that used a 'life' model of growth and restricted the participant's actions to very specific roles, such as seeding the growth of a dynamic work [2]. This work was time-based and certainly involved interaction, but the interaction was essentially quite simple. The complexity was more in the growth of the image over time. Mike Quantrill is a different case. He explored interactive drawing using an electronic whiteboard and made experimental works in which participant movement (detected by floor pads) determined the nature and dynamics of a visual display. The audience could almost play the work as if it was an audio-visual instrument (Edmonds and Quantrill, 1998). So in Quantrill's case, the interaction was continuous and fluid. Growth is the central interest in Bell's work and interaction is the central interest in Quantrill's.

There are a number of strands to my work and I have not only explored interaction. My central concern is with the implication of the notion of computation in art, of which interaction is certainly a significant example. At the time when I was not directly working with interaction (1980s and 1990s), I was largely concentrating on another implication of computation. That was generative time-based work, in which a set of rules that I designed led to the unfolding of an abstract work over a period of time, sometimes extending to hours or days [9]. The work was determined by the rules and not influenced by the audience. The generative works had come about through the realisation that as a computer program worked through the sets of rules that were intended to define the art system, it could display its progress. Hence the generative search could become the core of time-

based art rather than a route to a final object. The key issue here, for me, was finding ways of thinking about the rules and this time-based process. The only way that I found to do this was to build a platform, an art making software environment, that I could use to both experiment with rules and learn about their implications.

By 2001, however, I had seen how to incorporate interaction into my time-based generative works. The addition of interaction to the generative works represented a particular example of the category discussed above, Dynamic-Interactive (Varying). In this case, the variation came from the internal generative system. The interaction came from the analysis of images of the audience captured by a camera. The camera used was typically a small webcam.

The generative process in these works is dynamic in itself but what I added was an input to the art system that could cause a change in that dynamic process. The mechanism was to have the process consult data from the camera as part of the determination of the next action. Thus, activities external to the artwork itself, such as audience behaviour, altered the generative process. I used image processing, taking data from a video camera pointing at the audience and analysing movement or sound analysis of voice. To begin with, I made works in which the alteration was direct and immediately visible: audience actions caused visible responses.

4. Interaction: from reaction to influence

Most artists would probably say that they aimed for their work to encourage long-term engagement with their audience. Much interactive art, however, seems to emphasise attraction and immediate engagement. Why is this? There are two possible reasons for the focus on the immediate. One is the seductive appeal of direct interaction that has been so powerfully exploited in computer games. There is no doubt that the model of the game is interesting. However, it also represents a challenge to the artist taking the long-term view. How is the interactive artwork going to retain its interest once the initial pleasure has worn off? An answer may be implied in the second reason for the emphasis on the immediate, which seems to me to be an over reliance on an action-response model of interaction.

The psychological underpinning of interaction as it is employed in HCI as well as in art is the study of action and response. Each action leads to a response that, in turn, encourages or enables another action. This view of interaction is seen today by science as oversimplified. It does not take long-term influence properly into account and that point is clearly relevant to a concern for long-term engagement. Put simply, the key issue is that a system as complex as a human (or animal etc) must have internal states that represent memory, mood, state of development etc. An interaction, be it with another human, an artwork or a game, can influence internal states. This can happen whether or not any immediate action is made. Engagement over long periods of time almost certainly involves changes in these internal states and so an interactive artwork that is successful in these terms must take these things into account.

From my perspective, the psychological models most interesting for interactive art are not action response ones, but Systems Theory ones. In Systems Theory, the interchanges between interlinked entities are studied in a much broader context than in the action response case. For interactive art, this perspective introduces the possibility of considering interactions that have effects in the future and that may even have no observable response at the time. A simple example would be where an artwork has a memory of audience actions that is only used to affect the artwork's behaviour days or weeks later. I have suggested elsewhere that influence might be a better term than interaction to describe such cases [10].

4. Long term engagement

I started to explore the idea of moving from interaction to influence in 2003 and we might term it Dynamic-Interactive (Influencing). This idea matured in a series of artworks begun in 2007, called Shaping Form, in which images are generated using rules that determine the colours, the patterns and the timing. These are generative works that are changed by the influence of the environment around them. Movement in front of each work is detected by image analysis and leads to continual changes in the program that generates the images. People can readily detect the immediate responses of the work to movement but the changes over time are only apparent when there is more prolonged, although not necessarily continuous, contact with it. A first viewing followed by one several months later will reveal noticeable developments in the colours and patterns. The Shaping Form series are the latest works arising from my preoccupation with interaction and time expressed in a wide range of abstract generative forms over many years.

Digital artworks like Shaping Form are designed to interact with the environment in which they are found. Exactly how they behave depends on what kind of compositional elements or principles are being worked with at the time. I work with structural relationships between visual elements, the colours and shapes that determine how the images are constructed. Some works are made to learn from external movement such as a hand waving or a person walking by. The way the art systems accumulate information from these inputs, or 'learns', determines how they select future choices of colour and pattern in the images displayed. The behaviour of the works is not intended to always be obvious, so that if you continuously try to force a response by waving it might result in a period of quiet. Shaping Form has a generative element, a computer program, which produces a continuous stream of images using predefined rules that control the rectangular pattern, the pallet of colours and the timing. The program continuously analyses movements detected in front of the work. As a result of this analysis, the rules are steadily modified in a way that accumulates a history of experiences over the life of the work. The shaping of the form is a never-ending process of development.

5. Distributed interaction

My earlier concern for communication through digital systems, exemplified in the Communication Game works, continued and was revived firstly by making a version of Shaping Form that worked on the World Wide Web. This changed the structure to include a shared memory and the possibility of many remote users and so united the core ideas of Shaping Form with Communication Game. The main step, however, came about between 2008 and 2009 with the development of the Cities Tango series [11]. I call this type of interactive art 'Dynamic-Interactive (Communicating)'. This category more-or-less corresponds to Ascott's early concept of Telematic Art, which advocates the use of computer-mediated networks as an art medium.

In Cities Tango, two or more 'nodes', consisting of Shaping Form like works with camera input, are connected over the Internet. The first major example had one node in Sydney and a second in Belfast. In addition to the typical colour bands that I use, I added two other elements. First, I used photographs of a single location at each site at different time of the day as abstract elements that substituted for certain colours and gave a sense of the remote site. Second, occasional live stills were transmitted from one site to another, typically at a time of significant audience activity. In this way, we have the idea of distributed interactive art systems that can involve instant response and/or communication as well as long term influence in the Shaping Form sense.

6. Interaction engagement and experience

The physical way in which the audience interacts with a work is a major part of any interactive art system. Three main approaches are used. The first is as in #Datapack, where members of the audience physically manipulate the work in some way (typing at the teletype in #Datapack). The second approach is where members of the audience are provided with special devices of some kind, such as headsets as in Char Davies' works using virtual reality [16] or Cardiomorphologies [15]. The third approach is ambient, such as many of the examples described in this book, where audience movements, or states, are detected by non-invasive devices, such as cameras, floor pads or infrared beams.

We can term these approaches:
• Direct
• Facilitated
• Ambient

In making Dynamic-Interactive works, issues about the audience reaction to them are significant and have gained increasing attention, in particular, by many of the contributors to this book. One specific area of interest is engagement. Do people become engaged with the artwork? Is that engagement sustained? What are the factors that influence the nature of the engagement? Does engagement relate to pleasure, frustration, challenge or anger, for example? Of-course, the artist can use themselves as typical of the audience and rely on their own reactions to guide their work. Much art is made like that, although asking the opinion of expert peers, at least, is also normal. However, understanding audience engagement with interactive works is quite a challenge and needs more extensive investigation than introspection.

There are many forms of engagement that may or may not be desired in relation to an artwork. For example, in museum studies, people talk about 'attractors', that is, attributes of an exhibit that encourage the public to pay attention and so become engaged. The immediate question arises of how long such engagement might last and we find that the attributes that encourage sustained engagement are not the same as those that attract. Another form of engagement is one that extends over long periods of time, where one goes back for repeated experiences such as seeing a favourite play in many performances throughout ones life. We often find that this long-term form of engagement is not associated with a strong initial attraction. Engagement can grow with experience. These issues are ones that the interactive artist needs to be clear about and the choices have significant influence on the nature of the interaction employed.

The discussion of engagement needs to be significantly extended in order to cover the complexities of Dynamic-Interactive (Communicating) art systems. This is an area that remains in need of exploration and research. However, there is another aspect that interactive art research has brought very much top our attention. This is the nature of the experience that audiences have during their engagement with an interactive art system.

In my own practice, I have considered just three kinds of engagement. Let's call them
- Attracting
- Sustaining
- Relating

'Attracting' is a matter of drawing attention, so that a sudden noise (or a sudden silence) will attract attention. 'Sustaining' is the process of retaining that attention for a period of time. 'Relating' is developing a long term interest, which occurs when the audience wants to experience the work again and again, perhaps over many years. Attracting and relating do not always go together. Sometimes, what is most immediately engaging is also easily discarded. My Shaping Form works, for example, clearly aim at a 'Relating' type of engagement. The challenge is to provide just enough attracting and sustaining engagement to draw the audience in, but not so much as to induce boredom.

7. Categories of Interaction Re-visited

I have discussed three kinds of classification in relation to interactive art. The first was the one that dealt with what kind of art 'systems' are at play, based initially on the Cornock and Edmonds set. The second was of the different kinds of way that the physical exchange takes place. The third was the set of different kind of experience that the interaction encourages in the audience.

The 'systems' categories that have been discussed above extend the early Cornock and Edmonds terminology. To make the naming more consistent, we can replace 'Dynamic-Interactive' by 'Dynamic-Interactive (Responding)'. This implies that the system responds directly to audience action, at the time of that action, and so is directly reactive.

Thus we now have:
    Static
    Dynamic-Passive
    Dynamic-Interactive:
    Responding
        Varying
        Influencing
        Communicating

The central interest in relation to interactive art in this paper, and in the book, is in the dynamic-interactive cases, so we might simplify our categories by saying that we have four kinds of interactive art systems:

- Responding
- Varying
- Influencing
- Communicating

Naturally, art systems may fall into more than one of these categories. For example, the Shaping Form works are both 'Varying' and 'Influencing'. The Communication Games are both 'Responding' and 'Communicating'. All four categories apply to Cities Tango.

As discussed above, the physical interactions might be any of:
- Direct
- Facilitated
- Ambient

Each kind of system might be implemented with various physical interfaces. However, we can see that the 'Influencing' case, for example, may not be easily realised by the 'Facilitated' method, for the simple reason that it may not be practical to facilitate over long periods of time.

In relation to experience, I have discussed
- Attracting
- Sustaining
- Relating

Thus we have three dimensions in which to consider interactive art systems.

7. Conclusion

As interactive art developed since the various innovations of 1960s, I have become more concerned with the nature of interaction itself. There are many aspects to this issue, which I have explored above. As the developments in my art practice have unfolded a concern for the active audience's perspective on the work has grown. This is where my discussion of the issues of interaction, engagement and experience is important.

Interactive art systems involve artefacts and audiences equally. The artist sets up situations that develop in ways that are, at least in part, determined by the audience. The cybernetic and systems principles that informed the early developments are now applied more completely than at first, by the equal and reflexive consideration of art object and active audience experience. As a result, the frameworks that inform our thinking and practice have had to evolve appropriately. There is no question that they will evolve still further as new opportunities, new understandings and new practices emerge.

References

[1]   Ascott, R. "Behaviourist art and the cybernetic vision". *Cybernetica,* Vol. 9, 1966. pp. 247-264.

[2]   Bell, S. PhD Thesis: *Participatory Art and Computers.* Loughborough University, UK. Available at http://nccastaff.bournemouth.ac.uk/sbell/. 1991.

[3]   von Betralanffy, L. "An outline of General Systems Theory" *Brit. J. Philos. Sci.* Vol 1, 1955. pp. 139-164.

[4]   Bower, T. G. R. *Development in Infancy.* Freeman and Company, San Francisco, CA. 1974.

[5]   Candy, L. and Edmonds, E.A.. "Interaction in Art and Technology". *Crossings: Electronic Journal of Art and Technology* - http://crossings.tcd.ie/issues/2.1/Candy/ Vol. 2 (1). 2002.

[6]   Cornock, S. and Edmonds, E. A. "The creative process where the artist is amplified or superseded by the computer" *Proceedings of the Computer Graphics '70 Conference,* Brunel University, UK 1970, and later published in a revised form in *Leonardo,* Vol.16, (1973), pp. 11-16.

[7]   Doran, M. (ed) *Conversations with Cezanne*, University of California Press. 2001.

[8]   Edmonds, E. A. "Art systems for interactions between members of a small group of people". *Leonardo,* Vol. 8, 1975. pp. 225-227.

[9]   Edmonds, E. A. "Logics For Constructing Generative Art Systems". *Digital Creativity*, Vol. 14 (1). 2003. pp 23-38.

[10]   Edmonds, E. A. "Reflections on the nature of interaction". *CoDesign: International Journal of Co-Creation in Design and the Arts*. Vol. 3 (3), 2007. pp 139-143.

[11]   Edmonds, E. A. "Cities Tango: between Belfast and Sydney, 2009" (installation). In Mey, K. E. A. (Ed.) *ISEA: Interface,* University of Ulster. Belfast, Ireland, 2009.

[12]   Edmonds, E. A. and Quantrill, M. "An Approach to Creativity as Process*", Proceedings of CAiiA Conference "Reframing Consciousness",* Ascott (editor), Intellect Books, 1998. pp. 257-261.

[13]   Johnson, B. S. *The Unfortunates.* Panther Books, London. 1969.

[14]   Kirby, M. "Allan Kaprow's Eat" *Tulane Drama Review* Vol 10 (2), 1965. pp. 44-49.

[15]   Khut, G. & Muller, L. "Evolving Creative Practice: A reflection on working with audience experience in Cardiomorphologies". In Anastasiuo, P., Smithies, R., Trist, K. & Jones, L. (Eds.) *Vital Signs: Creative Practice & New Media Now.* RMIT Publishing, Melbourne, Australia. 2005.

[16]   McRobert , L. *Char Davies's Immersive Virtual Art and the Essence of Spatiality.* Univ of Toronto Press. 2007.

[17]   Weizenbaum, J. "ELIZA — A Computer Program For the Study of Natural Language Communication Between Man And Machine", *Communications of the ACM* Vol. 9 (1) 1966. pp. 36–4

[18]   Wiener, N. *Cybernetics.* MIT Press, Cambridge Mass. 1965.

Brief History of Computer Art and New Media Art in Latvia

Solvita Zariņa
Institute of Mathematics and Computer Science
University of Latvia
Riga, Latvia
solvita.zarina@lumii.lv

Abstract—The Soviet and particularly Latvian computer art is not a well-known topic of digital art history. This paper attempts to analyze this computer art in context of the 20th century art, considering the political circumstances in Soviet Union. At the turn of the 21st century after gaining the independence new media art examples and collaboration between scientists, computer scientists, software programmers and the artists are to be found in Latvia. Some recent media art events are mentioned from this viewpoint.

Keywords-computer graphics; computer art; digital art; ASCII art; new media art

I. INTRODUCTION

Latvia, a small state of the Baltic region, was incorporated into the Soviet Union after the Second World War. The whole art process during the period 1945 – 1991 to a certain degree was affected by this political fact. Computer art in Latvia developed differently as it happened in the US, Western Europe and Japan.

The emergence of computer graphics and early computer art in Latvia as well as elsewhere completely depended on availability of the computer technique here. Since the moment when the graphical output devices became available (in Latvian case – so called – "the wide print") some people started to use them for experiments in image making. These first computer drawings were as realistic as possible. After regaining of independence in the early 1990s the Soviet-style art became extremely unpopular, but now this period in Latvian art history of in the 20th century is going to be reassured. This early computer art in context of its visual form seems to be original and even weird from the viewpoint of Western digital art history. Some disparities of what is considered to be art in perception of common audience at that time in Soviet Latvia should be mentioned.

Since the mid-1990s the Internet possibilities became available for the artists worldwide. Some informal artist communities (*E-Lab*) and new media festivals (*ART + COMMUNICATION*) emerged. During the next fifteen years new media art gained popularity among the artists and now it is to be considered in the mainstream of Latvia's visual culture.

II. COMPUTER ART DEVELOPMENT FROM THE MID-20TH CENTURY

The first visual examples created by using an analogue computer appear in the mid-1950s in the United States and Germany. Some experiments with oscilloscope images are to be found even before the stage of electronic graphics. The point of interest, taking into account the Soviet art background, is why anybody dares to call these pieces art. We can prove it from the viewpoint of the 20th century Western art history. The art forms, such as cubism, Dada, futurism, naïve art, primitivism, constructivism, suprematism and kinetic art had emerged and were widely considered to be art forms at that time. Abstract expressionism was one of the major stylistic approaches in the US during the 1950s. Therefore, three things characteristic of the first examples of computer art:

- art as a process not only as a result (Dada),
- non-professional artists (naïve and primitive art),
- abstract, non-representative art forms (such as suprematism, constructivism, abstractionism)

have already been accepted by art theoreticians, gallery and museum curators, as well as by general public in the Western world. [1]

The first authors of the computer images are mathematicians, computer scientists and engineers. It seems to be self-understandable considering the availability of at that time extremely expensive computer resources and necessity for high level technical skills. They boldly developed their artistic careers, participated in the exhibitions, and broadened their academic experience by developing courses about computer art and aesthetics. Herbert W. Franke (1927) and 'Three big N' - A. Michael Noll (1939), Frieder Nake (1938) and Georg Nees (1926) can be mentioned as good examples of this highly skilled society of scientists and other well furnished minds.

It has to be remarked that they had their own theoretical viewpoint on the style and aesthetics of the newly created art form. Roger F. Malina (1912 - 1981) even was a creator and the first editor of the journal *Leonardo*. This medium was started as an international peer-reviewed research journal that featured articles written by artists on their creative work, and focused on the display of the interactions between the contemporary arts with the sciences and new

1550-6037/11 $26.00 © 2011 IEEE
DOI 10.1109/IV.2011.25

technologies [2]. *Leonardo* remains a significant medium till nowadays and it is covered by Arts & Humanities Citation Index and Current Contents/Arts & Humanities of Thomson Reuters.

Herbert W. Franke states: "Art can be regarded as a special form of communication. It is the task of the artist to provide a message, which in this particular case is also subject to certain aesthetic considerations, however they may be defined. Formerly, colours, sounds and tones were regarded as the raw material of art; today they would be considered information carriers. The elements of art are data, i.e. immaterial components. Even though this statement may sound rather sober, it does imply that art is not a material but rather an intellectual process" [3].

Almost ten years later the informal communities consisting of professional artists (visual artists, as well as musicians, filmmakers, etc.) of the one part and scientists, engineers of the other part began to spread out in order to combine the creative potential of art with computer technologies. The foundation of non-profit organization *Experiments in Art and Technology (E.A.T.)* in New York and its later activities (1967 - ca. 1989) is a well-known example.

III. BEGINNINGS OF COMPUTER ART IN THE SOVIET UNION

The emergence of computer art was tightly connected with the computer industry development in the Soviet Union. The first Soviet project of an electric programmable computer was started in 1948 by S. A. Lebedev in Kiev. In 1951 both this project and a competing project by I. S. Brook were completed. The famous gap in computation possibilities between the West and the Soviet block then was much smaller than at a later time but graphical output devices appeared later and in essentially lesser quantities. This, of course, influenced the development of computer art in the Soviet Union. Experimentation with computer art at that period was done only in centres were computers were constructed. It was half impossible to buy even the Soviet technique, and the imported machinery was a very rear phenomenon.

Already in 1964 Yu. M. Bayakovsky and T. A. Shuskevich created a visualisation demo of the process of plasma flow around a cylinder. In 1967 the Institute of Applied Mathematics, Academy of Sciences, USSR obtained a foreign made graph plotter *CalCamp*. This started a series of short animation movies. The frame sequence was done by printing out every computer made still, photographing it and then putting together. G. K. Borovin, I. I. Karpov and N. N. Kozlov, et al. participated in this project. In 1968 the animation film "*Koshechka*" (Little Cat) made by a team led by N. N. Konstantinov achieved the popularity.

It was created on the Soviet 2nd generation computer BESM-4. It boasted with the realistic movement performance of a living creature. This was achieved by describing these movements by a system of differential equations.

Figure 1. A still from animation film *Koshechka*.

The papers covering the topics of computer aesthetics and computer music appeared in the Soviet Union, particularly in Soviet Russia starting from the 1970s.

IV. ASCII ART IN SOVIET LATVIA

In the former Soviet Latvia the first generation computer was constructed by a team lead by Jānis Daube in 1962. Some graphics features became available at the end of the 1960s. In 1969 a second generation computer GE-415 was bought from France to set it at the premises of the Computing Centre in Riga. This was the first machine with an output device printing more than twenty symbols in one line. Engineers called it "the wide print".

During the Cold War no connections with the Western modern art were officially allowed. In view of the political situation of that time in Soviet Latvia (especially from the second half of the 1940s till 1970s) the art forms, such as Dada, abstract art (and its variations), and even impressionism, and postimpressionism (in the 1950s), were forbidden and practically unknown to a wider audience including the first authors of the computer drawings - computer scientists and engineers in Soviet Latvia. They hardly had any information about the contemporary art forms of the 20th century. The politically dictated mainstream of art was the *Socialist Realism*. This term was introduced in 1934, and it was the only officially permitted style of Soviet art.

The very first examples of computer drawings can be found in the late 1960s. Undoubtedly, it is owing to the appearance of better output devices and more appropriate printing possibilities for graphics. The political background dictates a completely different approach to the style and aesthetics of this art form. Nobody, including the authors of computer drawings, accepted them as art. These examples are anonymous, and only a very small part of them has survived till nowadays. They are not signed at all due to their completely different status in perception of the society, as well as the authors' own position. The computer scientists and engineers were not tended to position their experiments with data visualization as any form of visual art. None of them in Latvia considered describing any aspect of computer aesthetics.

The most common in Latvia were ASCII art forms. These drawings have always tended to be realistic. Sometimes they have the features characteristic to caricatures or cartoons. The Museum of Computer Technique, IMCS UL in Latvia possesses the examples of the first computer drawings.

Figure 2. Portrait of Computer Scientist Eižens Āriņš; Portrait of Engineer Jānis Daube; Portrait of Chief Accountant Jānis Kaugars.

The realistic series of portraits seems to be the best and more serious part of all drawings. The sitters were close colleagues, hence warm and more personal attitude penetrate these artworks.

Portrait of Lenin is a digitalisation from the communist party leader's portrait in the Kremlin Congress Palace, Moscow (known from photos in newspapers). The authors of this digitalisation have made an attempt to produce an artwork following the Soviet art standards. *Mother and Child* is a similar digitalisation of some Soviet style drawing or painting. It was done in honour to the International Women's day (an official holiday in USSR).

Even prohibited 'underground' things (no wonder, considering the political status of Latvia at that time) like drawings of nudes appeared.

Figure 3. Portrait of Lenin; Mother and Child; Nude.

V.   CONCEPTUAL AND KINETIC ART UNDER THE DESIGN UMBRELLA

Despite the official politics in Soviet Latvia some kinetic and even conceptual, as well as environmental art examples made by professional artists have emerged since 1970. This kind of contemporary art was often presented as design proposals and some of them were realized in cooperation with engineers and programmers. Political criteria in this new zone were not clearly stated, and it allowed making much more independent experiments. Artists used the terms "applied art" and "design" to cover up many contemporary artworks. "An important zone for new pursuits in art during the 1970s in Latvia developed in the border area between fine arts and applied arts – both offered innovative solutions in form and focused on the issues of space and environment... Among them the most avant-garde phenomena were kinetic art (actually the first installations in Latvian art) and visionary environment proposals... works of art created within this zone were accepted by the institutions and enjoyed much more publicity. At the same time the number of artists representing this zone was tiny and the effect caused by them in the complete art picture was perceived rather ambiguously. 'Is that art at all?'- the question was asked many a time." [4]

Most of these artworks appeared only few times in the exhibitions dedicated to design. Some kinetic objects were built and the communication design samples appeared. In 1980 the Riga Central Railway Station renovation project was hold. A multi-program light system sinhronized with a flow of time at the clock tower was realized. In nowadays terms we can call it a synthesis of communication design and conceptual art.

Figure 4.   Artūrs Riņķis. Kinetic Painting. 1978; Riga Central Railway station clock tower with multi-programme synchronous lighting system. 1980.

In 1994 Journal *Leonardo* dedicated the whole issue to the art, science and technology in the former Soviet Union. Two Latvian artists – Valdis Celms and Artūrs Riņķis – artists with a design background published their articles here.

Environmental designer and artist Jānis Borgs even had created an artwork simulating the computer drawing, instead of computer using traditional technique. "I contributed [at the exhibition of work by the teaching staff of the high school of art– S.Z.] with an entirely incongruous work –

three sheets of technical drawings, consisting of arrangements of black lines. This was 'programmed art', where the will of the artist plays no role. It had been created entirely by means of a programme, using the principle of complete randomness to determine the composition of the elements. The works were intended to be created by computer, but in those days there was no technical equipment of this kind available, and so everything had to be done by hand. In other words – it was the imitation of computer art. From the traditional prospective of art it was absolute nonsense. But I'd decided on a shameless display of conceptualism, which was so important to me at the time, and because of which I'd already established extensive international connections with like-minded people. It seems that my traditionalist colleagues, who had no experience in this field, deliberately hung them the wrong way up, or so they thought. The joke flopped, because in this case the arrangement had no significance, and I kept a straight face." [5]

VI. NEW MEDIA ART DEVELOPMENT AT THE TURN OF THE 21ST CENTURY

In 1991, after the collapse of the Soviet Union, the borders were opened and the new media art (now computer art is often considered as a part of it) began to develop in Latvia. It happened at the same time as in the world elsewhere. The development of the World Wide Web was the main precondition. Young Latvian artists (Rasa Šmite, Raitis Šmits, Arvīds Alksnis and others) actively started wide international collaboration. They established *E-Lab* (later renamed as *RIXC*) – an electronic art and media centre in Riga, and created the mailing list '*Xchange*' as an information and communication channel for the net broadcasters.

Annual new media festival in Riga "*Art and Communication*" first organized by RIXC (*Centre for New Media Culture* in Riga) in 1996 has acquired international recognition amidst the world's digital community. Artists prompted to cover such issues as *Transbiotics* (2010), *Energy* (2009), *Spectropia* (2008), *Spectral Ecology* (2007), *Waves* (2006), *Media Architecture* (2003).

Latvian artists Ieva Auziņa and Raitis Šmits initiated an international art project called '*Milk project*'. It won the Prix Ars Electronica '*Golden Nica*' in 2005.

"The *MilkLine* is one of the countless movements of the international food trade, in this case milk, produced by Latvian farmers, made into cheese by a local factory with the help of an Italian expert, transported to the Netherlands, stored in a charming Dutch cheese warehouse to ripen, sold at the Utrecht market and finally eaten by Dutch citizens. This map follows the milk from the udder of the cow to the plate of the consumer, by means of the people involved. All those involved were given a GPS device for a day: one of the days when they were somehow occupied with the movements of this dairy. Special GPS-visualization software developed for Milk project by Marcus The, in collaboration with Esther Polak and Ieva Auziņa. The aim of the visualization was to share GPS-information by showing as clearly as possible how, when and at what speed the movements through the landscape had taken place. In the privacy of their own homes, we showed the paths to each of the participants, and are happy to be able to share them with you. Finally, we would now like to invite you to enter the website, to meet all the nice people who drew the line on the Map." [6]

Professional artists were initiators of collaboration with scientists and the IT industry. Some Latvian contemporary artists have successful cooperation with our computer scientists and physicists in developing their art projects. In 2007 new media artist Gints Gabrāns (1970) created project "Paramirrors" and presented it in the Latvian pavilion on the 52nd International Art Exhibition of La Biennale di Venezia, Venice, Italy. It was done in collaboration with Elmārs Blūms, Institute of Physics of the University of Latvia, Ilze Aulika, Vismants Zauls, Mārtiņš Rutkis, Institute of Solid State Physics of the University of Latvia and Jānis Spīgulis, Institute of Atomic Physics and Spectroscopy, University of Latvia.

CONCLUSIONS

Some crucial differences between Western and Soviet Latvia computer art should be mentioned.

- Due to political reasons the scientists and engineers – the first authors of the computer art – were not familiar with modern art theories and practice of the 20th century.
- The common style of computer drawings should be considered as realistic style ASCII art.
- Some artifacts done by professional artists in collaboration with engineers and programmers of kinetic art were covered under the term *design*.

Internet art and the new media art development established the role of Latvian art in the digital field during the second half of the 1990s.

REFERENCES

[1] S. Zariņa, "Computer Scientists as Early Digital Artists," *Scientific Papers of the University of Latvia*, vol. 752, Riga: University of Latvia, 2011, in press.

[2] Electronic Publication: http://www.leonardo.info/isast/leostory.html

[3] H. Franke and H. Helbig, "Generative Mathematics: Mathematically Described and Calculated Visual Art," *Leonardo*, vol. 25, 1992, pp. 291–294.

[4] Exhibition catalogue, "AND OTHERS. Movements, Explorations and Artists in Latvia 1960 – 1984," Riga: The Latvian Centre for Contemporary Art, 2010.

[5] J. Borgs, "Taking a different direction... ," *Studija*, vol. 76, 2010, pp. 38–44.

[6] Electronic Publication: http://milkproject.net/en/index.html

Digital Photo Painting as an Artistic and Cultural Phenomenon

Vladimir Geroimenko
School of Art and Media
University of Plymouth
Plymouth, UK
vladimir.geroimenko@ plymouth.ac.uk

Abstract—Digital photo painting is a newly emerging phenomenon in both fine art and everyday life. The latest versions of specialist software, such as Corel Painter or Adobe Photoshop, allow anyone to turn their selected photographs into enchanting paintings, produced in any style desired. The first book on this subject 'The Art of Digital Photo Painting' by Marilyn Sholin was published quite recently, in 2009.

This paper explores the conceptual, creative and cultural aspects of turning photos into paintings using popular software and plug-ins. It argues that the mass production of original digital paintings and fine art prints may signal a new era in the relationship between photography and painting. The paper discusses why digital photo painting might be the 'next big thing' in digital art and become a new hobby for millions.

Keywords - digital art; digital painting; photo painting; digital photography; fine art

I. A NEW REVOLUTION IN ART

The latest developments in digital cameras and image-editing software have dramatically changed the very nature of both photography and painting. As a result, digital photography has moved toward the next level of expression, removing the boundary between photography and painting. A new field of digital photo painting has been born which combines the artistic tools found in photography and painting.

A. Digital Photo Painting vs. Photo Painting

Although digital photo painting is a newly emerging field in both amateur and professional art, the use of a camera as a sketchbook is as old as photography itself.

The development of paintings from photographs to completed works of art is a very common approach in traditional painting, despite the well-known fact that many painters prefer not to talk about it. By using a camera as a sketchbook, artists are able to collect unique visual references in order to inform and inspire their creative work.

In her book 'Painting Great Pictures from Photographs' [2], Hazel Harrison states that "although there is a lingering prejudice against using photographic references, to many professional artists the camera is essential". She also points out that there is a considerable difference between taking photographs for their own sake and taking them as painting references. Good paintings can be made from such particular photographs but seldom by direct copying.

Digital photo painting has opened new opportunities for the use of photographs. Artists can still use them as painting references in a traditional way, just by looking at them and painting digitally from scratch. But they are also able to put them into the underlying layer of specialist software in order to paint 'over them'. Furthermore, amateur painters can use popular software or plug-ins for turning their digital photographs into paintings automatically, with a single mouse click.

B. The Nature of the Revolution

Digital photo painting is a form of digital art. Without doubt, digital art has changed the landscape of art forever. But are those changes serious enough to be considered as a new revolution in art?

Scott Ligon in the book 'Digital Art Revolution' [3] analyses five key reasons why digital art is causing a revolution: (1) Everything is connected, (2) Endless experimenting, (3) Process, not product, (4) Eliminate the middleman, (5) No limitations.

More specifically, digital technology is redefining the creative process because it: "(1) blurs the boundaries between mediums to the point of irrelevance, (2) possesses potential for endless experimentation and variation, (3) allows for infinite duplication with no loss of quality, (4) is able to reach large audiences directly with no middleman, and (5) contains no inherent aesthetic or technical limitations" [3, p.13].

Of course, it is possible to name several other factors that define the nature of the digital revolution, such as, for example, the scope and the depth of the ongoing changes. The digital revolution in art is affecting not just a particular small group of artists, but everyone who deals with either professional or amateur photography or fine

1550-6037/11 $26.00 © 2011 IEEE
DOI 10.1109/IV.2011.26

art. Also, the revolutionary changes are going so deep that it is difficult to name any artistic form or technique that might not be influenced by digital technologies.

C. Painting vs. Photography

The birth of digital painting has raised many questions about a new relationship between photography and painting. What is going to happen to them in the future? Is photography dead, and is it just a first step in the production of digital photo paintings? Is traditional physical painting dead and to be replaced with the digital techniques?

To answer those questions, a deep and essentially philosophical reflection is required. Putting the relationship between photography and painting in a historic perspective will make the whole picture much clearer. Ever since the invention of photography, the proportion of 'paintings to photographs' has constantly changed in the same direction as an ever increasing number of photographs were being produced worldwide each and every day.

As of today, almost everyone seems to be a digital photographer and millions and millions of the resulting photographs are uploaded to the Internet. Comparing this with the number of paintings produced at the same period in time, the complete dominance of amateur photography is obvious. According to Hegel's dialectical method, such monotonous development cannot continue forever. At a certain point in time, a transition from quantity to new quality has to take place. Usually, such transitions happen in the form of a sudden jump that in some cases can more properly be called a revolution. The jump from traditional photography to digital painting is just such a revolution, and it is worth considering the concept in more detail.

II. THE CONCEPT OF DIGITAL PAINTING

A. Computer-generated Art?

In general, digital painting is associated with the process of painting on a computer using Corel Painter or similar software and some specialist hardware, such as a pressure-sensitive Wacom tablet and pen. This process results in an image that is visually manifested on a computer display as an array of coloured pixels. Each digital painting is born in this initial 'virtual' form. It can stay in it forever or it can be physically rendered on paper or canvas using a printer.

Is digital painting therefore a kind of computer-generated art? Since the main goal of digital painting is to simulate traditional painting using new electronic tools, the answer is negative. It is formulated very well by Jeremy Sutton in the Preface to his book 'Painter 11 Creativity': "The digital painting referred to in this book is no more 'computer-generated' than a Van Gogh painting was 'oil brush generated'. It involves original handmade brush strokes on a digital canvas. The act of painting is very similar to the act of traditional painting, only with electronic media instead of physical media..." [5, p.xvi]. The main idea of today's digital painting is to produce a piece of art that looks human made, but to do this using computer-generated brushes and digital paint.

B. Between Photography and Painting

Digital photo painting takes photography to the next level of expression, allowing us to turn digital photographs into artworks that look hand-painted rather than created on a computer. With popular software and little effort, everyone can alter digital images so that they will replicate traditional media like oils or watercolours. But when all desired painterly effects are applied and photographs are successfully transformed into paintings, are the final pieces genuine digital paintings or do they remain essentially digital photographs?

This question reflects the intimate goal and the main issue of digital photo painting. As Marilyn Sholin pointed out in her book 'The Art of Digital Photo Painting', "It is always the goal of the digital painter to create paintings that do not look either too photographic or too computer generated" [4, p.13]. In other words, the answer to the philosophical question 'To be or not to be' could in this particular case be as follows: To be a masterpiece, your digital photo painting should not be too photographic and at the same time it should not be too computer generated.

The art of digital photo painting is that of treading the narrow path between clearly computer generated and clearly photographic appearances of artwork.

C. Going beyond Digital

Digital paintings are digital only by their birth. With the latest technologies, they can be printed on a solid physical substrate, such as paper or canvas, using practically any medium, such as Giclée, acrylic, watercolour or oil. This allows digital paintings to exist in the physical world of art in the same way as any traditional paintings on canvas or paper. After such 'materialization', digital paintings are no longer just files on a computer; they are something physical that can be held in galleries and private collections around the world.

Jeremy Sutton concludes that "digital painting is now established as a respected and accepted medium, or collection of media, with digital paintings being exhibited in galleries and museums worldwide" [4, p.xvi]. Also, Marilyn Sholin emphasizes that "digital painting is one of the most popular and fastest growing art forms, and digital art is finding its way into galleries around the world, creating an entirely new niche of art and art prints that are being sold and collected worldwide" [4, p.7].

The digital revolution has changed the nature of the relationship between physical and virtual, between the original and reproduction. If you have scanned a famous oil or watercolour painting, it will enter the world of digital imagery and will be in exactly the same form as any digital painting. Only an external relationship to the physical original makes us to think that this is something completely different.

The question of the originality has also become more difficult to answer in the digital era than in all the previous history of art. "What can we classify as the 'original', anyway, in digital art? Surely, it's not the file itself, which is simply a collection of ones and zeros… Is it the image we see on screen? Is it a physical print made from the artwork? None of these possibilities offers a satisfying and definitive answer" [3, p.17].

The world famous Corel Painter master Jeremy Sutton writes: "I describe my completed artwork as a painting, not a digital painting or computer art. The literal description, as I may put on a label in an exhibition, depends on the media I use. An example is: 'pigment ink and acrylic on canvas.'" [5, p.xvi].

Indeed, if, for example, an acrylic painting is the print of 'a limited edition of 1', does it really matter that a digital copy of this painting existed before it's production and was actually it's digital original?

III.   CULTURAL AND TECHNOLOGICAL ASPECTS OF DIGITAL PHOTO PAINTING

A.   Can everyone be an Artist?

Surprisingly, the most likely answer to this question is positive. At least from the technological point of view, all limits seem to be removed and everyone can easily afford and try to be a digital artist. Of course, to succeed as an amateur or a professional artist, they must have not only painting software and hardware, but also imagination, creativity and talent.

The digital revolution makes it possible for everyone to try to be artistic. New affordable software boosts creativity, allowing endless options for experimentation. Now it is easier than ever, Marylyn Sholin points out, to take your photographs and digitally transform them into works of art that engage and mystify the viewer. The latest software programs on the market today are so sophisticated in their capabilities and so easy to use that anyone can be an artist and create their own style for their body of work [4].

The creative process of digital photo painting begins even before the shutter of the camera is clicked. The artist has to see the potential paintings as if they are 'embedded' into the real world. An alternative strategy is that the artist takes as many reference photographs as possible, but in this case, he or she faces the problem of selecting the photographs that will be rendered into paintings, but this selection itself is a difficult and mysterious process.

With digital art, everyone can create unique hand-painted images from their photographs because the possibilities of exploring different creative solutions are virtually endless. Digital artists can be fearless because they can always restore the original image. In the digital world, there are no mistakes because several hits of the Undo button can correct them immediately.

B.   Software and Hardware for All

The current painting software and hardware is affordable and easy to operate. It can all be controlled by the artist to achieve truly unique paintings and to create interesting and realistic painting effects.

But which software and hardware to use? "Combining multiple programs is the best method to create personalized digital art that does not look like it was created in a computer" [4, p.17]. "Corel Painter is your digital art studio in your computer. It is a complement to, not a competitor with, Adobe Photoshop, your digital darkroom. I recommend, as a minimum, that your digital painting toolbox includes both Painter and Photoshop" [5, p.xvi].

In terms of hardware, a Wacom graphic tablet and its pressure-sensitive pen is the key interface between artist and computer. 'Wacom' actually means the harmony between human and computer ('wa' is a Japanese word for harmony and 'com' stands for computer).

Let's take a look at one of my digital photo paintings that was created from a photo reference in Corel Painter and Adobe Photoshop using a mix of techniques with the help of a Wacom graphic tablet. The painting emulates the work of the impressionist masters, leaving out details and using a particular colour palette.

Figure 1. The original photograph.

Figures 1 to 3 show the original photograph and final digital results of a painting entitled 'Fowey II, Cornwall' and painted in 2010. These black and white images lack the main feature of the impressionist style – the creative use of color but they may nonetheless give some idea of the impressionist-style brush strokes. To see this digital photo painting in color, please visit *http://bit.ly/fowey-2*.

Figure 2. Impressionist-style digital photo painting.

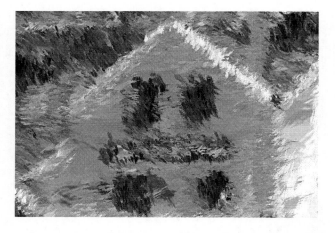

Figure 3. A detail view of the digital painting.

C. From Photography to Painting: Back to the Future

It is easier than ever to create unique digital artwork from photo references using popular software. "The bottom line is that digital paint is just another art medium (or collection of media), albeit an immensely powerful, efficient, versatile, non-allergenic, non-toxic and fun medium to use" [5, p.xvi].

Digital paint is gradually replacing the physical one and becoming the medium of choice for millions of people. It is affordable, always available on the computer and fun to try. This is why more and more ordinary people are getting involved in the production of digital paintings. The use of their own photographs as visual references or material for digital manipulation and transformation helps them enormously, and also fully guarantees that each of them is able to complete their artwork. If digital photo painting was not available, most of those people would never have been thinking about any contribution to visual art. Of course, not many of their artworks are masterpieces, but because of a dramatic increase in the number of people involved, the chances of finding new talents and producing real masterpieces are very high.

The Internet and its numerous photo-sharing websites, such as Flickr, make it possible to present your achievements in digital painting not only to your friends, but to the rest of the world as well. All the major photo-sharing websites have many specialised groups that state "No photos please, digital paintings only".

From a technological point of view, all the necessary painting tools are widely and easily available and they are good enough to move digital photo painting to a revolutionary new level of popularity similar to the current use of digital photography. From a cultural point of view, it is highly possible but not yet quite clear, whether digital photo painting will become a mass hobby on this planet.

Current research indicates that the answer is more likely 'yes' than 'no'. The historical and conceptual perspective of the relationship between photography and painting supports this positive claim. The dominance of photography has reached the point of dialectic negation and transformation into the form of art that was dominant before the invention of photography, namely painting.

Digital photo painting leads us 'back to the future', where a huge proportion of visual artworks will be not photographs but truly unique paintings produced from reference photographs.

IV.   CONCLUSIONS AND FUTURE WORK

Digital photo painting is an emerging phenomenon in fine art and everyday life that has the potential to be 'the next big thing'. Since at the moment it is in its juvenile stage, the main body of research into its features and development still lies ahead, forming a novel and exciting field for in-depth analysis and theoretical reflection.

REFERENCES

[1] M. Addison, Painter X for Photographers: Creating Painterly Images Step by Step. Focal Press, 2007.

[2] H. Harrison, Painting Great Pictures from Photographs. David & Charles PLC, 1999.

[3] S. Ligon, Digital Art Revolution. New York: Watson-Guptill Publications, 2010.

[4] M. Sholin, The Art of Digital Photo Painting. New York / London: Lark Books, 2009.

[5] J. Sutton, Painter 11 Creativity: Digital Artist's Handbook. Focal Press, 2009.

PieVis: Interactive Graph Visualization Using a Rings-Based Tree Drawing Algorithm for Children and Crust Display for Parents

Adrian Rusu[1], Andrew Crowell[2], Bryan Petzinger[1], Andrew Fabian[1]

[1]Department of Computer Science, Rowan University, U.S.A.

[2]Federal Aviation Administration, U.S.A.

rusu@rowan.edu, andrew.crowell@faa.gov, {petzin02,fabian78}@students.rowan.edu

Abstract

The quality of a graph drawing algorithm is often measured by its edge crossings, angular resolution, aspect ratio, and node labeling. Algorithms for drawing trees in general are segregated from algorithms for drawing graphs. In this paper we present a graph visualization system that uses a novel interconnection between a tree drawing algorithm and graph drawing techniques. First, the graph is transformed into a tree and nodes that have multiple parent connections within the graph are duplicated within the tree. While some of the connection information is lost during this transformation, the multiple connections can be regained by interactively displaying the details based on the degree of interest. We use an edgeless rings-based visualization which allows edge crossings and angular resolution issues to be eliminated and has a desirable aspect ratio of 1. Finally, a circular labeling method is used that provides user-friendly labels that do not overlap and clearly show node affiliation.

1 Introduction

Graph drawing algorithms aim at creating aesthetically pleasing graphs. Among the most important graph visualization aesthetics are minimizing edge crossings, increasing the angular resolution, and providing a desirable aspect ratio close to 1 [1]. Adding text to a graph visualization may encounter challenges, so various algorithms have been developed attempting to find the most efficient way to label a graph (see for example [2]). Labels typically should be displayed in a way that allows as much important information as possible to fit inside the label without having labels overlap each other. It is also important to ensure the user can easily distinguish which label is affiliated with which node. In this paper we present a novel graph drawing algorithm that addresses these four issues using an interactive visualization and a tree drawing algorithm.

Often, tree drawing and graph drawing, though similar areas of research, are treated as two separate domains. Generally, trees, being simpler structures, allow for simpler drawing algorithms. Our visualization interconnects these two domains, using a tree drawing algorithm and graph drawing techniques to create an interactive focus+context graph visualization system. Several different means of interaction are provided, in order to allow the user to gain several different levels of detail about interesting areas of the graph. We first transform the graph into a tree, and then use a rings-based tree drawing algorithm that represents connections via enclosing smaller rings inside larger rings. Because of this unique way of showing connections between nodes, it allows for the removal of directed edges within the visualization. As a result, edge crossings and angular resolution issues are eliminated. We display parent nodes along the edge of the main ring, similar to the crust of a pie.

The interaction between tree drawing algorithms and graph visualization techniques has been explored in previous work as follows. A graph visualization created by adding a set of curved edges to a Treemap drawing had been presented in [3]. A fisheye view and several other interactive techniques have been applied in [8], in order to remove clutter from a small section of a large graph drawing. Previous work which is the closest to our contribution has been presented in [5]. The author introduces a force-directed graph visualization that provides interactive means to display a section of a graph as a tree which can then be incrementally explored. A smooth animation between transitions is used to help the user remain oriented within the visualization. Several concepts used by these previous systems are applied in our visualization, including incremental exploration, using a tree drawing algorithm for node placement, and applying user interaction to gain more information about an area of the graph.

2 Drawing Algorithm

The first step of our graph drawing algorithm is to transform the input graph into a corresponding tree, without losing connections (relationships). In order to achieve this outcome, we duplicate all vertices of the graph, as needed. The result is a tree which has all edges from the input

1550-6037/11 $26.00 © 2011 IEEE

DOI 10.1109/IV.2011.68

graph, but in which the number of nodes exceeds the number of vertices in the input graph (see Figure 1).

From an implementation standpoint, the data is stored as a graph using Object Oriented Design principles that allow references to be made to the same node (the Object) multiple times, without creating multiple physical copies of the same node. The tree drawing algorithm can then be applied to the graph structure, without inefficiently creating many copies of a single node.

Once the graph has been converted into a tree, we use the top-down FastRings tree drawing algorithm [6] that was extended from original bottom-up RINGS algorithm [7]. Our visualization is intended for interaction with and display of large graph structures, such as the World Wide Web, and FastRings is most practical because it allows for quick access to top levels of large trees. Although many of the techniques we introduce in this paper can be applied to RINGS, a bottom-up algorithm requires the entire tree to be analyzed before it can be displayed. The FastRings algorithm allows the removal of edges, since connections are represented by child nodes being drawn inside the parent node, and since FastRings draws the tree in a circular format, this naturally provides the desirable aspect ratio of 1. The navigation of our graph visualization system also follows a similar strategy as the one described in [6].

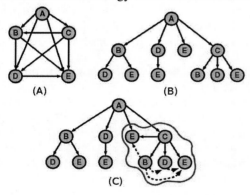

Figure 1: (A) A directed graph. (B) A tree corresponding to the graph in (A). (C) Connections are re-established when more detail is shown of sections of the drawing based on Degree of Interest interactions.

Another feature of the FastRings algorithm is that the tree is visualized from the point of view (POV) of a particular node, called the focal node. Instead of displaying the entire tree structure at once, a node of interest is chosen as the focal node and then several levels down from that node are drawn. This results in a visualization of a subtree of interest rather than a visualization of the entire tree, which would be impractical for large trees.

When a subtree is in focus, the root node of that subtree is drawn as the largest circle and each child of that root

node is drawn as a circle inside of it. In this same manner, several levels of the tree are drawn recursively. The number of levels drawn can be specified by the user.

Once the graph has been transformed into a tree, and displayed using the FastRings algorithm, methods of recreating the graph must be applied to allow the user to retrieve the details he or she requires.

2.1 Node and Subtree Highlighting

In order to re-establish the missing links within the graph being displayed by the PieVis system, a means of displaying the multiple connections that were lost, without introducing edges, is required. Highlighting the common nodes when the user hovers over one provides a way to recreate multiple connections to a single node in an area of interest. When the user hovers the mouse over any node in the visualization, that node will be highlighted by filling it in with a transparent color. Likewise, every copy of that node within the current view will be highlighted (see Figure 3). This highlighting recreates the lost connections of the node of interest without drawing any edges, and therefore introducing no edge crossings.

Although highlighting can help the user recreate the multiple connections to the node, it does not always allow the user to see where these multiple connections actually exist. When a user highlights a node that is several levels deep within the current visualization, although his primary interest would be the highlighted node, the immediate subtree of that node is also of interest. Consider the example that B is a child of A and A is a child of both C and D (see Figure 2). When the graph is transformed into a tree, A would be duplicated to be a child of both C and D. Now, if the user hovers over the B node that is inside the A_C node, the user is likely interested in A, B, and C, although the primary interest is on B. The B node will be highlighted inside of A_C and A_D, but the user will not be able to know that both A_C and A_D are actually the same A node.

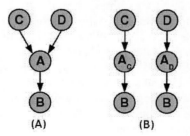

Figure 2: (A) The original graph as described. (B) The graph transformed into a tree: using only node highlighting, the connections of C and D to B will not be correctly portrayed as through a common node A.

The immediate subtree is defined as the entire subtree, beginning at level 1, of the currently highlighted node. If the highlighted node is at level 1 in the current view, then the immediate subtree is only the node itself. Otherwise, it is the level 1 node that the highlighted node is inside, and recursively each node below level 1 that the highlighted node is inside. In the example in the previous paragraph, the immediate subtree of the B node inside the A_C node would be $C - A - B$. In order to show the connections of these interesting nodes each level is highlighted a darker color as the level gets closer to the hovered node (Figure 3). Each copy of the highlighted subtree nodes are also highlighted with the same color. Highlighted subtrees are drawn with a thick line of a distinguishable color, as opposed to highlighted nodes which are filled with a translucent color.

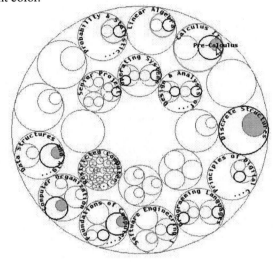

Figure 3: Subtree highlighting: when the user hovers over a deep node, the subtrees containing that node are highlighted.

Subtree highlighting along with node highlighting allows the user to see multiple connections and the level at which each connection is made, without introducing edges. In turn, much of the data that was lost is now regained. Although this does not recreate every connection to the node of interest, it attempts to recreate all of the connections that are interesting to the user.

3 Parent Display

Because the FastRings algorithm creates a drawing intended for incremental exploration, there is some data that may be interesting to the user that is lost in the visualization. If the user navigates to a node of interest, with the traditional FastRings algorithm only the subtree of the focal node is visible. This means only the children of that node, as well as its children's children and so forth, are displayed. However, the user may also be interested in the parents of the focal node. In a traditional graph visualization, the user would be able to retrieve parent information

by backtracking the directed edges coming into the node he is interested in. When the graph is converted into a tree this information is lost unless the entire tree is displayed. Since the FastRings algorithm does not draw the entire tree, parent information of the focal node is lost.

In order to address this issue, the FastRings algorithm is applied to the children and the resulting image is extended to display the parents of the focal node. The parents of the node are displayed in a crust around the outer edge of the largest circular node similar to the crust of a pie (see Figure 4). This provides a visualization of one level up in the graph from the current focal node. Combined with the traditional FastRings, the visualization now displays one level up and several levels down from a focal node helping to recreate the graph without introducing edges.

The user may interact with parent nodes in the same manner as child nodes, and node and subtree highlighting are also applied to parent nodes. Hovering over a parent will highlight the respective node in all other parts of the visualization, and hovering over a child will cause connected parent nodes to be highlighted accordingly.

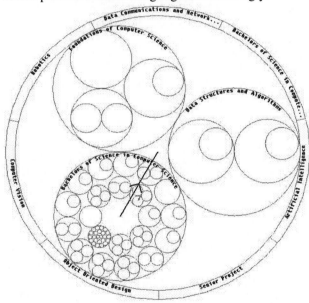

Figure 4: Parents of the focal node are displayed around the outer edge of the node, in a format similar to a pie crust.

4 Degree of Interest

As discussed, the PieVis system uses a feature called incremental exploration that allows the visualization to display a subset of the graph drawn from the focal point of a single node as chosen by the user. Much of the graph data is abstracted into tree data to avoid unwanted issues such as edge crossing and overcrowding. However, the graph data can be reconstructed using the interactive node and subtree highlighting features that are provided. These features are an important part of the PieVis system and combined create a feature called the Degree of Interest (DOI).

DOI is a method of suppression in which each node in the graph is applied a value of interest, and any node not over a threshold value is not displayed. In our visualization, several thresholds are used to decide the level of detail that is displayed. The first threshold is used to decide whether or not a child node should be displayed. This value can be set by the user, and decides how many levels down from the current focal node are displayed. The second threshold value tells whether a parent should be displayed or not and is currently hard-coded to one level above the focal node. Finally, there is a threshold that decides whether to display the details of the connections of a particular node. This threshold is concerned with the node highlighting and marking.

Conventionally, DOI is a numerical value assigned to each node in a graph, and there are several graph visualizations that use this DOI function to decide the level of detail of a node to display [9]. Although our visualization does not use a conventional DOI function, the results are similar.

5   Labeling

Since the nodes are represented as circles, a circular labeling method was implemented (see Figure 4). These circular labels provide a way to fit as much text as possible inside the space provided by each node. Since only the first level of nodes and the parent nodes are labeled, and the label is contained completely inside the node, label overlap is impossible. The circular labels are easy to read and it can easily be determined which label is affiliated with which node.

Although the circular labels provide more room for text than straight labels would, with no overlap, and they provide an aesthetically pleasing means of labeling, it is preferable to limit the child node labels to using 270° of the circle. This is to limit the amount of the label that is displayed upside-down to a minimum and to help distinguish the start of a label from the end. Often, the label for a node is longer than that which can fit within the 270° limitation. In order to display entire labels, an interaction was implemented in which when the user hovers over a node the label of the hovered node is extended straight and the entire label is displayed. In this same way, labels for deeper level nodes can also be provided. The label shown when hovered is still connected to the node and follows the mouse cursor around so as to place the label directly where the user's attention is focused.

The labeling algorithm uses character width and height and node radius to determine label placement. Arclength is used to determine the rotation of each character and the length of the string that can fit within the 270° limit. If this limit is reached before the end of the label text, an ellipsis is appended.

6   User Study

A user study was organized to demonstrate PieVis, gauge its effectiveness and locate areas for improvement. Eight subjects participated in our study, with experience ranging from those with non-technical backgrounds to graduate level computer science students familiar with visualization techniques. The participants were categorized as either technical or non-technical, where technical subjects have backgrounds in science or mathematics-related fields where they are familiar with concepts such as directed graphs. Of the total eight participants, five were determined to be technical and three non-technical. This determination was made based on an evaluation questionaire given at the end of the study through which the participants provided information about their respective backgrounds.

6.1   Procedure

Each subject participated in the same study on a one-on-one basis with the proctor, who was one of the authors of the paper. Participants were first given a short introduction to PieVis, and its basic features were explained. Each participant was then given a short tutorial to familiarize themselves with the system.

After the introduction and preliminary training period, a series of 24 tasks were presented which tested the participant on data from the web, a file system, and a series of directional graphs. In each case, participants used PieVis alongside a traditional tool such as a web browser, file system explorer or static graph generated by the GraphViz graph visualization software. After completing each task the participant was asked to rate the degree to which PieVis was used compared to the other tool. These ratings were recorded on a scale ranging from one to five, where a score of one would indicate they did not use PieVis at all and a five would indicate they were able to complete the task using only PieVis.

Both objective and subjective questions were used in the study. Objective questions were those that had a definitive correct answer such as browsing to a given node, counting or locating specific information. Subjective tasks were open to interpretation, for example identifying the most popular account in a social network or comparing homogeneous directories in a file system. When answering subjective questions, participants were asked to provide an explanation for their reasoning in addition to their answer. These subjective tasks were incorporated as a means to promote critical thinking and problem solving using PieVis instead of just following directions.

Participants were not given a strict time limit for the tasks, but were advised to move on if they could not complete it in five minutes. After completing all tasks the participant was given a brief evaluation sheet containing eleven questions and an open ended area for comments.

6.2 Results

We present PieVis as a supplementary visualization system to enhance existing methods for browsing data (e.g. web, file system, directed graph), and the goal of this study is to evaluate PieVis in that role. The results are presented in Table 5. Our evaluation is based on three factors: the answers to each task, how the tasks were rated and feedback from the evaluation questionnaire.

There was only one task which was answered incorrectly by all participants. The task involved a graph representing the Computer Science program at Rowan University, and required participants to count the number of children of a particular node. All participants counted each node visible in PieVis, however there were several nodes that were not visible due to a hard limit being set to prevent crowding. This limit caused several nodes to not be included in the visualization, which all participants failed to realize. This issue can be attributed to two main factors, first the participants inexperience with the PieVis visualization system and second the lack of visual indicator that the limit has been reached.

For the remaining tasks there was no obvious pattern or consistency between participants in regard to tasks being answered incorrectly. However, trends can be seen in how questions were rated. Tasks that require skills such as browsing or searching were rated among the highest tasks with an average rating of approximately 4.5 and 4.7, respectively. These results are very promising, as PieVis is targeted as an incremental exploration tool, these are the main areas of interest.

Tasks that required contextual information were rated the lowest with an average rating of approximately 2.8. This is an expected result as PieVis does not attempt to visualize content, this area is well handled by existing methods which PieVis is meant to supplement. Another area of weakness was for tasks requiring counting. There were only two of these tasks, however one was the task which all participants answered incorrectly and the other was either answered incorrectly or given a poor rating (meaning that PieVis was not used to answer it).

Overall, PieVis performed very well in the areas that we target, and its areas of weakness are outside the scope of the system. Some minor issues were discovered that are labeled as items for future work. Overall the study was very successful with an average task rating of 4.15/5, which indicates that PieVis is a valuable supplementary visualization system.

6.3 Subjective Ratings

The subjective questions revealed some interesting aspects to the visualization. For example in situations where participants would use PieVis to compare nodes they would tend to focus on the context as means for comparison, whereas using the more traditional method they would focus more on relationships. For example when asked to find two similar directories, one participant chose a directory containing pictures and another containing video, reasoning that they were similar because they both contain visual media. However when the same participant later was asked to perform a comparison and used the provided static node-link diagram, they based their comparison on the number and direction of edges. Similar results occurred for other participants, which leads the question of why this happened; one possibility could be the lack of edges in PieVis, although more extensive research is necessary.

7 Future Work

Additional feedback collected after the study revealed general user opinions concerning the overall usefulness of PieVis and how it performs in terms of speed, ease of use, and user orientation. From this feedback and the results discussed in the previous section we identified the following areas for future work:

- the history node should be more distinguishable from other regular nodes

- add the ability to look beyond one level of parents

- label the focal node

- smoother or alternative animation for semantic zoom

- provide a visual cue when limit of nodes being drawn is reached

8 Conclusion

PieVis is a novel, interactive graph visualization that has many useful applications. It is an incremental exploration system that uses a tree drawing algorithm and user interaction to display details of interesting areas of the graph. The tree drawing algorithm used allows for the removal of edges and, therefore, the elimination of edge crossing and angular resolution issues. Its circular format provides a desirable aspect ratio of 1, and the circular labeling method presented allows aesthetically pleasing labels to be displayed based on Degree of Interest without overlap.

PieVis has potential for various applications, including World Wide Web visualization, social network visualization, database analysis, and network structure displays.

The PieVis system is not without its drawbacks, however. Although the PieVis system's incremental exploration feature allows large graphs, such as the WWW, to be

task	type	User 1	User 2	User 3	User 4	User 5	User 6	User 7	User 8	User Average
1	browsing	5	5	5	5	5	5	5	5	5
2	content	1	1	1	1	1	1	1	1	1
3	browsing	4	5	4	5	4	5	5	4	4.5
4	browsing/content	3	3	1	3	5	2	1	5	2.88
5	content	3	3	3	4	3	1	1	5	2.88
6	browsing	3	5	1	3	5	5	1	2	3.13
7	browsing	4	5	5	5	5	5	5	2	4.38
8	browsing	4	4	5	4	5	5	5	5	4.63
9	browsing	5	4	5	5	5	5	5	5	4.88
10	browsing	5	4	5	4	5	5	5	4	4.63
11	content	5	5	5	5	5	5	3	4	4.63
12	search	5	5	5	4	5	5	5	4	4.75
13	search	5	5	5	5	5	5	3	3	4.5
14	subjective	5	5	5	5	5	5	4	5	4.88
15	search	5	5	5	5	5	5	5	5	5
16	search	5	5	5	5	5	5	5	5	5
17	counting	x	x	x	x	x	x	x	x	x
18	browsing	x	5	5	4	5	5	5	4	4.75
19	browsing	5	5	5	5	5	5	5	1	4.5
20	counting	5	5	5	3	1	1	3		3.5
21	search	5	1	5	5	3	5	5	x	4.14
22	search	5	5	5	5	5	5	5	x	5
23	subjective	5	5	1	5	3	1	3	x	3.29
24	subjective	5	3	1	5	5	3	3	x	3.57
										4.15

Figure 5: Tabulated results from the user study. Tasks have been grouped into five types; browsing, content, search, counting and subjective. Ratings marked 'x' indicate tasks that were incomplete or incorrect. In the User Average column, results less than 3 are marked in red as that implies PieVis was used less than the standard tool.

displayed quickly and efficiently, it is limited in how many levels from the focal node it can display. The level of children does not have a hard limit, but most graphs become too crowded at more than three levels. Some users may desire to see much more of the graph structure than PieVis allows for. For some large graphs, it may even be desirable to display the entire graph structure before focusing on a small area of interest.

In the future, research will be devoted to connecting PieVis with another graph visualization, such as Walrus [4], that provides a good view of the overall graph structure. Providing a multi-windowed visualization using overview and details on demand, in addition to the current focus and context feature, should eliminate many of the drawbacks of the PieVis system and create a powerful tool for graph visualization and analysis.

References

[1] G. DiBattista, P. Eades, R. Tamassia, and I. G. Tollis. *Graph Drawing: Algorithms for the Visualization of Graphs.* Prentice Hall, 1999.

[2] U. Dogrusoz, K. G. Kakoulis, B. Madden, and I. G. Tollis. On labeling in graph visualization. *Information Sciences: An International Journal,* 177:2459–2472, June 2007.

[3] J. Fekete, D. Wang, N. Dang, A. Aris, and C. Plaisant. Overlaying graph links on treemaps. *Proc. of the 2003 IEEE Symposium on InfoVis,* pages 82–83, 2003.

[4] Y. Hyun. Walrus - a graph visualization tool. http://www.caida.org/tools/visualization/walrus/index.xml, 2002.

[5] A. Pavlo. Interactive, tree-based graph visualization. Master's thesis, Rochester Institute of Technology, May 2006.

[6] Adrian Rusu, Confesor Santiago, and Radu Jianu. Real-time interactive visualization of information hierarchies. In *Proceedings of 11th International Conference Information Visualisation,* pages 117–123, 2007.

[7] S. T. Teoh and K. L. Ma. RINGS: A technique for visualizing large hierarchies. In *Proceedings 10th International Symposium on Graph Drawing,* volume 2528, pages 268–275, 2002.

[8] C. Tominski, J. Abello, F. van Ham, and H. Schumann. Fisheye tree views and lenses for graph visualization. *Proceedings of 10th International Conference Information Visualisation,* pages 17–24, 2006.

[9] F. van Ham and A. Perer. "Search, show context, expand on demand": Supporting large graph exploration with degree-of-interest. *IEEE Transactions on Visualization and Computer Graphics,* 15:953–960, December 2009.

Improving the Evaluation Performance of Space-Time Trellis Code through Visualisation

H. Harun

Aerospace Engineering Department
Engineering Faculty, University Putra Malaysia (UPM)
43400 Serdang, Selangor, Malaysia
harlisya@eng.upm.edu.my

U. A. I. Ungku Chulan and K. Khazani

Developing Reality
22A-1, Jalan 7/7, Seksyen 7
43650 Bandar Baru Bangi, Selangor, Malaysia
proactive.azmi@gmail.com,
proactive.khamizon@gmail.com

Abstract—**In this paper we present a new visualisation approach in the effort of improving the evaluation strategy of space-time trellis code (STTC) generator matrix G. To our knowledge, although visualisation is widely used to handle a variety of problems, it has never been employed specifically to solve complexity problems that are related to generator matrix G evaluation. Most approaches are either mathematically or algorithmically inclined. As such, they tend to offer a series of refinement that enhances the current available method, but do not provide fresh insight on the problem at hand. By comparing it with the enhancement strategy that was discovered via the normal approach (i.e., by analysing algorithm) it was discovered that visualisation had inspired an entirely different pruning technique that outperformed the common approach by 20%.**

Keywords—Space-time trellis code; generator matrix; heuristic; visualisation tool.

I. INTRODUCTION

Great effort has been directed toward the search for optimal STTC code and the reduction of computational burden in calculating the minimum determinant. Fukuda *et al.* [1] and Lisya *et al.* [2] have developed high-speed and improved algorithm which is based on tree structure in calculating the minimum determinant effectively in obtaining optimal generator matrix **G**. As for now the improvement of the algorithm is done via the analysis of the pseudocode. This is not a productive way of understanding the actual impact of the design that is heuristically inclined. In the attempt of finding an effective solution of improving the performance of the current approach, the potential of visualisation is explored.

II. VISUALISATION

Visualisation is not a new approach in engineering. It has been employed widely in the process of analysing algorithms [3]. To our knowledge however, the effort to enhance the evaluation of generator matrix **G** in STTC has never been approached with visualisation.

To improve the design of evaluation, most approaches [4] rely on the analysis of algorithm, equation, matrix etc. As such they are mathematically or algorithmically inclined. This is only expected given the nature of the problem.

The analysis of heuristic algorithms could face the challenge of visibility. As such, analysing the behaviour via the pseudocode per se, may not reveal the actual behaviour of the algorithm. This is due to the fact that heuristic algorithms are not completely deterministic, where the algorithm can progress in a direction totally unforeseen by analysis.

Visualisation can help in resolving this visibility issue. In fact, it can contribute to the solution finding process in three aspects [5]:

1. Measuring the impact of change.
   Knowing the impact of changing a certain parameter is not an easy task. Visualisation can offer a concrete and controllable display of impact.
2. Testing of what-if scenarios.
   Once the impact of change has been understood, it is possible to test varying what-if scenarios without much complication and get the result immediately.
3. Simplification of processing.
   The complexity of information is simplified with visualisation. This way, it is easier for us to process it.

As some may argue, certain problems are just not innately visual. It must be remembered however that a design problem that is mathematical or algorithmic by nature need not remain that way. It is possible to re-frame [6] the mathematically-algorithmically inclined problem (MIP) into a visually inclined problem (VIP) that is more stimulating perceptually, as shown in Fig. 1.

Visualising the problem instead of just analysing the equation can promote an entirely different perspective on it. For instance, it could make research more sensitive to patterns that are readily apparent through visual means [7] but completely cryptic when analysed algorithmically.

III. DIMENSION OF ANALYSIS

To analyse the heuristic search based on the visualisation tool, these dimensions or features are given the emphasis [8]:

1. Size of search space
   The most fundamental way of analysing the efficiency of search is by studying the size of the search space. Search space corresponds to the

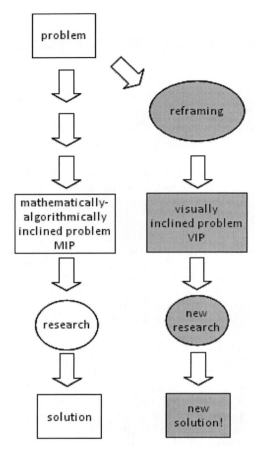

Figure 1. Effect of Re-framing.

amount of effort performed by an algorithm to search for the solution given a particular problem. The space expands in proportion to the number of trials made by the algorithm, as well as the mistakes. In effect, the higher the efficiency, the smaller the space would be.

2. Space structure.

    The space structure is defined by its branching factor and depth. Branching factor is the number of branches made by a particular node during the search process. Depth on the other hand, refers to how deep the search must progress to find a solution or cease from trying. Two other measures are also important. They are:

    a. Depth-node count.

        Depth-node count is the total number of nodes expanded for each level of the search tree. It reflects when the search is most active in term of tree level. The count is considered good when it is high at earlier level of the tree. This implies that the algorithm discriminates potential paths from trivial ones at early stages of the search instead of later.

    b. Time trace representation of node count.

Time trace shows the progression of search. Depth first search shows higher progression comparatively. Breadth first search shows slower progression.

3. Frequency domain analysis.

    Another aspect of search that is crucial is the extent of its backtracking. Frequency domain analysis shows how far search backtracks when reaching a dead end. Depth first search has higher frequency than breadth first search when it comes to backtracking. It implies that depth first search is more focused in the search process.

4. Problem – Search Space evolution.

    The space evolution is the change undergone by the search space when the input is changed. In order to analyse the evolution of a tree in comparison to their input, a series of similar trees can be analysed. Here, the concept of tree similarity or tree congruence is really imperative. The congruence of a tree can be measured via the external nodes shared by subtrees [9]. It is also possible to analyse congruence by studying the structural differences between trees [10, 11, 12]. Other approaches include the usage of an index to make the comparison process more economic [13].

The aforementioned methods can be materialised by visualising the search with a two dimensional tree that is highly interactive.

IV. STTC VISUALISATION TOOL (SVT)

STTC visualisation tool (SVT) is an application that translates the evaluation of the generator matrix **G** in STTC into a visual structure that allows researchers to interact directly with the elements that determine the minimal determinant of the tree.

SVT promotes a variety of interaction to occur [14], which includes zooming, abstracting, highlighting, separating etc. Users can immediately see the impact of a particular generator matrix **G** on the complexity of search without being bogged down by details.

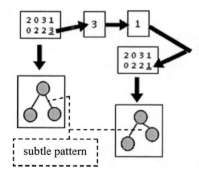

Figure 2. Iterative Exploration.

The tool is used in a cyclic manner, as shown in Fig. 2, where different generator matrix **G** is repeatedly generated and processed to uncover interesting patterns within the tree. This is performed using a simplified version of the P-Set Model [15] where variations of the generator matrix **G** are iteratively explored and the corresponding visualisations recorded.

The patterns of different constructs for the generator matrix **G** can be gathered (as in Fig. 2) by studying the evolution of the search tree from the visual aspect. For instance, the search tree is first generated for the generator matrix **G** [2 0 3 1 ; 0 2 2 3]. To gain insight on how the pattern could change, an element within the initial generator matrix **G** is changed from 3 to 1. The search tree for the new generator matrix **G** [2 0 3 1 ; 0 2 2 1] is then compared to the previous one to capture any subtle patterns that are inherently difficult to discover through analysis.

In using SVT, the main objective is to identify the patterns [16] that can assist the development of a high performance algorithm. That is, to become aware of insights that were previously elusive [17].

Knowing what to focus is a challenge in using any visualisation tools. In our context, emphasis is given to the patterns of interest that practically lies within the regions of the tree where:

1. Solutions are found most frequently.
   The region where solutions are frequently found is rich with potential insights. This is where most observation should focus on, to unveil the possible causality patterns that can direct the search more effectively towards the solution without unnecessarily traversal.
2. Solutions are found earliest.
   Fast solutions are highly useful in providing insights on the estimation of the initial upper bound for the search tree.
3. Pruning is employed most frequently.
   Frequently pruned regions can suggest a way of refining the pruning strategy such that pruning can be performed earlier to a small number of shallow branches instead of a high number of deep branches.

An important fact to note is that visualisation is partially experimental. There is no guarantee that it can improve the process of discovering better solutions for improving the evaluation approach of STTC generator matrix **G**. However, it posits a compelling alternative to the current way of perceiving analysis as being a completely sequential process.

V. CASE STUDY

In the following, the impact of approaching the problem with visualisation is illustrated. The first tree is generated via the original algorithm (Fig. 3) that evaluates the minimal determinant of a generator matrix **G** [1]. It is quite apparent that the tree spans a large search space.

To improve the original approach, the common method of research (i.e., mathematical-algorithmic analysis) was

Figure 3.   Original Algorithm.

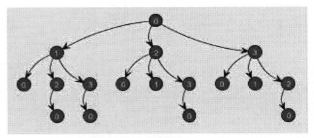

Figure 4.   Improved Inspired by Analysis of Algorithm.

employed. The algorithm of the original approach was analysed to identify the areas of which it can be further enhanced.

As shown in Fig. 4, with the improved approach, the search space was reduced by approximately 50%. By analysing the original algorithm, the last layer pruning was introduced [2].

The improvement inspired by analysing the algorithm was initially rather impressive. However, with visualisation, the best enhancement was discovered. By analysing the visual growth of the tree i.e., comparing the structural differences [10, 11, 12] between trees of different constructs of generator matrix **G**, an entirely new pruning strategy, called the optimal substructure pruning was developed. It can reduce a huge portion of the search space (approximately 70%) with only 3.7% of risk. This is shown in Fig. 5.

VI.   CONCLUSIONS

The discovery made by researching the original algorithm through visualisation is superior to the one done with algorithm analysis. For instance, the improved algorithm that was developed through algorithm analysis reduced the search space by approximately 50% as compared to the ≈ 70% reduction achieved by the enhancement found through visualisation. It is quite intriguing to acknowledge the fact that when the same problem was analysed visually, the research was suddenly provided with a set of new and empowering insights that were not previously visible with the mathematically or algorithmically inclined analysis. This had given rise to the formulation of an entirely different pruning strategy that enabled a more efficient reduction.

ACKNOWLEDGMENT

The authors would like to acknowledge UPM for supporting this research through grant number 91955 entitled "Investigation and Implementation of the Viterbi - MLSE STTC Decoder for Aeronautical Applications".

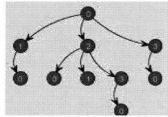

Figure 5. Improvement Inspired by Visualisation.

REFERENCES

[1] T. Fukuda, S. Otsu, Y. Tokunaga and H. Zhao, "A realization of determinant criterion for STTC design," Proc. of the 23rd International Technical Conference on Circuits/Systems, Computers and Communications (ITC-CSCC 2008), July 2008, pp. 61–64.

[2] H. Harun, "An improved algorithm for fast evaluation of space-time trellis code (STTC) generator matrix", Ph.D Thesis, Faculty of Engineering, University Malaya, Kuala Lumpur, Malaysia, June 2010, pp.1–204.

[3] C. Demetrescu, I. Finocchi, G. F. Italiano, and S. Naeher, "Visualization in algorithm engineering: tools and tTechniques," in Dagstuhl Seminar on Experimental Algorithmics, Springer Verlag, 2002.

[4] S. Nitinawarat, and N. A. Boston, "Complete analysis of space-time group codes," appeared in Proceedings of the 43rd Annual Allerton Conference on Communication, Control, and Computing, 2005.

[5] S. Carpendale, "Evaluating information visualizations," in Information Visualisation: Human-Centered Issues and Perspective, Springer, 2008, pp. 19–45.

[6] P. Linkow, "What gifted strategic thinkers do," Training & Development", vol. 53, no. 7,1999, pp. 34–37.

[7] M. Tory and T. Moller, "Human factors in visualization research," IEEE Transactions on Visualization and Computer Graphics, vol. 10, no. 1, 2004, pp. 72–84.

[8] Y. Kuwata and P. R. Cohen, "Visualization tools for real-time search algorithms," Computer Science Technical Report 93-57, 1993.

[9] H. V. D. Parunak, "Don't link me in: set based hypermedia for taxonomic reasoning," in Proc. of the Third ACM Conference on Hypertext (Hypertext'91), ACM Press, Dec. 1991, pp. 233-242.

[10] Y. Zhong, C. A. Meacham and S. Pramanik, "A general method for tree-comparison based on subtree similarity and its use in a taxonomic database," Biosystems, vol. 42, no. 1, 1997, pp. 1–8.

[11] T. N. W. Nye, P. Liò and W. R. Gilks, "A novel algorithm and web-based tool for comparing two alternative phylogenetic trees," Bioinformatics, vol. 22, no. 1, 2006, pp. 117–119.

[12] W. N. Wan Zainon and P. Calder, "Visualising phylogenetic trees," in Proc. Seventh Australasian User Interface Conference (AUIC 2006), pp. 145-152.

[13] D. M. De Vienne, T. Giraud and O. C. Martin, "A congruence index for testing topological similarity between trees," Bioinformatics, vol. 23, no. 23, 2007, pp. 3119–3124.

[14] J. S. Yi, Y. Ah Kang, J. T. Stasko and J. A. Jacko, "Toward a deeper understanding of the role of interaction in information visualization," IEEE Transactions on Visualization and Computer Graphics, vol. 13, no. 6, 2007, pp. 1224–1231.

[15] T. J. Jankun-Kelly, K. L. Ma, and M. Gertz, "A model and framework for visualization exploration," IEEE Transactions on Visualization and Computer Graphics, vol. 13, no. 2, 2007, pp. 357–369.

[16] R. A. Amar and J. T. Stasko, "Knowledge precepts for design and evaluation of information visualizations," IEEE Transactions on Visualization and Computer Graphics, vol. 11, no. 4, 2005, pp. 432–442.

[17] C. Plaisant, "The challenge of information visualization evaluation," In Proceedings of the Working Conference on Advanced Visual Interfaces (AVI), ACM Press, 2004, pp. 109-116.

Edge routing and bundling for graphs with fixed node positions

Miroslav Čermák, Jiří Dokulil
Department of Software Engineering
Charles University
Prague, Czech Republic
(cermak,dokulil)@ksi.mff.cuni.cz

Jana Katreniaková
Department of Computer Science
Comenius University
Bratislava, Slovakia
katreniakova@dcs.fmph.uniba.sk

Abstract—In some graph drawing scenarios, the positions of the nodes are already defined and cannot be modified (for example, they were provided by the user) and the graph drawing techniques are only used to draw edges between the nodes. The number of nodes in such cases tends to be relatively small (tens or hundreds of nodes at most) however the users want to see all of the edges. Various edge routing techniques can provide such services, but if the graph is dense, the drawing can get rather hard to read due to the high number of lines required to visualize the edges. In such cases, clarity can be improved by bundling individual edges (more precisely parts of their drawing) into larger groups and draw as a single line. In this paper, we provide several different techniques for edge bundling based on an edge routing algorithm, compare and evaluate them.

Keywords-edge routing; edge bundling

I. INTRODUCTION

There are applications for graph drawing techniques that do not allow the nodes to be repositioned. The most common reason for this limitation is that the nodes were positioned by the user to the locations where he or she wants them, so moving them around is out of question. If this is the case, the graph drawing is only called upon to handle drawing of the edges that connect the nodes. This rules out many graph drawing algorithms since they handle drawing of nodes and edges simultaneously – they position the nodes so that the edges can be nicely drawn between the nodes. Furthermore, the arbitrary positioning of the nodes may rule out even more algorithms, since the node positions may not be suitable for some edge drawing algorithms – for example the edges may not be positioned on layers. A common way of tackling the problem is to use some kind of edge-routing algorithm [1], [2], [3].

While these algorithms prevent edges from crossing the nodes, thus providing theoretically sound solution to the problem, the readability of such drawings can still be improved. One way of reducing the visual clutter created by routing many edges through a limited space is to use edge bundling. These techniques join some of the lines into larger bundles, thus cleaning up the drawing.

In the following text, we propose one such algorithm. It is an extension of an existing edge routing algorithm. It is aimed at relatively small graphs, where it should provide fast edge drawing with nodes drawn as rectangles, ideally allowing for real-time updating of the drawing while the user changes position of a node (or multiple nodes). The intended application of the algorithm is software like visual database schema designers [4] or UML modeling tools [5]. Such applications allow the user to position nodes (tables, UML classes, etc.) and connect them with edges. This lets the user place the nodes so that it suits his or her needs, for example to group them according to the subset of the problem they are related to. However, choosing the correct path for the edges is also often left to the users, which is a tedious task but the users usually do not put any semantics into the way the edges are routed – they only want to make the drawing clear and potentially aesthetically pleasing. Quite often, they just make sure that the edges do not cross any nodes along their path, which is a necessity [6].

These factors make the task an ideal opportunity for graph drawing techniques. It also provides us with a set of limitations and guidelines for creating a good algorithm. On one hand, it tells us what will the data look like, on the other hand, it provides us with the possibility to better evaluate the results by relating them to the specific real-world scenario. Measuring usability by performance on application specific tasks has already been successfully tried, for example by Purchase [7].

The rest of the text is organized as follows. First, in the Section II, we briefly describe the edge routing algorithm that our solution is based on and our modifications to the algorithm. The Section III describes our contribution – the edge bundling algorithms that we have designed on top of the edge routing algorithm. The ways in which we have evaluated the algorithms are described in the Section IV. Finally, the Section V concludes the text.

II. EDGE ROUTING ALGORITHM

In [2] we have proposed an algorithm for edge routing for fixed nodes positions in cases where the nodes do not overlap. The basic idea of the algorithm is quite straightforward. It starts by drawing the edge as a direct line between the source node and the destination node. Then it reroutes the line (creates a polyline in several steps where in each step it splits one segment of the polyline into two connected

1550-6037/11 $26.00 © 2011 IEEE
DOI 10.1109/IV.2011.47

segments) away from the nodes that intersect with the line. The algorithm does not alter the positions of the nodes and it is therefore possible to use it in conjunction with any node placement algorithm, or even in situations where the nodes are positioned by the user. Another advantage of the algorithm (the one we rely on heavily in our work) is the fact, that it only works locally with just one edge and is even able to process a line that connects arbitrary points in the drawing, not only lines that connect two nodes.

Let us briefly describe the way the algorithm works, since it may help the reader understand the rest of the paper and the drawings produced by our software. It starts with a straight line that connects two nodes. The algorithm then finds a node that intersects the line (there can be more of them, in which case any one of them can be used) and then reroutes the line so that it avoids the node by splitting the line – it adds a new "bend" and forms a polyline with two segments. The bend is positioned at one of the corners of the intersecting node. Which corner exactly is determined by a heuristic algorithm that attempts to find a locally optimal solution that provides the best chance of making the line completely avoid the node. Still, in some cases, splitting the line into two parts is not sufficient to completely avoid the node. In that case, the algorithm determines the best partial solution and the rerouting is completed in a subsequent iteration of the same algorithm. In any case, the algorithm is iterated until all crossings are eliminated.

One drawback of this solution is that it may create unnecessary bends on the line. For example, when the line is rerouted to avoid node a it bends around one of the corners of a. It may then be further rerouted to avoid node b, but this subsequent rerouting takes the line so far that it would avoid a anyway. Then it is unnecessarily bent near a. To avoid such situations, the line is straightened after the rerouting is complete. This means that each bend is tested, whether it is necessary and it is removed if it is not (if the line would still avoid all nodes even without the bend).

This way, the algorithm reroutes all edges so that they avoid all nodes. However, if more lines were bent around the same corner, they would pass the same spot and even bend there, which would make them impossible to distinguish. For that reason, these lines are then ordered according to another local optimization function and then placed at increasing distances from the corner. The optimization function tries to (locally) minimize the number of line crossings created by this step. For an example, see the Figure 1.

The optimization function used to order the lines used by our edge bundling algorithms is different from the one originally proposed (in [2]). Based on our experience and the images produced by our implementation, we decided to use a more simple, but much faster algorithm that also considers the angles at which the lines approach and leave the corner, but it uses a simpler algorithm to convert it to the final ordering. It checks the number of distinct angles on both sides (incoming and outgoing) and takes the order of angles from the side that has higher number of distinct values. This order is the final ordering of the lines at the corner.

As we were still not completely satisfied with the results, we have also added a *line snatching* feature to our corner handling algorithm. If there is a line passing close to the corner but without bending there, we add a new bend to the line at the corner and add it to the lines that are handled by the algorithm. This improved the drawings since such lines were often obscuring the tightly packed lines bending around a corner.

III. BUNDLING OF EDGES

The main idea behind edge bundling is to remove visual clutter in a drawing of a graph by partially reducing the number of distinct lines in the drawing by changing the drawing of the lines so that some of them follow the same path for a certain distance. The bundling effect is usually expressed visually by drawing the bundled portion as a thicker line, usually in proportion (logarithmic) to the number of lines that have been rerouted to follow that path [8], [9].

In the following text, we assume that all edges are drawn as polylines that consist of one or more connected segments. A *bundle* is a set of polylines that all share one or more segments, i.e., there is a segment s such that each polyline in the bundle contains a segment whose endpoints have exactly the same coordinates as s or s reversed (start- and end-points interchanged).

One of the requirements for the bundling algorithm is that all information has to be preserved, which means that the edges may not be bundled in such a way that the user will not be able to identify which edges were originally connected and which were not connected. An example of such situation is a double sided fork. There is no way of telling whether the top node on the left side is connected to the top or bottom node on the right side.

For this reason, we only do one-sided bundling. This means, that for any bundle b, all nodes of the bundle share a segment s where one of the endpoints of s is a node n. We call the node n the *root* of the bundle b. Furthermore, if any two polylines p_1 and p_2 share segments $s_1, \ldots, s_n$, these segments form a continuous line starting at n. In other words, once a polyline splits from the bundle, it may not join it again further along its path.

First, the graph is drawn without any bundling, only using the edge routing algorithm described in the previous section. This provides us with basic information on the directions in which the polylines that correspond to the edges of the graph should lead. Then we modify the drawing by bundling some of the edges.

Because we assume that the scenarios we target provide high chance of "central nodes" (nodes with high degree

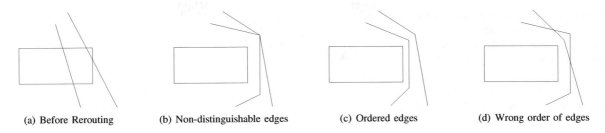

| (a) Before Rerouting | (b) Non-distinguishable edges | (c) Ordered edges | (d) Wrong order of edges |

Figure 1.   More edges passing the same corner

and high importance to the user), we start the bundling by selecting a node with the highest degree. If there are more such nodes, we pick one in such a way that on subsequent runs of the algorithm on the same data the same node is selected. In our implementation, we select the node with the lowest identifier (a number assigned to each node for easier manipulation). Then, we perform a local bundling steps. This is one of the algorithms described in the following sections that processes only edges incident to the selected node and tries to bundle them. This of course only creates bundles rooted at the selected node.

After bundling, we remove all edges that have been bundled from further bundling (to facilitate one-sided bundling) and also remove the selected node from the list of possible starting nodes. Then we repeat the algorithm until no more starting nodes are available. This means that we execute N iterations of the local bundling algorithm where N is the number of nodes in the graph.

A. Direction of the first segment

The first algorithm (referred to as "fixed-angle" in the rest of the text) is very straightforward. The area around the starting node n is split into k regions $r_1, \ldots, r_k$. The value k is a constant specified at the start of bundling. Each region r_i is defined by angles a_i and b_i. Then r_i contains all points whose angle in polar coordinates centered in n is in the half-closed interval $[a_i, b_i)$. The angles are defined so that they split the whole angle into equal slices, i.e. $a_1 = 0$, $b_k = 2 * \Pi$, $a_{(i+1)} = b_i$, and $b_i - a_i = \frac{2*\Pi}{k}$.

Then the polylines that correspond to the edges incident to the current node n are divided into k groups. Each group g_i contains polylines $l_1, \ldots, l_{|g_i|}$ such that for each of the polylines, the segment closest to the current node (denoted $start(l_i, n)$) lies in r_i. Since the segments are straight and start in the origin of the polar coordinate system we are using to divide them into groups, inner points of each segments lie in the same region as well as the opposite endpoint.

All polylines in a group are bundled into one bundle. To do so, we first need to find a good representation for the bundle in the drawing. We compute the average angle a_{avg} of all angles in which the starting segments $start(l_i, n)$ leave the node n. Then we compute the minimum of the lengths of segments $start(l_i, n)$, denoted d_{min}. This is the intended

direction and distance for the first segment in the bundle. However, such segment may cross a node (different from n), which is not acceptable. For this reason, we find d_{final}, which is the maximum distance that is less than d_{min} and which prevents the segment of such length (that leaves n in direction a_{avg}) from crossing any node (other than n). We denote x the point that lies d_{final} distance away from n in the direction a_{avg}.

Then, we replace all polylines l_i with new ones, that are formed by two sets of segments: the segment that connects n to x (the bundled segment) and the polyline from x to the original endpoint $end(l_i, n)$ of l_i. This polyline is created by applying edge routing algorithm to a straight segment that connects x to $end(l_i, n)$.

This would only create bundles with one bundled segment. To create longer bundles, the algorithm is then repeated on a slightly different input:

- point x is used instead of node n
- edges from the bundled group (i.e., those that have been just bundled and their drawings pass the point x) are considered to be the edges adjacent to the point x
- the bundled segment connecting n and x is not considered to be part of the polylines that represent the edges in further steps of the algorithm.

In other words, the algorithm is then run as if we added a new node to the position of x and split all edges from the group at that point.

B. Variable angle

The "variable-angle" algorithm is a modification of the first algorithm. It only changes the way polylines are split into groups. The difference is that the number of groups is not a pre-defined constant. Instead, it is determined each time polylines are split int groups. First, a *critical angle* is determined. The process is iterative and starts with the value of $\Pi/2$. The system then checks whether the maximal angle between any two adjacent segments from $start(l_i, n)$ is larger than the critical angle. If not, the critical angle is halved and the process is repeated until a suitable angle is found.

After the critical angle is found, polylines are grouped into groups like this:

1) Find a gap large enough to contain the critical angle. Set the end of the gap as the current position.
2) Take the first segment s_1 after the current position and all other segments s_i such that s_1 and s_i form an angle that is smaller than the critical angle. Create a new group which consists of polylines that contain these segments. Set current position to the end of the group.
3) If there are ungrouped polylines, goto 2.

The idea behind this algorithm is to provide high number of groups for nodes that have edges leaving in all directions. Otherwise, smaller groups (larger critical angle) is used.

C. First bend

The "first-bend" variant is yet another variant of the first algorithm. In this case, a group is formed by the polylines whose first bend (the end of the segment $start(l_i, n)$) is at the same position.

D. Routing to node clusters

A different approach to edge bundling is based on node clustering. Instead of making a decision only based on the direction in which the polylines leave the origin and then iterating the algorithm to create longer bundles, this approach first determines the point where the bundle splits and them creates the path to and from that point.

However, it keeps the basic structure of repeatedly selecting the node with the highest degree, bundling adjacent edges and removing the starting node and bundled edges from further processing. The difference is in the way the adjacent edges are bundled.

First, the nodes connected to the starting node are clustered according to their position on the plane. The clustering algorithm works like this:

1) For each node, create a cluster that contains only that node. The center of that cluster is the position of the node.
2) Find two clusters c_1 and c_2 whose centers are closest to each other.
3) Create new cluster c_n by joining c_1 and c_2. The center of the cluster is obtained by averaging the coordinates of the nodes in the cluster.
4) Remove clusters c_1 and c_2.
5) If the minimal distance between centers of any two clusters is below a specified threshold, goto 2.

The threshold specified in the last step is computed from the dimensions of the area occupied by the nodes adjacent to the center. At the moment, we are using one quarter of either width or height of the area, depending on which is larger.

Each cluster is then processed individually. First, we find a bounding box for each cluster. Then, we find a route to the cluster by applying the edge routing algorithm to a line connecting the starting node to the bounding box of the

	G1	G2	G3
No bundling	3,03	2,15	3,36
Fixed angle	3,18	3,02	3,12
First bend	3,23	2,14	3,29
Variable angle	2,96	3,21	3,18
Clustering	2,47	2,62	2,40

Table I
WEB SURVEY RESULTS – AVERAGE RATING FOR DIFFERENT GRAPHS

cluster. This creates a polyline m. Then we only take the part of the polyline that is outside the bounding box (denoted m'). The end of the polyline is the point x.

The polyline for each edge is obtained by concatenating m' and the polyline created by applying the edge routing algorithm to the line from x to the destination of the edge (the node connected to the starting node by the edge).

An example of the result is shown in the Figure 2.

IV. EVALUATION

We have evaluated the algorithms proposed in the Section III in three ways. To quickly get some basic feedback from a large group of users, we posted an online survey where the visitors could rate drawings produced by the individual algorithms. To get a more detailed results, we also performed a user study in a controlled environment. The last set of results was obtained by measuring objective criteria like number of edge crossings.

We have focused more on the first two ways of evaluation the algorithms, since they are currently believed to be better for assessing the readability of graph drawing techniques. As an illustration, in [10] authors state that commonly used graph drawing aesthetic criteria (as listed for example in [11]) are not based on experimental data.

A. Web survey

The online survey was intentionally simple, requiring the visitors to spend only a few minutes (the average time was 5 minutes). It consisted of three sets of five images. Each set was a drawing of the same graph, but created using the five possible bundling algorithms (four from section III and no bundling at all). All images from the set were presented to the user along each other (but in a random order) and the user was requested to rate them on a 1 to 5 scale, with 1 being the best and 5 being the worst. The aggregate result may be sen in the Table I. Columns labeled G1, G2, and G3 show the results for each of the three different graphs used in the survey.

When the survey ended we had nearly 120 responses. The actual number ranges from 110 to 118 for the individual images, since not everyone rated all of them.

The results are similar for G1 and G3, but not so with the G2 graph. It was a small and relatively simple graph with 10 nodes and 20 edges. With this graph, the users clearly preferred the version without any bundling. This is not as

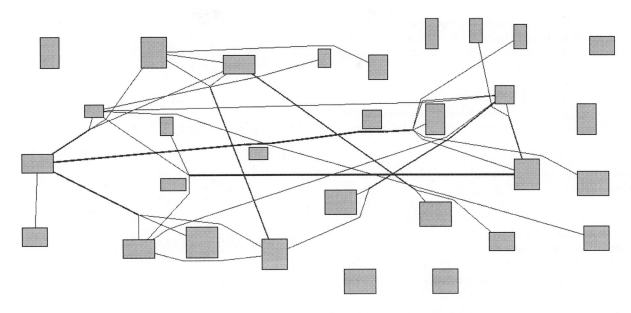

Figure 2. Example of clustering-based edge bundling

surprising, since in such a small graph it is easily possible to track each individual edge even without bundling. The "first bend" algorithm performed just as well, but it is due to the fact, that it was not able to create any bundles, thus producing the same graph as the no-bundling version. The clustering-based algorithm also scored quite well, but again, it was only able to create two bundles. The other two (fixed and variable angle first segment bundling) did create more bundles (about twice as much), but scored badly.

The G1 and G3 graphs were much larger (both contained 50 nodes and 40 edges). In these cases, all options reached similar scores, except for the clustering-based algorithm which reached significantly better scores for both graphs.

B. User study

For the "offline" user study, we asked the users to come to us and perform a test on our computers under our supervision. First, each user was individually briefed on the tasks to complete, then a series of 100 tasks was performed by the user uninterrupted. Each task displayed a new random graph with the same properties (50 nodes, 40 edges) where edges were bundled by an algorithm chosen randomly from the same five possibilities as in the online survey.

Purchase [12], [13] and Ware [14] used evaluation based on the response time and correctness rate and we decided to follow in their footsteps. For this reason, we faced the user with the following two types of tasks, mixed at random:

1) Two nodes of the graph were displayed in a clearly visible color and the user was asked to determine if the two nodes are directly connected by an edge. The answer was given by clicking `Yes` or `No` button.

	type 1	type 2	type 1	type 2
No bundling	96.2%	99.0%	2.77s	0.25s
Fixed angle	95.3%	98.4%	3.88s	0.32s
First bend	97.5%	99.2%	3.97s	0.22s
Variable angle	92.4%	98.5%	4.34s	0.27s
Clustering	97.0%	99.6%	3.88s	0.20s

Table II
USER STUDY RESULTS – ACCURACY AND TIME

2) One of the nodes was displayed in a clearly visible color (different from the colors used in the other task type). The user was asked to mark (click) all nodes directly connected to the highlighted node and then click the `Done` button.

The type of each task was also selected at random, but the probability of the first task type was 80%, leaving 20% chance for the second type. This ratio was chosen to reduce the time required by the test, since the second task type is significantly more time consuming. Since the tasks are very repetitive, we wanted to keep the total time of the test low. With this setup, one test took about 10 minutes (plus the briefing and debriefing).

The average results are displayed in the Table II. The first two columns show the accuracy with which the users picked the Yes/No answer correctly (task type 1) and the accuracy with which they picked the right nodes (task type 2). The second two columns show the time elapsed before the user clicked the Yes or No button (task type 1) and the average time it took the user to select a single node (task type 2). The results suggest that it is best to use no bundling at all for determining whether two nodes are connected (it is a bit less accurate, but much faster), but clustering seems to be the best choice for the second task type (it is both faster and more accurate). Still, the no-bundling solution also provides decent performance.

C. Measurements without user involvement

Another set of tests we have performed to evaluate different bundling methods is measuring some objective properties of the drawings.

The first, most obvious, criterion is the number of edge crossings in the drawing. An important factor to note that if a line crosses a bundled segment, we only count is as one crossing, not the number equal to the number of bundled edges. As a result of this, the number of edge crossings is significantly reduced when bundling is used, since there are fewer lines to cross. This means that there are fewer occurences of two lines crossing each other in the produced drawing but not necessarily a lower number of edge crossings from the formal point of view.

There is no bundling method that clearly outperforms the other methods under all circumstances. The average values for 10 graphs with 50 nodes and 100 edges are shown in the Table III. The number of crossings may seem high, but it is a very dense graph.

Another measure we explored was the reduction of the total length of all polylines used in the drawing. As Ware states [14], this is one of the most important edge drawing criteria (along with the number of crossings and continuity), but it is often overlooked. Our rationale for including the criterion is, that we want to make the drawing as clear as possible and the lines are what makes it more difficult to read. Thus reducing the space taken by the lines should help. We cannot reduce the number of the lines, due to the requirement that all information has to be preserved – the number of lines has to stay equal to the number of edges. We can only make the lines occupy less space by making them shorter or bundling them.

Once again, no algorithm was able to come out best in all tests, but all of them managed to provide significant reduction of the total line length, except for the first-bend bundling algorithm, which consistently provided the worst results, some times being able to reduce the length only by less then 10%. The rest of the algorithm was able to provide between 20% and 45% reduction of the total line length. The average values are once again shown in the Table III.

Furthermore, we assessed the size of the maximal bundle. These test showed us some clear trends: not surprisingly, the first-bend algorithm produced the smallest bundles. But more interesting were the results of the cluster-based bundling, which creates smaller (maximal) bundles than fixed- and variable- angle bundling. This may not necessarily be a negative result for the cluster-based bundling but we think it is an interesting observation. Again, for the average value of the maximal bundle size, refer to the Table III.

	number of crossings	length reduction	maximal bundle
No bundling	1935	0%	1
Fixed angle	775	35%	21.2
First bend	1065	21%	8.8
Variable angle	747	38%	23.3
Clustering	818	40%	12.2

Table III
OBJECTIVE CRITERIA – NUMBER OF CROSSINGS, LENGTH REDUCTION AND SIZE OF THE MAXIMAL BUNDLE

	min	2°	5°	10°
No bundling	0.1°	58.5	68.8	86.3
Fixed angle	0.24°	11.2	14.7	20.8
First bend	0.22°	18.2	27.9	44.3
Variable angle	0.22°	10.9	14.0	19.0
Clustering	0.24°	11.1	14.9	21.5

Table IV
CRITERIA BASED ON ANGULAR RESOLUTION

The last set of criteria are concerned with the angular resolution, i.e. the minimal angle between two segments that leave a certain node. We measured the exact value of the angle, but also counted the number of situations where two neighboring segments form an angle smaller than a specified threshold. In other words, the number of situations, where the angle between lines that leave a node is small and it may be difficult to clearly distinguish them. The values of the minimal angle are not very encouraging, since it is usually well below one degree, but they are usually improved when edge bundling is used.

The angular resolution shows no clear trends that would differentiate the various bundling algorithms. However, the statistics that show the number of segment pairs that form angle smaller then a threshold do provide more interesting reading. In all of the test that we performed, the numbers decreased significantly for all bundling algorithms and all three values of threshold (2, 5 and 10 degrees). Once again, the first-bend bundling consistently scored last, with the other three techniques providing very similar results, usually reducing the numbers by about three quarters. The result for the same data sets as in previous cases are shown in the Table IV.

The last metric we tested was the time required to generate the drawing. The Table V shows times taken by the algorithms on graphs with varying number of nodes and edges (10 nodes – 20 edges, 50 nodes – 100 edges, 200 nodes – 1000 edges). For small graphs (10 nodes, 10 edges), the time required by all the algorithms was less than 15 milliseconds. For slightly larger (50 nodes, 40 edges) the times ranged from 20 to 60 milliseconds, with the first-bend bundling being by far the fastest bundling algorithm, and variable-angle bundling finishing last, but only slightly slower than the fixed-angle bundling. The clustering-based

	10N 20E	50N 100E	200N 1000E
No bundling	1.6ms	83ms	3.7s
Fixed angle	6.3ms	197ms	11.6s
First bend	2.4ms	105ms	5.6s
Variable angle	5.0ms	226ms	11.3s
Clustering	3.9ms	124ms	5.8s

Table V
PERFORMANCE (TIME TO COMPUTE LAYOUT)

algorithm took slightly longer than the first-bend algorithm, but still significantly outperformed the fixed- and variable-angle bundling. The same relative speeds were maintained even in further test with large graphs. Graphs with 50 nodes and 100 edges took between 62 and 222 milliseconds to draw. This is roughly the size of the graphs we expect to be present in the scenarios where our edge bundling techniques would be used. The largest graph we tested (200 nodes, 1000 edges) can no longer be drawn in real-time while the user changes node positions – they took from 3.7 to 16 seconds depending on the algorithm, node positions and edges (we tested several random graphs with the desired node and edge count).

The implementation of the algorithms used in the test was not heavily optimized. A great improvement in the speed could be for instance gained by using spatial indexing structures for crossings detection and segment lookup.

V. CONCLUSIONS

In this text, we have presented several edge bundling algorithms. Based on the evaluation we have performed with the algorithms, the best version is the clustering-based variant. It scored best in the usability study and also in the online survey. It is also on of the fastest variants. On the whole, it is able to provide better experience to the user while having small impact on the performance on the application.

There are several ways in which our results may be improved. During the user evaluation and debriefing interviews we have identified critical situations, which caused errors in user's understanding of the graph. We detected two main problems. First, we need to eliminate edge bends near edge crossings (especially near edge crossings with bundled edge). In some drawings, the distance between the edge bend and the edge-crossing was under the resolution capabilities of a humans eye and this caused the two edges to be indistinguishable. Second, the point at which the bundle leading to a cluster splits into individual lines should be further from the bounding box of the cluster.

ACKNOWLEDGMENT

This work was supported by the grant SVV-2011-263312 and the grant 28910 of the Grant Agency of the Charles University. The work was also supported by the grant 202/10/0761 of the Czech Science Foundation.

REFERENCES

[1] T. Dwyer and L. Nachmanson, "Fast edge-routing for large graphs," in *Graph Drawing*, ser. Lecture Notes in Computer Science, D. Eppstein and E. Gansner, Eds. Springer Berlin / Heidelberg, 2010, vol. 5849, pp. 147–158.

[2] J. Dokulil and J. Katreniakova, "Edge routing with fixed node positions," in *IV '08: Proceedings of the 2008 12th International Conference Information Visualisation*. Washington, DC, USA: IEEE Computer Society, 2008, pp. 626–631.

[3] K. Freivalds, "Curved edge routing," in *Fundamentals of Computation Theory*, ser. Lecture Notes in Computer Science, R. Freivalds, Ed. Springer Berlin / Heidelberg, 2001, vol. 2138, pp. 126–137.

[4] E. M. Haber, "Visual schema management for database systems," Ph.D. dissertation, The University of Wisconsin - Madison, 1995, supervisor-Ioannidis, Yannis.

[5] G. Booch, J. Rumbaugh, and I. Jacobson, *Unified Modeling Language User Guide, The (2nd Edition) (Addison-Wesley Object Technology Series)*. Addison-Wesley Professional, 2005.

[6] K. Sugiyama, *Graph drawing and applications for software and knowledge engineers*, ser. Series on software engineering and knowledge engineering. World Scientific, 2002.

[7] H. C. Purchase, J.-A. Allder, and D. A. Carrington, "Graph layout aesthetics in uml diagrams: User preferences," *J. Graph Algorithms Appl.*, vol. 6, no. 3, pp. 255–279, 2002.

[8] A. Lambert, R. Bourqui, and D. Auber, "Winding roads: Routing edges into bundles," *Comput. Graph. Forum*, vol. 29, no. 3, pp. 853–862, 2010.

[9] A. Telea and O. Ersoy, "Image-based edge bundles: Simplified visualization of large graphs," *Comput. Graph. Forum*, vol. 29, no. 3, 2010.

[10] W. Huang and P. Eades, "How people read graphs," in *proceedings of the 2005 Asia-Pacific symposium on Information visualisation - Volume 45*, ser. APVis '05. Darlinghurst, Australia, Australia: Australian Computer Society, Inc., 2005, pp. 51–58.

[11] I. G. Tollis, G. Di Battista, P. Eades, and R. Tamassia, *Graph Drawing: Algorithms for the Visualization of Graphs*. Prentice Hall, July 1998.

[12] H. C. Purchase, "Which aesthetic has the greatest effect on human understanding?" in *Graph Drawing*, ser. Lecture Notes in Computer Science, G. D. Battista, Ed., vol. 1353. Springer, 1997, pp. 248–261.

[13] H. Purchase, "Performance of layout algorithms: Comprehension, not computation," *Journal of Visual Languages & Computing*, vol. 9, no. 6, pp. 647 – 657, 1998.

[14] C. Ware, H. Purchase, L. Colpoys, and M. McGill, "Cognitive measurements of graph aesthetics," *Information Visualization*, vol. 1, pp. 103–110, June 2002.

Node-attribute graph layout for small-world networks

Helen Gibson, Joe Faith

School of Computing, Engineering and Information Sciences
Northumbria University
Newcastle-upon-Tyne, UK
{helen.gibson,joe.faith}@northumbria.ac.uk

Abstract—**Small-world networks are a very commonly occurring type of graph in the real-world, which exhibit a clustered structure that is not well represented by current graph layout algorithms. In many cases we also have information about the nodes in such graphs, which are typically depicted on the graph as node colour, shape or size. Here we demonstrate that these attributes can instead be used to layout the graph in high-dimensional data space. Then using a dimension reduction technique, targeted projection pursuit, the graph layout can be optimised for displaying clustering. The technique outperforms force-directed layout methods in cluster separation when applied to a sample, artificially generated, small-world network.**

Keywords-**Graph Layout; Dimension Reduction; Node-attribute; Clustering; Small-world**

I. INTRODUCTION

Many real-world networks display a small-world network structure, characterised by the fact that they are highly clustered and have smaller than average shortest path lengths. Small-world networks are likely to contain cliques (a fully connected subgraph) or at least highly connected subgraphs of nodes. Real world examples include neural networks, social networks and the connectivity of the World Wide Web [1]. It has been found that when users arrange such graphs manually, they will seek to organise the graph such that nodes in clusters are grouped together [2]. It would therefore be useful for graph layout algorithms to also emphasise these clusters – but most layout algorithms fail to do this.

Node-attribute graphs are graphs in which all nodes have a set of attributes associated with them. These attributes can be thought of as a new type of node to which that nodes links or, vice-versa, that other nodes in the graph could instead be defined as attributes. For example, membership of a group in a social network could be represented as an attribute of those nodes representing its members, or as a link from a group node to the member nodes. Here we demonstrate that attributes associated with cluster membership can position each node in a high-dimensional attribute space such that dimension reduction techniques can then be used to layout the nodes in the graph in two dimensions. The aim of this technique is first to show the clustering in the graph and ultimately to use this information to analyse which attributes are most influential in the clustering and the layout in general.

This pilot study uses a dimension reduction technique developed for vector data, targeted projection pursuit, to show cluster structure more clearly than other layout algorithms.

II. SMALL-WORLD NETWORKS

Many real-world networks can be approximated by small-world networks. In fact, Albert and Barabási [3] have hypothesised that the prevalence of small-world networks in biological systems is due to inherent structural advantages. A small-world network is where, despite the fact that the network is large, it takes very few steps to move between any two nodes. Specifically, they have a smaller than average shortest path length and a high clustering coefficient meaning they are also more likely to contain clusters of nodes. The most common real-world example of a small-world network is from the six degrees of separation experiment; the concept that most people in the United States are separated by only six people in a chain of friendship, as suggested by psychologist Milgram [4]. Other examples of small-world networks include the collaboration of actors in films [5], social networks, neural networks of the brain [6], and the connectivity of the World Wide Web [7].

Given that small-world networks are such a commonly occurring graph structure, it is then a surprise that so few layout algorithms display them well [8]. Force-directed layouts, in particular, do not optimise the visualisation for small world networks. This is, in part, because of the short path length (graph-theoretic distance) small-world networks have. Force-directed layouts such as Kamada and Kawai's [9] energy-based layout try to represent graph-theoretic distance as Euclidean distances and so if all pairs of nodes have a small graph-theoretic distance then most pairs of nodes are placed close together and the clustered structure of the graph is lost. Therefore layouts which can accentuate this clustered structure offer advantages over traditional layouts for small-world networks.

III. NODE ATTRIBUTE GRAPHS

Node-attribute, or multivariate, graphs are graphs that incorporate attributes on the nodes as well as displaying the links between the nodes [10]. Node attributes on graphs are quite common and the ability to represent them by colour, shape or size is a functionality included in many pieces

1550-6037/11 $26.00 © 2011 IEEE
DOI 10.1109/IV.2011.64

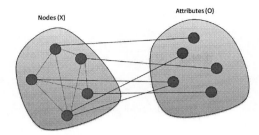

Figure 1: A node-attribute graph where the blue circles are nodes and the red are attributes. Links exist between the blue nodes and between the blue and red nodes.

of graph drawing software such as Cytoscape [11], Gephi [12], Pajek [13] and others. However, there is a limit to the number of attributes that can be represented this way. One way of representing a node attribute in a graph would be to add an extra node representing the attribute and a (weighted) link to the graph from the node whose attribute it is, as in Fig. 1. Obviously actually representing the graph this way would add a significant number of extra nodes and links to the view and most likely make the graph harder, not easier, to read.

Instead, defining the graph this way means the graph can be divided into two separate graphs: the original graph with no attributes shown and a bipartite graph where links only exist between nodes and their attributes. This type of graph structure contains a subset of graphs termed semi-bipartite graphs [14] where a semi-bipartite graph has second type of nodes as opposed to a set of attributes. Real-world graphs which have this semi-bipartite structure include Xu et al.'s [14] network containing genes and gene ontology terms where genes are connected to their ontology terms and the terms are linked to each other hierarchically. Other possible real-world examples could be a drug and protein network where similar drugs (or similar proteins) are linked and a drugs are linked to proteins they target [15]. Similarly in social networks, such as those from Facebook, links are made between friends and a second set of links can be added for connections to groups, activities, 'Likes', 'Fan of', etc.

Another example of multi-modal graphs are those from formal concept analysis, known as Galois or concept lattices. These are similar to bipartite graphs but for which a specific graph visualisation has been developed. The set of nodes are divided into non-disjoint subsets each of which contains nodes that share the same attributes; and the relations between subsets are then shown using a Hasse diagram [16]. The composition of each subset is then shown using by annotating the glyph representing it. Freeman and White [17] used Galois lattices to show social networks with three types of link: node-node, attribute-attribute and node-attribute. However they are different from the graphs we are visualising here as only node-attribute data is used and

then the visualisation is used to imply the node-node and attribute-attribute relationships rather than taking them as a given from the start.

IV. GRAPH CLUSTERING

Users value clustering in graphs and they try to recreate this structure when laying out graphs manually [2]. Traditional force-directed layouts do not reproduce the clusterings in graphs well; this is because they tend to place all nodes of high degree at the centre of the graph and also try to adhere to the aesthetic criteria of keeping edge lengths uniform which makes cluster separation more difficult [8]. One attempt to visualise clusterings in graphs is due to Noack [8], [18] who demonstrated an energy layout algorithm for clustering graphs, calling them 'interpretable layouts' since the links are not shown in the visualisation but are instead used to position the nodes; the nodes are then also sized depending on their degree. The graph is not clustered prior to layout, rather it is clustered based on the graph-partitioning idea of cuts and then visualised. A cut is a simple measure of the coupling between two sets of disjoint nodes, and Noack [18] proposes two models: node-repulsion and edge-repulsion. The node-normalised cut is the ratio of number of edges between the two partitions to the total possible number of edges between the two partitions. The edge-normalised cut is then defined as the ratio between the number of edges between the partitions and the product of the sums of the degrees of the nodes in each partition. The edge-repulsion model is preferred as it is less likely to place nodes of high degree in the centre of the graph.

Other attempts for visualising clustered graphs include Huang and Nyguen's [19] approach where the graph is divided into densely connected subgraphs that are each placed on their own separate rectangular partition for layout. Chung Graham and Tsiatas [20] use a version of Kamada and Kawai's force-directed layout and the PageRank algorithm for computing a clustered layout while Balzer and Deussen [21] use a 3-D graph with pre-defined clusters to first wrap spheres around clusters and then use implicit surfaces to further emphasise cluster separation.

V. DIMENSION REDUCTION AND TARGETED PROJECTION PURSUIT

Dimension reduction takes some data in high-dimensional space and computes a lower dimensional representation of that data, which for visualisation purposes is likely to be two dimensions. Methods of dimension reduction include multidimensional scaling, principal component analysis and other linear and non-linear methods.

Targeted projection pursuit (TPP) [22] is a linear projection method of dimension reduction such that, instead of searching for the most interesting projection (as with projection pursuit), the user can interact with the data by attempting to move the points around to fit their intuition and the algorithm will try to find a projection that best matches the users desired view. This is an effective technique because it allows users to explore and interact with the data in real-time as well as to iteratively make and test hypotheses about how the data can be projected and what that projection then means in the context of the original high-dimensional data set. TPP works by the user suggesting a view of the data they wish to see and then searches for a projection that best matches that target view. So by taking an $n \times k$ matrix X and a $n \times 2$ target view T TPP tries to find a $k \times 2$ projection matrix P that minimises the difference between the two, where n is the number of points and k the number of dimensions. That is

$$\min \|T - XP\| \tag{1}$$

As an alternative to user-directed layout, TPP can also search for a projection that separates the data into pre-defined classes by trying to maximise the distance between classes through projecting the data on to the vertices of a simplex [23].

VI. NODE-ATTRIBUTE GRAPH LAYOUT

Define a node-attribute graph to be $G(V_X, V_O, E_{XX}, E_{XO})$ where V_X are the nodes in first partition, V_O are the nodes in the second partition, E_{XO} are the edges linking nodes in V_X to V_O and E_{XX} are the edges between the nodes in partition V_X. We call the nodes in V_X our entity nodes and the nodes in V_O our attribute nodes.

One pre-requisite for this visualisation is that each node needs to be defined as a being a member of a particular cluster before the analysis can be carried out. This can be done by using particular cluster structure that occurs naturally in the dataset or by using an unsupervised clustering algorithm first, such as k-means, to impose a clustered structure on the dataset.

The visualisation of the graph will show the V_X nodes and the E_{XX} edges while the layout will depend on the clustering of the nodes and the edges E_{XO} between the V_X nodes, that are visualised, and the V_O nodes, that are not. In order to layout the points, for each node in V_X a vector, p_i with binary entries is constructed based on their links to the V_O nodes, i.e. if an edge between V_{X_i} and V_{O_j} exists

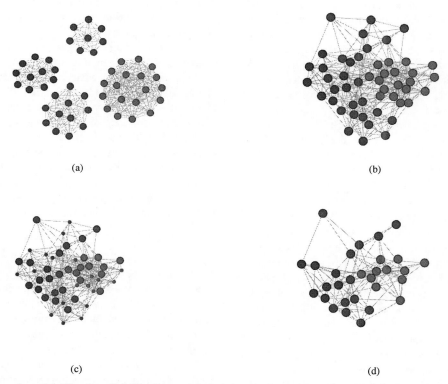

(a)

(b)

(c)

(d)

Figure 2: Dataset creation. (a) The four initial cliques of nodes. (b) Random links are added between cliques and removed within cliques. (c) Nodes that are chosen as attributes are indicated as the smaller nodes. (d) The attribute nodes and their connections are removed leaving only the $x - x$ links. All layouts produced using Yifan Hu's force directed layout in Gephi.

then the entry takes value one and if it does not then takes value zero.

$$p_i = \{(p_{i1}, p_{i2}, p_{i3}, \ldots)^T \mid$$
$$p_{ij} = 1 \text{ if } E_{X_i, O_j} \text{ exists and 0 otherwise}\} \quad (2)$$

This can be extended to include relationships to attributes which are not only binary but also nominal and real-valued data too, especially if the link is considered to have a weighting. From this each V_X can be described as $V_X(c, p_i)$ in $|V_O + 1|$ dimensional space where one of those dimensions describes the cluster, c, to which the node belongs.

The aim is then to use TPP to visualise the position of each node in two-dimensional space and use it to separate the clusters in the graph as far as possible. In this case the vector p_i for each of the V_{X_i} nodes is taken as one of the n rows forming the $n \times k$ matrix, where k is the number of attribute nodes. A two-dimensional projection is found that minimises the difference between the target projection defined by the user and itself. The nodes can be coloured according to their cluster membership or if no clustering is proposed then an unsupervised clustering algorithm can be used to define one. The links between the entity nodes can then be added to the visualisation.

From this point the user can then either repeatedly select and drag nodes to move them to fit their idea of how the graph should appear and the closest possible projection will be shown or the process can be automated. In this case to have the centre of each cluster to be positioned over the vertices of a simplex is seen as the optimum target view, i.e. where each of the clusters will be most separated from each of the other clusters. This automated process is akin to just the user trying to separate the clusters themselves by dragging points but achieves maximum separation.

VII. EXAMPLE APPLICATION

In this pilot study, TPP was used to visualise a clustered small-world network with node-attribute data, and the results compared with the same graph visualised using the Yifan Hu layout in Gephi [12] and Noack's LinLog layout [18].

An example graph with the required properties (small-world, known clusters, and node attributes) was constructed by starting with several fully-connected cliques that will define the clusters in the graph (Fig. 2a). Specifically, using an artificially generated data set allows control over the properties of the graph in order to evaluate the potential success of the technique for real-world data in the future without having to account for noise or unexpected variations. The adjacency matrix that defines the graph was then randomly mutated to add new links between cliques and removing some links within cliques (Fig. 2b). Nodes were then randomly divided into entities and attributes (Fig. 2c) and any remaining links between two attributes are removed. From this there is data for two graphs: the bipartite

graph between attribute and entity nodes and the graph of connections between the entity nodes only (Fig. 2d).

In this case the graph original consisted of 50 nodes with 318 links divided unequally into 4 cliques of sizes 11, 12, 19 and 8 and the addition of noise to the dataset increased this to 350 edges. Then the nodes were split into entity and attribute node groups with 30 nodes in the entity group and 20 nodes in the attribute group. This resulted in cluster sizes of 7, 7, 11 and 5 in the entity group and 4, 5, 8 and 3 in the attribute group. In terms of links this gives 132 links in the visualisation, 173 links used in the projection and 45 links between the attributes were removed. The graph is then laid out in three ways: the Yifan Hu force-directed approach from Gephi [12] (Fig. 3); TPP (Fig. 4); and Noack's LinLog layout in Fig. 5.

TPP clearly achieves a greater visual separation between clusters than the force-directed layout. This is especially the case with some nodes which would be difficult to determine which cluster they belong to without colouring. This could be advantageous in the future as it would free the use of colour to show some other attribute. The use of TPP to separate the clusters is different to just using user choice to position the nodes, as in Fig. 3, since in that case the position of the nodes is purely dependent on where the user want to put them. In TPP, however, the position of the nodes is the product of a linear projection. Additionally moving one node, or a group of nodes, in TPP rarely affects only the chosen nodes; other nodes are moved as a consequence of trying to fit the selected nodes to their preferred position. That is, the position of the nodes using the TPP algorithm is purely dependent on the attribute nodes and to a lesser extent cluster membership.

LinLog also creates clear spatial separation; however it imposes its own clustering on the data which makes clear comparisons difficult. While the lack of links in this layout makes the clustering very clear – and the distances between clusters gives an indication of the number of links between them – the lack of links means some of the understanding of how the clusters are related to each other is lost. It also affects the ability to see if there are individual links between nodes in different clusters that show interesting information.

VIII. CONCLUSION

The aim of this approach is to show the clustering that occurs in most small-world networks and its relationship to node attributes. It can be seen that the layout produced by TPP does show the clustered structure of the graph more clearly than a simple force-directed layout did where the separation of clusters is mostly discernible by their colour.

Further validation on this layout and its success will include measuring both the intra-node distances within clusters and the inter-node distances between clusters and comparing them between the layouts. Secondly, as it is known that users also prefer fewer edge crossings [2] in their graphs,

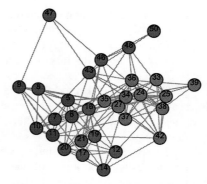

Figure 3: Yifan Hu's force-directed approach from Gephi

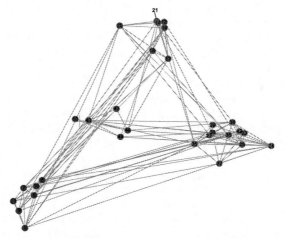

Figure 4: Target Projection Pursuit with clusters separated as far as possible

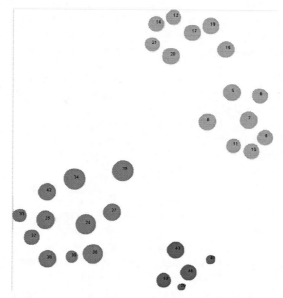

Figure 5: Noack's linlog layout which imposes its own clustering on the graph. The blue cluster corresponds to the purple cluster, the red to the green and the two green clusters to the red and blue clusters in the other layouts.

it will be useful to measure the difference between the numbers of edge crossings between the two layouts that show links. The purpose of using attributes for layout is not only important for producing a good layout, they may also be able to give more insight into the structure of the graph. Particularly, being able to assess which attributes may be the most influential in the layout and which attributes are the least, or even completely irrelevant.

Further extensions to this dataset would be to alter the ratio of entities to attributes and measure how this affects the ability to cluster the data and the layout in general. This was also an artificially created dataset and so most real-world graphs may contain more noise, specifically it would be useful to investigate how introducing known exceptions into the data, such as misleading attributes and wrongly classified nodes may give an indication of how great an effect they have on the layout and how easy is it to identify any errors. It will also be important to test how this technique can scale to graphs with hundreds or even thousands of nodes.

REFERENCES

[1] D. J. Watts and S. H. Strogatz, "Collective dynamics of 'small-world' networks," *Nature*, vol. 393, no. 6684, pp. 440–442, Jun. 1998.

[2] F. van Ham and B. Rogowitz, "Perceptual Organization in User-Generated Graph Layouts," *IEEE Transactions on Visualization and Computer Graphics*, vol. 14, no. 6, pp. 1333–1339, Nov. 2008.

[3] R. Albert and A.-L. Barabási, "Statistical mechanics of complex networks," *Reviews of Modern Physics*, vol. 74, no. 1, pp. 47–97, Jan. 2002.

[4] S. Milgram, "The small world problem," *Psychology Today*, vol. 2, no. 1, pp. 60–67, 1967.

[5] D. Auber, Y. Chiricota, F. Jourdan, and G. Melancon, "Multiscale visualization of small world networks," *Information Visualization, IEEE Symposium on*, vol. 0, p. 10, 2003.

[6] O. Sporns, D. R. Chialvo, M. Kaiser, and C. C. Hilgetag, "Organization, development and function of complex brain networks." *Trends in cognitive sciences*, vol. 8, no. 9, pp. 418–25, Sep. 2004.

[7] R. Albert, H. Jeong, and A. Barabási, *Nature*, no. 6749, pp. 130–131.

[8] A. Noack, "An energy model for visual graph clustering," in *Graph Drawing*, ser. Lecture Notes in Computer Science, G. Liotta, Ed. Springer Berlin / Heidelberg, 2004, vol. 2912, pp. 425–436.

[9] T. Kamada and S. Kawai, "An algorithm for drawing general undirected graphs," *Information Processing Letters*, vol. 31, no. 1, pp. 7–15, 1989.

[10] M. Wattenberg, "Visual exploration of multivariate graphs," in *Proceedings of the SIGCHI conference on Human Factors in computing systems*, ser. CHI '06. New York, NY, USA: ACM, 2006, pp. 811–819.

[11] P. Shannon, A. Markiel, O. Ozier, N. S. Baliga, J. T. Wang, D. Ramage, N. Amin, B. Schwikowski, and T. Ideker, "Cytoscape: a software environment for integrated models of biomolecular interaction networks," *Genome Research*, vol. 13, no. 11, pp. 2498–504, Nov. 2003.

[12] M. Bastian, S. Heymann, and M. Jacomy, "Gephi: An open source software for exploring and manipulating networks," in *Third International AAAI Conference on Weblogs and Social Media*, 2009, pp. 361–362.

[13] V. Batagelj and A. Mrvar, "Pajek analysis and visualization of large networks," in *Graph Drawing*, ser. Lecture Notes in Computer Science, P. Mutzel, M. Jnger, and S. Leipert, Eds. Springer Berlin / Heidelberg, 2002, vol. 2265, pp. 8–11.

[14] K. Xu, R. Williams, S.-H. Hong, Q. Liu, and J. Zhang, "Semibipartite Graph Visualization for Gene Ontology Networks," ser. Lecture Notes in Computer Science, D. Eppstein and E. R. Gansner, Eds. Berlin, Heidelberg: Springer Berlin Heidelberg, 2010, vol. 5849, pp. 244–255–255.

[15] S. J. Cockell, J. Weile, P. Lord, C. Wipat, D. Andriychenko, M. Pocock, D. Wilkinson, M. Young, and A. Wipat, "An Integrated Dataset for in Silico Drug Discovery," *Journal of Integrative Bioinformatics*, vol. 7, no. 3, pp. 116–128, Jan. 2010. [Online]. Available: http://journal.imbio.de/index.php?paper_id=116

[16] U. Priss, "Formal concept analysis in information science," *Annual Review of Information Science and Technology*, vol. 40, no. 1, pp. 521–543, 2006.

[17] L. C. Freeman and D. R. White, "Using Galois Lattices to Represent Network Data," *Sociological Methodology*, vol. 23, pp. 127–146, 1993.

[18] A. Noack, "Energy models for graph clustering," *Journal of Graph Algorithms and Applications*, vol. 11, no. 2, pp. 453–480, 2007.

[19] M. L. Huang and Q. V. Nguyen, "A fast algorithm for balanced graph clustering," in *Information Visualization, 2007. IV '07. 11th International Conference*, july 2007, pp. 46 –52.

[20] F. Graham and A. Tsiatas, "Finding and Visualizing Graph Clusters Using PageRank Optimization," in *Algorithms and Models for the Web-Graph*, ser. Lecture Notes in Computer Science, R. Kumar and D. Sivakumar, Eds. Berlin, Heidelberg: Springer Berlin Heidelberg, 2010, vol. 6516, pp. 86–97–97.

[21] M. Balzer and O. Deussen, "Level-of-detail visualization of clustered graph layouts," *Asia-Pacific Symposium on Visualization*, vol. 0, pp. 133–140, 2007.

[22] J. Faith, "Targeted projection pursuit for interactive exploration of high- dimensional data sets," pp. 286–292, 2007.

[23] J. Faith, R. Mintram, and M. Angelova, "Targeted projection pursuit for visualizing gene expression data classifications," *Bioinformatics*, vol. 22, no. 21, pp. 2667–2673, Nov. 2006.

Using the Gestalt Principle of Closure to Alleviate the Edge Crossing Problem in Graph Drawings

Amalia Rusu[1], Andrew J. Fabian[2], Radu Jianu[3], Adrian Rusu[2]

[1]Department of Software Engineering, Fairfield University, Fairfield, CT 06824, USA
[2]Department of Computer Science, Rowan University, Glassboro, NJ 08028, USA
[3]Department of Computer Science, Brown University, Providence, RI 02912, USA

arusu@fairfield.edu, fabian78@students.rowan.edu, jr@cs.brown.edu, rusu@rowan.edu

Abstract

Graphs, generally used as data structures in computer science applications, have steadily shown a growth in mapping various types of relationships, from maps to computer networks to social networks. As graph layouts and visualizations have been at the forefront of graph drawing research for decades, it consequently led to aesthetic heuristics that not only generated better visualizations and aesthetically appealing graphs but also improved readability and understanding of the graphs. A variety of approaches examines aesthetics of nodes, edges, or graph layout, and related readability metrics. In this paper we focus on the edge crossing problem and propose a solution that incorporates Gestalt principles to improve graph aesthetics and readability. We introduce the concept of breaks in edges at edge crossings. A break is a gap in an edge drawing occurring in the vicinity of an edge crossing. At every edge crossing, one of the incident edges is broken, which will prevent any unintentional gestalts that occur at edge crossings that reduce the readability of a graph drawing. We present our preliminary results and user studies that show that this technique could play a role in improving graph readability.

Keywords--- **graphs, graph drawings, edge crossings, Gestalt principles.**

1. Introduction

Graph drawing algorithms can be qualitatively compared by how successfully they meet certain aesthetic requirements, such as minimizing the number of edge crossings, minimizing the area of the drawing, maximizing angles between edges, conformance to a desired aspect ratio. Aesthetic requirements are indicators of a graph drawing's readability, understanding, and overall aesthetic value, therefore given two drawings of a graph structure, the 'better' drawing is more successful in meeting one or more of these aesthetic requirements than the other.

Most graph drawing algorithms focus on placement of the nodes constrained by the aesthetic requirements, or proceed further. The algorithm in [1] proceeds from node

placement by subsequently coloring the edges of the graph through application of the principles of grouping from Gestalt psychology. These principles derive from the law of prägnanz, which argues that people tend to order experience in a matter that is simple, orderly, symmetric, and regular [3]. The principles of grouping suggest that predictions can be made on how the mind will interpret visual stimuli since it naturally seeks order and patterns based on certain rules. The principles are ordered into the following seven categories (Figure 1):

1. Proximity - elements that are close together are perceived collectively, whereas elements that are far apart are perceived separately.
2. Similarity - like elements are perceived collectively, whereas differing elements are perceived separately.
3. Closure - incomplete or partially obscured elements tend to be completed by the mind.
4. Symmetry - elements displaying symmetry are perceived collectively in spite of distance.
5. Continuation - when elements intersect or overlap, each is perceived separately and as uninterrupted.
6. Common fate - when elements are moving at the same velocity, they are perceived collectively.
7. Figure-ground - elements can be distinguished from their surroundings by dividing a scene into foreground and background.

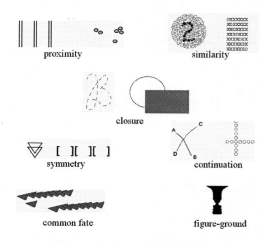

Figure 1. Gestalt principles.

Such experimental studies as [2] provide evidence that edge crossings are the primary inhibitor to readability. However, not all graphs are planar so it is impossible to guarantee that a drawing is free of edge crossings in the general case. Therefore, we propose a new graph drawing algorithm whose focus is on utilizing the principle of closure to improve readability inhibited by edge crossings. At each edge crossing, assign one edge to be primary and the other to be secondary. The secondary edge will then have a gap in continuity on the portion immediately passing through the area of the edge crossing. The primary edge is trivially easy to trace through the area of the edge crossing, and the secondary edge is still easily perceived as a whole edge due to the Gestalt principle of closure. In the unusual case of multiple edges crossing at the same point, a number of them are assigned as primary, while the rest are assigned as secondary, then each set is treated as in the typical case.

2. Background

This research furthers the work done in [1] by investigating ways of applying Gestalt principles to a drawing of a graph after it has been embedded in the plane. The method in [1] relies on coloring the entire drawing. However color is not always appropriate for graphs or displays might be restricted to monochrome in which case colors are not an option. Moreover, edge crossings cannot always be avoided so other techniques are needed and some of the Gestalt principles seem to fill in the need. The method presented here only affects the areas immediately around the edge crossings and can still be employed when restricted to black-on-white drawings. We are unaware of any other research employing edge breaks in the graph drawing with perceptual support. However, researchers in [4-6, 12] provide evidence of the cognitive ability of the human mind to correctly interpret highly distorted images or shapes, useful in applications such as human interactive proof systems and CAPTCHAs (Figure 2). Using the high success rate as evidence that the humans use Gestalt principles, such as closure, in order to interpret distorted images, we predict that our minimal effects will not hinder readability; in fact, we expect to enhance readability by breaking other unintentional gestalts.

Buffalo

Lockport

Oakland

a) English (city) words as CAPTCHA to distinguish humans from automatic programs (bots) in online services.

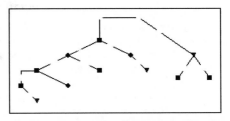

Instructions: **click on all 90 degree bends in the tree.**
b) Tree structure as CAPTCHA.

Figure 2. Visualizations transformed according to Gestalt principles which pose no problem to human recognition.

3. Technical Approach

We chose an embedding algorithm with few edge crossings that is interactive, easy to implement, and adapt. The Force Directed Placement (FDP) [8] algorithm meets these requirements. In FDP, the nodes can be imagined as point masses connected by springs. The total energy of the system is then minimized iteratively by adjusting the lengths of the springs. The final embedding is the minimum energy state found. The original algorithm has a costly time complexity of $O(n^3)$, though [9] and [10] present optimizations to produce algorithms with a time complexity of $O(n^2)$ and [11] further improves it with a hybrid algorithm utilizing approximations by both sampling and interpolating, achieving an algorithm with time complexity of $O(n^{5/4})$.

A sweep line algorithm can be used to efficiently find all edge crossings. For example, the Bentley-Ottman algorithm [7] performs with a time complexity of $O((n + k)\log n)$, where n is the number of edges and k is the number of edge crossings. A simpler algorithm would be a pairwise comparison of edges where minimum bounding boxes are used to quickly eliminate spatially distant edges. Although it has a poorer time complexity, the latter option was chosen in our implementation since it offers a natural way to select the primary and secondary edges. We chose an implementation where the edge being compared to all others is the secondary edge. This choice naturally leads to the secondary edges indexing the edge crossing positions so that intermediate points can be easily determined using the same angle for each by using the following formulas:

$$x = x_{ec} \pm r\cos(\theta)$$

$$y = y_{ec} \pm r\sin(\theta)$$

where (x_{ec}, y_{ec}) is an edge crossing, r is the break radius, and θ is the angle that the secondary edge makes with the x-axis. These intermediate points (x, y) lie on the intersections of the break area and the secondary edge, so that the entire edge can be represented as a series of line segments where the first line segment starts at the parent node's coordinates and ends at the first intermediate point, and the last line segment starts at the last intermediate point and ends at the child node's coordinates (Figure 3). When the intermediate points are being determined, some may need to be discarded if two break areas overlap so that a line segment is not drawn in this area. Drawing primary edges is trivial in this system since they are represented as secondary edges with no intersections, causing the lines to be drawn through the intersection points creating the desired Gestalt effect over the secondary edges with which they cross.

We have used C++ and the G3D extension library for OpenGL for implementation. The Human Protein Reference Database has been used to provide the underlying data used to create our graph drawings.

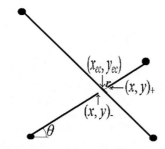

a) The geometry of the secondary edge.

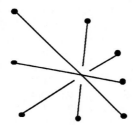

b) Multiple primary and secondary edges intersecting at the same edge crossing point.

Figure 3. Examples illustrating our algorithm for edge crossings that incorporates Gestalt principles.

4. User Study

The program presented in [1] has been adapted to incorporate the new approach we described for rendering the graph. Various graphs were drawn using our program. Each was rendered with and without the gestalt effect (Figure 4-7). We were also interested in the effect of our approach when applied to a graph with fewer edge crossings vs. very large number of edge crossings. A preliminary study was performed with fourteen participants having various educational backgrounds. Each participant were shown the four testing figures, in the order shown, and asked to identify all nodes

connected to a node chosen at random five times for each graph and rendering. The participants were asked to rate the ease of this task for each graph on a five-point Likert scale, where one denotes 'very difficult' and five denotes 'very easy.' The participants were also asked to give general feedback regarding the test at the end. Table 1 shows the results of preliminary user studies. The columns heading include a number corresponding to the testing figure and also identify whether that figure is 'traditional' (T) or has the Gestalt effect added (G) (i.e., 4T corresponds to Figure 4 left - traditional, whereas 7G corresponds to Figure 7 right - with breaks in edges at edge crossings). The cells with lighter shading highlight an improvement in readability over the traditional graphs whereas the cells with darker shading highlight difficulty when introducing Gestalt effect, as perceived by the participants in our study.

	4T	4G	5T	5G	6T	6G	7T	7G
1	5	5	3	4	3	4	5	5
2	4	4	5	5	3	2	1	1
3	5	5	4	5	3	4	3	3
4	5	5	5	5	4	5	4	3
5	5	5	5	4	5	4	5	4
6	4	4	5	5	2	1	3	2
7	5	5	5	5	5	4	5	4
8	5	5	5	5	4	4	4	4
9	5	5	5	5	5	5	5	5
10	4	4	4	4	4	4	4	4
11	4	5	4	5	4	5	4	5
12	5	4	3	5	4	3	5	5
13	5	5	5	5	4	4	3	4
14	5	5	5	5	4	4	4	4

Table 1. Graph readability results (5 is 'very easy' and 1 is 'very difficult').

More qualitative data has been recorded through the general feedback on the exit survey. Out of the 14 participants, 13 left feedback of which one did not relate to the study. Three of them felt that the gaps were distracting and aesthetically unpleasing making the tasks more difficult whereas two felt that the gaps made the graph more aesthetically pleasing though had no impact on the difficulty of the tasks. Three felt that the breaks were distracting in sparse drawings but were very effective in densely clustered drawings, while another four had no preference for either rendering after the study. These preliminary tests are encouraging especially for the graph drawings with clusters of edge crossings or larger graph drawings.

In future work, considering some of the feedback received in the initial study, we will perform more tests in which edge crossings must meet certain requirements before a gap is introduced. Such requirements may be local node density, angle at which edges intersect, number of edge crossings on a single edge, and whether gaps have already been introduced on an edge.

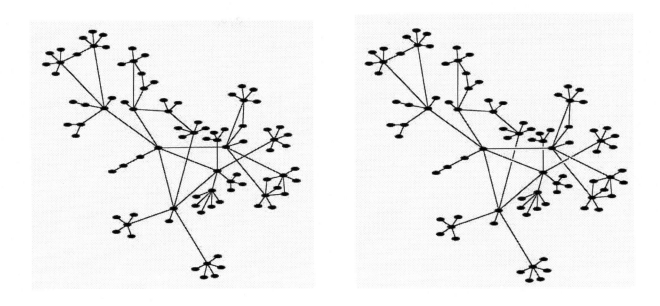

Figure 4. Graph drawing with few edge crossings (traditional on the left; Gestalt effect introduced on the right).

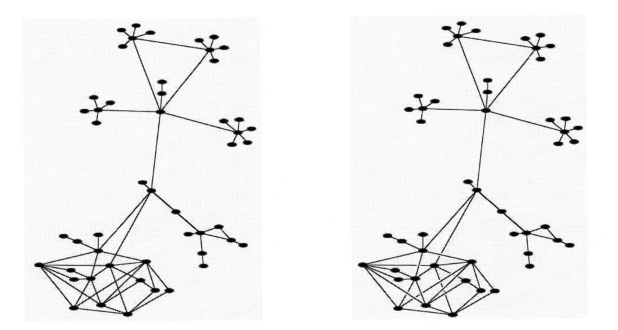

Figure 5. Graph drawing with a cluster of edge crossings (traditional on the left; Gestalt effect introduced on the right).

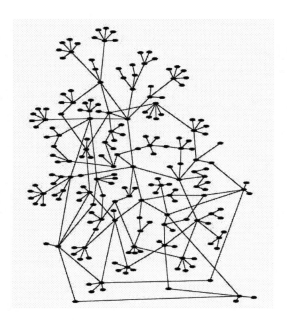 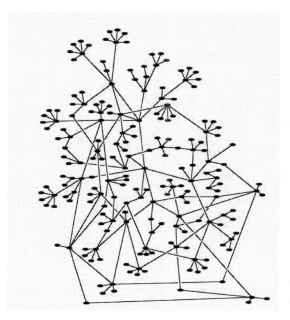

Figure 6. Larger graph drawing with edge crossings (traditional on the left; Gestalt effect introduced on the right).

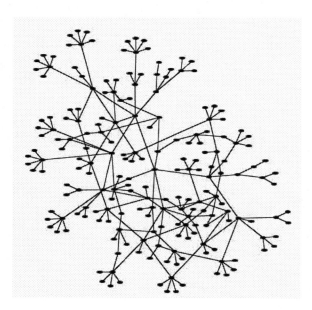 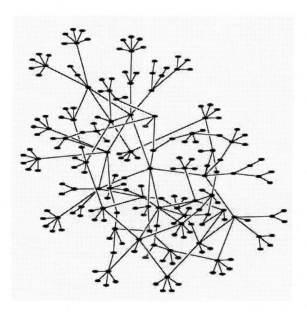

Figure 7. Graph drawing with a high density of edge crossings (traditional on the left; Gestalt effect introduced on the right).

5. Conclusions

We present a method that uses Gestalt principle of closure for increasing graph drawings aesthetics and readability, by introducing gaps into a graph at every edge crossing. Similar Gestalt principles applied as deformations to handwriting samples or shapes have been proven to work well without altering human recognition abilities. We adapted the FDP algorithm to accommodate these gaps as part of the secondary edges when crossing primary edges.

We conducted a preliminary study to collect evidence that our hypothesis holds merit. Initial results and user feedback have been promising and provided important information for our future work. We consider conducting additional studies in the future on adding gaps at edge crossings after certain requirements are met. Additional experiments will be considered by varying the size of the edge breaks in order to determine any influence on graph readability.

6. References

[1] R. Jianu, Ad. Rusu, A.J. Fabian and D.H. Laidlaw. A coloring solution to the edge crossing problem, *Proceedings of the 2009 13th International Conference on Information Visualization.*

[2] H. Purchase. Which aesthetic has the greatest effect on human understanding? *Proceedings of the 5th International Symposium on Graph Drawing*, pp. 248-261, 1997.

[3] C.G. Boeree. *Gestalt Psychology,* <http://webspace. ship.edu/cgboer/gestalt.html>, 2000.

[4] Am. Rusu and V. Govindaraju. Visual CAPTCHA with handwritten image analysis, *Proceedings of the 2nd International Workshop on Human Interactive Proofs,* Lecture Notes in Computer Science, Vol. 3517, pp. 42-52, 2005.

[5] Am. Rusu and V. Govindaraju. A human interactive proof algorithm using handwriting recognition, *Proceedings of the 8th International Conference on Document Analysis and Recognition*, IEEE Computer Society, Vol. 2, pp. 967-971, 2005.

[6] Am. Rusu, A.O. Thomas and V. Govindaraju. Generation and use of handwritten CAPTCHAs, *International Journal on Document Analysis and Recognition*, Springer-Verlag, Vol. 13, Issue 1, pp. 49-64, 2010.

[7] J. Bentley and T. Ottman. Algorithms for counting and reporting geometric intersections, *IEEE Transactions on Computers*, Vol. C-28, Issue 9, pp. 643-647, 1979.

[8] T. Fruchterman and E. Reingold. Graph drawing by force-directed placement, *Software – Practice and Experience*, Vol. 21, Issue 11, pp. 1129-1164, 1991.

[9] M. Chalmers. A linear iteration time layout algorithm for visualizing high-dimensional data. *Proceedings of the 7th IEEE Visualization Conference*, IEEE Computer Society, p. 127ff, 1996.

[10] E. Tejada, R. Minghim and L.G. Nonato. On improved projection techniques to support visual exploration of multidimensional data sets, *Information Visualization*, Vol. 2, Issue 4, pp. 218-231, 2004.

[11] A. Morrison and M. Chalmers. A pivot-based routine for improved parent-finding in hybrid MDS, *Information Visualization*, Vol. 3, Issue 2, pp. 109-122, 2003.

[12] Am. Rusu and R. Docimo. Securing the Web using human perception and visual object interpretation, *Proceedings of the 2009 13th International Conference on Information Visualization.*

6. Geometric Modeling and Imaging
IV 2011

G¹ Continuity Conics for Curve Fitting using Particle Swarm Optimization

Zainor Ridzuan Yahya*, Abd Rahni Mt Piah† and Ahmad Abd Majid‡

School of Mathematical Sciences,
Universiti Sains Malaysia, 11800 USM, Pulau Pinang, Malaysia
Email: *zainor.usm@gmail.com, †arahni@cs.usm.my, ‡majid@cs.usm.my

Abstract—We solve curve fitting problems using Particle Swarm Optimization (PSO). PSO is used to optimize control points and weights of two conic curves to a set of data points. PSO is used to find the best middle control point and weight for both conic curves to provide piecewise conics that preserve tangent continuity. We present the numerical result and an application using our proposed curve fitting technique.

Keywords-curve fitting; particle swarm optimization;

I. INTRODUCTION

Curve fitting[1] is the process of constructing a curve, or mathematical function, that has the best fit to a series of data points, possibly subject to constraints. Curve fitting can involve either interpolation, where an exact fit to the data is required, or smoothing, in which a 'smooth' function is constructed that approximately fits the data. A related topic is regression analysis, which focuses more on questions of statistical inference such as how much uncertainty is present in a curve that is fitted to data observed with random errors. Fitted curves can be used as an aid for data visualization, to infer values of a function where no data are available, or to summarize the relationships among two or more variables. Extrapolation refers to the use of a fitted curve beyond the range of the observed data, and is subject to a greater degree of uncertainty since it may reflect the method used to construct the curve as much as it reflects the observed data.

Particle Swarm Optimization(PSO) is an optimization technique proposed by Kennedy and Eberhart by means of particle swarm [1]. PSO incorporates swarming behaviours observed in flocks of birds, school of fish, swarm of bees and even social behaviour, from where the idea emerged. PSO is a population-based optimization tool, which could be implemented and applied easily to solve various function optimization problems, or problems that can be transformed to function optimization problems. As an algorithm, the main strength of PSO is its fast convergence, which compares favourably with many global optimization algorithms like Genetic Algorithm (GA) [2], Simulated Annealing (SimA) [3] and other global optimization algorithms. To apply PSO succesfully, one of the key issues is finding how to map the problem solution into the PSO article, which directly affects its feasibility and performance.

[1] http://en.wikipedia.org/wiki/Curve_fitting

II. CONICS CURVE

A standard form of conics is given by [4] and [5]:

$$r(t) = \frac{B_0^2(t)b_0 + wB_1^2(t)b_1 + B_2^2(t)b_2}{B_0^2(t) + wB_1^2(t) + B_2^2(t)} \quad (1)$$

where $b_i(i = 0, 1, 2)$ are the control points of the Bezier curve and w is the middle weight. Here we list some useful properties of conics:

1) for $w < 1$, we obtain an ellipse; for $w = 1$, a parabola; and for $w > 1$, a hyperbola.
2) the straight line segments $[b_0, b_1]$ and $[b_1, b_2]$ are *tangents* to r at $r(0) = b_0$ and $r(1) = b_2$, respectively.
3) for $w \geq 0$, the curve segment (1) lies in the convex hull of the control polygon.
4) the point $s = r(1/2)$ of a conic segment in its standard form is called the shoulder point. It can be computed from

$$s = \frac{1}{2}q_0 + \frac{1}{2}q_1,$$

where

$$q_0 = \frac{b_0 + wb_1}{1 + w}, q_1 = \frac{wb_1 + b_2}{1 + w},$$

the characteristic points. The shoulder tangent is spanned by q_0 and q_1. Note that the shoulder tangent is parallel to $[b_0, b_2]$; see Fig. 1(a). As a consequence,

$$w = \frac{\|s - m\|}{\|b_1 - s\|}$$

where m is the midpoint of b_0 and b_2.
5) The curvature κ of r at the endpoints is given by:

$$\kappa(0) = \frac{\tau}{w^2\rho^2}, \kappa(1) = \frac{\tau}{w^2\lambda^2} \quad (2)$$

where τ denotes the area of the triangle formed by the control polygon; i. e. $\tau = \frac{1}{2}det(b_1 - b_0, b_2 - b_1)$, $\rho = \|b_1 - b_0\|$ and $\lambda = \|b_2 - b_1\|$. Note that κ denotes the signed curvature, since τ may be positive or negative.

Suppose we have two conic curves $P(t)$ with control points p_0, p_1 and p_2 and $Q(t)$ with control points q_0, q_1 and q_2 (refer Fig. 1(b)). From [5], to achieve G^2 continuity , the two curves $P(t)$ and $Q(t)$ must share the same curvature at $p_2 = q_0$ with

$$\frac{\tau_P}{w_P^2\lambda_P^2} = \frac{\tau_Q}{w_Q^2\rho_Q^2} \quad (3)$$

1550-6037/11 $26.00 © 2011 IEEE
DOI 10.1109/IV.2011.27

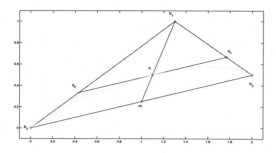

(a) Shoulder point: A rational quadratic with shoulder point **s** and shoulder tangent through **q**$_0$ and **q**$_1$

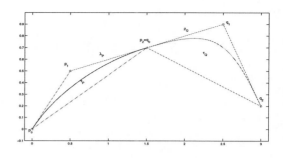

(b) Curvature continuity: Two adjacent conic segments

Figure 1.   The properties of conic curves

where τ, λ and ρ are as described in equation (2).

III. PARTICLE SWARM OPTIMIZATION

PSO starts by having a population of particles initialized with random positions marked by vector $\vec{x}_i$ and random velocities $\vec{v}_i$ [6]. The population of such particles is called a 'swarm' S. Each particle P has two state variables viz., its current position $\vec{x}(t)$ and its current velocity $\vec{v}(t)$. It is also equipped with a small memory comprising its previous best position $\vec{p}(t)$, i.e., the personal best experience and the best $\vec{p}(t)$ of all P, $\vec{g}(t)$, i.e., the best position found so far in the neighbourhood of the particle. The PSO scheme has the following algorithmic parameters:

- V_{max} or maximum velocity which restricts $\vec{V}_i(t)$ within the interval $[-V_{max}, V_{max}]$;
- an inertia weight factor ω;
- two uniformly distributed random numbers, $0 \leq \varphi_1, \varphi_2 \leq 1$ on the velocity update formula.
- two constant multiplier terms C_1 and C_2 known as 'self-confidence' and 'swarm confidence', respectively.

Initially, $\vec{p}(t)$ and $\vec{g}(t)$ are set as $\vec{p}(0) = \vec{g}(0) = \vec{x}(0)$ for all particles. Once the particles are all initialized, an iterative optimization process begins, where the positions and velocities of all the particles are altered by the following recursive equations (4) and (5). The equations are presented for the dth dimension of the position and velocity of the ith particle.

$$V_{id}(t + 1) = \omega.v_{id}(t) + C_1.\varphi_1.(p_{id}(t) - x_{id}(t)) \quad (4)$$
$$+ C_2.\varphi_2.(g_{id}(t) - x_{id}(t))$$
$$x_{id}(t + 1) = x_{id}(t) + v_{id}(t + 1) \quad (5)$$

The first term in the velocity updating formula represents the inertial velocity of the particle. Since the coefficient C_1 has a contribution towards the self-exploration (or experience) of a particle, we regard it as the particle's self-confidence. On the other hand, the coefficient C_2 has a contribution towards motion of the particles in global direction, which

takes into account the motion of all the particles in the preceding program iterations, naturally its definition 'as swarm confidence' is apparent. After having calculated the velocities and position for the next time step $t + 1$, the first iteration of the algorithm is completed. Typically, this process is iterated for a certain number of time steps, or until some acceptable solution has been found or until an upper limit of CPU usage has been reached. The algorithm can be summarized in the following pseudo code:

The PSO Algorithm
Input: Randomly initialized position and velocity of the particles: $\vec{X}_i(0)$ and $\vec{V}_i(0)$
Output: Position of the approximate global optima $\vec{X}^*$
Begin
    While terminating condition is not reached
    Begin
        for i=1 to number of particles
        Evaluate the fitness:=$f(\vec{X}_i)$;
        Update $\vec{p}_i$ and $\vec{g}_i$;
        Adapt velocity of the particle
            using equation 4 and 5;
        Update the position of the particle;
        increase i;
    end while
end

IV. BI-CONIC G^1 CURVE FITTING

Most of the techniques used in conic curve fitting choose weight = 1 as the initial value and using the least square technique to estimate the control points. Once we get the data points, we find the midpoint of the data point which is the endpoints for both left and right curves. Then, we approximate the intermediate control point of the left curve using least square. After that, we choose the size of the search area to find the best value for point control. Different from the original PSO, we have the search space size = 1, where control points are searched in the search space (see

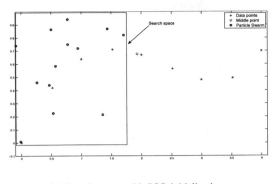

(a) Search space with PSO initialization

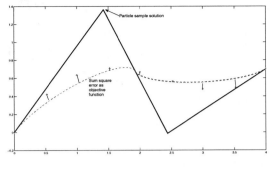

(b) Sample solution

Figure 2.   The process to obtain sample solution

Fig. 2(a)). For each particle from the initialization, we find the location for the intermediate point of the right curve to achieve G^1 continuity (see Fig. 2(b)). Evaluation will be done for each particle solution using sum square error [7]. To find the weight, the initial value of the weight will be chosen at random in the range of [0,1]. Our proposed PSO algorithm starts with having an initial swarm position of swarm size= 25. PSO is used to find the best control point and weight to provide the best fitted curve the given data. For the PSO scheme, we set inertia $\omega = 1.0$ and $C_1 = C_2 = 2.0$. For our stop criterion, the iterations will stop if the same error is repeated 20 times. The pseudo code of our proposed technique is given below. Fig. 3(a) and 3(b) explained our research findings.

Our Proposed PSO Curve Fitting Algorithm
For each segment until last segment
    Get data points;
    Find middle point from chord length
        parameterization;
    Use Least Square to approximate the
        intermediate point for left curve;
    Determine search space for finding intermediate
        control points;
    Initialization
    Initialize intermediate control point for each particle;
    Initialize weight (random choose from [0,1])
        for each particle;
    For $i = 1$ until last iteration
        For $j = 1$ until number of particle
        Update the left control point of the particle;
        Calculate the right control point to achieve G^1;
        Update the left conic weight;
        Calculate the right conic weight;
        Evaluate solution (newSolution);
        If newSolution better than bestSolution
            bestSolution=newSolution;
            bestControlPoint=newControlPoint;

Table I
PSO ITERATIONS FOR FITTED CURVES

#	# iter.	Best error	Average error	CPU time(sec)
1	225	0.01676684	0.017172396	3.0108193
2	182	0.015141434	0.015233733	2.4648158
3	167	0.019376049	0.019597467	2.2308143
4	224	0.014112258	0.014575132	2.9952192
5	255	0.020400675	0.020483788	3.4632222
6	212	0.012698477	0.012934463	2.8392182
7	208	0.015141952	0.015270387	2.808018
8	293	0.012909775	0.012998558	3.9156251
9	307	0.01270423	0.012880085	4.0716261
10	**347**	**0.01180574**	**0.01194918**	**4.6488298**
11	397	0.012711394	0.012805794	5.2728338
12	162	0.024681615	0.025241859	2.1684139
13	226	0.015162703	0.015243114	2.9952192
14	239	0.012309645	0.012562997	3.2136206
15	223	0.014611253	0.014725769	2.9796191
16	216	0.015168622	0.015281159	2.9172187
17	210	0.017129725	0.017432969	2.7768178
18	204	0.022841566	0.023161461	2.7456176
19	349	0.014626932	0.014918098	4.7268303
20	**162**	**0.016766049**	**0.016946505**	**2.1528138**

            bestWeight=newWeight;
        end If
        Update velocity for control point and weight;
        increase j;
        end For
    increase i;
    end For;
end

V. NUMERICAL RESULTS AND APPLICATION

We look at the efficiency of using PSO to optimize biconic G^1. Iterations will be done 20 times and we compare the efficiency of the algorithm based on their CPU time, number of iterations and best error. Table I explains our findings. It is shown that best error occurs at the 10th iteration. The fastest iteration is at the 20th iteration. Therefore the result is acceptable. We use font design to show an application of soft computing for curve fitting. We match our conic curves

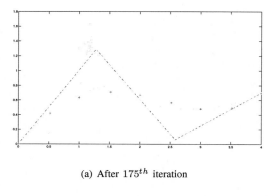

(a) After 175th iteration

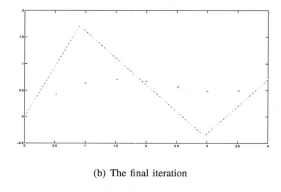

(b) The final iteration

Figure 3. G^1 continuity conics for curve fitting using Particle Swarm Optimization

to an arabic font 'Li'. In the pre-processing, we need to perform some image processing techniques on the image. At first, we find the boundaries of the image (Fig. 4(a)) . Then, we use the SAM06 technique [8] to identify the edges of the image (Fig. 4(b)). Finally, curve fitting is performed to obtain the best conic curve(Fig. 4(c)).

VI. CONCLUSION

Instead of using a direct technique, we use an indirect technique to perform curve fitting. To find the best solution, we need to map the curve fitting problem to the best PSO scheme. In future, we will try to use similar algorithm to solve surface fitting problem. The effects of changed parameters found in PSO scheme will also be studied. It can be shown that PSO does not give a very good solution, but the error is within acceptable region.

ACKNOWLEDGEMENTS

The authors would like to thank Universiti Sains Malaysia for supporting this research under its RU grant 1001/PMATHS/817049.

REFERENCES

[1] T. Weise, *Global Optimization Algorithms Theory and Application* , T. Weise, Ed. http://www.it-weise.de/, 2009.

[2] A. Eiben and J. Smith, *Introduction to Evolutionary Computing*, Springer, Ed. Springer, 2007.

[3] S. Kirkpatrick, J. Gelatt, C. D., and M. P. Vecchi, "Optimization by simulated annealing," *Science*, vol. 220, no. 4598, pp. 671–680, 1983. [Online]. Available: http://www.sciencemag.org/cgi/content/abstract/220/4598/671

[4] X. Yang, "Curve fitting and fairing using conic splines," Department of Mathematics, Zhejiang University , Hangzhou 310027, China, Tech. Rep., 2003.

[5] G. Farin, "Curvature continuity and offsets for piecewise conics," *ACM Trans. Graph.*, vol. 8, no. 2, pp. 89–99, 1989.

[6] S. Das, A. Abraham, and A. Konar, "Particle swarm optimization and differential evolution algorithms: Technical analysis, applications and hybridization perspectives," *Advances of Computational Intelligence in Industrial Systems*, pp. 1–38, 2008.

[7] F. Yahya, J. M. Ali, A. A. Majid, and A. Ibrahim, "An automatic generation of G^1 curve fitting of arabic characters." Los Alamitos, CA, USA: IEEE Computer Society, 2006, pp. 542–547.

[8] M. Sarfraz, *Interactive Curve Modeling With Applications to Computer Graphics, Vision and Image Processing.* Springer, 2008.

(a) Boundary extraction

(b) Corner detection: corner detected with red circle

(c) Curve fitting: fitted curve in blue colour

Figure 4.   From boundary extractions to curve fitting

Generating a simple polygonalizations

V. Muravitskiy, V. Tereshchenko
National Taras Shevchenko University of Kiev
vmyrik@gmail.com, vtereshch@gmail.com

Abstract

We consider the methods of construction simple polygons for a set S of n points and applying them for searching the minimal area polygon. In this paper we propose the approximate algorithm, which generates the simple polygonalizations of a fixed point set and finds the minimum area polygon, in $O(n^3)$ time and using $O(n^2)$ memory.

Keywords—**simple polygon, approximate algorithm, minimal area polygon, polygonalizations.**

1 Introduction

Problem statement. The problem of generating random geometrical figures, except existing theoretical interest, is motivated by the need to generate test data to verify the correctness and time complexity of algorithms of computational geometry [1]. There is a wide range of possible applications for the algorithms, associated with the construction of simple polygons of minimum area, in GIS systems, [2, 3]. Another direction of application in this area is geo-sensor networks [4, 5].

One of the problems is the impossibility of calculating the number of simple polygons in a given points set, in polynomial time. An important problem is finding a simple polygon that have certain properties. In particular, search of the minimum area polygon among all possible polygons which can be generated on a given set of points. The problem of finding a simple polygon of minimal area has got certain weight in pattern recognition problems. Therefore the search for the optimal algorithm that can generate a simple polygon of minimal area is till now actual.

Analysis of recent research. For today, there are several approaches to the solution of the problem, that based on using Delaunay triangulation or Voronoi diagram. In [6, 7] the authors introduce "α-shape" -notion for the generalization of a convex hull that allows to develop methods of constructing the simple polygons with using Voronoi diagram. In [8-10], "A-shape" used to "onion-peeling"- method, by removing the boundary edges of triangulation [11]. The papers [12,13] propose algorithms using Delaunay Triangulation. The approach allows us to develop a simple, flexible and efficient algorithm for constructing a simple poly-

gon using the notion of *characteristic form*. The *characteristic form* is varied from a convex hull to the uniquely defined form of a minimum area. It experimentally confirms that the algorithm, using an appropriate parameterizations, can precisely construct the characteristic forms for different sets of points. Another algorithm was proposed in [14]. The algorithm starts with constructing a convex hull, and then uses the procedure of "divide-and-conquer, successively inserting additional edges and smoothing zigzags. A complexity of the algorithm is limited by complexity of constructing the initial convex hull - $O(nlogn)$.

Moreover, we can distinguish two approaches to the generation of simple polygons for a given set of points. The first suggests that we need to find a single polygon without consideration its properties [1]. The second approach provides algorithms that generate "random" polygons for this set. This problem is more complicated, but for its solution were proposed efficient algorithms [1, 15]. Attempts to solve the problem of finding a polygon of minimal area also have been undertaken, and have achieved certain results for its solution [16].

The novelty and idea: In the paper we propose a polynomial approximation algorithm for the minimum area polygon.

Paper's aim: Explore algorithms for generation of simple polygons given set of vertices, and develop an algorithm for determining the minimum possible area polygon.

2 Problem and algorithms

Problem. *Let S – given set of n points on the plane. 1. It is necessary to specify the order of connection by edges of points from set S so to generate simple polygons. 2. Find among the generated polygons the minimum area polygon.*

In solving the given problem, we can distinguish algorithms that build a simple polygon (unique requests), algorithms that generate all possible set of simple polygons (mass requests) and algorithms for finding the minimum area polygon.

2.1 Constructing a simple polygon for a given set of points (unique requests)

In this case, we can suggest the following algorithms.

Algorithm 1. Choose $P_0 \in S$ as anchor point. It is the start of bypass. Sort all other points $\{ S \backslash P_0 \}$ with polar angle relative P_0. As a result, we get one of the possible polygons for a given set S. Sorting can be done in $O(n \log n)$ time.

Algorithm 2. Constructing convex hull for S. If all points of S belong to a contour, then problem solved. If not, look for a point P_1, which is at minimum distance from the contour – even this minimum distance to the side pieces (P_{k-1}, P_k). If several such points, we take any of them. Insert point P_1 in the contour that is instead of (P_{k-1}, P_k) will be (P_{k-1}, P_1, P_k). For all the points that remain, we repeat the above procedure until the last point will be inserted in the contour.

Algorithm 3. Building convex hull for S. If all points of S belong to a contour, then problem solved. Otherwise, denote all the internal point S_1 of a convex hull. Building for a new set S_1 convex hull V_1 (contours V and V_1 do not intersect). Sticking together two contours. Choose a pair of consecutive vertices u, v and u_1, v_1 on contours V respectively, so that in the quadrangle with vertices u, v, v_1, u_1 not lay any more points from contours. V and V_1. Severing contours V and V_1 (removing edges (u, v) and (u_1, v_1)) and connecting them (adding edges (u, u_1) and (v, v_1)).

If V_1 does not contains the points, the problem is solved. Otherwise, we conduct the same operations with internal points: we find the convex hull and a pair of consecutive points on the contours; we couple and uncouple contours until we get a convex hull which includes 0, 1 or 2 points. If count of points equal 0, then problem solved. Otherwise, we add points to the contour so that the figure remained polygon (can be conducted joining, as in previous case).

2.2 Generating the simple polygons for a given set of points (mass requests)

In this case we can use the following algorithm [15].

Steady Growth . At initialization, **Steady Growth** randomly selects 3 points s_1, s_2, $s_3 \in S$ such, that no other points no lie outside $CH(\{s_1, s_2, s_3\})$. Let $S_1 = S \backslash \{s_1, s_2, s_3\}$. During the i-iterations ($1 \leq i \leq n - 3$) we perform the following operations:

1. We choose randomly $s_1 \in S_i$, but to no points $S_{i+1} = S_i \backslash \{s_i\}$ that lie outside $CH(P_{i-1} \cup \{s_i\})$.

2. Finding an edge (v_k, v_{k-1}) in P_i that completely visible of s_i and replace it by edges (v_k, s_i) and $(s_i, v_{k+1})(s_i, v_{k+1})$.

Permute & Reject. This algorithm works as follows: generates one possible permutations of the set S and involves checking whether is this permutation a simple polygon. If yes - we got the result, otherwise generate another permutation. This algorithm is inefficient when all (or most) points lie on the convex hull, because only $2n$ of

$n!$ permutations corresponding to simple polygons. Permute & Reject can generate all possible polygons.

So if we need to generate a simple polygon for a given set of points, we can do this by using the above algorithms.

2.3 Generating the minimum area polygon

The problem of finding the minimum polygon area known as MAP - Minimum Area Polygon. It is NP-complete, which was proved in [16]. That is, for a minimum polygon area, we must review all the possible polygons for a given set S of n points.

Consider now the same problem with the position of the minimum polygon approximation. Since MAP - NP-complete problem, it is unlikely we can find an exact polynomial algorithm for finding the minimum area polygon, so it's interesting to find a good approximation method. The main reason lies in the complexity of approximation of complex geometric relationship between the boundary simple polygon and its area. So can be trying some heuristics to try and get a minimum polygon area. One of effective approaches to solve a problem based on the idea of greedy algorithm "Greedy - build" [16]. We start with the smallest not degenerate triangle in the set S. While the vertex is not included in the polygon, we choose the smallest not degenerate triangle that formed the current polygon edge and vertex outside polygons that completely "sees" edge. We adding to the triangle polygon and back to previous step.

We propose the following algorithm for finding the minimum area simple polygon.

3 The proposed (greedy) approximation algorithm) for minimum area polygon

It is invite the following approximation algorithm:

1. Jarvis method for building the convex hull of the set S (Figure 1) (this method is best approximations, because if the basic number of points not lying on the convex hull, we'll get it in time $O(hn)$, where h – points that lie on the convex hull).

2. While the vertex is not included in the polygon: choose among the points that are inside this polygon point P, which will form one of the edges (u, v) the maximum triangle area, and one that does not contain other points, and also does not intersects the edges of this polygon (the edge "seen" from the point).

3. Let (u, v)- edge, P - points that formed a triangle of maximum area that satisfied the specified conditions. Severing edge (u, v) and form two new (u, P) and (P, v). Is returned to p.2

For the proposed greedy algorithm we obtain the following estimates of complexity. Building convex hull $O(hn)$, in the worst case $O(n^2)$, but this case is both the best, because once we get the solution of the original problem. We need to insert n points to the polygon. To insert

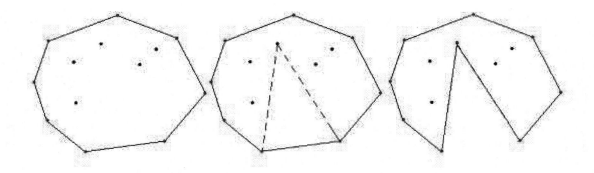

Figure 1: Convex hull and point selection and inserting point into the contour

each of them we take over all edges of this polygon, and for each edge we take all remaining points. For each point in question we check whether the triangle contains no other points, and whether it crosses no the edges of this polygon. This gives us a total complexity of $O(N^4)$, where N − number of points that lie inside the convex hull, $N = n - h$. Using memory - $O(n)$.

Optimization of the proposed algorithm. It is possible conduct preliminary processing of the set S, which will improve time characteristics of the complexity of this algorithm, but slightly increased while costs memory. In [18] algorithm, which provides preparation for a set S $O(n^2)$, using the $O(n^2)$, memory that will check whether a triangle contains a set of other points in constant time. The total complexity of this greedy algorithm will be $O(n^3)$. The algorithm builds a matrix stripe $[p_i, p_j]$, elements of which - the number of points that are in the vertical segment below p_i, p_j.

Algorithm.

1) Fill all elements stripe [*,*] zeros.

2) Sort out all points on the x-coordinate of left to right. This gives the sequence $p_1 \ldots p_n$

3) For each point, sort all the points that lie left of the clockwise around. This will give consistency

4) For $p_i := p_2$ to p_n:

For $j := 2$ to -1:

1) if p_j^i left lying on p_{j-1}

Stripe$[p_j^i, p_i]$ = stripe$[p_{j-1}^i, p_i]$+stripe$[p_j^i, p_{j-1}^i]$ + 1

2) if p_j^i right lying on p_{j-1}

Stripe$[p_j^i, p_i]$ = stripe$[p_{j-1}^i, p_i]$-stripe$[p_j^i, p_{j-1}^i]$

During the study the approximation algorithms , it was found that impossible to find a method that would approximates polygon minimum area for a given set of points with constant accuracy. Therefore there is a question on existence of such method in general. It is possible prove that

the approximation of the polygon with constant accuracy it is NP-complete problem. To prove we'll use the principle of reduction problems [19].

As a prototype we will use Minimum Area Triangulation(MAT) problem, for which we have a proof of NP-completness.

Minimum Area Triangulation problem (MAT). *On a given set P of 3n points on a plane find a set of disjoint triangles T_i, $i = 1..n$, such that the total area $\sum_i AR(T_i)$ is smallest possible.*

Theorem. *Minimum Area Triangulation (MAT) problem is reducible to the problem of construction simple polygons in a linear time.*

Proof. The set S of n points in the plane is an input data for the approximation problem. The same set is an input data for MAT. So input data of approximation problem can be transformed into input data of MAT in the time of $O(1)$. We have a proof of NP-completeness of MAT [16].

Output data of approximation problem can be transformed into output data of MAT in linear time. We can use some of triangulation algorithms for it. Hence we have that MAT problem is reducible to the approximation problem. So the approximation problem has the same estimation of complexity as MAT and the polynomial algorithm for solving this problem does not exists.

4   Implementation

To test the efficiency of the proposed method we made implementation on Java. To obtain reliable data on the algorithm was necessary to compare results with other algorithms. For comparison was elected algorithm of exhaustive search which is based on the above Permute & Reject: all possible permutations are generated and checked for simplicity. Although the problem is NP-complete for sets of small capacity it gives the result. Moreover, this result is best possible (Figure 2).

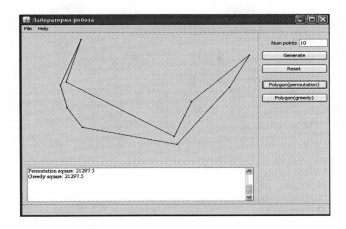

Figure 2: The result of the program.

Figure 2 shows that for the given test set with 10 points, minimum polygon area, which constructed by algorithm of exhaustive search and which generated by greedy algorithm, have coincided.

5   Conclusions

The paper had investigated the problem of generation of simple polygons for a given set S of n points. It was revealed that this problem can have different interpretations, namely one-time generating of a simple polygon or generating some set of simple polygons - random generation. There are efficient algorithms for solving the first problem. They give the result in a polynomial time. There are algorithms for the second case too, but their efficiency is lower. Examples of such algorithms were presented.

Concerning the problem of finding the minimum area polygon, there were some difficulties. Initially it was found that the problem of counting the number of simple polygons for a given set of points is NP-complete, so algorithm of simple exhaustive search is ineffective even if the set S has a small capacity. So researches were switched to approximation methods. It was found that the proposed greedy algorithm with a time complexity $O(n^4)$ and memory usage $O(n)$ can be improved, and we will get the time complexity $O(n^3)$ and memory usage $O(n^2)$. But in practice the methods gave results that differed from the optimum. Further investigation showed that constant-factor approximation is impossible and it was proved.

References

[1] C. Zhu, G. Sundaramb, J. Snoeyink and Joseph S. B. Mitchell. Generating random polygons with given vertices. *Jur.Computational Geometry: Theory and Applications*,6 (5): 277-290, Elsevier, 1996.

[2] H. J. Miller and J. Han. Geographic Data Mining and Knowledge Discovery. CRC Press, 2001.

[3] A. Galton and M. Duckham, "What is the region occupied by a set of points?" in GIScience. *Lecture Notes in Computer Science*, 4197:81-98, Springer, 2006.

[4] A. Galton, "Dynamic collectives and their collective dynamics," in COSIT. *Lecture Notes in Computer Science*, 3693:300-315,Springer, 2005.

[5] M. F. Worboys and M. Duckham. Monitoring qualitative spatiotemporal change for geosensor networks.*International Journal of Geographic Information Science*, 20 (10):1087-1108, 2006.

[6] H. Edelsbrunner, D. G. Kirkpatrick, and R. Seidel. On the shape of a set of points in the plane. *IEEE Transactions on Information Theory*, IT-29(4):551-558, 1983.

[7] M. Melkemi and M. Djebali.Computing the shape of a planar points set.*jur. Pattern Recognition*, 33:1423-1436, 2000.

[8] M. J. Fadili, M. Melkemi, and A. ElMoataz. Non-convex onion-peeling using a shape hull algorithm. *jur.Pattern Recognition Letters*, 25:1577-1585, 2004.

[9] A. R. Chaudhuri, B. B. Chaudhuri, and S. K. Parui. A novel approach to computation of the shape of a dot pattern and extraction of its perceptual border. *Computer Vision and Image Understanding*, 68 (3):257-275, 1997.

[10] N. Amenta,S. Choi and R. K. Kolluri. The power crust, unions of balls, and the medial axis transform. *jur.Computational Geometry: Theory and Applications*, 19(3):127-153, 2001.

[11] B. Chazelle. On the convex layers of a planar set. *IEEE Transactions on Information Theory*, 31:509-517, 1985.

[12] H. Alani, C. B. Jones, and D. Tudhope.Voronoi-based region approximation for geographical information retrieval with gazetteers. *International Journal of Geographical Information Science*, 15(4):287-306, 2001.

[13] A. Arampatzis, M. van Kreveld, I. Reinbacher, C. B. Jones, S. Vaid, P. Clough, H. Joho, and M. Sanderson.Web-based delineation of imprecise regions. *Computers, Environment, and Urban Systems*, 30 (4):436-459, 2006.

[14] G. Garai and B. B. Chaudhuri.A split and merge procedure for polygonal border detection of dot pattern. *Image and Vision Computing*, 17:75-82, 1999.

[15] Thomas Auer and Martin Held.Heuristics for the generation of random polygons. *In CCCG'96 Proceedings of the 8th Canadian Conference on Compu. Geom.* , pages 38-43, 1996.

[16] S.P. Fekete, W.R. Pulleyblank. Area Optimization of Simple Polygons. *In SoCG'93 Proceedings of the 9th Annual ACM Symposium on Computational Geometry*, pp. 173-182, 1993.

[17] Goodman J.E., O'Rourke J.*Handbook of Discrete and Computational Geometry*, 2ed, CDC,Press, New York, 2004

[18] D. Eppstein, M. Overmars, G. Rote, and G. Woeginger. Finding minimum area k-gons. *Jur.Disc. Comp. Geom.*, 7(1):45-58, 1992.

[19] F. Preparata and M.I. Shamos. *Computational Geometry: An introduction*. Springer-Verlag, Berlin, 1985.

Growing B-spline Model for Efficient Approximation of Complex Curves

Asif Masood

Military College of Signals
National University of Sciences and Technology
Islamabad, Pakistan
amasood@mcs.edu.pk

Sundas Bukhari

Military College of Signals
National University of Sciences and Technology
Islamabad, Pakistan
s_bukhari@mcs.edu.pk

Abstract— Growing B-spline model of curve approximation exploits local control of B-spline which leads to efficient approximation of complex curves, even with higher order B-splines. Approximation is carried out progressively (growing) in this model which is another factor for efficient approximation. Control points are adjusted / re-positioned in each iteration of approximation based on error between two curves. Proposed method can avoid any need of parameterization and complex computations. Proposed growing model can be applied with any degree of B-spline curve.

Keywords-B-spline; Curve Approximation; Control points

I. INTRODUCTION

Curve approximation is one of the basic areas of graphic designs and modeling. Researchers are investigating for better and better algorithms in curve approximation for last few decades. Use of B-spline in curve approximation is an attractive approach due to local control and simplicity of computations. Some latest techniques of curve approximation using B-spline can be seen in [1-13]. When modeling any shape with B-spline curve, there are various factors need to be addressed during approximation. These factors may include degree of approximating curve, number of control points to be used, position of these control points and location knots. Computational efficiency and accuracy are few other concerns. Researchers tried to address one more of these issues in their work.

In literature, many iterative processes were used to determine the location control points for approximating curve [2-7]. Inclusion, deletion and adjustment of knots also help in computing the accurate approximation. Paper in [9,10,13,14] propose this approach. In another technique [15], dominant points are used to compute the knot vector for error bounded curve approximation. Approximation based on least square minimization and parameterization can be seen in [14]. In [7], a B-spline curve is fit to a point cloud data using curvature based squared distance minimization. The techniques discussed above are mostly performing iterative processes for data points detection, thus involve

computational complexity, performance loss and increase in processing time. These problems make them unfavorable in approximating lengthy complex curves.

Proposed curve approximation technique addresses most of these issues. Growing B-spline model and use of error vector for repositioning of control points is something different that is proposed in this paper. The paper is structured as follows. Section 2 presents curve approximation method using error vector. Section 3 gives the growing B-spline model for approximation. Results are presented in Section 4 and section 5 concludes the paper.

II. CURVE APPROXIMATION WITH B-SPLINE

B-spline is the most widely used model in curve approximation due to local control and efficient computation. Computation of B-spline curve $P(u)$ is given as:

$$P(u) = \sum_{k=0}^{n} p_k B_{k,d}(u), \quad \begin{matrix} u_{min} \le u \le u_{max}, \\ 2 \le d \le n+1 \end{matrix} \quad (1)$$

Where p_k represent the set of $n+1$ control points and $B_{k,d}$ represent B-spline blending function which is a polynomial of degree $d-1$. Range of parameter u is divided into $n+d$ subintervals with knot values labeled as $\{u_0, u_1, \ldots, u_{n+d}\}$. The blending function for B-spline curves are defined using Cox-deBoor recursion formula given as:

$$B_{k,1}(u) = \begin{cases} 1, if\, u_k \le u \le u_{k+1} \\ 0, \quad otherwise \end{cases} \quad (2)$$

$$B_{k,d}(u) = \frac{u - u_k}{u_{k+d+1} - u_k} B_{k,d-1}(u)$$

$$+ \frac{u_{k+d} - u}{u_{k+d+1} - u_{k+1}} B_{k+1,d-1}(u)$$

1550-6037/11 $26.00 © 2011 IEEE
DOI 10.1109/IV.2011.86

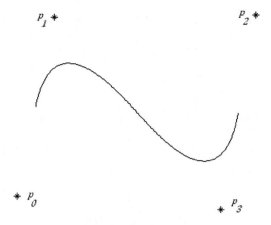

Figure 1.   Quadratic B-spline curve with 4 control points

Fig. 1 shows the Quadratic B-spline curve with four control points. The curve consists of 300 points. In proposed model of curve approximation, position of control points are determined from the error between given and computed curve. Let's take a piece of this curve, first 150 points of curve shown in Fig. 1 and see how the proposed model will approximate this curve. Selected piece of curve is shown in Fig. 2. Let's approximate this curve with Quadratic B-spline using three control points (p_0, p_1, p_2). Let's take position of control point p_1 at some random position and see how it moves to its correct position. Position of control points p_0 and p_2 is given as:

$$p_0 = 2P_{start} - p_1 \qquad (3)$$

$$p_2 = 2P_{end} - p_1$$

Where P_{start} and P_{end} represent the first and last point of (original) curve, to be approximated. Curve computed with initial position of control points (having p_1 at random position) is shown in Fig. 3. Control point p_0 and p_{n+1} are not shown in these figures for clarity.

Figure 2.   Selected piece of curve

Error between original (O) and computed (C) curve is computed as:

$$\begin{aligned} E_x &= O_x - C_x \\ E_y &= O_y - C_y \end{aligned} \qquad (4)$$

Where O_x and C_x represent the x - coordinates of original and computed curve respectively. Similarly O_y and C_y represent the y- coordinates of original and computed curve. E_x and E_y represents the array errors in x and y direction. Note that the number of points of both original and computed curves is same.

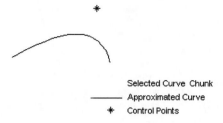

Selected Curve Chunk
—— Approximated Curve
∗   Control Points

Figure 3.   Selected piece of curve with random control point

In proposed method control point p_1 will be repositioned/displaced using the error E_x and E_y . Displacement of control point p_1 in x and y direction can be represented by vectors $\overrightarrow{D_x}$ and $\overrightarrow{D_y}$ respectively. These vectors can be computed as:

$$\overrightarrow{D_x} = \sum_{i=1}^{m} \left(E_x(i) \times \hat{B}_{1,3}(i) \right) \qquad (5)$$

$$\overrightarrow{D_y} = \sum_{i=1}^{m} \left(E_y(i) \times \hat{B}_{1,3}(i) \right)$$

Where $\hat{B}_{1,3}$ is the normalized blending function of quadratic curve for control point p_1 . Symbol m represents the number of array points, which must be equal for both (i.e. E and $\hat{B}$). Normalized blending function is computed as:

$$\hat{B}_{k,d}(u) = \frac{\alpha B_{k,d}(u)}{\sum_{u=u_k}^{u_{k+d}} B_{k,d}(u)} \qquad (6)$$

$$u_k \leq u \leq u_{k+d}$$

B-spline curve is defined only in the interval from knot u_{d-1} up to knot value u_{n+1}. Therefore, part of normalized blending function spanning out of this range must be truncated. Symbol α is an approximation constant. The value of $\alpha = 3$ in current approximation. Impact of α in curve approximation will be explained in the end of this section. New position of control point is determined as:

$$p_{1x} = p_{1x} + \overrightarrow{D_x} \qquad (7)$$

$$p_{1y} = p_{1y} + \overrightarrow{D_y}$$

$$p_1 = \left[p_{1x}, p_{1y} \right]$$

Where p_{1x} represents x-coordinate value of current position of control point and p_{1y} represents y-coordinate value respectively.

*

Figure 4.   Computed curve after repositioning of control point

New position of control points p_0 and p_2 will also be recalculated using eq. 3. Fig. 4 shows the curve after repositioning of control points p_1 . Demonstrated approximation achieves acceptable level of approximation in single iteration. However this approximation may take many iterations especially incase of higher degree curves. Another set of results are shown in Fig. 5. Fig. 5a is the curve with some randomly selected position of control point and Fig. 5b shows its approximation after single iteration. Similarly, Fig. 5c is the curve by selecting control point at the midpoint of original curve and Fig. 5d shows its approximation after single iteration. The value of constant $\alpha = 3$ in these examples.

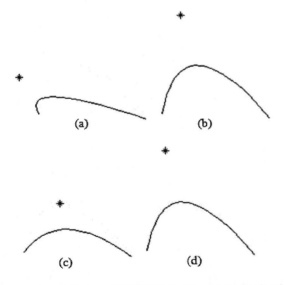

Figure 5.   Approximation with Quadratic B-spline. (a) Randomly selected control point position, (b) After reposition control point, (c) Control point at curve centre, (d) After reposition control point

Cubic B-spline can also be used to approximate the curves in similar method. Incase of cubic B-spline with four control points, control point p_1 and p_2 will be repositioned using above method. Obviously there will be two normalized blending function ($\widehat{B}_{1,4}$ and $\widehat{B}_{2,4}$) in this case. $\widehat{B}_{1,4}$ will

span from knot u_3 to u_5 and $\widehat{B}_{2,4}$ will span from knot u_4 to u_6 . Fig. 6a shows the curve selected for approximation. Initial position of control points is also shown. Fig 6b and 6c show results after first iteration of approximation with cubic B-spline having $\alpha = 3$ and $\alpha = 6$ respectively.

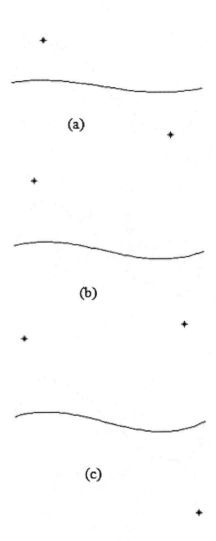

Figure 6.   One iteration of Cubic B-spline approximation. (a) Input curve, (b) Approximation with α = 3, (c) Approximation with α = 6

In most cases control point(s) will not be able to reach their destination in one run. Therefore approximation procedure should be repeated iterative till required level of approximation has been obtained. Some threshold value can be defined to determine the level of approximation achieved. We have used threshold τ in our approximation. The approximation error is computed as:

$$\varepsilon = \sqrt{E_x^2 + E_y^2} \tag{8}$$

Results proposed in this paper are based on threshold $\tau = 0.5$. Approximation constant α plays an important role in speeding up the approximation process. Higher value α (more than 1) leads to bigger jumps and quick approximation but may overshoot the target. In worst case it may start oscillating around the target and never reach to its optimal position. On the other hand small value of α (less than 1) will probably fine tune to optimal position but it may take many iterations in this process. Ideally, value of α should be high if away from its target position and α value should be small when control point has reached closer to its destination. Our investigations in this regard are under way.

III. GROWING B-SPLINE MODEL FOR CURVE APPROXIMATION

Approximation method presented in section 2 was confined to approximation of single curve section. In case of complex / lengthy curves (as shown in Fig 7a), it becomes difficult to decide the number of control points to be used for approximation. Further such an approach can be computationally very heavy. Keeping in view these problems, approximation with growing B-spline is the most suitable solution. Local control of B-spline does not impose excessive computation burden in growing B-spline model.

Basic idea of approximation using growing B-spline is to take initial chunk of given curve and approximate it using method described in section 2. Then, include more points of given curve in the initial chunk and reposition the control points, using the method described in section 2. Add a control point if error (ε) does not come below specified threshold limit (τ). This process will continue till whole curve was approximated. In B-spline reposition of any control point affects the shape of curve at most d curve sections. Therefore, previous sections of approximated curve (at the distance of $\frac{d}{2} - 1$ sections) remain unaffected during readjustments of current sections.

Fig. 7b shows the initial chunk of curve (of Fig. 7a) taken for approximation. This chunk is approximated using Quadratic B-spline (explained in section 2) and is shown in Fig. 7c. Now more points are added in this chunk and control point p_1 is re-adjusted again. Fig. 7d shows approximation at this stage. Approximation error will go beyond threshold limit ($\tau = 0.5$) if this approximation is grown any further. Therefore we add one more control point and readjust its position. Fig. 7e shows approximation at this stage. This process will continue till whole curve was approximated. Fig. 7f shows approximation of complete curve using growing B-spline model.

Complete procedure of approximation with growing B-spline model is given in Fig. 8. The growing B-spline approximation is also experimented using Cubic B-splines for approximation and the approximation results are shown in Fig. 9. Fig. 9a is the given curve. Fig. 9b is the approximation of first chunk, Fig. 9c shows approximation at an intermediate stage and Fig. 9d show the final result of approximation. For all approximation shown in this section $\alpha = 1$.

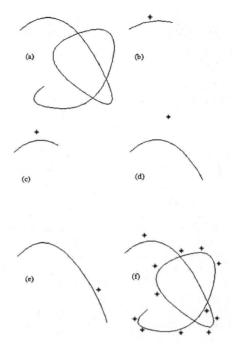

Figure 7. Approximation with growing B-spline. (a) Original curve, (b) Initial piece of curve, (c) Approximation of initial piece, (d) Approximation after growing initial piece, (e) Approximation after growing and adding one control point, (f) Final result of growing B-spline approximation

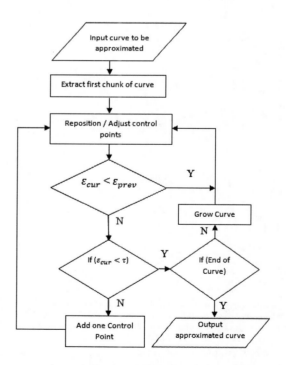

Figure 8. System Flow Diagram

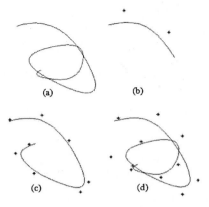

Figure 9. Approximation with growing Cubic B-spline. (a) Original curve, (b) approximation with two control points, (c) Growing curve at an intermediate level, (d) Final approximation results.

IV. RESULT DEMONSTRATION AND ANALYSIS

This section represents the curve approximation results achieved using the proposed technique. The experiments using the proposed model are carried out on curves and 2D objects. Approximation procedure of curves is explained in section 2 and 3 and it is not repeated here. Approximation with growing B-spline of two curves is given in Fig. 10. Fig. 10a shows the approximation with growing quadratic B-spline. Fig 10b shows the computed curve over original. Similarly, Fig 10c shows another approximation with growing cubic B-spline. Fig. 10d shows approximated curve over original. The approximation constant α is assigned a value 1 for both approximations.

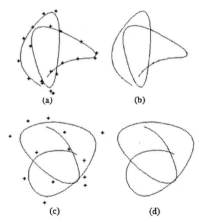

Figure 10. Growing B-spline Approximation. (a) Quadratic B-spline Approximation, (b) Computed Curve over Original, (c) Cubic B-spline Approximation, (d) Computed Curve over Original

The curve approximation results achieved using proposed technique involves minimal computational complexity. Comparing the techniques given in [2-7], the presented curve model effectively performs approximation of curves in terms of processing time and complexity. Unlike the conventional

iterative approach of locating the data points for curve approximation, the proposed model is approaching towards the optimal position of control point for a particular chunk of curve and ultimately locates the best position.

Another factor that makes the proposed technique unique and useful is the progressive growing of curve chunk till end of the curve. This helps in reducing the processing overhead, thus improves the approximation efficiency. Another advantage is that the progressive growing of curve helped in restriction or controlling the number of control points needed to approximate the curve. The computed control points represent the possible minimum set of points to perform curve approximation. The opted technique for repositioning of control point is also simple and does not require complex calculations unlike the curve approximation techniques presented in [4-5].

Proposed curve approximation method can be applied to model the shape outlines with equal ease and efficiency. Such a result is shown in Fig. 11. Before applying curve approximation, corner points were detected. The shape was segmented from the detected corner points. Fig 11a is the shape of bottle and Fig 11b shows its outline with marked corner points. Few segments were approximated with straight line and few required curve approximation. Approximation for the shape of bottle is shown in Fig. 11c. Computed shape is drawn over original to demonstrate the accuracy of results. Similarly, another result for the shape of music symbol can be seen in Fig. 11d, 11e and 11f.

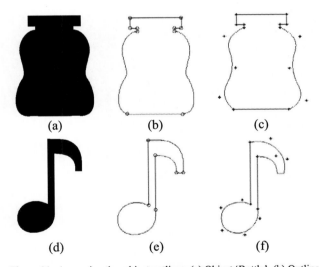

Figure 11. Approximation object outlines. (a) Object 'Bottle', (b) Outline of bottle shape with marked corner points, (c) Approximation of bottle shape, (a) Object 'Music Symbol', (b) Outline of music symbol shape with marked corner points, (c) Approximation of music symbol shape

V. CONCLUSION

A growing B-spline model for curve approximation is presented in this paper. The proposed technique is basically for the approximation of complex / lengthy curves and does not involve complex computations for the repositioning of control points. The technique is initiated by approximating the selected chunk of curve and progressively adds curve points and performs approximation. The presented technique is effectively overcoming the drawbacks of discussed approaches and provides a simple solution.

REFERENCES

[1] A. Razdan, "A knot placement for B-spline curve approximation", PRISM Publications, 1999.

[2] J. Hoscheck, D. Lasser, "Fundamentals of computer aided geometric design", London : AK Peters, 1993.

[3] H. Park, "An error bounded approximate method for representing planar curves in B-splines," Computer Aided Geometric Design, May 2004, pp. 479–497, doi:10.1016/j.cagd.2004.03.003.

[4] L. Piegl, W. Tiller, "The NURBS Book", Second Ed., NewYork: Springer-Verlag, 1997.

[5] D.F. Rogers, N. Fog, "Constrained B-spline curve and surface fitting," Computer Aided Design, Dec. 1989, pp. 641-648, doi:10.1016/0010-4485(89)90162-0..

[6] B. Sarkar, C. Menq, "Parameter optimization in approximating curves and surfaces to measurement data," Computer Aided Design, Oct. 1991, pp. 267-290, doi:10.1016/0167-8396(91)90016-5.

[7] W. Wang, H. Pottmann, Y. Liu, "Fitting B-spline curves to point clouds by curvature based squared distance minimization", ACM Transaction on Graphics, April 2006, pp. 214-238, doi:10.1145/1138450.1138453.

[8] X.D. Chen, W. Ma, J.C. Paul, "Cubic B-spline curve approximation by curve unclamping", Computer Aided Design, June 2010, pp. 523-534, doi:10.1016/j.cad.2010.01.008.

[9] W. Li et al, "Adaptive knot placement in B-spline curve approximation", Computer Aided Design, Elsevier Science, July 2005, pp. 791-797, doi:10.1016/j.cad.2004.09.008.

[10] A. Masood, M. Sarfraz, S.A. Haq, "Curve approximation with Quadratic B-splines," Proc. IEEE Symp. 9th International Conference on Information Visualization (IV'05), July 2005, pp. 419-424, doi:10.1109/IV.2005.39.

[11] W.Y. Ma, J.P. Kurth, "Parameterization of randomly measured points for least squares fitting of B-spline curves and surfaces," Computer Aided Design, Sept. 1995, pp. 663-665, doi:10.1016/0010-4485(94)00018-9.

[12] H. Pattmann, S. Leopoldseder, M. Hofer, "Approximation with active B-spline curves and surfaces," Proc. 10th Pacific Conference on Computer Graphics and Applications (PG'02), IEEE Computer Society Press, pp. 8-25, ISBN: 0-7695-1784-6.

[13] H. Binder, W. Sauerbrei, "Increasing the usefulness of additive spline models by knot removal," Computational Statistics and Data Analysis, Aug. 2008, pp. 5305-5318, doi:10.1016/j.csda.2008.05.009.

[14] H. Park, J.H. Lee, "B-spline curve fitting based on adaptive curve refinement using dominant points", Computer Aided Design, June 2007, pp. 439-451, doi:10.1016/j.cad.2006.12.006..

[15] H. Park, J.H. Lee, "Error bounded B-spline curve approximation based on dominant point selection," Proc. Computer Graphics, Imaging and Vision: New Trends (CGIV'05), 2005, pp. 437-446, doi:10.1109/CGIV.2005.36.

[16] M. Eck, J. Hadenfeld, "Knot removal for B-spline curve," Computer Aided Geometric Design, May 1995, pp. 259-282, doi:10.1016/0167-8396(94)00012-H.

Evaluation of Volumetric Medical Images Segmentation using Hidden Markov Random Field Model

Samy Ait-Aoudia, Ramdane Mahiou, Elhachemi Guerrout

ESI - Ecole nationale Supérieure en Informatique, BP 68M, O-Smar 16270 Algiers, Algeria

s_ait_aoudia@esi.dz, r_mahiou@esi.dz, e_guerrout@esi.dz

Abstract. *Medical image segmentation is a crucial step in the process of image analysis. An automatic aid in interpretation of huge amount of data can be of great value to specialists that hold final decision. Hidden Markov Random Field (HMRF) Model and Gibbs distributions provide powerful tools for image modeling. In this paper, we use a HMRF model to perform segmentation of volumetric medical images handling inter-image similarity. This modelling leads to the minimization of an energy function. This problem is computationally intractable. Therefore, optimizations techniques are used to compute a solution. We will use and compare promising relatively recent methods based on graph cuts with older well known methods that are Simulated Annealing and ICM.*

Keywords. *Medical image segmentation, Hidden Markov Random Field, Gibbs distribution, Simulated Annealing, Gibbs sampler, Metropolis Sampling, Iterated Conditional Modes, Graph cuts.*

I. INTRODUCTION

Classical medical exams can produce large sets of images. The huge amount of produced data sets makes the analysis and interpretation a tiresome and delicate task. An automatic aid in interpretation can be of great value to specialists that hold final decision. Automatic medical image segmentation is thus an important phase that can rapidly partition the images in different tissues (normal or abnormal).

Several methods were used to perform this segmentation. HMRF Model and Gibbs distributions provide powerful tools for image modelling [10, 11, 14] that lead to a solid basis to the final image segmentation. Since the seminal paper of Geman and Geman [7], Markov Random Fields (MRF) models for image segmentation have been largely investigated [1, 9, 15, 17]. In this paper, we use a Hidden Markov Random Field (HMRF) model to perform segmentation of volumetric medical images (3D datasets). This modelling leads to the minimization of an energy function. This problem is computationally intractable. Therefore, optimizations techniques are used to compute a solution. Choosing a good optimization method is a crucial task. A poor optimization process can lead to "disastrous" results. We will use and compare well-known optimization techniques that are Gibbs Sampler with Simulated Annealing scheme (Gibbs-SA), Metropolis Sampling with Simulated Annealing scheme (Metropolis-SA), the Iterated Conditional Modes (ICM), and the Graph Cuts promising method [16]. When we have the ground truth images (a priori segmented images known), the segmentation evaluation is made by calculating Dice coefficients (Kappa Indexes) that gives the similarity between segmented images and the a priori labeled images.

This paper is organized as follows. We remind in section 2 basis of Markov Random Field model. In section 3, we give principles of Hidden Markov Field model in the context of image segmentation. The optimization techniques used are explained in section 4. Experimental results on medical samples datasets are given in section 5. Section 6 gives conclusions.

II. MARKOV RANDOM FIELD MODEL

In this section we remind some important notions relative to Markov Random Field model and some terms used in the context of image analysis issues.

A. Neighborhood system and clique notion

The pixels of the image are represented as a lattice S of $M=n*m$ sites.

In an MRF, the sites (pixels in our case) in S are related by a neighborhood system $V(S)$.

The first and second order neighborhood systems are the most commonly used. In these systems, a site has four and eight neighbors respectively. When a site has four or eight neighbors, we speak about a 4-neighborhood (4-N) or an 8-neighborhood (8-N).

A clique c is a subset of sites in S relatively to a neighborhood system. c is a singleton or all the distinct sites of c are neighbors.

A *p-order* clique noted c_p contains p sites i.e. p is the cardinal of the clique.

B. Markov Random Field

Let $X=\{X_1, X_2,...,X_M\}$ be a family of random variables on the lattice S. Each random variable taking values in the discrete space $\Lambda=\{1,2,...,K\}$. The family X is a random field with configuration set $\Omega = \Lambda^M$.

A random field X is said to be an MRF on S with respect to a neighborhood system $V(S)$ if and only if :

$$\forall x \in \Omega, P(x) > 0$$

$$\forall s \in S, \forall x \in \Omega, P(X_s = x_s / X_t = x_t, t \neq s) = P(X_s = x_s / X_t = x_t, t \in V_s(S))$$

1550-6037/11 $26.00 © 2011 IEEE
DOI 10.1109/IV.2011.83

The Hammersley-Clifford theorem establishes the equivalence between Gibbs fields and Markov fields. The Gibbs distribution is characterized by the following relation:

$$P(x)= Z^{-1} e^{-\frac{U(x)}{T}}$$

$$Z=\sum_{y\in\Omega}e^{-\frac{U(y)}{T}}$$

where T is a global control parameter called temperature and Z is a normalizing constant called the partition function. Calculating Z is prohibitive. $Card(\Omega)=2^{2097152}$ for a 512x512 gray level image. $U(x)$ is the energy function of the Gibbs field defined as :

$$U(x)=\sum_{c\in C}U_c(x)$$

C. Standard Markov Random Field

Standard Markov random fields have been used for image analysis purposes.

Ising model

This model was proposed by Ernst Ising for ferromagnetism studies in statistical physics. The Ising model involves discrete variables s_i (spins) placed on a sampling grid. Each spin can take two values, $\Lambda=\{-1,1\}$, and the spins interact in pairs. The first order clique potential are defined by $-Bx_s$ and the second order clique potential are defined by :

$$U_{c=\{s,t\}}(x_s,x_t)=-\beta x_s x_t=\begin{cases}-\beta & if \ x_s=x_t \\ \beta & if \ x_s\neq x_t\end{cases}$$

The total energy is defined by :

$$U(x)=-\sum_{c=\{s,t\}}\beta x_s x_t +\sum_{s\in S}Bx_s$$

The coupling constant β between neighbor sites regularizes the model and B represents an extern magnetic field.

Potts model

The Potts model is a generalization of the Ising model. Instead of $\Lambda=\{-1,1\}$, each spin is assigned an integer value $\Lambda=\{1,2,...,K\}$. In the context of image segmentation, the integer values are gray levels or labels. The total energy is defined by :

$$U(x)=\beta \sum_{s,t\in C_2}(2\delta(x_s,x_t)-1)$$

where δ is the Kronecker's delta.

When $\beta>0$, the probable configurations correspond to neighbor sites with same gray level or label. This induces the constitution of large homogenous regions. The size of these regions is guided by the value of β.

III. HMRF MODEL

A. Hidden Markov Random Field

A strong model for image segmentation is to see the image to segment as a realization of a Markov Random Field $Y=\{Y_s\}_{s\in S}$ defined on the lattice S. The random variables $\{Y_s\}_{s\in S}$ have gray level values in the space $\Lambda_{obs}=\{0..255\}$. The configuration set is Ω_{obs}.

The segmented image is seen as the realization of another Markov Random Field X defined on the same lattice S, taking values in the discrete space $\Lambda=\{1,2,...,K\}$. K represents the number of classes or homogeneous regions in the image.

In the context of image segmentation we have a problem with incomplete data. Two different information are associated to every site $i\in S$. Observed information expressed by the random variable Y_i and a missed or hidden information expressed by the random variable X_i. The Random Field X is said Hidden Markov Random Field.

The segmentation process consists in finding a realization x of X by observing the data of the realization y representing the image to segment.

B. MAP estimation

We seek a labeling $\widehat{x}$ which is an estimate of the true labeling x^*, according to the MAP (Maximum A Posteriori) [18] criterion (maximizing the probability $P(X=x|Y=y)$).

$$\widehat{x}=\underset{x\in X}{arg\,max}\{P(X=x|Y=y)\}$$

$$P(X=x|Y=y)=\frac{P(Y=y|X=x)P(X=x)}{P(Y=y)}$$

$$P(X=x|Y=y)=Ke^{ln(P(Y=y|X=x))-\frac{U(x)}{T}}$$

$$P(X=x|Y=y)=Ke^{-\Psi(x,y)}$$

The labeling $\widehat{x}$ can be found by maximizing the probability $P(X=x|Y=y)$ or equivalently by minimizing the function $\Psi(x|y)$.

$$\widehat{x}=\underset{x\in X}{arg\,min}\{\Psi(x,y)\}$$

The searched labeling $\widehat{x}$ can be found using some optimization techniques.

Assuming that the pixel intensity follows a Gaussian distribution with parameters μ_k (mean) and σ_k^2 (variance) and using the Potts model, we have :

$$\Psi(x,y)=\sum_{s\in S}\frac{(y_s-\mu_{x_s})^2}{2\sigma_{x_s}^2}+ln(\sqrt{2\pi}\sigma_{x_s})+\frac{\beta}{T}\sum_{s,t\in C_2}(1-2\delta(x_s,x_t))$$

514

IV. OPTIMIZATION

The MAP estimation leads to the minimization of an energy function. This problem is computationally intractable. Therefore, optimizations techniques are used to compute a solution. We will use and compare relatively recent methods based on graph cuts with older well known methods that are Simulated Annealing and ICM.

Graph cuts algorithms are stemming from combinatorial optimization. The two most popular graph cuts algorithms used in our experiments are due to Boykov et al. [3,4]. The two algorithms used (called swap-move and expansion-move) find a local minimum with respect to two types of moves that are swap moves and expansion moves. These moves allow large number of pixels to change their labels simultaneously. Algorithm 1 and algorithm 2 briefly describe these two methods.

Simulated annealing is a neighborhood based optimization method inspired from a technique used to have states of low energy of a material. This technique is called metallurgic or physics annealing. Inspired from the principles of the metallurgic annealing, Kirkpatrick [13] proposed the well-known simulated annealing optimization method shown by algorithm 3. We will use in our experiments Gibbs Sampler with Simulated Annealing scheme (Gibbs-SA) and Metropolis sampling with Simulated Annealing scheme (Metropolis-SA).

The Iterated Conditional Modes (ICM) algorithm proposed by Besag [2], is a deterministic relaxation scheme with a constant temperature. Performances of the ICM algorithm tightly depend on the initialization process. It converges toward the local minimum close to the initialization. Algorithm 4 summarizes the ICM technique.

Algorithm 1 : α-β swap algorithm
1. Start with an arbitrary labeling x
2. Set success := 0
3. For each pair of labels $\{\alpha, \beta\} \subset L$
   3.1. Find x* = argmin E(x') among x' within one α-β swap of x
   3.2. If E(x*) < E(x), set x := x* and success := 1
4. If success = 1 goto 2
5. Return x

Algorithm 2 : α expansion algorithm
1. Start with an arbitrary labeling x
2. Set success := 0
3. For each label $\alpha \subset L$
   3.1. Find x* = argmin E(x') among x' within one α-expansion of x
   3.2. If E(x*) < E(x), set x := x* and success := 1
4. If success = 1 goto 2
5. Return x

Algorithm 3 : simulated annealing
1. Initialization: n=0 and T0=Tmax a high temperature; the configuration x(0) is randomly chosen.
2. Repeat:
   - *Generate a perturbation x(n+1)*
   - *Accept this state under condition*
   - *Decrease the temperature T according to the annealing function f(T)*
   Until reaching a minimum temperature T_{min} that guarantees the convergence to a global minimum

Algorithm 4 : ICM
1. Initialization: Start with an arbitrary labeling x^0 and let *n=0*.
2. At step *n* :
   Visit all the sites according to a visiting scheme and in every site s :
   $$x_s^{n+1} = \arg \min_{x \in \Omega^{card(S)}} U_s(x_s = \lambda), \quad \lambda \in \Omega.$$
3. Increment *n*. Goto 2, until a stopping criterion is satisfied.

V. EXPERIMENTAL RESULTS

The evaluation of the segmentation is made on volumetric medical data samples. All images were gray-level, and were scaled to 8 bits/pixel.

The implementation of the segmentation model requires estimating the parameters μ and σ for each class. Since the segmentation is unsupervised as in [6,12], the expectation-maximization (EM) algorithm [5,8,19] is used to compute μ and σ.

The segmentation model needs also the estimation of several parameters that are: the parameter β, the initial temperature T_0 for the simulated annealing process, the constant τ and the neighborhood system. This is a non trivial task. We have conducted several tests with different parameter choices. The choice of wrong parameters can have "dramatic" consequences on image segmentation quality and the time needed to do this segmentation.

The convergence of Simulated Annealing algorithm is tightly linked to the annealing process. The logarithmic decrease of the temperature $T(n) \geq \frac{\tau}{log(1+n)}$ (where τ is a constant) proposed by Geman and Geman [7] is very slow. In practice, a geometric decrease $T(n+1) = \tau . T(n)$ is used without noticeable degradation of results.

The following examples give some results showing the results of the segmentation of medical and synthetic images.

Figure 4 shows an IRM scan and its corresponding segmentations in four classes varying the parameter β.

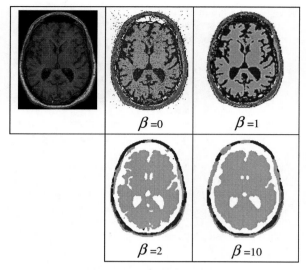

Figure 4. Segmentation varying β.

Figure 5 shows an IRM scan and its corresponding segmentations in three classes with β=1 and T_0=4 varying the parameter τ.

Figure 6 shows a synthetic image and its corresponding segmentations in five classes with β=1 and τ=0.98 varying the parameter T_0.

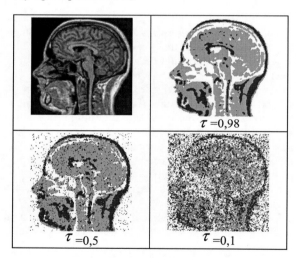

Figure 5. Segmentation varying τ.

Based on an evaluation phase, the following parameters values were chosen: β=1, T_0=4, τ =0,98, 6-neighborhood. They give good results and a better compromise in terms of segmentation quality and processing time: The 6-neighborhood system is a 3D neighborhood system as shown in figure 7.a. The use of 3D 18- neighborhood (figure 7.b) and 26- neighborhood systems imply more computing time without bringing noticeable quality in segmentation.

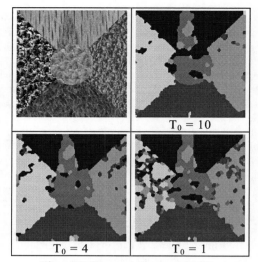

Figure 6. Segmentation varying T_0.

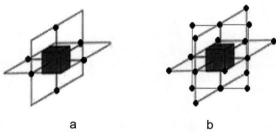

a   b

Figure 7. 6-neighborhood and 18-neighborhood systems

Evaluating the quality of the segmentation can only be made on synthetic images where the a priori segmentation is known. For this purpose, we have used the Brainweb[1] database largely used in the evaluation of brain segmentation. The Dice Coefficient *DC* or Kappa Index given hereafter measures the quality of the segmentation.

$$DC=2\times\frac{TP}{2\times TP+FP+FN}$$

where *TP* stands for True positive, *FN* False Negative and *FP* False Positive.

The Dice coefficient equals 1 when the two segmentations are identical and 0 when no classified pixel matches the true segmentation.

Figure 8 shows some slices and their corresponding segmentation of the volumetric dataset for the subject 04 T1w (181 slices, 256x256 pixels per images) taken from the Brainweb database.

_____

[1] http://www.bic.mni.mcgill.ca/brainweb/

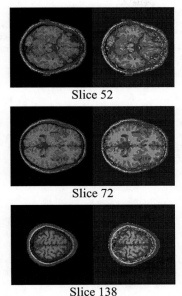

Slice 52

Slice 72

Slice 138

Figure 8. Brainweb Segmented examples.

Some slices of subject T1_ICBM (from Brainweb database) are shown in figure 9. Their corresponding segmentations are given in figure 10. The ground truth segmentations for the white matter and gray matter are given in figure 11 and 12 respectively.

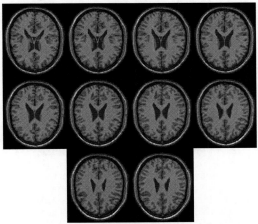

Figure 9. MR brain images sample.

The means of Dice coefficients calculated for these slices considering white matter and gray matter are given in table 1. The neighborhood systems used are 4-neighborhood (4-N), 6-neighborhood (6-N) and 18-neighborhood (18-N). With the 4-neighborhood, the interactions between slices are not taken into account since this is a 2D neighborhood. 6-neighborhood and 18-neighborhood are 3D neighborhood. The use of the 18-neighborhood don't bring noticeable quality in segmentation but requires more computing time.

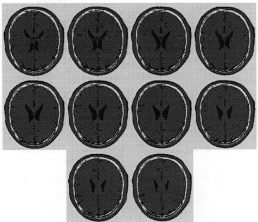

Figure 10. Segmented images.

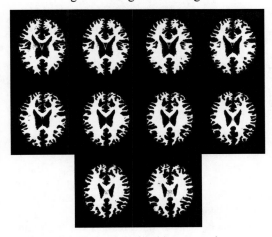

Figure 11. Ground truth white matter images.

	4-N	6-N	18-N
ICM	0,84	0,85	0,85
Gibbs-SA	0,86	0,87	0,88
Metropolis-SA	0,87	0,89	0,89
GC α,β swap	0,92	0,93	0,94
GC α expansion	0,94	0,95	0,95

White Matter

	4-N	6-N	18-N
ICM	0,79	0,80	0,81
Gibbs-SA	0,80	0,82	0,82
Metropolis-SA	0,81	0,83	0,83
GC α,β swap	0,85	0,87	0,87
GC α expansion	0,86	0,87	0,88

Gray Matter

TABLE I. Mean Kappa Index

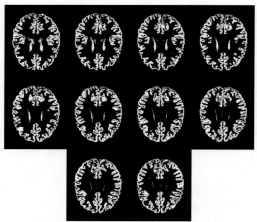

Figure 12. Ground truth gray matter images.

From table I, we see that the two graph cuts algorithms (α-β swap-move and α expansion-move), give remarkable best results than the older methods (ICM and Simulated Annealing).

The implementation was also parallelized on a cluster of PCs. The processing time was reduced to less than a minute on a cluster of 16 PCs (Intel Pentium 4, CPU 3.60GHz, RAM 1 Go).

VI. CONCLUSION

This paper attempts to evaluate the segmentation of Brain Magnetic Resonance Images using Hidden Markov Random Field Model. Different optimization techniques (Graph Cuts, Simulated Annealing and ICM) were used and compared.

From the results obtained, Graph Cuts technique outperforms the Simulated Annealing and ICM classical techniques. When the ground truth is known, the segmented images are very close (in similarity) to the a priori segmented images when using graph cuts techniques.

Nevertheless, further works must consider segmenting sets of MR brain images taken from other sources. The opinion of specialists must also be considered in the evaluation when no ground truth is available to have a more synthetic view of the whole segmentation process.

REFERENCES

[1] E.D. Angelini, T. Song, B.D. Mensh, & A.F. Laine, "Brain MRI Segmentation with Multiphase Minimal Partitioning: A Comparative Study", Int. J. Biomed Imaging, volume 2007, 15p.

[2] J. Besag, "On the statistical analysis of dirty pictures (with discussion)," J. of Royal Statist. Soc., ser. B, 1986, vol. 48, no. 3, pp. 259–302,.

[3] Y. Boykov, O. Veksler and R. Zabih, "Fast Approximate Energy Minimization via Graph Cuts", IEEE Transactions on PAMI, vol. 23, no. 11, pp. 1222-1239

[4] Y. Boykov and V. Kolmogorov, "An Experimental Comparison of Min-Cut/Max-Flow Algorithms for Energy Minimization in Vision", In IEEE Transactions on PAMI, Vol. 26, No. 9, pp. 1124-1137, Sept. 2004.

[5] A.P. Dempster, N.M. Laird, D.B. Rubin, "Maximum likelihood from incomplete data via the EM algorithm", Journal Royal Stat. Soc., B1:1-38, 1977.

[6] H. Deng, D.A. Clausi, "Unsupervised image segmentation using a simple MRF model with a new implementation scheme", Proc. of the 17th International Conf. on Pattern Recognition, Aug. 2004, 691- 694.

[7] S. Geman, D. Geman, "Stochastic relaxation, Gibbs distributions and the Bayesian restoration of images". IEEE Trans. Pattern Anal. Machine Intell., 1984, 6(6), 721-741.

[8] D.B. Gu, J.X. Sun, "EM image segmentation algorithm based on an inhomogeneous hidden MRF model", Vision, Image and Signal Processing, IEE Proceedings, Volume 152, Issue 2, 8 April 2005, 184 – 190.

[9] K. Held, E.R. Kops, B.J. Krause, W.M Wells, R. Kikinis, H.-W. Muller-Gartner, "Markov random field segmentation of brain MR images", IEEE Tran. on Medical Imaging, Dec. 1997, Vol. 16(6), 878-886

[10] .A. Huang, R. Abugharbieh, R. Tam, "Image segmentation using an efficient rotationally invariant 3D region-based hidden Markov model", IEEE Computer Vision and Pattern Recognition Workshops, June 2008, Anchorage, AK, USA, 1-8.

[11] M. Ibrahim, N. John, M. Kabuka and A. Younis, "Hidden Markov models-based 3D MRI brain segmentation", Image and Vision Computing Volume 24, Issue 10, Oct. 2006, 1065-1079.

[12] Z. Kato, J. Zerubia, M. Berthod, "Unsupervised parallel image classification using Markovian models", Pattern Recognition 32 (1999) 591-604.

[13] S. Kirkpatrick, C.D. Gelatt, M.P. Vecchi, "Optimisation by simulated annealing", Science, vol. 220 (4598), pp 671-680, 1983.

[14] S. Z. Li. Markov Random Field Modeling in Computer Vision. New York: Springer-Verlag, 2001.

[15] J.L. Marroquin, B.C. Vemuri, S. Botello, E. Calderon, A. Fernandez-Bouzas, "An accurate and efficient Bayesian method for automatic segmentation of brain MRI", IEEE Trans. on Med. Imaging, vol. 21(8), Aug. 2002, 934-945.

[16] R. Szeliski, R. Zabih, D. Scharstein, O. Veksler, V. Kolmogorov, A. Agarwala, M. Tappen, C. Rother, "A Comparative Study of Energy Minimization Methods for Markov Random Fields with Smoothness-Based Priors", IEEE Trans. on Pattern Analysis and Machine Intelligence, Vol. 30(6), June 2008.

[17] K. Van Leemput, F. Maes, D. Vandermeulen, and P. Suetens, "A Unifying Framework for Partial Volume Segmentation of Brain MR Images", IEEE Trans. on Medical Imaging, vol. 22(1), pp.105-119, January 2003.

[18] P. Wyatt and J.A. Noble, "MAP MRF joint segmentation and registration of medical images", Medical Image Analysis, Volume 7, Issue 4, December 2003, 539-552

[19] Y. Zhang, M. Brady, S Smith, "Segmentation of Brain MR Images through a Hidden Markov Random Field Model and the Expectation-Maximization Algorithm", IEEE Trans. on Medical Imaging 20(1), Jan. 2001, 45-57.

Efficient Curvature-optimized G^2-continuous Path Generation with Guaranteed Error Bound for 3-axis Machining

Jevgenija Selinger, Lars Linsen

Jacobs University, Bremen, Germany

j.selinger@jacobs-university.de; l.linsen@jacobs-university.de

Abstract

Path generations are a necessary integral part of any automated machining approach using 3-axis robots. Given an input path in form of a piecewise linear curve, we automatically generate an optimized path that lies within a given error bound or tolerance band of the input path. The optimization is targeted at minimizing the processing time of the machining process. As sharp turns require the robot to slow down, we want to minimize the local curvature at each point of the curve. Our approach is an efficient offline algorithm that consists of several processing steps. In a preprocessing step, we analyze the input path and split it into small groups. The groups are categorized and can be handled independently and locally. We apply a local sleeve concept for complicated groups and a local Bézier approximation for simple groups. In a postprocessing step the groups are combined to form a G^2-continuous path. Our approach achieves high-quality results that are comparable to the sleeves approach while being significantly more efficient (speed-up of one order of magnitude) when applied to real-world problems.

1 Introduction

Milling with 3-axis robots is one of the major topics in computer-aided manufacturing. One main step in this context is the generation of a milling path. Various strategies exist to generate a suitable path. However, the paths frequently contain sharp turns, which forces the robot to slow down significantly during the milling process. As such, sharp turns in the milling path lead to a substantial increase in milling time. We present an approach that optimizes a given milling path with a guaranteed error bound.

According to common industry standards, the milling path is typically given in form of a piecewise linear curve representation. Hence, the input to our algorithm is a workpiece which we want to mill and a milling path in form of a polygonal line that connects consecutive path points. The milling machine cuts along this path to obtain the required shape of the workpiece. We developed an offline calculation algorithm for a smooth milling path with low oscillations from the initially given path. The constructed curve

should be contained in a given prescribed small *tolerance* neighborhood of these points.

The resulting curve shall be represented as a B-spline curve

$$\mathbf{C}(u) := \sum_{j=0}^{n} \mathbf{P}_j N_j^d(u), \ a \le u \le b$$

where the interval $[a, b]$ can be any, $\mathbf{P}_j$ denotes the j-th control points, and N_j^d denotes the j-th normalized B(asis)-spline function of degree d. The B-spline basis functions are defined over a nonperiodic knot vector

$$\mathbf{U} = (\underbrace{a, \cdots, a}_{d+1}, u_{d+1}, \cdots, u_{m-d-1}, \underbrace{b, \cdots, b}_{d+1}),$$

where $m = n + d + 1$.

In order to generate a B-spline curve with the restrictions described above, we construct a channel around the initial points with given tolerance and require the resulting curve to lie inside this channel. The sharper the angle between the initial points is, the more complicated, and thus slower, movements the milling tool has to make. To reduce the overall processing time of the milling procedure, we want to minimize the curvature of the resulting curve while keeping the curve within the channel (see Figure 1a). In addition, it is desirable that the solution satisfies certain shape constraints of the milling path to obtain proper results. In particular, one wants to obtain symmetrical solutions for single angles and turns (see Figure 1b and Figure 1c).

The idea of the proposed method is to appropriately partition the input curve in form of connected initial points into small groups, to handle the groups individually, and to combine the local solution for the groups to a global solution in form of a G^2-continuous curve. The partitioning step is described in Section 3.2. The handling of the groups depends on their complexity. Complex groups are handled using a sleeve approach, see Section 3.3. Simple groups can be handled with a more efficient local cubic curve approximation, see Section 3.5. In case the G^2-property is not required and the construction of a G^1-continuous curve suffices, the even simpler solution in Section 3.4 can be applied to the simple groups. Finally, the local curves need to

1550-6037/11 $26.00 © 2011 IEEE

DOI 10.1109/IV.2011.31

be combined to form a global one as described in Section 3.6. The result is represented by a smooth B-spline curve of degree three.

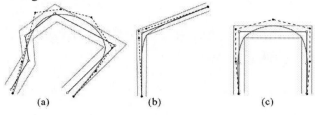

Figure 1: (a) Smooth milling path generation (red) in B-spline form with a certain control polygon (black) from a given piecewise linear input curve (blue) within a certain tolerance defining a channel (green). (b) Symmetric solution for single angles. (c) Symmetric solution for turns.

2   Related Work

A method for obtaining a smooth, jerk-bounded feed rate profile in high-speed machining has been developed in papers about adaptive interpolation for NC machining [10, 11]. Those studies propose a NURBS interpolator based on adaptive feed rate control with a look-ahead algorithm. By using a windowing scheme the feed-rate profile, obtained after look-ahead, is re-interpolated to obtain a continuous velocity and acceleration profile which reduces the jerk related problems (see Figure 2).

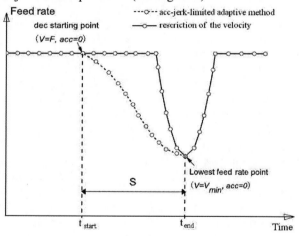

Figure 2: Adaptive parametric interpolation scheme with limited acceleration and jerk values for NC machining [10]. As we arrive at the decreasing starting point, the feed rate must be reduced. However, the feed rate depends on the radius of curvature. To achieve the point with the lowest feed rate, the feed rate is adaptively adjusted such that the error does not exceed the allowable maximum value.

There is no adjustment of the milling curve beforehand. All the calculations are taking place during milling by minimizing an error between the interpolated path and the gen-erated curve. Our approach would allow for an application of feed-rate adaptation to the optimized curve. Since curvatures are minimized, it is to be expected that results would be significantly improved.

Many approaches for a global approximation of the input path with higher-order piecewise polynomials exist. Most of them do not fit all the constraints that are imposed to our problem, e.g., they do not allow for curvature minimization or cannot provide guaranteed error bounds. An approach that would be applicable to our problem is the one of data approximation using biarcs [9]. Given two points P_s, P_e and two unit end tangents T_s and T_e, a piecewise circular arc is sought such that:

- it passes through P_s and P_e;
- it is tangential to T_s at P_s, and to T_e at P_e;
- the arcs join in G^1 continuity.

The solution is given in form of $P_1 = P_0 + \alpha T_s$,

$$P_2 = \frac{\beta}{\alpha + \beta}P_1 + \frac{\alpha}{\alpha + \beta}P_3 \text{ and } P_3 = P_4 + \beta T_s,$$

where α and β are scalar values, such that $|P_1 P_2| = \alpha$ and $|P_2 P_3| = \beta$. The method is a fast and useful in engineering applications, where simple curves are required to drive machine tools, or where the application necessitates a piecewise curve with piecewise constant curvature. However, it only generates G^1-continuous curves and curvature control is limited.

A standard local approximation scheme is provided in the NURBS book [8] produce a nonrational G^1–continuity cubic B-spline curve. It provides a fast solution for simple initial data. The details of this approach are described in Section 3.4. We build upon this idea to create a new approach for the generation of G^2-continuous cubic B-spline. This extension is described in Section 3.5.

The latter three approaches take care about how far the control points move from initial points. Our goal is to keep the curve inside the tolerance band. Closeness of the control points to the initial points is not required. We use the idea of smooth paths in a polygon channel to achieve this. The details are given in Section 3.5.

3   Smooth Path Generation
3.1   Overview

As part of our approach, we build upon two existing algorithms. For complicated regions of the path we apply the idea of threading splines through 3D channels (see Section 3.3), for simple ones we use the idea of local non-rational cubic approximation (see Section 3.5). The former algorithm provides us a solution with the curvature close to optimal. However, this algorithm involves time-expensive calculations using methods from linear programming. Though the second algorithm provides acceptable approximation results only for the simple parts of the workpiece, it is substantially faster than the first one. Since an average workpiece consists mostly of simple parts, the computation times of our combined algorithm are significantly lower.

Our method can be described by the following steps:

- Split the sequence of initial points into small groups.

- For each group, estimate all properties of the current group and decide which algorithm to apply (see Section 3.2) and generate the solution for the group using the appropriate algorithm (see Sections 3.3 and 3.5).

- Connect all groups to one B-spline curve (see Section 3.6).

3.2 Splitting into Groups

As a first step, we need to partition the given curve into small curve segments. As the input curve is given as a sequence of points, the curve segments are represented as groups (or sequences) of consecutive input points. We want to distinguish between simple and complicated groups. As handling complicated groups will be done in a more time-consuming processing step, it is desirable to keep the number of complicated groups as small as possible and to keep the complicated groups themselves as small as possible. A complex group is a group that contains at least one sharp corner, i.e., an angle smaller than a certain threshold α_{sharp}. Consequently, simple groups are those with no sharp corners.

We implement different grouping criteria based on the distances between consecutive input points and the incident angles between the two edges connecting three consecutive input points.

First, we deploy some global splitting criteria. As processing time for groups increases superlinearly with increasing group size, groups shall not exceed a certain upper limit of points n_{max}. Also, very long distances between consecutive points may make it difficult to optimize for curvature. Hence, if two consecutive input points exhibit a distance larger than a certain threshold d_{max}, the two points shall belong to two different groups.

To make the simple groups as large as possible, we proceed as shown in Figure 3. We iterate through the points of the input curve. When a new group contains more than five points with no sharp corner, we generate a new group that is marked as simple. We keep on growing that group until the maximum number of points n_{max} is reached or we are approaching a sharp corner. To detect an approaching sharp corner, we use a look-ahead method of n_{ahead} points. If this look ahead reports a sharp corner, we finalize the simple group and start a complicated group.

If a sharp corner is reported before the group reaches the n_{ahead} point, the group is marked as complicated and we keep on adding points. A complicated group is finalized when n_{ahead} points have been added since the last sharp corner and no new sharp corner has been reported by the look ahead. If the look ahead reports a sharp corner but we are about to exceed the n_{max} restriction, we investigate the angles of the last $2n_{ahead}-1$ points, and finish the group with the point that is situated in the middle of the two look-ahead points with the sharpest corners. It prevents the group to stop at the input point with the sharpest corner.

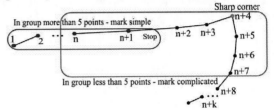

Figure 3: Complicated and simple regions.

The described solution produces complicated groups of minimum size. Moreover, the solution for a complicated group with a single sharp corner is symmetric in the sense that the sharp corner is at the middle point of the group, see Figure 4. Such a symmetric solution is desirable for milling applications, as it ensures that the milling result to both sides of the sharp corner is similar.

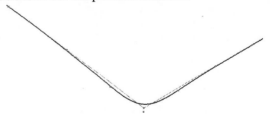

Figure 4: Symmetric solution for a single corner point.

Such a symmetric behavior is also desirable when dealing with a group of multiple sharp corners. In particular, a common geometric feature of milling paths is that of a turn, i.e., a small sequence of points where the direction of milling in changed to its inverse direction at some offset. We handle such turns explicitly to assure that the middle of the turn corresponds to the middle of the generated group.

Depending on which criterion caused the formation of a group, we have different methods of how a group is to be connected with the subsequent group when generating the overall curve. We distinguish between two types of connections, namely a *line connection* and an *overlapping connection*. As mentioned above, if we have a pair of neighboring points a_k and a_{k+1} in distance more than d_{max}, we are finalizing the current group with the point a_k and start the next group with point a_{k+1}. This type of connection is what we call a line connection. Examples for line connections are shown in Figure 5.

To fulfill continuity requirements, we insert three additional points lying on the line $a_k a_{k+1}$ such that each inserted point has distance d_{line} from the previous point. We adjust the two groups by adding the three additional points to the end of the first group (i.e., after a_k) and to the beginning of the second group (i.e., before a_{k+1}). When optimizing the curve segments as described in the subsequent sections, we restrict the solutions to keep inserted points on the line $a_k a_{k+1}$.

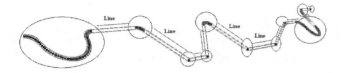

Figure 5: Line connections between groups of points that are further apart than distance d_{max}.

Note that individual points can form a group, if they are more than distance d_{max} away from both its preceding and succeeding point. In this case that single point is connected with two line segments in a symmetric fashion as shown in Figure 4.

If two successive groups have not been separated by the maximum-distance criterion, the two groups are close together and, in general, have not been split in an area of low curvature. Figure 6 shows such a critical area, where the two groups come together at an area of rather large curvature. In this case, it is likely that the optimization of the first group generates a solution with the endpoint on the border of the tolerance channel. This fact will make it hard to produce a G^2-continuous transition with low curvature terms between the two groups. Thus, we want the two groups to overlap, i.e., we want the groups to share a small area. Consequently, we call this connection an overlapping connection. The overlap is handled as follows: we first get a solution for the first group and then we insert at the beginning of the second group first overlapping point and for next to points present G^2-continuity restrictions (see Section 3.6). Now the starting point of the second group, in general, lies well within the tolerance channel making it easier to construct a good solution for the second group.

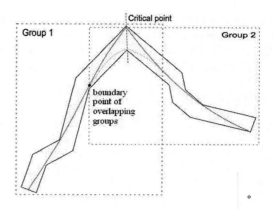

Figure 6: Necessity for overlapping connection at critical area.

The generated groups are sufficiently small to efficiently generate optimized solutions using the algorithms described in Sections 3.3 and 3.5. However, in some cases the algorithms cannot find a solution. If that happens, additional points are added to the initial sequence and the algorithms start over again with the refined point sequence. In our experiments, it turned out that this successive refinement and optimization step can be rather computationally intense. Instead, we empirically found a criterion that estimates whether this refinement step is likely to happen. If yes, we insert points beforehand, which can significantly reduce the computation costs. Using the notations of Figure 7, the criterion can be formulated as follows: We insert the midpoint between B and C, if the angle α at B is small and the distance between B and C is large when compared to the tolerance ϵ of the channel. Those two criteria are combined such that the midpoint is inserted, if the point $(cos(\alpha), \|BC\|/\epsilon)$ lies above the graph of the empirically found curve shown in Figure 7.

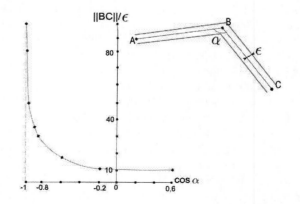

Figure 7: Point insertion criteria. If the $\|BC\|$ divided by the tolerance ϵ lies above the graph of the curve then we insert the midpoint between B and C.

3.3 Local Sleeve Approach for Complicated Groups

The handling of complicated groups is done by executing a local method based in the slefe approach by Lutterkort and Peters [2, 3, 4]. Slefe is short for "subdividable linear efficient function enclosure". The idea is to generate two polygons that represent lower and upper boundaries of a given B-spline curve. The construction can be generalized to curves in space by applying the construction in both coordinate-axis directions of the underlying 2D domain, see Figure 8. It is, then, referred to as the sleeve approach. After construction of the piecewise linear sleeve, it it is sufficient to constrain this sleeve rather than the original nonlinear curve to stay within the channel. Carefully formulated, this approximation results in a linear feasibility problem that is solvable using linear programming.

The construction of a sleeve around the spline curve is equivalent to enclosing the spline curve with linear pieces. However, in the channel problem, the coefficients of the spline curve are unknown and are sought as the solution of the feasibility problem.

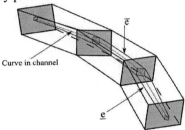

Figure 8: Sleeve $\bar{e}$ $\underline{e}$ and channel.

Given a B-spline curve

$$C(u) = \sum_{j=0}^{m} P_j N_j^d(u),$$

with control points P_j. Let the B-spline basis functions N_j^d of degree d be defined over a knot vector (u_k). The control polygon $l(u)$ of the spline is the piecewise linear interpolant to the control points P_j at the Greville abscissa

$$u_j^* = \sum_{i=j+1}^{j+d} u_i/d,$$

i.e. $l(u_j) = P_j$.

The weighted second differences $\Delta_2 P_i$ of the control points are defined as

$$\Delta_2 P_i = P_i', \quad P_i' = \frac{P_i - P_{i-1}}{u_i^* - u_{i-1}^*}$$

In addition, we define $\Delta_i^- = \min\{0, \Delta_2 P_i\}$ and $\Delta_i^+ = \max\{0, \Delta_2 P_i\}$.

Over the interval $[u_k^*, u_{k+1}^*]$ the contribution of the i-th B-spline to the distance between a spline and its control polygon is captured by the non-negative and convex functions

$$\beta_{ki}(u_k^*) := \begin{cases} \sum_{j=i}^{\bar{k}} (u_j^* - u_i^*) N_j^d, & i > k, \quad (1) \\ \sum_{j=\underline{k}}^{i} (u_i^* - u_j^*) N_j^d, & i \le k, \end{cases}$$

$$(2)$$

where $\bar{k}$ and $\underline{k}$ are the indices of the first and last (at most) $d+1$ B-spline basis functions N_j^d whose support spans u_k^*.

Then, we can formulate the restrictions for our curve by

$$\underline{e}(u) \le C(u) \le \bar{e}(u)$$

where

$$\bar{e}(u) = l(u) + \mathcal{L}(\sum_i \Delta_i^+ \beta_{ki}(u_k^*), \sum_i \Delta_i^+ \beta_{k+1,i}(u_{k+1}^*)),$$

$$\underline{e}(u) = l(u) + \mathcal{L}(\sum_i \Delta_i^- \beta_{ki}(u_k^*), \sum_i \Delta_i^- \beta_{k+1,i}(u_{k+1}^*)),$$

where $u \in [u_k^*, u_{k+1}^*]$ and

$$\mathcal{L}(a_1, a_2) = a_1 \frac{u_{k+1}^* - u}{u_{k+1}^* - u_k^*} + a_2 \frac{u - u_k^*}{u_{k+1}^* - u_k^*}.$$

The constraints force the sleeve, and thus the spline, to stay inside the channel. We solve the linear programming problem using a simplex approach. The target function we intend to minimize is $\sum_{i=1}^{m-1} \sum_{j \in \{x,y,z\}} (\Delta_{i,j}^- + \Delta_{i,j}^+)$. By minimizing the absolute second differences we are minimizing the curvature of the spline. Sometimes the constraints cannot be met. In this case, we need to insert further points as described in 3.2.

3.4 Local G^1- continuous Approximation for Simple Groups

In this section, we present the approach by Piegl [8] to generate G^1-continuous approximations and how it can be applied in our context to the local approximations for simple groups. In Section 3.5, we generalize the ideas to generate G^2-continuous approximations.

Given a short sequence of initial points $q_k, \ldots, q_{k+n}$, we try to approximate them by fitting a Bézier curve of the degree three that stays within in the channel. As Bézier curves are endpoint interpolating, we set the first and last point P_0 and P_2 of the Bézier curve to the first and last point q_k and q_{k+n} of the given sequence, respectively (see Figure 9). We must determine two inner control points P_1 and P_2 with

$$P_1 = P_0 + \alpha T_s \quad \text{and} \quad P_2 = P_3 + \beta T_e,$$

where T_s and T_e are the start and end unit tangents. The unit tangents T_s and T_e as well as the values for α and β

are defined by the continuity constraints with the preceding and succeeding group. The resulting control polygon with control points P_0, P_1, P_2, and P_3 determine the sought Bézier curve.

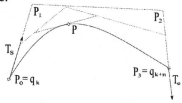

Figure 9: Local G^1-continuous Bézier curve approximation.

For a longer sequence of input points, the solution may be a rather crude approximation. It needs to be checked whether the approximating curve fulfills the error tolerance constraints. If not, it needs to be further refined. To check for validity, we build the tolerance channel and the sleeve as described in Section 3.3. If the sleeve lies inside the tolerance channel, the approximation is sufficiently precise. If not, we reduce the number of input points of the sequence by removing the last point and try to solve for the reduced sequence.

If the sequence only consists of two points, it cannot be further reduced and we have to insert an additional point. In general, we insert the midpoint of the two input points. In the case, where the two tangents point in opposite directions (i.e., the angle between start and end tangent is larger than the angle between start tangent and AB and larger than the angle between end tangent and AB) as in Figure 10, inserting the midpoint would lead to oscillations. Instead, we try to minimize curvature by shifting the midpoint in the direction of the start tangent when projected onto the plane perpendicular to the line that connects the input points. The shifting distance is equal to the distance between the midpoint and the intersection point of the start tangent vector and the mentioned plane. The upper shifting limit is 0.7ϵ.

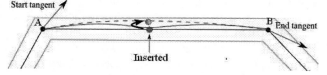

Figure 10: Moving inserted point to avoid oscillation.

3.5 Local G^2- continuous Spline Approximation for Simple Groups

Following the ideas described in Section 3.4, we generate a local approximation scheme for simple groups using two cubic Bézier curves to assure G^2-continuous connections. Given a sequence of input points $q_k,..., q_{k+n}$, we set the first control point of the first curve and the last control point of the second curve to q_k and q_{k+n}, respectively.

Using the notations of Figure 11, we set

$$P_0 = q_k, \quad R_3 = q_{k+n}$$

The endpoint interpolation property assures C^0-continuity. To assure G^1-continuity, we set

$$P_1 = P_0 + \alpha T_s \quad \text{and} \quad R_2 = R_3 + \beta T_e,$$

as in 3.4 and for G^2-continuity at the group's beginning we set

$$P_0 - 2P_1 + P_2 = A,$$

where A is determined by the preceding group (or A=0 for the first group, i.e., if k=0). The respective continuity requirements where the two Bézier curve stitch together are given by

$$
\begin{aligned}
P_3 &= R_0, \\
P_2 - P_3 &= R_0 - R_1, \\
P_1 - 2P_2 + P_3 &= R_0 - 2R_1 + R_2.
\end{aligned}
$$

Figure 11: Local Bézier curve approximation with G^2-continuous connections.

We, again, perform a validity check of the derived solution and refine the input sequence when necessary, see 3.4.

3.6 Combining Groups

Having described the local approximation schemes, we still need to explain how to obtain one global B-spline curve over a single knot sequence using the local schemes. We have to assure G^2-continuity at the connections. In case of a line connection, the construction described in Section 3.2 of choosing boundary control points on the connecting line delivers G^2-continuity.

For an overlapping connection of two groups, we need to distinguish whether the first group is a complicated or a simple one. If the first group is a complicated group, we calculate a new control point P lying on the curve. We obtain this by double knot insertion (see Figure 13), cutting off the control points after point P, and adjusting the knot sequence. The second group will then start with point P. We did not modify the shape of the first group's curve. If the first group is a simple group, we delete the last few control points until we find a control point that was an input point. Since Bézier curves are endpoint interpolating, we can start the second group with that control point. When solving for the second group, we have to pick the first three control points of that group such that G^2-continuity is achieved. G^0-continuity requires that the last control point of the first group has to be equal to the first control point of the second group, for G^1-continuity we need to have the proportional tangent vector of the adjacent parts, and the G^2-continuity condition requires is equality of the second derivatives of the adjacent parts. Using notations of Figure 12, we obtain:

$$
\begin{aligned}
P_k &= R_1, \\
\frac{P_{k-1} - P_k}{||P_{k-1}, P_k||} &= \frac{R_1 - R_2}{||R_1, R_2||}, \\
P_{k-2} - 2P_{k-1} + P_k &= R_1 - 2R_2 + R_3.
\end{aligned}
$$

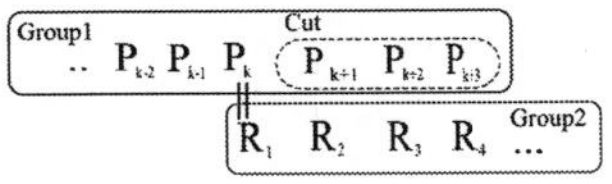

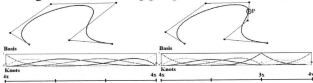

Figure 12: Connecting groups with G^2-continuity.

Figure 13: Double knot insertion to generate a control point P on the curve, where the curve can be cut off. Picture generated using [13]

4   Results and Discussion

For our experiments, we used two real-world examples, namely a reversible plate workpiece with a milling path of 5,952 input points and a comb structure with a milling path of 15,768 input points, see Table 1.

Workpiece	# Points	combined	local sleeve
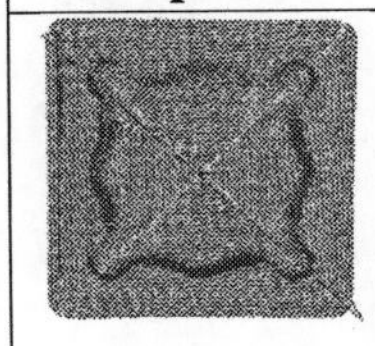 Reversible plate	5,952	35s	6min 28s
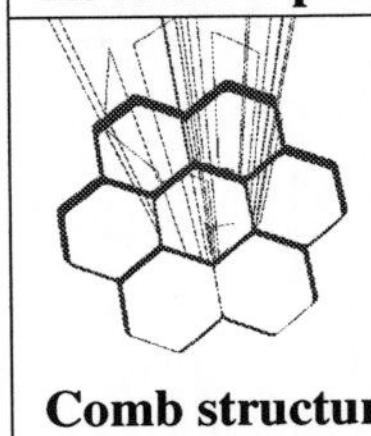 Comb structure	15,768	37s	5min 39s

Table 1: Computation times for two real-world workpieces.

As parameters for our experiment, we define distance measures as multiples of the tolerance ϵ, which is half of the width of the channel. A good value for the distance threshold d_{max} for splitting into separate groups was found to be $d_{max} = 300\epsilon$. Accordingly, the distance d_{line} for point insertion on a line connection can be set to $d_{line} = 16\epsilon$. An angle is reported as a sharp corner, iff its cosine is smaller than $cos(\alpha_{sharp}) = -0.85$. A good tradeoff in terms of computation time for solving individual groups and for splitting and joining overhead was found by setting the maximum number n_{max} of points per group to $n_{max} = 50$. The look ahead n_{ahead} shall be small to keep complicated groups small, and we set it to $n_{ahead} = 5$.

First, we want to investigate the effectiveness of the categorization of groups as simple or complicated. Figure 14 shows the points belonging to simple groups in blue and the ones belonging to complicated groups in yellow color. It can be observed that the more time-consuming algorithm of Section 3.3 is only used in high-curvature areas, while the more efficient algorithm of Section 3.5 is used in lower-curveture areas, as desired.

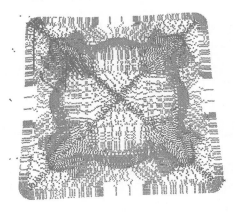

Figure 14: Our algorithm combines a local sleeve-like algorithm (yellow control points) with a local Bézier approximation (blue control points).

Next, we want to compare the computation times of our combined approach with (1) the classic sleeve approach as proposed by Lutterkort and Peters, (2) the sleeve approach when applied locally (Section 3.3) to all groups after splitting, (3) the local Bézier approximation (Section 3.5) when applied successively without our grouping, and (4) the local Bézier approximation (Section 3.5) when applied locally to all groups after splitting. As it was infeasible to run the classic sleeve approach to any of the presented workpieces, we restricted ourselves to the two outer loops of the reversible plate workpiece. While the classic sleeve approach required $1,325.0s$, its combination with our splitting reduced the time to $2.14s$. Even faster is the local

525

Bézier approximation with $0.093s$, which with our grouping was further reduced to $0.078s$. Our combined approach required $0.487s$, which means that the classic sleeve approach took about $2,721\times$ the time and the local sleeve approach with our grouping took about $4.4\times$ the time.

For the entire workpieces, we compared our combined approach to the local sleeve approach with our grouping. Table 1 reports computation times that are about one order of magnitude less for the combined approach.

To investigate the correctness of our approach, Figure 15 shows a zoomed-in view of an area with sharp corners next to straight lines. We can observe that the curve always stays within the tolerance channel, while exhibiting a smooth behavior.

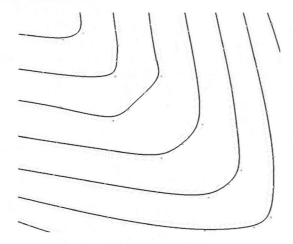

Figure 15: Smooth curve (blue) within tolerance channel (green) at sharp corners.

A special handling was proposed for turns. Its effectiveness is shown in Figure 16. A symmetric and similar result is achieved for all turns.

Figure 16: Behavior at turns: Non-symmetric without (left) and symmetric with additional treatment (right).

We compare the quality of the three local approaches with our grouping, i.e., local sleeve (left), local Bézier (right), and combined approach (middle), in Figure 17. It can be observed that the local Bézier approach is producing undesirable results, as there seem to be higher curvatures involved and the "offset curves" do not exhibit such a similar shape.

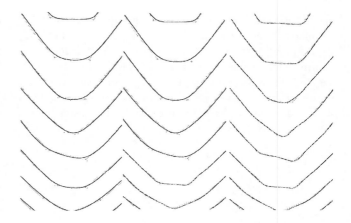

Figure 17: Results of local sleeve (left), local Bézier (right), and combined approach (middle) with our grouping.

We further investigated this by explicitly computing curvatures for the results generated by the three approaches. Figure 18 shows curvature plotted on a logarithmic scale over the arclength of the resulting curve. It can be seen that the local Bézier approach is, indeed, producing curves with higher curvatures, and that the combined algorithm tries to avoid that by switching to the local sleeve approach for the complicated groups.

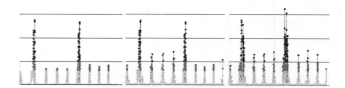

Figure 18: Curvature plots of local sleeve (left), local Bézier (right), and combined approach (middle) over the curve's arclength using a logarithmic curvature scale.

Moreover, Figure 19 shows areas of high curvatures for the results generated by the three approaches. It can be seen that the local Bézier approach is producing high curvatures in areas where the other two approaches can generate curves with lower curvatures.

Another undesirable property of curves that are used as milling paths is that of oscillation, even when curvatures are low. We also detected areas of oscillation for the results generated by the three approaches, see Figure 19. Oscillations are detected in form of inflection points after projection into the 2D domain. It can be observed that the local Bézier approach is producing oscillations in many areas where the other two approaches do not produce any.

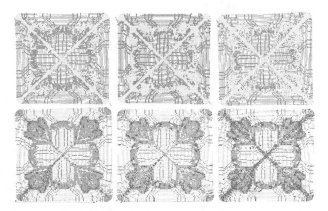

Figure 19: Upper row: High-curvature areas (more than 1) of the resulting curves for local sleeve (left), local Bézier (right), and combined approach (middle) are marked with green color. Lower row: Areas of oscillation of the resulting curves for local sleeve (left), local Bézier (right), and combined approach (middle) are marked with blue color.

5 Conclusions

We created an algorithm for generating a B-spline curve with optimized curvature that stays within a channel constructed around an input curve with given tolerance. To obtain an acceptable quality-speed ratio, we combine two algorithms: a local version of the sleeve-algorithm and a local Bézier approximation with G^2-continuity connections. The local schemes are applied to curve segments that need to be combined with G^2-continuity smoothness. Two types of connections were introduced. The splitting of the original curve into groups is performed with respect to the underlying application and the complexity of the groups. The local Bézier approximation algorithm is very efficient and produces good results for simple groups, while the local sleeve algorithm is less efficient but produces high-quality results even for complicated groups. For efficiency purposes, we keep complicated groups as small as possible and introduce a heuristic that inserts further points to a group when it is likely that no solution can be found.

The created algorithm can be used as a part of a micro milling process. This approach provides new possibilities for calculating velocity, acceleration, and jerk profiles. The benefits that profiles are easier to compute - and that the milling can generally be performed with a higher velocity is generally higher than the velocity. The latter is essential for practical purposes, since the higher is the velocity of the tool tip the faster is the manufacturing process.

6 Acknowledgments

This work was supported by BMWi within the InnoNet program under grant number 16IN0653. This work is done within the Knowledge Based Adaptive Micro Milling project. We like to thank Thorsten Schreiner, Lothar Glasmacher, Monika Mallok and Benedikt Gellißen from IPT Fraunhofer, Aachen, Germany, for valuable comments and feed back, provided data and cooperation. We also thank Paul Rosenthal and Steffen Hauth for a lot of useful talks.

References

[1] Abdulwahed Abbas, Ahmad Nasri and Takashi Maekawa. *Generating B-spline curves with points, normals and curvature constraints: a constructive approach.* The Visual Computer. Springer, 26(6-8):823-829, 2010.

[2] Ashish Myles and Jörg Peters. *Threading splines through 3D channels.* Computer-Aided Design, 37(2):139-148, 2005.

[3] David Lutterkort and Jörg Peters. *Tight linear envelopes for splines.* Numerische Mathematik, 89(4):735-748, 1999.

[4] David Lutterkort and Jörg Peters. *Smooth path in a polygon channel.* In: Proceedings of the 15th annual symposium on Computational Geometry. ACM Press, 316-321 1999.

[5] H.Prautzsch and W.Boehm and M.Paluszny. *Bézier and B-Spline Techniques.* Springer, 2002.

[6] Jörg Peters and Xiaobin Wu. *Sleeves for planar spline curves.* Computer-Aided Design, 21(6):615-635, 2004.

[7] Les A. Piegl. *On NURBS: a Survey.* IEEE Computer Graphics and Applications, 11(1):55-71, 1991.

[8] Les A. Piegl and Wayne Tiller. *The NURBS Book.* Springer, 1997.

[9] Les A. Piegl and Wayne Tiller. *Data approximation using biarcs.* Engineering with Computers. Springer 18:59-65 , 2002.

[10] Rong Zhen Xu, Le Xie, Cong Xin Li, and Dao Shan Du. *Adaptive parametric interpolation scheme with limited acceleration and jerk values for NC machining.* The International Journal of Advanced Manufacturing Technology. Springer, 36(3-4):343-354, 2008.

[11] Xianbing Liua, Fahad Ahmada, Kazuo Yamazakia, and Masahiko Mori. *Adaptive interpolation scheme for NURBS curves with the integration of machining dynamics.* International Journal of Machine Tools and Manufacture. Elsevier, 45(4-5):433-444, 2005.

[12] Xujing Yang and Zezhong C. Chen. *A practicable approach to G1 biarc approximations for making accurate, smooth and non-gouged profile features in CNC contouring.* Computer-Aided Design. Elsevier, 38(11):1205-1213, 2006.

[13] http://i33www.ira.uka.de/applets/.

Data Visualization using Shape Preserving C^2 rational spline

M. Sarfraz
Department of Information Science
P.O. Box 5969, Safat 13060, Adailiya Campus
Kuwait University, Kuwait
e-mail: prof.m.sarfraz@gmail.com

M.Z. Hussain, T.S. Shaikh, R. Iqbal
Department of Mathematics
University of the Punjab
Lahore-Pakistan.
e-mail: malikzawwar@math.pu.edu.pk

Abstract- **A rational cubic spline is developed to provide smooth curves(positive, monotone and convex). To control the shape of the curve, two families of parameters are introduced in its representation. Three schemes using rational cubic spline are elaborated to obtain positive curves through positive data, monotone curves through monotone data and convex curves through convex data. As well as degree of smoothness attained is C^2.**

Keywords- Data visualization; Rational spline; Positive spline; Monotone spline; Convex spline

I. INTRODUCTION

Interpolation is an essential part of scientific visualization because it provides a foundation for the visualization of the scientific data either in scientific research or in any computer field, etc. It provides a way to understand the inherited features of the data while other techniques fail to do so. The curve representation of the data being interpolated, gives a clear understanding of these hidden features. Spline interpolation plays an important role in this regard.

The technique used to interpolate the data must be effective in a way that it provides smoothness to the curve as well as has greater computational efficiency and accuracy. Ordinary spline interpolation schemes do so but do not provide control on the shape of the curve. Thus there must be such schemes that can provide all the desired features of the data.

In this paper such schemes are developed which not only control the shape of the curve but also provide smoothness in the representation of curves. When the data is positive, monotone and convex, then developed schemes produce positive, monotone and convex curves respectively.

This work is a motivation of the past work of many authors. Brodlie and Butt [1] introduced an algorithm to preserve convexity of the piecewise cubic interpolant. Butt and Brodlie [2] developed an algorithm that not only generates a cubic Hermite interpolant having first order smoothness but also preserves the positivity of the interpolant. To preserve the positivity of the interpolant, they introduced a method of inserting one or two extra knots, wherever required. Costantini [3] discussed the shape

preservation of boundary valued problems using polynomial spline interpolation. He defined arbitrary constraints for shape preservation. Delbourgo and Gregory [4] obtained the second order smoothness of strictly monotone data. They used rational quadratic spline interpolation in this regard. Duan et al. [5] discussed the accuracy of a rational cubic interpolant, they applied Peano-Kernnel Theorem in this regard. They discussed jump in the second derivatives. Duan et al. [6] discussed the scheme for second order smoothness of the rational interpolant, and discussed the accuracy of this schme. They used two shape parameters to control on the shape of the curve. Duan et al. [7] constructed a weighted rational cubic spline. They used two kinds of rational splines with second order smoothness. They applied it to preserve the convexity of the data. Fangxun et al. [8] developed a rational cubic function with quadratic denominator and have also discussed error analysis of the interpolant. Lamberti and Manni [10] constructed a shape preserving C^2 functional interpolant. This interpolant is a parametric cubic curve. They introduced tension parameters to control the shape of the curve. They also discussed the approximation order of the interpolant. Srafraz et al. [11] introduced schemes for the modeling of positive data using spline functions. The degree of smoothness they achieved is C^1. Sarfraz and Hussain [12] developed a C^1 piecewise rational cubic function in which they have introduced two shape parameters. They applied this scheme to preserve the shape of the positive, monotone and convex data.

There always has been a need of advancements in the methods developed earlier so that new techniques can be utilized for more accurate results. Many authors have been made their contribution for the advancement of such results. This paper is also a contribution towards this progress. The technique used in this paper has many salient features. The rational cubic spline developed in this paper not only visualizes the shaped data but also provides smoothness to visual images. Rational cubic spline (2.1) as compared to those defined in [7-10] has less computation. Additional knots are not required as in [2], because this rational cubic spline provides one or more than one free parameters which provide the desirable control on the shape of the curve. No arbitrary constraints are required as in [3] because of the necessary and sufficient constraints developed for positivity,

1550-6037/11 $26.00 © 2011 IEEE
DOI 10.1109/IV.2011.91

monotonicity and convexity which automatically conserve the shape of the data.

This paper is divided into six Sections. In Section 2, the rational cubic spline is developed for visualization of curve data. In Section 3 we derived constraints on shape parameters to visualize positive data in the view of C^2 positive curve. In Section 4 we derived constraints on shape parameters to visualize monotone data in the view of C^2 monotone curve. In Section 5 rational cubic spline is used to visualize convex data in the view of C^2 convex curve. Section 6 concludes the paper.

II. RATIONAL CUBIC SPLINE

In this section, a rational cubic spline is developed. Let (x_i, f_i), $i = 0, 1, 2, \ldots, n$ be given set of data points where $x_0 < x_1 < x_2 < \ldots < x_n$. The rational cubic spline, in each subinterval $I_i = [x_i, x_{i+1}], i = 0, 1, 2, \ldots, n-1$, is defined as:

$$S_i(x) = \frac{\alpha_i(1-\theta)^3 + \beta_i\theta(1-\theta)^2 + \gamma_i\theta^2(1-\theta) + \delta_i\theta^3}{\mu_i(1-\theta)^2 + (1+\mu_i\nu_i)\theta(1-\theta) + \nu_i\theta^2}, \quad (2.1)$$

where

$$\theta = \frac{(x-x_i)}{h_i}, \quad h_i = x_{i+1} - x_i, \ i = 0, 1, 2, \ldots, n-1.$$

In order to make the rational cubic spline (2.1) C^2, following interpolatory conditions are imposed on (2.1):

$$\left.\begin{array}{ll} S(x_i) = f_i, & S(x_{i+1}) = f_{i+1}, \\ S^{(1)}(x_i) = d_i, & S^{(1)}(x_{i+1}) = d_{i+1}, \\ S^{(2)}(x_{i+}) = S^{(2)}(x_{i-}), & i = 1, 2, \ldots, n-1 \end{array}\right\} \quad (2.2)$$

Now (2.2) provide the following manipulations:

$$\alpha_i = \mu_i f_i,$$
$$\beta_i = (1 + \mu_i + \mu_i\nu_i)f_i + h_i d_i \mu_i,$$
$$\gamma_i = (1 + \nu_i + \mu_i\nu_i)f_{i+1} - h_i d_{i+1}\nu_i,$$
$$\delta_i = \nu_i f_{i+1},$$
$$a_i d_{i-1} + b_i d_i + c_i d_{i+1} = e_i, \quad i = 1, 2, \ldots, n-1, \quad (2.3)$$

where

$$a_i = \mu_{i-1}\mu_i h_{i-1},$$
$$b_i = \mu_i h_{i-1}(1 + \mu_{i-1}\nu_{i-1}) + \nu_{i-1}h_i(1 + \mu_i\nu_i),$$
$$c_i = \nu_{i-1}\nu_i h_i,$$
$$e_i = \mu_i h_{i-1}(1 + \mu_{i-1} + \mu_{i-1}\nu_{i-1})\Delta_{i-1} + \nu_{i-1}h_i(1 + \nu_i + \mu_i\nu_i)\Delta_i$$

where $S^{(1)}(x_i)$ and $S^{(2)}(x_i)$ denote derivatives w.r.t x and d_i denotes derivative value at each knot x_i. Thus rational cubic spline (2.1) leads the to the following piecewise Hermite polynomial $S \in C^2[x_0, x_n]$, with shape parameters μ_i and ν_i defined in the interval $I_i = [x_i, x_{i+1}]$:

$$S(x) \equiv S_i(x) = \frac{P_i(\theta)}{Q_i(\theta)}, \quad (2.4)$$

where

$$P_i(\theta) = \alpha_i(1-\theta)^3 + \beta_i\theta(1-\theta)^2 + \gamma_i\theta^2(1-\theta) + \delta_i\theta^3,$$
$$Q_i(\theta) = \mu_i(1-\theta)^2 + (1+\mu_i\nu_i)\theta(1-\theta) + \nu_i\theta^2,$$

here $\alpha_i, \beta_i, \gamma_i$ and δ_i are as defined above.

It can be easily checked that when $\mu_i = 1$ and $\nu_i = 1$, the rational cubic spline (2.1) becomes the standard cubic Hermite polynomial. The desired shape of the curve can be obtained if variations are made for the values of μ_i's and ν_i's. The following section gives a brief description of this phenomena.

III. POSITIVE RATIONAL CUBIC SPLINE

In this section we will discuss the visualization of positive data by rational cubic spline (2.1). Sufficient conditions will be derived on shape parameters and derivative parameters so that visualization of C^2 positive rational curve is conserved.

Let us assume a positive data set: (x_0, f_0), $(x_1, f_1), \cdots, (x_n, f_n)$, with $x_0 < x_1 < x_2 < \ldots < x_n$, and $f_0 > 0$, $f_1 > 0, \cdots, f_n > 0$. Since $Q_i(\theta)$ is strictly positive for all $\mu_i, \nu_i > 0$, $\forall \ i = 0, 1, 2, \ldots, n-1$, to discuss the positivity of $S(x)$, it is therefore enough to discuss the positivity of $P_i(\theta)$. Rewrite $P_i(\theta)$ as follows:

$$P_i(\theta) = A_i\theta^3 + B_i\theta^2 + C_i\theta + D_i, \quad (3.1)$$

where

$$A_i = (1 + \mu_i\nu_i)f_i - (1 + \mu_i\nu_i)f_{i+1} + (\mu_i d_i + \nu_i d_{i+1})h_i,$$
$$B_i = (-2 + \mu_i - 2\mu_i\nu_i)f_i + (1 + \nu_i + \mu_i\nu_i)f_{i+1} - (2\mu_i d_i + \nu_i d_{i+1})h_i,$$
$$C_i = (1 - 2\mu_i + \mu_i\nu_i)f_i + \mu_i d_i h_i,$$
$$D_i = \mu_i f_i.$$

For the strict inequality (for positive data) in (2.1), according to Butt and Brodlie [2], $P_i(\theta) > 0$ if and only if

$$(P_i'(0), P_i'(1)) \in R_1 \cup R_2 \quad (3.2)$$

where

$$R_1 = \left\{ (a,b) : a > \frac{-3f_i}{h_i}, b < \frac{3f_{i+1}}{h_i} \right\},$$

$$R_2 = \left\{ \begin{array}{l} (a,b) : 36 f_i f_{i+1}(a^2 + b^2 + ab - 3\Delta_i(a+b) + 3\Delta_i^2) \\ +3(f_{i+1}a - f_i b)(2h_i ab - 3f_{i+1}a + 3f_i b) \\ +4h_i(f_{i+1}a^3 - f_i b^3) - h_i^2 a^2 b^2 > 0 \end{array} \right\}.$$

Now

$$P_i'(0) = \frac{f_i}{h_i}(1 - 2\mu_i + \mu_i \nu_i) + \mu_i d_i,$$

$$P_i'(1) = \nu_i d_{i+1} - \frac{f_{i+1}}{h_i}(1 - 2\nu_i + \mu_i \nu_i).$$

Further $(P_i'(0), P_i'(1)) \in R_1$,

$$\Rightarrow P_i'(0) > \frac{-3f_i}{h_i}, \quad P_i'(1) < \frac{3f_{i+1}}{h_i} \qquad (3.3)$$

This results in the following constraints:

$$\nu_i > m_i, \quad \mu_i > M_i, \qquad (3.4)$$

where

$$m_i = Max\left\{0, 2 - \frac{h_i d_i}{f_i}\right\},$$

$$M_i = Max\left\{0, 2 + \frac{h_i d_{i+1}}{f_{i+1}}, \frac{-4f_i}{-2f_i + h_i d_i + \nu_i f_i}\right\}.$$

Further, $(P_i'(0), P_i'(1)) \in R_2$, if

$$36 f_i f_{i+1}(\phi_1^2 + \phi_2^2 + \phi_1\phi_2 - 3\Delta_i(\phi_1 + \phi_2) + 3\Delta_i^2)$$
$$+3(f_{i+1}\phi_1 - f_i\phi_2)(2h_i\phi_1\phi_2 - 3f_{i+1}\phi_1 + 3f_i\phi_2) \qquad (3.5)$$
$$+4h_i(f_{i+1}\phi_1^3 - f_i\phi_2^3) - h_i^2\phi_1^2\phi_2^2 > 0,$$

where

$$\phi_1 = \phi_1(\mu_i, \nu_i) = P_i'(0), \quad \phi_2 = \phi_2(\mu_i, \nu_i) = P_i'(1).$$

To make the rational cubic spline smoother, second derivative continuity is applied at each knot. The values of derivative parameters are estimated by solving the system of linear equations (2.3), this system involves n-1 linear equations while the unknown values are n+1. So two more equations are required for unique solution. For this we imposed clamped end conditions at first and last knots such that:

$$S^{(1)}(x_0) = d_0, \quad S^{(1)}(x_n) = d_n. \qquad (3.6)$$

A summary of the above discussion is given as:

Theorem 1. Rational cubic spline (2.1) visualizes positive data in the view of C^2 positive curve if and only if either shape parameters μ_i, ν_i satisfy (3.4) or (3.5). And derivative parameters d_i's used, are derived by (2.3) and (3.6).

Remark 1. It is observed that the shape of the curve can be preserved as well as can be controlled if the constraints (3.4) are further modified. If there is no loss of generality, the parameters r_i, t_i, satisfying $r_i, t_i \geq -1$, can be found. This leads the constraints (3.4) to the following:

$$\nu_i = r_i + m_i, \quad \mu_i = t_i + M_i,$$

where one has freedom over the choice of r_i and t_i. The choice of $r_i = -1$ and $t_i = -1$ will be used as a default choice and can be considered the greatest lower bound.

Remark 2. The values of the shape parameters μ_i and ν_i satisfying (3.5) can be determined but this will take a lot of computation work. Therefore, for practical results, the choice of shape parameters in Remark 1, can be utilized.

TABLE I.   POSITIVE DATA.

i	1	2	3	4	5	6	7
x_i	2	3	7	8	9	13	14
y_i	10	2	3	7	2	3	10

Remark 3. It is observed in this paper d_i's are determined in such a way that the C^2 smoothness of the rational cubic spline (2.1) is gained.

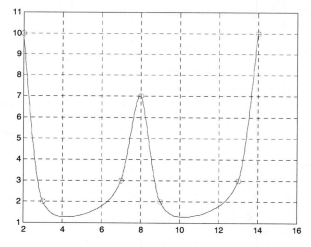

Figure 1.   Positive rational cubic curve.

530

3.1 Demonstration

We considered a positive data set in Table 1. Figure 1 is the graphical view of data set in Table 1 using rational cubic spline (2.1). Theorem 1 is applied for assigning the values of shape parameters μ_i, ν_i and derivative parameters d_i's. Figure 1 not only depicts the hidden behavior of the data but is smooth as well. In this Figure values assigned to free parameters are $r_i = t_i = 0.1$.

IV. MONOTONE RATIONAL CUBIC SPLINE

In this section we discuss the monotonicity of monotonic data. For this purpose we will use rational cubic spline (2.1) and impose conditions on shape parameters and derivative parameters. This requires some further mathematical treatment so that the desired shape of the curve is achieved. Assume the data set to be monotonic increasing so that

$$f_i \le f_{i+1}, \quad i = 0,1,2,...,n-1,$$

or equivalently

$$\Delta_i \ge 0, \quad i = 0,1,2,...,n-1.$$

For monotonicity, the necessary conditions satisfied by the derivative parameters are as follows:

when $\Delta_i \ge 0$, $i = 0,1,2,...,n-1$, $d_i \ge 0$, $i = 0,1,2,...,n$.

For monotonically increasing data, two cases are to be discussed, $\Delta_i = 0$ and $\Delta_i > 0$. When $\Delta_i = 0$, $S(x)$ reduces to

$$S_i(x) = f_i \quad \forall x \in [x_i, x_{i+1}], \quad i = 0,1,2,...,n-1,$$

hence is monotone. Now consider the case when $\Delta_i > 0$. The necessary and sufficient condition for $S(x)$ to be monotonically increasing is $S^{(1)}(x) \ge 0$, $\forall x \in [x_i, x_{i+1}]$. Now $S^{(1)}(x)$ can be written in the following simplified form:

$$S_i^{(1)}(x) = \sum_{j=1}^{5} A_{j,i} \theta^{j-1}(1-\theta)^{5-j} / \{Q_i(\theta)\}^2, \qquad (4.1)$$

where

$A_{1,i} = \mu_i^2 d_i,$

$A_{2,i} = 2(\mu_i + \mu_i \nu_i + \mu_i^2 \nu_i)\Delta_i - 2\mu_i \nu_i d_{i+1},$

$A_{3,i} = (1 + \mu_i + \nu_i + 6\mu_i \nu_i + \mu_i^2 \nu_i + \mu_i \nu_i^2 + \mu_i^2 \nu_i^2)\Delta_i$
$\quad - (1 + \nu_i + \mu_i \nu_i)\mu_i d_i - (1 + \mu_i + \mu_i \nu_i)\nu_i d_{i+1},$

$A_{4,i} = 2(\nu_i + \mu_i \nu_i + \mu_i \nu_i^2)\Delta_i - 2\mu_i \nu_i d_i,$

$A_{5,i} = \nu_i^2 d_{i+1}.$

Necessary and sufficient conditions for monotonicity on $[x_i, x_{i+1}]$ are respectively given as:

$$d_i \ge 0, \quad d_{i+1} \ge 0, \text{ and } A_{j,i} \ge 0, \quad j = 1,2,...,5. \qquad (4.2)$$

It is obvious that both $A_{1,i}$ and $A_{5,i}$ are non-negative. Now $A_{2,i}$, $A_{4,i} \ge 0$ if the following conditions are satisfied:

$$\Delta_i - \frac{\nu_i d_{i+1}}{1+\nu_i} > 0, \quad \Delta_i - \frac{\mu_i d_i}{1+\mu_i} > 0,$$

which lead to the following constraints:

$$\nu_i = \frac{\Delta_i}{l_i d_{i+1} - \Delta_i}, \quad \mu_i = \frac{\Delta_i}{k_i d_i - \Delta_i}, \qquad (4.3)$$

where $l_i, k_i > 0$, satisfying

$$\frac{1}{l_i} + \frac{1}{k_i} \le 1 \qquad (4.4)$$

The Equations (4.3) together with (4.4), lead to the following equations which are sufficient and provide the freedom over the choice of l_i and k_i:

$$l_i \ge 1 + \frac{d_i}{d_{i+1}}, \quad k_i \ge 1 + \frac{d_{i+1}}{d_i} \qquad (4.5)$$

The choice of l_i and k_i can be made, to the greatest lower bound as follows:

$$l_i = 1 + \frac{d_i}{d_{i+1}}, \quad k_i = 1 + \frac{d_{i+1}}{d_i}. \qquad (4.6)$$

This choice satisfies (4.4). On simplifying (4.3) and (4.4), the following sufficient conditions for monotonicity are obtained:

$$\nu_i = \frac{d_i + d_{i+1}}{\Delta_i} - 1, \quad \mu_i = \frac{d_i + d_{i+1}}{\Delta_i} - 1 \qquad (4.7)$$

This choice also satisfies $A_{3,i} \ge 0$. To control the shape of the curve according to the desire of the user, the constraints in (4.7) can be rewritten with shape parameters as follows:

$$\mu_i = \nu_i = r_i + Max\left\{0, \frac{d_i + d_{i+1}}{\Delta_i} - 1\right\}, \quad r_i \ge 0. \qquad (4.8)$$

All the above discussion is summarized as:

Theorem 2. Rational cubic spline (2.1) visualizes monotonic data in the view of C^2 monotone curve if and only if the shape parameters μ_i, ν_i satisfy (4.6) or (4.7) and derivative parameters d_i's used are derived by (2.3) and (3.6) satisfy $d_i = |d_i|$, $\forall i = 0,1,2,...,n.$

4.1 Demonstration

In Table 2 we considered a monotonic data. Figure 2 is graphical view of this data using rational cubic spline (2.1).

Theorem 2 is applied for assigning the values of shape parameters μ_i , ν_i and derivative parameters d_i's. Figure 2 not only depicts the hidden behavior of the data but is smooth as well. In this Figure values assigned to free parameters are $r_i = t_i = 5.5$.

TABLE II.　　AKIMA'S DATA SET.

i	1	2	3	4	5	6	7	8	9	10	11
x_i	0	2	3	5	6	8	9	11	12	14	15
y_i	10	10	10	10	10	10	10.5	15	50	60	85

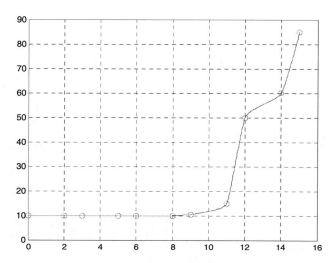

Figure 2.　Monotone rational cubic curve.

V.　CONVEX RATIONAL CUBIC SPLINE

In this section we briefly discuss the visualization of convex data in the view of convex curves. It can be done if appropriate values are assigned to shape parameters μ_i and ν_i. This requires mathematical treatment so that the desired shape of the curve is achieved. Assume the data set to be strictly convex so that

$$\Delta_i < \Delta_{i+1}, \ i = 0, 1, 2, ..., n-2$$

For convexity, the necessary conditions satisfied by the derivative parameters are as follows:

$$d_0 < \Delta_0 < ... < \Delta_{i-1} < d_i < \Delta_i < ... < \Delta_{n-1} < d_n,$$

Now the necessary and sufficient condition for $S(x)$ to be convex is $S^{(2)}(x) \geq 0$, $\forall \ x \in [x_i, x_{i+1}]$. Now $S^{(2)}(x)$ can be written in the following simplified form:

$$S_i^{(2)}(x) = \sum_{j=1}^{6} B_{j,i} \theta^{j-1} (1-\theta)^{6-j} / h_i [Q_i(\theta)]^3 \qquad (5.1)$$

where

$$B_{1,i} = \mu_i A_{2,i} - 2(1 + \mu_i \nu_i) A_{1,i},$$
$$B_{2,i} = 2\mu_i A_{3,i} - (1 - \mu_i + \mu_i \nu_i) A_{2,i} - 2(1 + 2\nu_i + \mu_i \nu_i) A_{1,i},$$
$$B_{3,i} = 3\mu_i A_{4,i} + 2\mu_i A_{3,i} - (1 + 3\nu_i + \mu_i \nu_i) A_{2,i} - 4\nu_i A_{1,i},$$
$$B_{4,i} = 4\mu_i A_{5,i} + (1 + 3\mu_i + \mu_i \nu_i) A_{4,i} - 2\nu_i A_{3,i} - 3\nu_i A_{2,i},$$
$$B_{5,i} = 2(1 + 2\mu_i + \mu_i \nu_i) A_{5,i} + (1 - \nu_i + \mu_i \nu_i) A_{4,i} - 2\nu_i A_{3,i},$$
$$B_{6,i} = 2(1 + \mu_i \nu_i) A_{5,i} - \nu_i A_{4,i}.$$

The denominator in (5.1) is clearly positive if $\mu_i, \nu_i > 0$. Therefore the sufficient conditions assumed for convexity on $[x_i, x_{i+1}]$ are

$$\mu_i, \ \nu_i > 0, \quad B_{j,i} \geq 0, \quad j = 1, 2, ..., 6, \qquad (5.2)$$

and necessary conditions are assumed as

$$\Delta_i - d_i \geq 0 \quad \text{and} \quad d_{i+1} - \Delta_i \geq 0. \qquad (5.3)$$

Rewrite $B_{1,i}$ and $B_{6,i}$ as follows:

$$\left. \begin{array}{l} B_{1,i} = 2\mu_i^2 \{(1 + \mu_i \nu_i)(\Delta_i - d_i) - \nu_i(d_{i+1} - \Delta_i)\} \\ B_{6,i} = 2\nu_i^2 \{(1 + \mu_i \nu_i)(d_{i+1} - \Delta_i) - \mu_i(\Delta_i - d_i)\} \end{array} \right\} \qquad (5.4)$$

If $\Delta_i - d_i > 0$ and $d_{i+1} - \Delta_i > 0$, then the sufficient conditions for (5.4) are given as follows:

$$\left. \begin{array}{l} (1 + \mu_i \nu_i)(\Delta_i - d_i) - \nu_i(d_{i+1} - \Delta_i) \geq 0 \\ (1 + \mu_i \nu_i)(d_{i+1} - \Delta_i) - \mu_i(\Delta_i - d_i) \geq 0 \end{array} \right\} \qquad (5.5)$$

These inequalities lead to the following constraints:

$$\nu_i = r_i + \frac{\Delta_i - d_i}{d_{i+1} - \Delta_i}, \quad \mu_i = t_i + \frac{d_{i+1} - \Delta_i}{\Delta_i - d_i}, \qquad (5.6)$$

where r_i and t_i satisfy $r_i, t_i > 0$. The sufficient conditions can also be written in the following form:

$$\mu_i = \nu_i = q_i + Min\left\{ \frac{\Delta_i - d_i}{d_{i+1} - \Delta_i}, \frac{d_{i+1} - \Delta_i}{\Delta_i - d_i}, \right\}, \ q_i \geq 0. \qquad (5.7)$$

Both the choices, (5.6) and (5.7), satisfy (5.2) and hence can be used for practical application of curve design.
A summary of the above discussion can be stated as:

Theorem 3. The rational cubic spline (2.1) visualizes convex data in the view of C^2 convex curve if and only if the shape parameters μ_i, ν_i satisfy (5.6) or (5.7) and derivative parameters $d_i's$ used are derived by (2.3) and (3.6) satisfy (5.3).

Remark 1. It can be observed that if $\Delta_i - d_i = 0$ or $d_{i+1} - \Delta_i = 0$, then the curve will be linear in the region where $d_i = d_{i+1} = \Delta_i$, i.e.

$$S(x) = f_i(1-\theta) + f_{i+1}\theta.$$

It can also be observed that if $\Delta_i = 0$, then both d_i and d_{i+1} are necessarily equal to zero. This leads to the following:

$$S(x) = f_i = f_{i+1},$$

which is constant on $[x_i, x_{i+1}]$.

All the above discussion shows that the rational spline (2.1) is convex together with the conditions (5.6) and (5.7). In case when data is convex but not strictly convex, the problem would be handled by dividing the data into strictly convex parts.

TABLE III.　　CONVEX DATA SET.

i	1	2	3	4	5	6	7
x_i	-9	-8	-4	0	4	8	9
y_i	7	5	3.5	3.25	3.5	5	7

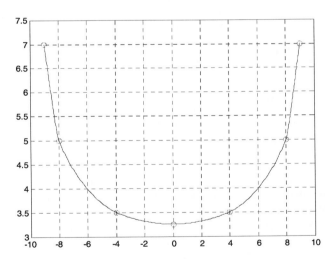

Figure 3.　Convex rational cubic curve.

5.1 Demonstration

In Table 3 we considered a convex data. Figure 3 is graphical view of this data using rational cubic spline (2.1). Theorem 3 is applied for assigning the values of shape parameters μ_i, ν_i and derivative parameters $d_i's$. Figure 3 not only depicts the hidden behavior of the data but is

smooth as well. In this Figure values assigned to free parameters are $r_i = t_i = 1$.

VI.　CONCLUSION

A rational cubic spline is constructed for the visualization of positive, monotone and convex data. To control the shape of data two shape parameters are inserted in the description of rational spline. Three main results are obtained for visualization of positive, monotone and convex data. User can easily control the shape of the curve according to his needs just by changing the values of the free parameters defined in the constraints for the shape parameters. To provide maximum smoothness to the curves, the degree of smoothness attained is C^2.

The present paper work can be extended for surface evolution as well. The authors are in progress of such a work and have intended to complete it in the near future.

REFERENCES

[1]　K. W. Brodlie and S. Butt, "Preserving convexity using piecewise cubic interpolation," *Computers and Graphics*, 15 (1), pp.15-23, (1991).

[2]　S. Butt and K. W. Brodlie, "Preserving positivity using piecewise cubic interpolation," *Computers and Graphics*, 17(1), pp.55-64, (1993).

[3]　P. Costantini, "Boundary-valued shape preserving interpolating splines," *ACM Transactions on Mathematical Software (TOMS)*, 23(2), pp.229-251, (1997).

[4]　R. Delbourgo and J. A. Gregory, " C^2 rational quadratic spline interpolation to monotonic data," *IMA Journal of Numerical Analysis*, 3, pp.141-152, (1983).

[5]　Q. Duan, H. Zhang, Y. Zhang and E. H. Twizell, "Error estimation of a kind of rational spline," *Journal of Computational and Applied Mathematics*, 200(1), pp.1-11, (2007).

[6]　Q. Duan, L.Wang and E. H. Twizell, "A new C^2 rational interpolation based on function values and constrained control of the interpolant curves," *Journal of Applied Mathematics and Computation*, 61, pp.311-322, (2005).

[7]　Q. Duan, L. Wang and E. H. Twizell, "A new weighted rational cubic interpolation and its approximation," *Journal of Applied Mathematics and Computation*, 168, pp. 990-1003, (2005).

[8]　B. Fangxun, S. Qinghua and Q. Duan, "Point control of the interpolating curve with a rational cubic spline," *Journal of Visual Communication and Image Representation*, 20, pp.275-280, (2009).

[9]　A. Kouibia and M. Pasadas, "Approximation by interpolating variational splines," *Journal of Computational and Applied Mathematics*, 218, 342-349, (2008).

[10]　P. Lamberti and C. Manni, "Shape-preserving C^2 functional interpolation via Parametric cubics," *Numerical Algorithms*, 28, pp.229-254, (2001).

[11]　M. Srafraz, M. Z. Hussain and Asfar Nisar, "Positive data modeling using spline function," *Applied Mathematics and Computation*, 216, pp.2036-2049, (2010).

[12]　M. Sarfraz and M. Z. Hussain, "Data visualization using rational spline interpolation," *Journal of Computation and Applied Mathematics*, 189, pp. 513-525, (2006).

[13]　M. H. Schultz, "Spline Analysis," Prentice-Hall, Englewood Cliffs, New Jersy, (1973).

A Hybrid Scheme Coding using SPHIT and Fractal for Mammography Image Compression

Benamrane Nacéra

Department of Informatics, Faculty of Science
USTOMB, B.P 1505, EL'Mnaouer
Oran, Algeria
nabenamrane@yahoo.com

Bentorki Soumia

Department of Informatics, Faculty of Science
USTOMB, B.P 1505, El'Mnaouer
Oran, Algeria
bentorki_mias@yahoo.com

Abstract— Medical imaging techniques produce very large amounts of data, that have to be transmitted or stored, and therefore, there is a need for image compression. Fractal image compression still suffers from a high encoding time. We propose a new optimization approach to reduce the time of fractal image encoding. This approach is a hybridization of the SPIHT algorithm and Jacquin-style coding scheme. Our approach was tested on mammography images of MIAS database.

Keywords- compression; bi-orthogonal Wavelets transformed; SPIHT; Fractals; mammography images.

I. INTRODUCTION

Fractal compression is a lossy compression method, introduced by Barnsley and Jacquin [1]. It is based on Iterated Function Systems (IFS) which exploits the self similarity between the parts of the image.

Different works shows that the Fractal compression method is one of very effective compression methods [2]. But the time of fractal image encoding is important, that is due to the great number of comparisons between the destination range blocks and the source domain blocks. The minimization of the source and destination blocks is one of the solutions of time reduction of fractal image encoding. Many approaches to solving this problem have been proposed [3][4].

This paper presents a hybrid scheme coding using SPHIT and fractal for mammography image compression.

II. PROPOSED APPROACH

Our proposed approach is based on the hybridization of fractals and SPIHT algorithm [5]. The source image to be compressed is first of all decomposed into Wavelets (decomposition using bi-orthogonal Wavelets). This gives place of the coefficients of high value; a scalar quantization will be then applied to the coefficients of the details by building a tree of the coefficients of the significant values. Then a coding with loss on the approximations of significant values is applied.

III. EXPERIMENTAL RESULTS

We have tested our approach on mammography images of size 256×256 using MIAS database.

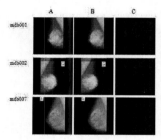

Figure 1. : A. Original images, B. Reconstructed images, C. Difference images.

TABLE 1. OBTAINED RESULTS

Image	CR (%)	PSNR (dB)	Time (s)
mdb001 (l)	67,29	43,05	4,25
mdb002 (r)	89,41	41,87	4,86
mdb007 (l)	85,70	42,81	4,99

Figure 1 shows that the quality of reconstructed images strongly depends on the number of quantified blocks and the errors of coding is located primarily at contours of the images. The obtained results (see TABLE 1) seem to show that the quality of the reconstructed mammography images is very good and the encoding time (evaluated in seconds) is reduced. The conclusion is that the obtained results seem to be satisfactory.

REFERENCES

[1] M. F. Barnsley and A. Jacquin, "Application of recurrent iterated function systems to images," Proc. SPIE, vol. 1001, pp. 122–131, 1988.

[2] D.Saupe and M.Ruhl, "Evolutionary fractal image compression," Proc. Int. Conf. on Image Processing, ICIP'96, Lausanne (1996).

[3] D.M. Monro and F. Dudbridge. "Approximation of Image Blocks." in Proc. Int. Conf. Acoustics, Speed, Signal Processing, Vol. 3, pp.4585-4588, 1992.

[4] Chandan Singh D. Rawat and Sukadev Meher "A Hybrid Coding Scheme Combining SPIHT and SOFM Based Vector Quantization for Effectual Image Compression" European Journal of Scientific Research, ISSN 1450-216X Vol.38 No.03, pp 425-440 2009.

[5] A. Said and W.A. Pearlman, "A New Fast and Efficient Image Codec Based on Set Partitioning in Hierarchical Trees," IEEE Trans. Circuits & Systems for Video Technology, Vol. 6, pp. 243-250, June 1996

1550-6037/11 $26.00 © 2011 IEEE
DOI 10.1109/IV.2011.69

7. Visualisation in Built and Rural Environments

IV 2011

Summarization and Visualization of Pedestrian Tracking Data

Hiroko Yabushita
Ochanomizu University
Tokyo, Japan
Email: yabu@itolab.is.ocha.ac.jp

Takayuki Itoh
Ochanomizu University
Tokyo, Japan
Email: itot@is.ocha.ac.jp

Abstract—We present a summarization and visualization technique for large-scale traffic path data. The research aims to visually distinguish the amount of similar traffic, by representing the similar traffic as bundles of lines. Our technique firstly quantizes the collection of paths, then categorizes the segmented paths, and finally renders the bundles of the segments. Our implementation also provides a graphical user interface (GUI) that allows users to interactively explore the various types of data, so that they can adjust the degree of summarization by controlling parameters in the GUI. The technique can visualize various kinds of path data recorded as chronologically ordered positions which form sequential segments, acquired from movies, sensors, and computer simulations. One of the features of the technique is that it can effectively visualize paths in the place where there are not expressly constructed ways. This paper demonstrates the effectiveness of the technique by applying it to two types of path data, where one is acquired by Radio Frequency IDentification (RFID) sensors, and the other is extracted from a movie.

Keywords-Visualization, summarization, movie tracking, RFID.

I. INTRODUCTION

Pedestrian traffic flows are critical factors for assessment of lands, buildings, and advertisements. Moreover, improvements of efficiency based on these flows are required in communal and public facilities such as medical institutions and airports. Therefore, observation of traffic paths of people is useful for various purposes. Recent computer vision and sensor technologies have provided the means to acquire accurate data about such traffic paths.

There have been several reports on the summarization and visualization of traffic flows of large numbers of people. Reported techniques can be categorized into two approaches: drawing flows into geographic spaces, and drawing as graphs. The technique presented in this paper can be categorized into the former approaches. Here, it may be difficult to look at or understand the paths with many of the early techniques, because the techniques directly draw the trajectories of the paths onto the display and therefore many of the paths clutter up the display results. Traffic summarization is therefore important to obtain more comprehensive visualization results in the geographic spaces. Several recent techniques have improved the visual representation of the paths. Some of the techniques attempt to integrate them onto known ways or automatically selected representative paths [5] [10]. However, there are still situations that cause these techniques to perform poorly. There may not be (or we cannot recognize) representative paths with certainty, when traffic is very tangled. Some of other techniques attempt to partition the geographic spaces and calculate transitions between adjacent regions [3] However, it may be difficult situations that the techniques cannot effectively partition the geographic spaces. For example, it may be difficult to discover characteristic regions of the flows when there may not be expressly constructed ways in wide spaces, such as parks, squares, and scrambled crossroads, and therefore pedestrians freely walk. We therefore think it is interesting to develop summarization and visualization techniques for such paths which can be used in a wide variety of environments.

This paper presents a technique for summarization and visualization of traffic paths which is available whether there are expressly constructed ways or not. The technique assumes that there are many paths across the given geographic space, and the paths consist of sequential points in the space. The technique firstly quantizes the paths with a grid surrounding the 2D space, by connecting intersection between grid-lines and the paths It then collects closely generated segments in each of rectangular regions divided by the grid. It then merges them by the average segments, and optionally connects the merged segments applying Hermite curves. Finally, it draws the segments with interactive operations. Also, the paper introduces two representative case studies: paths of pedestrians in a building tracked by RFID sensors, and paths of them in a wide space of a university campus captured from a movie file. These case studies demonstrate how the technique performs whether there are expressly constructed ways or not.

II. RELATED WORK

Many reports have discussed the visualization of traffic paths in the context of geographic spaces. Many early works straightforwardly draw traffic paths [4] [6]; however, it is obviously problematic for large-scale tracking data due to overlapping and cluttering of the drawn paths. Summarization of tracking data assists to realize comprehensive visualization of large-scale path data.

Andrienko et al. presented a technique that generates primary flows of crowds and then displays the results using

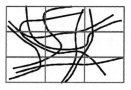 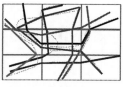  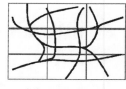
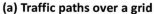

(a) Traffic paths over a grid   **(b) Quantization**   **(c) Bundling**   **(d) Connection**

Figure 1.   Brief procedure of the presented technique. (a) Generate a grid in a 2D space which traffic paths are tracked. (b) Quantize the paths by intersections with the grid-lines. (c) Bundle the quatized paths inside each grid subregion. (d) Connect the bundled paths by Hermite curves.

many ranged straight arrows [2] [3]. The technique extracts and groups characteristics points of paths, then partitions the regions, and finally calculates the transitions between adjacent territories. Consequently it represents the summarized paths as segments connecting specific adjacent points. The representation works very well with their examples including car traffic data; however, it is not clear if it works well with the tangled traffic data in freely walking wide spaces (e.g. parks or scramble crossroads), because it may be difficult to extract meaningful characteristic points from the tangled traffic.

At the same time, several other techniques attempt to generate primary flows of crowds and then represent them as thickness-varied arrow curves [5]. Such approach is usually appropriate not only for spaces that expressly constructed ways (e.g. roads or corridor) but also for wide spaces. However, primary flow extraction is not an easy problem. It may often fail to discover really important flows, or involuntarily merge different types of flows.

Several other reports expresses the summarization and visualization of traffic paths with graphs [7], [8], [9].

III. SUMMARIZATION AND VISUALIZATION

This section presents a new summarization and visualization technique of traffic paths. The technique first quantizes the path data and converts it into a set of rougher segments, because the data may be too fine and therefore contain meaningless noises. The technique then collects and categorizes the segments based on their directions, and bundles the categorized segments as average segments. Since the bundled segments may be discontinues, the technique optionally provides a process to smoothly connect them applying Hermite curves. Finally, the procedure interactively renders the summarized segments.

Following is the brief procedure of the proposed technique, and its illustration is shown in Figure 1:

1) **Quantization:** map a grid onto the 2D path space, calculate intersections, move intersections onto the vertices of the grid, and construct the quantized paths.
2) **Summarization:** categorize the segments of the quantized paths for each rectangular space, unify geometrically overlapping categories, bundle segments

belonging to the same categories. Optionally, connect the bundled segments applying Hermite curves.
3) **Rendering and interaction**.

A. Path Acquisition

We formalize a set of paths as $S = \{P_1, ..., P_n\}$, where P_i is a path and n is the total number of paths. A path consists of a sequence of passing points, $p_i = \{p_{i1}, ..., p_{im}\}$, where p_{ij} is the j-th point of the i-th path, and m is number of points of the i-th path. The point p_{ij} contains the time t_{ij}, and x/y-coordinates x_{ij} and y_{ij} in a 2D space.

We transformed an open RFID sensor data introduced in Section 4.1.1 into the above data structure. We also acquired an example of the traffic path data introduced in Section 4.1.2 from movie files taken by a fixed camera. The presented technique summarizes the traffic path data by constructing clusters of similar paths, and draws them as a set of segments.

The reader should note that traffic path data can come from a variety of different sources. While we discuss data acquired from movies and sensor data, data can also be produced from computer simulations.

B. Quantization

The technique then quantizes the set of paths. It maps a grid onto the 2D path space as shown in Figure 2(Left)(1). The grid lines are assumed to be much bigger than the average interval of the adjacent two points p_{ij} and $p_{(i(j+1))}$. The technique then calculates intersections between the paths and grid lines, shown as red circles in Figure 2(Left)(1). Let the intersections of the i-th path be $P_i' = \{p_{i1}', ..., p_{il}'\}$, while l is the number of intersections between the i-th path and grid lines. It then quantizes the paths by moving the intersections onto the vertices of the grid, shown as blue circles in Figure 2(Left)(1). Let the quantized intersections of the i-th path be $P_i'' = \{p_{i1}'', ..., p_{il}''\}$. Finally, the technique constructs the quantized paths by connecting the vertices of the grid, as shown in Figure 2(Left)(2). Here, the double-ringed, enlarged circles in Figure 2(Left)(2) denote that the quantized path passes these points twice.

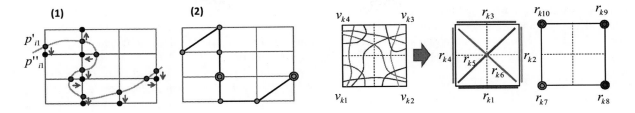

Figure 2. (Left) Quantization of paths. (Right) Patterns of path segments. Division of a rectangular space into four subspaces, and 10 patterns r_{k1} to r_{k10} according to quantized positions of start and end points of the segments.

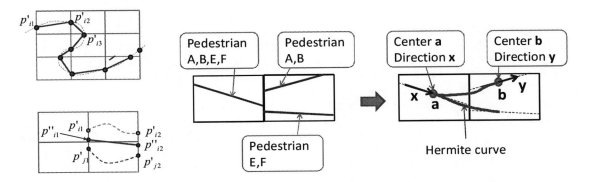

Figure 3. (Left) Bundling of segments. (Upper-Left)If there is only one segment in the patterns, the technique treats the segment as is. (Lower-Left)If the pattern has more than one segment, the technique treats the average of the segments as a bundled segment. (Right) Connection of bundled segments applying Hermite curves.

C. Collection, Categorization, and Bundling

The technique then categorizes the segments of the quantized paths for each rectangular space divided by the grid. Let the k-th rectangular space be r_k, and its four vertices be v_{k1} to v_{k4}. The technique collects all the intersection segments $P'_{ij}P_{(i(j+1))}'$ of the all paths P_1 to P_n passing through r_k. It then categorizes the segments into 10 patterns, r_{k1} to r_{k10}, according to the combination of the two vertices of the segments after the quantization. Figure 2(Right) denotes the ten patterns drawn in ten colors. Here, four patterns r_{k7} to r_{k10} denote that two end points of the quantized segments are at the same positions. Finally, the technique unifies geometrically overlapping categories. Supposing a rectangular space r_p and its lower adjacent r_q, the technique unifies the geometrically overlapping categories, r_{p1} and r_{q3}, r_{p7} and r_{q10}, r_{p8} and r_{q9}, respectively.

The technique then bundles segments for each pattern of each rectangular space r_k. Here, the technique divides the process according to the number of segments. If a pattern r_{pq} has only one segment $p'_{ij}p'_{(i(j+1))}$, the technique treats the segment as is. Figure 3(Upper-Left) shows an illustration that such segment is rendered. Note that the technique renders the segments connected by the intersections before the quantization p'_{ij}. If the pattern r_{pq} has more than one segment, the technique calculates the average path of the segments as a bundled segment. Figure 3(Lower-Left) shows

an example of an average path. Here, a sky blue segment p'_{i1} p'_{i2} and a green segment p'_{j1} p'_{j2} are the two segments those vertices are quantized to the same two vertices p''_{i1} and p''_{i2}. In this case, the technique treats the average of the two segments as a bundled segment, shown as a red segment in Figure 3(Lower-Left).

D. Connection of bundled segments

Segments bundled by the above process may be often discontinuous. The discontinuity is especially observable when we measured the paths of pedestrians at freely walkable spaces. For example, such discontinuity is not observable in the result at colliders of a building, shown in Section IV-A; however, it is especially observable in the result at free space of a university campus, shown in Section IV-B. For this problem, we developed a technique that connects the adjacent bundled segments which share at least one common pedestrian. The technique applies Hermite curves to smoothly interpolate the gaps between the adjacent bundled segments. Figure 3(Right) illustrates the process. The technique firstly finds pairs of segments which belong to adjacent grid-rectangles, and share at least one common pedestrian. It then generates Hermite curves connecting centers of the segments, where tangent vectors of the end points of the Hermite curves correspond to the direction of the segments. In Figure 3(Right), **a** and **b** denote the centers of the two segments, and correspond to the positions of the end points of the Hermite curve. Also, **x** and **y** denote the directions of the segments, and correspond to the tangent vectors of the end points of the Hermite curve.

IV. CASE STUDIES

This section introduces two case studies to demonstrate the capability of our path visualization.

A. Paths Acquired by RFID Sensors

First, we show the result of the visualization of paths acquired at a place where there are expressly constructed ways. The data is drawn from evacuation routes in a certain building, acquired by RFID sensors and published on the Web [1]. Figure 4(Left) shows a map of the building. In this figure, a bomb explodes at the bomb mark. People then evacuate through the doorways that have arrows and are circled in red. In a disaster situation such as this, lives will be saved if everyone can leave the building as quickly and orderly as possible.

Figure 5 (Left) shows captured paths. Many of paths overlap in the figure and therefore it is difficult to understand the quantity of overlapping paths from the figure, because many people may go along the same way during the evacuation. Figure 5 (Center) shows an intermediate result in which the walks are blurred by the quantization. Figure 5 (Right) shows a visualization result by the presented technique, which adequately represents the degree of congestion of the paths. Time required to escape from the building can be reduced if the people escape along less crowded ways for such refuge. We think this visualization result will suggest the improvement of the refuge course.

We discovered a thickened path at a left part in Figure 5 (Right). When we see the part more in detail, though it is one-way path, we discovered that in this part the summary line is thicker than the adjacent parts. We wondered why it was thickened. If people could smoothly escape from the building, we would not see such thickened segment. Looking at a video displaying the RFID sensor data, we could discover evacuees losing their ways. As just described, we could discover an extreme behavior of evacuees from the visualization result immediately, and understand the problem by looking at the video. We understood how important it is to make the escape route comprehensible from this discovery.

B. Paths Captured from Movies

We were also challenged to attempt to visualize paths that were acquired at a place without expressly constructed ways.

We recorded a movie file around a door of a cafeteria of a university for 30 minutes, from the higher floor of another building. Figure 4(Right) shows the position of the door of a cafeteria, garbage boxes, and vending machines. Our current implementation detects moving objects by Mean-Shift method, and assigns identical numbers to each of the objects. Our technique then extracts positions of the moving objects in the image space for each frame. We manually removed positions if the data contained the paths of non-human objects.

Figure 6 (Left) shows captured paths. Figure 6 (Center) shows an intermediate result, hence instead of looking like a very jagged line, it appears as a smoother arc because there are fewer sample points. Figure 6 (Right) shows a visualization result by the presented technique. The technique controls color and thickness of segments according to the number of passing persons, so that users can understand main flows of the traffic. We captured the movie around lunch time; therefore, we can observe the main flows from a lecture building to the door of the cafeteria. The result shows that the technique effectively simplified the path data and highlighted main flows. The example demonstrates that the presented technique can effectively visualize paths in places without expressly constructed ways.

Figure 7 shows the result of connection of merged segments. It is observable that merged segments shown in Figure 6 (Right) are somewhat discontinues; however, they are smoothly connected by applying Hermite curves and therefore the result is more comfortable to carefully observe. The technique can generate different resolutions of connected flows by varying the resolution of grids. This operation is useful for level of detail control of visualization results. Our implementation realizes interactive level of detail control since it spends less than 100 milliseconds for quantization, bundling, and connection with this dataset.

We were able to discover the main route as a result of observation of these results. Moreover, we were able to find that there were few people walking to the right side of the garbage box, though there were many people who walked in front of the garbage box. We understood that there were many people who stopped by the garbage box, before entering the cafeteria after leaving the main route, or after exiting the cafeteria before joining the main route. We think that such observation is useful for deciding how to arrange objects around the walking spaces.

V. CONCLUSION AND FUTURE WORK

We presented a technique for summarization and visualization of large collections of traffic paths As demonstrated in Section IV-B, the presented technique can effectively visualize paths in the place where there are no expressly constructed ways, which is an improvement over existing techniques that can only visualize results in places where there are expressly constructed ways.

As an on-going work, we are implementing a technique to convert the rendered segments into fewer numbers of smoothly connected curves. Another important issue is representation of direction of flows. Our current implementation does not consider the direction of segments during the

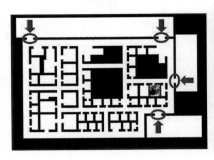

Figure 4. (Left) Map of the building. Scenery of around a door of a cafeteria of a university. (Right) (Red: Door of cafeteria, Blue: Garbage boxes, Yellow: Vending machines.)

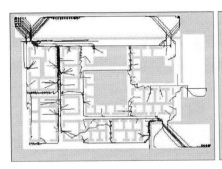
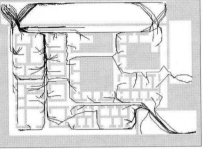
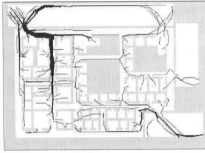

Figure 5. Rendering segments of the paths acquired by RFID sensors. (Left) The technique renders corresponding single segments as-is. (Center) The technique calculates intersections between the segments and grids, connects the intersections by straight segments, and renders the segments. (Right) The technique calculates the average of corresponding segments and renders according to relative density.

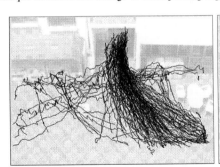

Figure 6. Rendering segments of the paths captured from a movie file. (Left) The technique renders corresponding one segment as is. (Center) The technique calculates intersections between segments and grids, connects the intersections by straight segments, and renders the segments. (Right) The technique calculates the average of the corresponding segments, and renders according to relative density.

categorization and rendering, so we would like to extend the implementation so that we can represent these directions.

The presented technique is not limited to path data obtained from movies and sensors: it can also visualize simulation-based path data. We would like to apply such path data to the presented technique in a future work.

REFERENCES

[1] IEEE 2008 VAST CHALLENGE, http://www.cs.umd.edu/hcil/VASTchallenge08/

[2] G. Andrienko, N. Andrienko, Spatio-temporal Aggregation for Visual Analysis of Movements, *IEEE Symposium on Visual Analytics Science and Technology 2008*, 51-58, 2008.

[3] N. Andrienko, G. Andrienko, Spatial Generalization and Aggregation of Massive Movement Data, *IEEE Transactions on Visualization and Computer Graphics*, 17(2), 205-219, 2010.

[4] T. Kapler, W. Wright, GeoTime Information Visualization, *Information Visualization*, 4(2), 136-146, 2005.

[5] K. Katabira, H. Zhao, R. Shibasaki, M. Sekine, K. Sezaki,

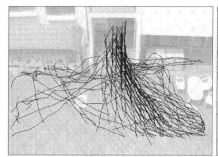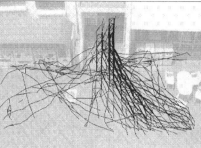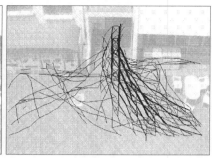

Figure 7. Connection of merged segments applying Hermite curves over various resolutions of grids. (Left) Using a grid dividing into 20×20 rectangles. (Center) Using a grid dividing into 15×15 rectangles. (Right) Using a grid dividing into 10×10 rectangles.

Crowds Flow Detection and Indoor Temperature Monitoring for Advanced Air-Conditioning Control, *The 27th Asian Conference on Remote Sensing*, 2006.

[6] M.-J. Kraak, The Space-Time Cube Revisited from a Geovisualization Perspective, *21st International Cartographic Conference*, 1988-1995, 2003.

[7] J. Li, J. Z. Wang, J. S. Larson, E. T. Bradlow, P. S. Fader, An Exploratory Look at Supermarket Shopping Paths, *International Journal of Research in Marketing* 22(4), 395-414, Dec. 2005.

[8] T. Schreck, J. Bernard, T. Tekusova, Visual Cluster Analysis of Trajectory Data With Interactive Kohonen Maps, *IEEE Symposium on Visual Analytics Science and Technology 2008*, 3-10, 2008.

[9] Z. Shen, K.-L. Ma, Path Visualization for Adjacency Matrices, *Eurographics/IEEE-VGTC Symposium on Visualization*, 83-90, 2007.

[10] P. Widhalm, N. Braendle, Learning Major Pedestrian Flows in Crowded Scenes, *20th International Conference on Pattern Recognition (ICPR)*, ThCT3.2, 2010.

Users' Responses to 2D and 3D Visualization Techniques in Urban Conservation Process

Turgay Kerem Koramaz

Istanbul Technical University, Faculty of Architecture,
Department of Urban and Regional Planning
Istanbul, Turkey
koramaz@itu.edu.tr

Nuran Zeren Gülersoy

Istanbul Technical University, Faculty of Architecture,
Department of Urban and Regional Planning
Istanbul, Turkey
gulersoy@itu.edu.tr

Abstract— This paper compares efficiency of two and three-dimensional visualization techniques which are developed for representation of spatial content of an urban historic site. The aim of this paper is to measure users' perception regarding the performance of these visualization techniques. Methodology is based on a questionnaire which is gathering the user's responses regarding comprehension and perception level of the case area's characteristics. The case study, which was held in Zeyrek urban historic site, comprises the application of 2D and 3D figures and schemes in order to represent the site characteristics, survey and analysis and proposals. As the fundamental finding of the study, it is concluded that spatial attributes and characteristics in 3D urban models are better defined than in 2D mapping technique. The study indicates that orientation sense of users and cognition of the townscape characteristics are the most prominent components of 3D urban model, generated within this case study.

Keywords- urban conservation; visualization techniques; 3D urban model; CAD

I. INTRODUCTION

Investigation of visualization technique's efficiency is important with the reliability of the technique regarding representation level of the spatial content in the process of urban planning, communication and interaction among user groups. Computer aided three-dimensional (3D) urban models as innovative visualization techniques, have more capability to attain communication between user groups and to visualize comprehensive spatial information than conventional two-dimensional (2D) visualization techniques [1]. But 3D urban models are occasionally used to represent the final view of the urban structure and expressions of planning and design proposals. In urban conservation and design process, these models produce realistic images and views to facilitate not only the actual urban pattern but also proposed urban structure and form in order to evaluate the planning decisions [2], [3].

Comprehensive spatial analyses and investigations are required in urban planning and conservation studies devoted to evaluation of urban historic sites. Efficiency levels of visualization techniques may vary in the different stages of urban conservation process. Then examination of negative and positive aspects of these techniques has been anticipated to provide contributions directly to communication and interaction between professions and other stakeholders in urban conservation process.

Two main parameters are identified in describing and developing the efficiency of visualization techniques. These are spatial abstraction level from high to low geometric content and functionality on spatial data analysis and visualization [4]. Spatial abstraction parameter investigates the level of geometric and spatial content that visualization technique represents in computer interface. Functionality parameter defines the reliability and accuracy level of visualized information in the technique while interpreting the representation level of real space in virtual interface [1].

By the technological improvements in CAD, especially 3D models offer more efficient and practical processes throughout developing capability of representation and abstraction level of spatial content [1]. Another function of these models is the communication and interaction capability in urban planning and design process among users in different background [2]. As the technology growth in CAD applications, 3D urban models are used not only for the purpose of a mere visualization media but also a design aid while achieving an efficient interface in communicative urban design process [5].

As the fundamental function of 3D urban models, communication and interaction function facilitate the participation and collaboration processes in urban planning. Then such communication and interaction tools develop learning skills [6] and cognition and perception abilities of users and professions in planning and design disciplines [7], [8]. Hence the discussions related to these abilities of learning, cognition and evaluation processes of users and stakeholders, especially professions and other authorities is necessary to enhance the functional efficiency of 3D visualization techniques.

The number of studies concerning the investigation of users' subjective responses for 3D visualization techniques in urban planning and architectural design processes has increased recently. These studies mainly focus on two research questions. The first one is to which degree of realism 3D virtual environments can represent the real environment [9], [10], [11]. The second research question in related literature is to what extent various visualization techniques can represent the spatial or visual content [12], [13].

1550-6037/11 $26.00 © 2011 IEEE
DOI 10.1109/IV.2011.22

Then this paper examines the efficiency of 2D and 3D visualization techniques those were developed for the case area, Zeyrek Urban Historic site, which is located in the north of the Historical Peninsula of Istanbul, Turkey.

The aim of this paper is to measure users' perception regarding the performance of 2D and 3D visualization techniques. Motivation of this paper is based on improving especially the tasks of 3D urban model as an active communication tool that is integrated with urban conservation. This examination was conducted using a questionnaire which compared the perceived level of spatial content of the site, represented by 2D mapping technique and 3D models.

II. METHODOLOGY IN THE QUESTIONNAIRE

This paper is based on the research held within the PhD study in 2009 [14]. A broader questionnaire study in 2008 was conducted to gather responses from various kinds of users, respectively graduate students in Faculty of Architecture, professions in planning and conservation institutions and high school students as the representatives of inhabitants. In the questionnaire, results of which are given in this paper, graduate students' responses have been investigated in two different groups; 2D mapping as the conventional representation technique and 3D urban model (in separate groups after separate presentations). Planning and design graduate students who are familiar to visual communication tools have assessed visualization techniques in terms of representation capability on urban conservation.

A. Visualization Techniques in Zeyrek

Zeyrek is located in the north of Historical Peninsula of Istanbul, on the slopes, viewing Golden Horn. In 1983 Zeyrek, as a quarter of Istanbul was included in the World Heritage List because of historical, aesthetical and architectural characteristics. Most important monument of the site is Mosque of Zeyrek that had been Monastery of Christ Pantokrator in Byzantium Period. Variety on cultural structure of the site is reflected to urban space that has traditional organic pattern, constituted with authentic timber Turkish houses [15].

In separate presentations, prepared within these 2D and 3D visualization techniques, "Zeyrek Urban Conservation and Design Project" [15] have been re-arranged within the purpose of the questionnaire. Presentation of "Zeyrek Urban Conservation and Design Project" which takes approximately ten-minute long is mainly formed of three stages. The first stage is preparation of base map and 3D urban model (Figure 1).

All maps and figures in both presentations, uses the same data, based on digital maps from municipality, on-site survey, and previous conservation and design studies and inventories prepared for Zeyrek urban historic site. Of all stages, as a CAD system AutoCAD 2004© is used to constitute 2D mapping technique and 3D urban model.

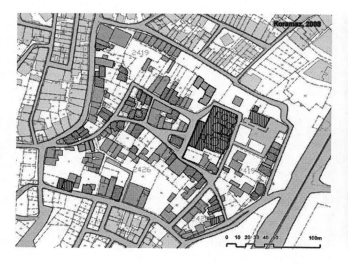 

Figure 1.   Existing Townscape on 2D Map (left) and 3D urban Model (right) (coloured in original)

After the preparation of the base map and 3D urban model, the second stage is surveying and evaluation of townscape. Survey and physical analysis was held in firstly conventional analysis which contains common evaluation of building and structures as, building uses, condition, construction material, built-up and inbuilt-up areas, and finally listed buildings. Then evaluation of townscape and conservation potential of the historic urban pattern was assessed in parameters titled as structure, façade, accessibility – privacy, and harmony with local architectural characteristics. All these survey and analysis were first constructed in 2D maps and then 3D urban model in the same topics and titles. The last stage is developing a plan proposal for the conservation of Zeyrek Urban Historic Site.

While the survey and analysis were held in both 2D mapping and 3D urban model techniques, opportunities were determined to define townscape and urban pattern parameters [14]. Contrary to the conventional survey and analysis, spatial data mostly related to privacy and façade characteristics were better represented in 3D urban models.

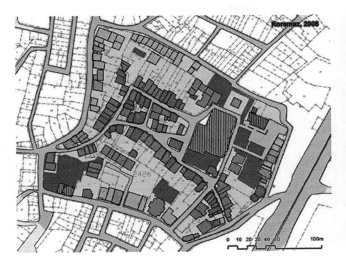

Figure 2.   Proposal for Townscape on 2D Map (left) and 3D urban Model (right) (coloured in original)

B.   Questionnaire

Questionnaire mainly consists of three parts as comprehension – perception level of site characteristics in the conservation and design project; efficiency of visualization and representation technique; and perception of components described in semantic scale. This paper comprises only the results of the first section the questionnaire. Each separate groups answered the same topics, covered the extent how they comprehend and perceived each figure and map and how they evaluated the efficiency of each techniques as 2D and 3D visualization technique.

All the questions in the questionnaire were conducted in a seven level - Likert scale with 1: "poor" and 7: "excellent". Ten-minute long presentations which were prepared with 2D mapping and 3D urban model were presented to two separate groups. Then respondents were asked to describe their comprehension and perception level for site characteristics in Zeyrek Urban Conservation and Design Project.

Results according to responses from graduate students have been analyzed with a specific statistical method, Linear Discriminant Analysis (LDA) which is a statistical analysis to attain weightings of variables to discriminate between separate groups [16]. LDA, which uses a function based on measuring the distance between two groups, has F-test analysis application module in SPSS software that allows indicating the significance of differences of means from separate groups.

C.   Participants

Forty-five graduate students, studying in Istanbul Technical University, Faculty of Architecture (30 urban planners, 8 architects, 7 landscape designer), took part in the questionnaire. First group, twenty students (12 PhD and 8 master students) were asked to evaluate the 2D mapping technique and the second group, twenty-five students (9 PhD and 16 master students) were asked to evaluate 3D urban model.

The respondents' ages in the professional group ranged from 21 to 32 years, with an average of 24,40 years (S.D.=2.624, median 24). Computer experience in the sample has been taken into consideration as the profile of respondents. 14 respondents have been using computer for less than nine years; 22 respondents between 10-14 years and 9 respondents between 15-19 years. Another indicator for computer experience is the use of computer aided design software. Of all respondents, only three graduate students do not use any computer aided design software in their professional and educational works or studies. But less respondents use 3D modelling software as in the quantity of 15 respondents. Of respondents in the first group, only four respondents use 3D modelling software. In the other group who evaluated 3D urban model, eleven persons use these techniques. Between respondent groups, no statistically significant differences were found for the variables of age or computer experience.

III.   RESULTS: COMPREHENSION – PERCEPTION LEVEL OF SITE CHARACTERISTICS

Comprehension and perception level of site characteristics of Zeyrek Urban Conservation Study is computed within four categories as general characteristics of the site (location, size, boundaries and topography of the site), conventional survey and analyses (building use, height, material, condition analysis, built-up and inbuilt-up and listed building), survey and analyses of townscape (analysis of structural condition, visual quality, accessibility and harmony) and proposal for the site (proposal for structural size and mass, façade characteristics, accessibility and architectural characteristics). Initially, it can be observed that respondents who were presented 3D urban model gives fairly higher scores to questions in the categories of general characteristics of the site, survey and analyses of townscape. On the contrary, first group who were presented 2D mapping techniques have higher mean scores in the categories of conventional survey and analyses and proposal for the site.

TABLE I. GROUP MEANS FOR COMPREHENSION – PERCEPTION LEVEL OF SITE CHARACTERISTICS

Variables / Questions		1. Group 2D map n:20		2. Group 3d model n:25	
		Mean	S.D.	Mean	S.D.
General Site Characteristics *To what extent do you perceive these?*					
A1.	the location of the site	2,85	1,69	3,20	1,53
A2.	the size of area	4,15	1,95	5,00	1,38
A3.	the boundaries of the site	4,80	1,47	**5,52**	1,16
A4.	the topography of the site	2,10	1,21	**4,68**	1,49
Conventional Survey and Analyses *To what extent can following building analysis define the site?*					
A5.	use analysis	**5,15**	0,67	4,92	1,55
A6.	height analysis	4,40	1,50	**4,72**	1,59
A7.	material analysis	**5,60**	0,94	5,28	1,21
A8.	condition analysis	**5,35**	1,35	5,00	1,12
A9.	built-up, inbuilt-up analysis	**4,95**	1,36	4,44	2,08
A10.	listed building analysis	**4,60**	1,60	4,28	1,79
Survey and Analyses of Townscape *To what extent can following analysis define the site?*					
A11.	structural condition	3,35	1,87	**5,08**	1,04
A12.	visual quality	2,45	1,61	**4,24**	1,48
A13.	accessibility	2,35	1,57	**4,04**	1,79
A14.	harmony	4,60	1,27	**5,00**	1,26
Proposal for the Site *To what extent are following proposals comprehended?*					
A15.	structural size and mass	**4,90**	1,65	4,00	1,58
A16.	façade characteristics	**4,80**	1,64	4,56	1,78
A17.	accessibility	**4,10**	1,74	3,56	1,47
A18.	architectural characteristics	**4,15**	1,69	3,96	1,79

Note: Question response format was seven-step scale from 1 to 7and highest mean values for each variable are printed in bold (S.D.= standard deviation).

TABLE II. COMPONENT LOADINGS AFTER VARIMAX ROTATION

Variables		Components			
		1	2	3	4
Comp1 Townscape Characteristics					
A12.	visual quality	**0,91**			0,26
A13.	accessibility	**0,82**			
A11.	structural condition	**0,73**			0,45
A14.	harmony	**0,68**	0,27	0,31	
A6.	building height	**0,53**	0,29		
Comp2 Proposal Characteristics					
A16.	façade characteristics		**0,85**		
A18.	architectural characteristics	0,26	**0,80**		
A15.	structural size and mass		**0,75**		
A17.	accessibility	0,47	**0,54**		
Comp3 Conventional Characteristics					
A7.	material analysis		0,26	**0,83**	
A8.	condition analysis		0,33	**0,81**	
A5.	use analysis			**0,66**	0,38
A9.	built-up, inbuilt-up analysis	0,36		**0,61**	
A10.	listed building analysis		0,46	**0,55**	
Comp4 General Characteristics					
A4.	topography of the site	0,34			**0,76**
A3.	boundaries of the site		0,27		**0,70**
A2.	size of area		0,33	0,34	**0,69**

Note : All component loadings > 0.25 are reported. Highest loadings for every variable are printed in bold. Kaiser-Meyer-Olkin measure of sampling adequacy is 0,679. Significance level within Bartlett's Test of Sphericity is 0,000.

To investigate comprehension – perception level of visualization and representation techniques, factor analysis is also performed with varimax rotation of 17 variables and developed indices for the whole data with the combination of two groups. The question of "To what extent do you perceive the location of the site?" (A1) has not been included in factor analysis because it decreased the sampling adequacy and had conflicts in the contribution of factor components in expected scales.

A four-factor solution has been chosen for the variables of comprehension – perception level of visualization and representation techniques (Kaiser-Meyer-Olkin measure of sampling adequacy: 0,679, Significance level within Bartlett's Test of Sphericity: 0,000). 67,07% of cumulative case loadings has been explained in component analysis with 1,201 Eigen value level. These levels reflect that factor analysis is adequately representing the case loadings in the sample size. These four factors could be termed as respectively townscape characteristics (Comp. 1), proposal characteristics (Comp. 2), conventional characteristics (Comp. 3) and general characteristics of the site (Comp. 4).

As the result of factor analysis, components reflect the same categories which were also identical in the questionnaire form. Only the loading scores of building height has been reported in another component terming townscape characteristics (Comp. 1), because building height analysis define the site more adequately in the second group (3D urban model) as the townscape survey and analysis.

As the first group examines and interprets a presentation with only 2D mapping techniques and the second group examines and interprets other presentation with only 3D urban model, a comparison has been assembled how much difference exists between two visualization and representation techniques in terms of delivering information for urban conservation study to the respondents. LDA processes each variables/questions and calculates values indicating whether there is a statistically significant difference.

As LDA analysis determines the mean values of each component from factor analysis and from each test group with the results of the F-test in the table n., Overall four components, townscape characteristics (Comp. 1) and general characteristics (Comp. 4) have positive mean values in the second group but negative values in the first group. However F-test significance indicates that statistically significant mean difference in the same components.

TABLE III.   LDA WITH GROUP MEAN VALUES

Variables / Questions		1. Group 2D n:20	2. Group 3D n:25	F	Sig.
Comp1	Townscape Characteristics	-0,449	**0,359**	8,502	0,006
Comp2	Proposal Characteristics	**0,307**	-0,246	3,602	0,064
Comp3	Conventional Characteristics	**0,274**	-0,219	2,819	0,100
Comp4	General Characteristics	-0,586	**0,469**	16,823	0,000

Since the group mean values from second group in component 1 and 4 are significantly (95% confidence interval) positive and higher, it can be reported that 3D urban model delivers more information on the components of townscape and general characteristics of urban conservation study. As the most distinctive component, general characteristics (M: 0,469 in the second group and M: - 0,586 in the first group; Sig : 0,000) which refer to size, boundaries and the topography of the site have been more intelligent to deliver information by means of 3D urban model rather than 2D mapping techniques. This finding may refer to the ability of visualization technique in terms of orientation sense of the use. Other component townscape characteristics (M ; 0,359 in the second group and M: - 0,449 in the first group; Sig: 0,006) which refer to analysis of structural condition, visual quality, accessibility, harmony and building height analysis have also been more intelligent to define the conservation site by means of 3D urban model.

Comp. 2 and Comp. 3 have higher mean values in the first group but in 90% confidence interval, because these components have significance level as respectively 0,064 and 0,100. It can be stated that to deliver information about decisions and proposals about the conservation study and conventional analysis such as building use, material, condition, built-up and inbuilt-up analysis and listed building analysis 2D mapping techniques are considerably adequate.

LDA calculates not only difference between group mean values but also Fisher's Linear Discriminant Function (FLDF), which is used as a threshold for dividing the answers into two groups at what extent these variable correspond these identical difference. Test of this function has been held by a chi square test for Wilk's lambda, too. The classification which is constructed by FLDF, is mainly measured on the discriminant scores, and the scores calculated with a linear equation. Classification for comprehension – perception level of defined characteristics in this case, which has been resulted with factor analysis with a four-factor component analysis have been calculated with the following equation;

$$D = 0,815 \cdot \times \text{Comp1} - 0,558 \cdot \times \text{Comp2}$$
$$- 0,498 \cdot \times \text{Comp3} + 1,064 \times \text{Comp4} \qquad (1)$$

Where D = Discriminant Function
Comp (n) = values for each component as comprehension – perception level of site characteristics

The coefficients of each component reflect the pre-eminence in the discriminant function as Comp4 have highest coefficient value as 1,064 and Comp3 has the lowest one as – 0,498. Test of this function has been proved with Chi Square test for Wilk's lambda (Chi-square = 36,069 and Significance = 0.000). This function indicates the similar trends with dominant components as F-test results represent, either. LDA gives possibility to estimate whether the group cases classifies correctly in a classification table as follows:

TABLE IV.   CLASSIFICATION TABLE OF LDA

Variables / Questions		Predicted Group Membership		Total
		1. Group 2D - n:20	2. Group 3D - n:25	
Count	1. group - 2D	**18**	2	20
	2. group - 3D	6	**19**	25
%	1. group - 2D	**90**	10	100
	2. group - 3D	24	**76**	100

Note : 82,2% of original grouped cases correctly classified.

Classification table indicates number and percent of respondents that belongs to correct groups. For instance, discriminant score from 18 out of 20 respondents in the first group could be grouped into first group. It means that only two respondents' answers in the first group had been more likely close to the scores of the second group. But on the contrary from 19 out of 25 respondents in the second group could be grouped into the same group. As 82,2% of original grouped cases correctly classified, it can be concluded that there are significant differences in comprehension level of defined characteristics of urban conservation study between separate presentations as 2D mapping and 3D urban model tools, and that the graduate students, who were presented 3D urban model, have higher perception level of urban conservation study's defined characteristics than the ones who were presented 2D mapping techniques.

IV.   CONCLUSIONS

As the fundamental finding of the study, it is concluded that spatial attributes and characteristics in 3D urban models are better defined by the comprehensive spatial analyses and investigations than in 2D mapping technique. 3D urban model has higher group mean values for most of the variables but the most prominently for variables describing "the comprehension of general characteristics" and "cognition of townscape characteristics" of urban historic site. In addition to the conclusion remarks of this paper, 3D urban models with virtual reality applications also strengthen the immersive experiences regarding the sense of orientation in virtual urban environments [17].

In accordance with the responses from graduate students, as one of the user groups among the planning and design professions, the most important skill of 3D urban models is stated as explanation ability of conservation project and interventions to structural and visual quality of urban historic environments. Representation ability of change and enhancement of cognition and perception level in urban historic townscapes are the other important capabilities of 3D visualization techniques. Responses of graduate students also overlapped with the community appraisals, especially for the statement which considers the 3D urban models' capabilities on representing the sense of historic site affection [18]. These community appraisals were described by the help of the research findings in 2009 [14] that main focus on the representation capability of 3D urban model is related to definition of architectural vernacular characteristics.

Graduate students in planning and design schools use 3D urban model mostly as "last visualization media" which is improved with material, texture and light modelling, in enriched artistic and realistic details. But planning and conservation project require visualization techniques in order to describe and represent spatial content in details. In conclusion, 3D models improve the user's perception regarding the representation of townscape characteristics and enhance the communication and interaction of spatial information among user groups in order to develop collaborative processes in urban conservation.

REFERENCES

[1] S.M. Pietsch. "Computer Visualisation in the Design Control of Urban Environments: a Literature Review." Environment and Planning B: Planning and Design, vol. 27, 2000, 521-536.

[2] P. Hall. "The Future of Cities." Computers, Environment and Urban Systems, vol. 23, 1999, 173-185.

[3] K, Al-Kodmany. "Visualization Tools and Methods in Community Planning: From Freehand Sketches to Virtual Reality. Journal of Planning Literature." vol. 17, no. 2, 2002, 189-211.

[4] M. Batty, D. Chapman, S. Evans, M. Haklay, S. Kueppers, N. Shiode, A. Smith, and P.M. Torrens. Visualizing the City: Communicating Urban Design to Planners and Decision Makers. url: http://www.casa.ucl.ac.uk/visualcities.pdf, 2000.

[5] D. Bertol. "Designing Digital Space, an Architect's Guide to Virtual Reality." New York, USA, John Wiley & Sons Inc., 1997.

[6] A. Hamilton, N. Trodd, X. Zhang, T. Fernando, and K. Watson. "Learning through Visual Systems to Enhance the Urban Planning Process." Environment and Planning B: Planning and Design, vol. 28, 2001, 833-845.

[7] J. Houtkamp, and H. van Oostendorp. "Virtual Vandalism: the Effect of Physical Incivilities on the Affective Appraisal of 3D Urban Models." In Proceeding Information Visualization 2007. IVS, IEEE, 559-566.

[8] B. Westerdahl, K. Suneson, C. Wernemyr, M. Roupe, M. Johansson, and C.M. Allwood. "Users' Evaluation of a Virtual Reality Architectural Model Compared with the Experience of the Completed Building." Automation in Construction, vol. 15, 2006, 150-165.

[9] E. Lange. "The limits of realism: perceptions of virtual landscapes." Landscape and Urban Planning, vol. 54, 2001, 163-182.

[10] N. Werglas and A Muhar. "The role of computer visualization in the communication of urban design – a comparison of viewer responses to visualizations versus on-site visits." Landscape and Urban Planning, vol. 91, no. 4, 2009, 171-182.

[11] J.M. Houtkamp and M.L.A. Junger. "Affective qualities of an urban environment on a desktop computer." In Proceeding Information Visualization 2010. IVS, IEEE, 597-603.

[12] P.L. Neto. "Evaluation of an urban design project: imagery and realistic computer models." Environment and Planning B: Planning and Design, vol. 28, 2001, 671-686.

[13] N., Bates-Brkljac. "Investigating perceptual responses and shared understanding of architectural design ideas when communicated through different forms of visual representations." In Proceeding Information Visualization 2007. IVS, IEEE, 348-353.

[14] T.K. Koramaz, and N. Zeren Gulersoy. "Evaluation of Users' Responses for 3D Urban Model in Urban Conservation Process." A|Z ITU Journal of the Faculty of Architecture, vol. 6, no. 2, 2009, 1-19.

[15] N. Zeren Gulersoy, A. Tezer, R. Yigiter, T.K. Koramaz, and Z. Gunay. "Istanbul Project: Istanbul Historic Peninsula Conservation Study; Zeyrek, Suleymaniye and Yenikapi Historic Districts, Volume 2: Zeyrek Case." Istanbul Technical University, Istanbul, TR, 2008.

[16] M.S. Srivastava. "Methods of Multivariate Statistics." John New York, USA, Wiley & Sons. 2002.

[17] T.K. Koramaz, and N. Zeren Gulersoy. "Comparison Between Users' Responses for Static 3D Model and VR Application in Zeyrek Urban Historic Site." In Proceeding 22nd CIPA Symposium, 2009, Kyoto, Japan.

[18] T.K. Koramaz, and N. Zeren Gulersoy. "3D Visualization of Transformation in Historic Townscape: Case of Zeyrek Urban Site." In Proceeding 14th IPHS Conference, Urban Transformation: Controversies, Contrasts and Challenges, vol.2, 2010, ITU, 360-371.

Optimized work flow through VR and AR technology on construction sites

Kim Kirchbach
Institute for Technology and Management in Construction (TMB)
Karlsruhe Institute of Technology (KIT)
Karlsruhe, Germany
Kim.Kirchbach@kit.edu

Christoph Runde
Virtual Dimension Center (VDC)
Competence Center for Virtual Reality
Fellbach, Germany
Christoph.Runde@vdc-fellbach.de

Abstract—The development of a physical building control center can support project management and -control to optimize the flow of the complex processes at a construction site. The concept consists of equipping vehicles with sensors and using VR and AR-techniques to visualize this realtime information and allow an optical adaption to current circumstances. The result will be shown by a more efficient utilization and enhanced cost effectiveness.

To analyse what is required you always start by clarifying the relevant object to be presented in VR. The instrument chosen was interview. The second step is to work out the necessary way of computing, viewing and manipulating this data. Finally a hardware setting is designed that would probably fulfill the derived requirements.

The results of the interviews are presented. By processing these data the information and objects, which shall be visualized within the use case of a control center as well as in an on-site use case, are elaborated and also introduced. For these reasons hardware settings are analyzed and the basis for an implementation is established.

Keywords-virtual reality; augmented reality; control center; process optimization; construction site; information visualization; user studies and evaluation;

I. INTRODUCTION

With the development of a physical building control center, project management and -control can be supported and the flow of the complex process at a construction site can be optimized. The task is to design a Human-computer-interface, which allows simple and secure handling even at complex building processes. "Virtual Reality" (VR) offers a good opportunity for doing so. Secondarily "Augmented Reality" (AR) shall be used to support the construction vehicle driver with additional information within the construction site. Building and digging works consist of many parallel processes, so that a slight accident or interruption can influence the workflow of a whole chain of building vehicles. This can cause delays, cost increase and quality may also suffer. To avoid or minimalize the impact of such an interruption it is necessary to reconsider the working cycle. It is impossible to foresee problems like these during the planning phase so that during the execution phase, tasks like this are handled by a participant, who is responsible to regain the work flow. Through imperfect information a reliable base of decision-making is missing, as a consequence vehicles act inefficient or nonproductive.

A planning and control system does not exist. By transferring concepts of the automobile ("digital factory", [1]) and manufacturing industry ("multi agent technology", [2], [3]) this problem can be tackled. The concept is to equip vehicles with sensors and act by means of software agents in teams. They are able to swap information among each other and eventually take further enquiry to a higher control center. The main objective is to get the involved components in continuous flow without any latency or downtime. The result is a more efficient utilization. Using this system, machine drivers shall be optimally supported. In addition, interferences with costs and deadlines can be visualized at the control center thus the construction manager is able to act positive and promptly to troubles.

For these problems the project "AutoBauLog" ("Autonomous control in construction site logistics", [4], [5]) can be used. Within the AutoBauLog project a requirements analysis has been done to identify the specific needs within the project's context. The instrument chosen was interview. The requirements analysis always starts by clarifying the relevant object to be presented in VR. The second step is to work out the required way of computing, viewing and manipulating this data. Finally a hardware setting is designed that would probably fulfill the derived requirements. [6]

II. CONTROL CENTER USE CASE

Conventional control centers consist of instruments, a planning table and communication devices [7]. Electronic control centers are assembled of capacity disposal and electric planning tables. Incurred information may be accessed and evaluated directly [8]. But this presented innovative control center makes use of information technology and state-of-the-art sensors to add an additional benefit to a "normal" control center.

The most important task is to provide information. Therefore building vehicles will be arranged with Topcon[1]-sensors. This is not a gps-receiver like a car sat, but rather a specific technology with increased accuracy. Additional sensors are able to collect the excavator bucket, shield tilting dozer

---

[1]Tokyo Optikal Company Nippon, one of the world largest affiliated groups within the field of geodetic surveying instruments

1550-6037/11 $26.00 © 2011 IEEE
DOI 10.1109/IV.2011.11

position and orientation exactly. Also technical data like maintenance interval, amount of diesel, engine oil pressure are known, so that a huge data basis exists. In this manner an overview of the entire site can be taken and a direct management is possible.

For example if a long queue of dumpers is recognized while removing binder soil, instructions can be displayed directly to the dumpers' drivers cab to adjust truck disposal. He can add refueling, bring forward his lunch break or be advised to slow down his dumper to rest its' material. As a result all dumpers can drive equally-distributed at the building site and all are in a continuous work flow again.

The control center information does not only show the direct environment but also vehicles working far away, which allows a global and not just a local optimization. Consequences of changes in the flow chart are automatically adjusting the time schedule. The impact will be shown directly. The same applies to the interaction of costs, so the site manager is knowledgeable at his best.

But help of the control center is not always required. Using multi-agent technology, every machine is allocated by a software-representative; as a result intelligent support for the machine driver stands by. For example, if no more dumpers are available, so an excavator is not able to dump the material to be removed. It now has got the alternative to retrieve truck data and get to know where the dumpers are. Optional extra work can be accomplished or more trucks requested.

In case of a simple breakdown or changes of ground conditions, the removal-team can arrange themselves and adapt their load to new circumstances - without any connection to the control center. Just if it is impossible to finish the task in the given time-frame or rather crossing a threshold, there will be an escalation to the control center layer. Using vr-visualization techniques an ergonomic and intuitional layout is possible, which professionally supports users with a background in construction management and not computer science. A simple, clear display on the basis of firm data allows to achieve an established decision.

For the control center the requirements analysis brought following results concerning the necessary aspects to be visualized:

terrain and subsoil
  initial DTM (digital terrain model), actual DTM, desired DTM (after end of activities), geometric difference between desired and initial DTM, geometric difference between desired and actual DTM.
soil type of soil, soil conditions, soil classification (reusable, sustainable, dump, ...), obstacles (e.g. rocks).
the structure to be build
  e.g. new road, difference between desired structure and status quo.
other structures
  vegetation, brooks, existing human-made structures (e.g. buildings, installations, tunnels, cables, pipes).
equipment and resources
  machines according to exact position, status, as-

signment, performance characteristics, machine data, installed webcams.
areas area dimensions, type of use, logistics capacity, road condition.
infrastructure on construction site
  fuel station, water and gas, external roads, dumps, storage area, signage.

The interaction with this data must allow making cross section cuts, panning, walking, zooming, and jumping to predefined camera positions. Further on there must be information retrieval from machine objects and area objects. The user should be able to open a communication channel to staff on the construction site and to open video streams from webcam installed on the construction site. Alarm messages (e.g. machine breakdown, machine performance permanently too low) need to be recognized and accepted.

It finally came out that a planning table hardware configuration could be very useful to install. It delivers a 2D layout from bird's perspective and a 3D view from inside the field. This allows having a quick overview in the familiar layout style as well as a intuitive 3D insight at the same time (see figure 1).

III. ON-SITE USE CASE

[9] does notice the benefit of AR for construction sites and recommends the adoption of ergonomic visualization to process-related information, especially for drivers. [10] and [11] also see AR as the adequate technique to optimize processes at construction sites. Workers are able to do their action simpler and more efficient, supported in a comfortable way by visual information, usable in different areas at the building site. For many building vehicles that are combined with state-of-the-art sensors, lots of application possibilities exist. Some examples are given below.

excavator
  visualization of the digging place and geometry or cable or tubes in the earth to present zones of care to the driver (transfer of [12] to construction sites).
roller compacter
  visualization of dynamic densification control; the drivers knows at which places he still has to compact and which he has to avoid to prevent overcompaction.
tower crane
  illustration of the place of delivery of a load, visualization of jib length and rotation limiting and also accessibility of not yet produced structures in the planning phase (see [13]).
general
  using mobile devices by an inspection of a construction site performance data can be embedded context sensitive, working processes visualized and target-performance comparison accomplished.

To realize these use cases, a computing background is necessary. The continuity of 3D-data from the planning to the execution phase has to be available. Media conversion

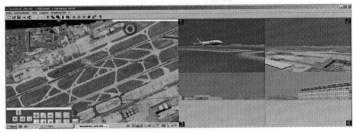

(a) visualization

(b) use case

Fig. 1.   Planning table for construction site monitoring

between these phases has to be deleted. The base may be the 5D Initiative (see [14], [15]).

For the on-site use case the requirements analysis brought following results concerning the necessary aspects to be visualized:

infrastructure
  display of subsurface infrastructure (e.g. tubes, cables).
process support
  for operators of excavator, compacter.
comparison digital model vs. reality
  evaluation of the digital model of existing man-made structures on construction site compared to reality.
navigation support and geo fencing
  for drivers on construction site.

Options 1 and 2 dropped out due to either a non precise data basis or due to already existing solutions. Options 3 and 4 in contrast are feasible and promise a good benefit.

Different AR hardware settings were analyzed. Head mounted displays and projection AR could be interesting in future but seem not to have reached enough practicable status today. Hand held displays on the other hand could be interesting as well as offline AR, which uses digital photographs to be augmented off-site at a desktop PC.

IV. CONCLUSION

The novel construction control center offers a global sight of the construction site. Real-time information is available and allows an optical adaption to current circumstances. Variance comparison in an operating state is the base for efficient project management/control and disposition and adaption of building vehicles to the current situation. In this way cost effectiveness and performance will be enhanced.

Newly developed and adapted VR and AR environments carefully designed for the specific use case, promise good benefits for the control centers and on-site use cases in the future.

REFERENCES

[1] W. Kuehn, *Digitale Fabrik: Fabriksimulation fuer Produktionsplaner.* Hanser Verlag, 2006.
[2] M. Bergmann and C. Motzko, "Ergonomiegestuetzte Multiagentensimulation im Baubetrieb," *BauPortal 05/10,* 2010.
[3] W. Dangelmaier, *Theorie der Produktionsplanung und -steuerung.* Springer-Verlag, 2009.
[4] Federal Ministry of Economics and Technology, "Autonomik - Autonome und simulationsbasierte Systeme fuer den Mittelstand," *Technologieprogramm AUTONOMIK, information brochure,* 2010.
[5] C. Frantzen and U. Rickers, "Raupe an Walze - bitte kommen..." *bd baumaschinendienst 09/2010,* 2010.
[6] J. Whyte, "Business drivers for the use of virtual reality in the construction sector," in *Chalmers University of Technology (editor): Conference on Applied Virtual Reality in Engineering & Construction. Applications of Virtual Reality. Current Initiatives and Future Challenges, Oct. 4.-5., 2001.* Goeteborg/Sweden: Chalmers University of Technology, 2001, pp. 99–105.
[7] G. Pawellek, *Produktionslogistik: Planung- Steuerung- Controlling.* Hanser Verlag, 2007.
[8] K. Kurbel, *Produktionsplanung und-steuerung im Enterprise Resource Planning und Supply Chain Management.* Oldenbourg Wissenschaftsverlag, 2005.
[9] S. Sanladerer, "Edv-gestuetzte Disposition mit Telematikeinsatz und mobiler Datenerfassung in der Baulogistik," *University of Munich, Dissertation,* 2008.
[10] D. H. Shin and P. S. Dunston, "Identification of application areas for augmented reality in industrial construction based on technology suitability," *Automation in Construction, Vol. 17, No. 7,* 2008.
[11] P. S. Dunston and D. H. Shin, "Key areas and issues for augmented reality applications on construction sites," X. Wang and M. A. Schnabel, Eds. Springer Science + Business Media B.V., 2009.
[12] G. W. Roberts, A. Evans, A. H. Dodson, B. Denby, S. Cooper, and R. Hollands, "The use of augmented reality, gps and ins for subsurface data," *FIG XXII International Congress: TS5.13 Integration of Techniques, Washington, DC,* 2002.
[13] A. Hammad, "Distributed augmented reality for visualising collaborative construction tasks," X. Wang and M. A. Schnabel, Eds. Springer Science + Business Media B.V., 2009.
[14] K. Kessoudis, "Umsetzung von BIM im Bauunternehmen," *buildingS-MART Forum 2008 - 12. IAI Industrietag,* 2008.
[15] Zueblin AG, "Position paper of the european construction industry for developing model-based it tools for planning, realising and operating buildings, facilities and infrastructure," *5D Initiative - Initiative of the European construction industry for the development of new IT tools for design, realisation and operation of buildings and infrastructure,* 2009.
[16] X. Wang and M. A. Schnabel, Eds., *Mixed Reality In Architecture, Design, And Construction.* Springer Science + Business Media B.V., 2009.

Some Drivers towards 3D Digital Master-plan Visualisation in the UK

John Counsell,
Cardiff School of Art and Design, University of Wales Institute Cardiff
{JCounsell@uwic.ac.uk}

Abstract

Master-planning in general, more particularly 3D interpretative visualisation of Master-plans, has not been the norm in the UK planning process. However the advent of the new Localism Bill, proceeding through the UK parliament, gives some indication that these will become much more common in English practice. It is argued that English planning departments will need to move towards implementing 3D Planning constraint exploration tools and standards for which they have little experience. In German planning in particular there have been many initiatives that point the way towards standards for masterplan visualisation. SmartCodes in the US indicate a similar approach for regulatory checking.

The Localism Bill is likely also to require substantial inclusive consultation and collaboration with neighbourhood groups. Tools for inclusive collaborative engagement were trialled in the VEPs Interreg IIIB project. This paper predicts that the combination of these or similar approaches will become necessary to cope with the demand.

1. Introduction

Over the past few years the rise of Information Master-planning in general, more particularly 3D interpretative visualisation of Master-plans, has not been the norm in the UK planning process. However the advent of the new Localism Bill, proceeding through the UK parliament, gives some indication that these will become much more common in English practice. The Minister, Greg Clark said that the Government wants "to restore the reputation of planning as a service that works for the public, and that the public feel is on their side. Instead of being principally a means of arbitrating disputes, it should be a positive process, where people come together and agree a vision for the future of the place where they live…. we want to create more options for local communities to exercise influence in the planning process."

Neighbourhood planning will let people come together at a very local level and decide, together, where the new homes, shops and businesses should go, and what they should look like. The local authority will provide technical support so that the proposals that local people draw up are of decent technical quality."[1] It is argued that English planning departments will need to move towards implementing 3D Planning constraint exploration tools and standards for which they have little experience. In German planning in particular there have been many initiatives that point the way towards standards for masterplan visualisation. Many cities have 3D digital models, and there is a move to standardising these models using CityGML. SmartCodes in the US indicate a similar approach for regulatory checking.

This paper discusses in particular the XPlanung E-Government project, and CityGML, as well as SMARTcodes and automated compliance checking. The Localism Bill is likely also to require substantial inclusive consultation and collaboration with neighbourhood groups. Tools for inclusive collaborative engagement in the context of 3D digital visualisation of planning proposals were trialled in the VEPs Interreg IIIB project described below. The paper concludes by predicting that a combination of such standards, smart codes, and collaborative commenting tools will become necessary to cope with the demand.

2. Background and Context

The UK coalition Government introduced the Localism Bill into Parliament on 13 December 2010. Among its ambitions is that it will introduce "reform to make the planning system clearer, more democratic and more effective". [2] "Instead of local people being told what to do, the Government thinks that local communities should have genuine opportunities to influence the future of the places where they live.

The Bill will introduce a new right for communities to draw up a "neighbourhood development plan."..."These neighbourhood development plans could be very simple, or go into considerable detail where people want."[2] The Bill's provisions include that these neighbourhood plans "would be approved if they received 50% of the votes cast in a referendum". [3] Local Authority Planning Departments are likely to be required to facilitate a local pressure group seeking to implement such a plan. To this end a "Neighbourhood Planning Vanguards scheme" is being trialled in advance of the Bill becoming law. [4] The minimum size of such a neighbourhood group was discussed in Parliament as perhaps about 20 persons. A neighbourhood

1550-6037/11 $26.00 © 2011 IEEE
DOI 10.1109/IV.2011.81

itself was thought to be possibly smaller or larger than or in the region of an electoral ward.

Master-planning has been a feature of selected key developments in the UK for many years, at times at City level, at times for a specific key site. For example in 1945 the projected outcomes of the Manchester City plan were illustrated in three dimensions. More recently in Birmingham the Brindley Place development was visualised during the lengthy planning negotiations. However master-planning in general, and 3D interpretation in particular have not been the norm.[5]

In Germany by contrast the statutory plan at local level is the Bebauungsplan (B-Plan), a plan which contains legally binding designations, drawn up to a scale of 1:5,000 or 1:1,000, regarding the proposed development and structure, and consequently it provides the basis for other measures required to allow planning to proceed. [6] In many cases the B-Plan contains sufficiently clear definition of the constraints in all three dimensions that it can in fact be visualised in three dimensions, showing massing and form and potential footprint. Similar detail can be derived in 3D from the French regulatory Plan Local d'Urbanisme (PLU) where these have been completed. [7]

The Virtual Environmental Planning system (VEPs) was an Interreg IIIB NWE funded project, with additional funding from the UK government to the UK partners, which ran from 2005 to mid-2008. [8] The project proposed an alternative approach to planning consultation by allowing people to view and leave comments about planning developments using 3D visualisation software in a web browser, within the context of an existing landscape or cityscape. It was held that comments could be as broad ranging as alternative planning proposals to instigate discussion, illustrate a point, or demonstrate a superior approach.

Some of the Case Study applications in the UK, Germany and France focused on a top-down authoritative delivery of information about the proposal (described later as 1 way access), together with at best the collation of comments to inform the decision makers. However the tools developed did not per se have this limitation and could be used by grass roots pressure groups. (It has been predicted [and some fear that] that the Localism Bill will open the flood gates to such pressure groups!) Thus the project also focused on easing the task of creating and comparing 3D modelling of proposals that do not already exist, within the bounds of an existing context. To this end both data about the proposals and intent were required and the tools then allowed modelling by any user to be created within the designated zone and in the context of the varying height of a 3D Digital Terrain Model (DTM). The consequent possibility of multiple alternatives was handled by version management.

3. Public Visualisation of Planning

Architectural practice has been greatly influenced by computer technologies such as computer-aided design (CAD) software packages. Similarly planning practice has been influenced by Geographic Information Systems (GIS) that have been extensively developed with urban planning as a major area of application. However research now indicates that recent moves towards computer generated visualisation models reflect the acknowledgement that conventional techniques fail to communicate environmental information either effectively or clearly. Pietch argues that with "increasing participation of non-design professionals such as elected council members and members of the public, the demand is there for a better communication medium than conventional 2D drawings". [9]

In the 2006 IV Paper on the VEPS project we held that the importance of visualisation is being recognised as crucial for almost all environmental and planning professionals who need to represent, communicate and evaluate design ideas and planning proposals. [10] According to Sawczuk "the design and planning process revolves around client's needs and therefore the client should be part of the team..." [11] It is thus significant that his findings revealed that while skilled participants appreciate traditional media, such as outline drawings, unskilled participants prefer more photographic representation. Similarly, it has been reported that when lay-people are exposed to architects' drawings the "plans had little meaning as the people could not understand what was represented".[12] Some research suggests that three-dimensional and interactive computer visualisation (based on using 3D VRML in research into community based 'Planning for Real') is one of the "most important developments in visual communication for urban planning and urban design since the development plan". [13][14]

There have been a number of initiatives in the UK to place planning application information in the public domain on line as part of a move to more transparent government. The UK Central Government has now started actively to seek ways to improve both the planning process in general and public participation in that process, since its e-Planning Blueprint, published in August 2004.[15][17] Among the resulting initiatives were the national PARSOL (Planning and Regulatory Services Online) project, a range of 'Pathfinder' projects and the Implementing e-Government (IeG) initiative. The main focus of these initiatives was to develop a set of toolkits, standards and 'demonstrator' projects with the aim of assisting planning authorities to implement e-Planning in forms that citizens will both comprehend and use in their dealings with the councils. New online planning portals aimed to introduce partnership working, bringing together planning, building control and licensing services.

Yet in several of the UK case study applications undertaken during the VEPs project it proved difficult to obtain digital data that shows the proposals, even in plan form. Despite the initiatives referred to above the approach taken most of the time to uploading planning applications to these new portals still remains the digital equivalent of paper, often PDF format, plans and elevations, but no 3D. In many instances the documents clearly state that they are not to scale. In others the scanning process has altered any original scale that the plans might possess, and there is not quality assurance to avoid dimensional shrinkage that is different in different axes. In these cases it takes some time and significant trial and error to rubber sheet stretch the proposed plan to fit as an overlay on the existing. Without this plan data it is difficult to model the proposals or to fully address the visual and massing implications, even with toolsets such as VEPs e-Planner or traditional CAD.

The VEPs project also argued that many people find it difficult to: access and comment on planning proposals during office hours; visualise what a proposed planning development will look like from looking at two-dimensional plans only; understand how planning decisions are made and how their comments are taken into account during the decision-making process. The software developed by VEPs was intended to overcome these difficulties. It allowed users to freely explore and interact with 3D models and make comments directly via an online system, which could be accessed from their 'home' PC over a 'normal' broadband connection at any time. Anyone accessing the web applications would be able to view & share comments online. The technical and 3D visual aspects of VEPs were presented at IVO5, IV06 and IV07 [6][15][16][25][18][19] and the evaluation outcomes at IV09. [20]

4. Resources and Tools

This paper argues that among the likely implications and intent of the Localism Bill is that Master-planning akin at least to the B-Plan or PLU will become much more common in England. Consequently Local Authority Planning Departments will be under pressure to acquire the expertise to facilitate this process effectively, and that in turn will require more digital engagement with the public, along the lines forecast by the VEPs project. It is also suggested that the 3D expression of Master-plans as implemented in some instances in Germany and France are a similar interpretation that is useful for informing discussion.

At a 2006 Workshop [21] entitled 'Preserving Our Past' was held by various UK research councils (AHRC, EPSRC, ESRC, NERC) together with English Heritage. In its 3rd Theme of 'Engagement and Interpretation' the cross-disciplinary experts present confirmed the continuing need for research to: move away from the concept of access (1-way) to participation / inclusion (2-way); and embrace social inclusion, interpretation, storytelling, authenticity, and interactive design.

Interpretative 'visions' of how a master plan might develop in practice are useful for provoking discussion. But this tends (due to the expertise required to use the tools and develop the illustrations) to be a one way communication from planners to the public, the approach critiqued as 'access' above! Planning for Real, and similar approaches to community engagement such as those implemented by the Princes Foundation 'Enquiry by Design' process, require significant facilitation by trained staff physically present with the community group. [22] This is highly resource intensive. In straightened circumstances Planning Departments in the UK are unlikely to have these resources available for many schemes.

The VEPs project explored in various case studies and with its partner Groundwork in particular the facility for neighbourhood groups to digitally explore the range of possible outcomes that could emanate from the legally binding planning process, more along the lines of virtual 'planning for real'. The VEPs tools did restrict exploration to within the development site boundary, but did not encompass other likely constraints such as height, position on plot, materials. In this respect work within the XPlanung E-Government project by Stuttgart Technical University [23][26] provides a useful indicator as to how an exploratory 3D planning constraint tool might work. For such tools to work comprehensively there need to be standards for the underlying description of the planning constraints.

The XPlanung approach offers promise, although it does not perhaps go as far in terms of materials and colour constraints as is promised to neighbourhood groups in the Localism Bill. In addition the tools need to work within the constraints of the existing context, including existing buildings, that is not part of the proposed area for change, and cannot therefore be modified. In this respect the German CityGML initiative [24] appears to point the way to a promising standard. However these standards do not in themselves include a facility for digital commentary by those participating. This perhaps is the other significant contribution of the VEPs project, the prototype Comment Mark-Up Language (COML) standard.

So the question remains as to where this leaves those who wish to comment on the emerging master plan for an area or a specific proposal, and perhaps suggest modifications or alternatives. The VEPs e-Planner tools were developed partly in response to this. These tools offered the ability to set a boundary only within which new buildings can be digitised or existing buildings 'modified' or 'deleted' allows a focus to be kept on a specific redevelopment site or area. Users could interactively sketch in new buildings or download template buildings from libraries. The system allowed those with administrator rights to upload new layers and overlays into the scene over the aerial photo. These could be the draped plan proposal, to serve as a context for discussion and digitising and debating new massing. The evaluation showed that these tools were still not sufficiently intuitive for many users. It remained apparent that any system analogous to CAD is likely to require some conceptual grasp and understanding or skill in the user.

5. XplanGML expressed in 3D

"XPlanGML is being developed for loss-free exchanges among IT systems of zoning plans, regional plans, and land use plans, which supports internet-based availability of plans, and allows evaluation and visualization of the contents of different plans." [23] Coors et al within this project developed an interface that read the maxima and minima of each parameter from the XPlanGML data and expressed it as an interactive 3D visualisation, with sliders to modify the proposed building form and footprint within the set parameters. [26] This approach requires interactive parametric objects. These are commonplace in recent architectural CAD programs, however use within a 3D master plan context may require specific libraries of downloadable or web based parametric objects suited to urban planning, such as dwellings trees and landscape features. Such libraries would also need to be customisable to suit local cultural variations and habitats.

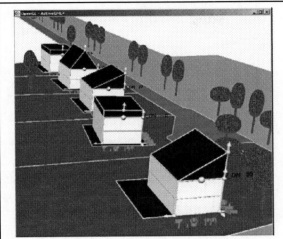

Figure 1 Xplan Constraint Based Model [22]

An alternative approach that is currently perhaps not quite so interactive is the US International Code Council SMARTcodes project, facilitated by British consultants AEC3.[27] They state that "the actual rules against which submissions will be checked can be automatically generated directly from the code mark-up. In fact, what results is a 'requirements model' that is captured in the form of a series of constraints". They state that the vision for the project is that "IFC based submissions from architects, engineers, contractors or others that are regulated should be able to be automatically checked for code compliance using computer systems before submission to building regulatory authorities. Within the terminology of the SMARTcodes development, an IFC file representing the building model is considered to be a

Figure 2 VEPs Frome Bare Earth DTM LOD0

'solutions model'. The intent is to test it against the SMARTcodes derived 'requirements model' and identify any conflicts or areas where the building model does not contain

the information necessary to assess compliance." The approach has been tested in software case studies in the USA.

Due partly to a desire to address climate change performance issues in the UK at the time of applying for planning approval, performance previously measured at a later building regulation approval stage are now increasingly checked at the earlier stage. There is therefore a convergence in the UK between planning and building performance regulation. Thus although a master-plan implementation would perhaps focus more on mass, form, height, position, in principle it could be similarly coded as minimal and maximal regulatory constraints. Some of the performance characteristics checked in the SMARTCodes project via building regulation would in fact need to be checked at this earlier stage. Compliance could be checked in the same manner.

6. CityGML as an emerging standard

CityGML defines 4 levels of detail for City Modelling.[28] The headings underlined on Levels of Detail (LOD) below are summarised from the more detailed description in 'Appraisal of standards for 3D City Models'.[24]

• LoD 0: Regional model (2.5D) contains only the DTM with Texture or Orthophoto. (See Image 1)
• LoD 1: A simple city model where buildings are modeled as blocks with flat roofs.
• LoD 2: A City model with roof shapes and textures for buildings and terrain, and with vegetation.

Freiburg University, one of the partners in the VEPs project have had significant success in automatically generating roof morphology from a LiDAR dataset. There remain limitations due to occlusion by overhanging or masking elements, together with complications of internal courtyards.

• LoD 3: This LoD includes highly differentiated, architectural models of buildings, Vegetation, and street furniture.
• LoD 4: Model of the interior of buildings, which includes constructive elements and openings such as windows and doors.

7. Comment Markup Language (COML)

The international partners in the VEPs project extensively debated how best to support tagging and commentary, leading to formulation of a standardised approach implemented across a range of prototypes termed COML. [29][30] Schill et al described COML as including geospatial comments that included "distinct types of comments: Comments that are attached to an object, comments that are attached to a view, and comments that are attached to the consultation as a whole (this is a special case of a "view comment)."

For example the requirements of the 'object' comment could be met as follows. "When the user navigates the 3D scene and wants to add an "object comment" (i.e. a comment attached to a specific object like a building), a ray tracing algorithm calculates the point of interest (the point where the ray from the camera intersects the surface of the object). This is the point geometry of the comment, the Point of Interest. The "direction of view" (DOV) is stored from the Point of Camera's point of view in yaw, pitch, distance, angle of view (roll is unnecessary..) Also the position of the POC is stored in real world coordinates. Most clients will use their own local coordinate system, so when loading a comment from the WFS, the client has to transform the position of the camera (POC - point of camera) and the PO1 from real world coordinates (e.g. epsg:4326) to the local coordinates of the virtual reality model, which uses a computer graphics coordinate system." [29]

In addition consensus was reached by the project partners that it should more broadly apply not only to tagging objects (CAD-like, so that selecting one or more objects invoked the comments or vice versa), and to comments associated with viewpoints making possible narrative sequences; but also encompass comments in the form of additions to or suppressions of parts of the model itself, enabling interventions and alternative proposals to be 'comments' as well.

8. Conclusion

The VEPs project was predicated on the basis that many people find it difficult to: access and comment on planning proposals during office hours; visualise what a proposed planning development will look like from looking at two-dimensional plans only; understand how planning decisions are made and how their comments are taken into account during the decision-making process.

This paper has thus argued that a highly probable outcome of the new Localism Bill is that much more 'Master-planning' will be required. Devolution means that the Localism Bill will not necessarily have such an immediate effect in Wales, Scotland and Northern Ireland, but it is predicted by the Coalition Government to have a major impact on the nature of planning in England, and thus on the bulk of the UK population.

Due to decreasing resources in all sectors of local government Planning Departments are already limited in resources. Current models of community engagement in planning at this stage are it is argued resource intensive. It has been suggested that the likely solution is that digital tools and 3D Visualisation and interpretation will be part of the solution. The models for those tools are likely to follow the leadership of Xplanung, CityGML, SMARTCodes and COML.

Acknowledgements

The VEPS project work presented in this paper was co-financed through the INTERREG IIIB North West Europe programme.

References

[1] G. Clark speech to Adam Smith Institute 2/2/2011 http://www.communities.gov.uk/speeches/newsroom/planninggrowth accessed 1May 2011

[2] A plain English guide to the Localism Bill available at http://www.communities.gov.uk/documents/localgovernment/pdf/1818597.pdf accessed 1 May 2011.

[3] http://services.parliament.uk/bills/2010-11/localism.html accessed 1 May 2011

[4] www.communities.gov.uk/planningandbuilding/planningsystem/neighbourhoodplanningvanguards/ accessed 1 May 2011.

[5] http://webarchive.nationalarchives.gov.uk/20110118095356/http://www.cabe.org.uk/case-studies/brindleyplace/info accessed 1 May 2011

[6] N. Bates-Brkljac, S. Duhr, J. Counsell "The VEPS project, Planning Information Visualisation", proceedings of IV'05, the 9th International Conference on, the IEEE Computer Society, California, pp 145-150, 2005.

[7] http://cartographie.issy.com/cartes/ accessed 1 May 2011

[8] Virtual Environmental Planning system ,funded Dec 2004 to 2008, by INTERREG IIIB NWE-ENO (a Community Initiative Programme funded by the European Regional Development Fund www.nweurope.org)

[9] Pietch S.M. (2000) Computer visualisation in the design control of urban environments: a literature review, Environment and Planning : Planning and Design, volume 21, pp 521-536

[10] McKechnie, G. E.(1997) Simulation techniques in environmental psychology in Stokols, D.(ed.) Psychological perspectives in environment and behaviour, Plenum Publishing Corp. New York

[11] Sawczuk, B (1992) The management of the design process, in Nicholson, M. (ed) Architectural management, E&FN Spon, London, pp 84-89

[12] Harrlichack M.A, (1993) The effect of rendering technologies on the evaluation of computer generated design simulation, Master thesis, College of Env. Science and Forestry, State University of New York, Syracuse, NY

[13] Smith., A.H. et al. (1998) Visual communication in urban planning and urban design, Paper 2, Online Planning Journal , http://www.casa.ucl.ac.uk

[14] Shiode, N.(2001) 3D Urban models: recent developments in the digital modeling of urban environments in threedimensions, GeoJournal 52, pp 263-269

[15] J. Counsell, S. Smith and N. Bates-Brkljac. "Web 3D Based Dialogue for Public Participation and the VEPs Project". Tenth International Conference on Information Visualisation (IV 06), pp. 343-348, 2006.

[16] Arayici Y, Hamilton A, 2005 'Modelling 3D Scanned Data to Visualise the Built Environment' in proceedings of IV05 9th Intl Conference on Information Visualisation London, edited by Banissi et al, published by the IEEE Computer Soc. Los Alamitos California

[17] ODPM: Office of the Deputy of Prime Minister, E-Planning Programme Blueprint, 2004 Available online http://www.odpm.gov.uk/stellent/groups/odpm_planning/documents/downloadable/odpm-plan_o30468.pdf accessed 8/4/2007

[18] A. Richman, A. Hamilton,. Y. Arayici, J. Counsell, B. Tkhelidze. "Remote Sensing, LiDAR, Automated Data Capture and the VEPS Project" in: proceedings of IV'05, the 9th International Conference on, the IEEE Computer Society, California, pp 151-156. 2005

[19] J. Counsell, S. Smith, A. Richman, "Overcoming some of the issues in Maintaining Large Urban Area 3D Models via a Web Browser" in: proceedings of IV'06, the 10th International Conference, IEEE Computer Society, California, pp 331-336. 2006.

[20] J. Counsell, A. Richman, A. Holding "Evaluation of 3D Visualisation in the Virtual Environmental Planning systems Project" in: proceedings of Viz'09, the 2nd International Conference in Visualisation Barcelona, IEEE Computer Society, California, pp 108 – 113. 2009

[21] The Preserving Our Past workshop was held at the Hilton Birmingham Metropole Hotel, NEC, Birmingham on 29 March 2006. The workshop was funded by AHRC, EPSRC, ESRC, NERC and English Heritage as a need was identified to build effective working relationships across discipline barriers in the historic environment research community.

[22] www.princes-foundation.org/content/princes-foundation-receives-grant-engage-local-communities accessed 1 May 2011

[23] XPlanGML http://www.iai.fzk.de/www-extern/index.php?id=679&L=1 accessed 1 May 2011

[24] Ewald K, Coors, V. 2005 : 'Appraisal of standards for 3D City Models' in proceedings of IV05 9th Intl Conference on Information Visualisation London, edited by Banissi et al, published by the IEEE Computer Soc. Los Alamitos California.

[25] Counsell, J, Smith, S, Richman A 2006: 'Overcoming some of the issues in maintaining large urban area 3D models via a web browser' in proceedings of IV06 10th Intl Conference on Information Visualisation London, edited by Banissi et al, published by the IEEE Computer Soc. Los Alamitos California.

[26] V. Coors, K. Hünlich and G. On "Constraint-based Generation and Visualization of 3D City Models" in Lecture Notes in Geoinformation and Cartography, Part II, pp 365-378, Chapter 23. Springer. 2009.

[27] AEC 3 - Projects International Code Council http://www.aec3.com/5/5_013_ICC.htm accessed 1 May 2011

[28] CityGML http://www.citygml.org/ accessed 1/5/2011

[29] C. Schill, B. Koch, J. Bogdahn, V. Coors , "Public Participation Comment Markup Language and WFS 1.1" in proceedings of the UDMS Annual Conference 2007 published by Taylor and Francis, p. 85 – 9 2007.

[30] P. Limbrick, Manchester Digital Development Agency 'Comment Markup Language' technical report on line at www.veps3d.org/site/files/28-feb-2007/16-32-37/13%20CoML%20Presentation_PL_200607.pdf accessed April 2009.

Trust and Risk in Collaborative Environments

James Harty, Richard Laing,

Copenhagen School of Design & Technology, KEA, Copenhagen, Denmark; Scott Sutherland School of Architecture & Built Environment, RGU, Aberdeen, UK

{jmh@kea.dk, r.laing@rgu.ac.uk}

Abstract

Many commentators and analysts are now saying that we are reaching the tipping moment in the adoption of building information modelling. By this they mean that the uphill struggle for implementation is finally falling into place and that it is beginning to gather its own momentum. This is to be welcomed.

But the construction industry is very fragmented and how implementation can be accomplished is appearing sluggish. Certain drivers like owners and developers are beginning to have an impact while others like architects and planners remain somewhat listless.

How to manage this risk, engender trust and make worthwhile collaboration can be helped with rated 'levels of detail' and calibrated 'metadata'.

Keywords--- Trust, Risk, Collaboration & Metadata.

1. Introduction

Initially it appeared that architects would herald the new process with the American Institute of Architects (AIA) thoroughly scrutinising the possibilities while proposing robust models of deployment [1]. But the response was middling. Architects are reflective types when designing [2] and boxing them into prescribed methods of designing is not easy. A designer cannot and possibly should not use contractual methods of procurement and application during concept phases just as there has to be development in the procedures by the time production information is at hand [3, 4]. There has to be a de facto acceptance of the data at each stage of the procurement and a method of improving or altering data if and when necessary. [5].

Practically speaking this can occur in two places, either within the model using the model phase's properties, or in a viewer programme such as Navisworks, Solibri or Tekla Viewer, which holds all the diverse entities, allowing them to be overlapped, collision tested or time line compared.

The former, permits objects to co-exist in time and space without displacing each other, but allows the data to be shared. This is a paradigm shift. Within the free viewers many formats can be assimilated into the same virtual time and space, allowing many operations to be completed and reported. Integrity and ownership is not challenged but everyone from planner to environmental activist can access the data for whatever reason [6, 7, 8].

2. Risk and its Assessment

Next with BuildingSMART it appeared that code checking would lead the assault [9], but to date it has only been implemented in Singapore with on-going trials in Norway. Tests are showing that government legislation, local planning controls and building regulations can be assessed in circa twenty minutes for specific types of permission and approval [10]. The only variable not included is the political lobbying and bargaining that can go on in mitigation circumstances. But planners appear unprepared to consign large municipal planning departments to the wayside.

As certainty came to the fore the merits of such a process became more apparent. Showcase projects were on time and to budget, which was virtually unheard of under traditional methods of procurement. Client demands therefore should be driving the implementation of modelling [11]. This should be the mainstay of adoption but word has not been as widespread as hoped, with contracts in this current recession occasionally reverting to traditional design-bid-build procedures [12, 13].

Vendors have also been slow to roll out compliant standards like full Industry Foundation Classes (IFC's) reading and writing, to adopt or offer better standardisation to users. This would reduce the implementation threshold that discourages acceptance [14]. The lack of standards also works on another level where not having compliant work necessitates vigilant translation processes with undependable outcomes [15]. It is also appearing that the lack of open standards clashes against a robust plateau where confidence could be nurtured and developed [16].

Sustainability is being pushed globally and by national legislatures meaning it is being implemented across the board in the developed world and this will ensure its uptake. Following the current recession, those firms who can document sustainable solutions will gain a clear advantage over more traditional operators [17]. With energy costs increasing and resources being finite, global warming has forced policy makers to implement targets and table deadlines to save the planet [18].

1550-6037/11 $26.00 © 2011 IEEE
DOI 10.1109/IV.2011.106

Having a virtual model allows performance analysis and climatic testing before deployment. Having quantifiable data from a direct analysis tool gets results [19].

3. Benefits of Adoption

Finally contractors and developers are reaping the rewards of modelling, because they can extract quantities and assign resources. This together with control on site is critical in leveraging the new mindset. The Association of General Contractors (AGC) recommends to its members not to bid on work that is not modelled and recently building contracts are penalising subcontractors who are not stakeholders in the model. This is done by excluding them from the site until those who have collaborated together have completed their work. A late comer too has been contractors and more importantly sub-contractors who now can see that a virtual model allows for better control regarding both collisions and time planning in the procurement process [20].

A follow on from the above is 'augmented reality' where data can be superimposed on situations to give better information in both time and place [21]. As Geographic Information Systems (GIS) improve in their accuracy the virtual model can be superimposed on to the reality, meaning new projects can be assimilated on site before execution and on-going work can be checked for delays and/or improvements.

Augmented reality also means Bots (a form of virtual robot) can mine information, and properly filtered, provide it conveniently to qualified personnel or place it in relevant data holders, all quietly in the background [22]. Within the model this could be product related where doors and windows are found to meet client/designer requirements and demands.

For a designer this can be generic or it can be initial prime cost sums. For the contractor it can compile a list of all products that meet the performance criteria so that when the product needs to be identified a qualified list exists to aid procurement. Outside the model it might be where utilities like water, electricity or gas can be identified below grade or where neighbouring buildings can be included to show context and terrain.

4. Collaboration

Parallel to this, financial viability is finding its way into building information modelling where computed area schedules are being mapped in early versions of the model which can be maintained and updated through the procurement of the project. Linking this to indexed price books ensures better cost control and improves project certainty. Facilities managers are also finding ways to map their requirements into the model which is giving life beyond procurement, making it possible to conduct life cycle analyses [23].

The early massing can also be tested for sustainable comparisons meaning that even at the early stages various options can be tried and tested leading to better informed designs. Similarly to sustainability, Life Cycle Assessment (LCA) is and will have a significant part to play in the procurement of buildings [24]. This is even more so, when the initial planning and post operations and maintenance issues are added. Suffice to say that best practice currently has three models running concurrently, one for the strategic policy makers or investors, one for the designers and procurers and finally one for the operations and maintenance people who pick up the pieces after practical completion. This is not optimal or efficient at all, because repeated input of data increases the likelihood of error, and encourages a knowledge drop at each point of the saw tooth knowledge acquirement diagram.

Better informed designs are possible, by bringing all stakeholders on board sooner in the process than previously. But while this is a bonus, it is also a potentially problematic issue. Not least is how this collaboration is managed. While there is clearly a need for a manager, there is also a need for bells and whistles, with regard to authorship, quality and level of detail, but this could well be dealt with using metadata.

The benefits of the model are not lost on some flexible entrepreneurs, already there are stakeholders who are entering into mutual agreements to work together to reap the rewards of completion on time and to budget. The biggest issue here is risk and how much or how well you trust your partner. Building trust in a business environment and especially in a fragmented market requires new skills and new procedures. Changing work practices from the adversarial to the collaborative, requires major changes in mindsets and even social behaviours [25].

Methods of integrating these diverse methods will improve how we make buildings and how we use them. Facilities Management (FM) has a critical role to play here and methods of facilitating designers without alienating them will consume many resources before an acceptable solution can be found. The driving force will be collaboration and already we are beginning to see consortia being formed where certain players can work purposefully and profitably together to mutual gain [26].

5. Trust

The major obstacle to collaboration is how trust is nurtured, how new blood can enter the mix and finally how information, competences and knowledge is shared for the benefit of the team, the project and society at large. Initially there were calls for sharing or giving away data for free, but with contractual obligations and recovery of costs there is a great reluctance to do so by the players and those who have invested so much into the project, to see others in the supply chain capitalise handsomely on their endeavours [27].

How this can be remedied rests with the client and the appointment of all the stakeholders in the project. First principles say that work effort must be remunerated, and secondly there cannot be subsequent adversarial disputes about the quality and correctness of the data.

The correctness of the data needs to be calibrated and one method is metadata [28].

6. Metadata

Metadata is data about data. It is typically embedded and is only of use to specific persons or things. This might be the size and quality of an image. Its dimensions, colour definition or the date it was created and by whom, the date modified and by whom. From this it can easily be seen that generally the interest is only in the image but occasionally more is needed for whatever reason, and especially when it is to be used by another downstream in the process [29].

This too can be applied to modelling and components of models so that the validity of any piece can be verified [30]. This is the first step in trusting a collaborator whether known or unknown. It is abstracted information and can be seen or hidden until required. It now makes the virtual element accountable for want of a better word, and it marks or informs the end user whether it is complete or just a holding-place for better informed data. This allows the authorship to be tagged and any information about amendments subsequently made or commented upon to be archived within the element.

7. Level of Detail

The process of architectural design is the moving from approximate information to more precise information [31], But digital model elements tend to be exact, whether or not intended. This can give false indications about the precision of the data. Coupled with its intended use, the author might not be qualified to release or stand over the data in its present form. All this needs a framework defining its precision and suitability, and this is called a Model Precision Specification (MPS).

The framework is essential for two reasons; the first *'that phase outcomes, milestones and deliverables be defined succinctly'* so that team members *'understand the level of detail at which they should be working, and what decisions have (and have not) been finalized'*, and the second; *'the idea of assigning tasks on a best person basis, even when that differs from traditional role allocations'* [32]. This caveat is purely because procurement is a process, and when the process is most vulnerable is when it is most open.

Five levels are defined. The first is *'Conceptual'* where there is little geometric data, typically block models, and only notional ideas about time and cost. There can also be analysis about programme, strategies and performance.

Next is *'Approximate Geometry'* where generic elements are shown, duration and cost estimates are better informed, specific functions and requirements are in place and the conceptual design is finished.

'Precise Geometry' as it suggests is a point where quantities can be extracted, the building can get approvals and permits issued and traditionally it can go to tender.

'Fabrication' is where shop drawings and production happen, where building parts are located, and components and assemblies are known. There is a committed price and specific manufacturing is in place.

Finally there is *'As Built'* which is the actual building with recorded costs and purchase documentation, where the building has been commissioned and performance can be measured.

8. Management (the Technology)

The cultural change required to implement integrated practice delivery is an enormous challenge defining *'true partners and collaborators with a mutual interest in a successful outcome'*. Essentially it alters the way and amount of time consumed in being adversarial and in expecting litigation. Increasingly contracts are explicitly saying that stakeholders will not sue each other, that future legal action is a no-value task and that trust with verification mechanisms will become standard, as in banking. The principle cause of a bank failure is often a loss of trust rather than insolvency, there is very little difference between a failed bank and a healthy one, Smith tells us.

How this impacts technology is principally in the transfer of information and the risk it imposes on the authoring party, who could be held responsible for the quality, completeness and accuracy of the handed over data. If a *'no fault'* policy is in place each stakeholder accepts the data as *'found'* and must validate it, appropriately to their needs. Validation consists of two parts, determining if the data is from a trusted source and confirming the integrity of the information itself. Smith calls this stewardship [33]. Where there are errors or omissions, methods will have to be effected to compensate the corrector or rectifier instead of identifying the responsible party or assigning blame. The blame culture interrupts the process and causes delays. There has to be a hand off of responsible control.

This greater dependence of stakeholders on each other can cause strain within the working relationship if trust is not present or more importantly earned [34, 35]. In order to minimise and in an endeavour to make the process more transparent standards are invariably required. This allows for a form of benchmarking and acts as a quality management control for all those involved. It covers the data richness, life cycle views, roles or disciplines, business process, change management, delivery method, timeliness response, graphical information spatial compatibility, information accuracy, and interoperability support. But it is only a skeleton which can offer the stakeholders an index to measure or check each other out, and to bolster their own pitch by giving them the tools to build their own argument and set out their own stall.

9. Partnering (the Business)

A compendium of principles as an application allows the stakeholders to value themselves, but value is added to projects through people [36]. Therefore the management of relationships becomes very important. The construction industry is accepted as being fragmented, rarely do the same people work together on subsequent jobs and often they do not complete the current job through either disruptions in the work phases themselves or the sheer length of the project which sees personnel either replaced or decanted to other projects.

Also the magnitude of small firms involved and the whole culture of sub contracting out engenders a state of flux and conversely a vested interest in protecting niches and expertise in the market. This is a huge element of risk in the construction industry.

But positive relationships do add value, improving project performance and client satisfaction. They also as mentioned induce less adversarial behaviour from the top down, and offer procurement led measures for proactive behavioural management throughout the enterprise. Relationship contracting is best seen in partnering and supply chain management.

One of the best examples is Terminal Five at Heathrow, completed on time and to budget, which is rare for a building of its size and complexity. T5 nurtured and encouraged such an environment [37]. It was based on the principles specified in the Constructing the Team [38] and Rethinking Construction [39]. Had BAA followed a traditional approach T5 would have ended up opening 2 years late, costing 40% over budget with 6 fatalities; this was not an option for BAA [40].

Conversely Eurotunnel had difficulties in motivating the suppliers once the contract had been awarded. Winch calls this moral hazard [41] where the client is somewhat unsure that the contractor will fully mobilise its capabilities on the client's behalf, rather than in its own interests or for some other client. The preferred option he calls consummate performance instead of more likely perfunctory performance.

The root to this situation can be found in the negotiation of the contract, essentially between banks and contractors. Here two cultures collide, on the one hand; the banks prefer to move the contractor to a fixed price which reduces their risk. On the other the contractor works on the basis that the estimates have to be low, to ensure that the project gets commissioned. *'In banking you bid high and then trim your margin: in contracting you bid low and then get your profits on the variations'* or as another said *'the project price... was put together to convince the governments, it was a variable price , a promoter's price. What it was not was a contract price'.*

10. Enlarging the Scope (Facility Management)

As if this was not enough to muddy the waters; beyond procurement, lies both appropriateness and life cycle assessment, -both of whom impact outcomes. Operational maintenance and on-going developments have an incredible bearing on how things are presented. The lengthening and enlarging of the scope and the focus and merit of the objective, mean that simple decisions

taken in good faith can have a detrimental effect on the success of the project. If we accept that the first 20% of the design decisions impact eighty per cent of the life cycle costs then the bottom line has to be to accept and moderate this situation [42, 43].

The International Facility Management Association (IFMA) defines FM as *'a profession that encompasses multiple disciplines to ensure functionality of the built environment by integrating people, place, process and technology'.* They are seen in a secondary function as supporting the core business.

Out of necessity FM adopts architectural floor plans for viewing the built environment [44]. But with the emergence of GIS scaling moves far beyond individual buildings and site maps. Traditionally it focused on the exterior environment and neither technologies ever crossed. But Enterprise Resource Planning (ERP) does not have such boundaries, and this introduces the holistic view that is now required [45].

GIS has now matured and is called a foundation technology that seamlessly provides *'world-to-the-widget'* scalability. This means that it can both drill down to very small scale (from the larger geographic scale) while also bringing layering of data into the matrix. On the one hand it can tell you how many unoccupied offices are within 500 meters of a parking space, or how many employees will have to travel more than half an hour to get to an office location, to the other extreme of mapping a property by building, floor, room - all the way down to the equipment and its usage in a Building Information Spatial Data Model (BISDM). *'This spatial data is the primary thread that holds together such functions as project, space, maintenance, lease and portfolio management,'* Rich et al tells us.

In his critique of BIM he sees it as being an ever enlarging file system, rather than a relational database, and that it works in a multi-user/concurrent user environment requiring highly specialised skills to implement and use. This might be true but what he fails to appreciate is that the entities created in BIM have the ability to hold property fields and property values. These properties can be blank (no value) and beyond the scope of the design team or they can be imported and read-in when making critical decisions.

These decisions might not be relevant or comprehensible to the design team directly but the Bots, mentioned earlier [46], might see fit to implement the data in the decision making process for someone else in the enterprise to use or act upon. The requirement of appropriate tools and software is being negated currently by the use of model viewers, which function similarly to PDF files, where they can be authored or read-only, depending on the need, meaning they are accessible to all.

Conclusions

Just as in design-and-build or partnering, collaborative consortia will go through a process of pre-qualification but not necessarily or singularly only project driven. It will be for a longer haul and over or through many projects. This pre-qualification will see the various members of the consortium indexing themselves with a view to both internally establishing their own worth and externally finding a compatible niche or setting the rate or level of engagement desired with the other members.

Central to this process will be the expectations of the collaboration and this will be built on faith and hope [47], giving rise to confidence and resulting in trust. The characteristics of trust were derived from the work of Lyons and Mehta (1997) bringing the economic and social analysis of trust to relationship management. There are essentially two elements involved, the first is the self interest part and the second is the socially orientated part which demands certain obligations in a social network of relationships. This introduces reputation and advocacy into the mix and it is prolonged through experience.

Already in the United States the National Building Information Modeling Standard (NBIMS) of America has deployed a compendium of principles called a Capability Maturity Model (CMM) to facilitate this process, but where the National Institute of Building Sciences (NIBS) see problems is how to bring the strategists and the operations and maintenance people on board the grand coalition of consortia. Essentially there

are three pipelines and each has a different model and a different purpose. But they all serve the same client and there is a need now for the client to step up to the plate and knock heads together.

Legislature has also a role to play here and as we have seen with sustainability it can be done. Those authorities with clout, like the major agencies in the States such as the military or the state agencies in Norway who actually commission work and have a portfolio of properties to maintain are beginning to set demands which require a broad response possible only through consortia.

The strategic alliances made through these consortia will see like minds using the same tools to use, reuse and exchange data. There will be an acknowledgement of each stakeholder's worth and expectations for each stakeholder's input. The rewards will be significant and in proportion to each stake. There will also be continuity as the same methods and processes are honed and improved with each project. It will transcend procurement, involving the strategists and developers at start-up, the procurement team through construction and the facility managers through operations until decommissioning and ultimately demolition.

References

[1] FALLON, K.K., 2007. Letter from the chair newsletter of the technology in practice knowledge community. [online] USA: AIA. Available from: http://info.aia.org/nwsltr_tap.cfm?pagename=tap_a_0704_chair [Accessed 4/9/2011 2011]

[2] SCHÖN, D., 1987. Educating the Reflective Practitioner: Toward a New Design for Teaching and Learning in the Professions. Proquest Info & Learning.

[3] COOMBE, M., 2011. Conceptual BIM Building Information Modelling for Concept Design. Denmark: Copenhagen School of Design & Technology.

[4] KOROLUK, K., 2009. BIM sure to bring creative disruption. [online] USA: Daily Commercial News. Available from: http://www.refworks.com/rwbookmark/bookmarklanding.asp [Accessed 4/9/2011 2011]

[5] MILLER, G.H. et al., 2008. On Compensation Considerations for Teams in a Changing Industry. USA: AIA.

[6] HARDIN, B., 2009. BIM and Construction Management

[7] HARDIN, B., 2008. REVIT - for real: It starts... interoperability and singular modeling. [online] Available from: http://bimcompletethought.blogspot.com/2008/11/it-starts.html [Accessed 27/11/2008 2008]

[8] HARTY, J. and LAING, R., 2010. Handbook of Research on Building Information Modeling and Construction Informatics: Concepts and Technologies. In: J. UNDERWOOD and U. ISIKDAG, eds. First ed. Hersey, New York, USA: Information Science Reference (an imprint of IGI Global). pp. 546-560

[9] CONOVER, D., 2008b. Smartcodes part-3. [online] ICC. Available from:

http://media.iccsafe.org/news/misc/smart_codes/smartcodes_part-3.html [Accessed 05/04/2008 2008]

[10] ROOTH, Ø., 2010. Public clients and buildingSMART Key issues in building policy. Keynote address ed. Copenhagen:

[11] FONG, S., 2007. One Island East, Hong Kong Swire Properties. Exhibition ed. Copenhagen:

[12] ERKESSOUSI, N.E., 2010. How Integrated Project Delivery is an Advantage to the Danish Building Industry, and how it can be executed. Unpublished Bachelor of Architectural Technology & Construction Management thesis, Copenhagen School of Design & Technology.

[13] BANDUREVSKAJA, I., 2010. Meaningful Management. Unpublished Bachelor of Architectural Technology & Construction Management thesis, Copenhagen School of Design and Technology.

[14] PAZLAR, T. and TURK, Z., 2008. Interoperability in practice: Geometric data exchange using the IFC standard. Electronic Journal of Information Technology in Construction, 13, pp. 362-380

[15] SMITH, D.K., 2010. BuildingSmart in the USA. University Lecture ed. Copenhagen:

[16] SMYTH, H. and PRYKE, S., 2008. Collaborative Relationships in Construction developing frameworks & networks. London: Wiley Blackwell.

[17] SMITH, D.K., 2011. International Standards. 6 April 2011. Bimbyen.

[18] ANDERSEN, M., 2009. The world reflects on Copenhagen process. [online] The Official Website of Denmark. Available from: http://www.denmark.dk/en/menu/Climate-Energy/COP15-Copenhagen-2009/Selected-COP15-news/The-world-reflects-on-Copenhagen-process.htm [Accessed 9/19/2010 2010]

[19] HARDIN, B., 2009. BIM and Construction Management Proven Tools, Methods and Workflows. Indianapolis, Indiana, USA: Wiley Publishing.

[20] YOUNG, N.W.J. et al., 2009. SmartMarket Report on The Business Value of BIM Getting Building Information Modeling to the Bottom Line. McGraw Hill Construction.

[21] BRAUN, A.K., 2010. Bips konference med internationalt snit | BIMbyen.dk CoSPACES; augmented reality. [online] Nyborg, Denmark: BIM Byen. Available from: http://www.bimbyen.dk/news/bips-konference-med-internationalt-snit [Accessed 9/19/2010 2010]

[22] OBONYO, E., 2010. TOWARDS AGENT-AUGMENTED ONTOLOGIES FOR EDUCATIONAL VDC APPLICATIONS. Journal of Information Technology in Construction, 15, pp. 318

[23] HARTY, J. and LAING, R., 2010. Handbook of Research on Building Information Modeling and Construction Informatics: Concepts and Technologies. In: J. UNDERWOOD and U. ISIKDAG, eds. First ed. Hersey, New York, USA: Information Science Reference (an imprint of IGI Global). pp. 546-560

[24] SØRENSEN, T. , 2010. Focus Group discussion on role of FM in BIM.

[25] SIGURÐSSON, S.A., 2009. BENEFITS OF BUILDING INFORMATION MODELING. Bachelor of architectural Technology and Construction Management ed. Copenhagen:

[26] SMYTH, H. and PRYKE, S., 2006. The Management of Complex Projects a relationship approach.

[27] WILLIAMS, C., 2009. Lawyers scared of computers. [online] The Register. Available from: http://www.theregister.co.uk/2009/12/23/cps_paper/ [Accessed 12/24/2009 2009]

[28] ONUMA, K.G., 2010. Location, Location, Location - BIM, BIM, BIM. 2010, Fall 2010

[29] BEDRICK, J., 2008. Organizing the development of a building information model. [online] AEC Bytes. Available from: http://www.aecbytes.com/feature/2008/MPSforBIM.html [Accessed 26 April 2011]

[30] BARRETT, P., 2008. Revaluing Construction. First ed. UK: Blackwell Publishing Ltd.

[31] CONOVER, D., 2008a. Smartcodes part-2. [online] ICC. Available from: http://media.iccsafe.org/news/misc/smart_codes/smartcodes_part-2.html [Accessed 05/04/2008 2008]

[32] ECKBLAD, S., RUBEL, Z. and BEDRICK, J., 2007. Integrated Project Delivery What, Why and How. 2nd May 2007. AIA.

[33] SMYTH, H. and PRYKE, S., 2006. The Management of Complex Projects a relationship approach.

[34] POTTS, K., 2006. Project management and the changing nature of the quantity surveying profession – Heathrow Terminal 5 case study.

[35] HASTE, N., 2002. Terminal Five Agreement; The Delivery Team Handbook (without PEP). Supply Chain Handbook ed. London:

[36] SMYTH, H. and PRYKE, S., 2008. Collaborative Relationships in Construction

[37] FERROUSSAT, D., 2008. The Terminal 5 Project - Heathrow. UK: BAA Heathrow.

[38] LATHAM, M., 1994. Constructing the Team The Final Report of the Government/Industry Review of Procurement and Contractual Arrangements in the UK Construction Industry. HMSO.

[39] EGAN, J., 1998. Rethinking Construction The report of the Construction Task Force. UK:

[40] POTTS, K., 2006. Project management and the changing nature of the quantity surveying profession – Heathrow Terminal 5 case study.

[41] WINCH, G., 2002. Managing Construction Projects: an information processing approach. Oxford: Blackwell Science.

[42] SMITH, D.K. and TARDIF, M., 2009. Building Information Modeling A Strategic Implementation Guide for Architects, Engineers, Constructors and Real Estate Asset Managers. Hoboken, New Jersey: John Wiley & Sons Inc.

[43] SAPP, D., 2010. Computerized maintenance management systems (CMMS) | whole building design guide. [online] Plexus Scientific. Available from: http://www.wbdg.org/om/cmms.php [Accessed 3/11/2010 2010]

[44] RICH, S. and DAVIS, K.H., 2010. Geographic Information Systems (GIS) for Facility Management. USA: IFMA Foundation.

[45] WIKIPEDIA CONTRIBUTORS, b. Logistics [online] Wikipedia, The Free Encyclopedia. 2010]

[46] OBONYO, E., 2010. TOWARDS AGENT-AUGMENTED ONTOLOGIES FOR EDUCATIONAL VDC APPLICATIONS. Journal of Information Technology in Construction, 15, pp. 318

[47] SMYTH, H. and PRYKE, S., 2006. The Management of Complex Projects a relationship approach.

Investigation & Research of Ancient Book Layout Culture on Chinese Sutras Edition – A Case Study on The "Jiaxing Tripitaka" Formation

Thzeng Chi-Shiung
Graduate School of Design
National Yunlin University of Science & Technology
YUNLIN, TAIWAN, R. O. C.
tsengch@yuntech.edu.tw

Hung I- TZU
Graduate School of Design
National Yunlin University of Science & Technology
YUNLIN, TAIWAN, R. O. C.
moon0621@ms57.hinet.net

Abstract

The case study in this research adopts the interpretation editions of Zibu (Philosophy Section) of Complete Library of the Four Treasures of Knowledge of Volume633, block-print edition of an ancient Buddhism scripture of Sutra Hall of Zhongdian of "Jiaxing Kuramoto" collections of National Library circulating from the regime of Emperor Wanli of Ming Dynasty to early Ching Dynasty. This research was conducted in essays derived from the comparison of documents. The focus is on the investigation of formation from modern design layout editing elements. With researches on Edition Study and related fields as a basis, we've reached quantity statistics in the form of character alignment through actual observation, arrangement and documentation. We intended to come up with a principle of regularity for the formation of the Jiaxing Tripitaka engraved Sutras through the relationship between title of volume and arrangement in the formation.

Below are research result:

1.) scripture title,names of translators, sub-title, the First Line of Article,the second line of article. It has been found this research that: the denomination principle was that the first character of the volume was used as the first character of the volume title and the first character of the first line of fist page of each of 214 scripture contents were used as the initial character of subject titles.

2.) For translator names in 28 books, related names for each writing were presented in one line. Characters of the whole paragraph in 56 books were all aligned to the lower line of the bottom column with a space of one word laid up above. Translator names in 241 books were engraved in front of sub-titles. Most sub-title characters reached the top cell. As for the first and second lines of articles, most of them also reached the top cell.

Keywords-"Jiaxing Tripitaka", Shurangama-temple Sutra, historiography, Buddhism, scripture format, print layout.

I. RESEARCH BACKGROUND

The Sutras is one of the classifications for ancient books. This is because Buddhism ancient books accounted for a major proportion of printed materials found in the early days. Buddhism originated in ancient India and it entered China in somewhere around 2 B.C. After the induction of Buddhism into China, large amount of Buddhism books were translated and this had opened the most prosperous period for Chinese printing. As a result, various versions of books from different dynasties were produced. From the hand-written contexts in the early period to the engraving printing evolved in later stage, a huge amount of character creation and editing were accumulated accordingly.

Among numerous editions of Tripitaka of Buddhist scriptures, the representative Jiaxing Tripitaka, which was engraved by private sector back in the Ming Dynasty, is a Chinese Tripitaka of the largest scale with the richest contents in the history of China. It is also the first thread-affixed ancient book of Tripitaka. The so-called "Tripitaka" is the generic term for Buddhist scriptures. It's a collection of Buddhist books that include scripture, law and theory on Mahayana and Hinayana, which were broadcasted from the China's ancient western region and India to China, as well as writings, chapters and annotations made by Chinese. It is equivalent to a collection of Han Dynasty ancient books. One Tripitaka includes thousands of Buddhist scriptures. Does Tripitaka have its own unique form of presentation? If yes, what form is it? Chinese Buddhist scriptures are an inseparable part of the Edition Philology. Numerous new vocabularies came from the translation of Buddhist scriptures. Meanwhile, Chinese Buddhist scriptures have significant influences over the way books were affixed, the organization and editing of large scale collections of books and Bibliography. Research on these issues will help establish the editing and design of books with Chinese characteristics.

II. PURPOSE OF RESEARCH

From the perspective of character editing and designing, we discussed the composition elements of editing the formation of the ancient Sutras of the "Jiaxing Lengyen Temple Ancient Book Tripitaka," which is a Dikan edition from the Wangli period of the Ming Dynasty to the early stage of the Qing Dynasty. We summarized the general principles for the engraved Sutras of the "Jiaxing Lengyen Temple Ancient Book Tripitaka" and came up with the formation editing and designing features, which will serve as references for the teaching and practicing of design, for ancient Sutras with Chinese traditional characteristics.

1550-6037/11 $26.00 © 2011 IEEE
DOI 10.1109/IV.2011.94

Focusing on the formation editing features of the ancient Sutras of the "Jiaxing Lengyen Temple Ancient Book Tripitaka," which is a Dikan edition from the Wangli period of the Ming Dynasty to the early stage of the Qing Dynasty, this research conducted various related studies and a compilation was processed through the gathering and comparison of statistics. With modern day design application research as a basis, we compared ancient Sutras features with contemporary editing and designing concepts in order to explore the unique presentation of formation editing for the"Jiaxing Lengyen Temple Ancient Book Tripitaka," which is a Dikan edition from the Wangli period of the Ming Dynasty to the early stage of the Qing Dynasty. We hope to find different point of views which will help provide true foundation for the history of editing and designing with Chinese characteristics when building editing standpoints. In the meantime, this research will focus on the formation features of the"Jiaxing Lengyen Temple Ancient Book Tripitaka."

This research conducted investigation on the formation composition elements for ancient engraved Sutras in order to find out formation editing element application phenomenon for ancient engraved Sutras of the"Jiaxing Lengyen Temple Ancient Book Tripitaka," which is a Dikan edition from the Wangli period of the Ming Dynasty to the early stage of the Qing Dynasty. We have also summarized general principles of formation editing composition elements for ancient engraved Sutras of the"Jiaxing Lengyen Temple Ancient Book Tripitaka." Finally, we have come up with the principle of style, which will serve as references for the teaching and practicing of design, for ancient Sutras formation with Chinese traditional culture.

III. RESEARCH METHOD

This research mainly focused on the scripture of the "Jiaxing Lengyen Temple Ancient Book Tripitaka", a 9975-chapter and 2247-volume Dikan edition from the Wangli period of the Ming Dynasty to the early stage of the Qing Dynasty listed in the category of Zi-Bu-Shi-Jia-Lei and collected by the National Central Library. Among them. This was conducted via the investigation and compilation of documents. From the perspective of research, we utilize research results from the study of edition, history of publication, history of printing, study of editing, editing and design, study of historical documents, study of Buddhist historical documents and editions of Buddhist scriptures as a basis. Through the discoveries on categorization statistics, we intended to summarize formation's principle of regularity hidden in the Buddhist scripture of the Jiaxing Tripitaka, which was engraved by private sector during the Ming Dynasty.

The names for the editing and major structures of Chinese ancient books include text, introduction, table of contents, postscript, notes, annotation, frontispiece, ending, appendix, additional collection, end of chapter, sub-title, main title, book mark, words of cloudy engraving, bye wen 、 punctuation marks, juan fa, mo wei, mo ding, formation, seal, Bon Shou and so on. Among these elements,

this research will focus on formation only because of the constraints on the size of this article. The so-called "formation" is actually the writing orders and formation of words. It includes orders for words and sentences. Through the statistics, analysis and understanding of formation, we hope to categorize formation characteristics of the Jiaxing Tripitaka, which was engraved by private sector back in the Ming Dynasty, in order to serve as a reference for modern day editing design.

Scope of this research was mostly based on the "Jiaxing Lengyen Temple Ancient Book Tripitaka" manuscript collected by the Manuscript Office of Special Collection Division of the National Central Library. According to the "National Central Library Documentary Manuscript First Draft," total Sutras manuscripts collected include: (1). Scripture: 452 books; (2). Law: 21 books; (3). Theory: 47 books; (4). Essays from Western Saints: 13 books; (5). Articles from Local Scholars: 100 books. The total volume is 633 books. This research mainly focused on engraved and movable-type printing books. Therefore, the handwritten copies, transcripts or Sutras engraved with dynasty will not be included in the scope of this research.

As for the research method, it was conducted in two ways.One way is through actual observation, documentation, and gathering of statistics under assistance from the National Central Library and consultation from experts on Textual Study. In this way, we hope to obtain quantity statistics on styles and features and use these data for the foundation of our theory. The other way is to use actual academic research results on Textual Study from both domestic and Chinese scholars as classification references during the research. Through this, we hope to come up with representative formation characteristics which will serve as references for the teaching and practicing of editing and design.

IV. INVESTIGATION RESULT

Based the space between the lines, the numbers of the tier of word and changes in combination of paragraphs derived from the number of words and lines of the formation, this research studied scripture title, names of translators, sub-title, the first line of article, the second line of article, combination of the first and the second lines. This research also analyzed the principle of regularity on the layout of the Buddhist scripture of the Jiaxing Tripitaka.

A. Scripture Title

This research observed that the naming of the Scripture Title started from the first word of the first line in the first chapter. All the 633 books in the Scripture Title appeared on the first line of the beginning page in the first chapter. For example, illustration 1 of the Jiaxing Tripitaka indicated that scripture tiles from the Buddhist scriptures all started from the first word of the first line in the beginning chapter. It was the most common scenario that scripture titles started from the first line of the first page in the beginning chapter. 104 books had smaller printing under scripture titles and 92 of them had dual lines of printings in one cell. As for the word of "Won-Yi" on lowest part of the scripture title in illustration 2, it indicated the serial number for the engraving of thousand words. such as illustrations of 3 and 4 which indicated two lines of smaller printings in one same cell under scripture titles.

Figure 1. Mohoyenpao- yen ching Chapter 1

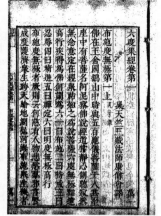

Figure 2. Liu tu chi ching Chapter 8

Figure 3. Shuo wu kou ch'eng ching Chapter 6

Figure 4. Liu tu chi ching Chapter 8

B.   Names of Translators

For Names of Translators on the Jiaxing Tripitaka, the names of translators were edited into one independent line with a space of 1 to 16 words laid up above. The number of empty cells varied depending on the different lengths of titles or respected names. The other way for a layout would be to leave spaces on both the top and the bottom ends. Words bearing translator's name would then be placed in the upper space within a line and this would make the lower space larger than the one up above. However, there were also cases that words for multiple lines all started in the same cell. That is, multiple lines of translators' names would each occupy one column with empty space of several words in both the upper and lower parts. Other lines would then be placed in the middle, or, be laid downwards to the edge of the parameter. dozens of words, which included the name of country, dynasty, temple, respected name, name, title, religious name, virtue name, Buddhist name, place of origin, order of emperor, order of monarch, level of translation and so on were cramped into a single line. There were a few

cases that the names of translator were printed in smaller fonts so that more words could be cramped into the line.

According to the statistics from table 1, sampling was based on the 633 Buddhist scripture of the Jiaxing Tripitaka. For ancient Buddhist scriptures, most of them are Buddhist scriptures translated from Indian Sanskrit into Chinese. Therefore, space originally reserved for the names of authors was filled with the names of translators. Words of "unknown translator(s)" would be engraved in the column of translator's name if translator(s) could not be found. This phenomenon differed a lot from the cases that, in Chinese ancient books, the space for author name would be left blank if there was no author name. The number of samples for translator name actual analysis was 633 books. Statistics and result from the analysis of translator name characteristics in Chinese ancient books from today's editing perspective are as follows:

TABLE 1   Statistics and Characteristics for Translators in the Jiaxing Tripitaka:

Code	Contents	Number of Books
A1	Multiple lines engraved for multiple authors in one book. That is, the related name for every author would each occupy a single line.	5
A2	2 or 3 translator names in one column.	3
A3	The whole paragraph was in line with the lower line of the bottom column with a 2-word space laid up above.	12
A4	The whole paragraph was in line with the lower line of the bottom column with a 3-word space laid up above.	56
B1	No translator name.	46

Code	Contents	Number of Books
B2	Lines started from the same cell.	6
B3	Lines varied in positions of both front and end.	273
B4	Positioned in the middle.	42
C1	Name(s) of author(s) engraved in front of sub-title.	102
C2	Smaller Printing	56
C3	Spanned Across Two Columns	32

(statistics compiled from this research)

The editing ways presented Buddhist scripture of the Jiaxing Tripitaka were closely related to engraving. Take illustration 5 for example. There was a half-cell space up above the "Chao" character right behind the translator's name. The whole of line of translators' names was positioned in the middle with a one-cell space both up and below. This is the only book with a one-cell space between the upper line of parameter and translator's name. In illustration 6, the name for each of the two translators occupied one line and in total the names spanned across two columns. One translator worked on "Chang Han" with the other one on the "Jong Sung." We have to point out here that most ancient Sutras engraved copies came from classical Chinese Sutras translated from Indian Sanskrit. That's the reason why translators' names were engraved in places where authors' names were originally supposed to be such as

566

the example in illustration 7. As for books that translators' names were unavailable, the words of "translator name missing" would be engraved on the author name columns. This is very different from Chinese ancient books where there would be no engraving at all if author's name was unavailable.

For a scripture translated by various translators, their names would be engraved in one single line or multiple lines. That is, the names would be presented in the way that each of the related translators occupied one line. The names for the writers of translation were spread among two columns in line with the lower line of the bottom parameter. In total, there were 45 characters occupying 4 columns such as the case in illustration 8. As for the words used for co-translation, they included "Gon", "Yu", "Ton" and so on.

 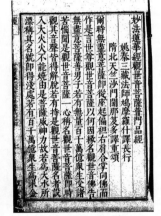

Figure 5 Tafang kuang manshu shihli ching Chapter 1

Figure 6 Miao Fa Lien Hua Jing Gwan Si Yin Pu Sa Men Pin Cing Chapter 1

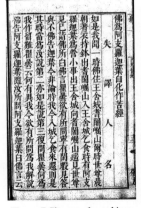 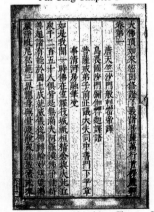

Figure 7 Shuo wu kou ch'eng ching Chapter 6

Figure 8 Liu tu chi ching Chapter 8

C. Sub –Title

One character for the sub-title of the Buddhist scripture of the Jiaxing Tripitaka was that most of these sub-titles would occupy one independent column no matter how many words were involved. Most of them have a 2-word space between them and the top of the cell. most of them had an 0-word of space between themselves and the upper line of the top parameter. Only two of them had a 2-word space as

demonstrated in illustration 9. In illustration 10, there were of praising words before the "Zhang Sin" text. This was done by someone in the later stage for the purpose of showing respect and these words were not essential. Cases of special presentation of sub-titles in the Buddhist scripture of the Jiaxing Tripitaka were presented in illustration 11. There were small printings of note in one single line laid in line with the right side of parameter line under the sub-title. The characters were slim and long. Words of "Chu-Yi-Zi-Yon" were engraved in the space down below with7-word of space in between. There was a 2-word of space between the top parameter line and the first line of the text for the 2nd paragraph. Characters for the sub-title in illustration 12 spanned across two columns.

Figure 9 Pan jo teng lun cing Chapter 15

Figure 10 Ta ch'eng ssu fa ching Chapter 1

Figure 11 Jon A Han Jing Chapter 60

Figure 12 Fo Shui Yi Che Ru Lai Jin Gan

D. The First Line of Article

Most starting points in the Buddhist scripture of the Jiaxing Tripitaka lied in the top of the lines, with cases of 2-word or 1-word of space between the top and the starting points came in the 2nd place. For the remaining, there was no space at all. The most common cases were presented in illustration 13. From the presentations of different printing changes, ink parameter and punctuation marks in the space before the first line in Table 2, we learned that presentations of top cell mainly focused on the Scripture.In illustration

14,there was also a line of praising words for the Buddha, the Dharma and the Sangha. These words stretched all the way to the other page on the same layout. The first line of the scripture actually started from the second line. For illustrations 15, there were honorific names to respect the Buddha, the Dharma and the Sangha before the text with 2-word of space from the top parameter line for 2 paragraphs.These printings would occupy 4 lines, or, be divided into 4 paragraphs with 1-word of space from the top parameter line and 4 printings for each paragraph.

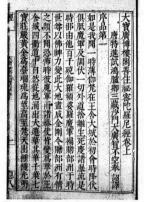

Figure 23 Tapao kuang po lou ko shan chou pi mi t'o lo ni ching Chapter 3

Figure 15 Pu Ti Sin Guan Si Chapter 1

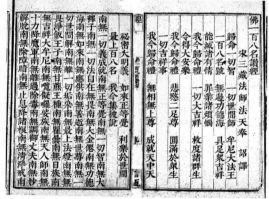

Figure 14 Fo i po pa ming tsan ching Chapter 1

TABLE 2 Statistics on the space in the first lines of the Buddhist scripture of the Jiaxing Tripitaka：

Space in the first lines	0	1	2	3	4	5
Scripture	452	426	26	0	0	0
Law	21	21	0	0	0	0
Theory	47	47	0	0	0	0
Essays from Western Saints	13	11	2	0	0	0
Articles from Local Scholars	100	59	13	28	0	0
Total	633	564	41	28	0	0

Note: X no chapter name   0 the top cell
1-5 space of words in the upper parameter line
(statistics compiled from this research)

E. The Second Line of Article

Most of the layouts for the 2nd line of articles in the Buddhist scripture of the Jiaxing Tripitaka concentrated on scriptures with Articles from Local Scholars trailing behind. This phenomenon is similar to the one for the first line of article. Most texts of the 2nd line came with the presentation of dual-line of small printings and this indicated changes occurred between big and small printings. As per statistics , there were 602 books with the 2nd line of article reached the top cell and there were 72 books with a 2-word of space between the 2nd line and the top parameter line.

V. CONCLUSION

This research focused on the layout editing features of the Jiaxing Tripitaka and research result was obtained after analysis and comparison on these features. We observed that there were various types of starting formation, scripture title, translator name, sub-title and the beginning of text involved. On the locations for scripture titles, they all started from the first word of the first line of chapter in these 633 books and most of them were spelled out in the first line of the page where the first chapter started. Sub-titles for 66 out of the 215 books reached the top cell. There were more changes on the combination of translator names. For a book with multiple translators, the names would be engraved in multiple lines. There were also cases that multiple names were cramped into the same column. There were 7 books that the name for every translator occupied one line each in a single column. There were 56 books that their whole paragraphs stayed in line with the lower parameter line with a 1-word of space up above. There were 466 books that their paragraphs did not go in line with each other in neither ends. There were 216 books that translators' names were engraved in front of sub-titles. Cases of sub-titles reaching the top cell accounted for the most part. As for the layout of the first and 2nd lines of article, most of them reached the top cell. This is a combination that both lines were parallel to each other.

The following special cases were observed: different printings for text and translator name, two translators cramped into one column, translator name spanned across 2 columns or multiple lines, translator name engraved in front of the sub-title, presentation in Sanskrit and 墨釘, dual lines and single line of small printings for notes, extension of word tier and flattening of words, and so on.

According to analysis result from this research, the layout editing features of the Jiaxing Tripitaka ancient Sutras followed the rules of 10 lines for each page and 20 engraved words on each line. As for layout editing characteristics, changes in layout were presented following the compliance of these rules. Statistics were obtained after analysis on the quantity concentration phenomenon. With this, we have come up with simulated most common formation structures for the"Jiaxing Lengyen Temple Ancient Book Tripitaka," which is a Dikan edition from the Wangli period of the Ming

Dynasty to the early stage of the Qing Dynasty. These structures will serve as references. The combined layout was presented in illustration 16 below:

The followings were derived from the research:
（1） Major Title：Starts with the first word of the first line in the beginning chapter.
（2） Sub-Title：Starts with the first word of the first line in the beginning chapter.
（3） Translator Name：For multiple translators on one book, related names for each item would occupy one line. There was a 2-word of space between the paragraph and the lower parameter line and a 3-word of space from the upper parameter line. Not in line with each other in neither ends. Translator name engraved in front of the sub-title.
（4） The first line of article: top cell.
（5） The 2nd line of article: top cell.

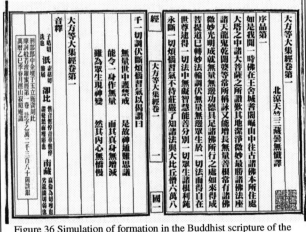

Figure 36 Simulation of formation in the Buddhist scripture of the "Jiaxing Tripitaka."

REFERENCES

[1] See Wang, Wen-Yen, "Observation on Buddhist scripture of Bie She Jing - with the scope of Buddhist scripture table of contents from the Tan Dynasty and previous dynasties," Cheng Da Chinese Newspaper, issue 2, 2004, pp.141-159.

[2] See Shen Jin, "Chinese edition collection" – Thoughts from the "Buddhist scripture," Table of Contents Quarterly, Chapter 38, Issue 4, 2005 pp.23-28.

[3] See Shen Jin, "Buddhist Scripture Jing Yen Lu – Engraved in Sung Dynasty and collected by the U.S., " Documentary, Issue 1, 1989 pp.195-210.

[4] See Wang, Je-Fu, "Book Marks on Ancient Books, " National Palace Museum Monthly, Chapter 7, Issue 8, 1989 pp.76-81.

[5] See Chou, Bo-Kan, "Hsu, Fu-Hua, Ho, Mei-Yi – Study on Han Dynasty Buddhist Scripture," New History, Chapter 16, Issue 2, 2005, pp.185-196.

[6] de Jong, J. W., 1996, Buddha's Word in China, East Asian History, Issue 11, pp.45-58.

[7] Zhu, Tianshu. "Buddhas and bodhisattvas emanators and emanated beings in the Buddhist art of Gandhara, Central Asia, and China." Ph. D. Dissertation, Ohio State University, History of Art, 2007.

[8] Kim, Sunkyung. "Decline of the law, death of the monk Buddhist texts and images in the Anyang Caves of late sixth-century China." Ph. D. Dissertation, Duke University, 2005.

[9] Pan, An-yi. "Li Gonglin's Buddhist beliefs and his Lotus Society Picture an iconographic diagram of the bodhisattva path " Ph. D. Dissertation, University of Kansas, 1997.

Cultural Data Sculpting: Omnispatial Visualization for Cultural Datasets

Dr Sarah Kenderdine,
Dept Chinese, Translation and
Linguistics
City University of Hong Kong
Hong Kong
email: skenderd@cityu.edu.hk

Dr Oscar Kin Chung Au,
School of Creative Media City
University of Hong Kong
email: kincau@cityu.edu.hk,

Prof Jeffrey Shaw
School of Creative Media
City University of Hong Kong
email: j.shaw@cityu.edu.hk

Abstract—This paper presents four research projects currently underway to develop new omnispatial visualization strategies for the collaborative interrogation of large-scale heterogeneous cultural datasets using the worlds' first 360-degree stereoscopic visualization environment (Advanced Visualization and Interaction Environment - AVIE). The AVIE system enables visualization modalities through full body immersion, stereoscopy, spatialized sound and camera-based tracking. The research integrates work by a group of international investigators in virtual environment design, immersive interactivity, information visualization, museology, visual analytics and computational linguistics. The work is being implemented at the newly established research facility, City University's Applied Laboratory for Interactive Visualization and Embodiment – ALIVE) in association with partners Museum Victoria (Melbourne), iCinema Centre, UNSW (Sydney), ZKM Centre for Art and Media (Karlsruhe), UC Berkeley (USA), UC Merced (USA) and and Europeana (in association with Israel Museum of Jerusalem). The applications are intended for museum visitors and for humanities researchers. They are: (1) Data Sculpture Museum; (2) Inside Europeana; (2) Rhizome of the Western Han; (4) Blue Dots AVIE (Tripitaka Koreana).

Keywords-3D; immersive; information visualization; interactive narrative; museum collections; archaeology; corpora

I. INTRODUCTION

Research into new modalities of visualizing data is essential for a world producing and consuming digital data at unprecedented rates [24, 40]. Existing techniques for interaction design in visual analytics rely upon visual metaphors developed more than a decade ago [25] such as dynamic graphs, charts, maps, and plots. Currently, interactive, immersive and collaborative techniques to explore large-scale datasets lack adequate experimental development essential to the construction of knowledge in analytic discourse [46]. Recent visualization research remains largely constrained to 2D small-screen based analysis and advances interactive techniques of "clicking", "dragging" and "rotating" [24, 48]. Furthermore, the number of pixels available to the user remains a critical limiting factor in human cognition of data visualizations [23]. The increasing trend towards research requiring 'unlimited' screen resolution has resulted in the recent growth of gigapixel displays. Visualization systems for large-scale data sets are increasingly focused on effectively representing their many levels of complexity. These include tiled displays such as HIPerSpace at Calit2 [20] and, next generation immersive virtual reality systems, StarCAVE at UC San Diego [9] and Allosphere at UC Santa Barbara [2].

In general, however the opportunities offered by interactive and 3D technologies for enhanced cognitive exploration and interrogation of high dimensional data still need to be realized within the domain of visual analytics for digital humanities [26]. The four projects described in this paper take on these core challenges of visual analytics inside the Advanced Visualization and Interaction Environment (AVIE) [1] [41] (also see Section 2.1) to provide powerful modalities for an omnispatial/omnidirectional (3D, 360-degree) exploration of heterogeneous datasets responding to the need for embodied interaction; knowledge-based interfaces, collaboration, cognition and perception [46]. The projects are developed by the Applied Laboratory for Interactive Visualization and Embodiment (ALiVE), CityU, Hong Kong [3]. A framework for 'enhanced human higher cognition' [16] is being developed that extends familiar perceptual models common in visual analytics to facilitate the flow of human reasoning. Immersion in three-dimensionality representing infinite data space is recognized as a pre-requisite for higher consciousness, autopoesis [39] and promotes non-vertical and lateral thinking [43]. Thus, a combination of algorithmic and human mixed-initiative interaction in an omnispatial environment lies at the core of the collaborative knowledge creation model proposed.

The four projects discussed also leverage the potential inherent in a combination of 'unlimited screen real-estate', ultra-high stereoscopic resolution and 360-degree immersion to resolve problems of data occlusion and distribution of large-scale data analysis in networked sequences revealing patterns, hierarchies and interconnectedness. The omnidirectional interface

1550-6037/11 $26.00 © 2011 IEEE
DOI 10.1109/IV.2011.102

prioritizes 'users in the loop' in an egocentric model [23]. The projects also expose what it means to have embodied spherical (allocentric) relations to the respective datasets. These hybrid approaches to data representation also allow for the development of sonification strategies to help augment the interpretation of the results. The tactility of data is enhanced in 3D and embodied spaces by attaching audio to its abstract visual elements and has been well defined by researchers since Chion and others [7]. Sonification reinforces spatial and temporal relationships between data (e.g. the objects location in 360-degrees/infinite 3D space and its interactive behavior (for example, see [57]). The multi-channel spatial array of AVIE platform offers opportunities for creating a real-time sonic engine designed specifically to enhance cognitive and perceptual interaction, and immersion in 3D. It also can play a significant role in narrative coherence across the network of relationships evidenced in the datasets.

II. EXPERIMENTAL PROJECTS

The four experimental projects included in this paper draw upon disciplines such as multimedia analysis, visual analytics, interaction design, embodied cognition, stereographics and immersive display systems, computer graphics, semantics and intelligent search and, computational linguistics. The research also investigates media histories, recombinatory narrative, new media aesthetics, socialization and presence in situated virtual environments and the potential for new psychogeography of data terrains. Each work takes place in AVIE system. The datasets used in these four works are:

- *Data Sculpture Museum*: over 100,000 multimedia rich heterogeneous museological collections covering arts and sciences derived from the collections of Museum Victoria, Melbourne and ZKM Centre for Art and Media, Karlsruhe, for general public use in a museum contexts.

- *Inside Europeana*: 5000 objects from the Israel Museum of Jerusalem, collaborative searching, live from Internet.

- *Rhizome of the Western Han*: laser-scan archaeological datasets from two tombs and archaeological collections of the Western Han, Xian, China culminating in a metabrowser and interpretive cybermap, for general public use in a museum contexts.

- *Blue Dots AVIE*: Chinese Buddhist Canon, Koryo version (Tripitaka Koreana) in classical Chinese, the largest single corpus with 52 million glyphs carved on 83,000 printing blocks in 13th century Korea. The digitized Canon contains metadata that links to geospatial positions, contextual images of locations referenced in the text, and to the original rubbings of the wooden blocks. Each character has been abstracted to a 'blue dot' to enable rapid search and pattern visualization. For scholarly use and interrogation.

A. Advanced Visualization and Interaction Environment

Applied Visualization Interaction Environment (AVIE) is the UNSW iCinema Research Centre's landmark 360-degree stereoscopic interactive visualization environment spaces. The updated active stereo projection system together with camera tracking s installed at ALiVE. The base configuration is a cylindrical projection screen 4 meters high and 10 meters in diameter, a 12-channel stereoscopic projection system and a 14.2 surround sound audio system. AVIE's immersive mixed reality capability articulates an embodied interactive relationship between the viewers and the projected information spaces. [41]

III. TECHNIQUES FOR CULTURAL DATA ANALYSIS AND VISUALIZATION

The intersection of key disciplines related to the projects in this paper includes multimedia analysis, visual analytics, and text visualization. An excellent review of the state of the art for multimedia analysis and visual analytics appeared in *IEEE Computer Graphics and Applications* [6]. The research projects also responds to core challenges and potentials identified in Visual Analytics [51, 25] and to key emerging technologies for the coming years such as Visual Data Analysis and Gesture Based Computing [22]. Visual Analytics includes the associated fields of Human Perception and Cognition where 3D technologies and immersive and interactive techniques hold significant potential for enhanced research applications [23]. Computational linguistics is providing many of the analytics tools required for the mining of digital texts (e.g. [48, 50]) The first international workshop for intelligent interfaces to text visualization only recently took place in Hong Kong, 2010 [35]. Most previous work in text visualization focused on one of two areas, visualizing repetitions, and visualizing collocations. The former shows how frequently, and where, particular words are repeated, and the latter describes the characteristics of the linguistic "neighborhood" in which these words occur. Word clouds are a popular visualization technique whereby words are shown in font sizes corresponding to their frequencies in the document. It can also show changes in frequencies of words through time [19] and in different organizations [8] and emotions in different geographical locations [17]. The significance of a word also lies in the locations at which it occurs. Tools such as *TextArc* [44], *Blue Dots* [5, 29, 30, 31, 32] and *Arc Diagrams* [56] visualize these "word clusters" but are constrained by the small window size of a desktop monitor. In the digital humanities, words and text strings is the typical mode of representation of mass corpora. However, new modes of lexical visualization such as *Visnomad* [50] are emerging as dynamic visualization tools for comparing one text with another. I another example the *Visualization of the Bible* by Chris Harrison where each of the 63,779 cross references found in the Bible are depicted by a single arc whose color corresponds to the distance between the two chapters [17].

Visual Analytics is closely related to HCI and the development of gesture based computing for data retrieval [22]. Microsoft's *Project Natal* and Pranav Mistry (MIT) *Six Sense* are examples of increasing use of intuitive devices that promote kinesthetic embodied relationships with data.

In the analytics domain of the humanities, *Cultural Analytics* as developed by UC San Diego, offers us visionary trends in large screen immersive system visualization. *Cultural Analytics* researches visualization of large-scale heterogeneous data in immersive system displays. It uses computer-based techniques from quantitative analysis and interactive visualization employed in sciences, to analyze massive multi-modal cultural data sets on gigapixels screens [37]. This project draws upon cutting-edge cyberinfrastructure and visualization research at Calit2 (including the aforementioned new generation CAVE and Powerwall).

IV. RELATED WORKS BY RESEARCHERS

Previous embodied and interactive systems visualization by the researchers collaborating on projects in this paper includes *T_Visionarium I & II* [49]. *T_Visionarium I* was developed by iCinema Centre, UNSW in 2003. It takes place in the Jeffrey Shaw's EVE dome, an inflatable (12 meters by 9 meters). Upon entering the dome, the viewer places a position-tracking device onto their head. The projection system is fixed on a motorized pan tilt apparatus mounted on a tripod. The database used here was recorded during a week-long period from 80 satellite television channels across Europe. Each channel plays simultaneously across the dome however, the user directs or reveals any particular channel at any one time. The matrix of 'feeds' is tagged with different parameters - keywords such as phrases, color, pattern, and ambience. Using a remote control, the viewer selects options from a recombinatory search matrix. On selection of a parameter, the matrix then extracts and distributes all the corresponding broadcast items of that parameter over the entire projection surface of the dome. For example, by selecting the keyword "dialogue" all the broadcast data is reassembled according to this descriptor. The viewer, by moving their head in different directions and thus the position of the projected image, shifts from one channel's embodiment of the selected parameter to the next. In this way, the viewer experiences a revealing synchronicity between all the channels linked by the occurrence of keyword tagged images. All these options become the recombinatory tableau in which the original data is given new and emergent fields of meaning (Figure 1). *T_Visionarium II* in AVIE (produced as part of the ARC Discovery, 'Interactive Narrative as a Form of Recombinatory Search in the Cinematic Transcription of Televisual Information') [49] uses 24 hours of free to air broadcast TV footage from 7 Australian channels as its source material. This footage was analyzed by software for changes of camera angle, and at every change in a particular movie (whether it be a dramatic film or a sitcom), a cut was

made resulting is a database of 24,000 clips of approx. 4 seconds each. Four researchers were employed to hand tag each 4 second clip with somewhat idiosyncratic metadata related to the images shown including emotion; expression; physicality; scene structure; with metatags including speed; gender; colour and so on. The result is 500 simultaneous video streams looping each 4 seconds, and responsive to a users search (Figures 2 & 3).

Figure 1.   *T_Visionarium I* © UNSW iCinema Research Centre.

An antecedent of the *T_Visionarium* projects can be found in Aby Warburg's, *Mnemosyne*, a visual cultural atlas, a means of studying the internal dynamics of imagery at the level of its medium rather than it content, performing image analysis through montage and recombination. *T_Visionarium* can be framed by the concept of aesthetic transcription, that is, the way new meaning can be produced is based on how content moves from one expressive medium to another. The digital allows the transcription of televisual data, decontextualising the original, and reconstituting it within a new artifact. As the archiving abilities of the digital allow data to be changed from its original conception, new narrative relationships are generated between the multitudes of clips and meaningful narrative events emerge because of viewer interaction in a transnarrative experience where gesture is all defining. The segmentation of the video reveals something about the predominance of close-ups, the lack of panoramic shots, the heavy reliance on dialogue in TV footage. These aesthetic features come strikingly to the fore in this hybrid environment. The spatial contiguity gives rise to news ways of seeing, and of reconceptualising in a spatial montage [4]. In *T_Visionarium* the material screen no longer exists. The boundary of the cinematic frame has been violated, hinting at the endless permutations that exist for the user. Nor does the user enter a seamless unified space but is confronted with the spectacle of hundreds of individual streams. Pannini's picture galleries also hint at this infinitely large and diverse collection, marvels to be continued beyond the limits of the picture itself.

Figure 2. *T_Visionarium II in AVIE* © UNSW iCinema Research Centre.

Figure 3. Datasphere, *T_Visionarium II* © UNSW iCinema Research Centre.

V. CURRENT WORK

A. Data Sculpture Museum

This project is being developed as part of the Australian Research Council Linkage Grant (2011 – 2014) "The narrative reformulation of multiple forms of databases using a recombinatory model of cinematic interactivity" (UNSW iCinema Research Centre [60], Museum Victoria [53], ALiVE City University [3], ZKM Centre for Built Media) [59]. The aim of this research is to investigate re-combinatory search, transcriptive narrative and multimodal analytics for heterogeneous datasets through their visualization in a 360° stereoscopic space [10]. Specifically, the exploration of re-combinatory search of cultural data (as a cultural artefact) as an interrogative, manipulable and transformative narrative, responsive to and exposing of multiple narrations that can be arranged and projected momentarily [10] over that which is purposefully embedded

and recorded in the architecture of data archive and metadata and witnessed [11]. This project builds upon the exploration and gains made in the development of *T_Visionarium I and II.*

The datasets used include over 100,000 multimedia rich records (including audio files, video files, high resolution monoscopic and stereoscopic images, panoramic images/movies and, text files) from Museum Victoria and the media art history database of the ZKM [60] that include diverse subject areas from the arts and sciences collections. The data is collated from collection management systems and from web-based and exhibition-based projects. Additional metadata and multimedia analysis will be used to allow for intelligent searching across datasets. Annotation tools will provide users with the ability to make their own pathways through the data terrain, a psycho geography of the museum collections. Gesture-based interaction will allow users to combine searches, using both image-based and text input methods. Search parameters include:

- Explicit (keyword search based on collections data and extra metadata tags added using the project accessible through word clouds)
- Multimedia (e.g. show me all faces like this face; show me all videos on Australia, show me everything pink!)
- Dynamic (e.g. show me the most popular search items; join my search to another co-user; record my search for others to see; add tags).
- Abstract (auto generate a flow of content based on my search input which results from an algorithm running through the data and returning abstract results)

This project seeks understanding in the developments of media aesthetics. Problems of meaningful use of information are related to the way users integrate the outcomes of their navigational process into coherent narrative forms. In contrast to the interactive screen based approaches conventionally used by museums, this study examines the exploratory strategies enacted by users in making sense of large-scale databases when experienced immersively in a manner similar to that experienced in real displays [33]. In particular, evaluation studies will ask: i) How do museum users interact with an immersive 360-degree data browser that enables navigational and editorial choice in the re-composition of multi-layered digital information? ii) Do the outcomes of choices that underpin editorial re-composition of data call upon aesthetic as well as conceptual processes and in what form are they expressed? [10]

Recent advent of large-scale immersive systems can significantly altered the way information can be archived, accessed and sorted. There is significant difference between museum 2D displays that bring pre-recorded static data into the presence of the user, and immersive systems that enable museum visitors to actively explore dynamic data in real-time. This experimental study into the meaningful use of data involves the development of an experimental browser capable of engaging the user by enveloping them in an immersive setting that delivers information in a way that can be sorted, integrated and represented interactively. Specifications of the proposed experimental data browser include:

- immersive 360-degree data browser presenting multi-layered and heterogeneous data;
- re-compositional system enabling the re-organization and authoring of data;
- scalable navigational systems incorporating Internet functions;
- collaborative exploration of data in a shared immersive space by multiple users;
- intelligent interactive system able to analyze and respond to user's transactions.

B. Inside Europeana

Another prototype project under development at ALiVE which forms the basis for upcoming projects is focused on providing a multi-user interactive visualization of the online cultural collection portal Europeana [13]. Around 1500 institutions have contributed to Europeana and their assembled collections of over 14 million records in multiple languages (Figure 4). The recently released future directions report for Europeana [14] emphasized the need to look for innovations in delivery of content. Our prototype uses 5000 objects coming from the collection of Israel Museum of Jerusalem, inside AVIE (Figures 5, 6). We are using the limited five-field metadata that is the basis for Europeana portal for this visualization, and the data itself will come live from the internet repository using the API.

Figure 4. Europeana online portal - current search return © Europeana.

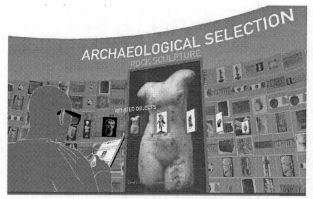

Figure 5. 3D data distribution of IMJ Europeana dataset in AVIE. Image: Tobias Gremmler © ALiVE, CityU

Figure 6. iPad interface and 3D data distribution of IMJ Europeana dataset in AVIE. Image: Tobias Gremmler © ALiVE, CityU

C. Rhizome of the Western Han

This project investigates the integration of high-resolution archaeological laser scan and GIS data inside AVIE. This project represents a process of archaeological recontextualization, bringing together remote sensing data from the two tombs (M27 & The Bamboo Garden) with laser scans of funerary objects, in a spatial context. This prototype builds an interactive narrative based on spatial dynamics, and cultural aesthetics and philosophies embedded in the archaeological remains. The study of Han Dynasties (206 BC 220 A.D.) imperial tombs has always been an important field of Chinese archaeology. However, only a few tombs of the West Han Dynasty have been scientifically surveyed and reconstructed Further, the project investigates a reformulation of narrative based on the application of cyber mapping principles in archaeology [15, 28].

The application engine has been developed in order to be completely dynamic and not dependent on the application data. Every environment, information, models and behaviors are specified and loaded from a configuration file. When the application starts, the user is surrounded by an introductory 3D level. This scenario allows the user to select between various real 3D archaeological reconstruction scenarios through intuitive iconic representations. This Scene Browser is dynamically created according to the total amount of models available for the application (in the Western Han case of study it is possible to select between two different tomb reconstructions and an 3D objects browser). The engine is able to generate two type of scenario with different behaviors and user experiences (Figure 7).

The second type of environment (the Object Viewer) displays multiple virtual reconstructions of objects around the user in a circular manner. The user can browse, magnify and manipulate every object independently. The object browser experience is also improved thanks to the visualization of a facultative cloud of point where the objects are floating in.

Figure 7. *Rhizome of the Western* Han: inhabiting the tombs at 1:1 scale © ALiVE, CityU.

At the nexus of this work is the embodiment of the user in 360-degree 3D space. There is ample discourse to situate the body at the forefront of interpretive archaeology research as a space of phenomenological encounter. Post-processual frameworks for interpretive archaeology advance a phenomenological understanding of the experience of landscape. In his book, Body and Image: Explorations in Landscape Phenomenology, archaeologist Christopher Tilley for example usefully contrasts iconographic approaches to the study of representation with those of kinaesthetic enquiry [52]. Tilley's line of reasoning provides grounding for the research into narrative agency in large-scale, immersive and sensorial, cognitively provocative environments [26]. This project examines a philosophical discussion of what it means to inhabit archaeological data 'at scale' (1:1). It also re-situates the theatre of archaeology in a fully immersive display system, as 'the (re)articulation of fragments of the past as real-time event' [45].

This prototype has led to a new project to build an interactive installation (*Inside Dunhuang*) using laser scan data from the UNESCO World Heritage site of the Dunhuang Caves (Magao Grottoes), Gobi Desert, China.

Figure 8. Visualizations of CAVE 220 inside AVIE. Image: Tobias Gremmler © ALiVE, CityU/Dunhuang Academy

This work is in collaboration with the Dunhuang Academy and the Friends of Dunhuang. Initially data from CAVE 220 will be incorporated into AVIE, together with multiple interactive features (Figure 8). The work uses ultra high resolution imaging data to tell stories about the extraordinary wealth of paintings found in the caves at Dunhuang, a nexus of cultural interchange via the Silk Road between China, India, Persian, Greco-Roman and Central Asia. The site is world renown for its art treasures and has been subject to extensive digital imaging for conservation and preservation.

D. *Blue Dots AVIE*

This project integrates the Chinese Buddhist Canon, Koryo version Tripitaka Koreana into the AVIE system (a project between ALiVE, CityU Hong Kong and UC Berkeley). This version of the Buddhist Cannon is inscribed as UNESCO World Heritage enshrined in Haeinsa, Korea. The 166,000 pages of rubbings from the wooden printing blocks constitute the oldest complete set of the corpus in print format (Figure 9). Divided into 1,514 individual texts the version has a complexity that is challenging since the texts represent translations from Indic languages into Chinese over a 1000-year period (2nd-11th centuries). This is the world's largest single corpus containing over 50 million glyphs and it was digitized and encoded by Prof Lew Lancaster and his team in a project that started in the 70s [29, 30, 31, 32].

1)   *Amount of content*

- 1.504 texts
- 160.465 pages
- 52.000.000 glyphs
- 1 text includes 107 pages (34674 glyphs)
- 1 page includes 324 glyphs arranged in 23 rows and 14 columns

2)   *Contextual information*

- 1.504 colophons with titles, translators, dates, places, and other information.
- 202 people names (translators, authors, compilers)
- 98 monastery names

The *Blue Dots* [5] project undertaken at Berkeley as part of the Electronic Cultural Atlas Initiative (ECAI) which abstracted each glyph from the Canon into a blue dot, and gave metadata to each of these *Blue Dots* allowing vast searches to take place in minutes which would have taken scholars years. In the search function, each blue dot also references an original plate photograph for verification. The shape of these wooden plates gives the blue dot array its form (Figure 10).

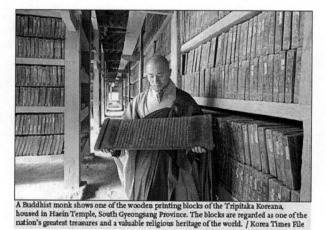

A Buddhist monk shows one of the wooden printing blocks of the Tripitaka Koreana, housed in Haein Temple, South Gyeongsang Province. The blocks are regarded as one of the nation's greatest treasures and a valuable religious heritage of the world. / Korea Times File

Figure 9.   Tripitaka Koreana © Korean Times
(http://www.koreatimes.co.kr/www/news/art/2010/03/293_61805.html)

As a searchable database, it exists in a prototype form on the Internet. Results are displayed in a dimensional array where users can view and navigate within the image. The image uses both the abstracted form of a "dot" as well as color to inform the user of the information being retrieved. Each blue dot represents one glyph of the dataset. Alternate colors indicate position of search results. The use of color, form, and dimension for a fast understanding of the information is essential for large data sets where thousands of occurrences of a target word/phrase may be seen. Analysis across this vast text retrieves visual representations of word strings, clustering of terms, automatic analysis of ring construction, viewing results by

time, creator, and place. The *Blue Dots* method of visualization is a breakthrough for corpora visualization and lies at the basis of the visualization strategies of abstraction undertaken in this project. The application of an omnispatial distribution of this text solves problems of data occlusion, and enhances network analysis techniques to reveal patterns, hierarchies and interconnectedness (Figures 11 & 12). Using a hybrid approach to data representation audification strategies will be incorporated to augment interaction coherence and interpretation. The data browser is designed to function in two modes: the Corpus Analytics mode for text only, and the Cultural Atlas mode that incorporates original texts, contextual images and geospatial data. Search results can be saved and annotated.

The current search functionality ranges from visualizing word distribution and frequency, to other structural patterns such as the chiastic structure and ring compositions. In the *Blue Dots AVIE* version, the text is also visualized as a matrix of simplified graphic elements representing each of the words. This will enable users to identify new linguistic patterns and relationships within the matrix, as well as access the words themselves and related contextual materials. The search queries will be applied across classical Chinese and eventually English, accessed collaboratively by researchers, extracted and saved for later re-analysis.

The data provides an excellent resource for the study of dissemination of documents over geographic and temporal spheres. It includes additional metadata such as present day images of the monasteries where the translation took place, which is will be included in the data array. The project will design new omnidirectional metaphors for interrogation and the graphical representation of complex relationships between these textual datasets to solve the significant challenges of visualizing both abstract forms and close-up readings of this rich data (Figures 13 & 14). In this way, it we hope to set benchmarks in visual analytics, scholarly analysis in the digital humanities and, the interpretation of classical texts.

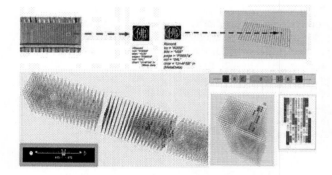

Figure 10. *Blue Dots*: abstraction of characters to dots and pattern arrays
© ECAI, Berkeley.

Figure 11. Prof Lew Lancaster interrogates the Prototype of *Blue Dots AVIE* © ALiVE, CityU.
Image: Howie Lan

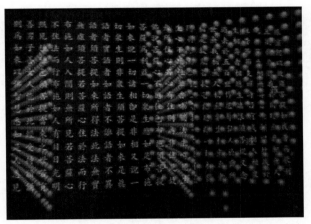

Figure 12. Close up of blue dots & corresponding texts, Prototype of Blue Dots AVIE © ALiVE, CityU. Image: Howie Lan

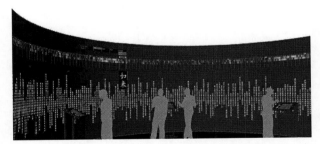

Figure 13. Visualization of *BLUE DOTS AVIE*. Image: Tobias Gremmler © ALiVE, CityU.

Figure 14. Visualization of BLUE DOTS AVIE. Image: Tobias Gremmler © ALiVE, CityU.

VI.   CONCLUSION

The four projects described begin to take on core challenges of visual analytics, multimedia analysis, text analysis and visualization inside AVIE to provide powerful modalities for an omnidirectional exploration of museum collections, archaeological laser scan data and multiple textual datasets. The research is responding to the need for embodied interaction and knowledge-based interfaces that enhance collaboration, cognition and perception and, narrative coherence. For instance, through AVIE, museum users and scholars are investigating the quality of narrative coherence of abstract and multimedia data, through interactive navigation and re-organization of information in 360-degree 3D space. There will be ongoing reporting related to the *Data Sculpture Museum*, which has recently commenced as part of a three-year project, and the *Blue Dots AVIE*. The upcoming work on the interactive installation *Inside Dunhuang* will also be the subject of separate reports.

ACKNOWLEDGEMENTS

This paper contains information appearing in Kenderdine & Hart 2011 [26]. The principle author would like to acknowledge the contribution of colleagues at ALiVE: Prof Jeffrey Shaw, William Wong and Dr Oscar Kin Chung Au and Tobias Gremmler. Also the contributions of members of the Department of Chinese, Translation and Linguistics, CityU, in relation to textual analytics, Prof Jonathan Webster and Dr John Lee. The title 'Cultural Data Sculpting' is inspired Zhao & Vande Moere [54]. *Data Sculpture Museum: The narrative reformulation of multiple forms of databases using a recombinatory model of cinematic interactivity*. Partners: UNSW iCinema Research Centre, Museum Victoria, ZKM, City University of Hong Kong. Researchers: Assoc Prof Dr Dennis Del Favero, Prof Dr. Horace Ip, Mr Tim Hart, Assoc Prof Dr Sarah Kenderdine, Prof Jeffrey Shaw, Prof Dr Peter Wiebel. This project is funded by the Australian Research Council 2011-2014. [10]. *Rhizome of the Western Han*. Partners: ALiVE, City University of Hong Kong, UC Merced,

Researchers: Assoc Prof Dr Sarah Kenderdine, Prof Maurizio Forte, Carlo Camporesi, Prof Jeffrey Shaw. *Blue Dots*: *Tripitaka Koreana*. Partners: ALiVE, City University of Hong Kong, UC Berkeley, Researchers: Assoc Prof Dr Sarah Kenderdine, Prof Lew Lancaster, Howie Lan, Prof Jeffrey Shaw, Tobias Gremmler

REFERENCES

[1] Advanced Visualization and Interaction Environment (AVIE) (http://icinema.unsw.edu.au/projects/infra_avie.html). Consulted Nov 30, 2010.

[2] Allosphere, Available (http://www.allosphere.ucsb.edu/). Consulted Nov 30, 2010.

[3] Applied Laboratory for Interactive Visualization and Embodiment – ALiVE, CityU, Hong Kong (http://www.cityu.edu.hk/alive). Consulted Nov 30, 2010.

[4] Bennett, J. 2008, *T_Visionarium: a Users Guide*, University of New South Wales Press Ltd.

[5] *Blue Dots* (http://ecai.org/textpatternanalysis/). Consulted Nov 30, 2010.

[6] Chinchor, N, Thomas, J., Wong, P. Christel, M. & Ribarsky, W., 2010, Multimedia Analysis + Visual Analytics = Multimedia Analytics, September/October 2010, *IEEE Computer Graphics*, vol. 30 no. 5. pp. 52-60.

[7] Chion, M., *et al.* (1994), *Audio-Vision*, Columbia University Press.

[8] Collins, C. Carpendale, S. & Penn, G. (2009), DocuBurst: Visualizing Document Content using Language Structure. Computer Graphics Forum (*Proceedings of Eurographics/IEEE-VGTC Symposium on Visualization* (EuroVis '09)), 28(3): pp. 1039-1046.

[9] DeFanti, T. A., *et al.* 2009. The StarCAVE, a third-generation CAVE & virtual reality OptIPortal. *Future Generation Computer Systems*, 25(2), 169-178.

[10] Del Favero, D., Ip, H., Hart, T., Kenderdine, S., Shaw, J., Weibel, P. (2009), Australian Research Council Linkage Grant, "Narrative reformulation of museological data: the coherent representation of information by users in interactive systems". PROJECT ID: LP100100466

[11] Deleuze, G. 1989 *Cinema 2: the Time Image*. Translated by Hugh Tomlinson and Robert Galeta, Minnesota: University of Minnesota.

[12] Electronic Cultural Atlas Initiative (www.ecai.org). Consulted Nov 30, 2010.

[13] Europeana (http://www.europeana.eu). Consulted Nov 30, 2010. Consulted March 30, 2011.

[14] Europeana, 2011, *Comité des Sages*, The New Renaissance, Europeana Report (http://ec.europa.eu/information_society/activities/digital_libraries/comite_des_sages/index_en.htm). Consulted April 30, 2011.

[15] Forte, M. (2010), Introduction to Cyberarcheology, in Forte, M (ed) *Cyber Archaeology*, British Archaeological Reports BAR S2177 2010.

[16] Green, T. M., Ribarsky & Fisher (2009), Building and Applying a Human Cognition Model for Visual Analytics. *Information Visualization*, 8(1), pp. 1-13.

[17] Harris, J. & Kamvar, S. (2009), *We feel fine*. New York, NY: Scribner.

[18] Harrison, C. & Romhild, C. (2008), *The Visualization of the Bible*. (http://www.chrisharrison.net/projects/bibleviz/index.html). Consulted Nov 30, 2010.

[19] Havre, S., *et al.* (2000), ThemeRiver: Visualizing Theme Changes over Time. *Proc. IEEE Symposium on Information Visualization*, pp. 115-123.

[20] HIPerSpace CALIT2. 2010. Research Projects: HIPerSpace. (http://vis.ucsd.edu/mediawiki/index.php/Research_Projects:_HIPer Space). Consulted Nov 30, 2010.

[21] Horizon Report, 2010, Four to Five Years: Visual Data Analysis. Available from (http://wp.nmc.org/horizon2010/chapters/visual-data-analysis/). Consulted Nov 30, 2010.

[22] Johnson, L., et al. 2010. The 2010 Horizon Report. Austin, Texas: The New Media Consortium. <http://wp.nmc.org/horizon2010/>.

[23] Kasik, D. J., *et al.* (2009), Data transformations & representations for computation & visualization. *Information Visualization* 8(4), pp. 275–285.

[24] Keim, D. A., et al. (2006), Challenges in Visual Data Analysis. Proc. Information Visualization (IV 2006), pp. 9-16. London: IEEE.

[25] Keim, D. A., *et al.* (2008), Visual Analytics: Definition, Process, & Challenges. *Information Visualization: Human-Centered Issues and Perspectives*, pp. 154-175. Berlin, Heidelberg: Springer-Verlag.

[26] Kenderdine, S. (2010), 'Immersive visualization architectures and situated embodiments of culture and heritage' *Proceedings of IV10 - 14th International Conference on Information Visualisation*, London, July 2010, IEEE, pp. 408-414.

[27] Kenderdine, S. & Hart, T. 2011, Cultural Data Sculpting: Omnispatial Visualization for Large Scale Heterogeneous Datasets, In D. Bearman & J. Trant (Eds.) *Museums and the Web, Selected papers from Museums and the Web 2011*. Philadelphia: Archives & Museum Informatics (http://conference.archimuse.com/mw2011/papers/cultural_data_scu lpting_omni_spatial_visualiza). Consulted April 30, 2011.

[28] Kurillo, G. Forte, M. Bajcsy, R. (2010), Cyber-archaeology and Virtual Collaborative Environments, in Forte, M. (ed) 2010, BAR S2177 2010: *Cyber-Archaeology*.

[29] Lancaster, L. (2007), The First Koryo Printed Version of the Buddhist Canon: Its Place in Contemporary Research. *Nanzen-ji Collection of Buddhist Scriptures and the History of the Tripitake Tradition in East Asia*. Seoul: Tripitaka Koreana Institute.

[30] Lancaster, L. (2008a), Buddhism & the New Technology: An Overview. *Buddhism in the Digital Age: Electronic Cultural Atlas Initiative*. Ho Chi Minh: Vietnam Buddhist U.

[31] Lancaster, L. (2008b), Catalogues in the Electronic Era: CBETA and *The Korean Buddhist Canon: A Descriptive Catalogue*. Taipei: CBETA (electronic publication).

[32] Lancaster, L. (2010), Pattern Recognition & Analysis in the Chinese Buddhist Canon: A Study of "Original Enlightenment". *Pacific World*.

[33] Latour, Bruno. (1988). Visualization and Social Reproduction. In G.Fyfe and J. Law (Eds.). *Picturing Power: Visual Depiction and Social Relations*. London: Routledge, pp. 15-38.

[34] Lee, H., *et al.* 2010. Integrating Interactivity into Visualising Sentiment Analysis of Blogs. *Proc. 1st Int. Workshop on Intelligent Visual Interfaces for Text Analysis*, IUI'10.

[35] Liu, S., et al. (eds.) (2010), *Proc. 1st Int. Workshop on Intelligent Visual Interfaces for Text Analysis*, IUI'10.

[36] Manovich, L. (2008), The Practice of Everyday (Media) Life. In R. Frieling (Ed.), The Art of Participation: 1950 to Now. London: Thames and Hudson.

[37] Manovich, L. (2009), How to Follow Global Digital Cultures, or Cultural Analytics for Beginners. *Deep Search: They Politics of Search beyond Google*. Studienverlag (German version) and Transaction Publishers (English version)

[38] Many Eyes. (http://www.manyeyes.alphaworks.ibm.com). Consulted Nov 30, 2010.

[39] Maturana, H. & Varela, F. (1980), *Autopoiesis and cognition: The realization of the living*, vol. 42, Boston Studies in the Philosophy of Science, Dordrecht: D. Reidel.

[40] McCandless, D. (2010.) The beauty of data visualization [Video file]. (http://www.ted.com/talks/lang/eng/david_mccandless_the_beauty_ of_data_visualization.html). Consulted Nov 30, 2010.

[41] McGinity, M., *et al.* (2007), *AVIE*: A Versatile Multi-User Stereo 360-Degree Interactive VR Theatre. *The 34th Int. Conference on*

Computer Graphics & Interactive Techniques, SIGGRAPH 2007, 5-9 August 2007.

[42] Museum Victoria, example collections include Social History (http://museumvictoria.com.au/collections) & Bio-security (http://www.padil.gov.au). Consulted Nov 30, 2010.

[43] Nechvatal, J. (2009), *Towards an Immersive Intelligence: Essays on the Work of Art in the Age of Computer Technology and Virtual Reality (1993-2006)* Edgewise Press, New York, NY.

[44] Paley, B. 2002. *TextArc* (http://www.textarc.org). Consulted Nov 30, 2010.

[45] Pearson, M. & Shanks, M. (2001) *Theatre/Archaeology*, London: Routledge.

[46] Pike, W. A., *et al.* (2009), The science of interaction. *Information Visualization, 8*(4), pp. 263–274.

[47] Ricoeur, P. (2004), *Memory, History, Forgetting*, University of Chicago Press.

[48] Speer, R., et al. (2010), Visualizing Common Sense Connections with Luminoso. *Proc. 1st Int. Workshop on Intelligent Visual Interfaces for Text Analysis* (IUI'10), pp. 9-12.

[49] T_Visionarium (2003-2008), (http://www.icinema.unsw.edu.au/projects/prj_tvis_II_2.html). Consulted Nov 30, 2010.

[50] Thai, V. & Handschuh, S. 2010. Visual Abstraction and Ordering in Faceted Browsing of Text Collections. *Proc. 1st Int. Workshop on Intelligent Visual Interfaces for Text Analysis* (IUI'10), 41-44.

Revealing the Celt: digitilising Irish placenames in Australia

Dymphna Lonergan and Theodor Wyeld
Flinders University, Australia
{ dymphna.lonergan@flinders.edu.au, twyeld@gmail.com}

Abstract

This paper describes the integration of various kinds of historical and geographic information about place-naming and immigration. Information about space, place names and cultural meanings is usually disparate and fragmented in location and time. The digital resource described in this paper addresses this fragmentation by providing an interface that is both searchable and navigable. As a pilot study, it presents a rich visualisation of Irish migration and heritage within the Australian landscape and history. The resource will be used as a foundation structure for the digital collation of other cultures and migrations, internationally. It has proven to be useful for researchers from a variety of disciplines.

*Keywords--- **GPS, Irish, placenames, Google Maps, history, migration**.*

Introduction

Many places around the world bear a name that is representative of the ethnicity of the immigrants who settled there. However, the stories behind these settlements and their naming are often lost in the time that has passed since their establishment. In an attempt to recapture some of that history the authors of this paper have begun the process of collating the history of migrant named places and the stories behind them. In its first iteration, as a pilot study, the project focuses on Irish placenames in Australia. The database uses Google Maps with markers and pop-up texts to provide a searchable interface which correlates placenames with their geographical locations (see Figure 1). In future iterations it is expected the project will expand to include placenames applied by immigrants of different ethnic origin – in Australia and internationally. This is potentially a huge project. The pilot study is being used to provide the framework for the larger databases to come. While the process itself is not novel what the searchable map provides is a tool for correlating placename with location, context and its history. Preliminary evaluation suggests the tool's ability to provide visual and other cues to correlations between placename history, location and dates has been effective.

In particular, the tool facilitates the ability to visualise the migratory movements across Australia at particular times as migrants followed employment opportunities such as mining and farming – a feature not possible with existing text-only searchable databases. The visualisation of this information opens up possible research trajectories not otherwise apparent with the text-only tools.

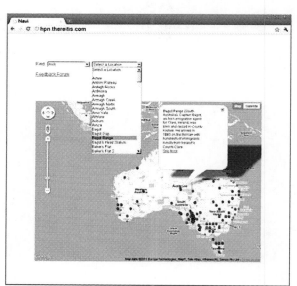

Figure 1. Irish Place Names interface showing pull-down menu of placenames and pop-up text box for Bagot Range in South Australia (see wyeldbydesign.com/irishplacenames).

Overview of Existing Interfaces

There are various existing searchable online place name databases (see, for example: nona.net, familyhistorysa.info, gazetteer.com.uk). They allow the user to search for a place name and its occurrence in multiple global locations. Selecting one will show that location in relation to surrounding areas. For example, the *Nona Net* [1] website at http://nona.net/features/map allows the user to select a placename such as Dublin. This is returned as Dublin in the state of Virginia, US

1550-6037/11 $26.00 © 2011 IEEE
DOI 10.1109/IV.2011.99

(see figure 2). However, the history behind the naming of Dublin in Virginia is not provided.

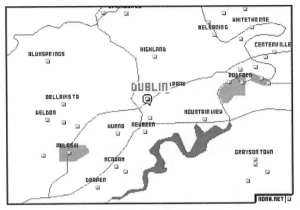

Figure 2. nona.net search for Dublin, Michigan [1]

Similarly, the website, *Genealogy Australia* [2] provides access to interactive maps for the various states and territories at www.familyhistorysa.info/australia.html. However, users can only drill down to a place. Again, no history is provided to the origins of the place name. The *United Kingdom Gazetteer* [3] is another example at http://www.gazetteer.co.uk. A search for a place name reveals some geographical details such as county name and coordinates, but there is no visual reference such as an interactive map and no historical detail is provided for the place name. By contrast, the framework provided by the Irish placenames in Australia project (URL currently http://www.wyeldbydesign.com/irishplacenames/) provides a searchable interface that can reveal location, history, and ethnic connection. For example, in searching for Bagot Range its location in South Australia is revealed as a green dot. Clicking on the dot drills down to a more specific location and at the same time a textbox provides the history behind the name, including the information that the range is named after an Irish-born immigrant, Captain Hervey Bagot.

Overview of the Tool

While Irish placenames and their history in Australia can be found in various books or online databases that include GPS coordinates, to-date there has been no attempt to collate these and apply this information to a visual, searchable, navigable map. Collating the existing information and linking it to its GPS coordinates was the first task necessary to establish a searchable map. Using Google Maps with placename data fed into it, one can now type in or search via a drop down menu Irish placenames in Australia and be taken to that location on the map. By clicking on the marker for that location a summary history is provided in a pop-up text box. Clicking on the link in the pop-up text box takes the user to a more detailed historical overview of the location. Administrative tools allow the database managers to add

and edit placenames which are automatically updated on the map. A feedback button allows for continuous updating of the database through input from the public.

Background

According to the historian Patrick O'Farrell [5, p5] the Irish language in Australia "…died out on reaching these shores." A subsequent PhD study by Lonergan [6] claims this to be untrue. Instead, she claims, the Irish language has played a significant role in the development of Australian English. Several iconic Australian words such as *didgeridoo* and *sheila*, for instance, have an Irish language origin. Indeed, the Irish origins of a word or place can be hidden in its anglicizing. For example, Belfast comes from *Béal Féirste* (a sandy ford mouth); Dublin from *Dubh Linn* (a black pool). The Irish name Inis Fáil, 'island of destiny', a mythological name for Ireland, is an example of the Australian town of *Inisfail* – with its anglicized pronunciation (the original Irish name *Inis Fáil* is pronounced 'Innish fawl').

Our focus here is on placenames originating in the Irish language or with another Irish connection, the relationship between these ethnic placenames and settlement, and to what extent place names reflect the original settlement patterns. The current database of placenames and their historical background has been built up from a number of resources. The South Australian research was drawn from place name books, family histories, and other texts such as Mary Burrows' [7] *Riverton: Heart of the Gilbert Valley*, Reg Butler's [8] *The Quiet Waters By: The Mount Pleasant District 1843-1993*; Rob Charlton's [9] *The History of Kapunda* ; Teresa Donnellan's [10, 11] *Home of the East Wind: Hornsdale* and her *Tarcowie: Place of Washaway Water* ; and Julie Anne Ellis's [12] *Yacka: The Story of a Mid North Town in South Australia*.

Placename books and family histories can be found in public libraries and genealogical centres, and in government electronic databases. For example, all states in Australia have electronic placename databases available to the public such as Western Australia's Landgate website [13]; Victoria's *Vicnames* website [14]; and the South Australian *PlaceNames online* website [15]. These electronic databases provide information such as feature code (whether the place is a town, locality, or geographical feature); postcode; status (official or unofficial); and its GPS coordinates. Some sites provide the history behind the name. For example, the Western Australian Landgate site provides for the place name 'O'Connor':

> *The suburb of O'Connor was named in 1955 in honour of Charles Yelverton O'Connor. O'Connor was Engineer in Chief and General Manager of the Railways of Western Australia in the 1890's, and is remembered for his genius that resulted in construction of the Goldfields Water Supply, Fremantle Harbour and Perth's suburban rail system. He died in 1903.* [13 n.d.]

However, the Irish background of Charles O'Connor is not mentioned. By contrast, the *Australian Dictionary of Biography* online gives the information that Charles O'Connor was Irish-born, but does not mention the place named after him:

> CY (Charles Yelverton) O'Connor was born in 1843 in Meath, Ireland. He was apprenticed to an Irish railway before emigrating to New Zealand and then Australia. [16]

What this study does is to bring together a place name's geographical, spatial, historical, and ethnic information in a single resource. Hence, what this project adds to the collection of Irish-related placenames in Australia is the historical background linked to its location in a visible way that opens up new possibilities for interpretation and further research.

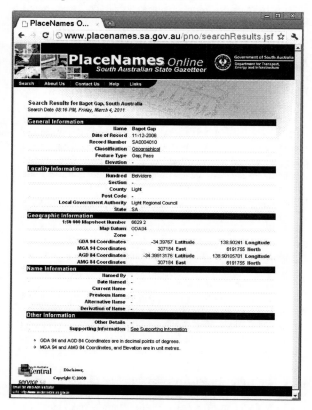

Figure 3. Search for Bagot Gap [15].

South Australian Study

Existing electronic placename websites provided by the various government authorities tend to focus primarily on geographical data. According to Knowles [17] these sites are mainly interested in the application of geographic information systems (GIS) to the study of history. The history behind the place name is of secondary interest evidenced by the absence of so much place name history from sites such as Geoscience Australia. Moreover, when the history part of a place name has been recorded ethnic data such as that provided

in this project is often not included. For example, a search for Bagot Gap on the South Australian Government place name website shows that the Name Information section remains blank. This is because, for this database, the historical information is of secondary importance compared to the geographical information (see figure 3).

The history behind Irish and other ethnic settlement in relation to placenames is a little researched field, not just in Australia, but worldwide. There are place name websites but what is missing from most of them is historical detail that reveals an ethnic connection. With the framework this study sets up this ethnic connection will be accessible electronically by researchers in history, settlement, migration, and cultural studies linked to existing studies of migration patterns and their GPS coordinates in a visual interface.

Motivation for the Study

The idea to use a GPS coordinate system in the collection of Irish-related placenames in Australia was first considered in viewing *The Australian Word Map* website [18]. This site provides a searchable database of Australian colloquial words. It provides information on their ethnic origins. The continent is divided into regions where the words are used. For example, a search for the word 'Gabba' reveals it as being used in the Sydney and Brisbane regions and these regions are highlighted when the curser is passed over the name. The word 'Gabba' is known nationally as the name of the cricket ground in Brisbane. It is a shortening of the suburb the cricket ground is located – Woolloongabba – an Australian Aboriginal term with undefined meaning (see Figure 4).

The Australian Word Map project's word collection initiated the idea to collect and collate Irish and other ethnic place names in Australia and transfer the database to a similar searchable interface. At that time the database contained a number of recurring Irish place names. This raised the question whether this represented signified settlement in Australia from a particular area in Ireland or whether the name was chosen because it was Irish or simply at random. This is significant if further study shows that place names played a significant part in attracting new settlers to an area. For example, many would be familiar with the placename 'Irishtown'. Occurring worldwide wherever there has been Irish settlement, it is often an unofficial placename and one seldom chosen by the Irish themselves. Yet, the placename 'Irishtown' signals Irish settlement, and so it follows that more Irish might choose to settle there [6]. Choosing a place name to attract a particular ethnic group has been part of Australian European settlement. An 1839 address to Irish landlords who may want to downsize their tenantry by paying for the passage of some to South Australia, a suggestion was made that, in Ireland, the society might immediately purchase 100,000 acres of land and call it "New Dublin," "St. Patrick's Land," or any other patronymic, and locate on it such surplus of their tenantry as would cultivate their new country [19].

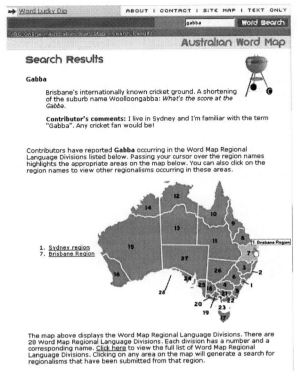

Figure 4. Australian Word Map search for 'Gabba' [18].

Historical Boundaries

As was seen in the example from the South Australian place names data base, a hierarchical focus has been geographical information taking precedent over historical. At the same time, historical studies such as family histories and histories of ethnic groups are not usually digitilised. One reason the historical background to placenames is often missing or truncated in the electronic databases is that the disciplines of geography and history tend to follow different paths of enquiry. Hence, bringing these two disciplines together using the searchable map tool promotes a reconsideration of the research divide of settlement and migration studies.

Preliminary Evaluation

Once the searchable map tool was developed a survey was conducted to ascertain user reception. Respondents included international and national users. Participants were asked to attempt a search with the tool and answer three questions:

1. In what ways is the site helpful in researching Irish-related placenames?
2. What areas are working well?
3. How could the site be better?

Participant feedback tended to focus on the value of the background information (coordinates, location, and stories) and the ability to locate a place on the map which previously may have only been part of a list in a book. The fact that all Irish placenames in Australia could be seen in a single glance of the map highlighted just how many such named places there are in Australia. It also shows clusters of Irish-named places which suggests further investigation is needed to answer questions, such as: what, if any, is the correlation between Irish settlement and Irish-related place names?

Participants commented that the searchable map 'provides researchers with "starting points" and possible sources of further information'. They also commented that when conducting research on an unrelated site they could quickly and easily 'check to see what, if any, "Irish" detail [we had] listed for the area'. More generally, the map was 'useful in clarifying [the general] spread of Irish placenames across the landscape'.

Users were interested in the information and were positive about the tool. They wanted more context, especially to be able to continue to see the place when reading the pop-up text against a background of Australia. Context has been improved since the survey was conducted by making sure the entries have the full name of the state or territory, as international users may not know that SA stands for South Australia, for example. The GPS coordinates need to be checked using a proper digital survey, as some locations listed by the official placenames websites are incorrect.

Conclusion

This paper has demonstrated an existing gap in the inquiry into migration settlement and place names. Place names are found in every habited and uninhabited region in the world. These names are associated with people who lived in these places or travelled to these places. Place names carry our histories but in a fast moving age of new technologies the slow work of the individual researcher in collecting these histories means over time there is a danger of the histories being lost. The database search tool described here can lead to disparate geographical and historical studies of places and peoples that have been traditionally separated being brought together in a new way that creates a new type of research tool that generates new ways to enquire and pose new questions about their connections.

References

[1] *Nona Net*, http://nona.net/features/map
[2] *Genealogy   Australia*   (2001), http://www.familyhistorysa.info/australia.html.
[3] *United   Kingdom   Gazetteer*   (2010), http://www.gazetteer.co.uk
[4] http://www.wyeldbydesign.com/irishplacenames/
[5] O'Farrell, P. 2000, *The Irish in Australia*, University of New South Wales Press, Sydney

[6] Lonergan, D.2006, 'A Place named Irishtown', Placenames Australia, http://www.anps.org.au/documents/Sept_2006.pdf

[7] Burrows, M. 1965, *Riverton: Heart of the Gilbert Valley* , Griffin Press, Adelaide

[8] Butler, R. 1993, *The Quiet Waters By: The Mount Pleasant District 1843-1993,* District Council of Mount Pleasant, Adelaide

[9] Charlton, R. 1971 *The History of Kapunda*, Austaprint, Adelaide

[10] Donnellan, T. 1995, *Home of the East Wind: Hornsdale*, Open Book Publishers, Adelaide

[11] Donnellan, T. 1998, *Tarcowie: Place of Washaway Water*, Tarcowie Book Publishers Association, Adelaide

[12] Ellis, J. A. 1995, *Yacka: The Story of a Mid North Town in South Australia*, Yakka Historical Group, Adelaide

[13] Landgate Western Australia Land and Information Authority 2011, accessed 4 March 2011 <http://www.landgate.wa.gov.au>

[14] *Vicnames*, accessed 4 March 2011 <http://services.land.vic.gov.au/vicnames>

[15] *PlaceNames online* (2000) South Australian Gazetteer, Department for Transport, Energy, and Infrastructure, accessed 4 March 2011, <www.placenames.sa.gov.au> South Australia

[16] *Australian Dictionary of Biography* 2006, accessed 4 March 2011 <http://adbonline.anu.edu.au/adbonline.htm>

[17] Knowles, A. K.2005, 'Emerging Trends in Historical GIS', *Historical Geography* (Vol 33) 2005, pp. 7-13

[18] *The Australian Word Map* (2005) http://www.abc.net.au/wordmap/.

[19] *Dublin University Magazine*, Vol. X1V, September, 1839

The Contemporisation of Dante's Inferno

Jenefer Marquis and Theodor Wyeld
University of New South Wales and Flinders University
{sust.solutions@gmail.com, twyeld@gmail.com}

Abstract

This paper discusses the contemporisation of Dante's Inferno [1]. It attempts to highlight the role of contemporary media in recasting this culturally significant work in a new light. More accessible to the current generation in the form of a computer game, the contemporisation of Dante's Inferno loses none of its impact and meaning. More than this, the game facilitates the search for a virtual soul-space previously reserved only for those vested with the 'given powers' (in Medieval times and prior). In this sense, the contemporisation of the Inferno also brings with it much of the mythological intensity it once sought.

*Keywords--- **Dante, Inferno, Game.***

Dante's Soul Space

The gravity of human vice and virtue in Medieval Christian theology shaped the topography of what Wertheim [2] calls 'soul-space'. Towards the end of the Gothic era, Dante's [3] *La Divina Commedia* (The Divine Comedy) mapped the three kingdoms of Christian metaphysical reality: *Paradisio, Purgatorio,* and *Inferno* (Paradise, Purgatory, and Hell) in a virtual soul space that could be visited on its reading – at least in one's imagination. The gateway or portal to the three realms he maps out is death. Dante's entry to the afterlife is to embark on an allegorical, archetypal quest of the Christian soul's return to God.

But Dante's *Divine Comedy* is much more than this. It is seen by many as the culmination of the medieval worldview developed by the Western church in the thirteenth Century [5]. This worldview did not distinguish between physical reality and the reality of the soul as two distinctive spaces. It reflected a medieval geocentric (heaven above and hell below) cosmology: "Heaven was co-incident with the celestial realm, metaphorically surrounding and enveloping mankind in an ethereal embrace" [2, p53]. Hell was in the bowels of the Earth, and Purgatory was still attached to the Earthly plane but stretched up towards the Heavens, providing a bridge between the two realms.

Dante's travels through each realm was accompanied by his guide Virgil; there is a demon psychopomp that facilitates entry into the afterlife, who takes the soul to the gates of Hell; and, an angel who ferries the soul to the shores of *Purgatorio*. Then, from the peak of Mount Purgatory, the purified soul ascends into the heavenly realms - that equates with the model of the Medieval geocentric universe - eventually returning to the state of beatification and into the presence of God.

Figure 1. La Commedia Illumina Firenze. Domenico di Michelino (1417-1491) [4].

Regular Christians could never expect to enter any of the ten levels of Heaven immediately after death as this sanctified state was reserved for saints and martyrs only. Instead, *Purgatorio* was a transitory space or state on the way to *Paradisio*. *Inferno* was forever. Depending on the severity of the soul's sin, incarceration on one of the series of descending levels in the pit of Hell denoted the torment that the soul would endure for all eternity. The Gate of Hell is the portal to the subterranean realm with Satan situated at the centre of the Earth.

Dante's topography of the Medieval Christian afterlife is thus a vertical axis crossed by approximately fifteen horizontal axes with various portals or gateways into the soul space. The ascension of Dante and Virgil from the darkest depths of *Inferno* to the highest light of the heavenly realms parallels the metaphorical polarities and oppositions of up/down, light/dark, good/evil, heaven/hell, heavy/light – mapping out a multi-

1550-6037/11 $26.00 © 2011 IEEE
DOI 10.1109/IV.2011.97

dimensional space. Until, in the final canticle of *Inferno*, he describes his and Virgil's emergence from the subterranean metaphysical reality:

> *By that hidden way*
> *my guide and I did enter, to return*
> *To the fair world: and heedless of repose*
> *We climbed, he first, I following his steps,*
> *Till on our view the beautiful lights of heaven*
> *Dawn'd through a circular opening in the cave:*
> *Thence issuing we again beheld the stars.* (*Inferno* Canto XXXIV [3, pp126-133])

Dante's Inferno – the Game

The story of Dante's multileveled world of the soul has evolved through many incarnations over time (in literature, sculpture, music, the fine arts, cinema, multimedia and computer games). Of interest here is the interactive computer game: *Dante's Inferno* [6]. In a similar manner to Dante's experiences of a 13th century metaphysical 'walkthrough' of *Inferno*, it is possible to experience its 21st century equivalent in the form of a virtual 'walkthrough' of the nine levels of Dante's Hell. The goal is to pass through successfully in order to save Beatrice (who was abducted by demons) from Lucifer's grasp. Thus, the topographies of 'soul space' [2] can now be navigated not entirely through one's imagination but interactively as a cyberspatial experience. Gamers manoeuvre through virtual space in the form of an avatar version of Dante. Various blogsites are available online to explain the degrees of 'infernal difficulty', cheats and codes for (amongst others) 'auto-absolve', 'holy cross-attacks', and 'divine armour'.

Figure 2. Screenshot from 'Dante's Inferno' Xbox360 game [6].

Despite the shift in technology, Dante's Christian symbolism remains. Its moral and ethical dilemmas endure as gamers descend through the levels to be faced with increasing challenges to physical and spiritual transcendence.

Christian cultural mythology has endured the seven centuries separating Dante's original poem from its contemporary, interactive, version. However, the interactive version of Dante's Inferno bears witness to the development of cultural thought as, unlike the Medieval poem, in the game it is possible for Dante to defeat Death and, taking his scythe into the levels of Hell, use

the power of Death to absolve and redeem hapless souls on his epic quest. Hence, 21st century Dante is no passive observer of metaphysical revelation. He is a warrior of impeccable integrity and moral purpose who navigates the multi-levelled topographies of the underworld, eventually redeeming his lost love from the very grasp of Satan himself. Dante, as an avatar, also has the capability of returning to the physical realm, unlike his original medieval souls who remained eternally damned.

In contemporary society, Dante's *Inferno*, as a game, sees the shift in metaphysical grounding of Christian values that once produced a symbolism by which a culture navigated moral and ethical challenges [7]. In the contemporary version, self-responsibility and self determination enable the transcendence of the avatar, Dante, into demi-godlike status. It denotes the possibility of a return of superhuman powers to the merely mortal human aspirant. These more-than-human sensibilities and powers are the driving forces behind the motivation to play the game.

Feedback from gamers describes Dante's Inferno as being 'heavy', 'full-on' and 'unrelenting'. Nine levels of constant battling with the forces of the underworld, human vice and sin still has an impact. The metaphorical conquest of Death and the vanquishment of Satan, within the virtual *Inferno*, affects the course of contemporary metaphysical reality by changing the rules of the quest and introducing iterations that would have been considered blasphemous to thirteenth century Dante. Yet, the results of these expanded parameters enable the liberation of numerous souls and the avatar from eternal incarceration in hell.

The contemporisation of the affects of Dante's poem have rendered them largely unchanged. The ethnographer of mythologies, Eliade [8, p57], describes the powers of navigation through metaphysical realms and easy communication with the 'gods' during mythological human history reflected a "nostalgia for Paradise... [and] a regression into the mythical time of the Paradise lost". Where once the 'paradisiac myth' in which humankind travelled into the realms of the immortal gods and communicated with them face to face, this was replaced after the mythical 'Fall' – (from religious following or faith) by increasing distance, spatially and temporally – from the metaphysical kingdoms of the overworlds and underworlds and decreasing communications with their more-than-human inhabitants. Today, these more-than-humans are the avatars standing in for gamers in games based on medieval mythology.

Eliade's [8] distinction between the physical reality of everyday living as being 'profane space' and that of the metaphysical realms as 'sacred space', where the normal laws of physics are suspended, also describe two existential modes. This is highlighted in changing perceptions of space and views of reality. In Crary's [9] 'genealogy of attention' and it's role in the modernization of subjectivity, the privileging of visuality and the 'capturing of attention' during the age of empiricism has resulted in a fixation on the physical process and production dominated by the visual. This is no more so pronounced than in the interactive computer game – with its simple keyboard, mouse and screen.

Within the gaming culture, the interface is the threshold, the boundary, in the journey from profane to sacred space. The avatar transcends the profane world through the portal, creating a new and constantly changing territory that is "qualitatively distinct from the surrounding milieu" [8, p12].

Twenty-first century Dante navigates multiple iterations of metaphysical reality, communicating with superhuman beings. As the avatar moves from plane to plane, it becomes apparent that the 'sacred' space is actually a state of numinosity – induced by the revelation of an aspect of divine power [8] – from which he draws forces equivalent to powers that are divine-like or 'wholly other'.

Dissolution

Whether the reality is virtual or physical, the 'irruption of the sacred' [2] in the game *Dante's Inferno* creates a portal of communication between cosmic planes – heaven, earth, and the underworld – creating the possibility of passage from one state to another and the navigation of otherworldly realms, albeit virtual. In this sense, the cyberspace of the game can be thought of as the modern equivalent of the mystic or shamanic experience: a movement outside conventional physical laws where the aspirant or initiate dreams themselves as something greater than mere reality allows and creates

superhuman powers. Hence, 'cyber-imagination', as Wertheim [2] calls it, shapes a virtual world within which the metaphysical forces of sacred space have the capacity to be as powerful as those of a physical reality. This is evident in the contemporisation of *Dante's Inferno* as a computer game and espoused by those who play it and existentially claim those powers.

References

[1]   Alghieri, D. *The Vision: or Hell, Purgatory, and Paradise of Dante Alighieri*. Transl. by The Rev. Henry R. Cary (1844). London: Frederick Warne and Co.

[2]   Wertheim, M. (1999) *The Pearly Gates of Cyberspace: A History of Space From Dante to the Internet*. New York: W.W. Norton & Company.

[3]   Alghieri, D. *The Divine Comedy*. Transl. by C.H. Sisson (1993) Oxford: Oxford University Press

[4]   Web Gallery of Art, online, http://www.wga.hu/frames-e.html?/html/d/domenico/michelin/dante.html,   23-04-2011

[5]   Russell, J.B. (1997) *A History of Heaven: The Singing Silence*. Princeton: Princeton University Press.

[6]   Dante's Inferno Game Official Site, Visceral Games, Electronic Arts, www.dantesinferno.com, 23-04-2011

[7]   Geertz, C. (1973) *The Interpretation of Cultures*. New York : Basic books

[8]   Eliade, M. (1959) *The Sacred and The Profane: The Nature of Religion*. London : Harcourt Brace

[9]   Crary, J. (1999) *Suspensions of Perception: Attention, Spectacle and Modern Culture*. Camb. Mass: MIT Press

Mediation of Knowledge Construction of Historic Sites through Embodied Interaction

Kristine Deray[1], Michael Day[1],
University of Technology, Sydney[1]
kristine.deray@uts.ed.au, Michael.Day-1@uts.edu.au

Abstract

This paper focuses upon the reframing of cultural heritage as bodily experience articulated through narrative based media. The concept of mediation is introduced and explored, as a knowledge intensive process that integrates the production and construction of information interfaces. Such interfaces are negotiated through, and translated by, bodily interaction and bodily reasoning. As such, the mediation process is shaped through the reformulation of kineasthetic, somatic and embodied experiences, that both, customize the interaction process, and shape the resultant outputs that effect construction of knowledge. For enhancement of the mediation process, guidelines for maintaining the integrity of the mediation are discussed. The approach is demonstrated over several projects that explore these concerns through low fidelity prototypes executed in an experimental manner.

Keywords-- - cultural heritage, mediation, embodied interaction, information visualisation, visual analytics.

1. Introduction

The work in this paper references theoretical framework drawn from discourses that seek to go beyond documenting cultural heritage through predominantly textual modes of representation focused on the documentation of specific sites. With the rapid growth in participative media, embodied in Web 2.0, the focus has shifted to creative production as a primary means of interaction that overshadows previous modes of interaction such as basic access with databases, archives and search engines [1]. As such, meaning is increasingly expressed in relation to a person's experience and interaction with various bodies of information that provide scenarios for exploration and knowledge construction. Such a shift, from passive mode of production to interactive and dynamic production, generates a different model to merely providing access to information. For cultural archives, such as Heritage Housing, this provides issues for representational strategies and innovative access to archival narratives within the heritage sites.

The value of interactive narrative for increased understanding of site - specific cultural content through embodied knowledge has advantages. This is in line with the work of phenomenological archaeologists who have supported the construction of knowledge systems that reference embodied sensory experience. Importantly for this work such experience is situated, considering interpretation of the past as subjective and relational. One of the benefits of such a shift in relation to cultural heritage is, the centrality of the body to create and engender dialogue based upon how the body represents the affective, corporeal and sensuous dimensions of human knowledge [2], [3].

Taking an embodied view of heritage housing provides the opportunity to decode what is often a static hierarchical geometry. Rather, the space when considered somatically becomes a space of bodily movement and sensory experience. It has been argued that kinesthetic experience is fundamental to any experience of space grounding that experience in the body itself. Through the years researchers have suggested that: (i) skilled movement is a form of thinking [4], [5]; movement is predominant in all forms of human intellectual activity [6], [7], [8], and, children learn to communicate with gestures before they learn to speak. There is research supporting the use of metaphoric thought and schemata based upon motion as a fundamental basis for the understanding of space by humans. People constantly create relations in their lives between physical reality and abstract concepts. People's conceptual structure of information space often references particular metaphors where the underlying visual schemata are based upon physical motion [9]. These form deep recurrent patterns developing image schemata. This is in line with recent research in neuroscience that indicates a neural basis for embodied understandings, specifically, in relation to mental imagery, association and memory. Some researchers now support the perspective that many, if not all, higher-level cognitive processes are body-based in the sense they make use of (partial) simulations or emulations of sensorimotor processes. Such simulation is through the re-activation of neural circuitry that is also active in bodily perception and action [10]. The argument is given that such constructs embodied in sensorimotor processes will still reference the physical system they are derived from, even when they are linked to abstract concepts.

Similarly, understandings of basic spatial concepts are intrinsically linked to how we orientate and move in the physical world. Such bodily reasoning references the experience of the structure of our bodily movement in space.

In this paper we explore three projects that demonstrate, through low fidelity prototyping, aspects of these issues and experimental solutions. We report on an interdisciplinary lab for university design students. The students were required to respond to the brief of, how can mediation be 'framed' in cultural heritage through narrative driven interactive media. The aim of the project was to design and simulate an act of mediation into a historic house in Sydney, Australia. Two sites were selected, Elizabeth Bay House and Vaucluse House, shown in Figs 1, and 2. Both sites are under the governance of the Historic Housing Trust (HHT) of NSW, who actively contributed to the dialogue in their role as an industry partner. HHT is a statutory authority within Communities NSW. It is "one of the largest state museums in Australia and is entrusted with the care of key historic buildings and sites in New South Wales.[1] HHT was interested in engaging with archival material through bodily experience. A focus of the work was to heighten the experience of the visitors to historic housing through low budget solutions that still engender creative production as a primary means of interaction.

Discussions of embodiment are framed from the perspective of the cultural heritage visitor as end user. The work was completed over one semester and involving little, or no budget, allocation.

2. Mediation

Mediation in this work is considered a knowledge intensive process that shapes how information is retrieved through bodily reasoning. Mediation is considered site specific and is an interaction with a previously existing, or present, space that can reflect traces of habituation, layers of materiality, topologies of structures, landscapes, atmospherics, and / or artifacts. Mediation can be mapped through a system framework, that is, considering the context of the building and its ecology. The building is reconceived as a multi - dimensional information system open to interpretation from different views rather than investigated through static image making. The process of information inquiry and bodily reasoning shape the construction of knowledge as dynamic events contributing to the narrative. Through 'framing' duration is addressed providing a certain set of information, one that is informatic. This set of information is only one in a field of relations within the whole.

It was central to the approach to keep the mediation within the confines of the heritage buildings. This was a deliberate choice given the HHT's desire to increase the visibility and experience of visitors within the physical boundaries of each site.

Figure 1. Elizabeth Bay House

Figure 2. Vaucluse House

Thus, the direction explored centered on augmenting the physical world, rather than utilizing online repositories of knowledge. The act of mediation is perceived as a 'change agent', where the experience is shaped through the visitor's form and modality (or modalities) of interaction. It is this process that provides the individual semantics derived from the context. In this sense the visitor is also being transformed by the experience derived from the mediation.

2.1. Maintaining the integrity of the mediation

Creating well-constructed and consistent visual representations remains a challenge (see Chapter 3 in [11] for some of the issues facing designers of visual representations). Information visualization needs to be embedded in a framework that provides leverage, through reasoning, to the human knowledge construction process. It is important to provide the right tools and methods for this process to unfold. Concentrating on this process, of how humans create and communicate knowledge of cultural heritage through interaction, the following ways of representing the production of cultural heritage were explored.

- *Sense-scapes*. First person methodologies, that is, to learn through the experience of the self, engender concepts that value attention to the senses. Dealing with the body, through its materiality and senses, provides meaning to experience, and generates the notion of archival content being explored through

---

1 http://www.hht.net.au/about

sense making. The embodied subject with its multiple concomitant ways of sensing, feeling, knowing performing and experiencing offer dynamic routes to different perceptions of the human relation to the material. Narrative agency supports personalized kinaesthetic and haptic experience.

- *Soft spaces*. Space is perceived as performative and experiential, capable of constructing and mediating dialogue. Modelling space as performative and mutable supports engagement with space as material presence, represented as flows and interactions. Space is no longer only described through its Euclidian geometry.
- *Social collaboration*. The sharing of experience enables visitors to explore narrative content through implicit and /or explicit collaborative encounters, such as, physical proximity. Semantics can be derived from social and bodily interaction.

Through these ways, singularly or in combination, cultural heritage embedded in the sites becomes visible through the application of broad and accessible digital technologies. The digital circulation of information, images, and interaction constitute a mixed reality space, which can continually produce new and personalized narratives for re-inhabiting, constructing and experiencing cultural heritage. In this process feedback loops become an integral component in the design providing the reflective, in addition to, the productive aspects of design.

2.2. Interaction: the central construct

Interaction is placed as the central unit to the modeling and the visualization of narrative. Interactions communicated through convergent media generate the feedback loops noted above. As interaction is placed as *both* the representation *and* the inquiry, an argument can be advanced that it is necessary to reflect upon the nature of interaction and the relationship between interaction and cognition. Pike et al (2009) [12], state that interaction and inquiry are inextricably connected and that it is through the interactive co-junction of parties at a visual interface that knowledge can be constructed, shared, evaluated and refined. Importantly, such displays need to be embedded in an interactive framework that supports human cognitive reasoning based on bodily knowledge. To accomplish such a task certain tools and methods are required. In the next section we discuss design guidelines for visual interfaces. As in visual analytics the central premise is that human insight is aided by interaction with a visual interface.

3. Design Guidelines for Mediation of Cultural Heritage

In this project mediation implies the process of a middle agent effecting communication in some innate way. The mediator is an instrument dedicated to processing information that creates the environment and the means for the visitors to derive knowledge in a collaborative manner. Convergent media are well suited to communicate narrative structures, as they offer unique abilities to converge time and space. Inherent in such media are design guidelines that inform knowledge construction.

We can group these guidelines into a group, namely (i) ambience. Adapted from [13] the ambient aspects of delivery of information about narrative interactions through the visualization include the following principles:

Information capacity: This design principle relates to the trade-off between the size of the visual elements, the space for the display of the elements, and the time for presenting an information segment.

Attention attracting capacity: This design principle relates to the ability of visualization and respective media to demonstrate critical patterns in interaction, capable of rising person's alert and the need for immediate consideration during the decision - making.

Expressive power: This design principle relates to the semiotics [14] of the discrete elements that constitute the visualisation and their combinations that constitute the mediation, i.e. how the information about cultural heritage is encoded into patterns, pictures, words, or sounds that eventually convey the information about the site. Such visual semiotics relates directly to how condensed is the information delivered by the visualisation. The range is from direct presentations of low - level data for monitoring visitor interaction to metaphorical reasoning based on bodily knowledge and other graphical displays of complex and latent information structures (see [15] for a survey of diverse displays) that convey condensed information.

Aesthetics: This design principle concerns to what extent a graphical display is considered visually pleasing. Extraction and sense making of information about interactions relate to the ability to gain insights, hence, this design principle is closely connected with the principles of information capacity and attracting attention capacity.

Table 1. Design guidelines

Design principle	Semantics
Disjunction	The degre of disjunction between the medaition and physical frame, or fames, within the building requires transitions that people can map to the site.
Reflectivity	This design principle addresses the identification of context. In the process of interaction, parties' contexts help them identify relevant concepts and link them into appropriate structures.
Accessibility	Information design needs to be accessible to visitors for knowledge to be actively constructed. Information design of the visualizations is indexed to enabling efficient interaction and analytics capabilities of respective media.

In addition to these guidelines we consider the

following design principles are of value. In Table 1 these principles are grouped and briefly covered, with corresponding knowledge semantics.

The quest for implementing these principles acts as constraints in the development and deployment of the act of mediation perceived as a change agent. In the next section these principles are utilized to discuss the projects produced in the interdisciplinary lab.

4. Emergent Narratives

We adapt the notion of delayering applied to urban design [16]. McGrath sees this process as a way of deriving archaeological modeling: a method to unpack embeddedness. Fundamentally delayering deconstructs complexity. The process of delayering is a three dimensional operation of uncovering cultural production in the various strata of the sites as materiality constructed over time. Delayering can be unpacked through the application of the method of metaphor that maps a trajectory from the physical site to the mediation. Recent work in the application of metaphors has demonstrated the opening up of metaphor modeling from the linguistic basis commonly associated with metaphor usage. Current work is inclusive of cognitive structures that have a neurological basis upon which such modeling can function. The notion of conceptual metaphor [17] considers a conceptual metaphor is a cognitive mechanism that derives abstract thinking from the way we function in the everyday physical world. Lakoff and Nuhez (2000) argue that such conceptual systems align with our body, that the conceptual system is embodied and shaped by our physical processes, and by 'being in the world.' The process of delayering enables the isolation and analysis of the relationships between the explicit archival content displayed in artifacts, such as furniture, of the building and the embedded content.

Figure 3. Playing with re-scaling through the use of simple technology

This is an act by the designer to change the boundaries of the site by establishing new sets of relationships that modify how cultural production is experienced. In the design process, noted by [16], rescaling techniques can be introduced to create transitions between layers of information. For instance, the project, 'In the Dark,' discussed in this paper, plays with re-scaling. Through the use of simple technology the visitor is 'zoomed in' to selected tableaux that are subsequently augmented via projected content as shown in Fig. 3.

A further way to deconstruct the unified construct of heritage building can be derived from repositioning points of view. This is accomplished through different modes of representation, or, as represented in Fig 4a, 4b, through spatial proximity of information to infer connectivity. Here the image of the visitor is added to those already projected on the floor as they enter into the performative role of being both in the role of within, and without, the creative production. The visitor can then, juxtapose the perspectives of both first and third person.

a

b

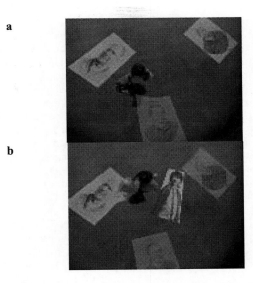

Figure 4. Inscribing performativity into the space

The projects considered all shared the common approach of tracing cultural production through actors embedded in the archival content of the sites. Actors can be traced and cross - referenced in time and space thus providing networks of relations from which to derive semantics.

4.1. The projects

Three projects executed by design students are considered. These are:
- Tears
- Butterflies
- In the dark

All projects looked to narratives constructed around the personas derived from prior human habituation. It was recognized across the projects that the archival content of the historic houses reflected the presence of the inhabitants through various artifacts, such as, clothing, furniture, natural collections, books and so on. Yet the lived experience of significant inhabitants was noticeably absent.

The groups selected different aspects of lived experience of past inhabitants to analyse and explore through convergent technologies. The retrieval of information, in relation to these narratives, was deployed through various perceptual interactions that reflected metaphorically the form, semantics, and function of the specific mediation. Formal approaches utilise the concept of semantic visualisation, defined as a visualisation method, which establishes and preserves the semantic link between form of the visual elements and their function in the context of the visualisation metaphor [18].

4.1.1. In the dark

This project defined itself through an interactive narrative exploring the concept of hierarchy as a navigational and spatial paradigm. The hierarchy referenced the 'upstairs- downstairs' spatial portioning between servant and 'master'. In the simulation visitors were guided through the narrative by cues perceived as measures of light - dark. The semantics for light - dark metaphorically modeled were mapped through illumination of selected objects in the house. These objects referenced set tasks associated with the work of servants. For instance, turning down the bed, winding up the grandfather clock, or lighting the fire in the drawing room.

The overriding theme of hierarchy was mapped through the narrative of life in the house and how this narrative would have effected spatial partitioning between owners and servants. Then, as noted, objects grouped as tableaux, were selected to demonstrate the daily life for servants as a series of tasks. The project was performative and theatrical. Each visitor was provided with a 'kit' that included a LED flashlight. The action of shining this light into darkened rooms, located through radii set by sensors, triggered the projection of a task associated with the object(s). The aim of such layering was to create through the embodied response of participants the somatic and kinesthetic experience of such tasks. Fig. 5 shows a simple example of how this narrative was composed as a series of events.

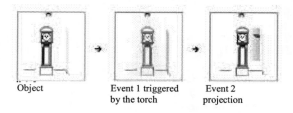

Object   Event 1 triggered   Event 2
             by the torch   projection

Figure 5.   Event driven interaction

Figure 6. Augmentation of the drawing room

Figure 6 provides an example of the augmentation in the drawing room of Elizabeth Bay House.

4.1.2. Tears

The project 'Tears' focused on representations with strong kinaesthetic associations embedded within the materiality. The prime leverage to visual display was the performative basis of the selected artifacts upon which semantics were founded. Embodied in the form of a dress two states of spectatorship were presented. The states referenced the life of a key actor in the heritage house and her struggle to be recognized by the 'society 'of the day. Her ball gown was framed as a conceptual metaphor for acceptance / rejection of her personage in society. As such, the state of turning signifying acceptance (Fig.7) is contrasted to the state of rejection where the gown lies crumpled on the floor, inert and motionless. The relationship between the two performative modes rests on the difference that is expressed in the sense – scapes, as the project deals with the body, materiality and the senses. The basis of bodily knowledge that finds correspondence in these relations provides the framing for the narrative in this project.

Figure 7. Kinaesthetic association constructed through the materiality of performance

4.1.3. Butterfly affect

Butterfly affect defined boundaries to visual display through the chorography of traces utilizing multimodal inputs. Butterfly affect traced the theme of fragility and decay of the production of heritage culture through the motif of the butterfly. This referenced Alexander Macleay's (the person responsible for the building of Elizabeth Bay House) life long obsession with entomology. Mediation of the space was framed through the projection of butterflies. The fragility of this was emphasized by the affect the presence of visitors, communicated through sensors, had on the visual display that reflected a progression from birth, to decay, to death.

Figure 8. Knowledge construction through association

Conclusions

In this paper we have demonstrated, through an initial study, that mediation is a knowledge intensive process that integrates information discovery and embodied interaction. Mediation provides a method that can be positioned to deconstruct the layering of archival content contained in cultural heritage, by reshaping content through analogical reasoning. The potential of mediation, for augmentation of cultural heritage, supports further investigation of the inherent subjective information generation of cultural heritage. Referencing the embodied experience of the present through mediated knowledge can contribute to new strategies of knowledge construction for the visualisation of heritage sites.

Acknowledgements

This research is supported by the University of Technology, Sydney. We gratefully acknowledge the support and advice of, the Historic Housing Trust of New South Wales, particularly the assistance of Scott Hill and Scott Carlin; and, the input of the design students, from the University of Technology, Sydney.

References

[1] Manovich, L. 2008, The Practice of Everyday (Media) Lie. In R. Frieling (ed.), *The Art of Participation: 1950 to Now*. London: Thames and Hudson.

[2] Tilley, C., 1994, *The phenomenology of landscape*, Oxford, Berg.

[3] Deray, K., and S. Simoff, 2008, 'Human Movement as a Framework for Understanding Interactions', Computers and Philosophy, Lavel, France, May 2006 in *Computers and Philosophy, an International Conference, Proceedings, 3-5 May 2006 Laval France*, (ed) Schmidt, Colin, European Office for Aerospace Research and Development, LIUM, Lavel, France, pp. 173-188.

[4] Seitz, J.A. 1994, 'Thinking kinesically: Theory and practice', *24th Annual Symposium of the Jean Piaget Society*, Jean Piaget Society, Chicago.

[5] Sudnow, D.W. 1978, *Ways of the Hand: The Organization of Improvised Conduct*, Harper & Row, New York.

[6] Laban, R. and Lawrence, F.C. 1974, *Effort: Economy of human movement*, 2nd edn, Plays, Boston.

[7] Seitz, J.A., 2000a, *The Bodily Basis of Thought*, Department of Political Science & Psychology, York College, City University of New York, New York.

[8] Seitz, J.A. 2000c, 'Embodied cognition', 12th Annual Convention of the American Psychological Society, Miami, FL

[9] Maglio, P.P., and Matlock. T. 1999, 'The conceptual structure of information space', in A.J. Munro, K. Hook, and D. Benyon, (eds), *Social Navigation of Information Space*, Springer-Verlag, London.

[10] Larssen, A.T. 2004, 'Physical computing-representations of human movement in human-computer interaction', *Computer Human Interaction Proceedings: 6th Asia Pacific Conference, APCHI 2004*, Rotorua, New Zealand.

[11] Thomas, J. J., and K. A. Cook, 2008, *Illuminating the Path: The Research and Development Agenda for Visual Analytics*, IEEE, CS Press.

[12] Pike, W. A., Stasko, J., Chang, R., and O'Connnell, T., 2008, 'The Science of Interaction', *Information Visualization*, vol 8, 4. 263-274.

[13] Pousman, Z. and Stasko, J. 2006. A taxonomy of ambient information systems: four patterns of design. In *Proceedings of the Working Conference on Advanced Visual Interfaces*. ACM, Venezia, Italy.

[14] Chandler D, 2004, *Semiotics: The Basics*. Routledge, London.

[15] Chen C. 2004. *Information Visualization: Beyond the Horizon*. Springer, London.

[16] Mcgrath, B., 2008, *Dgital Modelling for Urban Design* Wiley, Chichester, UK

[17] Lakoff, G. and R.E. Nunez, 2000, *Where Mathematics Comes From: How the Embodied Mind Brings Mathematics into Being*, Basic Books, New York.

[18] Simoff, S. 2008, 'Form-Semantics-Function, 'A framework for designing visual data representations for visual data mining, ' in S. J. Simoff and M.H. Böhlen and A. Mazeika (eds*), Visual Data Mining: Theory, Techniques and Tools for Visual Analytics: Lecture Notes in Computer Science 4404*, Springer Verlag, Heidelberg, Germany, pp. 30-45.

8. BioMedical Visualization

IV 2011

Preprocessing for Automating Early Detection of Cervical Cancer

Abhishek Das, Avijit Kar

Dept. of Computer Sc. & Engineering
Jadavpur University
Kolkata, India
email:adas.us@ieee.org

Debasis Bhattacharyya

Dept. of Gynecology & Obstetrics
SSKM Hospital
Kolkata, India

Abstract- **Uterine Cervical Cancer is one of the most common forms of cancer in women worldwide. Most cases of cervical cancer can be prevented through screening programs aimed at detecting precancerous lesions. During Digital Colposcopy, colposcopic images or cervigrams are acquired in raw form. They contain specular reflections which appear as bright spots heavily saturated with white light and occur due to the presence of moisture on the uneven cervix surface and. The cervix region occupies about half of the raw cervigram image. Other parts of the image contain irrelevant information, such as equipment, frames, text and non-cervix tissues. This irrelevant information can confuse automatic identification of the tissues within the cervix. Therefore we focus on the cervical borders, so that we have a geometric boundary on the relevant image area. Our novel technique eliminates the SR, identifies the region of interest and makes the cervigram ready for segmentation algorithms.**

Keywords- cervix; segmentation; clustering

I. INTRODUCTION

Uterine Cervical Cancer is one of the most common forms of cancer in woman worldwide. It is ranked 11th in incidence and 13th in mortality in the developed countries, due to the ability to detect the precancerous lesions through government-sponsored Cervical Cancer Screening Program. This success in the developed countries has been achieved through a synergy between Cervical Cytology Screening for Cervical Intra-epithelial Neoplasia (CIN) before they become invasive and their effective treatment directed by colposcopy.

Colposcopy is a very effective, non-invasive diagnostic tool. In colposcopy, the cervix is examined non-invasively by a colposcope which is a specially designed binocular stereo-microscope. The abnormal cervical regions turn to be white after application of 5% acetic acid and are called Acetowhite (AW) lesions which are then biopsied under colposcopic guidance for confirmation by histopathological examination. Modern colposcopes can produce a digital image of the cervix. Colposcopy today is considered the *gold standard* for detection and treatment of pre-cancerous lesions of the cervix. However, there is currently a void in specialized image processing software which has the ability

to process images acquired in colposcopy. Nevertheless, trained personnel are required for evaluation of the results.

II. LITERATURE REVIEW

Uterine Cervical Cancer is one of the most common form of Cancer in women worldwide, and 80% of cases occur in the developing world, where very few resources exist for management[1]. Most cases of cervical cancer can be prevented through screening programs aimed at detecting precancerous lesions. Screening for cervical neoplasia using the Papanicolaou (Pap) smear, followed by colposcopy, biopsy, and treatment of neoplastic lesions has dramatically reduced the incidence and mortality of cervical cancer in every country in which organized programs have been established[2]. This is due to the fact that the precursors, denoted as cervical intraepithelial neoplasia (CIN) or squamous intraepithelial lesions (SIL) can take 3 to 20 yr to develop into cancer. However, due to lack of resources and infrastructure, 238,000 women die every year of cervical cancer; more than 80% of these deaths occur in developing countries[1],[3]. We are interested in applying optical technologies to replace expensive infrastructure for cervical cancer screening in the developing world. The use of direct visual inspection (DVI), visual inspection with acetic acid (VIA), and visual inspection with Lugol's iodine (VILI) are being explored as alternatives to Pap smear and colposcopic examination in many developing countries[4]-[8]. Recent reviews of the performance of these methods found that they have sufficient sensitivity and specificity, when performed by trained professionals, to serve as viable alternatives to Pap screening in low-resource settings[9]-[10]. The results of a review by Sankaranarayanan[11] favorably compares these methods for human papillomavirus (HPV) testing and conventional cytology. Because DVI relies on visual interpretation, it is crucial to define objective criteria for the positive identification of a lesion and to train personnel to correctly implement a program based on these criteria. Denny et al.[10] noted that restricting the definition of a positive VIA test to a well-defined acetowhite lesion significantly improved specificity, while reducing sensitivity. In a series of 1921 women screened in Peru, Jeronimo et al found that the DVI false positivity rate dropped from 13.5% in the first months to 4% during

1550-6037/11 $26.00 © 2011 IEEE
DOI 10.1109/IV.2011.89

subsequent months of a 2-yr study; the drop in positivity rate was hypothesized to be due to a learning curve for the evaluator[12]. Bomfim-Hyppolito et al. investigated the use of cervicography as an adjunct to DVI. A simple Sony digital camera was used to photograph the cervix before and after the application of acetic acid[13]. Photographs were later interpreted by an expert colposcopist. The addition of cervicography improved both sensitivity and specificity. However, this approach prevents the implementation of see-and-treat strategies in low resource settings because of the need for expert review.

Recently, optical techniques have been investigated as alternative detection methods in a quantitative and objective manner. Several studies have demonstrated that optical spectroscopy has the potential to improve the screening and diagnosis of neoplasia. Ferris et al. studied multimodal hyperspectral imaging for the noninvasive diagnosis of cervical neoplasia[14]. They reported a sensitivity of 97% and a specificity of 70%. Huh et al. [15] measured the performance of optical detection of HGSIL using fluorescence and reflectance spectroscopy, finding a sensitivity of 90% and a specificity of 70%. As another promising application of optical techniques for cervical cancer screening, a number of studies investigated whether digital image processing techniques could be used to automate the interpretation of colposcopic images[14]-[19]. Craine and Craine[16] introduced a digital colposcopy system for archiving images and visually assessing features in the images. Shafi et al.[17] and Cristoforoni et al.[18] used a digital imaging system for colposcopy, which enables image capture and simple processing. To assess various colposcopic features, the acquired images were manually analyzed by an expert. By examining the relationship between colposcopic features and histology outcomes, Shafi et al.'s study provided information about features that are most useful to the expert observer.

Image interpretation in these early studies mainly relied on experts' qualitative assessment of colposcopic images and provided limited quantitative analysis. Li et al. developed a computer-aided diagnostic system using colposcopic features such as acetowhitening changes, lesion margin, and blood vessel structures[19]. They prototyped image processing algorithms for detection of those features and showed promising preliminary results. However, the diagnostic performance of the system has not been reported. Recently, advances in consumer electronics have led to inexpensive, high-dynamic-range charge-coupled device (CCD) cameras with excellent low light sensitivity. At the same time, advances in vision chip technology enable high quality image processing in real time. Moreover, automated analysis algorithms based on modern image processing techniques have the potential to replace clinical expertise, which may reduce the cost of screening.

The purpose of the paper is to present an image preprocessing method to remove specular reflection and detect ROI.

Several challenges for diagnostic digital colposcopic image analysis remain. First, previous studies have investigated only a few features and have not taken advantage of the mature field of image analysis and computer-automated techniques. Second, previous studies have compared image features of selected normal and abnormal areas of the cervix, but have not applied the approach to the entire image to identify whether lesions are present. Finally, previous studies have used biopsies from selected areas as the gold standard. A gold standard is necessary for the entire field of view to address the issue of lesion localization.

III. AUTOMATED SYSTEM

An automated system is proposed in this paper that is used for diagnosis of CIN. The scheme is presented as a block diagram in Fig. 1. The process of translating raw cervix image acquired using a Digital Colposcope into a thorough diagnosis of CIN is decomposed into four modules: 1) removal of specular reflection (SR) from raw cervigrams; 2) segmentation of cervix region of interest (ROI); 3) segmentation of cervix ROI into acetowhite (AW), columnar epithelium (CE) and squamous epithelium (SE); 4) classification of AW regions into AW, mosaic, or punctation tiles; However, we are presenting the first two modules in this paper.

A. Algorithms for Segmentation

Salient features observed in cervical images consist of the cervix ROI, SR, AW, SE, and CE. While the AW region is the single most important region for detecting the presence and extent of CIN, the ROI must also be extracted. SR, which adversely affects the AW segmentation process, must be removed. During the AW segmentation procedure, the CE and SE are designated as distinct regions. The classification process of these macro features constitutes the first three modules of the automated diagnosis system illustrated in Fig. 1.

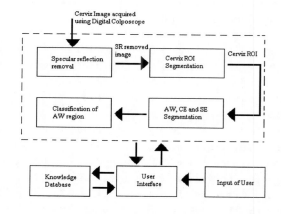

Fig1: Block Diagram of the proposed Automation tool for CIN detection

B. Removal of Specular Reflection

Specular Reflections (SR) appear as bright spots heavily saturated with white light. These occur due to the presence of moisture on the uneven cervix surface, which act like mirrors reflecting the light from the illumination source. Apart from camouflaging the actual features, the SR also affects subsequent segmentation routines and hence must be removed. At first, the RGB Image (Raw Cervigram) is separated into Red, Green and Blue Planes. The Specular Reflections (White Areas) are identified by selecting the white pixels from each plane and logically AND -ing them. Standard Morphological methods viz. dilation is used that utilize a structuring element (SE). Once the dilated binary images with outlines are identified, the borders of all the reflections on the original grayscale image using the coordinates are returned. A filling Algorithm is used which smoothly interpolates inward from the pixels on the boundary of the polygon (White SR Areas) by solving *Laplace's equation*. The idea is to find an interpolating function y that satisfies Laplace's equation in n dimensions,

$$\Delta y = 0 \quad \text{where } \Delta \text{ is the } Laplace\ operator$$

and its homogenous version, *Poisson's equation* $-\Delta y = f$. We also say a function y satisfying Laplace's equation is a harmonic function.

Now we try to find the fundamental solution. Consider Laplace's equation in $\mathbf{R^n}$, $\Delta y = 0 \quad x \in \mathbf{R^n}$

There are a lot of functions y which satisfy this equation. In particular any constant function is harmonic. In addition, any function of the form $y(x) = a_1 x_1 + \ldots + a_n x_n$ for constants a_i is also a solution. However here we are interested in finding a particular solution of the Laplace's equation which will allow us to solve Poisson's equation. Given the symmetric nature of Laplace's equation, we search for a *radial* solution. That is we look for a harmonic function y on $\mathbf{R^n}$ such that $y(x) = z(|x|)$. In addition to being an automatic choice due to the symmetry of Laplace's equation, radial solutions are automatic to look for because they reduce a PDE to an ODE, which is easier to solve. Therefore we look for a radial solution.

If $y(x) = z(|x|)$, then $\quad yx_i = \frac{x_i}{|x|} z'(|x|) \quad |x| \neq 0$,

which implies

$$yx_i x_i = \frac{1}{|x|} z'(|x|) - \frac{x_i^2}{|x|^3} z'(|x|) + \frac{x_i^2}{|x|^2} z''(|x|) \quad |x| \neq 0.$$

Therefore,

$$\Delta y = \frac{n-1}{|x|} z'(|x|) + z''(|x|)$$

Letting $r = |x|$, we find that $y(x) = z(|x|)$ is a radial solution of Laplace's equation implies z satisfies

$$\frac{n-1}{r} z'(r) + z''(r) = 0.$$

Therefore,

$$z'' = \frac{1-n}{r} z'$$

$$\Rightarrow \quad \frac{z''}{z'} = \frac{1-n}{r}$$

$$\Rightarrow \ln z' = (1-n) \ln r + C$$

$$\Rightarrow z' = \frac{c}{r^{n-1}},$$

which implies

$$z(r) = \begin{cases} c_1 \ln r + c_2 & n = 2 \\ \dfrac{c_1}{(2-n)r^{n-2}} + c_2 & n \geq 3. \end{cases}$$

From these calculations we see that for any constants c_1, c_2, the function

$$y(x) = \begin{cases} c_1 \ln |x| + c_2 & n = 2 \\ \dfrac{c_1}{(2-n)|x|^{n-2}} + c_2 & n \geq 3. \end{cases} \quad (1.1)$$

For $x \in \mathbf{R^n}$, $|x| \neq 0$ is a solution of Laplace's equation in $\mathbf{R^n} - \{0\}$. We notice that the function y defined in (1.1) satisfies $\Delta y(x) = 0$ for $x \neq 0$, but at $x = 0$, $\Delta y(0)$ is undefined. The reason for choosing Laplace's equation (among all possible partial differential equations, say) is that the solution to Laplace's equation selects the smoothest possible interpolant.

B. Cervix ROI Segmentation

The cervix region involves about half of the cervigram image. Other parts of the image contain irrelevant information, such as equipment, frames, text, and non-cervix tissues. This irrelevant information can confuse the automatic identification of the tissues within the cervix. The first step is, therefore, focusing on the cervical borders, so that we have a geometric bound on the relevant image area. The cervix region is a relatively pink region located around the image center. The reason for choosing the Lab Color space (among all other color models) as it is display device independent and conducive to human perception.

The Lab color space is derived from CIE XYZ tristimulus values. The Lab space consists of a luminosity layer 'L', chromaticity layer a indicating where color falls along red-green axis, and chromaticity layer b indicating where color falls along blue-yellow axis. All of the color information is in 'a' and 'b' values. The difference between two colors using Euclidean distance metric can be measured. Now the cervigram consists of distinct SE, CE & AW Regions which are relevant to our context. Hence we need to segment them using a Clustering Algorithm.

Clustering is a way to separate groups of objects. Clustering in pattern recognition is the process of partitioning a set of pattern vectors into subsets called clusters. The general problem in clustering is to partition a set of vectors into groups having similar values.

In traditional clustering there are K clusters $C_1, C_2, \ldots, C_K$ with means $m_1, m_2, \ldots, m_K$

K-means clustering treats each object as having a location in space. It finds partitions such that objects within each cluster are as close to each other as possible, and as far from objects in other clusters as possible. The K-means algorithm[23] is a simple, iterative hill-climbing method which can be expressed as follows.

Form K-means clusters from a set of n-dimensional vectors.
1. Set ic (iteration count) to 1.
2. Choose randomly a set of K means $m_1(1), m_2(1), \ldots, m_K(1)$.
3. For each vector x_i compute $D(x_i, m_K(ic))$ for each k=1,….K and assign x_i to cluster C_j with the nearest mean.
4. Increment ic by 1 and update the means to get a new set $m_1(ic)$, $m_2(ic)$, ….,$m_K(ic)$.
5. Repeat steps 3 and 4 until $C_k(ic) = C_k(ic+1)$ for all k.

Applying the above algorithm, the Cervigram Image is segmented. When the resulting ROI consists of several disjoint areas in the image, the largest one is chosen, and the others are ignored. The image is cropped to include the ROI region, and subsequent steps of the process are performed within it, thus avoiding the confusing patterns and colors that occupy the rest of the image.

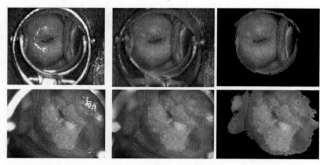

Fig2: Raw Cervigram(left), Specular reflection removed image(centre), ROI detected using the clustering algorithm(right)

IV. RESULTS

We have taken a dataset of 210 Normal cervigrams and 42 Acetowhite cervigrams. On visual inspection by Gyneco-oncologists of previous research results [19]-[21], our method of removal of specular reflection is far better, as it smoothly interpolates using our algorithm. Previous methods have considered only replacing the specular reflections by blobs.

V. CONCLUSION

In this paper, we have presented an image preprocessing method to remove specular reflection and detect ROI for further detection of acetowhite lesions from the cervigram. The first two modules as proposed in our model has given satisfactory results. The work on next two modules is ongoing. Future scope of this research is to explore whether digital colposcopy, combined with recent advances in camera technology and automated image processing, could provide an inexpensive alternative to Pap screening and conventional colposcopy.

ACKNOWLEDGMENT

The authors would like to thank the Department of Biotechnology, Government of West Bengal, India for providing financial support to the research.

REFERENCES

[1] Cancer Facts & Figures 2010, available at: http://www.cancer.org.
[2] L. G. Koss, "The Papanicolaou test for cervical cancer detection. A triumph and a tragedy," *J. Am. Med. Assoc. vol.*261, 737–743 ,1989.
[3] D. M. Parkin, F. Bray, J. Ferlay, and P. Pisani, "Global cancer statistics," *Ca-Cancer J. Clin. vol* 55, 74–108, 2005.
[4] S. J. Goldie, L. Gaffikin, J. D Goldhaber-Fiebert, A. Gordillo-Tobar, C. Levin, C. Mahé, and T. C. Wright, "Cost-effectiveness of cervical cancer

screening in five developing countries," *N. Engl. J. Med. vol* 353, 2158–2168 ,2005.
[5] B. M. Nene et al., "Early detection of cervical cancer by visual inspection: a population-based study in rural India," *Int. J. Cancer. vol* 68,770–773,1996.
[6] R. Wesley, R. Sankaranarayanan, B. Mathew, B. Chandralekha, A. Aysha-Begum, N. S. Amma, and M. K. Nair, "Evaluation of visual inspection as a screening test for cervical cancer," *Br. J. Cancer. vol* 75, 436–440, 1997.
[7] P. Basu et al., "Evaluation of downstaging in the detection of cervical neoplasia in Kolkata, India," *Int. J. Cancer.vol* 100, 92–96, 2002.
[8] M. J. Germar and M. Merialdi, "Visual inspection with acetic acid as a cervical cancer screening tool for developing countries. Review for postgraduate training course in reproductive health/chronic disease, 2003."
[9] R. Sankaranarayanan et al., "The role of low-level magnification in visual inspection with acetic acid for the early detection of cervical neoplasia," *Cancer Detect. Prev. vol* 28, 345–351, 2004.
[10] L. Denny, L. Kuhn, A. Pollack, and T. Wright, "Direct visual inspection for cervical cancer screening: an analysis of factors influencing test performance," *Cancer vol* 94, 1699–1707, 2002.
[11] R. Sankaranarayanan, R. Rajkumar, R. Theresa, P. O. Esmy, C. Mahe, K. R. Bagyalakshmi, S. Thara, L. Frappart, E. Lucas, R. Muwonge, S. Shanthakumari, D. Jeevan, T. M. Subbarao, D. M. Parkin, and J. Cherian, "Initial results from a randomized trial of cervical visual screening in rural south India," *Int. J. Cancer vol* 109, 461–467, 2004.
[12] J. Jeronimo, O. Morales, J. Horna, J. Pariona, J. Manrique, J. Rubinos, and R. Takahashi, "Visual inspection with acetic acid for cervical cancer screening outside of low-resource settings," *Rev. Panam Salud Publica, vol* 17(1), 1–5, 2005.
[13] S. Bomfim-Hyppolito, E. S. Franco, R. G. Franco, C. M. de Albuquerque, and G. C. Nunes, "Cervicography as an adjunctive test to visual inspection with acetic acid in cervical cancer detection screening," *Int. J. Gynaecol. Obstet. vol* 92, 58–63, 2006.
[14] D. G. Ferris, R. A. Lawhead, E. D. Dickman, N. Holtzapple, J. A. Miller, S. Grogan, S. Bambot, A. Agrawal, and M. L. Faupel, "Multimodal hyperspectral imaging for the noninvasive diagnosis of cervical neoplasia," *J. Low. Genit. Tract Dis. vol* 5(2), 65–72 2001.
[15] W. K. Huh, R. M. Cestero, F. A. Garcia, M. A. Gold, R. M. Guido, K. McIntyre-Seltman, D. M. Harper, L. Burke, S. T. Sum, R. F. Flewelling, and R. D. Alvarez, "Optical detection of high-grade cervical neoplasia *in vivo*: results of a 604 patient study," *Am. J. Obstet. Gynecol. vol* 190, 1249–1257 ,2004.
[16] W. E. Crisp, B. L. Craine, and E. A. Craine, "The computerized digital imaging colposcope: future directions," *Am. J. Obstet. Gynecol. vol* 162, 1491–1497,1990.
[17] B. L. Craine and E. R. Craine, "Digital imaging colposcopy: basic concepts and applications," *Obstet. Gynecol. Clin. North Am. vol* 82, 869–873, 1993.
[18] M. I. Shafi, J. A. Dunn, R. Chenoy, E. J. Buxton, C. Williams, and D. M. Luesley, "Digital imaging colposcopy, image analysis and quantification of the colposcopic image," *Br. J. Obstet. Gynaecol. vol* 101, 234–238, 1994.
[19] P. M. Cristoforoni, D. Gerbaldo, A. Perino, R. Piccoli, F. J. Montz, and G. L. Capitanio, "Computerized colposcopy: results of a pilot study and analysis of its clinical relevance," *Obstet. Gynecol. (N.Y.,NY, U. S.) vol* 85, 1011–1016, 1995.
[20] W. Li, V. Van Raad, J. Gu, U. Hansson, J. Hakansson, H. Lange, and D. Ferris, "Computer-aided diagnosis (CAD)for cervical cancer screening and diagnosis: a new system design in medical image processing," in *Lect. Notes Comput. Sci.*, vol 3765, 240–250 , 2005.
[21] S. Gordon, G. Zimmerman, R. Long, S. Antani, J. Jeronimo, and H.Greenspan, "Content analysis of uterine cervix images: Initial steps towards content based indexing and retrieval of cervigrams," in *Proc. SPIE Conf. on Medical Imaging*, San Diego, CA, Mar. 2006, vol. 6144, pp. 1549–1556.
[22] W. Press, S. Teukolsky, W. Vetterling, B. Flannery, "Numerical Recipes: The Art of Scientific Computing" Cambridge Univ. Press, 3rd edn. 2007
[23] L. Shapiro, G. Stockman, "Computer Vision" Prentice Hall 2001

Accelerating Tumour Growth Simulations on Many-Core Architectures: A Case Study on the Use of GPGPU within VPH

Baoquan Liu[1], Gordon J. Clapworthy[1], Feng Dong[1], Eleni Kolokotroni[2], Georgios Stamatakos[2]

[1] Centre for Computer Graphics & Visualisation, University of Bedfordshire, UK

[2] Institute of Communication and Computer Systems, National Technical University of Athens, Athens, Greece

Abstract

Simulators of tumour growth can estimate the evolution of tumour volume and the quantity of various categories of cells as functions of time. However, the execution time of each simulation often takes several dozens of minutes (depending upon the dataset resolution), which clearly prevents easy interaction. The modern graphics processing unit (GPU) is not only a powerful graphics engine but also a highly parallel programmable processor featuring peak arithmetic performance and memory bandwidth that substantially outpaces its CPU counterpart. However, despite this, the GPU is little used in the context of the Virtual Physiological Human (VPH).

This paper provides a case study to demonstrate the performance advantages that can be gained by using the GPU appropriately in the context of a VPH project in which the study of tumour growth is a central activity. We also analyse the algorithm performance on different modern parallel processing architectures, including multi-core CPU and many-core GPU.

Keywords

Tumour simulation, Virtual Physiological Human, VPH, *in silico* oncology, CUDA, GPGPU, multi-GPU

1. Introduction

This paper describes a case study in which CPU-based code being used in a VPH project was replaced by equivalent GPU code. This work took place within the Contra Cancrum project.

The rapid increase in resolution of many of the devices used to produce biomedical data and the multiscale nature of much of the work on the Virtual Physiological Human (VPH) has led to most VPH projects being confronted with huge amounts of data. This, in turn, has tended to cause a concentration on the use of Grid and other high-performance computing (HPC) resources to process it.

A survey undertaken by the authors found that, apart from Contra Cancrum, only 3 of the original VPH projects made any use of GPUs and all of these used them purely for tasks related to visualisation and imaging – collision detection, image processing, etc.

From the above, it is clear that, as a whole, VPH projects have largely overlooked the possibilities offered by

the rapidly increasing power of the Graphics Processing Unit (GPU) and have thus failed to take advantage of the immense potential afforded by general purpose GPU programming. The motivation for this paper is to demonstrate its value to the VPH community and to bring to its attention the level of performance gain that use of the GPU can provide. We are not suggesting that GPUs should supersede large-scale HPC installations for huge compute-intensive applications, but we do contend that they could usefully play a much larger role in VPH than currently.

Contra Cancrum is developing an advanced multiscale simulation platform of tumour growth and response to treatment, driven by real clinical needs, and is instigating clinical translation of the simulation system within the context of clinical trials/tests. The project has developed molecular-level and tissue-level models and integrated components concerned with patient-specific tissue biomechanics and medical image analysis. A dedicated repository has been provided to allow remote access to a large number of multi-modal and temporal datasets of glioma and lung cancer patient data. The initial validation experiments with models have been both data-driven and data-driving, as novel concepts on cross-scale model integration have demanded the acquisition of further molecular, patient-specific information. The ultimate goal is the demonstration of its clinical usefulness in current treatment practice and cancer therapy optimisation.

Within Contra Cancrum, the particular application that forms the focus of this paper relates to the modelling of tumour growth. Statistical approaches to tumour growth using a Monte Carlo method have been in use for some time [1,2]. They may require hundreds of simulations to be run to provide a statistical picture of the likely tumour behaviour due *inter alia* to the uncertainties in the estimation of various model parameters within the clinical context. Depending upon the outcome, the clinician may subsequently need to slightly tune a few parameters to obtain a new simulation result, so the interactive response time of the simulator is critical.

Ideally, for efficient interaction, each execution should be performed in seconds. However, for the type of data used in this application, a simulation instance will generally take several dozens of minutes on a desktop PC, so the process cannot take place interactively. This severely limits the level of experimentation that can take place. The work described below was designed to overcome this problem.

1550-6037/11 $26.00 © 2011 IEEE
DOI 10.1109/IV.2011.45

The remainder of the paper is arranged as follows. Section 2 provides an overview of the salient features of the GPU that make it particularly suitable in the application described and Section 3 introduces the application and the processes by which the results are obtained. Section 4 describes the original program structure and how it is parallelised, while Section 5 explains how the parallelised code is then mapped to the GPU architecture of a single GPU. Section 6 discusses how the GPU code is adjusted to deal with a multi-GPU approach. Section 7 presents the results and Section 8 provides a summary of the outcomes.

2. The GPU

Parallel computing offers fast computing by splitting tasks into small components and distributing them among multiple processors/threads. Many computing tasks exhibit a parallel nature and are hence suitable for parallel computing. Conventional parallel computing takes place using multi-core CPUs or via distributed, grid, high performance computers. The remarkably increased power of the GPU in recent years offers a very attractive alternative, which can handle many demanding tasks by harnessing the local computing resources to be found in low-cost computer platforms.

Probably the most important development in GPUs in recent years has been the increase in their versatility as a result of recent advances in GPU hardware and software architecture. Although GPUs were initially designed for use in highly visual tasks, mostly associated with computer games development, they are now being used in many computational areas - this is known as general purpose GPU programming (GPGPU). A state-of-the-art GPU can perform 1.35 trillion arithmetic operations per second [3], and this represents a tremendous computational resource when utilised for general purpose computing. The GPU does, however, demand very specific skills to ensure that its potential is fully realised.

The GPU has always offered multi-thread processing, but it has now become the most powerful processor in a desktop computer – its development continues to outpace progress in CPUs due not only to its highly data-parallel nature but also to its ability to achieve higher arithmetic intensity. Figs. 1 and 2 show the huge advantage of the latest GPUs over CPUs in terms of both GFLOPS[1] and memory bandwidth[2], and as the gap continues to widen, this trend is set to become more extreme in the future.

The major factors inhibiting GPU use have previously been low on-board memory and poor double-precision performance. These have largely been overcome in the current generation of GPUs and GPU clusters, with the current NVIDIA GPUs (codename Fermi) having an 8-fold

---

[1] GFLOPS: Giga Floating Point Operations Per Second

[2] Memory bandwidth: the rate at which data can be moved between memory and the processor

improvement in performance at double precision, which further extends the performance gap over CPUs.

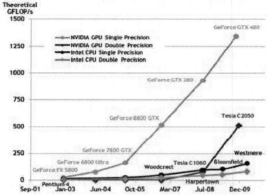

Figure 1. CPU vs GPU Performance in GFLOPS
(image courtesy of NVIDIA)

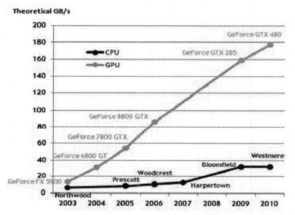

Figure 2. CPU vs GPU Performance in Memory Bandwidth
(image courtesy of NVIDIA)

Another significant factor is that GPU computational power is inexpensive and is now widely available in many moderate computers with basic configurations (e.g. desktop PCs, laptops). A typical latest-generation card costs only a few hundred euros, and these prices drop rapidly as new hardware emerges. Moreover, off-the-shelf GPU clusters are now commercially available at low cost, for example, the latest-generation NVIDIA Tesla S2050 4-GPU cluster retails at around €8,500. These can be set up with virtually no technical knowledge and they deliver exceptional computing power on the desktop.

The parallel nature of the GPU can provide vast speed gains for applications in which the computational requirements are large and parallelism is substantial. Given their wide availability, GPUs are particularly suitable for medium-sized computing tasks in which frequent interaction and adjustments of parameters are needed. Even if the final target for an application is a remote supercomputer, early testing and experimentation is often important before a major commitment is made to the use of high performance computing facilities, which are normally expensive and require advance booking.

Originally, the programming of the GPU used high-level shading languages which were designed for graphics rendering and thus require some familiarity with computer graphics. At that time, adapting these for general-purpose computation was less than straightforward.

In 2006, the NVIDIA Corporation released a new computing architecture for the GPU, the Compute Unified Device Architecture (CUDA) [3]. This is the general-purpose parallel-computing architecture of modern NVIDIA GPUs. Having been designed for general-purpose usage, CUDA greatly lowers the knowledge threshold for using GPUs for non-graphical computation. In CUDA, the GPU is regarded as a multi-threaded coprocessor to the CPU with a standard C language interface.

The CUDA programming model is based upon the concept of a kernel: to define the computational task for the GPU, programmers should provide a C-like function – the kernel. This is a function that is executed multiple times in parallel, each instance running in a separate thread. A unique thread ID is given to each thread in order to distinguish between them.

The threads are organised into one-, two- or three-dimensional blocks, which in turn are organised into one- or two-dimensional grids. The blocks are totally independent of each other and can be executed in any order. However, threads within a block are guaranteed to be run on a single multiprocessor. A feature that proved very useful in this application is that this makes it possible for them to synchronise and share information efficiently using the on-chip memory, as CUDA allows all threads in a block to share data via fast on-chip shared memory to avoid redundant memory access.

CUDA maintains a separated view of the two main actors in the computation – the host (CPU system) and the device (GPU card/system). The host executes the main program, while the device acts like a coprocessor.

The above discussion focused on NVIDIA GPUs because these were used in the work described later. Other manufacturers' cards are generally similar in character.

3. Tumour simulation

In the simulation method used in Contra Cancrum, a cubic discretising mesh is superimposed upon the anatomical region of interest to create a regular set of *geometric cells* (GCs) on which the tumour simulation is computed. This regular structure provides a suitable foundation on which to base the parallelisation.

A set of basic biological rules is applied locally to each of the GCs at regular timesteps (generally an hour) to model the spatiotemporal evolution of the tumour system.

The local biological, physical and chemical dynamics of the region are described, explicitly or implicitly, by the use of a hypermatrix, i.e. a mathematical matrix of matrices of

matrices…of (matrices or vectors or scalars) corresponding to the anatomic region of interest [4-7].

The following parameters are used to identify a cluster of biological cells (BCs) belonging to a given equivalence class within a particular GC at a given time point:

I. the spatial coordinates of the discrete points of the discretisation mesh with spatial indices i,j,k, respectively; it is noted that each discrete spatial point lies at the centre of a GC

II. the temporal coordinate of the discrete time point with temporal index l

III. the mitotic potential category (i.e. stem or progenitor or terminally differentiated) of the BCs with mitotic potential category index m

IV. the cell phase (within or out of the cell cycle) of the BCs with cell phase index n; the following phases are considered: {G1,S,G2,M,G0,A,N,D}, where G1 denotes the G1 cell cycle phase, S the DNA synthesis phase, G2 the G2 cell cycle phase, M mitosis, G0 the quiescent (dormant) G0 phase, A the apoptotic phase, N the necrotic phase, and D the remnants of dead cells.

For the BCs belonging to a given mitotic potential category AND residing in a given cell phase AND accommodated within the GC whose centre lies at a given spatial point AND being considered at a given time point; in other words, for the BCs clustered in the same equivalence class denoted by the index combination $ijklmn$, the following state parameters are provided:

i. local oxygen and nutrient provision level,

ii. number of BCs,

iii. average time spent by the BCs in the given phase,

iv. number of BCs hit by treatment,

v. number of BCs not hit by treatment.

The initial biological, physical and chemical state of the tumour has to be estimated based on the available medical data through the application of pertinent algorithms. This state corresponds to the instant just before the start of the treatment course to be simulated.

The simulation can be viewed as the periodic and sequential application of a number of sets of algorithms (operators) on the hypermatrix of the anatomic region of interest, which are performed in the following order:

A. Time updating i.e. increasing time by a unit (e.g. 1h),

B. Estimation of the local oxygen and nutrient level.

C. Estimation of the effect of treatment (therapy) – this refers mainly to cell hitting by treatment, cell killing and cell survival. Available molecular and/or histological information is integrated at this point.

D. Application of cell cycling, possibly perturbed by treatment. Transition between mitotic potential cell categories such as transition of the offspring of a terminally divided progenitor cell into the terminally differentiated cell category is also tackled here.

E. Differential expansion or shrinkage or, more generally, geometry and mechanics handling.

F Updating the local oxygen and nutrient provision levels following application of the remaining algorithm sets at each time step. Stochastic perturbations about mean values of several model parameters are considered (hybridisation with the Monte Carlo technique).

Utilisation of the models described above is designed to take place within the Oncosimulator [5]. Fig. 3 shows a synoptic diagram of its envisaged functioning [5,6].

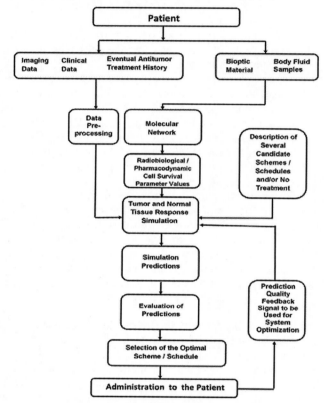

Figure 3. Use of the Oncosimulator

The Oncosimulator reflects multilevel integrative cancer biology. It is a complex algorithmic construct, a biomedical engineering system and (eventually, in the future) a clinical tool to support the clinician in optimising cancer treatment in the context of the individual patient by allowing experiments to be conducted *in silico*, i.e. on the computer, across a range of different scenarios.

Additionally, it is a platform for simulating, investigating, improving understanding and exploring the natural phenomenon of cancer, supporting the design and interpretation of clinicogenomic trials and training doctors, researchers and interested patients, alike.

4. CPU implementation and parallelisation

In this paper, the data for the modelling is the same as that in a recent study on breast cancer [7]. The initial state is a spatially macroscopically homogeneous tumour of spherical shape – while this construct is simple, it is, in fact, a reasonable model for an early breast tumour [7].

As mentioned in Section 3, a cubic discretising mesh is superimposed upon the anatomic region of interest to create an array of GCs. This is scanned every hour, at which time a set of rules is applied locally within the GC to find the changes that will occur in the next time period.

In this paper, a GC corresponds to a volume of 1 mm³. A standard assumption, particularly in radiobiological models [8], is a cell density of 10^6 cells/mm³, so each GC belonging to the tumour is considered initially to accommodate 10^6 BCs. This (mean) cell density is conserved throughout the simulation.

Each GC of the discretising mesh (which constitutes the region of interest around a tumour) contains a number of BCs. All cells in all GCs follow cytokinetic diagrams (see Fig. 4), which are general cytokinetic models that can be adapted and/or expanded for specific tumour data and drugs under consideration by adjusting the corresponding simulation parameters (e.g. the probabilities of the various transitions between phases, the cell cycle durations, etc.) [1,2,7]. The discrete character of the simulation model enables the consideration of various exploratory initial percentages of the cells in the various equivalence classes.

Fig. 4 depicts the cytokinetic model adopted for tumour growth. An extension of this diagram can be used in order to model chemotherapy-treated tumour cytokinetics. The following types (categories) of cells can be identified:

- *stem/clonogenic cells* – cells assumed to possess unlimited proliferative potential,
- *limp (limited mitotic potential) or progenitor cells* – cells with limited mitotic potential (3 divisions are assumed before terminal differentiation occurs),
- *differentiated (diff) cells* – terminally differentiated cells,
- *necrotic cells* – cells that have died through necrosis
- *apoptotic cells* – cells that have died through apoptosis.

A more detailed description of the tumour growth (and response to treatment) model is provided in [7]. Two sets of real clinical spatiotemporal tumour data have been used for the clinical adaptation of the model in that paper. The basics of the model under consideration have been used *inter alia* for the implementation of the entire ContraCancrum project [9].

Commodity PCs are now typically built with general purpose CPU hardware containing up to two or four cores (dual core or quad core) on the same die, with higher core counts on the horizon. They deliver high performance by exploiting modestly parallel workloads arising from either the need to execute multiple independent programs or individual programs that themselves consist of multiple parallel tasks, yet maintain the same level of performance as single-core chips on sequential workloads [10].

In our experiments, we used an AMD Phenom 9650 Quad-Core CPU processor, which is an x86-based multi-threaded multi-core architecture that offers four parallel cores on the same die, running at 2.3 GHz. Each core is backed by a 512KB L2 cache, and all four cores share a 2MB L3 cache. On such a multi-core system, the multiple CPU threads will actually run at the same time, with each core running a particular thread or task. So we can split up the computational task according to the number of available cores, and assign different parts of the GCs to different CPU threads for parallel computing. Since different threads in the same process share the same address space, this allows concurrently-running code to couple tightly and conveniently.

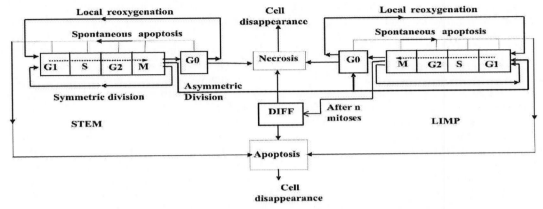

Figure 4. The generic cytokinetic model for tumour growth

5. Adaptation to a single GPU

To accelerated the C program, we create a CPU thread that communicates with, and sends orders to, the GPU. The pre-processing and initialisation is still handled by the CPU, but, the data is transferred to the GPU memory at the beginning of the time-step procedure. Then, each routine that was previously performed on the CPU by looping over each iterative scan of the GCs, is replaced by CUDA routines that process all cells in parallel on the GPU.

To accelerate such numerical calculation for tumour simulation on stream processors, we designed algorithms using CUDA to parallelise the tumour simulation based on the biological mathematical model.

The CUDA architecture is built around a scalable array of multithreaded streaming multiprocessors. NVIDIA's current GPU consists of an array of multiprocessors, each able to support up to 1024 co-resident concurrent threads. Our decomposition is based on fine-grain task parallelism that balances the load among the GPU multiprocessors.

The GPU and CPU have separate memory spaces requiring data to be copied into the GPU or CPU memory before the processing can take place. Data transfers of this type occur over the PCI-express bus at a relatively slow speed (compared with the GPU memory bandwidth of up to 144 GB/s). We try to minimise data transfer by moving as many routines as possible on to the GPU – we gather all the result data from the GPU into a single buffer to reduce the size and number of the memory copies to the CPU.

The overall process is as described in Section 3. In their initial state, the tumours are assumed to be spatially macroscopically uniform and all GCs are initialised in the same way. We use parallel threads to perform the computation for each GC independently and execute hourly scanning steps via parallel GPU kernels, which allow the local application of basic biological rules. In this way, the tumour evolution is computed by iteratively scanning the biological parameters in the GCs, and at the same time applying the biological rules to them to spatiotemporally simulate the evolution of the tumour system. By buffering the parameters of neighbouring GCs in the shared memory, we can reduce the number of memory transactions hugely.

In a carefully structured way, at each iterative scan, we assign one GPU thread to perform the computation associated with a single GC. To simulate tumour expansion and shrinkage, we execute the following 3 scanning steps via parallel GPU kernels.

1) *Cell growth*: each thread computes all the cell-cycle phase transitions and cell deaths due to chemotherapy or radiotherapy that have occurred inside the GC.

2) *Cell transfers* are computed in parallel by unloading excess cells from the current GC into the 26 adjacent GCs, using 27 subpasses that interleave the 27 neighbouring GCs at each subpass. This novel implementation takes full advantage of all the GPU resources available under the CUDA programming model. Cell transfers among the 27 local neighbouring GCs (a box) are evaluated in a single thread, with each thread block responsible for a row of boxes. All threads in a block simultaneously iterate through the neighbouring GCs in shared memory, computing the transfers on the boxes in their individual registers. Since all threads in a block access the same shared memory

location, data are broadcast to all threads by the hardware, and no bank conflict penalty is incurred.

3) *Differential tumour shrinkage* is dealt with by freeing the GCs containing too few cells, or creating new GCs for differential tumour expansion. Tumour contiguity is also restored if fragmentation has taken place.

The above process is repeated continuously until the completion of the time interval $T_{interval}$ (in hours) being studied. Finally, we read back the results from the GPU memory to the CPU buffer over the PCI-express bus.

6. Multi-GPU implementation

Here, we investigate the performance factors of a multi-GPU system for tumour simulation. In particular, we focus on NVIDIA's Tesla multi-GPU solution, which combines four GT200 GPUs, making up to 4 TFLOPS of computational power available. Our test bench, the NVIDIA Tesla S1070, can be connected to a single host via two PCI Express connections (shown in Fig. 5).

We show that the multi-GPU system greatly benefits from using all four of its GPUs on very large data volumes – computation using the four GPUs was only slightly short of four times faster than using a single GPU.

Performance was measured on an NVIDIA Tesla S1070 containing four GT200 GPUs. The S1070 contains 30 multiprocessors, each with 8 streaming processors (for a total of 240 processor cores), 16KB 32-bit registers and 16 KB of shared memory. The theoretical global-memory bandwidth is 102 GB/s and the available global memory of each GPU is 4GB. The Tesla S1070 has up to 4 TFLOPS of computational power.

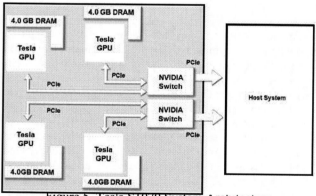

Figure 5. Tesla S1070 System Architecture
(image courtesy of NVIDIA)

The connection to the host CPU is through PCIe Host Interconnection Cards (HIC), with a single PCIe slot on the host being connected to two GPUs using a PCIe HIC card. This provides a transfer rate of up to 12.8 GB/s between the host CPU and the Tesla S1070.

The GPUs are linked through the host system. This kind of interconnection requires communication to set up cooperation in order to solve a massive data parallelism task. In our implementation, we try to minimise data transfers or other communication flow between the GPUs. We only send data from the host to the GPUs or read back the resulting data from the GPUs to host. We also move as many routines as possible to the GPU, since the GPU has a much higher bandwidth than the PCI-express bus, over which the data transfers between GPUs take place.

The NVIDIA CUDA Runtime API gives the programmer the possibility to select the device on which to execute the kernels. By default, device 0 is used, and the devices can be numbered progressively for the other GPUs.

The general idea of multi-GPU computing is to split up the computational task according to the number of available GPUs. To do this, we let each part of the array be handled by one of the installed GPUs to achieve the greatest utilisation of the multiple GPUs.

To use multiple CUDA contexts (one for each GPU), we can associate them with different CPU threads, one for each GPU. For the multi-GPU implementation, each CPU core runs a separate thread and controls one of the GPUs by using the corresponding CUDA context. For optimal performance, the number of CPU cores should be greater than, or at least equal to, the number of GPUs in the system. Our bench host CPU satisfies this requirement.

To use multiple GPUs in our implementation, we spawn 4 CPU worker threads from the CPU master thread (usually each will run on a different CPU core), one for each individual GPU. A worker thread will hold a CUDA context and be responsible for an individual GPU, while the CPU master thread can send messages or data to the 4 worker threads. Thus, we have a one-to-one relationship between the CPU threads and the GPU devices. As a result, the 4 worker threads can launch the 4 GPUs simultaneously and run the kernels in parallel.

The idea is that each CPU host thread, the worker thread, will attach to a different GPU device with a unique device ID for each CPU thread.

All data to be allocated and manipulated on the GPU should be created in the context of the CPU thread that is attached to its appropriate GPU device. By this means, we can run the GPU kernels from these CPU threads with different parts of the data that we want to process. Finally, after all four GPUs finish their computation, we copy the results back from the GPUs to the CPU master thread.

In this way, all the GPUs run the same code but operate on different parts of the input dataset in a parallel mode.

7. Results

7.1 Baseline CPU and GPU implementation

We performed our experiments of free tumour growth (based on cytokinetic models) on a desktop computer with AMD Phenom 9650 Quad-Core CPU processor, which has 4 CPU cores all running at 2.30 GHz.

At first, we tested the baseline CPU implementation, which used only a single CPU thread. The first GPU hardware in the experiments is an NVIDIA GTX 285 GPU, which contains 30 multiprocessors, each of which contains 8 streaming processors (for a total of 240 processor cores). We implemented our single GPU algorithm using the CUDA programming language [3]. The performance improvement of the GPU implementation compared to the baseline CPU implementation is shown in Table 1, where $time_b$ and $time_{g1}$ are the computing times (in milliseconds) of the baseline single CPU thread and the GTX 285 GPU implementation, respectively.

From Table 1, it can be seen that the more demanding the calculation becomes, the greater the benefit derived from using the GPU. The speedup increases both with an increase in $T_{interval}$ and an increase in the number of GCs (that is, an increase in spatial resolution).

TABLE 1
BASELINE CPU AND GPU PERFORMANCE

resolution of GCs	$T_{interval}$ (hours)	$time_b$ (ms)	$time_{g1}$ (ms)	speed-up factor
32^3	500	8604	173	49.7
32^3	5000	85332	1563	54.6
64^3	5000	970888	7905	122.8

This is due to an increase in the GPU occupancy (that is, the proportion of the hardware's threads that are actively in use) which, in essence, determines how successfully the hardware is kept busy. This can also help to reduce the effect of memory latency and dependencies.

The performance gain is particularly noticeable in the 64^3 example, in which the processing time was reduced from 16 minutes to 8 seconds, which can radically change the approaches that users employ to investigate their data.

7.2 Parallel multi-thread CPU implementation

The multiple-thread CPU implementation took place on an AMD Phenom 9650 Quad-Core CPU processor with 4 CPU cores running at 2.30 GHz. On this multi-core system, we split the computational task according to the number of available cores and assigned different parts of the GCs to different CPU threads for parallel computing. The multiple CPU threads run at the same time, with each core running a particular thread, and each CPU thread processes a different part of the data in parallel.

TABLE 2
MULTI-THREAD CPU PERFORMANCE

resolution of GCs	$T_{interval}$ (hours)	# of threads	$time_t$ (ms)	speed-up factor
64^3	5000	1	970888	1
64^3	5000	2	492580	1.97
64^3	5000	4	263522	3.68
64^3	5000	8	264655	3.67

The performance improvement of the multi-thread CPU implementation compared to the baseline single thread CPU implementation is shown in Table 2, where $time_t$ is the multi-thread CPU computing times in milliseconds for different numbers of CPU threads. From Table 2, we can see that the performance is slightly below linear for threads up to 4 in number and, thereafter, it does not improve.

The best performance of the parallel multi-thread CPU implementation is achieved when the number of threads is equal to the number of cores in the CPU hardware. In this case, each thread runs on a real CPU core, so that the horsepower of the multi-core CPU hardware can be fully utilized. More or fewer threads can only result in worse performance, since fewer threads cannot fully employ the power of the multi-core hardware, while more threads will entail more overheads than necessary.

7.3 Multi-GPU implementation

We performed the multi-GPU experiments on tumour growth based on cytokinetic models on an NVIDIA Tesla S1070 computing system, which (as mentioned earlier) contains four GT200 GPUs. We implemented the GPU part of the algorithm using the CUDA programming language [3] and the CPU parts of algorithm using C++.

The performance of the multi-GPU computation compared to that on a single GPU is shown in Table 3, where $time_{g1}$ and $time_{g4}$ are the computation times for one GPU and four GPUs, respectively, in milliseconds.

TABLE 3
PERFORMANCE OF MULTI-GPU v. SINGLE GPU

resolution of GCs	$T_{interval}$ (hours)	$time_{g1}$ (ms)	$time_{g4}$ (ms)	speed-up factor
64^3	5000	7905	2157	3.66

This result shows that the multi-GPU system greatly benefits from using all of its GPUs on a very large dataset. Four GPUs were almost 4× faster than a single GPU.

Tables 1 and 3 show that a computation that took 16 minutes on the single-core CPU was completed in 2.157 seconds on the Tesla S1070, a speed up of over 450×.

We also found that the multi-GPU implementation may be slower than a single GPU implementation when the amount of work to be performed per GPU is very small (for example, when the volume resolution is very low); this is due to the overheads associated with creating multiple CPU threads to take care of each GPU separately.

So, the multi-GPU implementation is only worthwhile when you have a significant amount of work to perform per GPU (for example, very large data volumes), so that the overhead of creating multiple CPU threads can be amortised. If that is the case, the acceleration with the number of GPUs can be fairly close to linear.

7.4 Implementation on the new GTX480 GPU

Both the S1070 and GTX285 used in the above experiments belong to the category of GT200 GPU, where each GPU has 240 processor cores, 16KB registers per multiprocessor and 16KB shared memory. Below we perform experiments on the Geforce GTX480 (from the current generation of NVIDIA GPUs, as this is written), which has 480 processor cores, 32KB registers per multiprocessor and 48KB shared memory; it also has a much faster memory clock.

The performance improvement of the GTX480 GPU compared to that of the GTX285 is shown in Table 4, where $time_{g1}$ and $time_{g2}$ are the computation times for GTX285 and GTX480, respectively, in milliseconds.

TABLE 4

PERFORMANCE ON GTX480 GPU

resolution of GCs	$T_{interval}$ (hours)	$time_{g1}$ (ms)	$time_{g2}$ (ms)	speed-up factor
64^3	5000	7905	2684	2.94

The experiment showed that the GTX480 GPU is 2.94 times faster than GTX285 in this application due to a number of factors associated with the greater number of cores, larger register and shared memory, and the faster memory clock on the GTX480 GPU.

7.5 Precision

Current GPUs fully support single-precision float arithmetic and conform to the floating point standard in the same way as the SIMD units in CPUs do. Numerical codes executing on these architectures today typically yield bit-identical results, and any discrepancies are within the floating point standard [11].

Unfortunately, in previous-generation GPUs (e.g. the NVIDIA GTX 285), the double-precision arithmetic is not very mature, so we used only single-precision float arithmetic in both the CPU and the GPU implementations. We intend, in the near future, to update our implementation into double-precision arithmetic on the newer NVIDIA Fermi GPU (e.g. the Tesla S2050), which has been specifically designed to offer unprecedented performance in double precision [12], and we anticipate even greater performance gains when we do.

8. Conclusion

GPU technology is currently greatly under-utilised in the context of the Virtual Physiological Human, and this paper was written as a case study in applying GPGPU programming within a VPH project to highlight its benefits. The gain in performance in this application clearly demonstrates that the GPU warrants a much more prominent role in the future development of the VPH than it has had the opportunity to play in the past.

This paper considered a successful existing approach to tumour growth simulation and developed code specifically to run such simulations on a variety of platforms including multi-core CPUs and many-core GPUs. The existing code was designed to run on a single-core CPU, and this acted as a reference point for the experiments that followed.

In the application, tumour simulation was performed by executing hourly scanning of a set of geometric cells representing the tumour and its close neighbourhood. The method simulates the cell-cycle phase transitions based on biological rules, and the cell deaths due to chemotherapy or radiotherapy that have occurred inside each GC. As a result, we can estimate the tumour volume and the quantity of cells (stem, proliferating, etc.) as a function of time from a given set of input parameters.

As the speeds provided by the GPU mean that users no longer have to compromise on resolution to achieve acceptable computation times, our discussion below concentrates on the highest resolution case investigated.

Compared to the baseline version running on a single core, our parallel implementation delivered a speed up of approximately 3.66× when using the quad-core capabilities of the same CPU.

We also proposed a GPU-based approach to tumour growth simulation that is carefully constructed to take full advantage of the particular architecture of the GPU. We assign GPU threads to perform the tumour simulation by executing the hourly scanning via parallel GPU kernels under the CUDA programming model.

Use of a single previous-generation GPU produced a speed up of approximately 122.8× over the baseline. The experiments showed that the performance gain in using a GPU is particularly noticeable for cases in which there is high spatial resolution or a long scanning time.

A multi-GPU parallelisation was also performed using a Tesla S1070, and this delivered a 450× speed-up over the baseline CPU. In this, we split the computational task according to the number of available GPUs, so that each GPU computes only a part of the array. In this way, all the available GPUs in the system can run in parallel. Our experiments showed that the multi-GPU system greatly benefits from using all of its four GPUs on very large data volumes. We found that the four GPUs were almost four times (3.66×) faster than using a single GPU.

A single latest-generation GPU provided a speed up of approximately 2.94× over the previous generation GPU, equivalent to a speed up of 361× over the baseline CPU.

GPU use thus proved to be an effective way of reducing the computational time in an application similar to many others in VPH projects. The result was that the users can treat the data differently. A single run of the application previously took over 16 minutes but the latest-generation single GPU reduced this to 2.7 seconds. This means that interactive data investigation can now be considered for large datasets, even on commodity hardware, offering users the prospect of much greater experimentation with parameters and settings than was previously possible.

In Monte Carlo and other statistical methods in which multiple runs of the same simulation are required in order to build up a probabilistic picture of the outcomes, it also becomes feasible to increase the numbers of experiments, possibly leading to more robust outcomes.

The current cost of a GTX480 is approximately €400. That such performance gains can be achieved for such a small investment in hardware is truly remarkable.

9. Acknowledgment

This work received partial support from the European Commission within the project Contra Cancrum (FP7-ICT-223979) and the Marie Curie Fellowship GAMVolVis (023610). Dr D. Dionysiou is acknowledged for her contribution to the model development. Feng Dong is supported by the Open Project Program of the State Key Lab of CAD&CG (Grant No. A1012), Zhejiang University.

References

[1] Stamatakos, G.S., Antipas, V.P. & Uzunoglu, N.K. 2006 A spatio-temporal, patient-individualized simulation model of solid tumor response to chemotherapy in vivo: the paradigm of glioblastoma multiforme treated by temozolomide, *IEEE Trans Biomedical Engineering*, 53(8):1467-1477

[2] Dionysiou, D.D. & Stamatakos, G.S. 2006 Applying a 4D multiscale *in vivo* tumor growth model to the exploration of radiotherapy scheduling: the effects of weekend treatment gaps and p53 gene status on the response of fast growing solid tumors, *Cancer Informatics*, 2:113-121

[3] NVIDIA 2010 CUDA programming guide, NVIDIA

[4] Stamatakos, G.S. & Dionysiou, D.D. 2009 Introduction of Hypermatrix and Operator Notation into a Discrete Mathematics Simulation Model of Malignant Tumor Response to Therapeutic Schemes *in vivo*. Some Operator Properties, *Cancer Informatics* 7:239–251

[5] Stamatakos, G.S., Dionysiou, D.D., Graf, N.M., Sofra, N.A., Desmedt, C., Hoppe, A., Uzunoglu, N. & Tsiknakis, M. 2007 The Oncosimulator: a Multilevel, Clinically Oriented Simulation System of Tumor Growth and Organism Response to Therapeutic Schemes. Towards the Clinical Evaluation of *in silico* Oncology, *Proc IEEE Eng Med Biol Soc.*, Lyon, France, 23-26 Aug. 2007

[6] Stamatakos, G.S. 2010 In silico Oncology: PART I Clinically Oriented Cancer Multilevel Modeling based on Discrete Event Simulation", In *Multiscale Cancer Modeling*. (eds. T.S. Deisboeck, G.S. Stamatakos) Chapman & Hall

[7] Stamatakos, G.S., Kolokotroni, E.A., Dionysiou, D.D., Georgiadi, E.Ch. & Desmedt, C. 2010 An advanced discrete state - discrete event multiscale simulation model of the response of a solid tumor to chemotherapy: Mimicking a clinical study. *Journal of Theoretical Biology* 266, 124-139

[8] Steel, G. 2002 *Basic Clinical Radiobiology*. London: Arnold

[9] Marias, K., Sakkalis, V., Roniotis, A., Farmaki, C., Stamatakos, G., Dionysiou, D., Giatili, S., Uzunoglu, N., Graf, N., Böhle, R., Messe, E., Coveney, P.V., Manos, S., Wan, S., Folarin, A., Nagl, S., Büchler, P., Bardyn, T., Reyes, M., Clapworthy, G.J., McFarlane, N., Liu, E., Bily, T., Balek, M., Karasek, M., Bednar, V., Sabczynski, J., Opfer, R., Renisch, S. & Carlsen, I.C. 2009 Clinically Oriented Translational Cancer Multilevel Modeling: The ContraCancrum Project. In *World Congress 2009 on Medical Physics and Biomedical Engineering* (eds. O. Doessel & W.C. Schlegel), Sept 7-12, Munich, Germany, IFMBE Proceedings 25/IV, 2124-2127

[10] Garland, M. & Kirk, D.B. 2010 Understanding throughput-oriented architectures. *CACM* 53(11): 58-66

[11] Brodtkorb, A.R., Dyken, C., Hagen, T.R., Hjelmervik, J.M. & Storaasli, O.O. 2010 State of the Art in Heterogeneous Computing, *Journal of Scientific Programming*, 18(1):1-33

[12] NVIDIA 2010 *Fermi Compute Architecture Whitepaper*. NVIDIA

CCVis: A Software Plugin for Unified Visualisation in ContraCancrum based on VTK Extensions

Youbing Zhao[1], Gordon J. Clapworthy[1], Yubo Tao[1,2], Feng Dong[1], Hui Wei[1], Tao Wang[1]

[1] Centre for Computer Graphics & Visualisation, University of Bedfordshire, UK
[2] State Key Lab. of CAD&CG, Zhejiang University, China

{youbing.zhao, gordon.clapworthy, yubo.tao, feng.dong, hui.wei, tao.wang@beds.ac.uk}

Abstract

Medical visualisation is an indispensable means for doctors and researchers to better explore and analyse medical images. The EC-funded ContraCancrum project, which aims at more predictable tumour simulation and treatment, uses visualisation as an important tool to interactively display tumour development and tumour simulation. This paper presents CCVis – the visualisation tool in ContraCancrum – which is a Qt-based plugin of the DrEye platform. CCVis uses a unified architecture for visualisation of the patient image data and tumour simulation data. It provides axis-aligned and arbitrary slice views, isosurface rendering and volume ray casting as well as time-varying visualisation of patient image series and simulation data. Statistics in tumour simulation are plotted as 2D graphs. Major extensions of the Visualization Toolkit (VTK) are made to meet the demands for label highlighting and multi-dimensional transfer function.

Keywords: **ContraCancrum, DrEye plugin, VTK extensions, slice views, multi-layered isosurface, multi-dimensional transfer function, time-varying**

1. Introduction

ContraCancrum is an EC-funded project [1] which aims to boost the translation of clinically validated multi-level cancer models into clinical practice. To this end, the project has designed and developed a composite multi-level platform for simulating malignant tumour growth, as well as tumour response to therapeutic modalities and treatment schedules. In this process, accurate tumour identification in patient study images and reliable tumour simulation are key to the success.

Medical imaging technology continues to advance rapidly and the use of medical images from, for example, MRI or CT, have become indispensable for the diagnosis of a variety of diseases. Tumour simulation and evaluation in ContraCancrum is based on the accurate segmentation of tumours in patient study images. The traditional practice of radiologists was to study image slides by eye and analyse information in their heads. However, this method relies heavily on personal experience and is far from intuitive, especially for the analysis of complex shaped tumours and time-varying data series.

Visualisation is a powerful tool for presenting information in a more integrative and intuitive form. It can convert a huge amount of high dimensional data, which may be difficult for the human brain to process, into visual signals which can be more easily and quickly understood. Medical visualisation provides direct surface or volume rendering of tissues and organs in 3D space, which makes it easier to locate, highlight and analyse targets of user interest.

The aim of CCVis is to provide ContraCancrum researchers and doctors with a tailored tool to interactively view and analyse the progress of the tumour as to simulate the predicted outcomes of the proposed treatment, It provides functions that cannot be fully satisfied by existing software and enables the users to investigate tumour development and treatment interactively and to gain a more intuitive and comprehensive understanding of the tumour size, shape, position and composition at different time points.

For visualisation of the patient data in CCVis, slice views with highlighted tumour segmentation are useful to position tumours in 3D space. 3D surface and volume rendering of the segmented tumour is needed in order to display the shape of tumours and their relation to body tissues. For visualisation of simulation data, dynamic 3D rendering of the simulated tumour volume is required and the statistics of the tumour simulation have to be plotted as 2D graphs. Time-varying animation is needed for both the patient data and the simulation data to show tumour changes and to evaluate the effects of the treatment.

To achieve the above, the following facilities are provided:

- axis-aligned slice view
- arbitrary slice view
- isosurface rendering
- volume rendering
- time-varying visualisation
- 2D graph plotting of simulation statistics.

This paper presents the detailed design and implementation of CCVis for unified visualisation of patient images and tumour simulation data as a plugin of the DrEye [2] platform used by ContraCancrum. Major extensions of the Visualization Toolkit (VTK) [3] have

1550-6037/11 $26.00 © 2011 IEEE
DOI 10.1109/IV.2011.80

been made to meet the special visualisation demands of ContraCancrum

2. Architecture

DrEye [2] is used as the main platform for medical imaging processing in ContraCancrum. DrEye is .NET based software developed by the Foundation for Research and Technology – Hellas, Greece (FORTH) with the support of the Philips Research Centre and the University of Bern and is available freely to the scientific community [4]. It supports semi-automatic and manual segmentation of medical images in DICOM format. In ContraCancrum, DrEye is used for tumour segmentation and annotation – various layers of tumours are identified and annotated with different labels.

DrEye provides an architecture for customised plugins to accommodate additional imaging functionalities. Thus, interpolation and registration have been developed as DrEye plugins and integrated into DrEye. DrEye also provides basic isosurface visualisation of segmentation. However, the lack of advanced visualisation capabilities such as volume rendering and slice-based views made it too limited for the visualisation requirements of ContraCancrum. Consequently, a dedicated visualisation software tool was proposed by the participants of ContraCancrum and implemented as a DrEye plugin.

Figure 1 shows the architecture of CCVis which is based on VTK [3], Qt [5], GDCM [6] and is wrapped as a DrEye plugin.

As the most popular visualisation toolkit, VTK provides a variety of visualisation functions and widgets which may be used by or adapted into CCVis, such as isosurface rendering, orthographic slice view, simple volume rendering. CCVis uses VTK 5.6 as the base for its visualisation module. However, major extensions to VTK 5.6 have to be made as it lacks some important functions needed by ContraCancrum, such as arbitrary slicing with label highlighting, multi-dimensional transfer function based volume rendering, etc.

Qt is an open source, cross-platform application and UI framework with a large commercial and academic user community. The licence of Qt changed to LGPL from 2009, so increasing numbers of users have been joining the Qt community. For example, 3D Slicer [7] will shortly move from KWWidgets to the Qt platform. There are also many visualisation-related Qt-based open-source projects available, such as MITK [8]. In CCVis, Qt is used for implementation of the user interface. The Qt-based plotting library QWT [9] is used for the 2D graph plotting.

As mentioned earlier, CCVis has to provide slice views and volume rendering of both the patient data and simulation data. As patient image series and simulation data are both expressed as volume data, to avoid redundancy and improve reusability, these functions can be shared between the two data types. In the CCVis architecture, the patient data visualisation module and the simulation data visualisation module share a common visualisation core, but have their own data import interfaces, as shown in Figure 1. The benefit of this unified design is that the visualisation module can be separated and reused, thus reducing the complexity of the system as a whole.

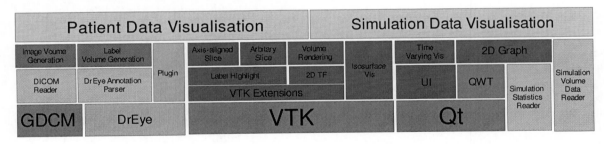

Figure 1. CCVis architecture

3. Patient image data visualisation

3.1. Data interface

In ContraCancrum, the patient data are DICOM [10] images from MRI or CT studies; tumour segmentation is subsequently generated by DrEye. In the DICOM model, a study comprises several image series, with each series generally equating to a position of the patient on the acquisition device or to a specific type of data. A series is usually composed of multiple sequentially scanned images which constitute a 3D volume. Each patient may have multiple studies taken at different times during the treatment, which can be visualised as a time-varying series. Segmentations of the tumour are generated semi-automatically in DrEye and stored as DrEye annotations. DICOM images with DrEye annotations form the patient data inputs for CCVis.

3.1.1 DICOM image reading

As CCVis is Qt-based while DrEye is .NET-based, CCVis cannot use the APIs from DrEye to read the DICOM images or parse the corresponding annotations. Moreover, our experience with the .NET based DICOM reading in DrEye was that it is slow compared to other C++ implementations, especially when reading large data sets.

To solve the problem, CCVis uses a popular DICOM image reader Grassroots DiCoM (GDCM) [6] to read the DICOM images, and designed our own C++ based DrEye annotation parser. GDCM is a C++ library which implements the DICOM base standard part 5 that concentrates on image file format. The Insight Toolkit (ITK) [11] also uses GDCM to read/write DICOM images.

3.1.2 DrEye annotation structure

Annotations generated by DrEye are labelled pixels on the corresponding images. In ContraCancrum, they represent segmentations of different layers of tumours. A DrEye annotation contains doctor name, time stamp, label name, colour and point list which are organised in an XML format as shown in Figure 2. Annotations can be stored as separate XML files or embedded in the corresponding DICOM images as TextValue Tags (0x0040, 0xa160). In an image series, annotations are essentially labelled 3D voxels; thus, a label volume can be generated after parsing all the annotations attached to a given image series. In ContraCancrum, a byte label volume is enough to represent all label values. Tumour volume size can also be estimated by calculating the number of labelled voxels in the annotations.

```
<Annotations>
 <Annotation>
  <Doctor>ADMINISTRATOR</Doctor>
  <Timestamp>2010/04/03/20:32:41</Timestamp>
  <Label>Tumor</Label>
  <Color>255 255 0 0</Color>
  <Points>339 224 340 224 339 225 340 225 338 226 </Points>
 </Annotation>
</Annotations>
```

Figure 2. A DrEye annotation example

3.2. Slice views

To better locate the tumour position and understand the shape of the tumours, the users need multiple slice views of the same data in the visualisation environment. Interactive slice views are provided for visualising both the patient images and the tumour simulations. There are two types of slice views: axis-aligned and arbitrary. Both allow the user to move the slices interactively. *vtkImagePlaneWidget* supports both axis-aligned and the arbitrary slicing of volume data but it does not satisfy the requirements of ContraCancrum. To meet this challenge, major extensions were made to *vtkImagePlaneWidget;* these will be described in detail in Section 3.2.3.

3.2.1 Axis-aligned slice view

Orthographic slice views are a familiar way of presenting medical image data to doctors and biomedical researchers. CCVis provides the usual three axis-aligned slice views parallel to the coordinate planes. Axis-aligned views show sagittal, coronal and transversal images in one or multiple views. Hence, the user can view the shape of the tumour from multiple directions at the same time, thus facilitating the understanding of the tumour shape and position, as shown in Figure 3.

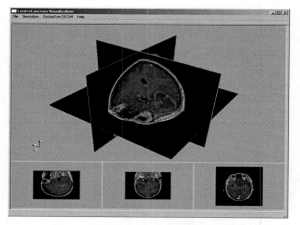

Figure 3. Axis-aligned slice view

3.2.2 Arbitrary slice view

Axis-aligned slices provide orthographic slice views of volume data, but the constraint on slice directions limits the freedom of interactive viewing and exploration. As the shapes of tumours are usually irregular, a cutting plane with arbitrary directions may further help the user to obtain information of the shape and interior of tumours from arbitrary angles, as shown in Figure 4.

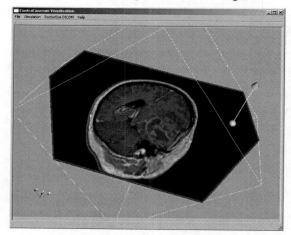

Figure 4. Arbitrary slice view

3.2.3 Unified implementation of axis-aligned slice and arbitrary slice

CCVis provides a unified implementation of both the axis-aligned slice and arbitrary slice based on extended *vtkImagePlaneWidget* to support overlay of a label volume. An auxiliary widget *vtkImplicitPlaneWidget* is used for user interaction to make the slice outline conform to the volume and remove black pixels outside the volume. Axis-aligned slicing is achieved by constraining the plane orientation to the coordinate axes.

- **External region removal**

While *vtkImagePlaneWidget* supports arbitrary slicing, its image slice (generated internally by *vtkImageReslice*) is always rectangular and does not follow the shape of the volume data. Regions outside the volume will be set to black. It is not possible to remove the external regions by use of a colour lookup table as there are also black voxels in the volume. This limitation makes it difficult to understand and estimate the true position of the tumour inside the volume.

To show the external regions as transparent, extensions to *vtkImagePlaneWidget* were made. A mask image is calculated based on the cutting plane. *vtkImageMask* is then used to unmask all the pixels outside the volume on the image slice.

- **Slice outline**

As *vtkImagePlaneWidget* uses rectangular slices, the widget outline is also rectangular and does not follow the shape of the volume data.

To show the widget outline as a polygon shape that conforms to the volume data, an auxiliary plane widget *vtkImplicitPlaneWidget* is used for user interaction and display of the outline. Synchronisation of plane position and orientation between *vtkImplicitPlaneWidget* and *vtkImagePlaneWidget* is made whenever there is user interaction.

- **Tumour highlighting**

vtkImagePlaneWidget does not support highlighting of additional label volumes, which is indispensable in ContraCancrum. To meet this challenge, major extensions of vtkImagePlaneWidget were made. An extended image slicing widget is derived from *vtkImagePlaneWidget*. An additional label volume is added and slicing is performed for both the data volume and label volume. The label values in the label slice are firstly converted into colours via the user-specified colour lookup table and then blended with the data slice by use of *vtkImageBlend*. As the transparency of the label slice can be adjusted through *vtkImageBlend*, the user can interactively change the transparency of the label overlay.

3.3. Multi-layer isosurface rendering

As tumours are generally composed of different layers, such as necrotic, cyst, oedema, proliferate, etc, isosurface rendering is useful to show the shape and composition of tumours.

The most popular algorithm for generating isosurfaces is the marching cube algorithm [12]. VTK provides two types of marching cube algorithm: *vtkMarchingCubes* and *vtkDiscreteMarchingCubes*. The former is for isosurface generation of continuous data types, while the latter is specially designed for discrete data types. As our volume has discrete scalars, *vtkDiscreteMarchingCubes* is used to generate the isosurfaces.

After isosurfaces of all scalar values are extracted, *vtkThreshold* is used to select the isosurfaces with the specified label value. These isosurfaces are stored in a list for future rendering. Layer isosurfaces with different label values can be selectively turned on and off. Isosurface rendering along with an axis-aligned slice is shown in Figure 5.

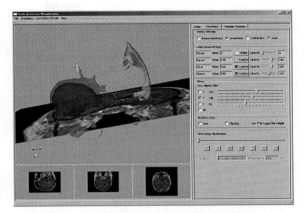

Figure 5. Isosurface rendering with an axis-aligned slice

3.4. Multi-dimensional transfer function based volume rendering

Volume rendering is helpful for visualising the contents of volume data. In ContraCancrum, it helps the doctors to understand the composition, position and shape of the tumour and the space relationship between the tumour and related tissues. Hybrid rendering of the isosurface and volume rendering is desirable to show layered tumours in relation to the structures of normal body tissue in 3D space.

Volume rendering based on multi-dimensional transfer functions [13] can improve detail presentation and discrimination compared to rendering based on 1D transfer functions. It is critical to discriminate tumours and their surrounding tissues in ContraCancrum. However, the intensity of the tumours encountered often differs very little from that of the surrounding tissue, thus a 1D transfer function can not distinguish sufficiently to produce a clear result. Consequently, multi-dimensional transfer function based volume rendering is preferred to accommodate this feature of the data.

VTK 5.6 provides several volume rendering classes (referred to as data mappers in VTK); however, none of them supports a multi-dimensional transfer function. Consequently, we extended VTK with our own class of GPU-based ray casting to provide a unified interface to volume rendering based on both 1D transfer functions or multi-dimensional transfer functions.

3.4.1 GPU-based ray casting and VTK

GPU-based ray casting was first proposed by Krüger and Westermann [14] and is widely accepted now as the leading technique for rendering volume data at interactive frame rates. For each pixel of the image plane, a ray is cast through the volume from the viewpoint; it samples the scalar values inside the volume along the ray. A transfer function is applied to each scalar value to obtain the colour and opacity of the sample, and these values are combined based on the volume rendering integral to generate the final colour of the associated pixel. Due to the programmability and flexibility of modern GPUs, this single-pass ray casting can be implemented in the fragment shader of the GPU, and the rendering efficiency is greatly improved.

VTK 5.6 already provides OpenGL-based GPU ray casting in *vtkOpenGLGPUVolumeRayCastMapper*, and its fragment shaders are written in the OpenGL shading language (GLSL) [15]. The GLSL code of the single-pass ray casting is decomposed into several files, such as the ray construction (*HeaderFS*), the ray cast loop (*CompositeFS* and *CompositeMaskFS*), and the composite mode (*OneComponentFS* and *FourComponentFS*). Thus, a new shading algorithm can be quickly implemented by providing only the different part of the code.

The entire volume is stored in a single 3D texture in VTK, and the fragment shader is invoked to cast the ray into the volume. The window coordinates of the ray are transformed to texture coordinates to obtain the starting position of the 3D texture. The colour and opacity of each sample is interpolated from the transfer function at the sampled scalar value. Currently, VTK 5.6 supports only a 1D transfer function (*vtkOpacityTable* and *vtkRGBTable*).

3.4.2 Implementation

vtkOpenGLGPUVolumeRayCastMapperMD is a new class that was implemented to support both 1D and 2D transfer functions within the VTK framework. It is inherited from *vtkGPUVolumeRayCastMapper*, so it can be used without a need to change the source code of original VTK application.

The new class has the same features as *vtkOpenGLGPUVolumeRayCastMapper*, and it further supports the widely used 2D transfer functions [13] which take the scalar value and gradient magnitude as lookup table entries. Two auxiliary classes, *vtkOpacityTable2D* and *vtkRGBTable2D* are provided to support 2D transfer functions. These are used to store the 2D opacity table and the 2D RGB table, respectively, in the CPU memory. As 2D transfer functions require gradient magnitude values, a new 3D texture is added to store the gradient magnitude volume in *vtkKWScalarField*. The gradient magnitude volume is evaluated and transferred to the GPU before volume rendering.

As discussed above, the GLSL code of the fragment shader comprises several code files. The framework can be reused and only new code dedicated to the 2D transfer function based volume rendering needs to be written. Three new GLSL files (*CompositeFS2D*, *CompositeMaskFS2D* and *OneComponentFS2D*) are added in our implementation. *CompositeFS2D* and *CompositeMaskFS2D* sample the opacity from the 2D opacity texture, while *OneComponentFS2D* samples the colour from the 2D RGB texture. These new files together with the original GLSL files can be dynamically composed into a run-time shading code to support various rendering algorithms.

The user can switch the classification between a 1D and a 2D transfer function at run time. The framework can automatically update corresponding textures and

transfer the composed GLSL fragment code to the GPU for rendering. The tumour can be rendered using either form of transfer function at interactive frame rates.

Although we have implemented only 1D and 2D transfer functions [13] in our framework, other dimensional transfer functions could easily be integrated in a similar way. Figure 6 is an example of a 2D transfer function based volume ray casting with isosurface rendering.

3.5. Time-varying visualisation

The visualisation of time-dependent patient image series and simulation data requires time-varying animation of the change of tumour shape and position. Patient studies are sorted in time order before they are visualised sequentially. This is achieved by user-specified ordering or by retrieving the StudyTime (0008,0030) tag in DICOM images.

Time-varying visualisation of patient data also demands the registration of patient data at different time points as they may have different positions, dimensions or even spacing. The registration of volume data and the transformation of their corresponding label volumes is performed by the University of Bern as a DrEye plugin using ITK registration. The registered patient image data and label volumes are then provided as inputs to CCVis.

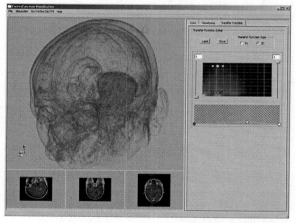

Figure 6. Hybrid 2D transfer function based volume rendering with isosurface rendering

4. Simulation data visualisation

Tumour simulation in ContraCancrum is undertaken by ICCS, Greece [16]. The generated simulation data are composed of simulation volume data series and related statistics. A special data import module is designed for reading simulation volume data and simulation statistics.

4.1 Simulation volume data visualisation

The simulation volume data are essentially label volumes with labels representing different tumour cell types, such as normal, necrotic, proliferate, etc. Each voxel in the label volume represents a certain number of cells in the tissue and the number of cells in the simulation is usually several orders of magnitude larger than the number of voxels. With the unified visualisation core, the visualisation of the simulation volume data is very similar to that of the patient volume data. Axis-aligned slice, arbitrary slice, multi-layer isosurface rendering and multi-dimensional volume ray casting are all available for simulation volume visualisation. The difference is that the simulation volume data themselves are label volumes and the size of simulation volume data is usually much smaller.

4.2 Simulation statistics visualisation

Simulation statistics are tumour related time-dependent quantities, such as the number of cells of each type and their percentage during tumour simulation.

2D plotting of polylines or fitted curves are used for visualising time-varying tumour simulation statistics. The implementation uses the Qt-based open source plotting library QWT [9]. As the numbers of different cell types can differ greatly from each other, an option of logarithmic drawing is provided to show each curve more clearly.

Visualisation of an examplar simulation data is shown in Figure 7.

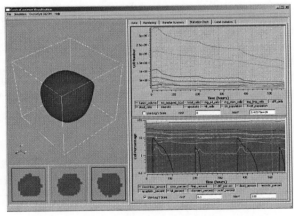

Figure 7. Visualisation of simulation volume data and statistics

Conclusions

The plugin is available to the ContraCancrum community freely. Responses from the end users show that CCVis is an effective visualisation tool for interactive viewing and analysis of tumour development, treatment and simulation.

Further work may include slice interpolation from multiple image series (saggital, coronal, transversal). As the inter-slice distance of medical images is usually much larger than the pixel distance in one image series, it is common that two of the three orthographic slices are in low resolution. If multiple image series are available, interpolation from more than one data set will enhance the resolution of slice views.

Another direction could be the integration of CCVis with a web service based data retrieval system we have implemented [17] for ContraCancrum. It would facilitate data acquisition and visualisation if data could be fetched directly from the online database.

Acknowledgements

We would like to thank the following partners in the project for their kind help and useful suggestions throughout the development of the work reported: Prof. Norbert Graf of Universitat des Saarlandes, Stefan Bauer of Universitat Bern, Prof. Georgios Stamatakos of the Institute of Communication and Computer Systems, Dr. Konstantinos Marias of FORTH and Dr Jörg Sabczynksi of Philips Research. Yubo Tao is partially supported by NFS of China (No. 60903133) and Feng Dong is partially supported by the Open Project Programme of the State Key Lab of CAD&CG (Grant No. A1012), Zhejiang University.

References

[1] ContraCancrum, http://www.contracancrum.eu/

[2] E Skounakis, C Farmaki, V Sakkalis, A Roniotis, K Banitsas, N Graf, K Marias, DoctorEye: A clinically driven multifunctional platform, for accurate processing of tumors in medical images, Open Med Inf J, 4:105-115, 2010

[3] The Visualization Toolkit (VTK), http://www.vtk.org

[4] DrEye, http://biomodeling.ics.forth.gr/?page_id=8

[5] Qt, http://qt.nokia.com/products/

[6] Grassroots DICOM (GDCM), http://sourceforge.net/projects/gdcm/

[7] 3D Slicer, http://www.slicer.org

[8] MITK, http://www.mitk.org/

[9] QWT - Qt Widgets for Technical Applications, http://qwt.sourceforge.net/

[10] DICOM, http://medical.nema.org/

[11] Insight Toolkit (ITK), http://www.itk.org

[12] W E Lorensen, H E Cline, Marching Cubes: A high resolution 3D surface construction algorithm. Computer Graphics, 21(4):163-169, 1987

[13] J Kniss, G Kindlmann, C Hansen, Interactive volume rendering using multi-dimensional transfer functions and direct manipulation widgets. IEEE Visualization 2001, pp. 255-262, 2001

[14] J Krüger, R Westermann, Acceleration techniques for GPU-based volume rendering. IEEE Visualization 2003, pp. 287-292, 2003

[15] OpenGL Shading Language, http://www.opengl.org/documentation/glsl/

[16] G S Stamatakos, V P Antipas, N K Uzunoglu, A spatiotemporal, patient individualized simulation model of solid tumor response to chemotherapy in vivo: the paradigm of glioblastoma multiforme treated by temozolomide. IEEE Trans Biomed Eng. 53(8):1467-77, 2006

[17] T Wang, Y Zhao, E Liu, G J Clapworthy, X Zhao, H Wei, F Dong, Using web services as functional-level plug ins for interactive 3D medical visualisation, Proc Information Visualisation 2010 (IV 2010), pp. 617-622, 2010

Intuition in Medical Image Segmentation: Visualizing Graph Edge Weights

Ryan A Beasley, Christopher R Wagner

Texas A&M University, College Station TX 77843, USA; Orthorun, Ltd., Ware, United Kingdom
beasley@entc.tamu.edu, chris@orthorun.com

Abstract

Weighting functions for graph-based medical image segmentation algorithms (e.g., Graphcut) have a significant effect on the segmentation, but to our knowledge no tool provides the user with intuition towards their proper selection. The large variety, their complexity, and the limited feedback hinders comparison of choices. This paper describes a package developed to visualize the effects of various edge weighting functions and parameters, in which the image of interest is overlaid with colors depicting the relative distances from the nearest seed to each voxel. By seeing the colors vary while changing parameters, the user gains intuition into the various options for the edge weighting function. A user study demonstrating the benefits of the package is presented. It is our hope that the intuition provided by the software will result in less time required to segment medical images in the clinical work-flow.

1 Introduction

The result of using a poorly-fitting segmentation algorithm is that labeling structures of interest in a medical image can take significant amounts of time to ensure the necessary accuracy, such as when quantifying cardiac ejection volume or designing patient-specific jigs for joint replacement [1]. Graph-based algorithms are popular for medical image segmentation (e.g., Graphcut is fast and suitable for either user-guided or autonomous operation), but the resulting segmentation is significantly based on the weighting function. The variety and complexity of possible weighting functions, as well as the lack of feedback beyond the resulting segmentation, hinders the development of intuition in the selection of the weighting function and any parameters.

Several papers have investigated the efficacy of specific weighting functions [2], evaluated the relative accuracy of segmentations performed using a range of values for parameters in a specific weighting function [3], or provided a weighting function tailored to a specific modality and organ [4]. Such works provide advice that is either very general or very specific, but do not tend to build the users intuition about the mechanisms by which different weighting

functions effect the segmentations. Meanwhile, graph visualization is an active area of research, often used to investigate the connectivity of a system [5]. Rather than being interested in how the graph is connected, we are concerned in combining the voxel position in the image relative to the seeds with the variations in the lengths of those graph connections, and thereby investigate the differences such variations will cause in segmentations.

This paper describes a package developed to visualize the effects of various edge weighting functions. The software shows the image of interest colored based on the distance as measured on the graph. The user thus gains intuition into the various choices for the edge weighting function based on the respective amount that different areas of the image change color. A user study demonstrating the benefits of the package is presented. It is our hope that the intuition provided by the software will result in less time required to segment medical images in the clinical workflow.

2 Methods

Graph-based segmentation algorithms treat each voxel in the image as a separate vertex, connected by "edges" to its neighbors. The likelihood that two neighboring voxels belong to the same area is determined by the weight (i.e., length or capacity) of the edge. The edge weight is calculated by the weighting function, typically based on the intensities of the voxels.

2.1 Options in graph-based segmentation

Various definitions of a "neighborhood" can be used, changing the layout or connectivity of the graph. Commonly either von Neumann or Moore neighborhoods are used, with a distance of 1. For two-dimensional images, the resulting neighborhoods are either 4-connected or 8-connected, where the number is how many edges connect to a centrally-located pixel. The former only allows edges between orthogonally-adjacent voxels, while the latter also places edges diagonally. Equivalent neighborhoods for three-dimensional volumes are 6-connected or 26-connected. The study presented in this paper uses

1550-6037/11 $26.00 © 2011 IEEE
DOI 10.1109/IV.2011.17

a three dimensional image, and a 6-connected (von Neumann) neighborhood is used to construct the graphs.

In addition to the parameters that affect the graph construction, once the graph has been constructed different algorithms can be applied to that same graph. For the segmentations performed in this paper we used Dijkstra's shortest path algorithm [6]. Using this algorithm, each graph vertex receives the label of the nearest seed point. The edge weights are therefore thought of as lengths, and the weight of an edge should be low between vertices that should share the same label. An example on another popular segmentation algorithm is Graphcut [7], in which the max-flow/min-cut approach is used to segment the image.

The edge weight function is an area of active research and many weighting functions have been proposed. Typically these functions are modifications to either the Gaussian form (1) or the Reciprocal form (2):

$$w_{ij,gauss} = \frac{1}{\text{dist}(v_i, v_j)} \exp\left(-\beta \text{diff}^2(v_i, v_j)\right), \quad (1)$$

$$w_{ij,recip} = \frac{1}{\text{dist}(v_i, v_j)} \frac{1}{1 + \beta \text{diff}^2(v_i, v_j)}, \quad (2)$$

where $g(v_i)$ is the image intensity at voxel v_i, diff $(\cdot)$ is the absolute value of the difference in intensities between two voxels, β is a free parameter, and dist $(\cdot)$ is the Euclidean distance between the centers of two voxels. As an example of modifications, the most popular may be an *a priori* intensity-distribution term used to estimate the probability that the two pixels belong to separate areas.

For the user study in this paper, four edge weight functions were implemented. The functions were chosen for minimal complexity, but with expected variation in performance. The simplest conceivable weighting function is a constant value (3), though equal weights result in very poor segmentation performance. Using the normalized difference between intensities (4) provides relatively good results except at weak boundaries. Squaring that value increases the effect of gradients, making it more likely that label boundaries will meet at high gradients in the image (5). The final function is the natural-log-reciprocal of the normalized difference (6). The functions implemented are thus:

$$w_{ij,constant} = 1, \quad (3)$$

$$w_{ij,delta} = \text{diff}(v_i, v_j)/max\_diff, \quad (4)$$

$$w_{ij,squared} = \left(\text{diff}(v_i, v_j)/max\_diff\right)^2, \quad (5)$$

$$w_{ij,ln\_recip} = -\ln\left(\frac{1}{1 + \text{diff}(v_i, v_j)/max\_diff}\right), \quad (6)$$

where *max_diff* is the maximum difference between any pair of neighbors in the volume.

2.2 Software

We have developed a C++ software package to assist users in visualizing the effects of various options in graph-based segmentation algorithms. The program utilizes the Boost Graph Library (BGL) to generate graphs and perform graph-based computations [8]. OpenGL is used for visualization.

The user starts by loading a medical image. The screen displays the image in a standard three-slice view, with slider bars to scan through the slices in each view, Fig. 1. The user can click on any of the views to place seeds of a specific label (i.e., color) determined by a drop-down box. The user can select different functions for the edge weight calculation via radio buttons. For the user study in this paper, the software contains radio buttons that select between the edge weighting functions above (constant, delta, squared, and reciprocal (3–6)).

Pressing a button labelled "Segment" will segment the image based on the current seeds and chosen edge weight function. Specifically we use BGL's implementation of Dijkstra's single-source shortest paths, with all the seeds set to a distance of zero. Prior to calculating the shortest paths, we convert our multi-source problem into a single-source problem by adding zero-length edges from one of the seeds (the source) to all the other seeds. A BGL "visitor" is used to propagate the labels. Once the segmentation is complete (13 seconds for a 126 x 175 x 85 voxel image, on an Intel Core2 2.4GHz CPU), the image is overlayed with the segmentation colors (i.e., labels).

Pressing a button labelled "Calculate heatmap" will color the image based on the shortest path distance to any seed. Voxels relatively close to any seed are given a hue closer to zero degrees (red), while voxels relatively far from all seeds are given a hue closer to 240 degrees (blue). To do so, a segmentation is performed as though the user had pressed the "Segment" button, but instead of overlaying the segmentation colors, the overlay is a "heatmap" derived from the resulting distance from each voxel to the nearest seed. The initially attempted calculation for the overlay color, c_i, for a given voxel, v_i, with distance, d_i, gave equal weight to the entire range of distances,

$$c_{i,hue,equal} = 240 \frac{d_i - min\_distance}{max\_distance - min\_distance}, \quad (7)$$

$$c_{i,saturation} = 1, \quad (8)$$

$$c_{i,value} = 1, \quad (9)$$

where *max_distance* is the maximum distance for any voxel in the image, and *min_distance* is the minimum distance for any voxel. Initial trials using (7) colored the majority of the image pure red for the squared function (5) as a result of the outliers the squared function creates in the voxel distances. Those outliers reduce the ability to differentiate between

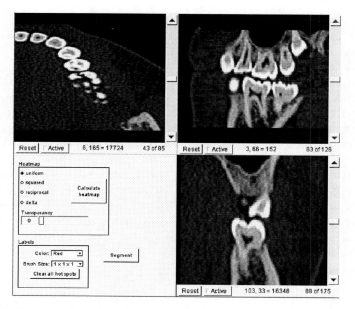

Figure 1: User interface, displaying CT of jaw. Utilizes a standard 3-plane view.

smaller (but still significant) differences in distance. As a result, the implementation for this paper clamps distances above a constant value, d^*,

$$c_{i,hue,clamped} = \begin{cases} 240\frac{d_i - min\_distance}{d^* - min\_distance} & \text{if } d_i < d^*, \\ 240 & \text{if } d_i \geq d^*, \end{cases} \quad (10)$$

where d^* was chosen to be twice the mean of the distances. Since the seeds are defined to have a distance of zero and all the edge weight functions used in this paper create positive-length edges, it was not necessary to clamp the low side of the distances.

Other buttons, sliders, and menu options enhance usability. The user can vary the transparency of any overlay using a slider widget. All seeds can be removed from the image with a button. Finally, the user can save and load segmentations and seeds.

2.3 User Study

A small user study was implemented to demonstrate the capabilities of the software package. The goal of the user study was to see if the subjects were able to choose the edge weighting fuction that best segments an image, solely by looking at the heatmap. Six subjects, males between the ages of 18 and 22 with no prior experience in medical image processing, were provided a computer running the software, on which had been loaded a CT image of one side of a human jaw (126 x 175 x 85 voxels). The image is a cropped version of a volume provided on the OsiriX imaging software website (Pixmeo SARL, Geneva, Switzerland) under the name INCISIX [9]. The image had

been pre-seeded on one sagittal slice and one coronal slice, with seeds of one label on the upper jaw and teeth, seeds of a different label on the lower jaw and teeth, and seeds of a third label on the non-bone tissue and air.

Subjects were provided with a short description of medical image processing, as well as the purpose of the study in evaluating the usability of the software package to visualize the effects of different segmentation algorithms. The proctor demonstrated selecting different radio buttons to change the edge weight function, and demonstrated how to observe the resulting heatmap by dragging the sliders for each view and by varying the transparancy of the heatmap. Fig. 2 displays the heatmaps on the same slices for each of the four functions.

Subjects were told that the overlay colors were a function of distance to the segmentation seed points, and therefore higher color gradients are more likely to correspond to boundaries between segmentation labels. Subjects were told they had as much time as they needed to determine which of the four radio buttons they thought would result in the segmentation that best labeled the upper and lower jaw bones (and teeth), as well as which radio button they thought would perform the worst such segmentation.

At no time did the subjects see the seeds or a segmentation. Neither were they allowed to add or remove seeds. Furthermore, the subjects had no knowledge of the different functions except for the labels on the radio buttons (in order, uniform (selected the "constant" function), squared, reciprocal, and delta). The subjects were observed while they manipulated the software to prevent operational errors, and to answer any questions on operation of the soft-

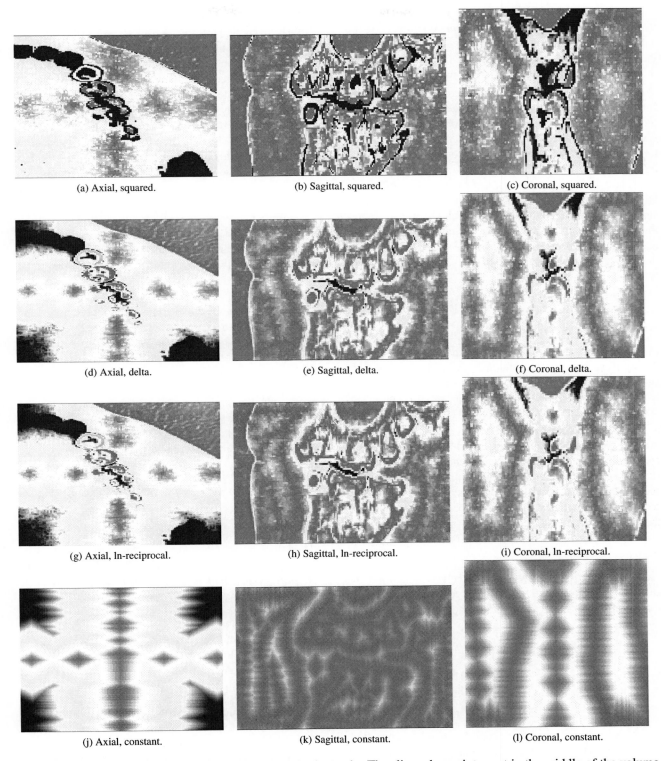

Figure 2: The "heatmaps" for the four functions used in the study. The slices shown intersect in the middle of the volume. The segmentation seeds were placed on the sagittal and coronal slices shown here. Colors indicate distance frome each voxel to the nearest seed. Ideally, each jaw would be surrounded by a blue outline, signifying significant separation, while the inside of the jaws would be red to signify similar areas.

ware. After the subjects indicated their choices for best and worst functions, they were asked for any comments on the software or the study. Then they were shown the segmentations that resulted from each function and any questions they had on the software or the study were answered.

After the experiment, the four segmentations (one per function) were generated from those seeds. The Dice Similarity Coefficient (DSC) was used to compare each of those segmentations with a manual segmentation. Here the DSC is calculated as twice the number of voxels that were labelled for the same jaw in both segmentations, divided by the sum over both segmentations of the number of voxels labelled as either jaw. A DSC of 1 would therefore represent that the segmentation labelled each voxel the same as the manual segmentation. Since the segmentations using each of the functions used the same seeds, and those seeds were only placed on one slice of the volume, much lower DSC's were expected, but higher DSC's still indicate better performance.

3 Results

Table 1 tallies the functions identified as best/worst by the subjects. For the best function, five of the six subjects selected the "squared" function (5), with one subject selecting the "delta" function (4). For the worst function, all six subjects selected the "constant" (3) function.

The DSC values between the segmentations and the manual segmentation are listed in Table 1. The squared function produced the segmentation that best matched the manual segmentation, only failing to label the very top of the upper jaw and very front portions of both jaws 3, and labelling almost no tissue voxels as bone. In comparison, the uniform function's segmentation had the lowest similarity, as it labelled many tissue voxels as bone and many bone voxels as tissue.

Table 1: Function quality: qualitatively as identified by subjects, and quantitatively calculated as the similarity (DSC) of the resulting segmentation to a manual segmentation.

Function name	# best	# worst	DSC
squared	5	0	0.890
delta	1	0	0.674
reciprocal	0	0	0.655
uniform	0	6	0.344

The subjects took an average of 6 minutes to manipulate the software and was observed to look through a range of slices in each view for each function. The few comments were positive on the software's ease of use. Following the study, each of the subjects asked for details on the specific functional forms indicated by the radio buttons.

Conclusions

We have created a software package that assists the user in visualizing the effects on graph-based segmentation algorithms of various edge weighting functions. The software allows the user to see the variations in vertex distance, which contains more information than the segmentation alone. A user study demonstrated that this approach has the potential to guide users in the understanding of how different graph edge weighting functions affect segmentations. We believe that this approach has the potential to reduce the amount of time necessary for medical image segmentation, by promoting accurate selection of edge weighting functions, parameters, neighborhood connectivity, etc.

Future improvements to the software would strive to investigate common choices in graph-based segmentations. The most significant enhancement would be allowing the user to choose between the shortest path segmentation approach used in this paper and the max-flow/min-cut approach (Graphcut). We also plan to add selection of the neighborhood connectivity, various edge weighting functions, the ability to vary parameters specific to each function, and possibly side-by-side comparisons. Finally, we will implement a user-modifiable transfer function for calculating the heatmap from the distances. The planned approach is to display a histogram of the distances and let the user pick the minimum and maximum distances (effectively a window/level operation). Following these technical and interface improvements, we will attempt to translate this package into the clinical work-flow.

Acknowledgements

ITK-SNAP was used extensively for image viewing and cropping [10].

References

[1] Hafez, M A, Chelule, K L, Seedhom, B B, Sherman, K P. *Computer-assisted Total Knee Arthroplasty Using Patient-specific Templating.* Clinical Orthopaedics & Related Research, vol. 444, pp. 184–192, 2006.

[2] Rother, C. and Kolmogorov, V. and Blake, A. *Grabcut: Interactive foreground extraction using iterated graph cuts.* ACM Transactions on Graphics (TOG), vol. 23, no. 3, pp. 309–314, 2004.

[3] Grady, L. and Jolly, M.P. *Weights and topology: A study of the effects of graph construction on 3d image segmentation.* Medical Image Computing and Computer-Assisted Intervention–MICCAI 2008, pp. 153–161, 2008.

[4] Funka-Lea, G. and Boykov, Y. and Florin, C. and Jolly, M.P. and Moreau-Gobard, R. and Ramaraj,

 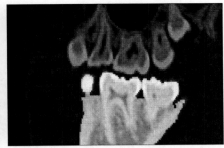

(a) Axial, segmentation from squared function.   (b) Sagittal, segmentation from squared function.

 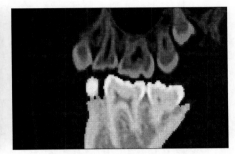

(c) Axial, manual segmentation.   (d) Sagittal, manual segmentation.

Figure 3: Sample segmentations, manual and based on the squared function. The upper jaw was seeded red. The lower jaw was seeded green. Soft tissue and air were seeded blue. The squared function performed the best of the functions tested in creating a segmentation similar to the manual segmentation (DSC 0.890). Still, some areas were incorrectly labelled (such as the incisors at the top of the axial view), due to the limited placement of seeds.

R. and Rinck, D. *Automatic heart isolation for CT coronary visualization using graph-cuts.* Biomedical Imaging: Nano to Macro, 2006. 3rd IEEE International Symposium on, pp. 614–617, 2006

[5] Kaufmann, M. and Wagner, D., *Drawing graphs: methods and models.* Springer Verlag, 2001.

[6] Dijkstra, E. W. *A note on two problems in connexion with graphs.* Numerische Mathematik 1, pp. 269-271, 1959.

[7] Boykov, Y., Jolly, M.P. *Interactive graph cuts for optimal boundary & region segmentation of objects in N-D images.* Proc. of ICCV 2001, pp. 105–112, 2001.

[8] Jeremy G. Siek, Lie-Quan Lee, and Andrew Lumsdaine. *The Boost Graph Library: User Guide and Reference Manual (C++ In-Depth Series).* Addison-Wesley Professional, December 2001.

[9] OsiriX, Dicom sample image sets. http://pubimage.hcuge.ch:8080/ retrieved February 2, 2011.

[10] Paul A. Yushkevich, Joseph Piven, Heather Cody Hazlett, Rachel Gimpel Smith, Sean Ho, James C. Gee, and Guido Gerig. *User-guided 3D active contour segmentation of anatomical structures: Significantly improved efficiency and reliability.* Neuroimage. vol. 31, no. 3, pp. 1116–28, 2006.

Real-Time Rendering of Temporal Volumetric Data on a GPU

Biao She, Pierre Boulanger, and Michelle Noga
Computer Science Dept., Computer Science Dept., Radiology Dept.
biao.she@ualberta.ca, pierreb@ualberta.ca, mnoga@ualberta.ca

Abstract

Real-time rendering of static volumetric data is generally known to be a memory and computationally intensive process. With the advance of graphic hardware, especially GPU, it is now possible to do this using desktop computers. However, with the evolution of real-time CT and MRI technologies, volumetric rendering is an even bigger challenge. The first one is how to reduce the data transmission between the main memory and the graphic memory. The second one is how to efficiently take advantage of the time redundancy which exists in time-varying volumetric data. We proposed an optimized compression scheme that explores the time redundancy as well as space redundancy of time-varying volumetric data. The compressed data is then transmitted to graphic memory and directly rendered by the GPU, reducing significantly the data transfer between main memory and graphic memory.

1 Introduction

The ability to image a heart in real-time, to visualize it, and to plan for treatments is key to reducing the cost of surgeries and to improving treatments. All heart disease treatments involve the establishment of critical competency assessment and require planning, rehearsal and predictive virtual tools. One advantage of high-resolution visualization is the possibility of virtual surgical training and planning. One study by Gallagher et al. [16] showed a six-fold improvement in avoiding vital structures after training with a surgical simulator. For accurate training, advanced visualization of the heart is key, given that it is a dynamic organ.

The processing speed of today's Central Processing Units (CPU) is not sufficient to achieve interactive visualization of real-time volumetric data. Fortunately, the recent development of high-speed Graphics Processing Units (GPU) capable of processing data at a rate of 1 Tera-flops is changing the landscape of today's computing power. Often a surface-based approach is used to render these data sets, but with the development of new graphics hardware, it is now possible to visualize, in real-time, volumetric data using texture-mapping or ray-casting techniques which are visually more accurate and do not require segmentation. This is a significant improvement because intra-anatomical structures cannot be visualized using surface techniques and many important details are lost. Volumetric visualization techniques are computationally much more expensive, making high-quality visualization of real-time dynamic cardiac data a challenge for current 3D rendering algorithms. Using a combination of tightly coupled scalar computing elements CPUs with a Graphics Processing Unit (GPU), the goal of this research project is to develop a GPU based algorithm capable of displaying large temporal volumetric data sets. The GPU contains multiple graphics processors that work in parallel, allowing the rendering of volumetric data in real-time. Using new volume texture based rendering techniques, one can dynamically bind volume data to the 3D rendering engine without degrading performance. The main problem with dynamic data is the high-bandwidth communication between the central memory and the GPU. In order to solve this problem, we present a novel algorithm to decompress the volumetric data within GPU in real-time, hence reducing the traffic on the main computer bus, to match the demands for real-time display and collaboration. This includes the development of techniques similar to video MPEG encoding, but for temporal volumetric data.

This paper is organized as follows, Section 2 reviews briefly the current state-of-the-art of medical volumetric visualization. Section 3 describes the system developed and its design objectives. Section 4 discusses the results of the implementation, and finally we conclude and present future research directions.

2 Literature Review

Volume rendering has been extensively studied for many years. Generally, there are five different optical rendering models for volume rendering, which are *Absorption Only [7] [2], Emission Only [8], Emission-Absorption Model [3] [1], Single Scattering [14] [4], and Shadowing [11] [9] and Multiple Scattering* [4]. Single Scattering and multiple scattering calculations are expensive in computer time, hence not suitable for real-time rendering yet.

1550-6037/11 $26.00 © 2011 IEEE
DOI 10.1109/IV.2011.85

The most widely used rendering technique is the Emission-Absorption Model. Both light emission and absorbtion in the volume are taken into account in this models. Solving the equation for volume rendering is both a computational and memory intensive process. Although many efficient software optimization techniques exist, it is difficult for general-purpose CPU, to deliver a real-time performance. Almost all existing real-time volume rendering algorithms one can find in the literature are either performed in parallel using multiple processors, GPU, or cluster. Most real-time rendering algorithms require volumetric data to be stored before hand on the GPU video memory as textures. When the size of volumetric data exceeds the capacity of the video memory, data exchange between video memory and other storage devices such as main memory and hard drive, is unavoidable reducing significantly the rendering speed as the data transmission between central memory and the GPU memory is usually not fast enough. The computational units in the GPU needs to wait for the data transmission to be done and then compute the rendering results. Therefore, data transmission time gradually becomes the main limit for real-time volume rendering. This is even more true in the case when visualizing time-varying volumetric data set as each time steps is in the order of 1 GB. For every individual time step, a complete copy of the volumetric data has to be transferred into graphic memory before rendering. To tackle the data transmission delay problem, a simple way is to add more video memory into the GPU. If all the time-steps could fit into the GPU memory, no data will be transmitted during the rendering stage, hence no transmission latency. The increasing capacity and lowering price of memory justify this unsophisticated approach in some sense. However, the size of volumetric data can possibly be infinite. Data compression is a more complex yet feasible way to deal with this issue as it has been used successfully in many video and audio applications over the Internet. A good compression algorithm can greatly reduce the amount of data that needs to be sent to the GPU. Many researchers [13] [5] [6] adopted data compression in their attempt to visualize real-time large volumetric data sets. Octree-structures, multi-resolution representation, wavelet-compression, run-length encoding and vector quantization are among the techniques used in some of those works. The trade-off for this compression strategy is the time needed to perform decompression. Any algorithm design should consider the cost of decompression in the rendering loop. If not a compression approach would not be useful if the decompression time takes longer than memory transfer time.

3   System Design

The proposed system is designed to render large time-varying volumetric data in real-time. In order to do so, we had to take flexibility and compatibility into account. The flexibility allows user to customize our system with their own algorithm easily and our shader programs can run on most GPUs, either NVIDIA or ATI.

Figure 1 shows an overview of the system. We generalize the process of visualizing volumetric data into four different modules. Each module is decoupled with each other, so that users have the flexibility to adopt their own algorithms into any module. The four different modules are: encoder, decoder, render, interaction handler. The interaction hander module provides parameters from input devices to the rendering module to generate interactive feedback and manipulations and is not described in this paper.

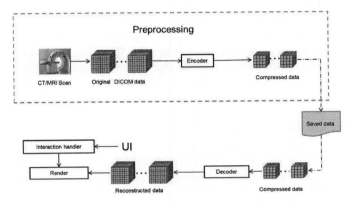

Figure 1: Overview of the rendering system.

The original volumetric data is usually obtained from a 4D CT or cardiac MRI scan. The scanner generates a large set of raw data in DICOM format which are saved into a hard disk or other massive storage devices. The encoder module then reads these DICOM files and processes them using the compression algorithms. The program then saves the compressed data into hard disk in a dedicated format. After preprocessing, the file reader reads the compressed data from the hard disk into main memory. The decoder module then upload the compressed data into GPU video memory for one time step. The decoding process is performed in the GPU after uploading. This is one of the most distinct features of our system. The combination of GPU decompression and volumetric rendering is not usual as most decompression algorithms are inherently serial, which makes an efficient decompression algorithm hard if not impossible to be implemented on GPU. However, vector quantization, which is the algorithm we adopted, is almost perfect for GPU decompression because of its parallel nature. The decoder module reconstructs the original data from the compressed file as 3D textures in the GPU video memory. This mechanism requires that the GPU must supports render to frame buffer object which can be directly read as 3D texture. After the decoder module reconstructs the original data in the GPU local memory as a 3D texture, the render module uses it for 3D texture-based volume rendering. The rendering algorithm slices and samples the texture memory to generate the final image displayed on screen. The interaction module allow user to interact with the system in real-time. In our implementation, user can switch between stereo mode and normal rendering mode. Our implementation also allows clipping along all three axis of the volume coordinates.

4 Implementation

As mentioned previously our system is composed of four sub-modules that will now be describe in some details.

4.1 Encoder Module

The main function of the encoder module is to reduce the size of the original data in order to reduce the traffic between the CPU and the GPU. To be real-time the decompression algorithm must be executed on the GPU very efficiently. Original data from 4D CT or cardiac MRI are usually not ready for vector quantization directly. There are a few preprocessing steps beforehand that need to be performed. We call these steps *Encoder Preprocessing*. The main components of the encoder preprocessing module are illustrated in Figure 2. In Figure 2, we define S_t as the original data sample of the volume at time t. Depending on the resolution of the sample data, the encoder module first decides if a re-sampling of the data is necessary. Trilinear interpolation is used to interpolate the value of the intermediate point from the original sample points. The reason for re-sampling is that our compression and rendering algorithm requires volume data with a size which is a multiple of the power of two in every dimension for efficient addressing.

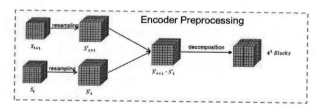

Figure 2: Preprocessing steps in the encoder module.

After re-sampling, all the data sets are at the desired dimension. The next step is to exploit the time redundancy of the re-sampled data. In our implementation, we subtract the re-sampled data of two consecutive volume, which is $S'_{t+1} - S'_t$. The time interval between the two consecutive samples are usually very short and the differences between them are usually small. Most of the difference values are actually 0, which give us lots of opportunity to compress the signal. Vector quantization perform better on these

sparse blocks. In our implementation, a higher signal-to-noise ratio (SNR) was observed when quantizing the sparse blocks instead of the original data.

Other than time redundancy, space redundancy is also used before final compression. Hierarchical decomposition is a very efficient way to analyze the relationships between neighboring sample points. Our system use the same decomposition method as in Schneider's paper [6]. The temporal difference $S'_{t+1} - S'_t$ is first divides into small blocks of size 4^3. Next, these blocks are decomposed into a multi-resolution representation. There are three steps to do this decomposition. Figure 3 illustrates the whole decomposition process. The first step is to divide the 4^3 block into 8 disjoint 2^3 blocks. Then the mean value of each 2^3 block are computed and stored in a new 2^3 block. We call this *detail level 0*. All the differences between the samples in 4^3 block and the corresponding mean value are stored in an array of size 64. We use *difference level 0* to represent the differences between two consecutive volume. The mapping from 4^3 block to the 64 array is given by $u = x + 4 * y + 16 * z$, where u is the corresponding index in the array for location (x, y, z) in 4^3 block. The last step of decomposition is basically the same process as in the second step. But it is applied to the detail 0 block. The results are one value which is essentially the mean value of the entire block and 8 values which are the subtraction of each sample in detail 0 level block relative to the mean value. The overall mean value is also a down-sampled version of the original 4^3 block. The 8 values differences from the last step will replace the values in detail level 0 to save memory space. At this point, all the preprocessing of the quantization are finished.

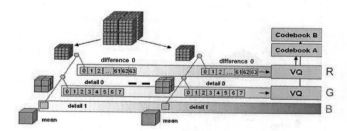

Figure 3: Data decomposition and vector quantization in the encoder module.

To quantize these blocks, we use a modified vector quantization algorithm. It is a more advanced algorithm than the conventional vector quantization algorithm. The advantages of the modified version comes from the way it gets the initial code-book. Normal algorithm, also called LBG-algorithm, recursively splits data set to get the code-book. Figure 4a shows the result of normal LBG-algorithm. It selects the geometric center of the entire input vectors as a first entry in the code-book, then split another entry by randomly setting an offset to the first entry. The two entries are then passed to a LBG-algorithm and processed. It stops until convergence is reached. The same splitting is then applied to the 2 entries to generate 4 entries. The whole algorithm ends until the desired bit-size is achieved, where the bit-size determine the size of the code-book. A bit-size of 8 means that a 256 length code-book is used. The normal procedure involves the process of finding nearest neighbors for n dimensional vector. It is very time consuming and the recursive splitting technique requires repeating the process several times. Hence, the LBG-algorithm is extremely slow in terms of speed. Pauly et al. [10] proposed a splitting technique where they addressed hierarchical clustering problems. The modified algorithm uses the same technique to split the original data as illustrated in Figure 4b. Like the normal splitting technique, it also starts with a single entry in the code book. Instead of getting another entry by random offset, it divides the entry into two entries with similar distortion rates. The next splitting continues with the entry with the largest distortion. Only the chosen entry splits into two smaller entries and each small entry has a smaller distortion. Only one more entry is generated after each split. The splitting process will stop until the desired number of entries are reached. The generated initial code-book is further refines by normal LBG-algorithm to get the final code-book. This splitting technology avoids significant number of time-consuming nearest neighbors search operation. Moreover, it also solve the empty cell problem which is common in the normal LBG-algorithm. Empty cell is not desired as it significantly increases the compression distortion. A more detailed description of the modified vector quantization algorithm can be found in Schneider's paper [6].

After vector quantization, we now have two code-books and a group of RGB color triplets. As shown in Figure 3, we denote the two code-books as code-book A and code-book B. Code-book A is the code-book for difference at level 0, which contains 64-dimensional arrays. Originally, there are $D'_x/4 * D'_y4 * D'_z/4$ arrays in total for the difference level 0. Those vectors are approximated by 256 different vectors after vector quantization. The R component in the RGB color triplets records the index in the code book of corresponding vector. The index is a 8-bits variable. The code-book B is the code-book for detail level 0. The same vector quantization applies to detail level 0 and results with 256 8-dimensional arrays. The index of corresponding array is stored in the G component in the RGB of the color triplets. The last element in the RGB color triplets stores the mean value of the corresponding 4^3 block. There are $D'_x/4 * D'_y/4 * D'_z/4$ such RGB color triplets in total. These

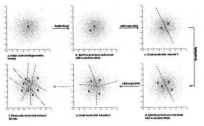

(a) LBG vector quantization

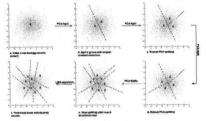

(b) Vector quantization using principal component analysis (PCA)

Figure 4: Procedures of two different vector quantization algorithms.

triplets, as well as the code-books A and B, are then saved to the hard drive for later use.

4.2 Decoder Module

The encoder preprocessing ends after the resulting files is saved on the hard drive. The first thing the decoder module needs to do is to read those saved files from the hard drive into main memory. The code books and the RGB color triplets are parsed and saved into main memory. The next step for the decoder module is to transfer the code-books and RGB triplets into GPU memory. This step is harder than it looks. Because the GPU memory model is not as flexible as the main memory model. There are certain data structures which GPU memory model does not support. We use the texture memory in GPU to store the code-books and the triplets from main memory for a time-step. The code books and RGB color triplets in main memory are then uploaded to these generated textures. Code book A and code book B are stored in two different 2D textures C_a and C_b. RGB color triplets are stored in a 3D texture I. The 2D textures C_a and C_b have $256 * 64$ and $256 * 8$ elements, respectively. To access the element in 2D textures, a 2-dimensional coordinates (s,t) are required. The s coordinate of C_a and C_b are given by the R and G components in RGB color triplets, which are now stored in the 3D texture I. Figure 5 shows the overview the texture memory structure of the decoder module.

Before we introduce how to implement the GPU decoding scheme, let us take a look at the equation used by the GPU in order to decode the data. In its simplest form, the

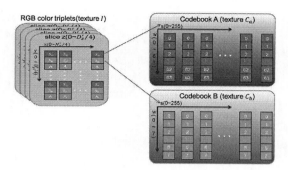

Figure 5: GPU textures memory structure for the decoder module.

equation is:

$$w(x,y,z) = I(x',y',z').b + C_b(s,w) + C_a(s,w). \quad (1)$$

In this equation, $w(x,y,z)$ is the scalar value at location (x,y,z); $I(x',y',z').b$ is the B component of the the RGB color triplets, which is also the mean value of the corresponding 4^3 block. Each (x,y,z) must belong to one of these blocks when we decomposed the volumetric data in the preprocessing step. The parameters $C_b(s,w)$ and $C_a(s,w)$ are the values which are returned by the code book B and code book A, respectively. To solve the equation, we need to somehow map all the coordinates on the right side of Equation 1 to a function of (x,y,z). Because (x,y,z) is the only coordinates we know during decoding. The main obstacle to implement a working decoding module is how to relate the different coordinates for different textures. The (x,y,z) coordinates are the actual coordinates of the re-sampled data. The coordinates (x',y',z') is for the texture I and needs to be calculated from (x,y,z). The s coordinates can be directly calculated from the returned values of texture I. The w coordinates of texture C_a and C_b are related to (x,y,z) as well. The relationship between (x,y,z) and (x',y',z') is not difficult to find. Texture I is essentially a lower resolution of the original data. Each dimension of the original data is divided by 4 to get the dimension of texture I. And only the integer part of the quotient is used. So the transformation between (x,y,z) and (x',y',z') can be expressed by:

$$\begin{array}{l} x' = \lfloor x/4 \rfloor, where\ 0 \leq x' \leq (D'_x/4 - 1)\ and\ 0 \leq x \leq (D'_x - 1) \\ y' = \lfloor y/4 \rfloor, where\ 0 \leq y' \leq (D'_y/4 - 1)\ and\ 0 \leq y \leq (D'_y - 1) \\ z' = \lfloor z/4 \rfloor, where\ 0 \leq z' \leq (D'_z/4 - 1)\ and\ 0 \leq z \leq (D'_z - 1) \end{array}$$
$$(2)$$

The previous equations only deal with integer numbers. In the implementation, we need to use texture mapping coordinate. Normal texture coordinates are not integers. We need to further transform the integer coordinates to float coordinates between 0.0 and 1.0.

The relationship between (x,y,z) and the (s,w) coordinates of C_a and C_b are less intuitive though. Let us examine the case for C_a first. The s coordinate is directly given by the R component of the RGB color triplets as illustrated in Figure 5. The w coordinate is an integer between 0 and 63. It is essentially a local index of (x,y,z) in the corresponding 4^3 block. The reminder of (x,y,z) divided by 4 can be used to calculate the local index. So the coordinate w and s can be computed by the following equations:

$$(s,w) = \left\{ \begin{array}{l} I(x',y',z').r \\ x\%4 + 4*(y\%4) + 16*(z\%4) \end{array} \right. \quad (3)$$

where $I(x',y',z').r$ represents the R component of the return value from the texture I sampling. The same equations applies to C_b as well. The only difference is that one needs to find the local index of corresponding 2^3 block instead of 4^3 block. The equation for C_b is the following:

$$(s',w') = \left\{ \begin{array}{l} I(x',y',z').g \\ \lfloor \frac{x\%4}{2} \rfloor + \lfloor y\%4 \rfloor + 2 * \lfloor \frac{z\%4}{2} \rfloor. \end{array} \right. \quad (4)$$

Now we have all the mapping equations. We need one equation to put them all together. The generalized equation should only contains coordinates of (x,y,z). Equations 2, 3 and 4 can be inserted into Equation 1 to get:

$$\begin{aligned} w(x,y,z) &= I(\lfloor x/4 \rfloor, \lfloor y/4 \rfloor, \lfloor z/4 \rfloor).b \\ &+ C_b(s',w') \\ &+ C_a(s,w) \end{aligned} \quad (5)$$

where (x,y,z) are integer values ranging from $[0, D'_x - 1]$, $[0, D'_y - 1]$, and $[0, D'_z - 1]$ respectively.

Equation 5 is the final equation which represents the whole decoding process related to the coordinates (x,y,z). Our decoder module needs a program in GPU to solve the equation efficiently. The GPU programming language which we choose to program the GPU is Cg from NVIDIA. One could have use CUDA instead but our program would have been usable only on NVIDIA hardware. This restriction would make our solution not potable to other GPU manufacturer such as ATI. Unlike CUDA, Cg can compile to GLSL for ATI GPUs. It enables us to deploy our proposed system on ATI machines as well. The decision to use Cg to implement the decoding module gives our system a better portability. To implement Equation 5 in GPU with Cg, there are some limitations which we must bear in mind:

1. The shift operations are not supported by Cg. In general programming, it is easy to get the results of $\lfloor x/4 \rfloor$ by shift operation $x >> 2$. Unfortunately, one cannot use this operation in Cg.

2. The bitwise operations are not supported by Cg. One efficient way to calculate $x\%4$ is to use bitwise AND operation. It is essentially the same as $x\&3$.

3. The texture coordinates in Cg are not integer. All our equations are based on an assumption that (x,y,z) are integers. We need to find a way to map the integer to float.

In the following, we will introduce ways to deal with those limitations. At first, let us take a look at the setup of viewing parameters for the decoding program. The projection mode is an orthogonal projection; and the view port is of size $D_x * D_y$. The volumetric data is reconstructed slice by slice. Either front-to-back or back-to-front order is fine for reconstruction. The rendering results are saved in the frame buffer for binding. Instead of integers, the coordinates need to be transformed are in the $[-1.0, 1.0]$ range. To convert to the new float coordinate, the integer is divided by $N_x - 1$, $N_y - 1$ or $N_z - 1$ and then subtract by 1.0 as in $x/(N_x - 1) - 1.0$.

To use the (x,y,z) coordinates in the GPU, there are still two problems that remains to be solved. The first problem is to figure out a way to get coordinates (x',y',z') for texture I from (x,y,z) without a shift operation or a direct floor function. The essence of the function $\lfloor x/4 \rfloor$ is to map four continuous integers to the same value. In texture mapping, there is a GL_NEAREST parameter for GL_TEXTURE_MAG_FILTER. When the pixel being textured maps to an area less than or equal to one texel, texture mapping returns the value of the texture element that is nearest (using the Manhattan distance) to the center of the pixel being textured. This way the nearest operation also maps different value to a single value. This gives us a way to overcome the first problem. Say we want to calculate the results of function $\lfloor x/4 \rfloor$ when $x = 4, 5, 6, 7$. If one can find a way to convert these integers to texture coordinates in a specific range and use the GL_NEAREST feature to texture map them, we are able to map all the texture coordinates to the same texture element. Thus, the function $\lfloor x/4 \rfloor$ can be simulated by texture mapping operation. Back to our application domain, one can prove that the following functions yields the correct coordinates for texture I:

$$
\begin{aligned}
x' &= (x*0.5+0.5)*\frac{D_x-1}{D_x-4} - \frac{3}{2*D_x-8}\\
y' &= (y*0.5+0.5)*\frac{D_y-1}{D_y-4} - \frac{3}{2*D_y-8}\\
z' &= (z*0.5+0.5)*\frac{D_z-1}{D_z-4} - \frac{3}{2*D_z-8}
\end{aligned}
\quad (6)
$$

where $D_n = \{2^n \mid n >= 3\}$. When the coordinates are less than 0.0 or greater than 1.0, we use GL_CLAMP to clamps the texture coordinate into the $[0.0, 1.0]$ range. The clamp-ing function handles the problem associated with texture border.

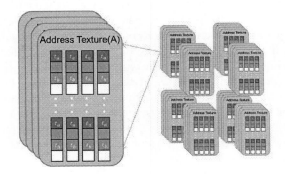

Figure 6: The structure and repeat pattern of address texture.

The second problem is to get the w coordinates for each small blocks. Address texture, as proposed by Schneider et al. [6], is a good solution for this problem. The basic idea is to use the address texture to hold the w coordinates of one single block and reuse it for other blocks. If we examine every block individually, the w coordinates of C_a and C_b for these blocks have the same pattern. So a single address texture which stores the pattern is enough for decoding all blocks. In our application domain, the address texture is a 4^3 block. We denote it texture A. Figure 6 illustrates the structure of address texture. Each element in the address texture has four components, RGBA. The R and B components store the w coordinates of the codebooks A and B. The G and A component are reserved for s coordinates which come from the R and G component of texture I. To get the pattern for the texture address, let us assume that the size of original data is the same as address texture. It is easy to calculate the w coordinates of C_a and C_b from Equation 5. One can use a progressively larger integer in every dimension to replace (x,y,z). Now we need a mechanism to use the address texture repeatedly. Fortunately, there is a GL_REPEAT parameter in texture mapping. It creates a repeating pattern by ignoring the integer portion of the texture coordinate. With the help of GL_REPEAT feature, the w coordinates calculations is reduced to a simple texture sampling operation. For every dimension, we need to repeat the texture coordinates $D_x/4$, $D_y/4$ and $D_z/4$ times respectively. It means that the texture coordinates for the texture address should be ranging from 0 to $D_x/4$, $D_y/4$ and $D_z/4$. A multiplication of (x,y,z) with $(D_x/4, D_y/4, D_z/4)$ will do the job. Equation 7 describes the transformation:

$$
\begin{aligned}
x_A &= (x*0.5+0.5)*(D_x/4)\\
y_A &= (y*0.5+0.5)*(D_y/4) \quad .\\
z_A &= (z*0.5+0.5)*(D_z/4)
\end{aligned}
\quad (7)
$$

where x_A, y_A, and z_A represent the texture coordinates for accessing texture A. Figure 6 illustrates where the texture address repeats itself with texture coordinates ranging from $[0.0, 2.0]$. Together with the R and G components of texture I, Equation 5 describes the decoding process mathematically as performed on the GPU. By combining Equation 5 with Equation 7 it is not hard to write its implementation in Cg. Because our decompressed data are the difference between two continuous time-varying volumetric data, there is one more step before rendering the volumetric data. We need to add the decompressed data with previous reconstructed volumetric data to yield the current reconstructed data. The addition of two volumetric data is also easy to implement using Cg.

The vector quantization algorithm is not a lossless compression algorithm. The bit-size of the index in the codebook affects the compression quality significantly. The bigger bit-size the lower the compression distortion is but at the expense of compression. It is possible to control the compression quality by setting up different bit-size. We decided to use a bit-size of 8. The initial time step of the time-varying volumetric data is transferred directly into GPU as a start point. Then for the subsequent time steps, we reconstruct the difference and add them to the previous time step. One problem associated with this scheme is the accumulated error. After several time steps, the error accumulated to a larger value. As in video compression, we need to use the concept of an I frame and P frame mechanism as in MPEG coding allowing us to reduce the accumulated errors. The I frames do not require other frames to be decoded. In our application domain, we define the original data as the the I frames. The P frames need previous data for decoding. We define the reconstructed volume data as the P frames. After several time steps, we transfer one copy of the original time step to GPU memory as an I frame to reset the accumulated errors.

4.3 Render Module

The render module is responsible for rendering in real-time the volumetric data. Numerous rendering algorithms have been proposed by researchers in the past decades. We use 3D texture-based volume rendering in our system. It is an object-order volume rendering algorithm because it use geometry primitives to iterate over the object. The whole rendering process is usually composed of the following steps:

1. Bind the volumetric data as 3D textures. The decoder module in our system did this step for the render module already.

2. Setup intractable rendering parameters, such parameters include: camera position, view direction, view port, number of slices, rendering mode, and so on.

3. Calculate a series of slices which intersect with objects in the scene. All the slices should be perpendicular to the viewing direction and have the same distance between two neighbor slices.

4. Render each slice using a 3D texture mapping operation and blend them to one final image.

5. Respond to any change of interaction parameters and repeat step 2 to step 5.

The first and second steps set-up all parameters which are required for the rendering algorithm. The most time-consuming process in the rendering algorithm starts from step 3. The calculation of cut-off slices are usually performed using the CPU. Rezk-Salama et al. [12] proposed a way to move the calculation to the GPU using vertex shader. Vertex shader is designed to transform the 3D position of each vertex to a 2D coordinate on the image plane. It can calculate the properties such as position, color and texture coordinates. The cut-off slice generation is essentially a transformation of vertex.

4.4 Implementation Results

In order to test our system, we use a desktop computer running Windows XP with a 4G memory Quadro FX 5800 graphics card. The interface between the GPU and main memory is performed by a PCI Express 2.0 bus. The volumetric data which we use in our system is a series of chest CT scan slices. We thank Dr. Michelle Noga at Department of Radiology & Diagnostic Imaging, University of Alberta, Edmonton, Canada, for providing us the data. The usefulness of our system relies on the assumption that the implemented GPU decompression mechanism saves time compare to direct data transfer through the PCIe bus. Otherwise, there is no point to use our system when rendering large time-varying data set. The first experiment which we did is to get measurements of the data transmission time for direct transmission and our proposed method. As our proposed method involves transmission of I frame and P frame, we present the results in two tables. In both tables, t_1 represents the transfer time between the main memory and the GPU without compression and t_2 is the total time to transfer the compressed data from main memory to GPU and to decompress the data on the GPU. Table 1 is the results for I frame. So t_1 is the same as t_2 and the compression ratio is 1. Table 2 shows the results for P frame transmission. In this table, p is defined as $(t_2 - t_2')/t_2'$. It is essentially the time spend on decompression vs the time spend on transmitting the compressed data. As the data size gets larger, more portion of time is dedicated to GPU decompression. These two examples are sufficient to validate the assumption which our system is based on. In essence, they are the amount of time it takes to get volumetric data ready for the rendering module. We call them *data*

Table 1: The data preparation time and compression ratio for an I frame.

Data Dimension	$t_1(ms)$	$b(Gb/s)$	$t_2(ms)$	$S_o(Mb)$	$S_c(Mb)$	r
512x512x32	4.2	1.905	4.2	8	8	1
512x512x64	8.9	1.798	8.9	16	16	1
512x512x128	17.8	1.798	17.8	32	32	1
512x512x256	35.1	1.823	35.1	64	64	1
512x512x512	70.9	1.805	70.9	128	128	1

Table 2: The data preparation time and compression ratio for a P frame.

Data Dimension	$t_1(ms)$	$b(Gb/s)$	$t_2(ms)$	$t_2'(ms)$	p	$S_o(Mb)$	$S_c(Mb)$	r
512x512x32	4.2	1.905	1.4	0.2	6.00	8	0.403	19.85
512x512x64	8.9	1.798	3.5	0.4	7.75	16	0.787	20.33
512x512x128	17.8	1.798	7.3	0.9	7.11	32	1.555	20.57
512x512x256	35.1	1.823	16.1	1.7	8.49	64	3.091	20.71
512x512x512	70.9	1.805	32.0	3.4	8.42	128	6.163	20.77

preparation time. If t_2 is less than t_1, it proves the GPU decompression mechanism is effective in terms of reducing GPU data waiting time. The two tables also contains the original data size (S_o), the compressed data size (S_c) and compression ratio (r). The compression ratio is defined by S_o/S_c.

We used five different data size ranging from 512x512x32 to 512x512x512 for the first test. They are actually the same data set. The original data dimension is 512x512x355. Figure 7a shows the curves of data size vs. data preparation time of P frame for the direct transfer without compression (red line) and our GPU decompression method (blue line). The GPU decompression method performs very well regardless of the data size. It saves more than half of the direct transferring time. When data size is small, it might not be necessary to use GPU decompression method since the direct transfer time is already short. Moreover, the GPU decompression algorithm is not a lossless decompression. The speedup is not worthy compare to the sacrifice of image quality. However, when the data size is large, the speedup is a desired factor rather than image quality for real-time rendering. From the experiment result, we conclude that our assumption is correct and the GPU decompression mechanism is effective in terms of reducing the data preparation time. The compression ratio is illustrated in Figure 7b. The bit rate of the vector quantization in our test is 8. Hence, the upper bound of the compression ratio is around 21.3, which is verified by Figure 7b. As our system is optimized for time-varying data set, we also need to prove that our proposed method deals with time-varying data set better than the conventional none optimized method. The benchmark with which we selected to compare our system with is based on Schneider's method. In their paper, they use mean square error (MSE), signal-to-noise ratio (SNR) and peak signal-

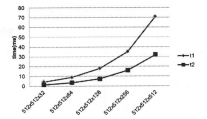

(a) Data data preparation time of uncompressed data to the GPU vs and data preparation time with GPU decompression. (P frame)

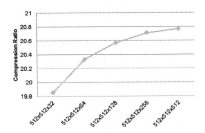

(b) Compression ratio for a P frame.

Figure 7: System performance for single time step with a P frame.

Table 3: Compression errors of our benchmark method.

Time Step	1	2	3	4	5	6
MSE	15.6504	15.8601	15.1026	15.2743	15.4127	14.9541
SNR(dB)	24.06	24.11	24.20	24.22	24.21	24.21
PSNR(dB)	36.01	36.02	36.20	36.26	36.22	36.35

to-noise ratio (PSNR) as performance indicators. The data we use is of size 512x512x256 and there are 6 different time steps in total. Table 3, 4, 5 show results which we got from the experiments. We did three different tests on these data. Table 3 is the benchmark test on Schneider's method. Their method treated different time steps individually and compressed them separately. The difference lies in the way they calculate the difference between different time steps. In Table 4, we get the difference from two original time steps; and in Table 5 we subtract the current original time step with the reconstructed previous time step. For example, suppose we have time step 2 and 3, the second method would compress the difference of time step 3 and time step 2, while the third method would reconstruct time step 2 at first, and then calculate the difference of time step 3 and the reconstructed time step 2. We call the second method the naive scheme and the third method the progressive scheme.

Figure 8 gives a visual overview of the performance for the three methods. The green lines in the graph are the testing results for the benchmark method. As the dif-

Table 4: Compression errors using the naive scheme.

Time Step	1	2	3	4	5	6
MSE	–	2.5064	12.4756	25.6068	44.2489	71.4553
SNR(dB)	–	32.12	25.03	21.98	19.63	17.42
PSNR(dB)	–	44.04	37.03	34.01	31.64	29.56

Table 5: Compression errors using the progressive scheme.

Time Step	1	2	3	4	5	6
MSE	–	2.5064	5.5752	5.7719	11.0158	20.5845
SNR(dB)	–	32.12	28.52	28.45	25.67	22.82
PSNR(dB)	–	44.04	40.53	40.48	37.68	34.96

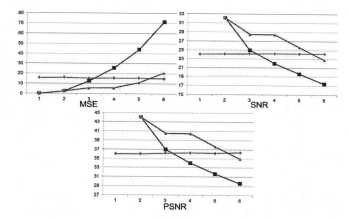

Figure 8: The error measurements of different methods

ferent time steps are separated from each other, the compression algorithm performance is quite stable. The green lines are almost horizontal in the graph. The naive scheme compression method is represented by the blue lines. As seen in the graph, the blue lines increase or decrease dramatically compare to other lines. The accumulated errors account for it. After reconstruction, the error due to compression is added to all previous errors, which also explains the monotone increase in MSE and monotone decreasing in SNR and PSNR. This is not the best method to compress the time-varying data set. As shown in Figure 8, the benchmark algorithm outperformed this method in every aspect after time step 3. The red lines, which represents the progressive scheme compression method, have much smoother slopes than the blue curve. It indicates that the compression error rate is smaller. At the sixth time step, the MSE for the progressive scheme compression method (red lines) begins to exceed the benchmark algorithm. We describe it as the turning point. The turning point is a good indicator to upload I-frame time step to reset the accumulated error.

Figure 9 are screen shots of the rendering results of time step 6. We use 3D texture-based volume rendering as described in the rendering module. On average, we managed to get 15 to 20 frames per second with our experiment data. In this graph, the distortion of Schneider's method is hardly noticeable at the given resolution. However, when we zoom the volume in our program, the distortion is fairly obvious. Both the naive scheme compression and progressive scheme compression yields severe distortions.

From those experiments, one can safely conclude that the progressive scheme compression yields a reduced compression distortion compare to the benchmark method. It efficiently exploit the time redundancy by encoding the difference of continuous time steps.

Conclusion

The goal of this paper is to explore an efficient way to render large sequence of volumetric data over time so that the end users can visually observe their evolution in time and space at real-time performance (min rate of 10Hz). This type of rendering is very memory and computationally intensive and is currently impossible with standard GPU algorithms. Even with one of today's fastest GPU, the transmission speed between main memory and GPU memory is still too slow for real-time rendering as the bandwidth of the PCI-E bus is at best 12 Gb/s. In this paper, we proposed and tested a new compression scheme to overcome this bottleneck. This compression scheme decompresses the data in GPU memory as if the GPU acted as a client in a video client-server configuration connected by a band limited network. Similar to standard video com-

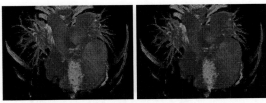

(a) Original volumetric data

(b) Volumetric data reconstructed using Schneider's scheme

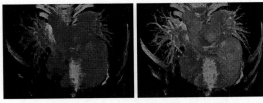

(c) Volumetric data reconstructed using naive scheme

(d) Volumetric data reconstructed using progressive scheme

Figure 9: The rendering result of time step 6 with different compression methods

pression technology like MPEG, the proposed algorithm takes advantage of time and spatial redundancies to reduce the data size to be transferred by the bandwidth limited PCI-E bus. Compare to other method which does not utilize time redundancy information, our proposed compression scheme manages to reduce compression distortion by a generalization of the concept of P and I frames used in the MPEG compression scheme. Once one time step of the volume data is transferred and decompressed in the GPU texture memory, it is immediately rendered using a fast GPU based 3D texture-based volume rendering algorithm. We have demonstrated that the progressive compression scheme using the I and P frames yields a reduce compression distortion compare to the benchmark method found in the literature. It efficiently exploit time redundancy by encoding the difference of continuous time steps.

References

[1] K. Akeley. Reality engine graphics. In *SIGGRAPH '93: Proceedings of the 20th annual conference on Computer graphics and interactive techniques*, pages 109–116, New York, NY, USA, 1993. ACM.

[2] J. Blinn. Light reflection functions for simulation of clouds and dusty surfaces. volume 16, pages 21 – 29. Computer Graphics, July 1982.

[3] E. E. Catmull. *A subdivision algorithm for computer display of curved surfaces*. Phd thesis, University of Utah, 1974.

[4] R. A. Drebin, L. Carpenter, and P. Hanrahan. Volume rendering. In SIGGRAPH88: Proceedings of the 15th annual conference on Computer graphics and interactive techniques, August 1988.

[5] E. Groller, I. Fujishiro (editors, Chaoli Wang, Jinzhu Gao, Liya Li, and Han wei Shen. A multiresolution volume rendering framework for large-scale time-varying data visualization abstract, 2008.

[6] R. Westermann J. Schneider. Compression domain volume rendering. In *In IEEE Visualization*, pages 293–300, 2003.

[7] A. V. Gelder J. Wilhelms. A coherent projection approach for direct volume rendering. volume 25, pages 275 – 284. Computer Graphics, July 1991.

[8] J. M. Kniss C. Rezk-Salama D. Weiskopf K. Engel, M. Hadwiger. *Real-Time Volume Graphics*. A K Peters. Ltd, 2006.

[9] E. Nakamae K. Kaneda, T. Okamoto and T. Nishita. Highly realistic visual simulation of outdoor scenes under various atmospheric conditions. n Proceedings of CG International 90, August 1990.

[10] L. Kobbelt M. Pauly, M. Gross. Efficient simplification of pointsampled surfaces. In Proceedings of IEEE Visualization 2002, 2002.

[11] Nelson Max. Atmospheric illumination and shadows. Computer Graphics, August 1986.

[12] C. Rezk-Salama and A. Kolb. A vertex program for efficient box-plane intersection. 2005.

[13] J. Gonser W. Straer S. Guthe, M. Wand. Interactive rendering of large volume data sets. pages 53–60, 2002.

[14] B. Sun and R. Ramamoorthi. A practical analytic single scattering model for real time rendering. *ACM Trans. Graph*, 24:1040–1049, 2005.

Web-Based 3D Visualisation for Biomedical Applications

Hui Wei, Enjie Liu, Xia Zhao, NJB McFarlane, GJ Clapworthy
Centre for Computer Graphics & Visualisation, University of Bedfordshire, UK
{hui.wei, enjie.liu, xia.zhao, nigel.mcfarlane, gordon.clapworthy@beds.ac.uk}

Abstract

This paper proposes an easy way to perform web-based 3D interactive visualisation, which accepts two data resources, local and remote, as input and copes with two types of algorithm, built-in and remote. The focus of this paper is the biomedical area. Today's web technology makes it possible to use software maintained on a remote server. The approach described provides a virtual client environment, in which users can employ remotely installed software interactively using any standard browser. The proposed approach is a generic one and can be used in many other application areas.

Keywords: 3D visualisation, medical data, web services, VTK, digital library.

1. Introduction

The Internet is being used increasingly for 3D applications. Despite the latency associated with any Internet operation, these applications can often involve user interactions of high complexity. For example, [1] involved the telecontrol of a robot via the Internet and included a successful live demonstration at a distance of over 8,000 km.

In recent years, 3D web visualisation techniques have sprung up in many fields. Their use interweaves our daily life and study. In the biomedical area, 3D visualisation gives end users an intuitive way to understand medical data.

This paper describes a web-based system for the 3D visualisation of biomedical applications. Its use is illustrated by a study in virtual surgery – this is a demonstrator that is a web-based extension of a system developed within the VPH2 project [2]. VPH2 is creating a surgical planning system for left ventricular dysfunction that will be deployed in the relevant clinical departments in the near future.

An independent web-based system for surgical planning and training involving medical personnel at different sites is described in [3]. It is likely that this is a precursor of further development in this area.

Users benefit from the usability of web-based applications: they are easy to use via a standard browser or slim client, and will be maintained by the service provider at the remote site which means no burden falls on the users. Since the application will be built, deployed and maintained by specialised companies, users can experience high-quality services at a low cost. The platform-independent and language-independent features of web services give developers great flexibility, and web service composition provides the possibility to re-use existing software as part of a completely new application at great cost saving.

A pure browser-server solution may lose some functionality when dealing with the graphical aspects of an application. However, an X3D browser such as Bitmanagement BS Contact [4] can be embedded in a web browser to support 3D visualisation. Transferring large data sets over Internet may also cause unacceptable delays in some cases, but the proposed approach provides a solution to this problem.

The method brings the following benefits:

- a cutting tool widget, which is an extension of an existing VTK [5] widget and described in [6,7] is wrapped as a web-based application;
- interaction speed is increased by using client-side visualisation; users operate on 3D medical data on their local machine rather than on the server, so, with the help of locally installed resources, the data processing is more efficient;
- the data transfer load is balanced between the client and server – users either read data from their local machines or from remote interfaces to the Storage Resource Broker (SRB) data grid used in projects such as LHDL [8] and VPHOP [9] to store 3D medical data;
- the proposed approach works in four different scenarios, in particular, the web server can include other necessary web services, thus extending the functionality that can be offered to the end user;
- the proposed approach is generic in web development, and can be used in many other applications.

A specific challenge in our approach is how to resolve local environment configuration and the corresponding data archiving and computation. There are two main desired goals: users do not needed to pre-install any software; anyone may interact with their local or remote medical data online without any prior knowledge of the software.

1550-6037/11 $26.00 © 2011 IEEE
DOI 10.1109/IV.2011.74

The remainder of the paper is organised as follows. In Section 2, we introduce related work on web-based visualisation. Section 3 describes the architecture design in detail, while some tools and techniques used in the implementation are described in Section 4. Finally, we present a summary and discuss future work in Section 5.

2. Related work

In recent years, several ways have been introduced for deploying 3D objects on the web.

JavaView, is visualisation software that allows the display of 3D geometries and interactive geometry experiments over the Internet. It offers full web integration and is independent of the operating system. However, it may not satisfy some requirements such as needed for the cutting tool used in our example application or for viewing medical volume data, as in Wang et al. [10]. However, VTK provides widgets that can easily extract parameters from the user side and it can also render volume data. [11,12] show some examples of the use of JavaView.

Java3D is an addition API to Java for displaying 3D graphics. It has a higher-level object-oriented interface compared with openGL, and calls openGL in the JNI layer. It also offers extensive 3D sound support. However, in some applications, a variety of data formats, such as DICOM, STL, VRML, and jpeg are used, and. VTK give us greater benefits on this aspect. [13] uses Java3D for 3D molecular visualisation.

JOGL is a Java wrapper library of openGL sponsored by Sun. It provides full access to the OpenGL functions, and integrates with the Java GUI: AWT and Swing. It enables hardware-supported 3D graphics written in Java. Cipriano et al. [14] presented a web server that allows users to quickly explore an abstracted protein surface using JOGL.

Comparing JOGL with VTK, the latter is more object-oriented for the Java API. It has a series of high-level design goals which make its API simple and it can be readily assembled into larger systems [15]. The former provides low-level bindings for OpenGL. VTK also provides many existing widgets which allow the user to flexibly choose accurate parameters. Furthermore, VTK also has a mechanism by which one can automatically generate a Java API, which is very helpful to extend it if using a C++ based server and Java based client.

Ajax3D [16] combines Ajax with x3d and is the standard for real-time 3D on the web. Ajax (Asynchronous JavaScript and XML) combines existing technologies, including html, css, JavaScript, Dom, XML, xmlhttpRequest object, and so on. It allows users to exchange data asynchronously between the browser and server without reloading the entire current page. X3D[17] is a royalty-free open standards file format and run-time architecture to represent and communicate among 3D scenes and objects using XML.

3. System design

The proposed system architecture shown in Fig. 1 indicates how we deploy modules in the system between the client and server.

Some of the modules are downloaded to the user's PC and run there in an applet form, so we separate the system into two parts, client and server, during our description. It is a relatively thin client. Whether the programs are executed on the server side or on the client's machine is transparent to the user.

The client side includes applets contained in the web pages and some libraries hosted in the user's machine for local interactive visualisation. Its main function is to configure the user environment, read the user's data and render the data in interactive way to assist further exploration. It is also used to retrieve and reset parameters for further processing on the server side.

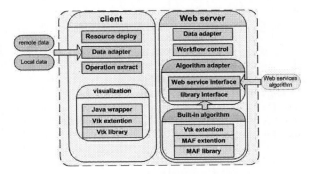

Figure 1. System Architecture

An applet is delivered to the client side, so it is executed on the user's machine after it has been retrieved from the server. This, allows us to use it as our client to realize local rendering by using resources from the user machine – CPU, RAM, etc. An applet running in a web browser is often restricted by a set of security policies – a sandbox. But it can be granted permission or be signed to perform tasks outside the sandbox. As granting permission requires users to configure the policy file in the client machine, it is not an easy thing for them to do. So, we choose to sign our applet to obtain the user's permission – the user needs only to click a button to confirm that they trust the applet. By this, the client may access restricted resources on the user's machine, such as the file system.

When users visit the web page, the *resource deploy* module detects if they have the necessary visualisation functions locally. If not, this module will deploy these resources on the user's machine. In our case, it will deploy the visualisation plug-ins for exploring the data on their local machine. Since this module lies on the client side, it can access the user's machine directly.

The *data adapter* module reads data from local or remote machines. The remote data interface may be SOAP, XML-RPC, HTTP, FTP or other web-based proxies. We access these data remotely and save them on the user's machine. Hence, the *visualisation* module can treat local and remote data in the same way, since both now lie on client side in an acceptable format.

3.1. Resource deployment

Visualisation resource libraries are stored in a folder on the web server, for any client to download, when needed – for this, the client program needs to know the URL of the web server. An applet can obtain the URL string of the host containing it in its *init* method. After these libraries are stored locally, the client program may load them into JVM.

The life cycle of an applet is determined by methods that are called by JVM automatically in the following sequence: *static block, init*, and *start*. To ensure that these libraries are loaded before use, and are loaded only once, the load operation is done in the *static* block of an applet. After that, the visualisation functions in these libraries are ready for use on the client side. However, this inevitably produces a conflict between the logic order and code execution order, which may mean that these tasks cannot be executed in a single applet.

A solution is to separate them into two applets(see Fig. 2)– the first fetches the server URL and stores the resources in the *init* method; and the second loads the libraries in the *static* block. To ensure that these two applets run in the correct order, a JSObject class, which is a wrapper of JavaScript objects, is used in the first applet to invoke a JavaScript function in the web page to redirect the current page to a new page containing the second applet.

Get server URL →store resource→ load libraries in JVM
Init()   →   init()   →   static block

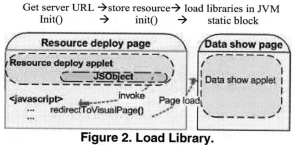

Figure 2. Load Library.

3.2. Visualisation

Applets can be run in any browser that has the appropriate version of a Java plug-in. Our web page, which contains an applet, will detect whether a user has the Java plug-ins installed, if not, the page will direct them to be installed.

The applet is now a mature technique and, with the latest development of Java plug-ins, an applet can be specified with a heap size larger than the default maximum through an HTML tag in the web page containing the applet. The heap size can be defined by the users for different applets individually, which makes a more flexible usage of the applet possible.

As a web technique, the applet also has a strong communication ability. It can visit an element value on the web page or a JavaScript method through the JSObject class. In contrast, a JavaScript method can visit

a public attribute or invoke a public method of an applet. An applet can communicate with a servlet, which is a lightweight application running on the server side, or with other applets. This feature is very useful – we can use sever applets to build a multi-view application, allowing users to explore data through different views (e.g surface and slice-based) simultaneously. These features of applets allow us to construct interactive, dynamic and informative applications.

Although VTK supplies a Java wrapper, the wrapper cannot work independently. It takes the form of an interface (JNI actually) and needs support from VTK dynamic-link libraries. When a method is called, through its Java API, the method invokes its library automatically through the interface. These *dll* files are deployed on the client side by the *resource deploy* module before running further functions, such as visualisation .

VTK supplies the developer with many examples of 3D widgets: interactive tools that can be embedded in the visualisation. The example in this paper is a 3D triangle-shaped widget, originally developed as a VTK extension in [6,7] as one of the surgeon-requested cutting tools in the surgical planner application mentioned earlier. The triangle widget features basic functions, such as resize, drag, rotate, plus some extra functionalities. It is intended to act as a tool for punching holes though a surface, so it should initially appear at a position facing the camera, and its allowable area of motion should not exceed the boundary of the input surface data. After each user interaction, it should readjust its position to "stick" as closely as possible to the surface and realign itself with the surface normal.

The VTK Java wrapper mechanism can also be used to extend a class. An extended VTK class will generate a corresponding *java.cxx file and a *.java file for the Java wrapper automatically. The newly generated .class file will be packaged in a vtk.jar file, which can be invoked by a Java applet. The main algorithm written in a C++ class will be exported as a shared library, which can be invoked automatically by its Java interface.

VTK gives the developer a pre-defined set of events and actions and a way to override default actions. It also provides a way to translate native mouse and keyboard events into vtk Events. This makes it possible to use Java UI events to interact with the vtk object. Our triangle widget VTK extension inherits these advantages.

Surface data as an input parameter data for a triangle widget is read separately in both Java code and native code on the client side. To avoid passing complex object parameters through JNI, a string of local paths is passed from Java code to native code. Both sets of code are stored on the client side, so they can both read the data easily.

3.3. Data resources

To access remote data resources, we embed our systems into PhysiomeSpace [18], which supplies users with an interface to download this data. The medical data

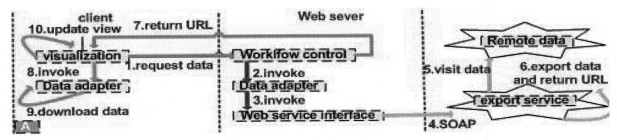

Figure 3-A Module collaboration of remote data rendering

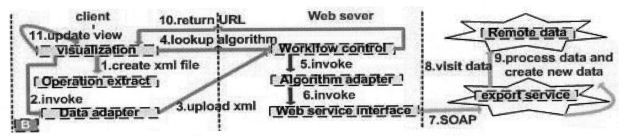

Figure 3-B module collaboration of using remote algorithm

defined in the project is the Virtual Medical Entity (VME) [19], which can be accepted directly in any MAF-related project. As our server integrated the MAF library as an algorithm set, this data format can be read directly from the server side. However, our client only contains VTK library, this data cannot be read directly. Fortunately, the web service function provided in PhysiomeSpace supplies an interface for visiting user data to be managed in the system in a VTK-acceptable file format (vtk, .stl, .vrml, etc). To process a case in which the data has to be read both on the client side for visualisation and on the server side for data processing, we use these two different ways of loading remote data separately for the client and server.

For the convenience of ordinary users viewing medical data on their local machine, a small interface for *file open* was created to allow them to choose the precise data from the file system. As rendering runs on the client side, once the permission is granted, users have the rights to visit the local file system and use local resources.

3.4. Algorithm set

PhysiomeSpace offers users many web-based algorithms for medical data processing. However, these services are pre-defined and limited.

To provide a more extensive and richer algorithm set, our built-in algorithm set is based on MAF. MAF is an open source framework containing several libraries such as VTK and ITK. We use MAF as an algorithm library, rather than an application. We classify these algorithms into three layers. The foundation layer is the MAF library. The upper two layers are both dynamic link libraries. The *extend layer* contains new algorithm classes extended from MAF and widget classes extended from VTK. The widget classes are needed on both the client and the server side. The server-side algorithms use

the widget class to transform a parameter object from an XML file and take further computational tasks. The classes in this layer are organised in an object-oriented way. To give a simple Java interface, the *function interface layer* includes many JNI functions. Every function answers for one algorithm by invoking classes in the two lower layers, so these functions can be invoked by the *algorithm adapter* module.

3.5. Module collaboration

3.5.1. Remote data visualisation

Once users log on to PhysiomeSpace, they are allocated their own sandbox to keep their own data. Through PhysiomeSpace, the user may choose data stored in the SRB repository with MAF VME format.

Fig. 3-A shows how to render the remote data at the client. An applet in *visualisation* module sends a request to a servlet in the *workflow control* module with the data id. The servlet informs the *data adapter* to get URL of the remote data in a VTK accepted format. *Data adapter* module invokes the right web based algorithm to process the remote data. The result data in VTK accepted format is then generated and the URL of the new data is returned to the client. Then the applet invokes the client side *data adapter* to download this data into a local data folder for further operations, such as visualisation.

3.5.2. Remote processing

When data are being processed on the server side, data and algorithm resources are needed. There are 4 cases for data and algorithm combinations to be dealt with:

- *Local data – built in algorithm:* the web server needs a copy of the data from the client, so the data must be uploaded from the client to the server by http proxy.
- *Local data – web service algorithm*: if the web service reads the data from the data repository, an import

service is needed to load the local data into data repository; the file id is passed to the server.

- *Remote data – built in algorithm*: the web server has to download the data in its original format; the data file id is passed to the server side from the client.
- Remote data – web service algorithm: the server side does not need to download the data, only the file id is chosen from the interface; data acquisition and data processing are done in the web services.

Fig. 3-B shows how to process remote data using web-based algorithms. An applet in the *visualisation* module invokes the *operation extract* module which extracts parameters from the widget object. The *operation extract* module will capture a snapshot of the run-time operation parameters and organise these in an XML file. The applet then invokes the *data adapter* module to upload the XML file to the server. It sends a request to the *workflow control* module to look up the algorithm for processing the data. If the *algorithm adapter* module finds a matching algorithm in the built-in algorithm set, the client then uploads the data file to the server, otherwise, the web service algorithm will read the data from the remote resource.

After processing the data, a new data set is created and, with the data file URL returned to the client, the *data adapter* module on the client side can use the URL to download the data to the local machine. Finally, the *visualisation* module uses the new data file to update the View produced.

4. Implementation

4.1. Configure client environment automatically

A trusted applet can access the properties of, and read or write files to, the client system. File systems on different clients are organised differently on different platforms, or even on the same platform. We leave the users free of trouble by setting up a configuration file. However, we do not want to keep this information in the database, so we create two local folders: a data folder and a library folder. The local data folder is used to store data downloaded from the remote site and the local library folder is used to store VTK libraries for visualisation. In this way, the reading of data and the execution of code can be performed locally at high speed. As the user now permits our code to visit the local system, two paths should be created.

The data folder is easy to choose. When users log on to their operating system (Windows, Unix or Linux), a home directory is given to them, separating the user data from the system-wide data. By reading a system property *user.home*, this unique path can be built, A new folder is then created to store the data downloaded from the remote site.

The library folder should be set to a path where JVM can read the library. Sun Java reads .dll files kept in the *java.library.path*. This system property contains the local path in the *path* environment variable. Libraries in this path can be loaded by JVM. However, when we run

Java code, JVM has already started when Java code is executing, and modification is difficult. To get around this, the declared static field *sys_paths* of the class *ClassLoader* which contains this *java.library.path* is set to null; the class can then be initialised automatically.

Another way to deal with it is to choose an existing path in *java.library.path*, manually or automatically. The latter would choose a JRE path that already exists (see Section 3.2).

4.2. Example application: simulated surgery

Fig. 4 shows a model of the left ventricle of a heart derived from an MRI image and visualised as a triangular mesh surface. The original desktop, client-side, version of this simulation has been described in [6, 7]. The user can interactively view the data on the web from any angle with two styles: position sensitive and motion sensitive.

A triangle widget, coded as a VTK extension appears on the surface. It has three shape handles and one normal handle. When one of the shape handles is active, the user can drag it to change the size and shape of the triangle. When the normal axis is active, the user can rotate the plane of the widget around the normal. When the normal handle or the edge of the triangle are active, the triangle can be dragged to a new position. A 3D x,y,z coordinate axis is shown as a position reference and set at the centre of the data bounds.

The triangle widget is a cutting tool – when the user is satisfied with the shape and position of the widget, they may use a *cutHole* button to punch a hole through the surface. The picture with a hole in the surface shows the resulting data, as processed by the server side built-in algorithm. The surface is cut by a triangular prism with parameters extracted from the triangle widget. From the wireframe graph we can see that the resulting data is decimated on the server side, in this case to 20% of the original size, to improve the speed of the interactive transfer between client and server.

5. Conclusions and future work

This paper has described a way of performing web-based 3D interactive visualisation – a virtual client environment. Users used a standard browser to perform simulated surgery and could decide on the shape and boundary of a 'cut' using remotely located visualisation tools. The approach accepts two data resources (local and remote) as input and two algorithm resources (built-in and remote). The proposed approach is generic and can be used in other projects that use VTK or, indeed, in other systems that use C++ in their applications.

In the future, for the remote algorithm aspects, we shall make use of the new axis2 features to create new web services, for example, invoking web services asynchronously. JAX_WS supports both polling and callback when calling web services asynchronously. Large datasets and complex graphics processing may cause delays, but these asynchronous mechanise may

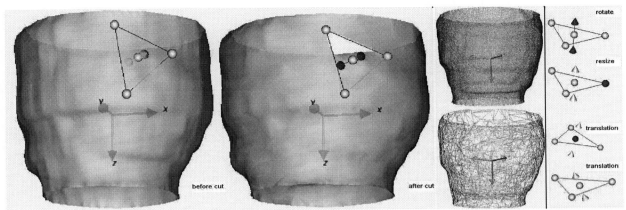

Figure 4 Heart

improve user satisfaction. They may go on to operate our interactive view on the client and after completing the processing, the view will be updated automatically. Another useful development is the support for Message Transmission Optimized Mechanism (MTOM), by which the user can send and receive binary attachments such as images or files along with web service requests. The binary data may be contained within the XML document or as an attachment outside it.

From the visualisation perspective, we shall create a multiview system to supply users with a broader variety of viewing modes with which to explore their data.

References

[1]   I R Belousov, R Chellali, G J Clapworthy, Virtual Reality Tools for Internet Robotics, Proc IEEE International Conference on Robotics & Automation (ICRA-2001), Seoul (Korea), May 2001, pp. 1878-1883

[2]   VPH2: www.vph-vph2.eu

[3]   Y Ning, X J Guo, X R Li, X F Xu, W J Ma, The Implementation of Haptic Interaction in Virtual Surgery, Proc. 2010 Int'l Conf on Electrical & Control Engineering, June 2010, pp. 2351-2354

[4]   Bitmanagement BS Contact: www.bitmanagement.com

[5]   VTK: www.vtk.org

[6]   X Lin, N J B McFarlane, Y Zhao, G J Clapworthy, F Dong, A Radaelli, Visualisation of Left Ventricular Dysfunction in the Virtual Pathological Heart, Proc. 7th Int'l Conf on Biomedical Visualisation (MediVis10), London, July 2010, pp. 635-640

[7]   N J B McFarlane, X Lin, Y Zhao, G J Clapworthy, F Dong, A Redaelli, O Parodi, D Testi. Visualisation and Simulated Surgery of the Left Ventricle in VPH2, Royal Society Interface Focus, 2011 (in press)

[8]   LHDL: www.livinghuman.org/

[9]   VPHOP: www.vphop.eu/

[10] T Wang, Y Zhao, E Liu, G J Clapworthy, X Zhao, H Wei, F Dong, Using Web Services as Functional-Level Plug Ins for Interactive 3D Medical Visualisation, Proc. 14th Int'l Conf on Information Visualisation (IV10), London, July 2010, pp. 617-622

[11] K Polthier, S Khadem, E Preuss, U Reitebuch, Publication of Interactive Visualisations with JavaView, in (Eds: J Borwein, M Morales, K Polthier, J F Rodrigues) Multimedia Tools for Communicating Mathematics, Springer Verlag, 2002

[12] M Majewski, K Polthier, Using MuPAD and JavaView to Visualise Mathematics on the Internet, Proc. 9th Asian Technology Conf in Mathematics, 2004, pp. 465-474

[13] R Ding, J Z Gao, B Chen, J I Siepmann, Y Liu, Web-Based Visualisation of Atmospheric Nucleation Processes Using Java3D, Proc 9th IEEE/ACM Int'l Symp. on Cluster Computing & the Grid, May 2009, pp. 597-602

[14] G Cipriano, G Wesenberg, T Grim, G N Phillips Jr, M Gleicher, GRAPE: GRaphical Abstracted Protein Explorer, Nucleic Acids Research Advance, May 2010, Published online Vol. 38, Web Server issue W595–W601,doi:10.1093/nar/gkq398

[15] W J Schroeder, K M Martin, W E Lorensen, The Design and Implementation of an Object-Oriented Toolkit For 3D Graphics and Visualisation, Proc 7th IEEE Visualisation 1996 (VIS '96), October 1996, pp. 93-101

[16] T Parisi. Ajax3d: The Open Platform for Rich 3D Web Applications, www.ajax3d.org/whitepaper/.

[17] X3D specifications. www.web3d.org/x3d/specifications/

[18] PhysiomeSpace: www.physiomespace.com

[19] M Viceconti, C Zannoni, D Testi, M Petrone, S Perticoni, P Quadrani, F Taddei, S Imboden, G J Clapworthy. The Multimod Application Framework : A Rapid Application Development Tool for Computer Aided Medicine, Comput. Methods Programs Biomed, 85(2):138–151, 2007

Author Index

Author Index

Author Index

Author Index

Notes

IEEE Computer Society
Conference Publications
Operations Committee

CPOC Chair
Roy Sterritt
University of Ulster

Board Members
Mike Hinchey, *Co-Director, Lero-the Irish Software Engineering Research Centre*
Larry A. Bergman, *Manager, Mission Computing and Autonomy Systems Research Program Office (982), JPL*
Wenping Wang, *Associate Professor, University of Hong Kong*
Silvia Ceballos, *Supervisor, Conference Publishing Services*
Andrea Thibault-Sanchez, *CPS Quotes and Acquisitions Specialist*

IEEE Computer Society Executive Staff
Evan Butterfield, *Director of Products and Services*
Alicia Stickley, *Senior Manager, Publishing Services*
Thomas Baldwin, *Senior Manager, Meetings & Conferences*

IEEE Computer Society Publications
The world-renowned IEEE Computer Society publishes, promotes, and distributes a wide variety of authoritative computer science and engineering texts. These books are available from most retail outlets. Visit the CS Store at *http://www.computer.org/portal/site/store/index.jsp* for a list of products.

IEEE Computer Society *Conference Publishing Services* (CPS)
The IEEE Computer Society produces conference publications for more than 250 acclaimed international conferences each year in a variety of formats, including books, CD-ROMs, USB Drives, and on-line publications. For information about the IEEE Computer Society's *Conference Publishing Services* (CPS), please e-mail: cps@computer.org or telephone +1-714-821-8380. Fax +1-714-761-1784. Additional information about *Conference Publishing Services* (CPS) can be accessed from our web site at: *http://www.computer.org/cps*

Revised: 1 March 2009

CPS Online is our innovative online collaborative conference publishing system designed to speed the delivery of price quotations and provide conferences with real-time access to all of a project's publication materials during production, including the final papers. The ***CPS Online*** workspace gives a conference the opportunity to upload files through any Web browser, check status and scheduling on their project, make changes to the Table of Contents and Front Matter, approve editorial changes and proofs, and communicate with their CPS editor through discussion forums, chat tools, commenting tools and e-mail.

The following is the URL link to the ***CPS Online*** Publishing Inquiry Form:
http://www.ieeeconfpublishing.org/cpir/inquiry/cps_inquiry.html